ANNUAL REVIEW OF
PLANT PHYSIOLOGY AND
PLANT MOLECULAR BIOLOGY

ANNUAL REVIEW OF PLANT PHYSIOLOGY AND PLANT MOLECULAR BIOLOGY

VOLUME 52, 2001

RUSSELL L. JONES, *Editor*
University of California, Berkeley

HANS J. BOHNERT, *Associate Editor*
University of Arizona, Tucson

DEBORAH P. DELMER, *Associate Editor*
University of California, Davis

www.AnnualReviews.org   science@AnnualReviews.org   650-493-4400

ANNUAL REVIEWS
4139 El Camino Way • P.O. BOX 10139 • Palo Alto, California 94303-0139

ANNUAL REVIEWS
Palo Alto, California, USA

International Standard Serial Number: 1040-2519
International Standard Book Number: 0-8243-0652-X
Library of Congress Catalog Card Number: 50-13143

Typeset by Techbooks, Fairfax, VA
Printed and Bound in the United States of America

PREFACE

In 1988, the *Annual Review of Plant Physiology* became the *Annual Review of Plant Physiology and Plant Molecular Biology* in recognition of the revolution that was occurring in molecular biology. At the close of the last millennium, we witnessed the genomics revolution that saw the sequencing of the entire *Arabidopsis* and rice genomes. New genomes are now being sequenced on a weekly basis. Functional genomics and proteomics will provide the foundation for an understanding of how genes function, and these discoveries will open the door to fundamental knowledge about how plants work, leading to improvements in the production of food and fiber. The extraordinary information explosion that new technologies bring poses problems for the researcher, and the management of information becomes critical. The dramatic advances in genomics and proteomics were made possible by the predictions of Moore's Law. Thus with each passing year, the capacity of the silicon chip to store and process information has doubled. The developments that allowed rapid advances in informatics also gave birth to the digital library, giving the scientist immediate access to almost all published work at the desktop and the ability to mine a myriad of databases. However, the task of distilling information is now daunting, and publications such as those in the *Annual Reviews* series will become even more important as reliable filters.

This volume has served the plant biology community well. This is evident from the high impact factor of this and other *Annual Reviews* volumes. In its listing of scholarly publications for 1998, ISI ranked the *Annual Review of Plant Physiology and Plant Molecular Biology* as twentieth among published journals and reviews in all fields. Changes have occurred in this volume over the last decade, some of which are evident to the reader, such as the inclusion of color illustrations, as well as the on-line availability of the *Annual Reviews* journals. Another milestone will be reached, beginning with Volume 53 in 2002, when this volume will appear as the *Annual Review of Plant Biology*, an event that marks the coming of age of plant biology as a discipline. Changes that may not be so apparent to the casual reader include the addition of the first member of the Editorial Board from outside of North America and the inclusion of two international advisors to the Editorial Board. We welcome Raoul Ranjeva to the Editorial Board for a five-year term, and Yuji Kamiya and Tony Trewavas are welcomed as international advisors. The inclusion of experts from countries outside North America is testament to the global nature of science and the influence that we hope the volume will continue to have on plant biology.

I have been privileged to have been associated with the *Annual Review of Plant Physiology and Plant Molecular Biology* since 1973; and after seven years as

Editor, I pass the baton to Debby Delmer. Debby has served as Associate Editor since 1998, and she brings a wealth of experience to the Editor's job. I leave this *Annual Review* with the very best of memories. Of all of the tasks that I have carried out in my career as academic and researcher, my association with the Editorial Board of this volume has been the most pleasurable.

Russell L. Jones

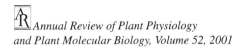

*Annual Review of Plant Physiology
and Plant Molecular Biology, Volume 52, 2001*

CONTENTS

RELATED ARTICLES

JAMES HM HENDERSON

Annu. Rev. Plant Physiol. Plant Mol. Biol. 2001. 52:1–28

FIFTY YEARS AS A PLANT PHYSIOLOGIST

James HM Henderson
Department of Biology, Tuskegee University, Tuskegee, Alabama 36088;
e-mail: jhenderson@tusk.edu

Key Words Tuskegee Institute, crown gall research, growth regulators, polio evaluation trials, ENHANCES

■ **Abstract** This chapter is a chronological and biographical sketch of the professional life of a botanist-plant physiologist. He just happens to be of African-American descent. He cites his early education and through college and graduate school, as well as his war years at the University of Chicago. His postdoc appointment at Caltech with James Bonner was really his professional beginning and highlight. Most of his teaching and research years were spent at Tuskegee University and the George Washington Carver Research Foundation. He spent several tours of research activity, in both the United States and foreign countries. His contact with plant physiologists was quite broad, both in the United States and overseas. Finally, in his senior years, he has turned to mentoring young students into careers in the biological and allied sciences. This activity, he states, has "kept me young beyond my chronological age."

CONTENTS

PREFACE

Professor Ann Oaks entitled her prefatory chapter in Volume 51, 2000: *Fifty Years of Plant Science: Was there Really No Place for a Woman?* My professional career in the field of botany and plant physiology also covers a span of 50 years (1940–1990), and I guess I could follow Professor Oaks' title and add *Was There Really No Place for an African American in the Field?* to my original title, *Fifty Years As A Plant Physiologist.*

EARLY LIFE AND SCHOOLING

I was born after midnight on 10 August, 1917, the second son of Edwin Bancroft Henderson and Ellen Meriwether Henderson, in Falls Church, a small Virginia town approximately six miles from the nation's capital, Washington, DC. Falls Church, which celebrated its three-hundredth anniversary in 1999, derives its name from two sources: Falls comes from an important geographical feature nearby, the Little Falls on the Potomac River, whereas church derives from the establishment of the Truro Parish. Vestrymen of this former Anglican church, now an Episcopal church, have included such prominent people as Augustine Washington, George Mason, Lord William Fairfax, and George Washington.

When Ned and Nellie Henderson married on 24 December 1910, they moved to Falls Church to live with his mother, because of the regulation that barred hiring of a husband and wife in the DC public school system. In 1912, they built their own home. This is where I spent my childhood days, on a farm (Figure 1). I often ask people, "Do you not think I was raised on a farm?" The farm consisted of chickens, hogs, cows, horses, guinea fowl, and of course dogs and cats, as well as fruit trees and all varieties of vegetables. One of my fondest memories was of the two American chestnut trees—and to this day chestnuts are among my specialties—but they died while I was still a youngster from *Cryphonectria parasitica*, a fungal disease that killed practically all of the chestnut trees in the country.

My mother was hired to teach in the two-room "colored" school in Falls Church. She taught the upper grades (4 through 6) while another teacher taught the lower grades (1 through 3). The school was about a mile from our house, and my mother walked the distance every day. Although my brother and I went with her to the school every day when we were ages one to six, we never were actual pupils there. When we reached school age, we went to school in Washington, DC, where my father taught. Normally, children from Virginia could not legally attend schools in DC, but because my father taught there, we were allowed to go to school

Figure 1 On the farm in Falls Church, Virginia, in 1918. My mother and my brother Edwin and me.

there. He was head of the Department of Physical Education and Athletics in the "colored schools," and the first Black American in the professional field of physical education in the United States. He had been taught under the tutelage of Dr Sargent at Harvard University from 1904–1907. In addition to his courses in physical education, he learned the new game of basketball, which had recently been invented by James Naismith at Springfield College in Massachusetts. He introduced the sport to the Washington-Baltimore area, and was the captain of the YMCA team, which never lost a game in 1909–1910. His last game was played the night before he married, on Christmas Eve 1910!

I began in the kindergarten at a model school, Garrison Elementary School, named for William Lloyd Garrison of Massachusetts, a leader in the abolitionist movement who felt that slavery was so wrong that he believed the Northern states should separate from the South. Garrison was a school where exceptional teachers taught. My years at Garrison were most enjoyable, replete with memories of bringing rabbits and other animals from the farm for the teachers and my school classmates to enjoy. I was fortunate that my grandmother lived just around the corner because I could go to her house for lunch and, after school, wait for my father to pick me up. When my father was unable to pick me up, my brother and I would take the train to Falls Church and walk the mile from the station to our house, where my mother would be getting dinner for us.

My childhood days in Falls Church were very happy and busy. As a young child my duties consisted of taking care of the chickens, feeding them, collecting eggs, and other small chores around the farm, later increasing to feeding horses and cows. At 14 or 15, I was responsible for milking our Guernsey cow, morning and evening, when my brother was not available. Most memorable and vivid in my mind was an incident that I felt was inhumanely wrong and terrible: Our favorite horse, Lighty, was hit by an automobile, which broke his leg. When the sheriff arrived, he shot the horse (in those days the legs could not be repaired). To add to this "tragedy", we had to pay for the damage to the driver's car!

After Garrison, I attended the Garnett-Patterson Jr. High School, where I enjoyed a wider social life. I was elected to the honor society, and took part in my first game of basketball. We formed a club, The Musketeers, and often played at the first Black YMCA in America, which my father helped to found.

Next, I attended Dunbar High School, named for the great Black poet, Paul Lawrence Dunbar. One of three Black high schools in DC, Dunbar was the first Black high school in the nation, established in 1870 to train young Black students for college. The first principal was the first Negro woman to graduate from college, Oberlin College in Ohio.

The official policy of segregation and discrimination in the nation's capital did, of course, include the public schools. Ironically, students and teachers at Dunbar benefited from the exclusion of "colored" teachers from white schools. Dunbar was therefore able to attract the cream of the crop of Negro teachers, many of whom were graduates of prestigious colleges in the North and Northeast such as Smith, Radcliffe, Yale, Amherst, or Harvard, some even with PhDs.

In addition to my scholastic activities, I took part in sports: swimming, football, and tennis. I also spent two years in drill, finally attaining the rank of sergeant—after which I dropped out to allow more time for sports. However, I stayed in long enough to march in the first inauguration parade for Franklin D Roosevelt on March 4, 1933, and as an ROTC cadet, in his second inauguration in 1937.

Naturally, my academic interests were enhanced by my farm experience with plants and animals; this obviously meant biology. In my freshman year in 1932, my first course of choice was biology; my father had to pull a few strings to get me in, at the tenth grade. It just happened that my father's office as Head of the Department of Physical Education and Athletics in the Negro schools was at Dunbar, across from the biology classroom. I was a member of the National Honor Society, graduating in the top 10% of a graduation class of 207 girls and 82 boys.

While I was at Dunbar, I met the girl I finally married. This event had been pre-ordained in 1917. The Hendersons and Francises were close friends—our mothers and fathers had gone to school together. We also shared a summer resort in the same small town of Highland Beach, near Annapolis, MD. Soon after I was born, her mother came to Falls Church to see her long-time friend, Nellie, and her newborn son. She brought her five-week old daughter, Betty Alice Francis. So, unknowingly, we met almost at birth, little knowing that 30 years later we would consummate that early meeting in marriage and from which would come two daughters, two sons, three granddaughters, and five grandsons.

After graduating from Dunbar in 1935, the choice of college was not difficult. In the midst of the country's worst depression, I chose a local university that allowed me to live at home. My choice for a major academic area was also easy, after 18 years on a farm among plants and animals; it was obviously biology.

COLLEGE YEARS

In September 1935, I enrolled at Howard University in Washington, DC, and majored in biology. Howard was then the only Negro university with a separate botany department; it now is a combined department of biology. Howard University, established in 1867 by Act of Congress, was designated "a university for the education of youth in the liberal arts and sciences." No mention of race was made; indeed, the first students were four white girls, daughters of some of the instructors or administrators. However, the role of the school, like many other institutions in the South, was the education of Negroes, recently freed by the Emancipation Proclamation. The curriculum soon expanded "to encompass more departments—normal, preparatory, collegiate, musical, theology, military, law, commercial, and medical." Its first president was a Civil War hero, Major General Oliver Otis Howard, for whom the institution was later named. The head of the Department of Botany, Dr Charles S. Parker, was a graduate of Penn State in Plant Pathology. A friend of the family, he also mentored me through my academic career. My minor was zoology, with a smattering of chemistry as a sub-minor. My years at Howard were successful and enjoyable, even though I could not participate in the usual activities on campus because I commuted daily from Falls Church; much of my social life therefore still revolved around my high school and local classmates.

Having entered as an honor student, I was placed in a special class called Orientation and Guidance, which gave only two credits. This left me two credits short of being a full-fledged sophomore at the end of my freshman year. However, this was overcome by the third semester, making me a bona fide sophomore. Although my major was biology, my most challenging and interesting courses were qualitative and quantitative chemistry, in which I received "A" grades.

I remember, in my senior year, discussing with my major professor the fact that, although I had done well academically (Phi Beta Kappa), I still did not feel confident that I had really jelled in a unified and comprehensive way the full body of knowledge gained through the individual courses. I could not integrate botany, combined with the adjuncts of chemistry, physics and zoology, into a unified body. That was normal, he told me, and when I went to graduate school, these areas would jell into a matrix of a unified subject.

There was one possible deterrent to my pursuing graduate school. It was 1939, with rumblings of world unrest, especially in Europe; the country was still deep in depression, and financing a graduate education was not going to be easy without outside funding. Therefore, I had taken as electives all the secondary education courses necessary to teach in the public school system, if graduate plans did not work out. However, with some aid from the state and an appointment as a work-study student, I was able to go to graduate school at the University of Wisconsin.

An odd circumstance allowed this to happen; in this case racial segregation played a serendipitous role. I applied to the University of Virginia for acceptance to graduate school. Of course the law then would not allow my admission, but I could not be turned down for lack of academic qualifications. Thus Virginia allowed me to receive a scholarship to a university of my choosing—outside the state. This was a standard practice in higher education for states in the South, in defiance of the Supreme Court's ruling in 1938, in *Missouri v. Gaines*, that the practice was unconstitutional. Thus, I was able to go to the University of Wisconsin to pursue my graduate degree in Botany, aided by a work assistantship.

My father accompanied me across the Midwest in my 1931 Model A Ford that I had bought for $125 in October 1938 during my senior year at Howard, with money saved from my summer job as a lifeguard at Dunbar High School. My father had never been west of Chicago, so he was anxious to help me get settled in Madison. Halfway across the 1000-mile trip we stopped at Wellington, Ohio, where relatives of my mother's family lived, and which became the stopping place on future trips between Madison and Falls Church.

UNIVERSITY OF WISCONSIN GRADUATE YEARS

My area of interest was plant physiology. Although I was not completely familiar with the specialties of the faculty, I was attracted by the name of Benjamin Minge Duggar, a well-known plant physiologist and mycologist. My major professor was John F Stauffer (Figure 2). I decided to obtain a master's degree first in case I had to stop my studies for financial or other reasons. I received an MPh, rather than an MS, at the end of my first year—a rare event considering the courses, especially in languages and education, that I had taken for my BS degree at Howard University. The title of my thesis was *The Growth of Tobacco Plants in Solution Culture Aerated with Air Containing Different Partial Pressures of CO_2*.

After the first year, I double-minored in chemistry and biochemistry, while majoring in plant physiology. Again, it was my interest in chemistry that spurred this decision, and just as in my undergraduate courses, it was the grade received in the chemistry course that seemed most rewarding. In biochemistry every graduate student had to take Biochem 110, taught by the entire faculty, which included some of the top biochemists of that day—Steenbock, Elvejhem, Peterson, Hart, Link, and their like. Regardless of where you had gone to school before coming to UW, Biochem 110 was compulsory.

I did not take organic chemistry at Howard, because I was unable to sched-ule it before my graduation, so I took it at UW. Perhaps if I been introduced

Figure 2 The "Wisconsin Gang," 1942. Front row, *left to right*: Joe Weybrew, Ed Ball, Fritz Stauffer, BM Duggar, Gene Elliott, Ed Spoerl. Back row, *left to right*: Rene Blondeau, J Curtis, Mack Dugger, Gus Gries, Joe Klotz, J Kuntz, J Henderson.

to organic chemistry in my undergraduate career, I might have made it my major. The most rewarding and challenging was a qualitative organic chemistry course taught by Professor Samuel McElvain on the characterization of organic compounds.

Since I was not in the draft and had not yet been called to a position as a junior chemist, for which I had applied, I continued to pursue my interest in qualitative organic chemistry. The course that followed was an advanced survey of organic compounds, taught by Professor Homer Adkins. He and Professor McElvain collaborated in the lab manual we used, entitled *An Introduction to the Practice of Organic Chemistry*. What a wonderful text that was! Originally published in 1933, in 1942 McElvain was revising this text together with his own *The Characterization of Organic Compounds*, using us students as guinea pigs. It was published in 1945, two years after I finished the course.

My four years in Madison were enjoyable in more ways than school work; it was not all work and no play. Learning to ski was one of those extracurricular activities. Taking advantage of the plentiful snow and long winters, I often went skiing on the slopes and hills surrounding Lake Mendota, as well as on the hills near Baraboo where there was a small skiing lodge. Some of the skiing was on the golf course near campus. One extremely cold night I almost lost an ear while skiing there! Fishing, swimming, and canoeing on Mendota and the four lakes of Madison were refreshing exercises, also.

My research involved the use of a relatively new technique, that of using isolated organs to study biochemical reactions in plants. Dr Phillip White had just recently isolated and cultured tomato roots in vitro. It was his method and technique that I used in my research. The title of my thesis was *The Effect of Respiratory Intermediates and Inhibitors on the Growth and Respiration of Tomato Roots*. The research resulted in my first publication (7).

BADGER ORDNANCE WORKS

My research essentially ended in the fall of 1942. The country was in the early stages of World War II and pressure was on to recruit armed forces. I had been declared IV-F (flat feet, they said) and was not in the first draft. I volunteered for flight training at nearby Middleton, but was turned down because of poor eyesight. However, I was accepted as a junior chemist at Baraboo, Wisconsin, at the Badger Ordnance Works (BOW). The military mission there was the production of smokeless powder. Baraboo was about 40 miles from Madison and my Model A made that trip many times during the winter of 1943 in $-35°$ weather, only managing not to freeze thanks to the five people in the car, a manifold heater, and blankets. I will always remember in January 1943 listening to radio accounts of what the Germans were going through at Stalingrad when the Russians started them on the retreat back to Germany in that terrible winter! I remained at BOW until the next spring, when I resigned in order to receive my PhD in June. My exam committee, in May 1943, was composed of my major professor, John F Stauffer, Assistant Professor of Botany (plant physiology); Norman C Fassett, Associate Professor of Botany and Curator of Herbarium (taxonomy); WE Tottingham, my minor professor, Associate Professor of Biochemistry (plant biochemistry); JW Williams, Professor of Chemistry (physical chemistry); and BM Duggar, Professor of Physiology and Applied Botany, and the senior professor of the committee. Although passing the exam was a relief and a satisfying feeling, I actually enjoyed the experience and, as I recall, was not in the least bit nervous. I had had that same feeling about my preliminary exam two years earlier.

UNIVERSITY OF CHICAGO AT UCTL

Seeking further employment in the national defense effort other than in an armed capacity, which was precluded because of my draft status, I applied for several positions in keeping with my research and graduate studies. One was at Lederlee Laboratories, New Jersey, where antibiotics were being produced. I also sent a letter of application to Johns Hopkins University where Folke Skoog was doing research in plant physiology. My final application was to a wartime project at the University of Chicago where toxic gases were being tested for gas warfare. I was accepted for this position in the laboratory of the University of Chicago Toxicology Lab (UCTL), administered by Dr Franklin C McLean, Professor of Pathological Physiology of the Department of Physiology. The project was under the US Office of Scientific and Research Development (OSRD) and the National Defense Research Committee (NDRC). The other two positions responded after I had accepted the position at the University of Chicago. The interesting one was an offer from Dr Subbaro, Director of Lederlee Labs, where Dr BM Duggar, my former professor, headed a group developing antibiotics. During the next year, Dr Dugger isolated Aureomycin, and I had missed the opportunity of being associated with one of the world's most effective antibiotics!

Also, belatedly, I received correspondence from Dr Skoog that he would be happy to have me join him at Johns Hopkins in Baltimore, but he advised me that because Johns Hopkins was located in a southern city, I would probably experience segregation. Folke and I have laughed over this many times. He had not realized that I had experienced segregation all of my life in Virginia and DC and even on the south side of the quadrangle at the University of Chicago, where I was refused housing. I lived on the campus at the Chicago Theological Seminary. Skoog advised me that I would fare much better with his friend, James Bonner, at CalTech. Neither of us realized at that time that I would enjoy two years with Bonner at CalTech five years later as a postdoctoral candidate. At the end of two years at UC and with the war's ending, I was now seeking a position in line with my graduate training.

TUSKEGEE INSTITUTE

In the spring of 1945, two professors from Tuskegee Institute visited me in Chicago and offered me a teaching and research position. They were Dr Russell W Brown, Professor of Microbiology and Director of the recently incorporated George Washington Carver Foundation (GWCF), and Dr Clarence T Mason, Professor of Chemistry at Tuskegee and Director of Research at GWCF. Our meeting was cordial and pleasant. They invited me out for the evening at Berghoff's Restaurant and Bar on Monroe Street. Even though I had been at UW where beer was served at the Rathskeller at the College Union, I had never imbibed, whereas they were veteran beer drinkers. So after a few beers, which I cordially accepted, I agreed to their offer to come to Tuskegee. They Shanghaied me! However, I never regretted the decision.

And so I packed my Model A, which had remained at Madison for use on skiing or fishing trips, and headed East. My first stop was at home in Falls Church before heading south to Alabama and Tuskegee.

Tuskegee University was founded by Booker Taliaferro Washington on 4 July 1881. He was the only American to make the long journey from a slave cabin to the Hall of Fame. It became the most famous school in the world for Negroes. Just 16 years after the Civil War, he went to the Deep South where his people needed him most. For the progress he made in advancing the cause of the Negro, he gained international stature and a prominent place in the life and legend of America.

Washington was born on April 5, 1856, in Franklin County, VA. His name, Booker, was probably derived from his slave owner named Bowker. His mother named him Taliaferro. He chose the name Washington. It was Washington, he reasoned, who was the father of his country, thus he chose his name. He enrolled at Hampton Institute in 1872, graduating in 1875. After six years teaching at Hampton, in 1881 he came to Tuskegee to become principal of a school. Upon arrival, the 25-year-old educator asked, "Where is the school?" "There isn't one—yet," he was told. Undismayed, Booker T. Washington went to work, and on July 4, 1881, the doors of a small shanty were opened to 40 students, mostly adults. That humble setting was the beginning of Tuskegee Institute. The school, a Normal School for Colored Teachers, so named by the Alabama legislature in establishing the school, in 1893 became known as Tuskegee Normal and Industrial Institute. The name changed to Tuskegee Institute in 1937, and Tuskegee University in 1985.

Tuskegee had become a hot national issue at the beginning of World War II, when Blacks attempted to enter the Army Air Corps. They were refused entry because the armed forces were segregated. However, with pressure from various groups, it was decided to organize a Negro unit at Tuskegee. The driving force came from Mrs Eleanor Roosevelt who had visited the primary training unit at Tuskegee and had been given a ride in a Piper Cub by flight instructor Charles "Chief" Anderson. When she went back to the White House, she convinced her husband,

President Franklin Roosevelt, that Blacks can indeed fly and asked him to authorize the formation of a Negro arm of the Army Air Corps at Tuskegee. This unit of fighter pilots, known as the Tuskegee Airmen, flew heroically in Italy during World War II, with a sterling record of fighter pilots escorting bombers in over 200 missions over Southern Europe and Germany in 1944 without losing a single bomber!

When I arrived at the end of the war in 1945, my early ambition to become a pilot was rekindled and, in June 1946, I took my first flight in a plane and began my pilot training. On August 7th I took my first cross-country flight with "Chief" Anderson, and received my private pilot's license after a check ride on November 9, 1946.

During the next two years, I taught general chemistry and biochemistry as well as courses in my special field of botany and plant physiology. My title also included Research Associate. I immediately engaged in research and directed master's degree students. My first graduate student was a transfer from the Department of Agriculture who needed a mentor. I took her on. She completed the research and received her MS degree in 1946 (8).

In the fall of 1947, I had two graduate students in biology. However, since I had been offered a position as a postdoctoral fellow at CalTech with James Bonner in the fall of 1948, these two students had to complete their MS degree in 12 months at Tuskegee University, whereas the MS degree typically requires a minimum of two years. However, they did complete all course work and research by August 1948 and published their research too (2, 12).

MY POSTDOCTORAL YEARS AT CALTECH

The summer of 1948 began another more significant phase of my life: I married my long-time girlfriend. We were off on a long journey from Falls Church and Washington to Pasadena and the California Institute of Technology, where I was to engage as a postdoctoral fellow with James Bonner. Our trip west took the long route to the Northwest that my distant relative, Meriwether Lewis, took in 1803; down the plains of Missouri and up that same river to the Rockies, and down the Snake and Columbia Rivers to the great Pacific, and in thus doing opened up the whole western US in that long trek between 1803–1804, known as the Lewis and Clarke Expedition. We did not take that circuitous route. We traveled northwest to Seattle and by boat to Vancouver to see an old friend whom I knew at Wisconsin, Bert Brink, at the University of British Columbia. From there we descended the coast through Washington, Oregon, Northern California, and finally, on to Southern California and Pasadena. As we descended into the valley of Los Angeles, we were met immediately with an unpleasant surprise that made our eyes smart and water! This was our first introduction to the environmental plague of Los Angeles—smog! However, after a few weeks, our eyes hardened and we were able to survive for the next two years.

The California Institute of Technology (CalTech) was founded as Throop University in 1891, later becoming the Throop Polytechnic Institute, and finally in

1920 it adopted its present name. It took its great step forward in 1921 when a Laboratory of Physics was established and in 1923 lured Nobel Laureate Dr Robert A Milliken from his position as Professor of Physics at the University of Chicago to head the Norman Bridge Physics Laboratory and chair the Executive Council as president. In 1945, Dr Lee A DuBridge assumed the office of president. While I was at CalTech, Dr Milliken and I had a nice friendly chat together. It was indeed an honor for me to be able to speak with this great man.

My appointment was as a Research Fellow in the Division of Biology, headed by Professor George W Beadle, Nobel Laureate in 1958. My immediate supervisor was Professor James F Bonner. The Biology Division consisted of 11 professors, headed by Professor Beadle, Chairman of the Department; 12 research associate, assistants, associate and assistant professors, followed by a host of others: 9 senior research fellows and 2 Gosney Fellows, 24 research fellows, 31 research assistants, and 11 graduate fellow assistants. Interestingly, among the research fellows in 1949–1950 was a James D Watson, who had recently received a BS degree from the University of Chicago. Little did I know then that I held the same position as one who was to make one of the greatest discoveries in the history of science, for which he received the Nobel Prize along with FHC Crick in 1962.

The plant group was headed by Professors Went and Bonner, assisted by Sam Wildman and Art Galston, senior research fellows. Among the research fellows in the plant group were George Laties, Howard Teas, Bob Bandurski, Guy Camus, and Jean Nitsch. Among other research fellows I remember well were Clem Markert, Dan Atkinson, Jean Mauron, Herb Hull, Jim Liverman, Bernard Axelrod, Andre Jangendorf, et al (Figure 3).

The emphasis of my research was on the development of an abnormal growth, known as crown gall, caused by a bacterium, *Agrobacterium tumefaciens*. This organism infects certain plants, causing a tumorous growth. The question raised concerned identification of the chemical agent that caused this proliferation of growth.

Much work had been done using tobacco as the system to study production of crown gall. The group at the University of Wisconsin under the supervision of Drs AJ Riker and BM Duggar had done considerable research on this. However, the tissue of the sunflower, *Helianthus annuus*, variety Great Russian, was the tissue of choice by several investigators, primarily Phillip White and Armin Braun. We decided to use this for our study.

The work of Went, Thimam et al determined that the naturally occurring organic growth factor or auxin, chemically indole-3-acetic acid (IAA), was the cause of cell proliferation. How did IAA play a role in crown gall production?

The results of our research showed the following:

> Crown Gall tumor tissue of the sunflower has been shown to contain significant amounts of free auxin even after prolonged culture on an auxin-free medium. Stem callus tissue, which requires a continual exogenous source of auxin in order to grow, contains so little free auxin

Figure 3 The Plant Physiology Group at CalTech, 1950. Front row, *left to right*: Bill Hiesey, AJ Haagen-Smit, FW Went, James Bonner, Rosamond Baker; second row, *left to right*: L Eggman, H Boroughs, R Bandurski, J Henderson, D Atkinson, J Nitsch, BJ Wood, H Garand; third row, *left to right*: S Honda, Herb Hull, B Axelrod, L Janson, J Livermore, A Jagendorf, G Camus. Missing: Art Galston, Norm Good, Sam Wildman.

that it was not detectable by the methods used. Lyophilized Crown Gall tumor tissue is capable of sustained and rapid production of auxin at the expense of endogenous substrates. This ability is absent or present to a much smaller extent in both non-tumor callus tissue and in the normal sunflower stem tissue from which both the tumor and callus were originally derived (4).

In order to make a comparison with in vitro crown gall tissue, culture of a normal sunflower tissue was necessary. This was accomplished by using the techniques established by RJ Gautheret and his students in France, and Phillip R White in the United States:

A technique for the production and subsequent culture in vitro of normal sunflower stem callus tissue has been described. This technique includes the use of a medium containing a supplement mixture of auxin (1AA), adenine, vitamins, and casein hydrolysate. This medium was found to support successfully the continued growth of the callus tissue. The addition of coconut milk to the nutrient medium greatly accelerates the growth of normal sunflower callus. Coconut milk and the supplement mixture together give significantly greater growth than any other combination of ingredients which have been tried. These results confirmed past reports that coconut milk contains an important growth promoting principle, a material different from other recognized plant growth factors (5).

Pasadena provided a wealth of interesting and wonderful experiences for me and my new family. In a sense this was our honeymoon. We had only been married five months, and had not had much free time since marrying in May 1948. We raised a family in Pasadena—two girls were born, Ellen and Dena, named for Pasa Dena. We gained many friends during our two years there, with many of whom I still correspond. Sadly, several with whom we had established friendly relations have died, including my research mentors, James Bonner and Frits Went.

We did enjoy and took advantage of the environment, from seashore to mountains. I skied in the Los Angeles Mountains, and we went grunion hunting in the surf at Santa Monica. One of my most enjoyable recreational activities was scuba diving. Several of us, including Clem Markert, Jean Nitsch, and Howard Teas, went often to the marine lab at Corona del Mar to dive. Our home-made spears were made in the shop in Kerkhoff at CalTech, using sturdy rubber bands as propellants. Our favorite targets were the flat, orange garibaldi, similar to perch. We make one grand trip to the offshore island of Catalina.

One of the greatest highlights at CalTech was the dedication of the world's first phytotron. This was the dream and creation of Frits Went. The dream became a reality through the influence of former president Robert Milliken. It was largely his persuasive powers, combined with his faith in the possibilities of the phytotron for furthering the plant sciences and its importance in developing fundamental knowledge in the border fields between physics, chemistry, and botany, that convinced his friend Harry Earhart to make such a royal gift to the California Institute of Technology.[1]

For a number of years, Went had grown plants under environmentally controlled conditions in a make-shift building, but the $ 407,000 Earhart Plant Research Laboratory was the first of its kind. The term phytotron was created by Sam Wildman who said, "The phytotron is to plant researchers what the cyclotron is to physical science researchers." This set the model and basic concept for others throughout the world.

One of my fondest memories was working in the *Avena* room in the basement of Kerkhoff. There I spent many an hour measuring *Avena* coleoptile curvatures on the assay for IAA. I was told this room played a significant role in the discovery of smog. Ventilation for the room came from the roof of Kerkhoff, and, at some point in time in the 1940s, Dr Went's coleoptiles were responding poorly to IAA. Careful analysis indicated that the accumulation of sulfur and nitrogen oxides and other noxious fumes caused by automobiles and other burnings was the cause of these reduced curvatures. Eventually, Arie Haagen-Smit, a colleague of Went's from Holland who had helped in the identification of IAA as the plant growth factor, was instrumental in the identification of smog for the state of California.

While at CalTech, a very close relationship developed with Jean Paul Nitsch, from France, who had come as a graduate student in 1949 to work under Frits Went. Together we spent many hours in the *Avena* room in the basement of Kerkhoff. On a personal note, he was the godfather of my older son.

My two years were coming to an end, and I had to make a decision about my professional future. I was interviewed for a position in Botany at Santa Barbara College (now University of California at Santa Barbara), but did not follow up on this for several reasons. I had gained a wealth of research experience and knowledge in plant physiology and biochemistry at one of the most prestigious scientific research and technical institutions, made many friends, both professional and personal, and had acquired a depth of experimental and technical knowledge. Since our families lived in the East, there was some feeling of wanting to be near them, but the overriding deciding factors were twofold: smog and an irresistible offer from Tuskegee.

The smog was not a pleasant environment, especially if one had the option of choosing other places to live. However, BIO-PEEPS, a CalTech bulletin, announced my return to Tuskegee with the comment, "Dr and Mrs. Henderson can testify that the California air is beneficial for the growth of more than plants; they will return to Alabama with two children born in California." But the overriding factor by far was an offer from Tuskegee of a $10,000 grant from the American Cancer Society—big money in 1950! I was to do research in my field of interest in plant physiology, especially as it related to plant cancer.

---

[1]The dedication program of The Earhart Plant Research Laboratory by FW Went, June 7, 1949.

Thus began my continuous tenure at Tuskegee University some 50 years ago. My role was in both teaching and research, with emphasis on the latter. This time I was appointed Research Associate Professor of Biology.

PROFESSIONAL AND ADMINISTRATIVE ROLE AT TUSKEGEE UNIVERSITY

For the next 15 years my research centered around in vitro culture of sunflower and growth regulators, including IAA, 2,4-D, and gibberellins. I continued the research begun at CalTech with crown gall in the sunflower. Since we had successfully shown the relationship between crown gall tissue and normal callus tissue in relation to IAA, the next goal was to produce the culture in between, known by the Gautheret group as "accoutumé" or habituated. This was a tissue that could be cultured in vitro without the addition of IAA, nor was it derived from *Agrobacterium tumefaciens*, or crown gall. This research was reported at a conference in the French Alps near Italy in the alpine town of Briançon and in several publications. Upon returning to Tuskegee University in 1950, I began my teaching solely in biology. My courses included botany and plant physiology. However, I still took an active role in research. One of my colleagues in the early 1950s was John Rier. Our research involved the sunflower tumor callus. One of the conditions that influenced growth was temperature. Armin Braun had shown that a tumor indication principle (TIP) showed temperature sensitivity at temperatures above $32°C$. Our work showed that another factor may work along with TIP, a tumor progression principle (TPP) to augment the action of TIP, or at least they are similar in nature in heat stress situations in tumor formation (8).

In 1957, I became the head of the Department of Biology, which had became a separate department with its own major in 1956. Previously biology had been taught in the School of Agriculture, which did not offer a BS degree in biology. On the other hand, BS and MS degrees had been awarded in chemistry for several years. The first BS degrees in biology were awarded in 1959 and the first MS degrees in biology in 1962. In 1968, I was appointed Director of the George Washington Carver Foundation, a position I was to serve in until 1975.

The Foundation was incorporated in 1940 with $40,000 that Dr Carver had saved over the years. Upon his death in January 1943, an additional $32,000 was bequeathed to the Foundation. The second Foundation Director, Mr. Austin Curtis, served only a year and in 1944 was succeeded by Dr Russell W Brown, who recruited me to come to Tuskegee University in 1945.

George Washington Carver, internationally renowned chemurgist, biologist, applied scientist, and educator, was born near Diamond Grove, Missouri, in 1864, of slave parents on the plantation of Moses Carver, a German emigrant. Moses Carver named him George Washington. In 1890, he was admitted to Iowa State College, where he studied agricultural science, earning the bachelor's degree in 1894 and the master's degree in 1896. He was then elected to the faculty of Iowa

State College and placed in charge of the greenhouse. There he devoted special attention to bacterial laboratory work in systematic botany.

In 1896, Booker T Washington invited Carver to come to Tuskegee Institute to serve as the Director of the newly established Department of Agriculture. Carver began his work on October 8, 1896. During his 45-year tenure at Tuskegee, Dr Carver developed a number of products from the peanut and sweet potato. He also introduced crop rotation to farmers of the South rather than one-crop agriculture, e.g. cotton. He died January 5, 1943.

CARL SAGAN AND TUSKEGEE

My association with Carl Sagan, world-famous astronomer, began in the summer of 1963. I was directing a summer institute on radiation biology, sponsored by NSF for high school teachers, and Dr Sagan was one of the lecturers. His topic was "Origin of Life." A year later he talked on the subject "Life Beyond the Earth," followed a few years later by "Is There Intelligent Life on Earth?" Thus began a close friendship spanning over 30 years.

His seventh visit to Tuskegee University, in 1988, was to receive an honorary Doctorate of Science degree, awarded at the fall Scholarship Convention. His speech ended with the following statement: "In this century, if it comes to pass, then I imagine sometime in the twenty-first century, the great expedition of human beings; Soviets, Americans, citizens of other nations landing on the planet Mars, setting foot for the first time on another planet. A step as momentous as when the first amphibians crept out of the sea on to the land. Every step of the way on national television, the US and the Soviet Union demonstrate that for a change they would do something on behalf of the people of the planet Earth. No one knows where the landing site will be, but maybe it will be in the vicinity of a small crater on Mars called Tuskegee."

The report of the landing of Viking C I on Mars in 1976 appeared in *Science* in that year. Dr. Sagan's first wife, Lynn Margulis, currently Distinguished University Professor of Geoscience at the University of Massachusetts, had this to say about the Viking probe: "In my opinion, the Viking Mission was a spectacular success: Everything worked...but the part of the mission which concerned itself with the search for life on Mars is over...."

There was a slight error in cartography, however, in the naming of the crater on Mars for Tuskegee. In a letter to me in September 1976, Carl wrote: "Dear Jim: Many thanks for your letter of September 2nd. I am on a committee of the International Astronomical Union dealing with Martian nomenclature. The committee decided that small impact craters on Mars would be named after towns and small cities on Earth with an attempt to achieve some substantial geographical and cultural distribution. A number of us made suggestions about appropriate places, and I am a strong supporter of Tuskegee, except I seem to remember that what I was originally supporting was Tuskeegee. But somehow it has mysteriously changed its spelling. In any case, there were many members of the committee who supported such a name. When I emerge from the present very taxing set of responsibilities, I would be delighted to visit my old friends at Tuskegee." (The first spelling in 1976 was Tuskeegee, the name of a small Indian village in Tennessee.)

Although Dr Sagan's main purpose in his visits to Tuskegee was to talk about subjects of his interest and expertise, he thoroughly enjoyed interaction with students. He gathered several around on the grass under a tree and discussed both technical subjects such as the universe and extraterrestrial life, especially prospects on Mars, and topics of general interest to young college students. During the 1960s, when students on Tuskegee's campus were deeply involved in the national struggle over civil rights, Carl would sit and discuss issues of great national concern. On one occasion he even paid the bail for a student who had been arrested in a civil rights protest.

In October 1994, I had the pleasure of being invited to the Astronomy and Science Symposium in Honor of Carl Sagan's Sixtieth Birthday. Sadly, two years later Carl Sagan died from myelodysplasia.

FOREIGN TRAVEL AND STUDY ABROAD

The 8th International Congress of Botany and Conference at Briançon

In the summer of 1954, I was invited to give a paper at the *Huitième Congrès International de Botanique* in Paris. I delivered a paper entitled *The Effect of 2,4-D on Auxin Destruction and Respiration* under the general heading of section II—*Physiologie de la Croissance*.

Of course, the experience of being among so many world-famous botanists, especially plant physiologists, was exciting. I stayed in a dormitory at the University of Paris on the south side of Paris, very near the laboratory where Mme Curie and her husband, Pierre, worked in the lab of Becquerel in the discovery of radioactivity in 1896.

Following the congress in Paris, a conference entitled *La Physiologie des Cultures de Tissus Végétaux* was held at Briançon, France, hosted by Professor RJ Gautheret and the *Union Internationale des Sciences Biologiques*. Over 50 plant physiologists from countries all over the world attended this one-week meeting in the high French Alps, bordering northwest Italy. Among those were such world-reknowned physiologists as Gautheret, Skoog, White, Steward, Riker, and Morel (Figure 4). Over 30 papers were delivered, including my presentation on *The Changing Nutritional Pattern from Normal to Habituated in Sunflower Callus Tissue in Vitro* (3).

Several things of interest occurred in Briançon. The group lived in a small hotel near the bottom of the town. Accommodations were meager and somewhat cramped and inconvenient, for example, the lavatory was half-way up (or down)

(*E. Ball, phot.*)

Les auteurs des communications.

Figure 4 Briançon Conference, 1954. First row, *left to right*: A Bitancourt, D Paris, G Duplessy-Graillot, E Ball, J Gautheret, PR White, Z Kulescha, FC Steward; second row, *left to right*: L Duhamet, C Lioret, SM Caplin, S Démétriadès, A Kovoor, R Bouriquet, R Heller, AJ Riker, F Skoog, GC Camus; third row, *left to right*: F Bertossi, LG Nickell, JHM Henderson, A von Wacek, O Kandler, C Lance, A Goris, RS Platt, G Morel, R Buvat.

the stairs in a corner. One thing stands out in my memory. I was badly in need of a hair cut. When I went for my haircut to the barber's shop next to the hotel, one or two of the group were already there, including Folke Skoog. While I was in the chair one of the barbers whispered to Folke, "Is that fellow Joe Louis?" pointing to me. I guess I was the first, last, and only Negro he had ever seen, and I had to be the famous boxer, Joe Louis! Folke and I have laughed over this many times. The week at Briançon was filled with field trips in the environs, especially in the mountains. There we found the elusive edelweiss and other rare plant specimens.

After the conference, Lou Nickell and I took off for nearby Milan. To compensate for the congested facilities at the hotel in Briançon we picked the biggest room we could find in Milan. Lou and I parted in Milan, he to explore more of Italy, I to travel down the Rhine into Germany and Holland and then on to England. I had the great pleasure of staying briefly with Frits Went's mother.

I spent a few days in London visiting the labs of two professors, one at Bedford College, the other at King's College of the University of London, both of whom I had met at the Botanical Congress and later at the 9th International Botanical Congress in Montreal, Canada.

MY SABBATICAL YEAR IN FRANCE

In 1961, I received a Senior Research Fellowship Grant from NSF for study abroad. In addition, I was given a sabbatical leave from Tuskegee University. The two were necessary to support a now growing family of four children, my wife, and myself.

We crossed the Atlantic on the German ship, *Bremen*. We had purchased a Peugeot station wagon, which was delivered at Cherbourg. From there we drove the 100 km to Paris.

My appointment was at *Le Phytotron* in Gif-Sur-Yvette in France, located about 30 km from Paris. south of Versailles. My association was with my former colleague at CalTech in 1949, Jean P Nitsch, the on-site program director of *Le Phytotron*—the actual director of the lab was a professor at the Sorbonne in Paris. In this small hamlet were located several research labs under the aegis of *Centre Nationale de Research Scientific* (CNRS), associated with the Sorbonne: Plant Biology (*Le Phytotron*), Photosynthesis, Genetics, Chemistry, etc. My research would be in *Le Phytotron*, which essentially mimicked the original one at CalTech, although many times larger and much more expensive!

Dr Nitsch had made all the arrangements for us in a small but adequate home, about two miles from the lab in the small town of Bures-sur-Yvette.

At the laboratory were two other Americans, Ed Oyer from Cornell and Frank Dennis from Michigan State. In true French custom, we were requested to communicate with our French colleagues in French, as well as in our research presentations. When talking to Nitsch, it was in English at the lab, as well as on social occasions. However, some of our French colleagues wanted us to speak English so they could learn it. Obviously, French was spoken in public.

RESEARCH AT *LE PHYTOTRON*

My primary research at *Le Phytotron* was on the synergistic role of certain phenolic compounds on auxin growth responses. Several reports in the literature had pointed out the synergistic role certain phenolic compounds can have in auxin growth responses. It had been demonstrated that such compounds can interfere with the metabolism of 3-indolylacetic acid (IAA). Some compounds reduce the destruction by IAA oxidase (polyphenols, especially ortho-diphenols such as caffeic and chlorogenic acids), whereas others enhance IAA destruction and act as co-factors of IAA oxidase (monophenols such as p-coumaric acid). In addition, certain phenols increase the yield of IAA produced from tryptophan (9, 10).

Nitsch & Nitsch had used as an assay to test these systems the *Avena* first internode test in place of the traditional *Avena* coleoptile curvature test developed by Went. In this test several compounds acted synergistically with IAA. Whether this effect was due to the sparing of IAA or to the formation of a chemical more active than IAA was the focal point of our research. The results point to the fact that o-diphenols such as caffeic and chlorogenic acids enhance the growth produced by IAA. These phenolics exert a similar synergistic effect on tryptophan, which acts as a precursor of IAA. Finally, these results show that monophenols (such as p-coumaric acid), which act as co-factors of IAA oxidase, can completely nullify the effect of phenolic synergists. These results point toward the inhibition of the IAA-oxidase system as the cause of the synergistic action of polyphenolic compounds (6).

Our four children enrolled in the elementary school in Gif, grades kindergarten through 7th grade. The school was divided by sex: l'école des filles for girls and l'école des garçons for boys. School was challenging for the children, but they got along very well, academically and socially, establishing strong ties with their colleagues. Our five-year-old had a harder time acclimating to the instructors and was switched back to l'école maternelle.

The home in which we lived was provided with a garage for the car and a modest-sized lawn and garden where fruit trees and vegetables were grown. We very soon set up a croquet game on the lawn where we played in the evening before dinner. Fortunately, our next-door neighbors, the Louvaux, were very friendly and helpful. Mme Louvaux spoke excellent English, as did their three children; M Louvaux spoke French only. Our other neighbors had a rather large farm with livestock and vegetables. We "inherited" a dog from them, named Gigi.

Our twelve months were filled with a thorough Cook's tour of Europe, especially Paris, where we went on Thursday, school days off. On vacation periods we toured the whole of Europe. On Christmas 1961 our trip took us southeast through Switzerland, Italy and Southern France. During the Easter break in April we toured east through Switzerland again, and Northern Italy, Austria (spending Easter in Vienna), Prague, Berlin, Hanover, Luxembourg, and back to Gif.

Our third and last trip came in July. This was our real vacation. This trip took us to Holland, where we borrowed tents and camping gear from friends in Wageningen. (We tearfully bade farewell to Gigi at a dog shelter outside of Paris.) This trip took us through North Germany, Denmark, Sweden, and Norway. We spent a few days in the home of Paul and Ellen Larson in Bergen. We were back home in Gif on August 3rd, after 3300 miles and 18 days of a wonderful summer vacation.

For the next three weeks, I spent the time wrapping up research and writing a manuscript at Le Phytotron while other members of the family busied themselves preparing for the exit from France and Europe. The trip back was on the longest ship in the world, La Normandie (2 feet longer than the Queen Mary). Our French by then was so good that the ship's crew thought we were "Black French"!

SABBATICAL LEAVE TO THE INTERNATIONAL INSTITUTE OF TROPICAL AGRICULTURE IN NIGERIA

I received a six-month sabbatical leave from Tuskegee in January 1986 to spend at the International Institute of Tropical Agriculture (IITA) at Ibadan, Nigeria, one of the laboratories under the Consultative Group of International Agricultural Research (CGIAR). It is related to The World Bank, Food and Agricultural Organization (FAO), and the United Nations Development Program, and is one of 13 centers worldwide that focus on international research on food commodities for the developing world.

I had been invited to do research at the lab in tissue culture. The major objectives of my research were, in the short term, to produce sweet potato plantlets and ultimately whole plants from subcultures of callus tissues and to develop from cell suspensions through embryogenesis, embryos that would produce new plants. In the longer term, I hoped to make available, through the techniques of protoplast culture, the possible advantages and avenues for genetic engineering, nuclear, and organelle fusion and propagate virus-free plants using these techniques.

My research was in the laboratory of Dr SK Hahn, Director of Root and Tuber Improvement (TRIP) of the station. The two main crops of interest were sweet potato and casava, two of the major food crops grown in tropical areas of developing countries. Again, my interest was in working with sweet potato culture since this was the crop of primary interest at Tuskegee. The research was done in the tissue culture lab under the direction of Mrs Young Ng.

During my six months there, most of the objectives were accomplished: We established cell suspension from callus cultures, regenerated plantlets, established meristem tip cultures, and carried our screening/indexing for virus.

THE TUSKEGEE UNIVERSITY HELA PROJECT IN THE POLIO EVALUATION TRIALS

On 8 February, 1951, George O Gey and his co-workers at the Johns Hopkins University Hospital isolated cell strain HeLa from epithelial tissue obtained by biopsy from a patient with cervical adenocarcinoma, a Black woman named Henrietta Lacks. The code name HeLa, designating the cell strain, was derived from the first two letters of Henrietta Lacks' first and last names. Henrietta Lacks died, but cells from her malignant cervical tissue have attained immortality because they continue to live in cell culture in vitro.

Poliovirus was first produced successfully in tissue culture by Albert Sabin and Peter Olitsky in 1936. In 1953 Scherer, Syverton, and Gey reported that poliovirus would infect cultures of the HeLa strain and that HeLa cells were more sensitive to the cytopathogenic effect of poliomyelitis virus than monkey testicular cells. In culture HeLa cells remained viable and unaltered in morphology. Furthermore, they were extraordinarily hardy when shipped by train or plane and would begin to proliferate again upon adding nutritive fluid.

After Jonas Salk developed his polio vaccine in 1952, it was anticipated that the 23 laboratories participating in the subsequent evaluation process would require large quantities of monkey cells to measure the amount of antibody developed in response to the three types of poliovirus antigen. However, the required supply of Rhesus monkeys became doubtful. HeLa cell strain was selected as an alternative source of primate host cells, and the National Foundation established a central source of supply of HeLa cultures to meet the anticipated demand.

The National Foundation for Infantile Paralysis wanted the HeLa cell project to conform to protocols they had developed, and thought that such conformity could be achieved best in a university organization with personnel experienced in research and development projects. The selection of Tuskegee for the HeLa project may have been influenced by confidence expressed by Basil O'Connor, chairman of the Board of Trustees, in the quality of research and cooperation available at Tuskegee. Dr Russell W Brown, Director of the Carver Research Foundation, was to act as principal investigator and I as his assistant (1). Dr Brown and I spent several weeks in January 1953 studying cell and tissue culture methods working with HeLa cells at the University of Minnesota under the supervision of Jerome T Syverton and William F Scherer.

The mission of the Tuskegee project was to culture HeLa cells on a relatively massive scale; to avoid viral, microbial, and other cellular contamination; to maintain the cells in a genetically unaltered condition; to prepare monolayer cultures of determined cellular population in tubes and bottles; and to ship these cultures to distant laboratories in such condition that they would be received ready for direct use in vaccine evaluation procedures.

In April 1953, Scherer made the first of many visits to Tuskegee as HeLa project consultant, bringing with him a culture of the HeLa cell. This culture was expanded to bottle culture monolayers, from which test tube cultures were prepared for experimental shipping. Beginning 11 May 1953, experimental shipments of cells were sent to Scherer and occasional shipments to Jonas Salk at the University of Pittsburgh. The objective was to develop the capacity to ship at least 10,000 cultures per week, beginning 1 June 1953.

Renovation of the area in the science building assigned to the HeLa project and installation of major items of equipment were accomplished in record time. The laboratory was designed to accommodate ten cell culture technicians and a laboratory supervisor.

By September 1953, we had six technicians at Tuskegee, including the laboratory supervisor. Shortly thereafter, the staff was increased to ten full-time cell culture technicians plus the supervisor, and additional full-time laboratory helpers and shipping clerks, as well as part-time student helpers. At one time during full-scale production 35 people were working on the HeLa project.

In February 1954, the laboratory achieved the projected level of production; it was then possible to supply the requirements of the many laboratories participating in the polio vaccine evaluation program. From 1 April through 30 September 1954, approximately 133,000 tube cultures and 1800 bottle cultures of HeLa cells were sent from Tuskegee laboratories in 23 cities throughout the United States. By 30 June we had shipped approximately 600,000 cultures.

In 1955, the first effective vaccine against polio was used. Initially, the live virus was used orally. However, owing to untoward effects, the injection of inactivated virus was used. This is the method used today. Thus, the plague of the poliomyelitis disease was essentially eradicated soon after the introduction of the vaccine in 1955.

In retrospect, although it may have been fortuitous that we at Tuskegee Institute became involved in a program that has had such momentous development in more recent decades, we are quietly proud of the role of the Tuskegee Institute in the fight against poliomyelitis.

AFFILIATION WITH PROFESSIONAL SOCIETIES

My first professional scientific meeting was as a new graduate student, to the 106th American Association for the Advancement of Science (AAAS) meeting at Philadelphia in December 1940. The American Society of Plant Physiologists (ASPP) was at that time meeting with AAAS. The Botanical Society was by far the predominant botanical science (15 program pages), followed by the American Phytopathological Society (APS) (11 pages), with ASPP only 7 pages. This was several years before the latter two began having their own meetings separately or at times jointly. At the meeting, Bernard S Meyer of North Carolina State University was Chairman of the Physiological Section of the Botanical Sciences of AAAS. He became the president of ASPP in 1943. He was coauthor with DB Anderson, of Ohio State University, of the most popular text in plant physiology at that time. I especially remember two papers delivered, one by Avery, Shalucha & Creighton, entitled *The Determination and Expression of Yields in Hormonal Extraction of Plant Tissue*, followed by a paper presented by Avery, Berger & Shalucha on *High Yields of Hormones from Maize Endosperm*. Among others who presented in that session were Thimann, Skoog, Overbeek, and Blakeslee.

I became a member of AAAS then and joined both the Botanical Societies of America and ASPP, the latter in 1950. In later years, my affiliation with the Botanical Society weakened whereas that with ASPP strengthened. I was made a fellow of AAAS in 1955, and received The Charles Reid Barnes Lifetime Membership Award from ASPP in 1998.

In 1958 I affiliated with the Southern Section of ASPP, but I could not meet with the section in Little Rock, Arkansas, because of segregation laws in the South. My first (integrated) meeting with the Southern Section came a year later in Memphis, Tennessee, where I was then and for several years subsequently the only Black present. In 1970, I became chairman of the section, and in 1984 received the fourth Distinguished Service Award.

In 1955, the annual AAAS meeting was held in Atlanta, Georgia. Despite the US Supreme Court decision in *Brown v. Board of Education* in May 1954, a year later the public accommodation laws in Atlanta had not changed to allow Blacks to meet in or stay in the major hotels. The then-president of AAAS, George Beadle, whom I had known when I was a postdoc at CalTech, was anxious to have the meeting integrated. He asked if I would be willing to serve as a guinea pig in attempting to do this. I agreed. Dr Beadle asked me to preside over a concurrent session of the American Phytopathological Society and the American Society of Plant Physiologists, my professional society. I agreed. The symposium was on the cotton plant—right in line with my patron saint, Dr George Washington Carver. In my introductory statement, I pointed out the role Dr Carver had played in the agricultural practices of the South in the early years of the twentieth century. In addition, I presented a research paper entitled *In Vitro and in Vivo Responses of Oat and Pea to 2,4-D*. However, even though the meeting sessions were integrated, the dining areas were not, so Dr Beadle moved the banquet to the cafeteria at Atlanta University, a Black school. Since AU was a considerable distance from the downtown hotels where the meetings were held, buses carried us to AU. At least one prominent Black scientist who was vice-president and subsequently president of the American Association for Anthropology, Dr W Montague Cobb, refused to attend because he felt it an insult to be subjected to the segregation policy of the hotels.

In 1976, because of my research in that area I joined the Tissue Culture Association (TCA), which changed its name to the Society for In Vitro Biology in 1995. I served as president of the Historical Section from 1994 to 1996 and received the society's Plant Fellow Award in 1998. My students and I presented many papers at the meetings of the society during that 20-year period.

In earlier years, when many of the national societies had southern sections that were closed to non-whites, Blacks formed their own scientific and technical societies. The National Institute of Science (NIS), begun in 1945 and still in existence, was primarily for senior scientists, i.e. mostly those who had received PhDs and were teaching predominantly in Negro universities. The Beta Kappa Ki Society was founded in 1923, at Lincoln University in Pennsylvania, to steer college students into the sciences and technology, hence its membership is primarily composed of students. It is also still very active. I was very active in both organizations, especially the former, NIS.

In 1971, President Nixon sent the following message to Congress: "Colleges and universities founded for Black Americans are an indispensable national resource. Despite great handicaps, they educate substantial numbers of Black Americans, thereby helping to bring about a more rapid transition to an integrated society. Black institutions are faced with an historic inadequacy of resources. To help these institutions compete for students and faculty with other colleges and universities, the combined help of government at all levels, other institutions of higher learning, and the private sector must be summoned." The Minority Schools Biomedical Support (MSBS) program aimed to promote the sciences and technology among students in Black colleges and universities. However, the name was changed to Minority Biomedical Support Program (MSB) to broaden its reach to minority students in colleges and universities nationwide. Its current name, Minority Biomedical Research Support program (MBRS), was adopted to emphasize the major purpose of the program—research. The program is still very active. At Tuskegee University there have been 387 participants in the program to date. I was program director of the MBRS program at Tuskegee University from 1973 until 1986.

MENTORING YOUNG STUDENTS IN THE SCIENCES

During my many years of participating in research meetings, presentations and publications, it was obvious to me that there were not many Blacks attending meetings of national or regional societies, especially in the South where large numbers of Blacks were in colleges and universities. I decided I would concentrate my last years at Tuskegee in trying to fill this void, especially in the biological and allied scientific areas.

Beginning in 1978, I directed the Research Education Apprenticeship Career in Health Opportunities for University Training (REACH-OUT). This program, funded by NIH, brought high school youngsters interested in the sciences, especially the biomedical sciences, to the campus of Tuskegee University to give them first-hand experience in research in biomedical areas under the supervision of senior research scientists. Between 1988 and 1994 this program engaged about 150 students in biomedical research, many of whom went on to college to receive undergraduate and graduate training in the biomedical fields.

I was the program director of ENHANCES (Educational Nurturing of Highly Academic National Candidates for Excellence in Science), a program funded by the Howard Hughes Medical Institute, beginning in 1989. An eight-week residential program was made available for talented minority high school students who were interested in the opportunity to receive college credits toward their freshman year. University faculty provided instruction in English and mathematics, using traditional and computer-based teaching techniques. Visiting lecturers introduced the students to research in the biomedical and chemical fields. Upon completion of the summer term, students enrolled in biology and chemistry programs at Tuskegee University. Another opportunity offered the ENHANCES students was the chance, once they reached their junior year, to apply for the MARC-U*STAR program, funded by NIH. This program is designed to increase the number of underrepresented minority students in programs in the biomedical sciences, including mathematics, up to doctoral-level training. Offered are a tuition waiver, stipend, internal research plus an external research experience at a major research university and travel to a national meeting to present the results of the external research activity. To date, the MARC-U*STAR graduates include 7 MDs, 6 PhDs, 2 DVMs, 1 DDS, and 2 MPHs. Most of the students in these programs have spent summers in research in laboratories all over the country, e.g. Harvard, University of California at Berkeley, New York University, St Jude's Hospital, Cold Spring Harbor Laboratory, Johns Hopkins University, Rockwell Cancer Center, and the University of Alabama.

Of almost 200 participants in the ENHANCES program, most have continued their college careers at Tuskegee, and at other Universities. Several have gone on to receive PhD and MD degrees. From the most recent graduates of this program in May 2000, of the 15 students who came to Tuskegee in the summer 1996 class, 12 remained at Tuskegee. Seven of those 12 students graduated with honors: four summa cum laude, two magna cum laude, and one cum laude. All of these students majored in either biology or chemistry and are all now pursuing PhDs, MDs, or other professional degrees in the health sciences.

In my last ten years or more at Tuskegee, I have changed my emphasis from training students in research to mentoring and promoting those youngsters on to successful college degrees and postgraduate positions and careers.

It has been this work with these youngsters that has kept me young beyond my chronological age. These students have been the impetus that has prevented me from actually retiring from university and academic activity, although my current title is professor emeritus.

My favorite Bible verse, Matthew 7:6–7, exemplifies the role of the scientist: "Ask, and it shall be given unto you; seek and ye shall find; knock and it shall be opened unto you. Everyone that asketh receiveth; and he that seeketh findeth."

ACKNOWLEDGMENT

I am greatly indebted to those persons who assisted me with this manuscript and without whose help it would not have met the deadline. First, Mrs. Mary Ballard, my secretary, who did the Herculean job not only of typing it, but even more difficult, of deciphering of my scratchy hieroglyphics. I am indeed most grateful for her patience in the typing, retyping, and revisions to this manuscript. I wish also to thank Diane Kenney for editorial assistance to make it flow more smoothly and coherently. And lastly, my wife, Gwen, for reading it, but more so for her patience in tolerating my late hours while I was writing this manuscript. I am forever in their debt for helping to make this sketch readable.

Visit the Annual Reviews home page at www.AnnualReviews.org

LITERATURE CITED

1. Brown RW, Henderson JHM. 1983. The mass production and distribution of HeLa cells at Tuskegee Institute, 1953–55. *J. Hist. Med. Allied Sci.* 38:415

2. Gordon WC, Henderson JHM. 1950. The alkaloidal content of blue lupine (*Lupinus angustifolius* L.) and its toxicity on small laboratory animals. *J. Agric. Sci.* 41:141

3. Henderson JHM. 1954. The changing nutritional pattern from normal to habituated sunflower callus tissue in vitro. *Ann. Biol.* 30:329

4. Henderson JHM, Bonner J. 1952. Auxin metabolism in normal and crown gall tissue of sunflower. *Am. J. Bot.* 39:444–51

5. Henderson JHM, Durrell ME, Bonner J. 1952. The growth of normal sunflower stem callus in vitro by the use of supplementary growth factors, including coconut milk. *Am. J. Bot.* 39:467–73

6. Henderson JHM, Nitsch JP. 1962. Effect of certain phenolic acids on the elongation of *Avena* first internodes in the presence of auxins and tryptophan. *Nature* 195:780

7. Henderson JHM, Stauffer JF. 1944. The influence of some respiratory inhibitors and intermediates on the growth and respiration of excised tomato roots. *Am. J. Bot.* 31:528

8. Henderson JHM, Veal MP. 1948. The effect of the inter-relationship of boron and magnesium in the growth and calcium uptake of blue lupine in solution culture. *Plant Physiol.* 23:609

9. Nitsch JP, Nitsch C. 1959. *Bull. Soc. Bot. France* 106:414

10. Nitsch JP, Nitsch C. 1961. *Bull. Soc. Bot. France* 108:349

11. Rier JP Jr, Henderson JHM. 1957. The relationship of temperature and nutrition to the growth of sunflower tissue in vitro. *Plant Physiol.* 32:494

12. West FR Jr, Henderson JHM. 1950. The effect of 2,4-dichlorophenoxyacetic acid and various other substances upon the respiration of blue lupine seedling roots. *Science* 111:579

Annu. Rev. Plant Physiol. Plant Mol. Biol. 2001. 52:29–66

ALKALOID BIOSYNTHESIS IN PLANTS: Biochemistry, Cell Biology, Molecular Regulation, and Metabolic Engineering Applications

Peter J Facchini

Department of Biological Sciences, University of Calgary, Calgary, Alberta T2N 1N4, Canada; e-mail: pfacchin@ucalgary.ca

Key Words   metabolic engineering, gene regulation, secondary metabolism, signal transduction, subcellular compartmentation

■ **Abstract**   Recent advances in the cell, developmental, and molecular biology of alkaloid biosynthesis have heightened our appreciation for the complexity and importance of plant secondary pathways. Several biosynthetic genes involved in the formation of tropane, benzylisoquinoline, and terpenoid indole alkaloids have now been isolated. The early events of signal perception, the pathways of signal transduction, and the function of gene promoters have been studied in relation to the regulation of alkaloid metabolism. Enzymes involved in alkaloid biosynthesis are associated with diverse subcellular compartments including the cytosol, vacuole, tonoplast membrane, endoplasmic reticulum, chloroplast stroma, thylakoid membranes, and perhaps unique "biosynthetic" or transport vesicles. Localization studies have shown that sequential alkaloid biosynthetic enzymes can also occur in distinct cell types, suggesting the intercellular transport of pathway intermediates. Isolated genes have also been used to genetically alter the accumulation of specific alkaloids and other plant secondary metabolites. Metabolic modifications include increased indole alkaloid levels, altered tropane alkaloid accumulation, elevated serotonin synthesis, reduced indole glucosinolate production, redirected shikimate metabolism, and increased cell wall–bound tyramine formation. This review discusses the biochemistry, cell biology, molecular regulation, and metabolic engineering of alkaloid biosynthesis in plants.

CONTENTS

1040-2519/01/0601-0029$14.00

INTRODUCTION

Alkaloids are a diverse group of low-molecular-weight, nitrogen-containing compounds found in about 20% of plant species. Many of the ~12,000 alkaloids for which structures have been described function in the defense of plants against herbivores and pathogens (19, 178). The potent biological activity of some alkaloids has also led to their exploitation as pharmaceuticals, stimulants, narcotics, and poisons. Plant-derived alkaloids currently in clinical use include the analgesics morphine and codeine, the anticancer agents vinblastine and taxol, the gout suppressant colchicine, the muscle relaxant (+)-tubocurarine, the antiarrythmic ajmaline, the antibiotic sanguinarine, and the sedative scopolamine. Other important alkaloids of plant origin include caffeine, nicotine, cocaine, and the synthetic O,O-acetylated morphine derivative heroin.

Research in the field of plant alkaloid biochemistry began with the isolation of morphine in 1806. Remarkably, the structure of morphine was not elucidated until 1952 owing to the stereochemical complexity of the molecule. Since then, three major technical advances have led to substantial progress in our understanding of plant alkaloid formation. The first was the introduction in the 1950s of radiolabeled precursors that allowed the chemical elucidation of alkaloid biosynthetic pathways. The second involved the increased use during the 1970s of plant cell cultures as an abundant source of biosynthetic enzymes that could be isolated, purified, and characterized. Finally, the widespread application in the 1990s of molecular techniques to the alkaloid field facilitated the isolation of several genes involved in indole, tropane, and benzylisoquinoline alkaloid biosynthesis (Table 1). The early events of signal perception, the pathways of signal transduction, and the function of gene promoters have since been investigated in relation to the regulation of alkaloid metabolism. Tissue-specific localization studies have shown that sequential biosynthetic enzymes can occur in distinct cell types. The predicted translocation of pathway intermediates between cells further demonstrates the intricate cell biology of alkaloid biosynthesis. Isolated genes have also been used to genetically engineer the accumulation of alkaloids and other secondary metabolites in plants. In this review, recent advances in the biochemistry,

cell biology, molecular regulation, and metabolic engineering of plant alkaloid pathways are discussed.

BIOCHEMISTRY AND CELL BIOLOGY OF ALKALOID PATHWAYS

Terpenoid Indole Alkaloids

Terpenoid indole alkaloids (TIAs) comprise a family of ~3000 compounds that includes the antineoplastic agents vinblastine and camptothecin, the antimalarial drug quinine, and the rat poison strychnine. Some TIAs have been proposed to play a role in the defense of plants against pests and pathogens (93). TIAs consist of an indole moiety provided by tryptamine and a terpenoid component derived from the iridoid glucoside secologanin. Tryptophan is converted to tryptamine by tryptophan decarboxylase (TDC; Figure 1), which is encoded by a single gene in *Catharanthus roseus* (31, 58) and by two autonomously regulated genes in *Camptotheca acuminata* (91). The *C. roseus TDC* gene exhibits both developmental and inducible regulation. In contrast, *C. acuminata TDC1* is expressed in tissues containing high levels of camptothecin including the shoot apex and bark, but the gene is not induced in response to elicitor treatment. However, *TDC2* is induced in elicitor-treated *C. acuminata* cell cultures, but is not developmentally expressed. The differential regulation of *TDC* genes in *C. acuminata* suggests that one participates in a developmentally controlled defense pathway, while the other is involved in an inducible defense mechanism.

The first committed step in secologanin biosynthesis is the hydroxylation of geraniol to 10-hydroxygeraniol. The enzyme geraniol 10-hydroxylase (G10H) was characterized as a P450 monooxygenase because it is membrane bound, dependent on NADPH and O_2, and displays light-reversible CO inhibition (106). G10H is specific for the C-10 position and exhibits similar affinity for geraniol and nerol, the *cis*-isomer of geraniol. The conversion of loganin to secologanin represents the last step in the pathway and is also catalyzed by a P450-dependent enzyme (180). The production of terpenoid precursors might play a regulatory role in TIA biosynthesis since the addition of secologanin or loganin to *C. roseus* cell cultures increases alkaloid accumulation (111, 113). Moreover, the level of G10H activity positively correlates with the accumulation of alkaloids when *C. roseus* cell cultures are transferred to alkaloid production medium (148). The enzyme 3-hydroxy-3-methylglutaryl coenzyme A reductase (HMGR), which is involved in the biosynthesis of mevalonate, was cloned and characterized from *C. roseus* (97) and *C. acuminata* (16, 99). The differential expression of *HMGR* genes in response to wounding and methyl jasmonate (MeJA) was suggested to contribute to the regulation of TIA biosynthesis. However, secologanin was recently shown to be derived from the triose phosphate/pyruvate pathway (22); thus, the correlation between *HMGR* expression and TIA accumulation is likely coincidental.

TABLE 1 Alkaloid biosynthetic enzymes for which the corresponding genes have been cloned

Enzyme	Function	Species	Type	Reference
Monoterpenoid indole alkaloid biosynthesis				
TDC	Tryptophan decarboxylase	*Catharanthus roseus*	Pyridoxal-5′-phospahate-dependent decarboxylase	31
		Camptotheca acuminata		91
STR	Strictosidine synthase	*Catharanthus roseus*	Vacuolar glycoprotein	104
		Rauwolfia serpentina		84
SGD	Strictosidine β-D-glucosidase	*Catharanthus roseus*	Membrane-associated glucosidase	55
T16H	Tabersonine 16-hydroxylase	*Catharanthus roseus*	P450-dependent monooxygenase	151
D4H	Desacetoxyvindoline 4-hydroxylase	*Catharanthus roseus*	2-Oxoglutarate-dependent dioxygenase	176
DAT	Deacetylvindoline acetyltransferase	*Catharanthus roseus*	Acetyl CoA-dependent acetyltransferase	164
Benzylisoquinoline alkaloid biosynthesis				
TYDC	Tyrosine decarboxylase	*Papaver somniferum*	Pyridoxal-5′-phospahate-dependent decarboxylase	38
6OMT	Norcoclaurine 6-*O*-methyltransferase	*Coptis japonica*	S-Adenosyl-L-methionine-dependent *O*-methyltransferase	114
4′OMT	3′-Hydroxy-*N*-methylcoclaurine 4′-*O*-methyltransferase	*Coptis japonica*	S-Adenosyl-L-methionine-dependent *O*-methyltransferase	114
OMT II;1-4	Norcoclaurine 6-*O*-methyltransferase	*Thalictrum tuberosum*	S-Adenosyl-L-methionine-dependent *O*-methyltransferase	49

CYP80A1	Berbamunine synthase	Berberis stolonifera	P450-dependent monooxygenase	81
CYP80B1	N-Methylcoclaurine 3'-hydroxylase	Eschscholzia californica	P450-dependent monooxygenase	133
		Papaver somniferum		72, 182
BBE	Berberine bridge enzyme	Eschscholzia californica	Flavinylated oxidoreductase	34
		Papaver somniferum		41
		Berberis stolonifera		21
SOMT	Scoulerine 9-O-methyltransferase	Coptis japonica	S-Adenosyl-L-methionine-dependent O-methyltransferase	171
COR	Codeinone reductase	Papaver somniferum	Aldo/keto reductase	173
Tropane alkaloid and nicotine biosynthesis				
ODC	Ornithine decarboxylase	Datura stamonium	Pyridoxal-5'-phospahate-dependent decarboxylase	112
PMT	Putrescine N-methyltransferase	Atropa belladonna	S-Adenosyl-L-methionine-dependent N-methyltransferase	167
		Nicotina tabacum		71
TR-I	Tropinone reductase-I	Datura stramonium	Short-chain dehydrogense	119
TR-II	Tropinone reductase-II	Datura stramonium	Short-chain dehydrogenase	119
H6H	Hyoscyamine 6β-hydroxylase	Hyoscyamus niger	2-Oxoglutarate-dependent dioxygenase	101
		Atropa belladonna		168
Purine alkaloid biosynthesis				
CS	Caffeine synthase	Camellia sinensis	S-Adenosyl-L-methionine-dependent N-methyltransferase	–

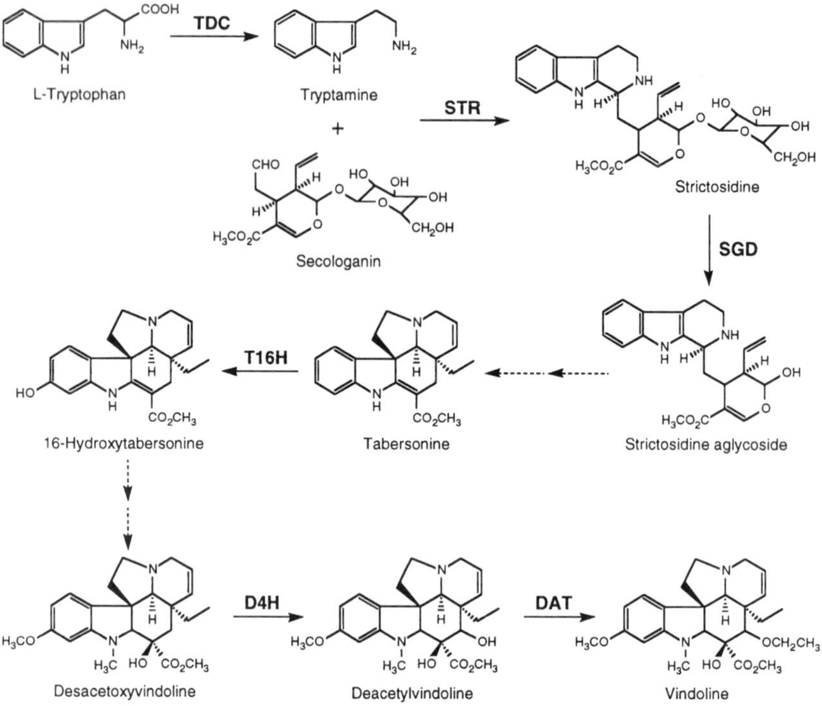

Figure 1 Reactions catalyzed by enzymes involved in monoterpenoid indole alkaloid biosynthesis for which the corresponding genes have been cloned. TDC, tryptophan decarboxylase; STR, strictosidine synthase; SGD, strictosidine β-D-glucosidase; T16H, tabersonine 16-hydroxylase; D4H, desacetoxyvindoline 4-hydroxylase; DAT, deacetylvindoline 4-O-acetyltransferase.

Tryptamine and secologanin are condensed by strictosidine synthase (STR) to form strictosidine, the common precursor to all TIAs (Figure 1). STR cDNAs have been isolated from *Rauvolfia serpentina* (84) and *C. roseus* (104, 132). The enzyme is encoded by a single gene in *C. roseus*, indicating that the multiple STR isoforms reported previously result from posttranslational modification of a single precursor (132). Strictosidine is deglucosylated by strictosidine β-D-glucosidase (SGD), which has been purified from *C. roseus* cell cultures (92). The native enzyme exhibits a high molecular mass, suggesting that it exists as an aggregate composed of multiple 63-kDa subunits. Digestion of SGD with trypsin causes the complex to disintegrate, solubilizing the enzyme without loss of activity. SGD is encoded by a single gene in *C. roseus* that shares ~60% homology with other plant glucosidases (55). Deglucosylated strictosidine is converted via several unstable intermediates to 4,21-dehydrogeissoschizine. Although several TIAs are produced from 4,21-dehydrogeissoschizine, few of the enzymes involved have been isolated (108). For example, none of the enzymes leading to catharanthine has been described.

However, the biosynthesis of vindoline has been characterized in considerable detail. Vindoline is ultimately coupled to catharanthine by a nonspecific peroxidase to yield vinblastine (157).

The first of six steps involved in the conversion of tabersonine to vindoline consists of hydroxylation at the C-16 position by tabersonine 16-hydroxylase (T16H; Figure 1), which was detected in total protein extracts of young *C. roseus* leaves (163). Based on its requirement for NADPH and O_2, and its inhibition by CO, cytochrome *c*, and specific inhibitors, T16H was characterized as a P450-dependent monooxygenase. A T16H cDNA was isolated from *C. roseus* cell cultures using a cloning strategy based on the activation of the enzyme by light (151). Several P450 sequences were amplified by polymerase chain reaction (PCR), using degenerate primers specific to the conserved heme-binding domain. The PCR products were hybridized to RNA from induced and noninduced cells, and one showed induction kinetics consistent with T16H. The isolated cDNA, encoding a P450 homologue designated CYP71D12, was expressed in *Escherichia coli* as a translational fusion with cytochrome P450 reductase (CPR) from *C. roseus* (107). CYP71D12 was identified as T16H based on its ability to convert tabersonine to 16-methoxytabersonine. Genomic DNA hybridization analyses suggest the presence of at least two *T16H* genes (151), but only a single copy of the *CPR* gene (90), in *C. roseus*.

Subsequent to the 16-hydroxylation of tabersonine, the next three steps in vindoline biosynthesis are now accepted as 16-*O*-methylation, hydration of the 2,3-double bond, and *N*-methylation of the indole-ring nitrogen (8, 27, 28). An *S*-adenosyl-L-methionine (SAM)-dependent *O*-methyltransferase (OMT) has been reported that methylates 16-*O*-demethyl-4-*O*-deacetylvindoline (45). Initially, two consecutive hydroxylations at the C-3 and C-4 positions were proposed to follow the 16-hydroxylation of tabersonine (45). However, the isolation of a SAM-dependent *N*-methyltransferase (NMT) specific for the indole-ring nitrogen of 16-methoxy-2,3-dihydro-3-hydroxytabersonine indicated that the *O*-methylation step precedes *N*-methylation, and that 16-hydroxytabersonine is the natural substrate of the OMT (28, 33). The enzyme involved in hydrating the 2,3-double bond has not been isolated.

The second-to-last step in vindoline biosynthesis is catalyzed by a 2-oxoglutarate-dependent dioxygenase that hydroxylates the C-4 position of desacetoxyvindoline (D4H; Figure 1) (23). The enzyme requires ferrous ions and ascorbate, occurs as three unique charge isoforms, and exhibits an "ordered ter ter" mechanism with 2-oxoglutarate binding first, followed by O_2 and desacetoxyvindoline (24). Degenerate primers, designed from amino acid sequences derived from the purified protein, were used to isolate cDNA and genomic clones encoding D4H (174). Two different cDNAs were isolated, representing dimorphic alleles of a single-copy gene.

The final step in vindoline biosynthesis is catalyzed by acetylcoenzyme A: deacetylvindoline 4-*O*-acetyltransferase (DAT; Figure 1) (26, 44). The purified enzyme is strongly inhibited by tabersonine and coenzyme A (50% inhibition at

45 μM and 37 μM, respectively), and weakly inhibited by tryptamine, secologanin, and vindoline (28%, 25%, and 40% inhibition, respectively, at 500 μM), suggesting that DAT activity is modulated by pathway precursors and products (135). The original purification of DAT led to the incorrect conclusion that the enzyme consists of two subunits with molecular weights of 33 and 21 kDa. However, the isolated *DAT* gene encodes a 50-kDa polypeptide, suggesting that the protein was cleaved as an artifact of purification (164). Moreover, the protein that cross-reacts with anti-DAT antibody in seedlings and leaves also has a molecular weight of 50 kDa (164).

Benzylisoquinoline Alkaloids

Benzylisoquinoline alkaloids (BIAs) are a large and diverse alkaloid group with $\sim$2500 defined structures. The pharmacological activity of BIAs renders many of them useful as pharmaceuticals and is often a clue to their biological role in the plant (19). For example, the effectiveness of morphine as an analgesic, colchicine as a microtubule disrupter, and (+)-tubocurarine as a neuromuscular blocker suggests that these alkaloids function as herbivore deterrents. The antimicrobial properties of sanguinarine suggest that it confers protection against pathogens. The BIAs berberine, sanguinarine, and palmatine were specifically shown to confer protection against herbivores and pathogens (149).

BIA biosynthesis begins with a metabolic lattice of decarboxylations, *ortho*-hydroxylations, and deaminations that convert tyrosine to both dopamine and 4-hydroxyphenylacetaldehyde (142). The only enzyme involved in these early steps that has been purified (100), and for which the corresponding cDNA has been cloned (38, 98), is the aromatic L-amino acid decarboxylase (TYDC) that converts tyrosine and dopa to their corresponding amines (Figure 2). TYDC is encoded by a family of $\sim$15 genes in *Papaver somniferum* (opium poppy) that can be divided into two subgroups based on sequence identity (38). Although the catalytic properties of the isoforms are similar, each *TYDC* subfamily exhibits a distinct developmental and inducible expression pattern (38, 40). TYDC cDNAs have also been reported from parsley (80) and *Arabidopsis thaliana* (172), which do not accumulate tyrosine-derived alkaloids. TYDC mRNAs were shown to be rapidly induced in response to elicitor treatment (40, 80, 172) and pathogen challenge (150) in various plants. Induction of TYDC mRNAs in parsley and *Arabidopsis* suggests that tyramine serves as the precursor to a ubiquitous class of defense-response metabolites, in addition to BIAs. Recent studies suggest that the synthesis and deposition in the cell wall of amides, composed of hydroxycinnamic acid-derivatives and tyramine, is central to the defense-response of many plants (105). Amides, together with other phenolics, are believed to reduce cell wall digestibility. The dual role of tyramine as a precursor for BIA and hydroxycinnamic acid amide biosynthesis suggests that the *TYDC* gene family in opium poppy encodes TYDC isoforms with diverse metabolic roles.

Dopamine and 4-hydroxyphenylacetaldehyde are condensed by norco-claurine synthase (NCS) to yield the trihydroxybenzylisoquinoline alkaloid (*S*)-norcoclaurine, which is the central precursor to all BIAs in plants (Figure 2) (158, 159). Due to the inability of NCS to discriminate between 4-hydroxyphenyl-acetaldehyde and 3,4-dihydroxyphenylacetaldehyde, and the nonspecificity of the

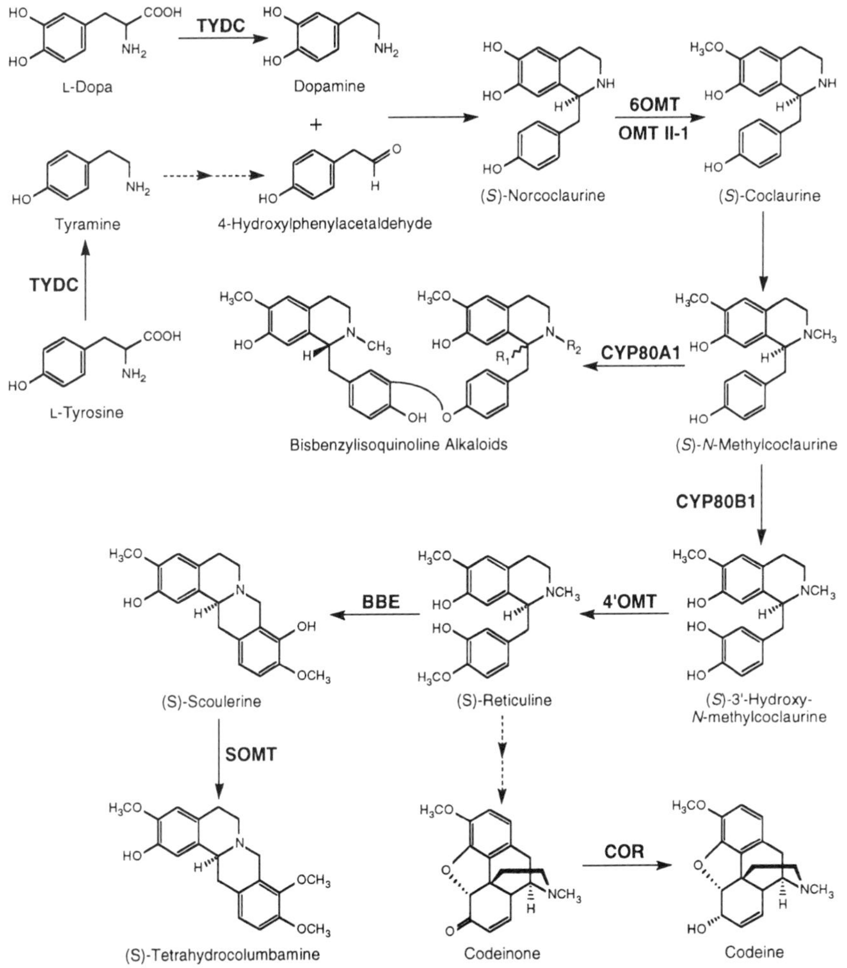

Figure 2   Reactions catalyzed by enzymes involved in benzylisoquinoline alkaloid biosyn-thesis for which the corresponding genes have been cloned. TYDC, tyrosine/dopa decar-boxylase; 6OMT, norcoclaurine 6-*O*-methyltransferase; 4′OMT, 3′-hydroxy-*N*-methylcoclaurine 4′-*O*-methyltransferase; OMT II-1, *O*-methyltransferase II-1; CYP80A1, berbamunine synthase, CYP80B1, (*S*)-*N*-methylcoclaurine 3′-hydroxylase; BBE, berberine bridge enzyme; SOMT, scoulerine *N*-methyltransferase; COR, codeinone reductase.

subsequent methyltransferase reactions, it was originally thought that the tetrahydroxybenzylisoquinoline alkaloid (S)-norlaudanosoline was the precursor to BIAs (141). However, only norcoclaurine has been found to occur in plants.

(S)-Norcoclaurine is converted to (S)-reticuline by a 6-O-methyltransferase (49, 147), an N-methyltransferase (47), a P450 hydroxylase (133), and a 4'-O-methyltransferase (48, 147). The SAM-dependent 6-O- and 4'-O-methyltransferases (6OMT and 4'OMT, respectively) have been purified from cultured Coptis japonica cells (147), and the corresponding cDNAs isolated and characterized (114). Although the two enzymes display similar enzymological properties, they exhibit distinct substrate specificities. Moreover, the 6OMT follows a "ping-pong bi bi" mechanism, whereas the 4'OMT catalyzes an "ordered bi bi" reaction (114). Four homologous O-methyltransferase cDNAs (OMT II;1-4) have also been isolated from MeJA-treated Thalictrum tuberosum cell cultures (49). Heterologous expression of the OMT II;1-4 cDNAs showed that homodimers and various heterdimeric combinations of the four isoforms exhibit broad substrate specificity. The O-methylated substrates included simple catechols, phenylpropanoids, and various BIAs, suggesting that some of the isoforms are involved in both BIA and phenylpropanoid metabolism. For example, the homodimer of OMT II;1 efficiently O-methylates (R,S)-norcoclaurine (Figure 2) and various catechol and caffeic acid derivatives. Remarkably, OMT II;4 differs from OMT II;1 by only one amino acid, but its homodimer does not catalyze the alkaloid methylations. Both the 6OMT and 4'OMT from C. japonica show relatively low identity (24 and 35%, respectively) to the various catechol OMT II isoforms (114). The in vivo contribution, if any, of the OMT II enzymes to BIA biosynthesis remains to be established.

Originally, the aromatic-ring hydroxylation involved in the conversion of (S)-norcoclaurine to (S)-reticuline was thought to be catalyzed by a nonspecific phenol oxidase (89). However, a P450-dependent monooxygenase (CYP80B1; Figure 2) isolated from Eschscholzia californica (133) and opium poppy (72, 182) exhibits a K_m for (S)-N-methylcoclaurine 39-fold lower than that of the phenolase; thus, CYP80B1 is now known to convert (S)-N-methylcoclaurine to (S)-3'-hydroxy-N-methylcoclaurine. CYP80B1 is encoded by two to three genes in E. californica (133) and opium poppy (72, 182).

Intermediates of the (S)-reticuline pathway also serve as the precursors to ~270 dimeric bisbenzylisoquinoline alkaloids such as berbamunine and (+)-tubocurarine. A phenol-coupling P450-dependent oxidase berbamunine synthase (CYP80A1) has been purified (160), and the corresponding cDNA isolated (81), from Berberis stolonifera. CYP80A1 couples two molecules of (R)-N-methylcoclaurine or one each of (R)- and (S)-N-methylcoclaurine by an ether linkage to form (R,R)-guattegaumerine or (R,S)-berbamunine, respectively (Figure 2). Additional variations in bisbenzylisoquinoline alkaloid structure include phenyl ring substitutions, the number of ether linkages, and regio- and stereoselection of monomers. CPR has also been purified from opium poppy, and the corresponding cDNAs isolated from opium poppy and E. californica (139). The CPR proteins share 69% amino acid identity and occur as two isoforms in each species. Coexpression of *E. californica* CPR and CYP80A1 in insect cell cultures resulted in an altered product profile compared to that obtained from the expression of CYP80A1 in the absence of the plant reductase.

(*S*)-Reticuline is a branch-point intermediate in the biosynthesis of many BIAs. Much research has focused on branch pathways that lead to benzophenanthridine alkaloids, such as sanguinarine and macarpine (85); protoberberine alkaloids, such as berberine and palmatine (66); and morphinan alkaloids, such as morphine and codeine (37). Most of the enzymes involved in these pathways have been isolated, many have been purified, and the corresponding cDNAs for three have been cloned. The first committed step in benzophenanthridine, protoberberine, and protopine alkaloid biosynthesis involves conversion of the *N*-methyl group of (*S*)-reticuline into the methylene bridge moiety of (*S*)-scoulerine by the berberine bridge enzyme (BBE; Figure 2). This conversion is unique in nature and cannot be achieved using synthetic chemical methods. The enzyme was purified from *Berberis beaniana* (161), the corresponding cDNAs were cloned from *E. californica* (34) and *B. stolonifera* (21), and *BBE1* genes have been isolated from opium poppy (41) and *E. californica* (68). The phenol coupling reaction catalyzed by heterologously expressed BBE (82) was recently identified as an ionic mechanism with a methylene iminium ion as the reaction intermediate (83).

(*S*)-Scoulerine can be converted to (*S*)-stylopine by two P450-dependent oxidases, (*S*)-chelanthifoline synthase (CFS) and (*S*)-stylopine synthase (SPS), which result in the formation of two methylenedioxy groups (9, 10). (*S*)-Stylopine is *N*-methylated by a substrate-specific methyltransferase, tetrahydroprotoberberine-*cis*-*N*-methyltransferase, that has been isolated from cultured *E. californica* and *Corydalis vaginans* cells (145), and purified from *Sanguinaria canadensis* cultures (122). The *N*-methylation step is followed by a third P450-dependent monooxygenase, (*S*)-*cis*-*N*-methylstylopine 14-hydroxylase (MSH), which catalyzes the formation of protopine and has been isolated from *C. vaginans* cultures (143). Conversion of protopine to sanguinarine involves hydroxylation by another P450-dependent enzyme, protopine-6-hydroxylase (PPH), followed by a spontaneous intramolecular rearrangement to yield dihydrosanguinarine, the first alkaloid with the benzophenanthridine nucleus (171). Dihydrobenzophenanthridine oxidase (DBOX), a cytosolic enzyme originally isolated from *E. californica* cultures (154) and recently purified from *S. canadensis* cultures (4), catalyzes the oxidation of dihydrosanguinarine to sanguinarine. Root exudates from many Papaveraceae species, such as *S. canadensis* and *E. californica*, are intensely red owing to the accumulation of sanguinarine and other benzophenanthridine alkaloids. Two novel enzymes, a P450-dependent monooxygenase dihydrochelirubine-12-hydroxylase and a SAM-dependent 12-hydroxydihydrochelirubine-12-*O*-methyltransferase, have been discovered in yeast-elicited *Thalictrum bulgaricum* cultures (76). These enzymes catalyze the final two steps in the biosynthesis of macarpine, the most highly oxidized benzylisoquinoline alkaloid found in nature.

In some plants, especially among the Berberidaceae and Ranunculaceae, (*S*)-scoulerine is methylated, rather than oxidized, to yield (*S*)-tetrahydrocolumbamine (Figure 2). The reaction is catalyzed by the SAM-dependent enzyme, scoulerine-9-*O*-methyltransferase (SOMT), which has been purified from *C. japonica* cells (146) and the corresponding cDNA isolated (170). Expression of the SOMT cDNA in *E. coli* produced a protein with a higher molecular weight than the native enzyme (51); thus, SOMT might be posttranslationally processed. Although the hydrophobic N-terminal region of SOMT is characteristic of a signal peptide, the enzyme has been reported to occur in the cytosol (116) and in the lumen of alkaloid-specific vesicles (52). The subsequent and second-to-last step in berberine biosynthesis involves the formation of a methylenedioxy bridge (52, 66). The enzyme activity originally thought to catalyze this reaction was actually a nonspecific peroxidase-mediated demethylation. The P450-dependent enzyme canadine synthase (CDS) was detected in members of the genera *Thalictrum* and *Coptis* and shown to catalyze methylenedioxy bridge formation in (*S*)-tetrahydrocolumbamine, but not in the quaternary alkaloid columbamine (144); thus, berberine biosynthesis cannot proceed via columbamine as once proposed. (*S*)-Canadine, also known as (*S*)-tetrahydroberberine, is oxidized to berberine either by (*S*)-canadine oxidase (CDO) or (*S*)-tetrahydroprotoberberine oxidase (STOX; 3). Although these enzymes catalyze the same reaction, their biochemical properties are quite distinct. STOX from *Berberis* is a flavinylated protein with a broad substrate range, whereas CDO from *Coptis* and *Thalictrum* contains iron and not flavin, proceeds via a different mechanism, and preferentially accepts (*S*)-canadine (66).

In some species of the genus *Papaver*, conversion of (*S*)-reticuline to its (*R*)-enantiomer represents the first committed step in morphinan alkaloid biosynthesis. An NADPH-dependent cytosolic enzyme 1,2-dehydroreticuline reductase, which catalyzes the stereospecific reduction of 1,2-dehydroreticuline to (*R*)-reticuline and is only found in plants that synthesize morphinan alkaloids, has been purified from opium poppy (25). Subsequent intramolecular carbon-carbon phenol coupling of (*R*)-reticuline by the P450-dependent enzyme salutaridine synthase (STS) results in the formation of salutaridine (56). The cytosolic enzyme, salutaridine:NADPH 7-oxidoreductase (SOR), found only in opium poppy and *P. bracteatum*, reduces salutaridine to (7*S*)-salutaridinol (57). Transformation of (7*S*)-salutaridinol into the morphinan alkaloid thebaine involves closure of an oxide bridge between C-4 and C-5 by the enzyme acetyl coenzyme A:salutaridinol-7-*O*-acetyltransferase (SAT), which has been purified from opium poppy cell cultures (87). SAT was also detected in *P. bracteatum*, but not in species that do not produce morphinan alkaloids.

In the remaining steps of the major pathway leading to morphine, thebaine is converted by enol-ether cleavage to codeinone, which is subsequently reduced to codeine. Ultimately, codeine is demethylated to yield morphine. The cytosolic enzyme codeinone reductase (COR), which catalyzes the NADPH-dependent reduction of (−)-codeinone to (−)-codeine, has recently been purified (88) and the corresponding cDNA isolated (173) from opium poppy (Figure 2). Four cDNAs encoding different COR isoforms were cloned and expressed in *E. coli*. The four isoforms are members of a family of at least six alleles, and exhibit similar physical and catalytic properties. COR shares 53% amino acid identity with 6′-deoxychalcone synthase from soybean, further supporting an evolutionary link between the enzymes of phenylpropanoid and alkaloid biosynthesis (49, 173). Both COR and 6′-deoxychalcone synthase are members of the aldo/keto reductase family of NADPH-dependent oxidoreductases found in several primary metabolic pathways.

Tropane Alkaloids and Nicotine

Tropane alkaloids (TPAs) occur mainly in the Solanaceae and include the anticholinergic drugs atropine, hyoscyamine, and scopolamine, and the narcotic tropical anesthetic cocaine. Although nicotine is not a member of the tropane class, the N-methyl-Δ^1-pyrrolinium cation involved in TPA biosynthesis is also an intermediate in the nicotine pathway. N-Methyl-Δ^1-pyrrolinium cation formation begins with the decarboxylation of ornithine and/or arginine by ornithine decarboxylase (ODC; Figure 3) and arginine decarboxylase (ADC), respectively. These enzymes are involved in the formation of putrescine either directly by ODC, or via agmatine and N-carbamoylputrescine in the case of ADC; thus, the early steps of TPA and nicotine biosynthesis are also common to polyamine metabolism. ODC occurs in all living organisms, but ADC is not found in mammals and many lower

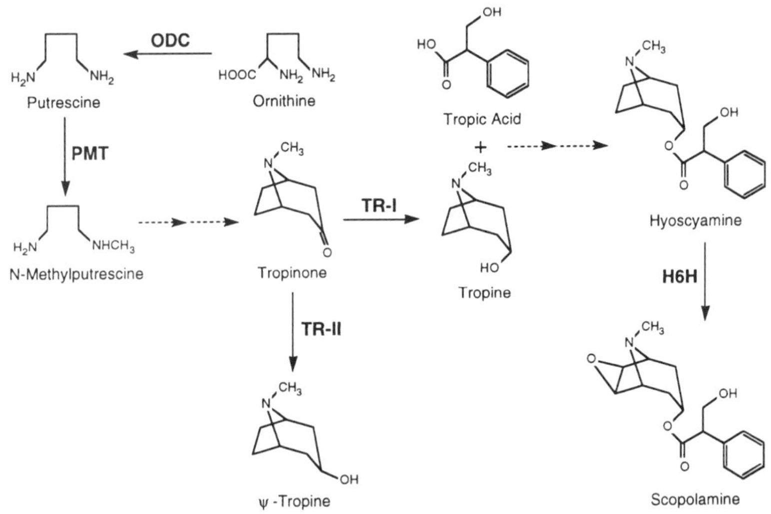

Figure 3   Reactions catalyzed by enzymes involved in tropane alkaloid biosynthesis for which the corresponding genes have been cloned. ODC, ornithine decarboxylase; PMT, putrescine N-methyltransferase; TR-I, tropinone reductase-I; TR-II, tropinone reductase-II; H6H, hyoscyamine 6β-hydroxylase.

eukaryotes. An ODC cDNA isolated from *Datura stramonium* (112) was shown to be similar to other eukaryotic ODCs, and both prokaryotic and eukaryotic ADCs. In *D. stramonium*, ODC is encoded by a small gene family and ODC mRNAs are most abundant in roots compared to stems or leaves. ADC cDNAs have been isolated from oat (11) and tomato (136). Despite the existence of two routes to putrescine, arginine has been suggested to supply most of the putrescine for alkaloid biosynthesis (65).

The first committed step in TPA and nicotine biosynthesis is catalyzed by a SAM-dependent putrescine *N*-methyltransferase (PMT; Figure 3). The PMT cDNA isolated from tobacco (71) shows strong identity to spermidine synthase from human (73%), mouse (70%), and *E. coli* (58%). Such homology is consistent with the remarkably similar active site models determined for partially purified PMT from *Hyoscyamus albus* and spermidine synthase (70). Subsequently, *N*-methylputrescine is oxidatively deaminated by a diamine oxidase to 4-aminobutanol, which undergoes spontaneous cyclization to form the reactive *N*-methyl-Δ^1-pyrrolinium cation (66). The *N*-methyl-Δ^1-pyrrolinium cation is thought to condense with acetoacetic acid to yield hygrine as a precursor of the tropane ring, or with nicotinic acid to form nicotine, although the enzymology of these steps is not known.

Tropinone is located at a branch point in the TPA pathway and is the first intermediate with a tropane ring. Two related dehydrogenases, tropinone reductase I (TR-I) and tropinone reductase II (TR-II), reduce the 3-keto group of tropinone to the 3α- and 3β- groups of the stereospecific alkamines tropine and Ψ-tropine, respectively (Figure 3). cDNA clones for TR-I and TR-II were isolated from *D. stramonium* and expressed in *E. coli* (118). The proteins exhibit 64% amino acid identity and are similar to enzymes in the short-chain, nonmetal dehydrogenase family. TR-encoding genes were identified in other TPA-producing species, but not in tobacco, which accumulates nicotine rather than TPAs. The exchange of various domains of TR-I and TR-II was performed to create a series of chimeric enzymes that could be expressed in *E. coli* (119). A C-terminal domain of about 120 amino acids was shown to determine the stereo- and substrate-specificity of each enzyme. These results suggest that the stereospecificity of TR is determined by the orientation of tropinone in the substrate-binding site, composed mainly of the C-terminal domain. The N-terminal region constitutes the NADPH-binding site required for short-chain dehydrogenases. The basis for the reaction stereospecificities of TR-I and TR-II were determined from the crystal structures of the two enzymes at 2.4- and 2.3-Å resolution, respectively (121). These studies showed that the folding of the two enzymes is almost identical and that the NADPH-binding sites and positions of the active site residues are conserved. Structural models revealed the role of charged amino acids among the predominantly hydrophobic residues that comprise the substrate-binding site in determining the binding orientation of tropinone.

Hyoscyamine is produced by the condensation of tropine and the phenylalanine-derived intermediate tropic acid. Hyoscyamine can be converted to its epoxide scopolamine by 6β-hydroxylation of the tropane ring followed by intramolecular epoxide formation via removal of the 7β-hydrogen (Figure 3). Cloning and heterologous expression of the H6H cDNA from *Hyoscyamus niger* showed that both reactions are catalyzed by a 2-oxoglutarate-dependent dioxygenase, hyoscyamine 6β-hydroxylase (H6H; 101).

Purine Alkaloids

Purine alkaloids such as caffeine, theobromine, and theacrine are widely distributed in the plant kingdom. Recent metabolic studies in tea and coffee have elucidated the biosynthesis of caffeine. The major route begins with xanthosine and proceeds through three *N*-methylations via 7-methylxanthosine, 7-methylxanthine, and theobromine (5, 6, 169), although a number of minor pathways have also been suggested (78, 152). The pathway contains three SAM-dependent *N*-methyltransferase activities found in young tea leaves, but absent in fully developed leaves (50). A partially purified enzyme preparation exhibited three activities, suggesting either that the *N*-methyltransferase steps in caffeine biosynthesis are catalyzed by a single enzyme, or by multiple enzymes with similar properties (78). However, an *N*-methyltransferase purified from the endosperm and leaves of coffee was active only toward 7-methylxanthine and theobromine (102). Moreover, an *N*-methyltransferase that catalyzes the methylation of methylxanthines and designated caffeine synthase (CS) was purified from young tea leaves (79). CS catalyzes two consecutive methylations involved in the conversion of 7-methylxanthine to caffeine, but is inactive toward xanthosine, indicating that the first methylation is catalyzed by a different enzyme. A CS cDNA has recently been isolated and expressed in *E. coli* (H Ashihara, personal communication). The predicted amino acid sequence shows that CS shares greater homology to salicylic acid *O*-methyltransferase than to other *N*-, *O*-, and *S*-methyltransferases, suggesting that CS belongs to a new methyltransferase class.

Subcellular Compartmentation of Alkaloid Biosynthetic Enzymes

Many alkaloid biosynthetic enzymes occur in subcellular compartments other than the cytosol. The compartmentation of these enzymes effectively sequesters toxic alkaloids and their biosynthetic intermediates away from the cytosol. The subcellular trafficking of pathway intermediates also creates an important level of metabolic regulation that could not occur if enzymes and substrates diffused freely in the cytosol. An understanding of the subcellular compartmentation of alkaloid pathways will reveal whether various enzyme characteristics observed in vitro, such as their inhibition by pathway intermediates, represent a true regulatory function in vivo.

Enzymes involved in vindoline biosynthesis have been localized to no fewer than five subcellular compartments. The conversion of tryptophan to tryptamine by TDC occurs in the cytosol (29, 162). Since STR is localized in the vacuole, tryptamine must be transported across the tonoplast before coupling to secologanin can occur (103). G10H, which catalyzes an early step in secologanin biosynthesis, is associated with provacuolar membranes (94). SGD, the enzyme catalyzing the deglucosylation of strictosidine, was suggested to be at least partly bound to the external face of the tonoplast (162). However, in vivo localization studies showed that SGD is associated with the endoplasmic reticulum (ER; 55). The P450-dependent monooxygenase T16H, which is involved in the C-16 hydroxylation of tabersonine, was also shown to be associated with the ER (163). NMT catalyzes the third-to-last step in vindoline biosynthesis and was found to be associated with thylakoid membranes (29, 33). However, chloroplast development is apparently not necessary since NMT activity was also detected in etiolated seedlings. The last two steps in vindoline biosynthesis, catalyzed by D4H and DAT, occur in the cytosol (23, 29). Vindoline must then be channeled back to the vacuole where nonspecific peroxidases necessary for coupling vindoline to catharanthine are localized (157). Overall, the complex compartmentation of the TIA pathway suggests the extensive subcellular trafficking of pathway intermediates. Although the vacuolar uptake of some TIAs, such as ajmalicine and serpentine, has been studied (15, 108), the mechanisms involved in channeling pathway intermediates to specific subcellular compartments are poorly understood.

Several BIA biosynthetic enzymes also occur in subcellular locations other than the cytosol. Of the five noncytosolic enzymes involved in the conversion of (S)-reticuline to dihydrosanguinarine, four (BBE, CFS, SPS, and MSH) are localized to a membrane fraction with a specific density of $\delta = 1.14$ g mL^{-1} (3, 9, 10, 143), while one (PPH) is associated with a membrane fraction with a density ($\delta = 1.11$ g mL^{-1}), consistent with that of the ER (171). The membrane-associated enzyme STS, which is involved in morphine biosynthesis, is also localized to a microsomal fraction with a density of $\delta = 1.14$ g mL^{-1} (56). With the exception of BBE, these noncytosolic enzymes are P450-dependent (14); thus, they must be membrane-bound proteins of the ER, or ER-derived compartments.

BBE appears to reside as a soluble protein within the lumen of a discrete subcellular compartment (3, 52). A putative N-terminal signal peptide was detected in the deduced amino acid sequence of BBE from *E. californica* (34). Other soluble enzymes involved in the biosynthesis of berberine are also associated with membranes of specific density $\delta = 1.14$ g mL^{-1}, including STOX (3), CDO (52), and columbamine *O*-methyltransferase (140). The association of these enzymes with a membrane fraction of greater density than the ER has led to speculation that distinct "alkaloid synthesizing vesicles" are found in certain cell types (3). Vesicles with a density of $\delta = 1.14$ g mL^{-1} and containing various alkaloids and biosynthetic enzymes have been visualized within vacuole-like compartments (3). Moreover, nascent BBE was found to contain a targeting domain comprised of an N-terminal signal peptide and an adjacent vacuolar sorting determinant (D Bird & P Facchini, unpublished results). Using the green fluorescent protein as a reporter, BBE was shown to be targeted to the ER lumen via the signal peptide. Subsequently, the protein is transported from the ER, possibly as a lumenal component of specific vesicles, to the vacuole. BBE is likely inactivated by the acidic conditions in the vacuole, suggesting that alkaloid synthesis occurs before the enzyme crosses the tonoplast membrane. The vacuolar accumulation of sanguinarine suggests that the entire contents of the transport vesicles, including BBE and various alkaloid intermediates, might be translocated directly from the ER to the vacuole.

Another example of novel subcellular compartmentation involves the biosynthesis of lysine-derived quinolizidine alkaloids, which occur in the mesophyll chloroplasts of legumes such as lupin (179). Recently, the biochemical localization of two acyltransferases that catalyze the last two acylations of $(+)$-p-coumaroylepilupinine and $(-)$-13α-tigloyloxymultifluorine showed that one enzyme occurs in the cytoplasm, whereas the other resides in the mitochondria of *Lupinus albus* (166). In animal cells, the acyl donor tigloyl-CoA is derived from isoleucine in the mitochondria, possibly explaining the mitochondrial localization of the terminal acyltransferase in plants. Although the quinolizidine nucleus appears to be synthesized in the chloroplast, subsequent modifications can occur only after alkaloid intermediates are transported to the cytosol and mitochondria. Ultimately, quinolizidine alkaloids are thought to accumulate in vacuoles of lupin epidermal cells, where their defensive properties are most effective (178).

REGULATION OF ALKALOID BIOSYNTHETIC GENES

Developmental Regulation and Tissue-Specific Localization

Alkaloid biosynthetic pathways are under strict developmental regulation in plants. This fact has severely restricted the exploitation of cultured plant cells for the production of valuable metabolites. For example, *C. roseus* cell cultures accumulate tabersonine and catharanthine, but not vindoline or vinblastine (108). Similarly, opium poppy cell cultures can be induced to accumulate sanguinarine, but do not synthesize morphine (37). The inability of dedifferentiated cell cultures to produce vindoline or morphine suggests that the biosynthesis of many alkaloids requires the differentiation of specific cell types.

The developmental regulation of TDC, STR, and four enzymes involved in vindoline biosynthesis (T16H, NMT, D4H, and DAT) has been studied in considerable detail. These enzymes are developmentally controlled in developing *C. roseus* seedlings, and some are further regulated by light (27, 30, 163). For example, *C. roseus* seedlings grown in the dark accumulate high levels of tabersonine and smaller amounts of four other vindoline pathway intermediates (8). The transfer of etiolated seedlings to light caused the turnover of tabersonine and other intermediates to vindoline, suggesting that some enzymes in the pathway are light regulated. The strict light activation of T16H in *C. roseus* seedlings (163) and cell cultures (151) was shown to be transcriptionally regulated. NMT activity increased $\sim$30% when etiolated *C. roseus* seedlings were exposed to light (30). D4H activity is also light induced (23), and the *D4H* gene has been shown to be under multilevel developmental and light-mediated regulation (175, 174). For example, D4H activity is low in etiolated seedlings despite an abundance of D4H transcripts. Exposure of etiolated seedlings to light caused a rapid increase in D4H activity without an increase in transcript levels (174). Despite the presence of only one *D4H* gene in *C. roseus*, several D4H isoforms were detected in etiolated and light-grown seedlings, suggesting that light modulates the developmental regulation of D4H at the posttranscriptional level (175). DAT activity was also shown to increase approximately tenfold in response to light, but the induction occurs primarily at the transcriptional level (30, 164). Phytochrome is clearly involved in the activation of vindoline biosynthesis by light (1) and has been shown to control expression of the *D4H* gene (175).

TDC and STR are most abundant in *C. roseus* roots, but also occur in photosynthetic organs (132). In contrast, T16H (163), D4H (174), and DAT (164) are restricted to young leaves and other shoot organs where vindoline biosynthesis occurs. In situ hybridization and immunocytochemical localization studies have shown that TDC and STR are localized to the epidermis of stems, leaves, and flower buds (32, 165). In roots, these enzymes occur in cells near the apical meristem. In contrast, D4H and DAT are associated with laticifers and idioblasts of shoot organs, but are absent from roots. Laticifers and idioblasts are distributed throughout the mesophyll in *C. roseus* leaves and are often several cell layers away from the epidermis; thus, vindoline biosynthesis involves at least two distinct cell types and requires the intercellular translocation of a pathway intermediate. The differential tissue specificity of strictosidine biosynthesis and the late steps of the vindoline pathway partially explain why vindoline is not produced in dedifferentiated *C. roseus* cell cultures.

Translocation of pathway intermediates also appears to occur in TPA biosynthesis (32). TPAs and nicotine are typically produced near the root apex, but accumulate within the vacuoles of leaves and roots (178). Histochemical localization of β-glucuronidase (GUS) activity in transgenic *Atropa belladonna* plants expressing a *PMT* promoter-GUS fusion showed that *PMT* expression occurs only in the root pericycle (167). Immunolocalization (64) and in situ hybridization studies (168) also demonstrated the pericycle-specific expression of H6H. In contrast, TR-I was immunolocalized to the endodermis and outer cortex, whereas TR-II was found in the pericycle, endodermis, and outer cortex (117). Similar, but not entirely identical, expression patterns of *TR-I* and *TR-II* promoter-*GUS* fusions were observed in transgenic *H. niger* (120). The localization of TR-I to a different cell type than PMT and H6H shows that an intermediate between PMT and TR-I moves from the pericycle to the endodermis and that an intermediate between TR-I and H6H moves back to the pericycle. Localization of PMT in the pericycle allows it efficient access to putrescine, ornithine, and arginine precursors unloaded from the phloem. Similarly, scopolamine produced in the pericycle can be readily translocated to the leaves via the adjacent xylem. Histochemical localization of GUS activity in transgenic roots of *H. niger*, *A. belladonna*, and tobacco expressing an *H6H* promoter-GUS fusion showed that the pericycle-specific expression of *H6H* is controlled by a mechanism that is specific to scopolamine-producing plants (77).

The tissue-specific localization of TYDC has been demonstrated in opium poppy (38). TYDC mRNAs are most abundant in the metaphloem of opium poppy stems and roots, and are found only at low levels in developing seed capsules (39). Metaphloem is closely associated with laticifers in opium poppy (37); thus, detection of TYDC mRNAs in metaphloem supports the association of opium poppy BIA biosynthesis with cells ontogenically related to laticifers. NCS, which catalyzes the first committed step in BIA biosynthesis, is also most active in roots and stems of opium poppy (N Samanani & P Facchini, unpublished results). CYP80B1 transcripts are most abundant in stems, followed by roots, leaves, and floral tissues (72, 182). The activities of STS and SOR, which convert (R)-reticuline to salutaridinol, also occur abundantly in roots and shoots (56, 57). In contrast, COR, which catalyzes the penultimate step in morphine biosynthesis, is present throughout the plant, but is most abundant in shoot organs (72, 173). These results suggest that pathway intermediates are translocated between the roots and various shoot organs. Originally, morphine biosynthesis was thought to occur in laticifers (37). However, neither STS nor SOR could be detected in a fresh latex fraction from opium poppy capsules (56, 57), suggesting that laticifers are a site of alkaloid accumulation, but not alkaloid synthesis. Moreover, several enzymes (STS, SOR, SAT, and COR) have been detected in dedifferentiated opium poppy cell cultures despite the absence of laticifers (56, 57, 87, 88).

The root-specific accumulation of sanguinarine in opium poppy (39) suggests that the enzymes involved in its biosynthesis occur only in roots. However, the substantial levels of BBE mRNA (41) and enzyme activity (161) in shoot organs suggest that pathway intermediates involved in sanguinarine biosynthesis are translocated from shoots to roots. Similarly, although berberine accumulates in the primary roots of *Coptis japonica*, low levels of SOMT activity suggest that the primary root is not the main site of berberine biosynthesis (51). Indeed, the highest levels of SOMT are found in lateral roots and stems.

Signal Transduction and Inducible Expression

Protection from environmental stress is a major role for secondary metabolites in plants; thus, their biosynthesis is often induced by factors such as pathogen challenge and wounding (178). The accumulation of many alkaloids is induced by fungal elicitors, heavy metal ions, UV radiation, and osmotic shock (66, 85, 108). Initially, research was focused on the induction of alkaloid biosynthesis in elicitor-treated cell cultures. Recently, molecular tools have been used to investigate the regulation of inducible alkaloid pathways.

Treatment of *C. roseus* cell cultures with a fungal elicitor increases the accumulation of tryptamine and alkaloids such as catharanthine (35). Fungal elicitors rapidly induced *TDC, STR*, and *SGD* gene expression (55, 132), suggesting that the elicitor-mediated signal transduction pathway consists of relatively few steps that activate pre-existing transcription factors. Fungal elicitors also induced jasmonic acid (JA) biosynthesis in *C. roseus* cell cultures (110). JA functions as a messenger in the activation of secondary metabolism and other defense mechanisms by environmental signals (61, 115). Treatment of *C. roseus* seedlings with methyl jasmonate (MeJA) caused an increase in TDC, STR, D4H, and DAT activity levels and enhanced the accumulation of vindoline (2). TDC and STR transcript levels were also induced in *C. roseus* cell cultures by MeJA or the JA precursor α-linolenic acid (110). An inhibitor of JA biosynthesis, diethyldithiocarbamic acid, blocked the elicitor-induced formation of JA and the activation of TDC and STR. Moreover, elicitor-induced JA biosynthesis and MeJA-induced *TDC* and *STR* expression were blocked by the protein kinase inhibitor K-252a, suggesting the involvement of protein phosphorylation in the transduction pathway. The JA-mediated induction of TDC and D4H in *C. roseus* seedlings was shown to involve transcriptional and posttranslational controls (176). For example, MeJA treatment activated *TDC* gene expression and appeared to increase the stability of the TDC protein, but did not result in higher TDC activity in light- and dark-grown seedlings. Similarly, exogenous MeJA resulted in higher D4H activity and protein levels, but only in light-grown seedlings.

A functional JA-producing octadecanoid pathway is necessary for TIA biosynthesis by *C. roseus* cells cultured in an auxin-starved medium (53). Auxin inhibited TIA accumulation and reduced *TDC* transcription (58), but alkaloid biosynthesis could be induced by transferring the cells to an auxin-free medium. Exogenous MeJA restored the ability of cells grown in the presence of auxin to produce alkaloids (53). In cells cultured in auxin-free media, MeJA or JA treatment caused a further increase in alkaloid accumulation, whereas alkaloid production was reduced in auxin-starved cells treated with octadecanoid pathway inhibitors. These results suggest that JA is produced in response to auxin depletion and function in coordinating biochemical events that lead to alkaloid biosynthesis. Although JA is clearly involved in linking physiological and environmental signals to alkaloid biosynthesis, JA treatment of etiolated seedlings did not enhance TDC activity, nor could it replace the light requirement for *D4H* expression (176). JA appears to modulate events in TIA biosynthesis already under the control of other regulatory mechanisms.

Leaf damage caused by herbivores increases JA and nicotine levels in *Nicotiana sylvestris* roots (7). Exogenous MeJA also induced nicotine production in roots, suggesting that JA functions in transferring the damage signal from the shoot to the root. MeJA also induced ODC, PMT, and *S*-adenosylmethionine synthase (SAMS) transcript levels, and the accumulation of putrescine, *N*-methylputrescine, and nicotine in tobacco cell cultures (74). However, the induction of *SAMS* and *PMT* gene expression by MeJA was blocked by cycloheximide, whereas *ODC* expression was not, suggesting that multiple regulatory mechanisms are involved in the MeJA-mediated control of nicotine biosynthetic genes.

Cell cultures of many Papaveraceae species accumulate benzophenanthridine alkaloids, such as macarpine and/or sanguinarine, in response to treatment with fungal elicitors (36, 95, 153). In general, the membrane-associated biosynthetic enzymes are induced by elicitors, whereas most cytosolic enzymes are not (14).

Several members of the *TYDC* gene family were rapidly and transiently expressed in opium poppy cell cultures in response to elicitor treatment (40, 42). CYP80B1 transcript levels were induced more than 20-fold in MeJA-treated *E. californica* cells (133) and fungal elicitor-treated opium poppy cells (72, 182). BBE was also transcriptionally activated in *E. californica* cells treated with a yeast elicitor (34) or MeJA (14, 85), and opium poppy cells treated with a fungal elicitor (41). The elicitor-mediated induction of other P450-dependent enzymes (CFS, SPS, MSH, and PPH) in the sanguinarine pathway has also been observed (10, 14, 171). Moreover, DBOX activity was reported to increase 4- and 14-fold in *S. canadensis* cells treated with MeJA or acetylsalicylic acid, respectively (73).

The induction of benzophenanthridine alkaloid biosynthesis in *E. californica* has been shown to occur at elicitor concentrations below the threshold required to stimulate events associated with the hypersensitive response, such as the production of phenolic compounds (138). Phenolic production could be selectively blocked by catalase at higher elicitor concentrations, suggesting that alkaloid biosynthesis is induced by a signal transduction pathway that is not mediated by reactive oxygen species involved in activating the hypersensitive response. Uncoupled induction mechanisms for phenylalanine ammonia lyase, TYDC, and downstream enzymes of sanguinarine biosynthesis have also been demonstrated in opium poppy (40). The elicitor-mediated induction of benzophenanthridine alkaloid biosynthesis requires a transient decrease in cytosolic pH caused by an efflux of protons from the vacuole (138). Artificial acidification of the cytosol was shown to induce alkaloid biosynthesis but not the hypersensitive response, whereas the depletion of vacuolar protons blocked the increase in alkaloid accumulation. Phospholipase A_2, a G-protein-controlled redox-dependent plasma membrane protein, might trigger the signal transduction pathway leading to the efflux of vacuolar protons (137). The role of G-proteins in the induction of benzophenanthridine alkaloid formation was also shown by treating *S. canadensis* cells with modulators of GTP-binding proteins and G-protein activators (96). The induction of alkaloid biosynthesis also appears to depend on an external source of Ca^{2+}, suggesting that Ca^{2+} and perhaps calmodulin participate in the signal transduction pathway (95).

Promoter Analysis

Recent studies have begun to reveal the location of *cis*-elements and the identity of transcription factors involved in the developmental and inducible regulation of *TDC*, *STR1*, and *CPR*. The activity of the *TDC* promoter linked to the *GUS* reporter gene was initially examined in transgenic tobacco plants and transfected protoplasts (59). Progressive 5′-truncations gradually reduced GUS activity levels until deletion to −112 essentially eliminated *TDC* promoter activity (59). Three functional regions involved in basal or elicitor-induced expression were identified in the *TDC* promoter from −160 to −37 by a loss-of-function assay (125). The −160 to −99 region was shown to act as the main transcriptional enhancer for basal expression, and two separate elicitor-responsive elements were found between -99 and -87, and between -87 and -37. In vitro binding of nuclear factors to the -572 to -37 region of the *TDC* promoter has also been described (126). Two binding activities that interact with multiple *TDC* promoter regions were identified as GT-1 and 3AF1 in tobacco and *C. roseus* nuclear protein extracts. Mutagenesis of the GT-1 binding sites did not affect basal or elicitor-induced expression, but did reduce *TDC* promoter activation by UV light. Only UV-B wavelengths were shown to induce TIA accumulation and TDC expression in *C. roseus*, suggesting the involvement of a specific receptor (123). Loss-of-function analysis revealed redundant UV-responsive elements in the *TDC* promoter between -99 and $+198$ (123).

The coordinate accumulation of transcripts suggests that *TDC*, *STR*, and *CPR* genes are regulated by common nuclear factors in response to elicitor treatment and UV light (108, 132). Deletion of the *CPR* promoter to -366 eliminated the elicitor-inducible expression observed with a 632-bp promoter (90). The -632 to -366 region of the *CPR* promoter also contains strong GT-1 binding sites. The main elicitor-responsive sequences of the *STR1* promoter were identified in the -339 to -145 region (131). Again, GT-1 was shown to bind to this and other regions of the *STR1* promoter. Despite the strong interaction of GT-1 with *TDC*, *STR1*, and *CPR* promoters, it remains to be determined whether GT-1 binding sites play a role in gene expression in vivo.

Other transcription factors are undoubtedly involved in the basal expression of the *TDC*, *STR1*, and *CPR* genes. A G-box motif at -105 was shown to bind G-box binding factors (GBFs) in vitro, but was not essential for the elicitor-induced expression of *STR1* in vivo (131). This G-box element also interacts with tobacco nuclear factors and the G-box-binding factor TAF-1 (124). Mutation of the G-box motif prevented binding of these factors and reduced the functional activity of constructs containing tetramers of the *STR1* G-box sequence. A G-box tetramer fused only to a TATA-box conferred seed-specific expression in transgenic tobacco, but required the enhancer region from the CaMV promoter for expression in leaves. These results suggest that sequences flanking the G-box motif determine *STR1* promoter activity in different tissues (124).

A GCC-box-like element in the -100 to -58 region of the *STR1* promoter is necessary and sufficient for JA- and elicitor-responsive expression (109). Two cDNAs encoding *C. roseus* AP2-domain (ORCA) proteins that bind the JA- and elicitor-responsive elements of *STR1* were isolated using a yeast one-hybrid screen. The ORCA2 protein *trans*-activates the *STR1* promoter, and expression of the *ORCA2* gene is induced by elicitor and JA treatment of *C. roseus* cell cultures. In contrast, the *ORCA1* gene is constitutively expressed. These results specifically identify a GCC-box-like element and ORCA2 in the JA- and elicitor-responsive expression of the *STR1* gene.

Deletion analysis has also revealed the location of regulatory domains necessary for *TYDC7* and *BBE1* promoter activities in a transient GUS assay system based on the microprojectile bombardment of cultured opium poppy cells (130). The

−393 to −287 region of the *TYDC7* promoter, and the −355 to −200 region of the *BBE1* promoter, were shown to be necessary for promoter function. Time-courses for the induction of TYDC7 and BBE1 mRNAs in wounded opium poppy cells were nearly identical to those for GUS activity in cells bombarded with promoter-*GUS* constructs when the −393 to −287 region of *TYDC7* and the −355 to −200 region of *BBE1* were present. These results suggest that the wound signal caused by the entry of DNA-coated microcarriers into opium poppy cells is sufficient to induce wound-responsive regulatory elements located from −393 to −287 in *TYDC7* and −355 to −200 in *BBE1*. Functional analysis of the *BBE1* promoter from *E. californica* showed that the −496 to −455 region is necessary for activity (68). Comparison of this region to the −355 to −200 region from opium poppy *BBE1* revealed a sequence with 55% nucleotide identity (130).

METABOLIC ENGINEERING APPLICATIONS

Metabolic engineering is broadly defined as the improvement of cellular activities by the manipulation of enzymatic, transport, or regulatory functions using recombinant DNA technology. Several alkaloid biosynthetic genes have been used to genetically alter the production of various secondary metabolites in plants (Table 2). Transgenic plants with altered or novel enzyme activities have also become a powerful tool to study the metabolic control architecture of alkaloid pathways.

Terpenoid Indole Alkaloids

A *TDC* transgene was first introduced into *C. roseus* cells by infecting seedlings with an oncogenic strain of *Agrobacterium tumefaciens* (60). Tumorigenic calli expressing the *TDC* transgene showed increased TDC activity and tryptamine content, but alkaloid levels were not affected compared to wild-type controls. These results contradicted previous conclusions that tryptamine is a limiting substrate for TIA biosynthesis, at least in some tissues (108).

Nontumorigenic *C. roseus* cell cultures transformed with a *STR1* transgene showed tenfold higher STR activity and accumulated higher levels of strictosidine and other TIAs, compared to wild-type cultures, but TDC activity was not affected (18). In contrast, high TDC activity conferred by a *TDC* transgene introduced alone, or in combination with the *STR1* transgene, did not affect alkaloid accumulation. These results further suggest that STR catalyzes a rate-limiting step of alkaloid biosynthesis in *C. roseus* cell cultures (18). The influence of precursor availability on TIA accumulation was investigated by feeding various concentrations and combinations of tryptamine and loganin to a transgenic *C. roseus* cell line overexpressing *STR1* (177). High rates of tryptamine synthesis were found to occur even when TDC activity was low. Moreover, efficient STR activity was possible even when the tryptamine pool was small. However, the overall formation

TABLE 2 Metabolic engineering of transgenic plants and tissue cultures using genes involved in alkaloid biosynthesis

Metabolic modification	Engineered enzyme(s)	Tranformed species	Source of gene(s)	References
Increased tryptamine	TDC	*Nicotiana tabacum*	*Catharanthus roseus*	155
Increased tyramine	TDC	*Nicotiana tabacum*	*Catharanthus roseus*	156
Increased serotonin	TDC	*Peganum harmala*	*Catharanthus roseus*	13
Reduced indole glucosinolates	TDC	*Brassica napus*	*Catharanthus roseus*	20
Redirection of shikimate metabolism; reduced phenylalanine; increased disease susceptibility	TDC	*Solanum tuberosum*	*Catharanthus roseus*	181
Increased tryptamine in crown gall tissue	TDC	*Catharanthus roseus*	*Catharanthus roseus*	60
Increased terpenoid indole alkaloids in cell cultures	TDC; STR	*Catharanthus roseus*	*Catharanthus roseus*	18
Increased quinoline alkaloids in root cultures	TDC; STR	*Cinchona officinalis*	*Catharanthus roseus*	54
Strictosidine production when supplied with exogenous secologanin	TDC; STR	*Nicotiana tabacum*	*Catharanthus roseus*	63
Increased cell wall–bound tyramine; decreased cell wall digestibility	TYDC	*Brassica napus*	*Papaver somniferum*	43
Increased cadaverine and anabasine	LDC	*Nicotiana tabacum*	*Hafnia alvei*	46, 69
Increased putrescine and nicotine	ODC	*Nicotiana tabacum*	*Saccharomyces cerevisiae*	62
Increased agmatine	ADC	*Nicotiana tabacum*	*Avena sativa*	17
Increased scopolamine	H6H	*Atropa belladonna*	*Hyoscyamus niger*	67, 183
Increased scopolamine	H6H	*Hyoscyamus muticus*	*Hyoscyamus niger*	75

of strictosidine was shown to require a sufficient supply of both secologanin and tryptamine, such that the efficient utilization of one depends on the availability of the other. Since precursor availability is a tissue-specific trait, different rate-limiting factors must occur in various cell lines, organs, and plants.

Transgenic tobacco expressing *C. roseus TDC* and *STR1* was used to establish a cell culture with high constitutive TDC and STR activity (62). This transgenic tobacco cell line accumulated tryptamine and produced strictosidine when secologanin was added to the culture medium. These results demonstrate that two consecutive steps in the TIA pathway can be cooperatively expressed in a foreign plant species that does not normally produce these metabolites. Examination of the integration frequencies and expression levels of *TDC* and *STR1* in tobacco showed that both transgenes were expressed in only 33% of the plants (86). Thus, the extensive phenotypic variation in alkaloid production in transgenic tissues (18) is partly caused by gene silencing phenomena affecting *TDC* and *STR1*.

Tropane Alkaloids, Nicotine, and Other Polyamine Derivatives

Some of the first attempts to metabolically engineer plant secondary products involved polyamine-derived alkaloids. Transgenic *Nicotiana rustica* root cultures expressing a yeast *ODC* gene produced higher levels of putrescine and nicotine (63). However, despite strong heterologous *ODC* expression, nicotine, putrescine, and *N*-methylputrescine levels increased only twofold, suggesting that ODC is not a rate-limiting step in nicotine biosynthesis. Overexpression of oat *ADC* in tobacco increased the accumulation of agmatine, the ADC reaction product (17). However, increased nicotine production was not detected despite suggestions that the putrescine required for nicotine biosynthesis is generated via ADC rather than ODC (66). It is possible that the additional agmatine was not accessible to the nicotine pathway.

Tobacco root cultures transformed with a bacterial lysine decarboxylase (*LDC*) gene produced higher levels of cadaverine, the product of the LDC reaction, and the alkaloid anabasine, produced by the coupling of cadaverine and *N*-methylputrescine (46). LDC activity, and cadaverine and anabasine accumulation, could be enhanced by fusing LDC to the RBCS transit peptide (69), demonstrating the importance of directing foreign enzymes to appropriate subcellular locations.

The *H6H* gene from *H. niger* was constitutively expressed in the hyoscyamine-rich plant *A. belladonna* (183). Transgenic plants exhibiting high H6H activity contained almost exclusively scopolamine. Similar results were obtained in transgenic root cultures of *A. belladonna* (67) and *Hyoscyamus muticus* (75). A large variation in TPA content was observed in root cultures of *H. muticus*, a species with a high capacity for tropane alkaloid accumulation, expressing *H6H*. One line produced over 100-fold more scopolamine than controls, but hyoscyamine conversion was still incomplete (75). Transgenic tobacco plants expressing an *H6H* were also capable of converting exogenous hyoscyamine and 6β-hydroxyhyoscyamine to scopolamine, which accumulated in leaves (184). Wild-type tobacco plants are unable to convert these intermediates to scopolamine.

Other Alkaloids

Cell cultures of *P. harmala* accumulate two simple and interrelated tryptamine-derived alkaloids: the harmane-type β-carboline alkaloids and serotonin. Serotonin levels in transgenic *P. harmala* cell cultures with elevated heterologous TDC activity were ten- to 20-fold higher than in control cultures (13). In contrast, β-carboline alkaloid levels were not affected, demonstrating that tryptamine supply is limiting for serotonin, but not for β-carboline alkaloid, biosynthesis. The mechanism for the metabolic channeling of tryptophan into serotonin and β-carboline alkaloids in *P. harmala* is not known. It is possible that two TDC isoforms occur in separate subcellular locations, and the additional tryptamine produced in transgenic cultures is available to only one pathway.

The metabolic engineering of BIA pathways has not been reported owing to the previous lack of transformation protocols for BIA-producing plants. However, procedures have recently been developed for the transformation of opium poppy plants (128), root cultures (129), and cell cultures (12), and *E. californica* plants (127) and root cultures (129). These transformation systems provide the opportunity to alter the activity of individual enzymes of BIA biosynthesis, and to examine the consequences of such modifications on the accumulation of end-products and pathway intermediates. Efficient transformation protocols for these species will also facilitate progress in dissecting the molecular regulation of BIA biosynthetic genes.

Other Uses of Alkaloid Biosynthetic Genes in Genetic Engineering

Enzymes that operate at the interface between amino acid and alkaloid metabolism have been used to alter substrate and product pools in a variety of plants. These studies provide insight into the control architecture of amino acid biosynthesis and relevant physiological processes. Tryptamine accumulation in tobacco plants expressing heterologous *TDC* was proportional to the level of TDC activity (60, 134, 155). Remarkably, plant growth was not affected despite the creation of a large sink for tryptophan and a large pool of soluble tryptamine. Moreover, no significant difference was detected in the activity of key aromatic amino acid biosynthetic enzymes (134), and IAA levels were identical in high-tryptamine and control plants (155). Transformed tobacco expressing *TDC* was also reported to accumulate more tyramine compared to controls (156). The most plausible explanation for this result is that the increased demand for tryptophan up-regulates the shikimate pathway resulting in increased tyrosine biosynthesis and, consequently, higher tyramine production via an endogenous TYDC activity.

Introduction of *TDC* into *Brassica napus* (canola) resulted in the redirection of tryptophan into tryptamine rather than indole glucosinolates (20). The indole glucosinolate content of seeds from transgenic plants was only 3% of that in wild-type seeds. In oilseeds, such as canola, the presence of indole glucosinolates decreases the value of the seed meal as an animal feed. This study is an elegant example of how a gene normally operating at an entry point in alkaloid biosynthesis can be used to divert metabolic flow and reduce undesirable product levels in crop species. In contrast, the introduction of *TDC* into potato altered the balance of substrate and product pools involved in phenylpropanoid metabolism (181). The redirection of tryptophan to tryptamine caused a decrease in wild-type levels of tryptophan, phenylalanine, and phenylalanine-derived phenolic compounds such as chlorogenic acid and lignin in transgenic potato tubers; thus, artificial metabolic sinks can also alter substrate availability even if the foreign gene operates outside the pathway involved in substrate supply.

Canola was also transformed with *TYDC* transgenes encoding TYDC isoforms from opium poppy (43). Plants expressing high levels of *TYDC1* showed fourfold higher TYDC activity, a 30% decrease in cellular tyrosine pools, a twofold increase in cell wall-bound tyramine, and reduced cell wall digestibility compared to wild-type plants. This study supports the involvement of *TYDC* and tyramine in cell wall formation via the synthesis of hydroxycinnamic acid amides. The engineering of amide metabolism could also provide an effective strategy to reduce crop susceptibility to a broad spectrum of pathogens by decreasing cell wall digestibility.

FUTURE PROSPECTS

Our understanding of the biological processes that permit the synthesis and accumulation of alkaloids in plants has advanced considerably over the past decade. This rapid progress has been facilitated by the availability of an impressive collection of alkaloid biosynthetic genes. These tools, combined with recent developments in plant genomics, will undoubtedly expedite the isolation of a multitude of genes involved in several alkaloid pathways. We have learned that plant alkaloid biosynthesis is more than a mere metabolic curiosity resulting in the formation of an immense array of biologically active products. Alkaloid pathways are highly regulated and involve novel cell-, tissue-, development-, and environment-specific controls. Many aspects of alkaloid biosynthesis, such as the elaborate subcellular compartmetation of enzymes and the intercellular translocation of pathway intermediates, reveal intriguing new variations in the complexity of plant metabolism. The expansion of our molecular toolbox will promote efforts to identify regulators associated with the development of cell types that can accommodate alkaloid pathways. Our emerging knowledge of the biochemistry, molecular biology, and cell biology of alkaloid biosynthesis will also lead to exciting opportunities to engineer alkaloid metabolism in transgenic plants. The inherent novelty of the pathways, and the socioeconomic importance of the products, are sure to encourage greater interest in alkaloid biosynthesis.

ACKNOWLEDGMENTS

I am grateful for support received from the Natural Sciences and Engineering Research Council of Canada, the Alberta Agricultural Research Institute, the University of Calgary Research Grants Committee, and Tasmanian Alkaloids Pty Ltd.

Visit the Annual Reviews home page at www.AnnualReviews.org

LITERATURE CITED

1. Aerts R, De Luca V. 1992. Phytochrome is involved in the light-regulation of vindoline biosynthesis in *Catharanthus roseus*. *Plant Physiol.* 100:1029–32
2. Aerts R, Gisi D, De Carolis E, De Luca V, Baumann TW. 1994. Methyl jasmonate vapor increases the developmentally controlled synthesis of alkaloids in *Catharanthus* and *Cinchona* seedlings. *Plant J.* 5:635–43
3. Amman M, Wanner G, Zenk MH. 1986. Intracellular compartmentation of two enzymes of berberine biosynthesis in plant cell cultures. *Planta* 167:310–20
4. Arakawa H, Clark WG, Psenak M, Coscia CJ. 1992. Purification and characterization of dihydrobenzophenanthridine oxidase from *Sanguinaria canadensis* cell cultures. *Arch. Biochem. Biophys.* 299:1–7
5. Ashihara H, Gillies FM, Crozier A. 1997. Metabolism of caffeine and related purine alkaloids in leaves of tea (*Camillia sinensis* L.) *Plant Cell Physiol.* 38:413–19
6. Ashihara H, Monteiro AM, Gillies FM, Crozier A. 1996. Biosynthesis of caffeine in leaves of coffee. *Plant Physiol.* 111:747–53
7. Baldwin IT, Schmelz EA, Ohnmeiss TE. 1994. Wound induced changes in root and shoot jasmonic acid pools correlate with induced nicotine synthesis in *Nicotiana sylvestris*. *J. Chem. Ecol.* 20:2139–58
8. Balsevich J, De Luca V, Kurz WGW. 1986. Altered alkaloid pattern in dark-grown seedlings of *Catharanthus roseus*. The isolation and characterization of 4-desacetoxyvindoline: a novel indole alkaloid and proposed precursor of vindoline. *Heterocycles* 24:2415–21
9. Bauer W, Zenk MH. 1989. Formation of both methylenedioxy groups in the alkaloid (*S*)-stylopine is catalyzed by cytochrome P-450 enzymes. *Tetrahedron Lett.* 30:5257–60
10. Bauer W, Zenk MH. 1991. Two methylenedioxy bridge forming cytochrome P-450 dependent enzymes are involved in (*S*)-stylopine biosynthesis. *Phytochemistry* 30:2953–61
11. Bell E, Malmberg RL. 1990. Analysis of a cDNA encoding arginine decarboxylase from oat reveals similarity to the *Escherichia coli* arginine decarboxylase and evidence for protein processing. *Mol. Gen. Genet.* 224:431–36
12. Belny M, Herouart D, Thomasset B, David H, Jacquin-Dubreuil A, David A. 1997. Transformation of *Papaver somniferum* cell suspension cultures with *sam-1* from *A. thaliana* results in cell lines of different *S*-adenosyl-L-methionine synthase activity. *Physiol. Plant.* 99:233–40
13. Berlin J, Rügenhagen C, Dietze P, Frecker LF, Goddijn OJM, Hoge JHC. 1993. Increased production of serotonin by suspension and root cultures of *Peganum harmala* transformed with a tryptophan decarboxylase cDNA clone from *Catharanthus roseus*. *Transgenic Res.* 2:336–44
14. Blechert S, Brodschelm W, Hölder S, Kammerer L, Kutchan TM, et al. 1995. The octadecanoid pathway—signal molecules for the regulation of secondary pathways. *Proc. Natl. Acad. Sci. USA* 92:4099–105
15. Blom TJM, Sierra M, van Vliet TB, Franke-van Dijk MEI, de Koning P, et al. 1991. Uptake and accumulation of ajmalicine into isolated vacuoles of cultured cells of *Catharanthus roseus* (L.) G. Don. and its conversion into serpentine. *Planta* 183:170–77
16. Burnett RJ, Maldonado-Mendoza IE, McKnight TD, Nessler CL. 1993. Expression of a 3-hydroxy-3-methylglutaryl coenzyme A reductase gene from *Camptotheca acuminata* is differentially

regulated by wounding and methyl jasmonate. *Plant Physiol.* 103:41–48

17. Burtin D, Michael AJ. 1997. Overexpression of arginine decarboxylase in transgenic plants. *Biochem. J.* 325:331–37

18. Canel C, Lopes-Cardoso MI, Whitmer S, van der Fits L, Pasquali G, et al. 1998. Effects of over-expression of strictosidine synthase and tryptophan decarboxylase on alkaloid production by cell cultures of *Catharanthus roseus. Planta* 205:414–19

19. Caporale LH. 1995. Chemical ecology: a view from the pharmaceutical industry. *Proc. Natl. Acad. Sci. USA* 92:75–82

20. Chavadej S, Brisson N, McNeil JN, De Luca V. 1994. Redirection of tryptophan leads to production of low indole glucosinolate canola. *Proc. Natl. Acad. Sci. USA* 91:2166–70

21. Chou WM, Kutchan TM. 1998. Enzymatic oxidations in the biosynthesis of complex alkaloids. *Plant J.* 15:289–300

22. Contin A, van der Heijden R, Lefeber AW, Verpoorte R. 1998. The iridoid glucoside secologanin is derived from the novel triose phosphate/pyruvate pathway in a *Catharanthus roseus* cell culture. *FEBS Lett.* 434:413–16

23. De Carolis E, Chan F, Balsevich J, De Luca V. 1990. Isolation and characterization of a 2-oxoglutarate-dependent dioxygenase involved in the second-to-last step in vindoline biosynthesis. *Plant Physiol.* 94:1323–29

24. De Carolis E, De Luca V. 1993. Purification, characterization, and kinetic analysis of a 2-oxoglutarate-dependent dioxygenase involved in vindoline biosynthesis from *Catharanthus roseus. J. Biol. Chem.* 268:5504–11

25. De-Eknamkul W, Zenk MH. 1992. Purification and properties of 1,2-dehydroreticuline reductase from *Papaver somniferum* seedlings. *Phytochemistry* 31:813–21

26. De Luca V, Balsevich J, Kurz WGW. 1985. Acetylcoenzyme A: deacetylvindoline *O*-acetyltransferase, a novel enzyme from *Catharanthus. J. Plant Physiol.* 121:417–28

27. De Luca V, Balsevich J, Tyler RT, Eilert U, Panchuk BD, Kurz WGW. 1986. Biosynthesis of indole alkaloids: developmental regulation of the biosynthetic pathway from tabersonine to vindoline in *Catharanthus roseus. J. Plant Physiol.* 125:147–56

28. De Luca V, Balsevich J, Tyler RT, Kurz WGW. 1987. Characterization of a novel *N*-methyltransferase (NMT) from *Catharanthus roseus* plants. Detection of NMT and other enzymes of the indole alkaloid biosynthetic pathway in different cell suspension culture systems. *Plant Cell Rep.* 6:458–61

29. De Luca V, Cutler AJ. 1987. Subcellular localization of enzymes involved in indole alkaloid biosynthesis in *Catharanthus roseus. Plant Physiol.* 85:1099–102

30. De Luca V, Fernandez JA, Campbell D, Kurz WGW. 1988. Developmental regulation of enzymes of indole alkaloid biosynthesis in *Catharanthus roseus. Plant Physiol.* 86:447–50

31. De Luca V, Marineau C, Brisson N. 1989. Molecular cloning and analysis of a cDNA encoding a plant tryptophan decarboxylase: comparison with animal dopa decarboxylase. *Proc. Natl. Acad. Sci. USA* 86:2582–86

32. De Luca V, St-Pierre B. 2000. The cell and developmental biology of alkaloid biosynthesis. *Trends Plant Sci.* 4:168–73

33. Dethier M, De Luca V. 1993. Partial purification of an *N*-methyltransferase involved in vindoline biosynthesis in *Catharanthus roseus. Phytochemistry* 32:673–78

34. Dittrich H, Kutchan TM. 1991. Molecular cloning, expression, and induction of berberine bridge enzyme, an enzyme essential to the formation of benzophenanthridine alkaloids in the response of plants to pathogen attack. *Proc. Natl. Acad. Sci. USA* 88:9969–73

35. Eilert U, De Luca V, Constabel F, Kurz WGW. 1987. Elicitor-mediated induction of tryptophan decarboxylase and stricto-sidine synthase activities in cell suspension cultures of *Catharanthus roseus. Arch. Biochem. Biophys.* 254:491–97

36. Eilert U, Kurz WGW, Constabel F. 1985. Stimulation of sanguinarine accumulation in *Papaver somniferum* cell cultures by fungal elicitors. *J. Plant Physiol.* 119:65–76

37. Facchini PJ, Bird DA. 1998. Developmental regulation of benzylisoquinoline alkaloid biosynthesis in opium poppy plants and tissue cultures. *In Vitro Cell. Dev. Biol. Plant* 34:69–79

38. Facchini PJ, De Luca V. 1994. Differential and tissue-specific expression of a gene family for tyrosine/dopa decarboxylase in opium poppy. *J. Biol. Chem.* 269:26684–90

39. Facchini PJ, De Luca V. 1995. Phloem-specific expression of tyrosine/dopa decarboxylase genes and the biosynthesis of isoquinoline alkaloids in opium poppy. *Plant Cell* 7:1811–21

40. Facchini PJ, Johnson AG, Poupart J, De Luca V. 1996. Uncoupled defense gene expression and antimicrobial alkaloid accumulation in elicited opium poppy cell cultures. *Plant Physiol.* 111:687–97

41. Facchini PJ, Penzes C, Johnson AG, Bull D. 1996. Molecular characterization of berberine bridge enzyme genes from opium poppy. *Plant Physiol.* 112:1669–77

42. Facchini PJ, Penzes-Yost C, Samanani N, Kowalchuk B. 1998. Expression patterns conferred by tyrosine/dihydroxy-phenylalanine decarboxylase promoters from opium poppy are conserved in transgenic tobacco. *Plant Physiol.* 118:69–81

43. Facchini PJ, Yu M, Penzes-Yost C. 1999. Decreased cell wall digestibility in canola transformed with chimeric tyrosine decarboxylase genes from opium poppy. *Plant Physiol.* 120:653–63

44. Fahn W, Gundlach H, Deus-Neumann B, Stöckigt J. 1985. Late enzymes of vindoline biosynthesis. Acetyl-CoA:17-O-deacetylvindoline 17-O-acetyltransferase. *Plant Cell Rep.* 4:333–36

45. Fahn W, Laussermair E, Deus-Neumann B, Stöckigt J. 1985. Late enzymes in vindoline biosynthesis. S-adenosyl-L-methionine:-11-O-demethyl-17-O-deace-tylvindoline 11-O-methyltransferase and an unspecific acetylesterase. *Plant Cell Rep.* 4:337–40

46. Fecker LF, Rügenhagen C, Berlin J. 1993. Increased production of cadaverine and anabasine in hairy root cultures of *Nicotiana tabacum* expressing a bacterial lysine decarboxylase gene. *Plant Mol. Biol.* 23:11–21

47. Frenzel T, Zenk MH. 1990. Purification and characterization of three isoforms of S-adenosyl-L-methionine: (R,S)-tetrahydro-benzylisoquinoline N-methyltransferase from *Berberis koetineana* cell cultures. *Phytochemistry* 29:3491–97

48. Frenzel T, Zenk MH. 1990. S-Adenosyl-L-methionine:3′-hydroxy-N-methyl-(S)-co-claurine 4′-O-metyltransferase, a regio and stereoselective enzyme of the (S)-reticuline pathway. *Phytochemistry* 29:3505–11

49. Frick S, Kutchan TM. 1999. Molecular cloning and functional expression of O-methyltransferases common to isoquino-line alkaloid and phenylpropanoid biosynthesis. *Plant J.* 17:329–39

50. Fujimori N, Suzuki T, Ashihara H. 1991. Seasonal variations in biosynthetic capacity for the synthesis of caffeine in tea leaves. *Phytochemistry* 30:2245–48

51. Fujiwara H, Takeshita N, Terano Y, Fitchen JH, Tsujita T, et al. 1993. Expression of (S)-scoulerine-9-O-methyltransferase in *Coptis japonica* plants. *Phytochemistry* 34:949–54

52. Galneder E, Rueffer M, Wanner G, Tabata M, Zenk MH. 1988. Alternative final steps in berberine biosynthesis in *Coptis japonica* cell cultures. *Plant Cell Rep.* 7:1–4

53. Gantet P, Imbault N, Thiersault M, Doireau P. 1998. Necessity of a functional octade-canoic pathway for indole alkaloid synthesis by *Catharanthus roseus* cell suspensions cultured in an auxin-starved medium. *Plant Cell Physiol.* 39:220–25

54. Geerlings A, Hallard D, Martinez Caballero A, Lopes Cardoso I, et al. 1999. Alkaloid production by a *Cinchona officinalis* 'Ledgeriana' hairy root culture containing constitutive expression constructs of tryptophan decarboxylase and strictosidine synthase cDNAs from *Catharanthus roseus*. *Plant Cell Rep.* 19:191–96

55. Geerlings A, Martinez-Lozano Ibañez M, Memelink J, van der Heijden R, Verpoorte R. 2000. Molecular cloning and analysis of strictosidine β-D-glucosidase, an enzyme in terpenoid indole alkaloid biosynthesis in *Catharanthus roseus*. *J. Biol. Chem.* 275:3051–56

56. Gerardy R, Zenk MH. 1993. Formation of salutaridine from (*R*)-reticuline by a membrane-bound cytochrome P-450 enzyme from *Papaver somniferum*. *Phytochemistry* 32:79–86

57. Gerardy R, Zenk MH. 1993. Purification and characterization of salutaridine: NADPH 7-oxidoreductase from *Papaver somniferum*. *Phytochemistry* 34:125–32

58. Goddijn OJM, de Kam RJ, Zanetti A, Schilperoort RA, Hoge JHC. 1992. Auxin rapidly down-regulates transcription of the tryptophan decarboxylase gene from *Catharanthus roseus*. *Plant Mol. Biol.* 18:1113–20

59. Goddijn OJM, Lohman FP, de Kam RJ, Schilperoort RA, Hoge JHC. 1994. Nucleotide sequence of the tryptophan decarboxylase gene of *Catharanthus roseus* and expression of *tdc-gus* A gene fusions in *Nicotiana tabacum*. *Mol. Gen. Genet.* 242:217–25

60. Goddijn OJM, Pennings EJ, van der Helm P, Schilperoort RA, Verpoorte R, Hoge JHC. 1995. Overexpression of a tryptophan decarboxylase cDNA in *Catharanthus roseus* crown gall calluses results in increased tryptamine levels but not in increased terpenoid indole alkaloid production. *Transgenic Res.* 4:315–23

61. Gundlach H, Mueller MJ, Kutchan TM, Zenk MH. 1992. Jasmonic acid is a signal transducer in elicitor-induced plant cell cultures. *Proc. Natl. Acad. Sci. USA* 89:2389–93

62. Hallard D, van der Heijden R, Verpoorte R, Lopes Cardoso MI, Memelink J, Hoge JHC. 1997. Suspension cultured transgenic cells of *Nicotiana tabacum* expressing the tryptophan decarboxylase and strictosidine synthase cDNAs from *Catharanthus roseus* produce strictosidine upon feeding of secologanin. *Plant Cell Rep.* 17:50–54

63. Hamill JD, Robins RJ, Parr AJ, Evans DM, Furze JM, Rhodes MJC. 1990. Overexpression of a yeast ornithine decarboxylase gene in transgenic roots of *Nicotiana rustica* can lead to enhanced nicotine accumulation. *Plant Mol. Biol.* 15:27–38

64. Hashimoto T, Hayashi A, Amano Y, Kohno J, Iwanari H, et al. 1991. Hysoscyamine 6β-hydroxylase, an enzyme involved in tropane alkaloid biosynthesis, is localized at the pericycle of the root. *J. Biol. Chem.* 266:4648–53

65. Hashimoto T, Yamada Y. 1992. Tropane alkaloid biosynthesis: regulation and application. In *Proc. Annu. Penn. State Symp. Plant Physiol., 7th,* pp. 122–34. Rockville: Am. Soc. Plant Physiol. Press

66. Hashimoto T, Yamada Y. 1994. Alkaloid biogenesis: molecular aspects. *Annu. Rev. Plant Physiol. Plant Mol. Biol.* 45:257–85

67. Hashimoto T, Yun D-J, Yamada Y. 1993. Production of tropane alkaloids in genetically engineered root cultures. *Phytochemistry* 32:713–18

68. Hauschild K, Pauli HH, Kutchan TM. 1998. Isolation and analysis of a gene *bbe1* encoding the berberine bridge enzyme from the California poppy *Eschscholzia californica*. *Plant Mol. Biol.* 36:473–78

69. Herminghaus S, Tholl D, Rügenhagen C, Fecker LF, Leuschner C, Berlin J. 1996. Improved metabolic action of a bacterial lysine decarboxylase gene in tobacco hairy root cultures by its fusion to a *rbcS* transit peptide coding sequence. *Transgenic Res.* 5:193–201

70. Hibi N, Fujita T, Hatano M, Hashimoto T, Yamada Y. 1992. Putrescine *N*-methyltransferase in cultured roots of *Hyoscyamus albus*. *Plant Physiol.* 100:826–35

71. Hibi N, Higashiguchi S, Hashimoto T, Yamada Y. 1994. Gene expression in tobacco low-nicotine mutants. *Plant Cell* 6:723–35

72. Huang F-C, Kutchan TM. 2000. Distribution of morphinan and benzo[*c*]phenanthridine alkaloid gene transcript accumulation in *Papaver somniferum*. *Phytochemistry* 53:555–64

73. Ignatov A, Clark WG, Cline SD, Psenak M, Krueger RJ, Coscia CJ. 1996. Elicitation of the dihydrobenzophenanthridine oxidase in *Sanguinaria canadensis* cell cultures. *Phytochemistry* 43:1141–44

74. Imanishi S, Hashizume K, Nakakita M, Kojima H, Matsubayashi Y, et al. 1998. Differential induction by methyl jasmonate of genes encoding ornithine decarboxylase and other enzymes involved in nicotine biosynthesis in tobacco cell cultures. *Plant Mol. Biol.* 38:1101–11

75. Jouhikainen K, Lindgren L, Jokelainen T, Hiltunen R, Teeri TH, Oksman-Caldentey K-M. 1999. Enhancement of scopolamine production in *Hyoscyamus muticus* L. hairy root cultures by genetic engineering. *Planta* 208:545–51

76. Kammerer L, De-Eknamkul W, Zenk MH. 1994. Enzymatic 12-hydroxylation and 12-*O*-methylation of dihydrochelirubine in dihydromacarpine formation by *Thalictrum bulgaricum*. *Phytochemistry* 36:1409–16

77. Kanegae T, Kajiya H, Amano Y, Hashimoto T, Yamada Y. 1994. Species-dependent expression of the hyoscyamine 6β-hydroxylase gene in the pericycle. *Plant Physiol.* 105:483–90

78. Kato M, Kanehara T, Shimizu H, Suzuki T, Gillies FM, et al. 1996. Caffeine biosynthesis in young leaves of *Camellia sinensis*: in vitro studies on *N*-methyltransferase activity involved in the conversion of xanthosine to caffeine. *Physiol. Plant* 98:629–36

79. Kato M, Mizuno K, Fujimura T, Iwama M, Irie M, et al. 1999. Purification and characterization of caffeine synthase from tea leaves. *Plant Physiol.* 120:579–86

80. Kawalleck P, Keller H, Hahlbrock K, Scheel D, Somssich IE. 1993. A pathogen-responsive gene of parsley encodes tyrosine decarboxylase. *J. Biol. Chem.* 268:2189–94

81. Kraus PFX, Kutchan TM. 1995. Molecular cloning and heterologous expression of a cDNA encoding berbamunine synthase, a *C-O* phenol-coupling cytochrome P-450 from the higher plant *Berberis stolonifera*. *Proc. Natl. Acad. Sci. USA* 92:2071–75

82. Kutchan TM, Bock A, Dittrich H. 1994. Heterologous expression of strictosidine synthase and berberine bridge enzyme in insect cell culture. *Phytochemistry* 35:353–60

83. Kutchan TM, Dittrich H. 1995. Characterization and mechanism of the berberine bridge enzyme, a covalently flavinylated oxidase of benzophenanthridine alkaloid biosynthesis in higher plants. *J. Biol. Chem.* 270:24475–81

84. Kutchan TM, Hampp N, Lottspeich F, Beyreuther K, Zenk MH. 1988. The cDNA clone for strictosidine synthase from *Rauvolfia serpentina*: DNA sequence determination and expression in *Escherichia coli*. *FEBS Lett.* 237:40–44

85. Kutchan TM, Zenk MH. 1993. Enzymology and molecular biology of benzophenanthridine alkaloid biosynthesis. *J. Plant Res.* 3:165–73

86. Leech MJ, May K, Hallard D, Verpoorte R, De Luca V, Christou P. 1998. Expression of two consecutive genes of a secondary

metabolic pathway in transgenic tobacco: molecular diversity influences levels of expression and product accumulation. *Plant Mol. Biol.* 38:765–74

87. Lenz R, Zenk MH. 1995. Acetyl coenzyme A:salutaridinol-7-*O*-acetyltransferase from *Papaver somniferum* plant cell-cultures. *J. Biol. Chem.* 270:31091–96

88. Lenz R, Zenk MH. 1995. Purification and properties of codeinone reductase (NADPH) from *Papaver somniferum* cell cultures and differentiated plants. *Eur. J. Biochem.* 233:132–39

89. Loeffler S, Zenk MH. 1990. The hydroxylation step in the biosynthetic pathway leading from norcoclaurine to reticuline. *Phytochemistry* 29:3499–503

90. Lopes Cardoso MI, Meijer AH, Rueb S, Machado JA, Memelink J, Hoge JHC. 1997. A promoter region that controls basal and elicitor-inducible expression levels of the NADPH: cytochrome P450 reductase gene (*Cpr*) from *Catharanthus roseus* binds nuclear factor GT-1. *Mol. Gen. Genet.* 256:674–81

91. López-Meyer M, Nessler CL. 1997. Tryptophan decarboxylase is encoded by two autonomously regulated genes in *Camptotheca acuminata* which are differentially expressed during development and stress. *Plant J.* 11:1667–75

92. Luijendijk TJC, Stevens LH, Verpoorte R. 1998. Purification and characterization of strictosidine β-D-glucosidase from *Catharanthus roseus* cell suspension cultures. *Plant Physiol. Biochem.* 36:419–25

93. Luijendijk TJC, Vandermeijden E, Verpoorte R. 1996. Involvement of strictisidine as a defensive chemical in *Catharanthus roseus. J. Chem. Ecol.* 22:1355–66

94. Madyastha KM, Ridgway JE, Dwyer JG, Coscia CJ. 1977. Subcellular localization of a cytochrome P-450-dependent monooxygenase in vesicles of the higher plant *Catharanthus roseus. J. Cell Biol.* 72:303–13

95. Mahady GB, Beecher CW. 1994. Elicitor-

stimulated benzophenanthridine alkaloid biosynthesis in bloodroot suspension cultures is mediated by calcium. *Phytochemistry* 37:415–19

96. Mahady GB, Liu C, Beecher CW. 1998. Involvement of protein kinase and G proteins in the signal transduction of benzophenanthridine alkaloid biosynthesis. *Phytochemistry* 48:93–102

97. Maldonado-Mendoza IE, Burnett RJ, López-Meyer M, Nessler CL. 1994. Regulation of 3-hydroxy-3-methylglutaryl-coenzyme A reductase by wounding and methyl jasmonate: implications for the production of anti-cancer alkaloids. *Plant Cell Tiss. Organ Cult.* 38:351–56

98. Maldonado-Mendoza IE, López-Meyer M, Galef JR, Burnett RJ, Nessler CL. 1996. Molecular analysis of a new member of the opium poppy tyrosine/3,4-dihydroxyphenylalanine decarboxylase gene family. *Plant Physiol.* 110:43–49

99. Maldonado-Mendoza IE, Vincent RM, Nessler CL. 1997. Molecular characterization of three differentially expressed members of the *Camptotheca acuminata* 3-hydroxy-3-methylglutaryl CoA reductase (*HMGR*) gene family. *Plant Mol. Biol.* 34:781–90

100. Marques IA, Brodelius PE. 1988. Elicitor-induced L-tyrosine decarboxylase from plant cell suspension cultures: I. Induction and purification. *Plant Physiol.* 88:47–51

101. Matsuda J, Okabe S, Hashimoto T, Yamada Y. 1991. Molecular cloning of hyoscyamine 6β-hydroxylase, a 2-oxoglutarate-dependent dioxygenase, from cultured roots of *Hyoscyamus niger. J. Biol. Chem.* 266:9460–64

102. Mazzafera P, Wingsle G, Olsson O, Sandberg G. 1994. S-Adenosyl-L-methionine:theobromine 1-*N*-methyltransferase, an enzyme catalyzing the synthesis of caffeine in coffee. *Phytochemistry* 37:1577–84

103. McKnight TD, Bergey DR, Burnett RJ,

Nessler CL. 1991. Expression of enzymatically active and correctly targeted strictosidine synthase in transgenic tobacco plants. *Planta* 185:148–52

104. McKnight TD, Roessner CA, Devagupta R, Scott AI, Nessler CL. 1990. Nucleotide sequence of a cDNA encoding the vacuolar protein strictosidine synthase from *Catharanthus roseus*. *Nucleic Acids Res.* 18:4939

105. McLusky SR, Bennett MH, Beale MH, Lewis MJ, Gaskin P, Mansfield JW. 1999. Cell wall alterations and localized accumulation of feruloyl-3′-methoxytyramine in onion epidermis at sites of attempted penetration by *Botrytis allii* are associated with actin polarisation, peroxidase activity and suppression of flavonoid biosynthesis. *Plant J.* 17:523–34

106. Meehan TD, Coscia CJ. 1973. Hydroxylation of geraniol and nerol by a monooxygenase from *Vinca rosea*. *Biochem. Biophys. Res. Commun.* 53:1043–48

107. Meijer AH, Cardoso MIL, Voskuilen JT, de Waal A, Verpoorte R, Hoge JHC. 1993. Isolation and characterization of a cDNA clone from *Catharanthus roseus* encoding NADPH: cytochrome P-450 reductase, an enzyme essential for reactions catalyzed by cytochrome P-450 monooxygenases in plants. *Plant J.* 4:47–60

108. Meijer AH, Verpoorte R, Hoge JHC. 1993. Regulation of enzymes and genes involved in terpenoid indole alkaloid biosynthesis in *Catharanthus roseus*. *J. Plant Res.* 3:145–64

109. Menke FL, Champion A, Kijne JW, Memelink J. 1999. A novel jasmonate- and elicitor-responsive element in the periwinkle secondary metabolite biosynthetic gene *Str* interacts with a jasmonate- and elicitor-inducible AP2-domain transcription factor, ORCA2. *EMBO J.* 18:4455–63

110. Menke FL, Parchmann S, Mueller MJ, Kijne JW, Memelink J. 1999. Involvement of the octadecanoid pathway and

protein phosphorylation in fungal elicitor-induced expression of terpenoid indole alkaloid biosynthetic genes in *Catharanthus roseus*. *Plant Physiol.* 119:1289–96

111. Mérillon J-M, Ouelhazi L, Doireau P, Chénieux J-C, Rideau M. 1989. Metabolic changes and alkaloid production in habituated and non-habituated cells of *Catharanthus roseus* grown in hormone-free medium. Comparing hormone-deprived non-habituated cells with habituated cells. *J. Plant Physiol.* 134:54–60

112. Michael AJ, Furze JM, Rhodes MJC, Burtin D. 1996. Molecular cloning and functional identification of a plant ornithine decarboxylase cDNA. *Biochem. J.* 314:241–48

113. Moreno PRH, van der Heijden R, Verpoorte R. 1993. Effect of terpenoid precursor feeding and elicitation on the formation of indole alkaloids in cell suspension cultures of *Catharanthus roseus*. *Plant Cell Rep.* 12:702–5

114. Morishige T, Tsujita T, Yamada Y, Sato F. 2000. Molecular characterization of the *S*-adenosyl-L-methionine: 3′-hydroxy-*N*-methylcoclaurine-4′-*O*-methyltransferase of isoquinoline alkaloid biosynthesis in *Coptis japonica*. *J. Biol. Chem.* 275:23398–405

115. Mueller MJ, Brodschelm W, Spannagl E, Zenk MH. 1993. Signaling in the elicitation process is mediated through the octadecanoid pathway leading to jasmonic acid. *Proc. Natl. Acad. Sci. USA* 90:7490–94

116. Muemmler S, Rueffer M, Nagakura N, Zenk MH. 1985. *S*-Adenosyl-L-methionine: (*S*)-scoulerine 9-*O*-methyltransferase, a highly stereo- and regio-specific enzyme in tetrahydroprotoberberine biosynthesis. *Plant Cell Rep.* 4:36–39

117. Nakajima K, Hashimoto T. 1999. Two tropinone reductases, that catalyze opposite stereospecific reductions in tropane alkaloid biosynthesis, are localized in

plant root with different cell-specific patterns. *Plant Cell Physiol.* 40:1099–107

118. Nakajima K, Hashimoto T, Yamada Y. 1993. Two tropinone reductases with different stereospecificities are short-chain dehydrogenases evolved from a common ancestor. *Proc. Natl. Acad. Sci. USA* 90:9591–95

119. Nakajima K, Hashimoto T, Yamada Y. 1994. Opposite stereospecificity of two tropinone reductases is conferred by the substrate binding sites. *J. Biol. Chem.* 269:11695–98

120. Nakajima K, Oshita Y, Yamada Y, Hashimoto T. 1999. Structures and expression patterns of two tropinone reductase genes from *Hyoscyamus niger*. *Biosci. Biotechnol. Biochem.* 63:1756–64

121. Nakajima K, Yamashita A, Akama H, Nakatsu T, Kato H, et al. 1998. Crystal structures of two tropinone reductases: different reaction stereospecificities in the same protein fold. *Proc. Natl. Acad. Sci. USA* 95:4876–81

122. O'Keefe BR, Beecher CWW. 1994. Isolation and characterization of S-adenosyl-L-methionine:(S)-tetrahydroberberine-cis-N-methyltransferase from suspension cultures of *Sanguinaria canadensis* L. *Plant Physiol.* 105:395–403

123. Ouwerkerk PBF, Hallard D, Memelink J. 1999. Identification of UV-B light-responsive regions in the promoter of the tryptophan decarboxylase gene from *Catharanthus roseus*. *Plant Mol. Biol.* 41:491–503

124. Ouwerkerk PB, Memelink J. 1999. A G-box element from the *Catharanthus rosues* strictosidine synthase (*Str*) gene promoter confers seed-specific expression in transgenic tobacco plants. *Mol. Gen. Genet.* 261:635–43

125. Ouwerkerk PB, Memelink J. 1999. Elicitor-responsive promoter regions in the tryptophan decarboxylase gene from *Catharanthus roseus*. *Plant Mol. Biol.* 39:129–36

126. Ouwerkerk PB, Trimborn TO, Hilliou F, Memelink J. 1999. Nuclear factors GT-1 and 3AF1 interact with multiple sequences within the promoter of the *Tdc* gene from Madagascar periwinkle: GT-1 is involved in UV light-induced expression. *Mol. Gen. Genet.* 261:610–22

127. Park S-U, Facchini PJ. 2000. *Agrobacterium*-mediated genetic transformation of California poppy, *Eschscholzia californica* Cham., via somatic embryogenesis. *Plant Cell Rep.* 19:1006–12

128. Park S-U, Facchini PJ. 2000. *Agrobacterium*-mediated transformation of opium poppy, *Papaver somniferum* L., via shoot organogenesis. *J. Plant Physiol.* 157:207–14

129. Park S-U, Facchini PJ. 2000. *Agrobacterim rhizogenes*-mediated transformation of opium poppy, *Papaver somniferum* L., and California poppy, *Eschscholzia californica* Cham., root cultures. *J. Exp. Bot.* 51:1005–16

130. Park S-U, Johnson AG, Penzes-Yost C, Facchini PJ. 1999. Analysis of promoters from tyrosine/dihydroxyphenylalanine decarboxylase and berberine bridge enzyme genes involved in benzylisoquinoline alkaloid biosynthesis in opium poppy. *Plant Mol. Biol.* 40:121–31

131. Pasquali G, Erven AS, Ouwerkerk PB, Menke FL, Memelink J. 1999. The promoter of the strictosidine synthase gene from periwinkle confers elicitor-inducible expression in transgenic tobacco and binds nuclear factors GT-1 and GBF. *Plant Mol. Biol.* 39:1299–310

132. Pasquali G, Goddijn OJM, de Waal A, Verpoorte R, Schilperoort RA, et al. 1992. Corrdinated regulation of two indole alkaloid biosynthetic genes from *Catharanthus roseus* by auxin and elicitors. *Plant Mol. Biol.* 18:1121–31

133. Pauli HH, Kutchan TM. 1998. Molecular cloning and functional heterologous expression of two alleles encoding

(S)-N-methylcoclaurine 3'-hydroxylase (CYP80B1), a new methyl jasmonate-inducible cytochrome P-450-dependent mono-oxygenase of benzylisoquinoline alkaloid biosynthesis. *Plant J.* 13:793–801

134. Poulsen C, Goddijn OJM, Hoge JHC, Verpoorte R. 1994. Anthranilate synthase and chorismate mutase activities in transgenic tobacco plants overexpressing tryptophan decarboxylase from *Catharanthus roseus*. *Transgenic Res.* 3:43–49

135. Power R, Kurz WGW, De Luca V. 1990. Purification and characterization of acetylcoenzyme A: deacetylvindoline 4-O-acetyltransferase from *Catharanthus roseus*. *Arch. Biochem. Biophys.* 279:370–76

136. Rastogi R, Dulson J, Rothstein SJ. 1994. Cloning of tomato (*Lycopersicon esculentum* Mill.) arginine decarboxylase gene and its expression during fruit ripening. *Plant Physiol.* 103:829–34

137. Roos W, Dordschbal B, Steighardt J, Hieke M, Weiss D, Saalbach G. 1999. A redox-dependent, G-protein-coupled phospholipase A of the plasma membrane is involved in the elicitation of alkaloid biosynthesis in *Eschscholtzia californica*. *Biochim. Biophys. Acta* 1448:390–402

138. Roos W, Evers S, Hieke M, Tschoepe M, Schumann B. 1998. Shifts of intracellular pH distribution as a part of the signal mechanism leading to the elicitation of benzophenenthridine alkaloids. *Plant Physiol.* 118:349–64

139. Rosco A, Pauli HH, Priesner W, Kutchan TM. 1997. Cloning and heterologous expression of cytochrome P-450 reductases from the Papaveraceae. *Arch. Biochem. Biophys.* 348:369–77

140. Rueffer M, Amman M, Zenk MH. 1986. S-Adenosyl-L-methionine: columbamine-O-methyl transferase, a compartmentalized enzyme in protoberberine biosynthesis. *Plant Cell Rep.* 3:182–85

141. Rueffer M, El-Shagi H, Nagahura N, Zenk MH. 1981. (S)-Norlaudanosoline synthase: the first enzyme in the benzylisoquinoline biosynthetic pathway. *FEBS Lett.* 129:5–9

142. Rueffer M, Zenk MH. 1987. Distant precursors of benzylisoquinoline alkaloids and their enzymatic formation. *Z. Naturforsch.* 42C:319–32

143. Rueffer M, Zenk MH. 1987. Enzymatic formation of protopines by a microsomal cytochrome P-450 system of *Corydalis vaginans*. *Tetrahedron Lett.* 28:5307–10

144. Rueffer M, Zenk MH. 1994. Canadine synthase from *Thalictrum tuberosum* cell cultures catalyzes the formation of the methylenedioxy bridge in berberine synthesis. *Phytochemistry* 36:1219–23

145. Rueffer M, Zumstein G, Zenk MH. 1990. Partial purification of S-adenosyl-L-methionine:(S)-tetrahydroprotober-berine-cis N-methyltransferase from suspension cultured cells of *Eschscholzia* and *Corydalis*. *Phytochemistry* 29:3727–33

146. Sato F, Takeshita N, Fitchen JH, Fujiwara H, Yamada Y. 1993. S-Adenosyl-L-methionine:scoulerine-9-O-methyltransferase from cultured *Coptis japonica* cells. *Phytochemistry* 32:659–64

147. Sato F, Tsujita T, Katagiri Y, Yoshida S, Yamada Y. 1994. Purification and characterization of S-adenosyl-L-methionine:noncoclaurine 6-O-methyltransferase from cultured *Coptis japonica* cells. *Eur. J. Biochem.* 225:125–31

148. Schiel O, Witte I, Berlin J. 1987. Geraniol 10-hydroxylase activity and its relation to monoterpene indole alkaloid accumulation in cell suspension cultures of *Catharanthus roseus*. *Z. Naturforsch.* 42c:1075–81

149. Schmeller T, Latz-Brüning B, Wink M. 1997. Biochemical activities of berberine, palmitine and sanguinarine mediating chemical defense against microorganisms and herbivores. *Phytochemistry* 44:257–66

150. Schmelzer E, Krüger-Lebus S, Hahlbrock

K. 1989. Temporal and spatial patterns of gene expression around sites of attempted fungal infection in parsley leaves. *Plant Cell* 1:993–1001

151. Schröder G, Unterbusch E, Kaltenbach M, Schmidt J, Strack D, et al. 1999. Light-induced cytochrome P450-dependent enzyme in indole alkaloid biosynthesis: tabersonine 16-hydroxylase. *FEBS Lett.* 458:97–102

152. Schulthess BH, Morath P, Baumann TW. 1996. Caffeine biosynthesis starts with the metabolically channelled formation of 7-methyl-XMP: a new hypothesis. *Phytochemistry* 41:169–75

153. Schumacher H-M, Gundlach H, Fiedler F, Zenk MH. 1987. Elicitation of benzophenanthridine alkaloid synthesis in *Eschscholtzia californica* cell cultures. *Plant Cell Rep.* 6:410–13

154. Schumacher H-M, Zenk MH. 1988. Partial purification and characterization of dihydrobenzophenanthridine oxidase from *Eschscholtzia californica* cell suspension cultures. *Plant Cell Rep.* 7:43–46

155. Songstad DD, De Luca V, Brisson N, Kurz WGW, Nessler CL. 1990. High levels of tryptamine accumulation in transgenic tobacco expressing tryptophan decarboxylase. *Plant Physiol.* 94:1410–13

156. Songstad DD, Kurz WGW, Nessler CL. 1991. Tyramine accumulation in *Nicotiana tabacum* transformed with a chimeric tryptophan decarboxylase gene. *Phytochemistry* 30:3245–46

157. Sottomayor M, Lopez-Serrano M, DiCosmo F, Ros-Barcelo A. 1998. Purification and characterization of alpha-3′4′-anhydrovinblastine synthase (peroxidase-like) from *Catharanthus roseus* (L.) G. Don. *FEBS Lett.* 428:299–303

158. Stadler R, Kutchan TM, Loeffler S, Nagakura N, Cassels B, Zenk MH. 1987. Revision of the early steps of reticuline biosynthesis. *Tetrahedron Lett.* 28:1251–54

159. Stadler R, Kutchan TM, Zenk MH. 1989. Norcoclaurine is the central intermediate in benzylisoquinoline alkaloid biosynthesis. *Phytochemistry* 28:1083–86

160. Stadler R, Zenk MH. 1993. The purification and characterization of a unique cytochrome P-450 enzyme from *Berberis stolinifera* plant cell cultures. *J. Biol. Chem.* 268:823–31

161. Steffens P, Nagakura N, Zenk MH. 1985. Purification and characterization of the berberine bridge enzyme from *Berberis beaniana* cell cultures. *Phytochemistry* 24:2577–83

162. Stevens LH, Blom TJM, Verpoorte R. 1993. Subcellular localization of tryptophan decarboxylase, strictosidine synthase and strictosidine glucosidase in suspension cultured cells of *Catharanthus roseus* and *Tabernaemontana divaricata*. *Plant Cell Rep.* 12:563–76

163. St-Pierre B, De Luca V. 1995. A cytochrome P-450 monooxygenase catalyzes the first step in the conversion of tabersonine to vindoline in *Catharanthus roseus*. *Plant Physiol.* 109:131–39

164. St-Pierre B, Laflamme P, Alarco A-M, De Luca V. 1998. The terminal *O*-acetyltransferase involved in vindoline biosynthesis defines a new class of proteins responsible for coenzyme A-dependent acyl transfer. *Plant J.* 14:703–13

165. St-Pierre B, Vázquez-Flota FA, De Luca V. 1999. Multicellular compartmentation of *Catharanthus roseus* alkaloid biosynthesis predicts intercellular translocation of a pathway intermediate. *Plant Cell* 11:887–900

166. Suzuki H, Koike Y, Murakoshi I, Saito K. 1996. Subcellular localization of acyltransferases for quinolizidine alkaloid biosynthesis in *Lupinus*. *Phytochemistry* 42:1557–62

167. Suzuki K, Yamada Y, Hashimoto T. 1999. Expression of *Atropa belladonna* putrescine *N*-methyltransferase gene in root pericycle. *Plant Cell Physiol.* 40:289–97

168. Suzuki K, Yun D-J, Chen XY, Yamada Y, Hashimoto T. 1999. An *Atropa belladonna* hyoscyamine 6-β-hydroxylase gene is differentially expressed in the root pericycle and anthers. *Plant Mol. Biol.* 40:141–52

169. Suzuki T, Ashihara H, Waller GR. 1992. Purine and purine alkaloid metabolism in *Camellia* and *Coffea* plants. *Phytochemistry* 31:2575–84

170. Takeshita N, Fujiwara H, Mimura H, Fitchen JH, Yamada Y, Sato F. 1995. Molecular cloning and characterization of *S*-adenosyl-L-methionine:scoulerine-9-*O*-methyltransferase from cultured cells of *Coptis japonica*. *Plant Cell Physiol.* 36:29–36

171. Tanahashi T, Zenk MH. 1990. Elicitor induction and characterization of microsomal protopine-6-hydroxylase, the central enzyme in benzophenanthridine alkaloid biosynthesis. *Phytochemistry* 29:1113–22

172. Trezzini GF, Horrichs A, Sommssich IE. 1993. Isolation of putative defense-related genes from *Arabidopsis thaliana* and expression in fungal elicitor-treated cells. *Plant Mol. Biol.* 21:385–89

173. Unterlinner B, Lenz R, Kutchan TM. 1999. Molecular cloning and functional expression of codeinone reductase: the penultimate enzyme in morphine biosynthesis in the opium poppy *Papaver somniferum*. *Plant J.* 18:465–75

174. Vázquez-Flota FA, De Carolis E, Alarco AM, De Luca V. 1997. Molecular cloning and characterization of deacetoxyvindoline 4-hydroxylase, a 2-oxoglutarate dependent dioxygenase involved in the biosynthesis of vindoline in *Catharanthus roseus* (L.) G. Don. *Plant Mol. Biol.* 34:935–48

175. Vázquez-Flota FA, De Luca V. 1998. Developmental and light regulation of desacetoxyvindoline 4-hydroxylase in *Catharanthus roseus* (L.) G. Don. *Plant Physiol.* 117:1351–61

176. Vázquez-Flota FA, De Luca V. 1998. Jasmonate modulates development- and light-regulated alkaloid biosynthesis in *Catharanthus roseus*. *Phytochemistry* 49:395–402

177. Whitmer S, Canel C, Hallard D, Goncalves C, Verpoorte R. 1998. Influence of precursor availability on alkaloid accumulation by a transgenic cell line of *Catharanthus roseus*. *Plant Physiol.* 116:853–57

178. Wink M. 1999. Plant secondary metabolites from higher plants: biochemistry, function and biotechnology. In *Biochemistry of Plant Secondary Metabolism, Annual Plant Reviews*, ed. M Wink, 2:1–16. Sheffield: Sheffield Academic

179. Wink M, Hartmann T. 1982. Localization of the enzymes of quinolizidine alkaloid biosynthesis in leaf chloroplasts of *Lupinus polyphyllus*. *Plant Physiol.* 70:74–77

180. Yamamoto H, Katano N, Ooi A, Inoue K. 2000. Secologanin synthase which catalyzes the oxidative cleavage of loganin into secologanin is a cytochrome P450. *Phytochemistry* 53:7–12

181. Yao K, De Luca V, Brisson N. 1995. Creation of a metabolic sink for tryptophan alters the phenylpropanoid pathway and the susceptibility of potato to *Phytophthora infestans*. *Plant Cell* 7:1787–99

182. Yu M, Facchini PJ. 2000. cDNA cloning and characterization of (*S*)-*N*-methylcoclaurine 3′-hydroxylase (CYP-80B1) from elicitor-treated opium poppy cell suspension cultures. *Plant Physiol.* 122:1457

183. Yun D-J, Hashimoto T, Yamada Y. 1992. Metabolic engineering of medicinal plants: transgenic *Atropa belladonna* with an improved alkaloid composition. *Proc. Natl. Acad. Sci. USA* 89:11799–803

184. Yun D-J, Hashimoto T, Yamada Y. 1993. Transgenic tobacco plants with two consecutive oxidation reactions catalyzed by hyoscyamine 6β-hydroxylase. *Biosci. Biotech. Biochem.* 57:502–3

Annu. Rev. Plant Physiol. Plant Mol. Biol. 2001. 52:67–88

How Gibberellin Regulates Plant Growth and Development: A Molecular Genetic Analysis of Gibberellin Signaling

Donald E Richards, Kathryn E King, Tahar Ait-ali, and Nicholas P Harberd

Department of Molecular Genetics, John Innes Centre, Colney Lane, Norwich NR4 7UJ, United Kingdom; e-mail: donald.richards@bbsrc.ac.uk; kathryn.king@bbsrc.ac.uk; tahar.aitali@bbsrc.ac.uk; nicholas.harberd@bbsrc.ac.uk

Key Words   signal transduction, genetics, aleurone layer, Arabidopsis, plant hormones

■ **Abstract**   Gibberellins are hormones that control growth and a wide variety of other plant developmental processes. In recent years, significant progress has been made on the biochemistry of gibberellin biosynthesis and on the mechanisms by which gibberellin levels are regulated in plants. There have also been major advances in the understanding of gibberellin signaling, with several key genes being cloned. This review discusses our current understanding of gibberellin signaling, as seen from the perspective of molecular genetic analysis, and relates these observations to previous biochemical studies. In particular, we highlight an important conclusion of recent years: that GAI/RGA and orthologs play major roles in gibberellin signaling in diverse plant species, and that gibberellin probably stimulates growth by derepression of GAI/RGA.

CONTENTS

1040-2519/01/0601-0067$14.00   **67**

INTRODUCTION

Gibberellins (GAs) are tetracyclic diterpenoid growth factors that are essential for normal growth and that affect a wide variety of plant developmental processes (39). The number of identified gibberellins is now over a hundred (see http://www.plant-hormones.bbsrc.ac.uk), but only a few of these are known to have biological activity. One of the most important structural features determining biological activity is 3β-hydroxylation. For example, in *Arabidopsis*, the 3β-hydroxylated GA_4 is biologically active, whereas its immediate non-3β-hydroxylated precursor GA_9 is not (15). In addition, the active 3β-hydroxylated form can be inactivated by hydroxylation at the 2β-position. GAs are thought to elicit biological responses via a specific GA-receptor interaction, and the structural limitations on biological activity described above suggest that the interaction receptor:GAs must be highly specific.

GAs affect varied and complex processes within the plant cell, and an understanding of how they perform their function is a fundamental question in plant biology. This review is concerned mainly with our current understanding of GA signaling. There have been several recent reviews on this subject (4, 30, 47, 61, 64, 85, 94, 98). Here we show how recent developments are enabling us to integrate a number of strands in GA biology that had previously seemed unconnected.

During signal transduction, an intra- or extracellular effector (a "signal") interacts with a cell, and its "message" is then relayed through one or more steps within the cell. Finally this process elicits a change in the behavior of the cell (a "response"). If the initial signal is a hormone, such as GA, the first step in signaling involves the interaction of that hormone with a receptor. Although no GA receptor, intra- or extracellular, has been isolated, the accumulated evidence suggests that GA is perceived at the extracellular surface (plasma membrane) of cells (27, 42, but see 2). Thus it seems likely that the GA-receptor is located in the plasma membrane. In this review we concentrate primarily on the molecular genetic analysis of GA-signaling components that are thought to operate downstream of the GA:receptor interaction. Since the mutations that affect these components have quite widespread effects on GA-regulated processes, it is likely that the components themselves are involved at a relatively early stage in GA signaling and precede the different individual processes controlled by GAs. Each of these processes presumably is controlled by a separate sub-branch of the GA signaling cascade. This concept is illustrated in Figure 1 (see color insert).

GA BIOSYNTHESIS MUTANTS REVEAL THE DEVELOPMENTAL ROLES OF GA

GA-deficient mutants are known in a wide range of plant species and exhibit a characteristic dwarf phenotype. One of the best studied of these, the *Arabidopsis gal-3* mutant (50, 106), provides a good illustration of the multiple effects of GA-deficiency. The *gal-3* mutation is a large deletion that abolishes the function of a gene *(GA1)* that encodes *ent*-CDP synthase, an enzyme involved in an early step of gibberellin biosynthesis (33, 50, 92, 93, 106). *gal-3* mutant plants, when compared to the wild-type, are dwarfed, bushier (apical dominance is reduced), and have darker green leaves. In addition, *gal-3* seeds fail to germinate, *gal-3* flowering is delayed [particularly in short days (102)], and *gal-3* flowers are male sterile (50). The addition of GA restores all the characteristics of the wild-type to the mutant (50). Although the precise phenotypic consequences of GA-deficiency vary slightly from species to species, the general effects are much the same. In particular, GA-deficiency results in a dwarfed plant phenotype, showing that GA is essential for normal plant growth.

Since GA-deficiency causes dwarfism, it might be expected that increased GA levels would have the opposite effect. Studies of a pea mutant that has reduced 2β-hydroxylase activity (56, 82) have shown this to be the case. This mutant contains elevated levels of bioactive GA, because the mutation prevents deactivation of bioactive GAs via 2β-hydroxylation. This mutant displays a phenotype similar to that of wild-type plants treated with exogenous GA: It is elongated compared to wild-type, and has light green leaves. Thus GA levels correlate directly with plant growth: Elevated GA levels are associated with taller plants, whereas reduced GA levels are associated with dwarfism.

GA LEVELS ARE AUTOREGULATED AND ARE ALSO CONTROLLED BY LIGHT

Many of the genes that regulate GA biosynthesis have been cloned. This subject has been recently reviewed (33), and here we highlight only a few points pertinent to the present topic. Many steps in the GA biosynthesis pathway are controlled by enzymes that are the products of small multigene families, with each gene family member having a specific pattern of expression (76, 81). The expression of genes encoding enzymes involved in the later steps of the GA biosynthesis pathway is often subject to regulation by GA itself, and by environmental signals such as light. GA regulates its own biosynthesis via negative feedback regulation on the accumulation of transcripts encoding the 20-oxidase and the 3β-hydroxylase (15, 33). Depending on the developmental stage of the plant and the species under study, the accumulation of these transcripts was also found to be phytochrome-regulated (1, 100, 105). More recently it was shown that GA feed-forward regulates the level of transcripts encoding the deactivating enzyme 2β-hydroxylase (96). Taken together, these observations indicate that during plant development, there is a tight regulation of the levels of GAs via the control of GA biosynthesis gene expression.

IDENTIFICATION OF GA-SIGNALING MUTANTS

Since elevating or reducing the endogenous GA levels in plants causes character-istic changes in plant phenotype, it should be possible to find mutants that exhibit these changes, but in which alterations in GA perception or signaling, rather than in GA levels, are primarily responsible for the mutant phenotype. There are many such mutants known, some of which mimic the effects of GA-deficiency, and some mimic the effects of elevated endogenous GA levels. In many cases, the genes affected in these mutants have been cloned, giving some indication of the biochemical function of the products that they encode. These various mutants are discussed below, beginning with the *Arabidopsis gai* mutant. The *GAI* gene was the first described member of what is now known to be a group of genes, found in *Arabidopsis* and in other species, that encode the GAI/RGA family of GA signal-transduction components.

THE GAI/RGA FAMILY OF GA SIGNAL-TRANSDUCTION COMPONENTS

In the past few years it has become clear that a family of proteins defined initially by *Arabidopsis* GAI and RGA play key roles in GA signal-transduction. In the following sections we describe the cloning of the genes encoding GAI and RGA, the cloning of orthologous genes from species other than *Arabidopsis*, and we draw some general conclusions about the role of the GAI/RGA family in GA signaling. We end with a discussion of the possible biochemical function of these proteins.

Arabidopsis *gai:* An Altered Function Mutant That Mimics GA Deficiency

The *Arabidopsis gai* mutant shares many of the phenotypic characteristics of GA-deficient mutants (Figure 2, see color insert): *gai* mutants are dwarfed (48, 69, 70), their leaves are darker green than wild-type (48, 71), and particularly in short days, they flower later than wild-type (102). However, the *gai* mutant phenotype is not reversed by the addition of GA (48, 70, 103), and *gai* mutant plants contain higher levels of bioactive GAs than do wild-type plants (73, 95). Unlike the GA-deficiency mutations, *gai* is a semidominant mutation (48, 69) and appears to be so because it encodes a product that is structurally and functionally different from the product encoded by the wild-type allele (30, 68, 69). In addition, the levels of 20-oxidase and *GA4* transcripts (which encode enzymes that catalyze late steps in the biosynthesis of GAs) are increased in *gai* (15, 68), consistent with the idea that *gai* has elevated endogenous GA levels because of perturbed feedback regulation.

gai Encodes a Mutant Product That Lacks a Small Segment of N-Terminal Amino Acid Sequence

gai was cloned by insertional mutagenesis (68). *GAI* (the wild-type allele) encodes a protein (GAI) that displays extensive C-terminal homology with a previously cloned presumed transcription factor known as SCARECROW (SCR), and which is now classified as belonging to the GRAS family of proteins (see below; 30, 68, 80). This homology is restricted to a region towards the C termini of GAI and SCR (the "C" region; Figure 3, see color insert), while the remainder of the GAI sequence (the "N" region, see Figure 3) is unrelated to that of SCR. The mutant *gai* allele contains a 51-base pair (in-frame) deletion mutation within the sequence that encodes GAI, resulting in the loss of a segment of 17-amino acid residues from the "N" region. This change in the structure of the protein confers reduced GA responses to the mutant. This suggests that the "N" region of GAI, the section that differs substantially from SCR, is crucial for normal GA responses.

Altered Function Mutations in *GAI Orthologs*: Maize *d8* and Wheat *Rht*

There are several examples of mutations in species other than *Arabidopsis* that confer phenotypes having similar properties to that conferred by *Arabidopsis gai*. For example, mutations at the maize *d8* locus, of which there are six dominant alleles of different severity, confer phenotypes that mimic that caused by GA deficiency (29, 77, 104). However, these phenotypes are unaffected by the addition of GAs (77, 104). The *D8-1* mutant is known to accumulate bioactive GAs to a higher level than do wild-type plants (22).

The mutant *Rht* genes of wheat confer a phenotype that has many characteristics in common with that conferred by the mutant *D8* alleles in maize. Wheat *Rht* mutants are dwarfed, dark green, and accumulate biologically active GAs to higher levels than are found in wild-type controls (24, 25, 38, 55, 101). There are 8 *Rht* homeoalleles, conferring different degrees of phenotypic severity (9), and these mutations behave genetically as dominant altered-function mutations (24). The *Rht* mutations are of great importance in agriculture, since they confer the higher yields that contributed to the postwar increases in world wheat production that characterized the so-called green revolution (26).

Since the *D8* and *Rht* mutations confer maize and wheat phenotypes with characteristics that resemble that of the *Arabidopsis gai* mutant, it seemed possible that these mutations might identify related or orthologous genes in these three species. This was shown to be the case. A rice expressed sequence tag (EST) containing sequence that was closely related to that of *Arabidopsis GAI* was used to isolate wheat and maize cDNA and genomic DNA clones via low stringency hybridization. These DNAs were then shown to map to regions of the wheat and maize genomes to which *D8* and *Rht* were already known to map. Finally, the dominant mutant *D8* and *Rht* alleles were shown to carry mutations in the sequences of these cloned genes (72).

Comparisons of the amino acid sequences of the Rht, D8, and GAI proteins identified two regions (domains I and II) of N-terminal sequence that are particularly well conserved (see 72). Interestingly, domain I is almost exactly coincident with the segment of protein that is deleted in the mutant gai protein. Furthermore, comparison of the sequences of the mutant alleles *D8-1*, *D8-Mpl*, and *D8-2023* in maize, and *Rht-B1b* and *Rht-D1b* in wheat with those of normal control alleles showed that each mutant allele encodes a protein that is altered in one or both of domains I and II. Taken together, these results show that deletions or truncations of the N terminus of the Rht/D8 proteins (equivalent to the "N" region of GAI, see Figure 3) result in reduced GA responses. This further emphasizes the importance of this region of the protein for GA signaling. In addition, these observations show that proteins related to GAI have a conserved function in GA signaling across a wide range of plant species, suggesting that this mechanism of GA signaling is of ancient origin.

Loss-of-Function Mutations in *GAI* and *RGA*

The *Arabidopsis RGA* gene was initially identified in an elegant screen for mutations that suppressed the phenotype conferred by *gal-3* (89). As described above, *gal-3* confers a severe dwarf phenotype, due to a dramatic reduction in endogenous GA levels. The screen involved a search for mutants that, although still homozygous for *gal-3*, now grew taller than the *gal-3* progenitor due to the presence of a new mutation. As a result of this screen, multiple alleles at a new genetic locus named *RGA* (for repressor of *gal-3*) were identified. These recessive *rga* alleles partially restore the stem elongation of the *gal-3* mutant, making *rga gal-3* plants taller than *gal-3* controls, but shorter than wild-type. However, *rga gal-3* plants, like *gal-3* plants, are sterile. The addition of GA restores the fertility of the mutant and further stimulates stem growth. The *rga* mutations suppress several of the phenotypic defects conferred by *gal-3*: reduced stem growth, reduced leaf abaxial trichome initiation, delayed flowering time, and apical dominance. Preliminary measurement of GA levels showed that the double mutants have the same levels of GA as *gal-3*, suggesting that the *rga* mutation is probably affecting gibberellin signal transduction and not the biosynthesis of gibberellins. The fact that the *rga* mutations suppress a broad spectrum of the phenotypes conferred by *ga1-3* indicates that RGA plays a major role in GA signaling. Furthermore, since *ga1-3* reduces endogenous GA levels, the fact that a *rga ga1-3* plant is taller than a *ga1-3* plant shows that RGA opposes the effect of GA, and that plants lacking RGA require less GA for growth than do normal plants. Thus RGA acts as a negative regulator of GA signal transduction.

Once *RGA* was cloned, it was found to be a homologue of *GAI*, identical to a previously cloned gene called *GRS* (for *GAI Related Sequence*) (68, 88). This was an exciting finding, because it clearly implicated two very closely related proteins in GA signaling. GAI, RGA, Rht, and D8 all share substantial homology in the "N" region (see Figure 3), whereas the equivalent region of SCR and of other members of the GRAS family is substantially different in sequence. This suggests that the "N" region in the GAI/RGA/Rht/D8 proteins is important for GA-related functions.

Molecular analysis of the *rga* alleles showed that some contain deletions that would be expected to abolish or destroy the activity of RGA, and thus can be described as loss-of-function alleles (88). Since loss-of-function *rga* alleles partially suppress the effects of GA-deficiency, do loss-of-function mutant alleles of *GAI* have the same effect? While such alleles of *GAI* confer a visible phenotype indistinguishable from that of a wild-type plant (69, 103), detailed studies of the effects of paclobutrazol (PAC), a GA biosynthesis inhibitor, revealed that they have increased PAC resistance (68). This observation confirmed that *GAI* loss-of-function alleles do partially suppress the effects of GA-deficiency, and it suggests that GAI, like RGA, acts as a negative regulator of GA-responses. Taken together with the high degree of sequence identity between the two genes, these results indicate that GAI and RGA may have overlapping roles in GA signaling. However, the roles of GAI and RGA do not entirely overlap as, if GAI and RGA could completely substitute for one another, then neither loss-of-function allele would confer a detectable change in phenotype.

The GA-Derepressible Repressor Model

As discussed above, the *GAI* gene can be mutated in two distinct ways. First, mutations that cause N-terminal deletions or truncations of GAI confer a dominant reduced GA-response phenotype that is due to the mutant protein having an altered function. Second, mutations that would be expected to abolish GAI function confer a reduced requirement for GA. In order to reconcile these observations a hypothesis that accounted for the action of GAI as a GA-derepressible repressor of plant growth was proposed (30, 68). Here we expand that model to propose a mechanism by which GAI and RGA may control plant growth, based on the premise that GAI and RGA have overlapping roles in GA signaling (Figure 4, see color insert).

Figure 4 outlines a hypothesis suggesting that GAI and RGA repress GA-mediated growth responses, and that GA derepresses growth by opposing the activity of GAI and RGA. According to this hypothesis, the altered structure of the gai mutant protein causes it to be less affected by GA. Thus, the gai protein constitutively represses plant growth, and this effect is dominant over the wild-type RGA, which can still recognize the GA signal. The converse also applies—a mutant RGA protein that lacks the equivalent amino acid sequence as is missing in the gai mutant protein confers a dominant, dwarfed reduced GA-response phenotype very similar to that conferred by *gai* (A Dill & T-p Sun, personal communication). In *GAI* loss-of-function mutants the repressor function of GAI is lost. However, this does not result in complete independence from GA, as wild-type RGA requires the GA signal to release its repression of plant growth.

One prediction of this model is that if GAI and RGA functions were both missing, GA would no longer be required for normal stem growth. This prediction has been tested experimentally: *Arabidopsis* plants lacking the *GA1* gene (a key gene in gibberellin biosynthesis, see above), and also lacking GAI and RGA are not dwarfed, and grow as tall as the wild-type (KE King & NP Harberd, unpublished results; A Dill & T-p Sun, personal communication).

Loss-of-Function Mutations in *GAI/RGA* Orthologs in Barley, Rice, and Pea

Barley plants homozygous for the recessive *slender* mutations (20) display phenotypes characteristic of plants treated with saturating levels of exogenous GAs. *slender* mutant plants have long internodes, narrow leaves, and are male sterile. In the *slender* mutant, but not in the wild-type, the secretion of α-amylase and other hydrolytic enzymes is induced in the absence of added GAs (13, 53; see below for discussion of the cereal α-amylase response). This suggests that the *slender* mutation is causing a constitutive GA response. Several lines of evidence are in favor of this hypothesis. First, the concentration of GAs is lower in the *slender* mutant than in the wild-type (16); second, the *slender* mutant is relatively resistant to inhibitors of gibberellin biosynthesis (16, 53); and finally, the progeny of crosses of *slender* with dwarf mutants that are either GA-deficient mutants or GA-sensitivity mutants have the *slender* phenotype (14).

Recently, barley *slender* mutants have been shown to carry mutations in a barley *GAI/RGA* ortholog (P Chandler, F Gubler, A Marion-Poll & M Ellis, personal communication). These mutations would be expected to result in a loss of gene function, consistent with the recessive nature of the *slender* phenotype. Thus it seems that the barley *SLENDER* gene is the functional ortholog of *GAI/RGA* in *Arabidopsis*.

A similar story is emerging from studies of rice *slender* mutants. These mutants also resemble plants supplied with an excess of exogenous GAs, exhibiting rapid growth and elongated leaf sheaths. Furthermore, the *slender* mutant rice plants are resistant to GA biosynthesis inhibitors, and they contain endogenous GA levels lower than those found in wild-type plants. Recently, the rice *SLENDER* gene has been cloned and shown to be a the rice ortholog of *Arabidopsis GAI/RGA*. One rice *slender* mutant carries what would be expected to be a null mutation in this gene: A frameshift mutation near the first nuclear localization signal produces a (potentially) truncated protein (J Yamaguchi, personal communication).

Although genetically more complex than the *slender* mutants of barley and rice (see above), the pea *la cry^s* double mutant has a phenotype very similar to them, resembling a plant treated with excess GAs: long, thin internodes, pale green foliage, and parthenocarpic fruit development (18, 63, 79). However, following the (by now) familiar pattern of the *slender* mutants, the pea *la cry^s* mutant has reduced levels of endogenous GAs (59, 79) and increased resistance to inhibitors of gibberellin biosynthesis (60, 79). Furthermore, the triple mutant *la cry^s na* has the same phenotype as the *la cry^s* double mutant (79), although the *na* single mutant is a gibberellin-deficient mutant with a characteristic dwarf phenotype (78). Preliminary mapping experiments (X Cubells, A Grenell, N Ellis, J Carbonel, personal communication) have indicated that pea *GAI/RGA* homologues map close to the known genetic locations of *la* and *cry^s*, suggesting that *LA* and *CRY* may also encode proteins belonging to the GAI/RGA family.

What Do We Know of GAI/RGA Function at the Biochemical Level?

The above sections show that the cloning of *GAI* and *RGA* initiated some important developments in our understanding of the genetics of GA signaling. Many of the "classical" GA-signaling mutants were shown to carry mutations in *GAI/RGA* orthologs. Furthermore, two mutant phenotypes, which had previously been thought to be genetically unrelated, dominant reduced GA-response, and recessive increased GA-response, were shown to be conferred by distinct classes of mutation in *GAI/RGA* and orthologs.

Given the importance of the *GAI/RGA* family in GA signaling, what do we know of the biochemical function of the proteins that these genes encode? *GAI/RGA/ Rht/d8* encode members of a recently discovered family of putative plant transcription factors, named GRAS (80), all of which share homology with the "C" region of GAI (see Figure 3). Other members of this family are *Arabidopsis SCR* (19), the first to be characterized, and a gene that regulates asymmetric cell divisions during root development; *LATERAL SUPPRESSOR* (86), a tomato gene involved in the control of production of lateral branches; *PAT1*, an *Arabidopsis* gene involved in phytochrome A signal transduction (10); and *SHORT-ROOT*, an *Arabidopsis* gene that is essential for both cell division and cell specification in root (36). The GRAS family members contain a number of characteristic features, including leucine heptad repeats and nuclear localization signals; they also contain LXXLL motifs (where L is a leucine residue and X any amino acid residue), which are necessary for the binding of transcriptional coactivators to nuclear receptors (34, 99). The nuclear localization signals of *Arabidopsis* RGA and GAI, and of rice GAI appear to be functional, since transiently expressed green fluorescent protein GFP-RGA or GFP-GAI (rice) fusion proteins localize in the nucleus of onion epidermal cells (67, 88); and in *Arabidopsis* plants transformed with *GAI::GFP* constructs, the GAI-GFP protein localizes to the nuclei of root and hypocotyl cells, as determined by confocal microscopy (B Fleck, personal communication).

Although the sequence comparisons and nuclear localization results are suggestive, the only direct evidence that the members of the GRAS family act as transcription factors is the report that the rice *GAI* homolog shows transactivation activity in a GAL4-dependent transactivation assay in spinach (67). As a further possible clue to the biochemical function of GAI/RGA/Rht/d8, visual analysis of the sequences of these proteins has led to the proposal that they contain an SH2-like domain and that they resemble the STAT proteins of metazoans and slime molds (17, 72, 83).

SPY: An *O*-GLcNAc Transferase Involved in GA Signaling

The first GA signaling component to be cloned was SPY, the product of the *SPINDLY (SPY)* gene of *Arabidopsis*. Recessive *spy* mutant alleles were isolated (44) in a screen where seeds were placed on medium containing paclobutrazol (PAC), an inhibitor of gibberellin biosynthesis. The concentration of PAC used prevented germination of wild-type seeds, but permitted germination of the PAC-resistant *spy* mutants. *spy* mutant plants resemble wild-type plants treated with exogenous GAs: Mutant plants have longer hypocotyls than wild-type, increased elongation of the main stem, light green leaves, and are early flowering. Addition of GAs to *spy* mutant seedlings caused a further increase in hypocotyl length, in a dose-dependent manner, indicating that *spy* mutants are not saturated in their responses to GAs (44). Double mutant studies showed that *spy* mutant alleles are partially epistatic to *ga1-2*, a gibberellin-deficiency mutation: *spy ga1-2* double mutant seeds germinated in the absence of exogenous GA and double mutant adult plants reached a height intermediate between that of wild-type and *ga1-2*. These observations suggest that the function of the SPY gene product is to act as a negative regulator of the GA signal transduction pathway.

SPY is a tetratricopeptide repeat (TPR) protein and exhibits extensive homology to *O*-linked *N*-acetylglucosamine (*O*-GlcNAc) transferases (43, 84). The TPR is a 34-amino acid repeated sequence motif that may act in protein-protein interactions. *O*-GlcNAc transferases are enzymes that, in animals, play a role in signal transduction pathways in the dynamic modification of proteins, in a manner similar to protein phosphorylation (31, 32, 51). Recent data suggest that SPY is indeed an *O*-GlcNAc transferase: When the SPY protein is expressed using the baculovirus expression system, it shows *O*-GlcNAc transferase activity toward gp40, a tobacco nuclear pore protein known to be *O*-GlcNAc modified (97).

Double mutant analysis has suggested that *spy* mutant alleles are epistatic to *gai* (12, 43, 68). In these experiments *spy gai* double mutants are less severely dwarfed than the *gai* single mutant. Perhaps SPY acts upstream of GAI/RGA (68, 88) and affects their function by *O*-GlcNAc modification. One possibility, considering the functions that *O*-GlcNAc-transferases play in mammalian systems (31, 32), is that SPY influences the nuclear localization of GAI/RGA.

SLY1: A Positive Regulator of GA Signaling?

The effects of GA are often antagonized by the action of another plant hormone, abscisic acid (ABA). For example, ABA promotes the establishment of seed dormancy. GA opposes this effect of ABA, promoting the breaking of seed dormancy and triggering germination. As found for the GAs, some *Arabidopsis* mutants are ABA deficient, whereas others have altered ABA-responses. ABA-insensitive mutants have reduced seed dormancy, germinating at ABA concentrations that prevent germination of the wild-type plants (49). One such mutant, *ABI1-1*, was used as the genetic background for a screen to identify extragenic *ABI1-1* suppressors (90). Plants containing such suppressor mutations were expected to exhibit an enhanced ABA response. *ABI1-1* can germinate in the presence of 3 μM ABA, a concentration of ABA that suppresses the germination of wild-type seeds. This concentration of ABA was used to identify suppressed *ABI1-1* mutants: mutants that contained *ABI1-1*, but that were unable to germinate on 3 μM ABA (but able to germinate in the absence of exogenous ABA).

In the course of this screen, as expected, intragenic suppressors of *ABI1-1* were identified (as *ABI1-1* is a semidominant mutation, and these intragenic suppressors probably represent loss-of-function derivative alleles of *ABI1*). In addition, and again as expected, a number of mutations conferring GA-deficiency were identified, including several *ga1* alleles (GA-deficient mutants would not be expected to germinate in these conditions). However, unexpectedly, and most interestingly from the perspective of this review, this screen also identified a new class of mutant: dwarf, dark-green plants that could not be rescued by the addition of GAs (or brassinosteroids). The mutants resemble severely GA-deficient mutants, showing reduced male fertility, an increased number of buds per inflorescence, reduced apical dominance, and delayed senescence. The mutations conferring these phenotypes were all recessive, and they were found to fall into a single complementation group, the *SLEEPY1 (SLY1)* gene. It seems that the reduced dormancy of the *ABI1-1* background allows germination of these severely GA-insensitive mutants: *sly1* mutants fail to germinate in a wild-type background. The recessive nature of the *sly1* alleles suggests that they may be loss-of-function mutations, perhaps in a GA receptor or some other key positive GA response regulator. Answers to these questions await the cloning of the *SLEEPY* gene.

THE RICE *DWARF-1* MUTANT IMPLICATES THE α-SUBUNIT OF A GTP-BINDING PROTEIN IN GA SIGNALING

dwarf1 mutants of rice are dwarfed, have broad, dark green leaves, and make smaller than normal grains. These phenotypes cannot be reversed by GA treatments, suggesting that this mutant is defective in GA signaling. Furthermore, aleurone layers from *dwarf-1* grains produce no detectable α-amylase in response to concentrations of GA that activate α-amylase production in wild-type aleurones

(62; see below for further discussion of the cereal aleurone GA response). Recently, two groups (3, 23) reported the cloning of the *Dwarf1* gene. This gene encodes a protein displaying high homology with the α-subunit of heterotrimeric G-proteins. These proteins play a key role in signaling in animals (see below for further details). However, unlike in animals, this gene seems to exist as a single copy in the rice genome. One of the *dwarf-1* mutant alleles appears to be a complete loss-of-function allele, suggesting that, although the α-subunit encoded by *DWARF-1* is involved in GA signaling, it is not essential for it, since the *dwarf-1* mutant grows and is fertile (23).

OTHER *ARABIDOPSIS* GENES THAT MAY BE INVOLVED IN GA SIGNALING

In this section we discuss genes that may have a role in the GA signal transduction pathway, but which are either not cloned, or whose involvement in the GA pathway awaits further clarification.

The *GAR2* gene is currently represented by a single mutant allele, *gar2-1*, that was first identified as a dominant extragenic partial suppressor of the phenotype conferred by *gai* (103). When crossed into a wild-type background (recombined away from *gai*), *gar2-1* confers PAC-resistant seed germination, and a visible phenotype that is not obviously different from that of nonmutant controls (68, 73). As described above, *spy* mutant alleles also cause partial suppression of *gai* phenotype. The triple mutant *gai spy-7 gar2-1* homozygote displays complete suppression of the dwarf (*gai*) phenotype, increased PAC resistance, and earlier flowering than seen in wild-type controls, showing that *spy-7* and *gar2-1* act additively. The triple mutants are still sensitive to a reduction of GA concentration, and in the presence of PAC, they are sensitive to the addition of GA. The triple mutant *gai spy-7 gar2-1* can also reduce to normal the higher levels of 20-oxidase transcript found in *gai*, and reverse the increased content of GAs found in *gai*, so that the triple mutant contains levels of active GAs comparable to the wild type. The *gar2-1* mutation seems to modify the GA dose-response relationship in such a way that less GA is needed for a given effect. This fact, together with the increased PAC resistance of the mutant in a wild-type background, suggests that the *GAR2* gene acts as a negative regulator of GA responses. These observations suggest that the *gar2-1* mutation perturbs normal GA responses, and that the GAR2 gene product is involved in GA signaling.

shi (for short internodes) is a semidominant dwarfing mutation, isolated following two-component *Activator/Dissociation (Ac/Ds)* transposon-tagging mutagenesis (21). The phenotype of the mutant resembles that of weakly GA-deficient mutants: dwarfism, reduced apical dominance, narrow leaves that are darker green than normal, and late flowering in short days. The dwarfism of the *shi* mutant is due to reduced cell elongation in the bolting stem and cannot be reversed by the addition of GAs. The *shi* mutant is as late flowering in short days as is *gai*, but with the addition of GAs the mutant flowered at the same time as wild type, although no effect on flowering time was seen in *gai*. As in *gai*, the levels of biologically active GAs are higher in the *shi* mutant than in wild-type controls. The *SHI* gene encodes a protein (SHI) that is likely to be a transcription factor: SHI contains a zinc-finger motif similar to the Zn_2Cys_6 cluster present in the DNA binding region of the yeast GAL4 transcriptional activator, two putative nuclear localization signals, and acidic and glutamine-rich stretches that are characteristic of transcriptional regulators. RNA gel-blot and RT-PCR analyses indicate that the *shi* phenotype can be attributed to overexpression of *SHI*, driven by the 35S promoter reading out of the transposon inserted in its promoter, leading to suggestions that SHI functions as a repressor of growth. However, *SHI* transcript is not detectable in *SHI* plants, so the *shi* phenotype could simply be due to ectopic expression of *SHI* or to a nonphysiologically high level of *SHI* transcripts. In the absence of loss-of-function mutant alleles, it is difficult to asses the role of SHI in GA signaling in normal plants.

Finally, the *pickle* mutant was obtained (65) in a screen for *Arabidopsis* mutants exhibiting abnormal root development, and further analysis of the *pickle* phenotype suggested that it may be involved in GA signaling. Recently, *pickle* has been cloned and found to be a CHD3 chromatin-remodeling factor conserved in eukaryotes (66). Further experiments are required to determine whether *pickle* is involved in the GA signaling pathway, and if so, what role it plays in it.

ANALYSIS OF DEVELOPMENTAL PROCESSES CONTROLLED BY GAs

GAs regulate many of the different processes that occur during the plant life cycle, from seed germination through fruit formation. In this section, we examine two processes that have received particular attention with respect to the controlling role of the GAs: the induction of hydrolytic enzymes in the cereal aleurone layer and the commitment of plants to flowering.

GAs Control the Production of α-Amylase by the Cereal Aleurone

During the germination of cereal grains, the aleurone layer (a layer of cells that surrounds the endosperm) secretes hydrolases (largely α-amylases) into the endosperm, thus releasing nutrients that feed the growing seedling. This process is controlled by GA. GA regulates α-amylase gene transcription and the secretion of α-amylase from the aleurone cells. This "cereal aleurone α-amylase response" has been the subject of intense investigation, resulting in many important advances in our understanding of GA signaling. Here, we review aspects of these studies that are particularly salient to the present discussion [for recent general reviews, see (4, 5)].

The addition of GAs to de-embryonated cereal grains, to isolated aleurone layers, or to aleurone protoplasts, stimulates the aleurone cells to produce enzymes, such as α-amylase, that are involved in the degradation of starch. Endogenous GAs are likely to be involved in the control of this process in intact plants, since some dwarf varieties of barley, which have reduced endogenous GA levels, also have reduced levels of α-amylase in the endosperm. Addition of exogenous GAs restores α-amylase activity to these varieties (107).

As mentioned above, studies using the cereal aleurone layer α-amylase response have indicated that GA is perceived by externally facing receptors located in the plasma membrane (27, 42). Following this initial GA perception event, there are several additional processes that are activated. There is an early increase of intracellular Ca^{2+} (11), and decrease of intracellular pH (35), followed by increases in the concentration of calmodulin (87) and cyclic GMP (74). After this, the transcription of a Myb-type protein GAmyb is activated, and this is followed by an increase in α-amylase activity (28). GAmyb may regulate the transcription of α-amylase, since in the absence of GA, the transient expression of GAmyb activates transcription of an α-amylase promoter fused to the reporter gene *GUS* (28). Protein phosphorylation also seems to be involved in the cereal aleurone α-amylase response, as the addition of okadaic acid, an inhibitor of protein phosphatases type 1 and 2A, prevented the GA-response of wheat aleurone layer cells (52).

How do these observations relate to the previous description of the genetics of GA signaling? Several of the recent discoveries described in previous sections establish a clear relationship between the α-amylase response and the GA-signaling components identified via the genetic approach. For example, both the wheat *Rht* mutants and the barley *sln* mutants are altered in their α-amylase responses: The *Rht* mutants have aleurone cells that are relatively insensitive to GA (24, 38), whereas *sln* mutant aleurones produce α-amylase constitutively and do not need GA to induce production (13, 53). These observations show that the GAI/RGA family of proteins are involved in the mediation of the cereal aleurone α-amylase response.

The cloning of the barley homologue of *Arabidopsis SPY* (*Hv-SPY*) allowed Robertson et al (84) to test whether the cereal *SPY* gene plays a role in the regulation of the α-amylase response. They co-bombarded aleurone layers with the barley high-pI α-amylase promoter-β glucoronidase (GUS) reporter gene construct, and the barley *SPY* gene in an overexpression effector construct. They showed that when the *SPY* overexpression effector construct was used, almost all of the increase in GUS activity seen in controls after the addition of GA disappeared. The results provide strong evidence that the *SPY* gene product is also a negative regulator of GA responses in cereal aleurones.

Several experiments have suggested that heterotrimeric G-proteins and the G-protein signaling pathway may be involved in mediating the GA regulation of cereal aleurone α-amylase production. The G-protein signaling pathway is well conserved among different species (91). These proteins transduce signals that arrive at extracellular receptors (G-protein-coupled receptors or GPCR), to downstream

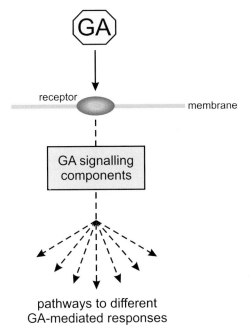

Figure 1 A generalized model for the pathway from GA perception, via a membrane-bound receptor, to the spectrum of GA-mediated plant growth responses.

Figure 2 *Arabidopsis* wild-type (*left*) and the *gai* mutant (*right*).

Figure 3 Representation of the GAI protein. The C terminus of GAI (the 'C' region) has homology to SCR. The N terminus (the 'N' region) is not related to SCR, and contains a region of 17 amino acids (the DELLA domain), which is missing in the *gai* mutant.

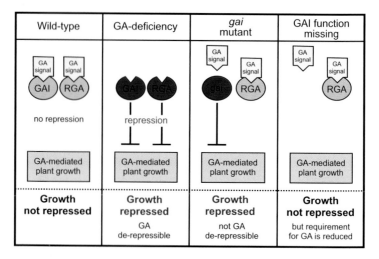

Figure 4 Derepression model for the regulation of plant growth responses by GA. The GAI and RGA proteins repress GA-mediated plant growth responses, and GA (via a signaling intermediate) derepresses growth by opposing this activity. The *gai* mutant no longer recognizes the GA signal and so constitutively represses growth. When the GAI repressor function is lost but RGA is active, GA is still required for derepression of growth, but the requirement is reduced. This model is an oversimplification for several reasons. First, it ignores the quantitative nature of GA responses. In addition, GAI and RGA do not have identical roles in GA signaling, although their functions overlap substantially. Finally, the representation of the interaction between GAI and RGA and the GA signal shown here is not meant to imply the nature of the interaction, as this may be transient or longer term.

signaling components. In plants [for reviews, see (40, 41, 58, 91)] the presence of G-proteins has been confirmed by the isolation of clones with homology to G-proteins. Concerning their possible role in GA signaling, indirect biochemical evidence has come from aleurone layer experiments (45). Adding GTP-γ-S, which mimics the activated state of G-proteins, slightly stimulated α-amylase expression, but the addition of GDP-β-S, which holds the α-subunit in its inactivated form, blocked completely the GA-induction of α-amylase. Further evidence comes from results obtained using a mastoparan analogue, Mas7. This compound stimulates GTP-GDP exchange by the heterotrimeric G-proteins, and is thought to mimic an activated G-protein-coupled receptor. When Mas7 was added to oat aleurone layers, it increased α-amylase secretion in a dose-dependent manner, and with a similar time course as adding GAs. ABA, which in the aleurone layer opposes the effects of GAs on α-amylase secretion, almost completely reverses the effect of Mas7. As mentioned by Fujisawa and co-workers (23), the interpretation of these results has to be tempered by the knowledge that Mas7 has effects on other signaling proteins, apart from G-proteins. However, the finding that the molecular defect in the *dwarf-1* mutant is in a protein with homology to the α-subunit of G-proteins (see above) suggests that G-proteins do indeed have a role to play in gibberellin signal transduction.

GAs Control Floral Initiation

The study of the role of GA in flowering is complicated because different species seem to respond differently to GA [for reviews see (57, 75)]. In *Arabidopsis*, a facultative long day plant, GAs have obvious effects on flowering, affecting both flowering time and flower morphology. The addition of exogenous GA makes the plants flower early, particularly in short days (54, 102). Mutants with reduced levels of endogenous GA, like *ga1-3* (see above), flower slightly later than wild type in long days (6, 89), and extremely late or not at all in short days (46, 89, 102). In long days, the mutant *ga1-3* is male sterile, with flowers that have poorly developed petals and stamens (50). All these flowering abnormalities seen in *ga1-3* can be restored to normal by the addition of exogenous GA (50, 54, 102). In addition, *spy* mutants, which behave as if the gibberellin signal transduction pathway is constitutively active, flower early (44). These observations show that GA have marked effects on flowering, but until recently, no details of the underlying molecular mechanisms were known.

Blázquez & Weigel (8) have argued that, because floral fate is specified by meristem-identity genes, the signals that regulate flowering must act through meristem-identity genes. One such meristem-identity gene is *LEAFY* (LFY) (7). In the wild-type plant, *LEAFY* is expressed in leaf primordia before the transition to flowering is made (7, 37).

The relation between GA and *LEAFY* expression has been studied in *Arabidopsis* by Weigel and colleagues. Application of GA to *Arabidopsis* in short days makes the plants flower early (54), and this effect is paralleled by an increase in

LEAFY promoter activity (7). As seen above, the exogenous application of GA makes *gal-3* flower early, and again this effect is accompanied by an increase in *LEAFY* promoter activity (7). Further studies with a *LFY* promoter–*GUS* construct (*LFY::GUS*) (6) introduced into the *gal-3* mutant showed that in long days, the initial levels of *LFY::GUS* were reduced, the up-regulation of *LFY::GUS* was delayed, and the maximum level of *LFY::GUS* was reduced, when compared to the wild type. The exogenous application of GA returned to normal both the flowering defect and *LFY::GUS* expression. In short days, where *gal-3* plants flower extremely late, or never flower (46, 89, 102), the expression of *LFY::GUS* was undetectable. Also, the effects on *LFY::GUS* expression seen in *gal-3* could be reproduced if wild-type plants carrying the *LFY::GUS* construct were treated with PAC, an inhibitor of gibberellin biosynthesis. Overexpression of *LFY* in *gal-3* plants (6) restored the capacity of this mutant to flower in short days. However, the mutant still flowered later than the wild-type transformed with the same construct. Taken together, these results suggest that GA regulates the activity of the *LFY* promoter and also the competence to respond to *LFY* activity (6).

Recently, a study of deletions of the *LFY* promoter fused to the *GUS* reporter gene has been published (8). A minimum promoter, GOF9, behaved with the same temporal pattern as the full *LFY* promoter, with fast up-regulation in long days, and a slower, gradual increase in short days; and this slow increase was enhanced by the addition of GA. Mutation of an 8-base pair sequence in this construct (GOF9m) had very little effect on the activity of the LFY promoter in long days, but the promoter remained inactive in short days, and this lack of activity could not be overcome by the addition of GA. This 8-base pair sequence is potentially a GA response element, and has a sequence that agrees with the consensus binding site for MYB transcription factors of animals (8). This is reminiscent of the well-studied effect of GA in inducing expression of the α-amylase gene in the cereal aleurone layer, where a MYB protein also seems to be implicated (see above). Perhaps this suggests a general mechanism by which GAs exert their effects.

CONCLUSIONS

The past few years have seen major advances in our understanding of the signaling mechanisms by which the GAs control the growth of plants. Although the GA receptor has not been isolated, it is thought to be associated with the plasma membrane. Pharmacological and mutant data suggest that the early stages of the signaling process may involve G-protein-coupled receptors and/or α-subunits of G-proteins. Genetic analysis in a variety of plant species has highlighted the importance of the GAI/RGA family of nuclear proteins in the mediation of the GA response, and it may be that these proteins are responsible for transmitting the signal from cytoplasm to nucleus. In addition, the *SPY* gene appears to encode an *O*-GlcNAc activity that modulates GA signaling. Finally, the involvement of Myb-type transcription factors has been implicated in two downstream GA-responses (the cereal α-amylase response and the initiation of flowering), suggesting that Myb-like proteins may be the point at which GA signaling diverges from the general pathway that is mediated by GAI/RGA and SPY to the specific branches that mediate specific responses.

Perhaps the most important consequence of all this exciting work has been to bring closer together the results of genetic studies with the wealth of biochemical and pharmacological information obtained from studies using the cereal aleurone layer. Although we are still far from a complete knowledge of GA signal transduction, these findings have opened many new avenues of research that will bring us nearer to that objective.

Visit the Annual Reviews home page at www.AnnualReviews.org

LITERATURE CITED

1. Ait-Ali T, Frances S, Weller JL, Reid JB, Kendrick RE, et al. 1999. Regulation of gibberellin 20-oxidase and gibberellin 3β-hydroxylase transcript accumulation during de-etiolation of pea seedlings. *Plant. Physiol.* 121:783–91
2. Allan AC, Trewavas AJ. 1994. Abscisic acid and gibberellin perception: inside or out? *Plant. Physiol.* 104:1107–8
3. Ashikari M, Wu J, Yano M, Sasaki T, Yoshimura A. 1999. Rice gibberellin-insensitive dwarf mutant gene *Dwarf 1* encodes the α-subunit of GTP-binding protein. *Proc. Natl. Acad. Sci. USA* 96:10284–89
4. Bethke PC, Jones RL. 1998. Gibberellin signaling. *Curr. Opin. Plant Biol.* 1:440–46
5. Bethke PC, Schuurink R, Jones RL. 1997. Hormonal signalling in cereal aleurone. *J. Exp. Bot.* 48:1337–56
6. Blázquez MA, Green R, Nilsson O, Sussman MR, Weigel D. 1998. Gibberellins promote flowering in Arabidopsis by activating the *LEAFY* promoter. *Plant Cell* 10:791–800
7. Blázquez MA, Soowal L, Lee I, Weigel D. 1997. *LEAFY* expression and flower initiation in *Arabidopsis. Development* 124:3835–44
8. Blázquez MA, Weigel D. 2000. Integration of floral inductive signals in *Arabidopsis. Nature* 404:889–92
9. Börner A, Plaschke J, Korzun V, Worland AJ. 1996. The relationships between the dwarfing genes of wheat and rye. *Euphytica* 89:69–75
10. Bolle C, Koncz C, Chua N-H. 2000. PAT1, a new member of the GRAS family, is involved in phytochrome A signal transduction. *Genes Dev.* 14:1269–78
11. Bush DS. 1996. Effects of gibberellic acid and environmental factors on cytosolic calcium in wheat aleurone cells. *Planta* 199:89–99
12. Carol P, Peng J, Harberd NP. 1995. Isolation and preliminary characterization of *gas1-1*, a mutation causing partial suppression of the phenotype conferred by the gibberellin-insensitive (*gai*) mutant in *Arabidopsis thaliana* (L.) Heyhn. *Planta* 197:414–17
13. Chandler PM. 1988. Hormonal regulation of gene expression in the "slender" mutant of barley (*Hordeum vulgare* L.). *Planta* 175:115–20
14. Chandler PM, Robertson M. 1999. Gibberellin dose-response curves and the characterization of dwarf mutants of barley. *Plant Physiol.* 120:623–32
15. Cowling RJ, Kamiya Y, Seto H, Harberd NP. 1998. Gibberellin dose-response regulation of GA4 gene transcript levels in *Arabidopsis thaliana. Plant Physiol.* 117:1195–203

16. Croker SJ, Hedden P, Lenton JR, Stoddart JL. 1990. Comparison of gibberellins in normal and slender barley seedlings. *Plant Physiol.* 94:194–200
17. Darnell JE Jr. 1997. STATs and gene regulation. *Science* 277:1630–35
18. de Haan H. 1927. Length factors in *Pisum*. *Genetica* 9:481–97
19. Di Laurenzio L, Wysocka-Diller J, Malamy JE, Pysh L, Helariutta Y, et al. 1996. The *SCARECROW* gene regulates an asymmetric cell division that is essential for generating the radial organization of the Arabidopsis root. *Cell* 86:423–33
20. Foster CA. 1977. Slender: an accelerated extension growth mutant of barley. *Barley Genet. Newsl.* 7:24–27
21. Fridborg I, Kuusk S, Moritz T, Sundberg E. 1999. The *Arabidopsis* dwarf mutant *shi* exhibits reduced gibberellin responses conferred by overexpression of a new putative zinc finger protein. *Plant Cell* 11:1019–31
22. Fujioka S, Yamane H, Spray CR, Katsumi M, Phinney BO, et al. 1988. The dominant non-gibberellin-responding dwarf mutant (*D8*) of maize accumulates native gibberellins. *Proc. Natl. Acad. Sci. USA* 85:9031–35
23. Fujisawa Y, Kato T, Ohki S, Ishikawa A, Kitano H, et al. 1999. Suppression of the heterotrimeric G protein causes abnormal morphology, including dwarfism, in rice. *Proc. Natl. Acad. Sci. USA* 96:7575–80
24. Gale MD, Law CN, Marshall GA, Worland AJ. 1975. The genetic control of gibberellic acid insensitivity in a "dwarf" wheat. *Heredity* 34:393–99
25. Gale MD, Marshall GA. 1975. The nature and genetic control of gibberellin insensitivity in dwarf wheat grain. *Heredity* 35:55–65
26. Gale MD, Youssefian S. 1985. Dwarfing genes in wheat. In *Progress in Plant Breeding*, ed. GE Russell, pp. 1–35. London: Butterworths
27. Gilroy S, Jones RL. 1994. Perception of gibberellin and abscisic acid at the external face of the plasma membrane of barley (*Hordeum vulgare*) aleurone protoplasts. *Plant Physiol.* 104:1185–92
28. Gubler F, Kalla R, Roberts JK, Jacobsen JV. 1995. Gibberellin-regulated expression of a *myb* gene in barley aleurone cells: evidence for Myb transactivation of a high-P*I* alpha-amylase gene promoter. *Plant Cell* 7:1879–91
29. Harberd NP, Freeling M. 1989. Genetics of dominant gibberellin-insensitive dwarfism in maize. *Genetics* 121:827–38
30. Harberd NP, King KE, Carol P, Cowling RJ, Peng J, et al. 1998. Gibberellin: inhibitor of an inhibitor of...? *BioEssays* 20:1001–8
31. Hart GW. 1997. Dynamic *O*-linked glycosylation of nuclear and cytoskeletal proteins. *Annu. Rev. Biochem.* 66:315–35
32. Hart GW, Haltiwanger RS, Holt GD, Kelly WG. 1989. Glycosylation in the nucleus and cytoplasm. *Annu. Rev. Biochem.* 58:841–74
33. Hedden P, Kamiya Y. 1997. Gibberellin biosynthesis: enzymes, genes and their regulation. *Annu. Rev. Plant Physiol.* 48:431–60
34. Heery DM, Kalkhoven E, Hoare S, Parker MG. 1997. A signature motif in transcriptional co-activators mediates binding to nuclear receptors. *Nature* 387:733–36
35. Heimovaara-Dijkstra S, Heistek JC, Wang M. 1994. Counteractive effects of ABA and GA3 on extracellular and intracellular pH and malate in barley aleurone. *Plant Physiol.* 106:359–65
36. Helariutta Y, Fukaki H, Wysocka-Diller J, Nakajima K, Jung J, et al. 2000. The *SHORT-ROOT* gene controls radial patterning of the *Arabidopsis* root through radial signaling. *Cell* 101:555–67
37. Hempel FD, Weigel D, Mandel MA, Ditta G, Zambryski P, et al. 1997. Floral determination and expression of floral regulatory genes in *Arabidopsis*. *Development* 124:3845–53
38. Ho T-HD, Nolan RC, Shute DE. 1981.

Characterization of a gibberellin-insensitive dwarf wheat, D6899. *Plant Physiol.* 67:1026–31

39. Hooley R. 1994. Gibberellins: perception, transduction and reponses. *Plant Mol. Biol.* 26:1529–55

40. Hooley R. 1998. Plant hormone reception and action: a role for G-protein signal transduction? *Philos. Trans. R. Soc. London Ser. B* 353:1425–30

41. Hooley R. 1999. A role for G proteins in plant hormone signalling? *Plant Physiol. Biochem.* 37:393–402

42. Hooley R, Beale MH, Smith SJ. 1991. Gibberellin perception at the plasma membrane of *Avena fatua* aleurone protoplasts. *Planta* 183:274–80

43. Jacobsen SE, Binkowski KA, Olszewski NE. 1996. SPINDLY, a tetratricopeptide repeat protein involved in gibberellin signal transduction in *Arabidopsis. Proc. Natl. Acad. Sci. USA* 93: 9292–96

44. Jacobsen SE, Olszewski NE. 1993. Mutations at the *SPINDLY* locus of Arabidopsis alter gibberellin signal transduction. *Plant Cell* 5:887–96

45. Jones HD, Smith SJ, Desikan R, Plakidou-Dymock S, Lovegrove A, et al. 1998. Heterotrimeric G proteins are implicated in gibberellin induction of α-amylase gene expression in wild oat aleurone. *Plant Cell* 10:245–54

46. King KE. 1999. *Genetic and molecular investigation of gibberellin signalling.* PhD thesis. Univ. East Anglia, Norwich, UK. 176 pp.

47. King KE, Carol P, Cowling RJ, Peng J, Richards DE, et al. 2000. Genetic approaches to the understanding of gibberellin-mediated plant growth regulation. In *Molecular Approaches to the Understanding of Plant Hormones*, ed. Palme, Schell. New York: Springer-Verlag

48. Koornneef M, Elgersma A, Hanhart CJ, van Loenen-Martinet EP, van Rijn L, et al. 1985. A gibberellin-insensitive mutant of *Arabidopsis thaliana. Physiol. Plant.* 65:33–39

49. Koornneef M, Reuling G, Karssen CM. 1984. The isolation and characterization of abscisic acid-insensitive mutants of *Arabidopsis thaliana. Physiol. Plant.* 61:377–83

50. Koornneef M, van der Veen JH. 1980. Induction and analysis of gibberellin sensitive mutants in *Arabidopsis thaliana* (L.) Heynh. *Theor. Appl. Genet.* 58:257–63

51. Kreppel LK, Blomberg MA, Hart GW. 1997. Dynamic glycosylation of nuclear and cytosolic proteins. *J. Biol. Chem.* 272:9308–15

52. Kuo A, Cappellutti S, Cervantes-Cervantes M, Rodriguez M, Bush DS. 1996. Okadaic acid, a protein phosphatase inhibitor, blocks calcium changes, gene expression, and cell death induced by gibberellin in wheat aleurone cells. *Plant Cell* 8:259–69

53. Lanahan MB, Ho T-HD. 1988. Slender barley: a constitutive gibberellin-response mutant. *Planta* 175:107–14

54. Langridge J. 1957. Effect of day-length and gibberellic acid on the flowering of *Arabidopsis. Nature* 180:36–37

55. Lenton JR, Hedden P, Gale MD. 1987. Gibberellin insensitivity and depletion in wheat—consequences for development. In *Hormone Action in Development—A Critical Appraissal*, ed. GV Hoad, JR Lenton, MB Jackson, RK Atkin, pp. 145–60. London: Butterworths

56. Lester DR, Ross JJ, Smith JJ, Elliot RC, Reid JB. 1999. Gibberellin 2-oxidation and the *SLN* gene of *Pisum sativum. Plant J.* 19:65–73

57. Levy YY, Dean C. 1998. The transition to flowering. *Plant Cell* 10:1973–89

58. Lovegrove A, Hooley R. 2000. Gibberellin and abscisic acid signalling in aleurone. *Trends. Plant Sci.* 5:102–10

59. Martin DN, Proebsting WM, Parks TD, Dougherty WG, Lange T, et al. 1996. Feedback regulation of gibberellin biosynthesis

and gene expression in *Pisum sativum* L. *Planta* 200:159–66

60. McComb AJ, McComb JA. 1970. Growth substances and the relation between phenotype and genotype in *Pisum sativum*. *Planta* 91:235–45

61. McCourt P. 1999. Genetic analysis of hormone signaling. *Annu. Rev. Plant Physiol.* 50:219–43

62. Mitsunaga S, Tashiro T, Yamaguchi J. 1994. Identification and characterization of gibberellin-insensitive mutants selected from among dwarf mutants of rice. *Theor. Appl. Genet.* 87:705–12

63. Murfet IC. 1990. Internode length and anatomical changes in Pisum genotypes *cry*^{s} and *cry*^{c} in response to extended daylength and applied gibberellin A1. *Physiol. Plant.* 79:497–505

64. Ogas J. 1998. Plant hormones: dissecting the gibberellin response pathway. *Curr. Biol.* 8:R165–67

65. Ogas J, Cheng J-C, Sung ZR, Sommerville C. 1997. Cellular differentiation regulated by gibberellin in the *Arabidopsis thaliana pickle* mutant. *Science* 277:91–94

66. Ogas J, Kaufmann S, Henderson J, Somerville C. 1999. PICKLE is a CHD3 chromatin-remodelling factor that regulates the transition from embryonic to vegetative development in *Arabidopsis*. *Proc. Natl. Acad. Sci. USA* 96:13839–44

67. Ogawa M, Kusano T, Katsumi M, Sano H. 2000. Rice gibberellin-insensitive gene homolog, *OsGAI*, encodes a nuclear-localized protein capable of gene activation at transcriptional level. *Gene* 245:21–29

68. Peng J, Carol P, Richards DE, King KE, Cowling RJ, et al. 1997. The *Arabidopsis GAI* gene defines a signaling pathway that negatively regulates gibberellin responses. *Genes Dev.* 11:3194–205

69. Peng J, Harberd NP. 1993. Derivative alleles of the Arabidopsis gibberellin-insensitive (*gai*) mutation confer a wild-type phenotype. *Plant Cell* 5:351–60

70. Peng J, Harberd NP. 1997. Gibberellin

deficiency and response mutations suppress the stem elongation phenotype of phytochrome-deficient mutants of Arabidopsis. *Plant Physiol.* 113:1051–58

71. Peng J, Harberd NP. 1997. Transposon-associated somatic *gai*-loss sectors in *Arabidopsis*. *Plant. Sci.* 130:181–88

72. Peng J, Richards DE, Hartley NM, Murphy GP, Devos KM, et al. 1999. "Green revolution" genes encode mutant gibberellin response modulators. *Nature* 400:256–61

73. Peng J, Richards DE, Moritz T, Caño-Delgado A, Harberd NP. 1999. Extragenic suppressors of the Arabidopsis *gai* mutation alter the dose-response relationship of diverse gibberellin responses. *Plant Physiol.* 119:1–10

74. Penson SP, Schuurink RC, Fath A, Gubler F, Jacobsen JV, et al. 1996. cGMP is required for gibberellic acid-induced gene expression in barley aleurone. *Plant Cell* 8:2325–33

75. Pharis RP, King RW. 1985. Gibberellins and reproductive development in seed plants. *Annu. Rev. Plant Physiol.* 36:517–68

76. Phillips AL, Ward DA, Uknes S, Appleford NEJ, Lange T, et al. 1995. Isolation and expression of three gibberellin 20-oxidase cDNA clones from *Arabidopsis*. *Plant Physiol.* 108:1049–57

77. Phinney BO. 1956. Growth response of single-gene dwarf mutants in maize to gibberellic acid. *Proc. Natl. Acad. Sci. USA* 42:185–89

78. Potts WC, Reid JB. 1983. Internode length in *Pisum*. III. The effect and interaction of the *Na/na* and *Le/le* gene differences on endogenous gibberellin-like substances. *Physiol. Plant.* 57:448–85

79. Potts WC, Reid JB, Murfet IC. 1985. Internode length in *Pisum*. Gibberellins and the slender phenotype. *Physiol. Plant.* 63:357–64

80. Pysh LD, Wysocka-Diller JW, Camilleri C, Bouchez D, Benfey PN. 1999. The GRAS family in Arabidopsis: sequence characterization and basic expression analysis of

the SCARECROW-LIKE genes. *Plant J.* 18:111–19

81. Rebers M, Kaneta T, Kawaide H, Yamaguchi S, Sekimoto H, et al. 1999. Regulation of gibberellin biosynthesis genes during flower and early fruit development of tomato. *Plant J.* 17:241–50

82. Reid JB, Ross JJ, Swain SM. 1992. Internode length in *Pisum.* A new slender mutant with elevated levels of C19 gibberellins. *Planta* 188:462–67

83. Richards DE, Peng J, Harberd NP. 2000. Plant GRAS and metazoan STATs: one family? *BioEssays* 22:573–77

84. Robertson M, Swain SM, Chandler PM, Olszewski NE. 1998. Identification of a negative regulator of gibberellin action, *HvSPY* in barley. *Plant Cell* 10:995–1007

85. Ross JJ, Murfet IC, Reid JB. 1997. Gibberellin mutants. *Physiol. Plant.* 100:550–60

86. Schumacher K, Schmitt T, Rossberg M, Schmitz G, Theres K. 1999. The *Lateral suppressor (LS)* gene of tomato encodes a new member of the VHIID protein family. *Proc. Natl. Acad. Sci. USA* 96:290–95

87. Schuurink RC, Chan PV, Jones RL. 1996. Modulation of calmodulin mRNA and protein levels in barley aleurone. *Plant Physiol.* 111:371–80

88. Silverstone AL, Ciampaglio CN, Sun T-p. 1998. The Arabidopsis *RGA* gene encodes a transcriptional regulator repressing the gibberellin signal transduction pathway. *Plant Cell* 10:155–69

89. Silverstone AL, Mak PYA, Martinez EC, Sun T-p. 1997. The new *RGA* locus encodes a negative regulator of gibberellin response in *Arabidopsis thaliana. Genetics* 146:1087–99

90. Steber CM, Cooney SE, McCourt P. 1998. Isolation of the GA-response mutant *sly1* as a suppressor of *ABI1-1* in *Arabidopsis thaliana. Genetics* 149:509–21

91. Strader CD, Fong TM, Tota MR, Underwood D. 1994. Structure and function of G-protein coupled receptors. *Annu. Rev. Biochem.* 63:101–32

92. Sun T-p, Goodman HM, Ausubel FM. 1992. Cloning the Arabidopsis *GA1* locus by genomic subtraction. *Plant Cell* 4:119–28

93. Sun T-p, Kamiya K. 1994. The *Arabidopsis GA1* locus encodes the cyclase *ent*-kaurene synthetase A of gibberellin biosynthesis. *Plant Cell* 6:1509–18

94. Swain SM, Olszewski NE. 1996. Genetic analysis of gibberellin signal transduction. *Plant Physiol.* 112:11–17

95. Talon M, Koornneef M, Zeevaart JAD. 1990. Accumulation of C19-gibberellins in the gibberellin-insensitive dwarf mutant gai of *Arabidopsis thaliana* (L) Heynh. *Planta* 182:501–5

96. Thomas SG, Phillips AL, Hedden P. 1999. Molecular cloning and functional expression of gibberellin 2-oxidases, multifunctional enzymes involved in gibberellin deactivation. *Proc. Natl. Acad. Sci. USA* 96:4698–703

97. Thornton T, Krepel L, Hart G, Olszewski NE. 1999. Genetic and biochemical analysis of *Arabidopsis* SPY. In *Plant Biotechnology and in-vitro Biology in the 21st Century,* ed. A Altman, M Ziv, S Izhar, pp. 445–48. New York: Kluwer

98. Thornton TM, Swain SM, Olszewski NE. 1999. Gibberellin signal transduction presents... the SPY who *O*-GlcNAc'd me. *Trends Plant Sci.* 4:424–28

99. Torchia J, Rose DW, Inostroza J, Kamei Y, Westin S, et al. 1997. The transcriptional co-activator p/CIP binds CBP and mediates nuclear-receptor function. *Nature* 387:677–84

100. Toyomasu T, Kawaide H, Mitsuhashi W, Inoue Y, Kamiya Y. 1998. Phytochrome regulates gibberellin biosynthesis during germination of photoblastic lettuce seeds. *Plant Physiol.* 118:1517–23

101. Webb SE, Appleford NEJ, Gaskin P, Lenton JR. 1998. Gibberellins in internodes and ears of wheat containing different dwarfing alleles. *Phytochemistry* 47:671–77

102. Wilson RN, Heckman JW, Sommerville CR. 1992. Gibberellin is required for flowering in *Arabidopsis thaliana* under short days. *Plant Physiol.* 100:403–8

103. Wilson RN, Sommerville CR. 1995. Phenotypic suppression of the gibberellin-insensitive mutant (*gai*) of Arabidopsis. *Plant Physiol.* 108:495–502

104. Winkler RG, Freeling M. 1994. Physiological genetics of the dominant gibberellin-non responsive maize dwarfs, *Dwarf8* and *Dwarf9*. *Planta* 193:341–48

105. Yamaguchi S, Smith MW, Brown RS, Kamiya Y, Sun T-p. 1998. Phytochrome regulation and differential expression of gibberellin 3-hydroxylase genes in germinating *Arabidopsis* seeds. *Plant Cell* 10:2115–26

106. Zeevaart JAD, Talon M. 1992. Gibberellin mutants in *Arabidopsis thaliana*. In *Progress in Plant Growth Regulation*, ed. CM Karssen, LC van Loon, D Vreugdenhil, pp. 34–42. Dordrecht: Kluwer

107. Zwar JA, Chandler PM. 1995. Alpha-amylase production and leaf protein synthesis in a gibberellin-responsive dwarf mutant of Himalaya barley (*Hordeum vulgare* L.). *Planta* 197:39–48

Annu. Rev. Plant Physiol. Plant Mol. Biol. 2001. 52:89–118

Cytokinin Metabolism and Action

David WS Mok and Machteld C Mok

Department of Horticulture and Center for Gene Research and Biotechnology,
Oregon State University, Corvallis, Oregon 97331-7304; e-mail: mokd@bcc.orst.edu;
mokm@bcc.orst.edu

Key Words   plant hormone, zeatin metabolic enzymes, cytokinin genes, cytokinin biosynthesis, cytokinin signal transduction

■ **Abstract**   Cytokinins are structurally diverse and biologically versatile. The chemistry and physiology of cytokinin have been studied extensively, but the regulation of cytokinin biosynthesis, metabolism, and signal transduction is still largely undefined. Recent advances in cloning metabolic genes and identifying putative receptors portend more rapid progress based on molecular techniques. This review centers on cytokinin metabolism with connecting discussions on biosynthesis and signal transduction. Important findings are summarized with emphasis on metabolic enzymes and genes. Based on the information generated to date, implications and future research directions are presented.

CONTENTS

DEDICATION

In memory of Professor Folke Skoog in whose laboratory cytokinin was discovered and a generation of scientists were inspired.

INTRODUCTION

Cytokinins are plant hormones promoting cell division and differentiation. Since the discovery of the first cytokinin, kinetin, by Skoog, Miller, and associates in 1955 (119), the number of chemicals fitting the definition of cytokinins has grown to include a large array of natural and synthetic compounds, adenine and phenylurea derivatives. The chemistry of these groups of cytokinins has been reviewed extensively by Shaw (160) and Shudo (162). The biological activities of cytokinins in whole plants and tissues cultures have also been summarized (126, 132). Moreover, endogenous cytokinins have been examined in many species (5, 84, 185). Despite the wealth of information concerning cytokinin chemistry and physiology, the transition from descriptive studies to molecular biology has been relatively slow compared with other hormones, particularly ethylene (86, 92) and gibberellin (71, 74, 169). It is still uncertain how cytokinins are synthesized in plants although it is generally assumed that the model adopted from *Agrobacterium* suffices (42a). Only recently have candidates for cytokinin receptors begun to emerge (89, 145). Although many metabolites have been identified, their significance and the regulation of the metabolic conversions are still largely unknown. In recent years, sophisticated methods have been employed to quantify a host of major and minor components. However, as the contribution of individual cytokinins to particular growth processes is uncertain, the relevance of cytokinin quantities is open to interpretation. In short, cytokinin research needs to capitalize on the power of molecular biology to resolve many of the critical issues.[1]

There are intrinsic challenges particular to cytokinins. In tissue culture bioassays, the effects of cytokinins are well defined. In contrast, the responses of whole plants to cytokinins are broad and unspecific, unlike the triple response, stem elongation, or abscission/dormancy induced by ethylene, gibberellins, and abscisic acid, respectively (117). The action of cytokinins is often masked by interaction with other hormones. For example, cytokinins can interact with auxins either synergistically or antagonistically and induce the production of ethylene; therefore,

---

[1] Abbreviations: AMP, adenosine-5'-monophosphate; BA, N^6-benzyladenine; CBP, cytokinin-binding protein; CPPU, N-phenyl-N'-[2-chloro-4-pyridyl]urea; DPU, N,N'-diphenylurea; i^6Ade, N^6-(Δ^2-isopentenyl)adenine; i^6Ado, N^6-(Δ^2-isopentenyl)adenosine; i^6AMP, N^6-(Δ^2-isopentenyl)adenosine-5'-monophosphate; ipn^{6}Ade, N^6-isopentyladenine; ipn^{6}Ado, N^6-isopentyladenosine; ipt, isopentenyltransferase; TDPG, thymidine-5'-diphosphoglucose; UDPG, uridine-5'-diphosphoglucose; UDPX, uridine-5'-diphosphoxylose; ZMP, zeatin riboside-5'-monophosphate.

phenotypic changes are not easily identifiable as directly related to cytokinins (15, 46, 61, 179). Because mutant phenotypes may not be distinguishable from lesions affecting other hormones and severe impairment of cytokinin biosynthesis or action is likely to be lethal, isolating cytokinin mutants has not been very successful. Moreover, as naturally occurring cytokinins are adenine derivatives, it is necessary to distinguish metabolic changes unique to cytokinins from those associated with the biochemistry of purines. These constraints explain to some extent the slow progress. Nevertheless, recent advances in the identification of genes involved in cytokinin metabolism, perception, and response have added impetus to cytokinin research, signaling a fast transition to molecular approaches. Therefore, a summary of key findings with interpretations and identification of research areas deserving attention is timely. We take liberty in the latter with the comforting thought that scientific investigation is a self-correcting process and any predictions/models will serve as invitation for rigorous tests. The choice of metabolism as the connecting theme is based on our research interests and the premise that enzymes and genes involved in inter-conversions provide useful clues to both cytokinin biosynthesis and mode of action. The review consists of four parts: an overview of cytokinin metabolites, description of metabolic enzymes and genes, recent progress regarding cytokinin action, and implications related to recent findings.

CYTOKININ METABOLITES

The natural cytokinins are adenine derivatives and can be classified by the configuration of their N^6-side chain as isoprenoid or aromatic cytokinins (Figure 1). Cytokinins with an unsaturated isoprenoid side chain are by far the most prevalent, in particular those with a *trans*-hydroxylated N^6-side chain, *trans*-zeatin (101, 161) and its derivatives. Dihydrozeatin, the counterpart of zeatin with a saturated side chain, has been identified in many species, while *cis*-zeatin and N^6-(Δ^2-isopentenyl)adenine (i^6Ade) are generally minor components although exceptions exist (51, 54). Kinetin and N^6-benzyladenine (BA) are the best known cytokinins with ring substitutions at the N^6-position. In the early years of cytokinin research, only cytokinins with an isoprenoid side chain were thought to be endogenous compounds; however, in the mid-1970s BA derivatives were identified as natural cytokinins (75, 76). The phenylureas constitute a group of synthetic cytokinins, some of which are highly active, e.g. CPPU (N-phenyl-N'-[2-chloro-4-pyridyl]urea) (170) and thidiazuron (130).

Adenine-Type Cytokinins

Modifications of the Adenine Ring   The discovery of a new natural cytokinin is almost invariably followed by the report of its nucleoside and nucleotide (Figure 2). These conversions are primarily related to purine metabolism and only incidental to cytokinin metabolism. Other possible modifications of the adenine ring (Figure 2) include glucosylation of the adenine ring at the 3-, the 7-, or 9-position

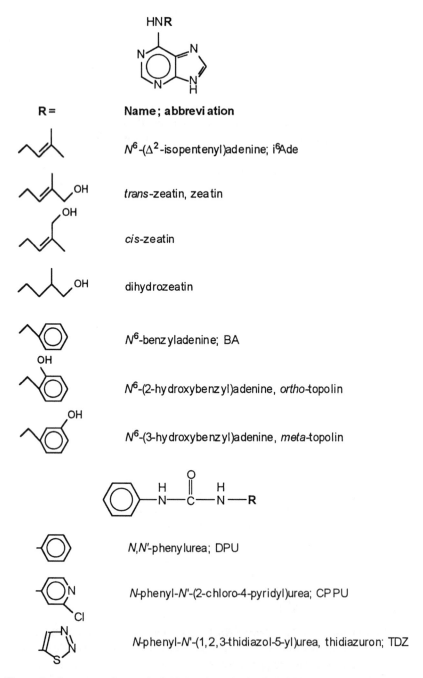

Figure 1 Structures of natural adenine and synthetic phenylurea cytokinins.

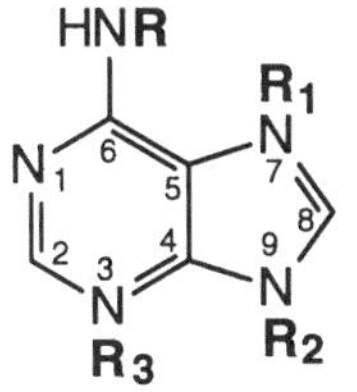

Figure 2   Modifications of the adenine ring.

R₁	β-D-glucopyranosyl

R_1 β-D-glucopyranosyl

R_2 β–D-ribofuranosyl
        β–D-ribofuranosyl-5'-monophosphate
        β-D-glucopyranosyl
        alanyl

R_3 β-D-glucopyranosyl

and conjugation of alanine at the 9-position of zeatin, forming lupinic acid (50, 84, 166, 178). These conversions presumably can occur with most adenine-type cytokinins provided there is no steric hindrance. With the exception of the 3-glucosides, the N-glucosyl and alanyl conjugates generally exhibit no or low activity in bioassays (103). The ribose moiety of cytokinin nucleosides can also be further glycosylated (173, 178).

Modifications of the N^6-Isoprenoid Side Chain   The most important changes are those affecting the N^6-side chain, since even small substitutions have pronounced effects on cytokinin activity, as demonstrated by extensive structure-activity relationship studies (100, 155, 156, 163). The modifications of the *trans*-zeatin side chain include reduction to dihydrozeatin, conjugation to O-glycosides (O-glucosides and O-xylosides), and side chain cleavage by cytokinin oxidases (Figure 3). O-Acetylation has been observed in a few species (84, 105). Modifications of the side chain of dihydrozeatin, such as O-glucosylation and O-xylosylation, are also known to occur (125, 182); however, an important difference between *trans*-zeatin and dihydrozeatin resides in the resistance of dihydrozeatin to cytokinin oxidases (3). The *cis*-isomer of zeatin is usually much less active than its *trans* counterpart in bioassays (156) and is somewhat susceptible to oxidases (3, 14). Evidence is emerging that the O-glucoside of *cis*-zeatin also occurs (111, 181) and isomerization of the *cis*- to the *trans*-configuration has been reported (11). Both i^6Ade and i^6Ado are highly susceptible to cytokinin oxidase attack (3) and can be converted to zeatin or zeatin riboside (38, 52), but reduction of the side chain from isopentenyl to isopentyl (to form ipn^6Ade or ipn^6Ado) has never been demonstrated.

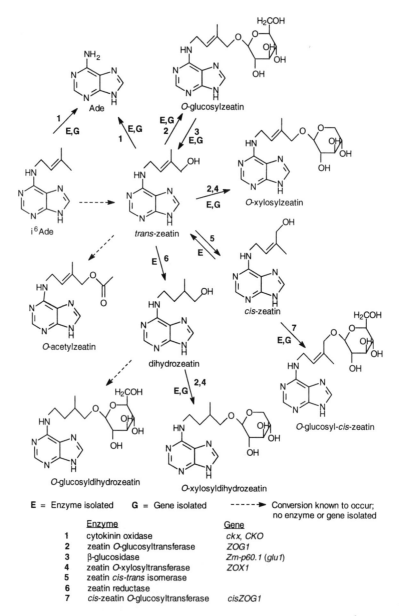

Figure 3   Enzymes (*E*) and genes (*G*) involved in the modifications of the N^6-isoprenoid side chain.

Aromatic Cytokinins   BA-type compounds were recognized as naturally occurring based on their isolation from poplar (75, 76), *Zantedeschia* (33), anise (58), and tomato (136). Modifications of the adenine ring on aromatic cytokinins mostly parallel those of the isoprenoid-cytokinins (Figure 2). Hydroxylated forms of BA, *meta-* and *ortho-*topolin, occur naturally, with the accompanying nucleosides, nucleotides, and *O*-glucosides (166). *meta-*Topolin is much more active than the *para* and *ortho-*derivatives. Other metabolites include 3-, 7-, and 9-glucosides and 9-alanine on the adenine ring (166) and a glucoside linked to the ribosyl moiety (6). It is not known if the distribution of BA derivatives is limited to a few species or is more widespread since plants analyzed in early experiments have often not been re-examined for their occurrence nor have these compounds been searched for routinely in recent analyses.

Phenylurea-Type Cytokinins

Diphenylurea (DPU) (Figure 1) was the first cytokinin-active phenylurea identified (159). Although this discovery was linked to detection of the compound in liquid coconut endosperm, it was later found to be a contaminant from prior chemical analyses of DPU. This fortuitous discovery, however, led to the synthesis of a number of potent analogues such as CPPU and thidiazuron (Figure 1), with cytokinin activity exceeding that of zeatin (130, 132, 162, 170). In contrast to zeatin, these active phenylureas are highly stable. Major metabolites isolated from bean callus tissues grown on medium containing ^{14}C-thidiazuron are glucosyl derivatives (129). There is no evidence that any phenylurea cytokinins occur naturally in plant tissues.

Perspectives on the Discovery and Quantitation of Metabolites

In the early years of cytokinin research, metabolites were isolated primarily by analyses of chromatographic fractions showing cytokinin activity in bioassays. This approach led to the identification of metabolites formed in relatively large quantities. Subsequent protocols for the isolation of cytokinins were often based on the structures and properties of metabolites discovered earlier. With the advent of more refined analytical tools such as HPLC combined with ELISA and/or mass spectral analyses (4, 7, 47, 63, 70, 174), metabolites present at minute concentrations can be detected, but the tendency to focus on known structures continues. Obviously, it is difficult to devise protocols for the isolation of unknown compounds; moreover, less common and novel cytokinin derivatives can be overlooked. Such may be the case with lupinic acid, isolated from lupin (104), and *O*-xylosylzeatin, found in *Phaseolus vulgaris* (99, 177), which could also occur in other species. Additional routes to identify new metabolites are now available. For example, determining the substrate specificity of metabolic enzymes would help predict the possible occurrence of unknown/unexpected compounds. As an illustration, the zeatin *O*-xylosyltransferase of *P. vulgaris* was found to convert dihydrozeatin to its *O*-xylosyl derivative (177; see below), which led to the isolation of *O*-xylosyldihydrozeatin from bean seeds (125). Prediction of metabolites could also be based on genomics. Newly cloned genes encoding cytokinin metabolic enzymes can be compared with GENBANK sequences to identify homologues. The recombinant proteins of candidate genes can then be tested in vitro to determine if (and which) cytokinins are substrates for the enzymes. Enzymatic products may represent cytokinin metabolites occurring in vivo even though they have not yet been revealed using conventional approaches. For instance, the cloning of a gene from maize encoding an *O*-glucosyltransferase specific to *cis*-zeatin (111; see below) suggests the presence of *cis*-zeatin-*O*-glucoside in this species. Eventually, metabolites may be predicted through the identification of sequences known to represent cytokinin binding sites.

Numerous studies have focused on measurements of cytokinin levels, but the significance of such quantitations is often unclear. Early on, levels of biologically active cytokinins were usually expressed as kinetin equivalents based on results of bioassays such as tobacco callus culture or chlorophyll retention tests. This approach, although seemingly undefined/unrefined, was operationally useful. As more cytokinin metabolites were discovered, results from cytokinin analyses gradually evolved into the display of arrays of metabolites and their quantities, the extent of which is limited mainly by the machinery and resources of the laboratories. The presentation of all measurable cytokinin components allows for a myriad of interpretations, but how such data sets relate to active cytokinin levels is not obvious. This is in part due to the uncertainty regarding the active form of cytokinin and the presumed reversibility of storage forms to active forms. The more cytokinin metabolites are discovered, the more difficult the task of interpreting the results of quantitative measurements becomes. As long as the function, or the qualitative importance, of each cytokinin remains unknown, the interpretation of prolific measurements will continue to be problematic. Moreover, current methods measure only extractable/free metabolites without including cytokinins bound to proteins or structural components. As the efficacy of each cytokinin is determined by a composite of factors such as cellular/tissue location, stability, and its metabolism, the quantity of that cytokinin extracted from mixed tissues or whole plants may or may not reflect its biological significance in vivo. Therefore, instead of relying on quantitation, it may be more informative to associate phenotypic variations or responses to environmental/chemical cues with changes in a specific metabolic step. In order for this approach to be successful, it is necessary to identify enzymes and genes regulating such metabolic conversions.

METABOLIC ENZYMES AND GENES

Conversions Between Cytokinin Bases, Nucleosides, and Nucleotides

Feeding experiments with cytokinin bases invariably result in the formation of corresponding nucleosides and nucleotides (102). Generally, such interconversions involve enzymes common to purine metabolism. These enzymes usually have higher affinity for adenine, adenosine, and AMP than for the corresponding cytokinins (reviewed in 34). For example, a 5′-nucleotidase (EC 3.1.3.5) from wheat germ (36) and tomato (26) converts AMP to adenine and cytokinin nucleotides to cytokinin bases but has higher affinity to AMP. Similarly, adenosine nucleosidase (EC 3.2.2.7) from wheat germ (37) has a lower K_m for adenosine than i^6Ado. Formation of cytokinin nucleosides from their free bases is mediated by an adenosine phosphorylase (EC 2.4.2.1), which prefers adenine over i^6Ade (41). Nucleotides of cytokinins can be formed from nucleosides by adenosine kinase (EC 2.7.1.20) or directly from free bases via the action of adenine phosphoribosyltransferase (APRTase; EC 2.4.2.7) (40). Mutants deficient in APRTase were isolated from *Arabidopsis* (123) and two genes encoding this enzyme were cloned (122, 158). Although one of the two recombinant enzymes (APT1) has much higher affinity for adenine than BA, the other (APT2) has threefold higher affinity for BA. The affinities for isoprenoid cytokinins were not reported. It is not known whether the male sterility of the *apt1* mutant is due to changes in cytokinin composition or purine metabolism (66). Another gene, encoding an adenosine kinase, was isolated from the moss *Physcomitrella* by complementation of a purine auxotrophic *E. coli* mutant, but its substrate specificity has not yet been determined (180).

Other Modifications of the Adenine Moiety

A glucosyltransferase (EC 2.4.1.118) catalyzing the formation of cytokinin glucosides at the 7- and 9-positions was isolated from radish cotyledons (55, 57). Although the enzyme recognizes a large number of adenine derivatives as substrates, the rate of conversion is highest for compounds with N^6-side chains of at least three alkyl carbons and roughly correlates with cytokinin activity (57). The formation of 7-glucosides is favored, but the relative amounts of 7- and 9-glucosides formed differ between substrates, with ratios of about 2:1 for BA and 10:1 for zeatin. The K_m for zeatin is 150 μM. The enzyme has a mass of about 46.5 kD and a broad pH range with an optimum of 7.3. Both UDPG and TDPG can serve as glucosyl donors.

A transferase (EC 4.2.99.13) converting zeatin to its 9-alanyl derivative, lupinic acid, was partially purified from lupin seeds (56). This enzyme has low substrate specificity but shows a preference for cytokinins since the rate of product formation is 14 times higher with zeatin than adenine and the K_m is 0.88 mM for zeatin versus 26 mM for adenine. The donor substrate is O-acetyl-L-serine (K_m 47 μM). The mass of the enzyme is estimated as 64.5 kD.

Modification of the Isoprenoid Side Chain

Cytokinin Oxidases   Cytokinin oxidases selectively degrade unsaturated N^6-isoprenoid side chains, converting active cytokinins such as zeatin and i^6Ade to adenine (Figure 3). Cytokinin bases and nucleosides but not the nucleotides are susceptible (3, 69, 87). The oxidation product of the i^6Ade-side chain has been identified as 3-methyl-2-butenal (23). Since the isolation of the first cytokinin oxidase from tobacco callus tissues 30 years ago (140), this type of enzyme has been obtained from maize, beans, poplar, wheat, and *Vinca rosea* crown gall tissues (reviewed in 3, 69, 87). The wide occurrence of oxidases is matched by their diversity. They vary in mass, from 25 kD for the enzyme from *Vinca rosea* to 94 kD for maize (3, 118). Most but not all of these enzymes are glycoproteins, with pH optima ranging from 6.0 to 9.0 (3, 90). Based on the degradation products, the use of oxygen, and the enhancement by copper imidazole complexes (32), oxidases were classified as copper-dependent amine oxidases (EC 1.4.3.6). This classification has recently been questioned (147) because copper-dependent amine oxidase seems to oxidize primary amines specifically (98), whereas cytokinins are secondary amines. The finding that the recombinant cytokinin oxidases of maize are flavoproteins (14, 77, 133; see below) also suggests that reclassification may be in order. However, the diverse properties of cytokinin oxidases indicate that there may be more than one class of cytokinin degradation enzyme.

Maize cytokinin oxidase genes were recently cloned in two laboratories (77, 133). Both groups based their strategies on determining partial internal amino acid sequences of enzymes purified from immature maize kernels. A partial gene sequence was then obtained using PCR with degenerate primers. Morris et al (133) isolated the full-length gene by screening a genomic library, while Houba-Hérin et al (77) cloned the cDNA via RACE PCR from a maize kernel cDNA library. The ORF was expressed in *Pichia* or moss protoplasts and an active oxidase was secreted into the culture medium. The two groups may have isolated alleles of the same gene family since the two clones differ only in seven nucleotides (three amino acids). The gene, *ckx* or *CKO*, consists of three exons separated by two small introns. The ORF of 1602 bp encodes a 57-kD enzyme with a flavin-binding domain and eight possible glycosylation sites. BLAST searches revealed homology to seven *Arabidopsis* accessions as well as the *fas5* gene of *Rhodococcus fascians* (14, 77). The *Arabidopsis* homologs are 39% to 47% identical to the maize gene at the amino acid level. Of the four homologs tested, three encode proteins displaying cytokinin oxidase activity (14). Western analyses detected high levels of the enzyme in maize kernels but low or no enzyme in other plant parts. The K_m values for the recombinant enzyme (i^6Ade, 1.5 μM; i^6Ado, 11 μM; zeatin, 14 μM; *cis*-zeatin, 46 μM) are in good agreement with those of the native enzyme, but differ somewhat from earlier estimates reported for maize cytokinin oxidase by other laboratories (3, 118). The molecular weight and the pH optimum also differ from earlier findings, again suggesting the likely occurrence of additional types of cytokinin oxidases.

Many studies have shown that phenylurea-type cytokinins such as thidiazuron and CPPU are strong inhibitors of cytokinin oxidase activity (3, 25, 31, 96). Although characterizations of maize and bean oxidases suggested such inhibition is noncompetitive (3, 25), the latest kinetic analyses of ckx1 recombinant protein indicate that CPPU is a competitive inhibitor, at least to this maize oxidase (14). It should be noted that adenine-type cytokinins such as BA and kinetin, which do not serve as substrates to the enzyme, did not inhibit oxidase activity in bean callus cultures (31). Whether these cytokinins show competitive inhibition with the ckx1 enzyme has not been determined.

Zeatin O-Glycosyltransferases   *O*-Glucosylzeatin seems to be a ubiquitous metabolite in plants (178), although *O*-xylosylzeatin has been detected thus far only in *Phaseolus* (99, 125). As *O*-glucosylzeatin is resistant to cytokinin oxidase attack (3) and can be converted to the active aglycone by *β*-glycosidases, *O*-glycosylation may serve an important function in regulating the level of active cytokinins. Two zeatin *O*-glycosyltransferases have been isolated thus far, an *O*-xylosyltransferase (EC 2.4.1.204) from *P. vulgaris* (177) and an *O*-glucosyltransferase (EC 2.4.1.203) from *P. lunatus* (49). The two enzymes are similar in mass (about 50 kD) but differ in charge. The *O*-glucosyltransferase uses UDPG and UDPX as donor substrates but has much higher affinity to UDPG, whereas the *O*-xylosyltransferase uses only UDPX. The cytokinin substrate recognition of the enzymes is also highly specific; besides zeatin, the only other substrate is dihydrozeatin, which is used by both transferases to form *O*-xylosyldihydrozeatin in the presence of UDPX (49, 109, 124). Interestingly, the *O*-glucosyltransferase does not catalyze the formation of *O*-glucosyldihydrozeatin in the presence of UDPG. This is rather unexpected since *O*-glucosyldihydrozeatin is known to occur in *P. vulgaris* (182); therefore, it is likely that other *O*-glucosyltransferases exist capable of mediating conversion of dihydrozeatin. Neither *cis*-zeatin nor any of the ribosides serve as substrates for the enzymes. The stringent substrate specificity for cytokinins and sugar donors suggests that *O*-glycosylation is precisely regulated, tailored to individual cytokinins.

Genes encoding the zeatin *O*-glucosyl- and *O*-xylosyltransferase have been cloned from *P. lunatus* and *P. vulgaris*, respectively (112, 113). The first gene, *ZOG1* (for zeatin *O*-glucosyltransferase), was identified by screening a cDNA library from immature *P. lunatus* seeds with monoclonal antibodies (110). The second gene, *ZOX1* (for zeatin *O*-xylosyltransferase), was obtained by inverse PCR with primers based on the *ZOG1* sequence. Neither gene contains any introns. The ORFs of *ZOG1* and *ZOX1* encode polypeptides of 459 and 454 amino acids, respectively, with a mass of 51 kD. The recombinant proteins (112, 113) exhibit properties identical to those of the native enzymes (49, 177). The two genes exhibit 93% and 87% identity at the DNA and amino acid level, respectively. Northern analyses showed high expression of the genes in immature seeds but low in vegetative tissues. Recently, additional homologues have been isolated from *Phaseolus* as well as *Glycine max* (X Shan, RC Martin, MC Mok & DWS Mok, unpublished results).

The regions of the *ZOG1* gene relevant to UDPG affinity were determined using hybrid enzymes derived from domain exchanges of parental *ZOG1* and *ZOX1* genes (109). The N-terminal half of the enzyme is of critical importance in this aspect since hybrid enzyme having the N-terminal half of ZOG1 and C-terminal half of ZOX1 had exactly the same patterns of UDPG and UDPX utilization as ZOG1. Substituting the region between bp 401 and 637 of the *ZOG1* ORF with the corresponding segment of *ZOX1* abolished utilization of UDPG as substrate, but UDPG still competed with UDPX when present in the reaction mix. Additional substitution of the segment from bp 74 to 400 eliminated binding of UDPG to the enzyme, as evidenced by the loss of competitive inhibition by UDPG in UDPG+UDPX incubation. Amino acids critical for UDPG binding to *ZOG1* may be pinpointed by site-directed mutagenesis.

Transgenic tobacco plants were generated harboring the *ZOG1* gene under the control of a constitutive (*35S*) and an inducible (*Tet*) promoter (114). Expression of the transgene resulted in elevated enzyme production and increased conversion of exogenous zeatin to its *O*-glucoside. In zeatin/NAA interaction experiments, Tet-*ZOG1* leaf discs cultured in the presence of tetracycline required tenfold higher zeatin concentrations for the formation of shoots and callus than the controls (Tet-no insert), which fits the hypothesis of *O*-glucosylzeatin being a storage product. On the other hand, 35S-*ZOG1* plants showed developmental variations including adventitious root formation on the lower stems and axillary shoot growth, the latter indicative of decreased apical dominance. Thus, increased zeatin *O*-glucosylation in detached, cytokinin-dependent tissues leads to cytokinin sequestering whereas in whole plants the effect can simulate a reduction or a rise in cytokinin activity, depending on the tissue and stage of development. The use of tissue- and stage-specific promoters will further clarify the role of cytokinin *O*-glycosylation and perhaps even allow targeted modifications of growth patterns.

Recently, a novel gene, *cisZOG1*, encoding a *cis*-zeatin *O*-glucosyltransferase, was isolated from maize (RC Martin, MC Mok, JE Habben & DWS Mok, unpublished results). This gene was cloned utilizing the sequence of *ZOG1* from *Phaseolus* to identify candidate genes from maize EST (expressed sequence tag) data banks of Pioneer Hi-Bred International (PHB). This gene also does not have any introns and the ORF of 1401 bp encodes a polypeptide of 50 kD. The enzyme recognizes *cis*-zeatin and UDPG as substrates, but not *trans*-zeatin, dihydrozeatin, *cis*-zeatin riboside, or UDPX. The *cisZOG1* and *ZOG1* genes are 60% identical at the DNA level and 40% at the deduced amino acid level. The occurrence of *trans*- and *cis*-specific enzymes again reinforces the precision of metabolic regulation. The finding suggests that *cis*-zeatin derivatives may play a more important role in cytokinin homeostasis than currently recognized and illustrates the possible use of genomic analyses to seek new cytokinin metabolites.

β-Glucosidases   In order to restore cytokinin activity, conversion of glucosides to the corresponding aglycones is necessary. Although *β*-glucosidases (EC 3.2.1.21) and genes encoding these enzymes have been identified, none showed specificity to cytokinins. A maize *β*-glucosidase of 60 kD (p60) was partially purified (27) and the gene cloned (24). The recombinant enzyme (64 kD) cleaves *O*-glucosylzeatin and kinetin-*N*3-glucoside (24) as well as a number of other artificial and natural substrates (42). The gene (*Zm-p60.1, glu1*) is about 5 kb in length and consists of 12 exons separated by 11 introns. A similar gene was isolated from *Brassica* *napus* (60). The recombinant enzyme converts zeatin *O*-glucoside to zeatin, but related substrates, such as cytokinin *N*-glucosides, were not tested. Considering the low specificity of β-glucosidases, hydrolysis of glucosides may not be highly regulated, in contrast to *O*-glucosylation. Separation of cytokinin glycosides from β-glucosidases in different subcellular locations may provide a measure of control, as suggested by the finding that the *O*-glucoside of dihydrozeatin is localized in vacuoles (65).

Zeatin Reductase   Reduction of the *trans*-zeatin side chain to form dihydrozeatin is mediated by a zeatin reductase isolated from immature seeds of *P. vulgaris* (115). The enzyme is highly specific for zeatin; it does not reduce *cis*-zeatin, *trans*-zeatin riboside, i^6Ade, or zeatin *O*-glycosides. The enzyme requires NADPH as a cofactor. Two isoforms of the enzyme, about 25 kD and 55 kD in size, were found in *Phaseolus* species. As dihydrozeatin is resistant to cytokinin oxidases, reduction of the zeatin side chain may preserve cytokinin activity, especially in tissues with high levels of oxidases.

Zeatin Isomerase   A *cis-trans* zeatin isomerase was partially purified from *Phaseolus* (11). The enzyme favors conversion from the *cis*- to the *trans*- isomer. As the indirect pathway of cytokinin biosynthesis involves the breakdown of cytokinin-containing tRNAs (146, 171), the isomerase provides a possible route to convert the less active *cis*-zeatin to the highly active *trans*-isomer.

Hydroxylase   Hydroxylation of the isopentenyl side chain was detected in a microsomal fraction of cauliflower (38). The enzyme catalyzed conversion of i^6Ade to zeatin and i^6Ado to zeatin riboside in the presence of NADPH. However, further purification and characterization of the enzyme has not been reported.

CYTOKININ ACTION

For close to 30 years, scientists have been searching for cytokinin-binding proteins (CBPs) that could serve as receptors (reviewed in 19–21; 18, 22, 64, 93–95, 120, 138). Many CBPs exhibit some of the properties expected of receptors, but clear proof for a true receptor is lacking. Based on the cytokinin concentrations in plant tissues, few of these proteins have K_d values low enough to qualify as receptors. Moreover, the function of these proteins is often unknown (reviewed in 15, 19, 20, 21).

The advent of molecular biology has brought about rapid progress in the field of plant hormone perception/signaling (61, 117). The patterns emerging for plant signal transduction resemble those established for other organisms (30, 117, 143). The first step involves binding of the hormone to a high-affinity receptor protein, resulting in a conformational change. This then sets into motion a signal transduction cascade, either through a his-asp phosphorylation/dephosphorylation chain or by guanine nucleotide binding and hydrolysis, eventually leading to changes in transcription of a specific set of genes. Although information on the components of cytokinin perception and signal transduction is still very limited, recent findings suggest that this model may be applicable to cytokinin signaling as well.

Phosphorelay Signal Transduction

A gene encoding a putative cytokinin receptor, CKI1, was isolated from *Arabidopsis* through *Agrobacterium*-mediated activational tagging using a 35S promoter (89, 135). Tissues of the transformant harboring the promoter upstream of the *CKI1* gene were cytokinin-independent in vitro, indicative of either increased cytokinin production or sensitivity. The CKI1 protein contains a putative input domain with two membrane-spanning regions, a sensor histidine kinase, and a receiver domain. The phenotype of the mutant together with the similarity of the protein to bacterial two-component systems and ETR1, an ethylene receptor (29, 154), render a cytokinin receptor function plausible. However, binding of CKI1 to cytokinins has yet to be demonstrated.

The existence of a his-asp phosphorelay chain is further suggested by the identification of other possible components of such a pathway (44, 45). *Arabidopsis* genes rapidly induced by cytokinin, *IBC6/ARR5* and *IBC7/ARR4*, were isolated by two groups (17, 80, 91, 172). The induction of gene expression does not require protein synthesis, indicative of a primary response function. Moreover, highly active cytokinins, including thidiazuron, were able to induce these genes, whereas adenine was only weakly active (17). Maize genes homologous to *IBC/ARR* have also been identified (152, 153). The gene products are similar to the receiver domain of bacterial two-component systems (30) and contain two invariant aspartate residues and an invariant lysine residue. Although 14 members of this family were reported for *Arabidopsis* (45, 79), only those containing a receiver domain and a short C-terminal region (A-type) were rapidly induced by cytokinins. Those having a receiver domain and a longer C-terminal region (B-type) were not induced by cytokinin. Divergence between the two types is indicated by the low homology of amino acid sequences of receiver domains between members of the two groups (24% to 30%), in contrast to the high homology between members of the same group (60% to 96%). B-type ARR proteins have properties suggestive of transcription factors, including the presence of a Myb-related motif, nuclear localization, and the ability to activate transcription when fused to the GAL4 DNA-binding domain (79, 107).

A gene family (*AHP*) with potential action in the same signal transduction pathway as A-type ARR members was obtained by scanning the *Arabidopsis* EST database for genes containing histidine phospho-transfer domains (121, 168). Purified AHP1 and AHP2 protein, when previously phosphorylated by crude bacterial membranes, could phosphorylate ARR3 and ARR4 in vitro, indicating a possible role upstream of ARR in the pathway. It should be noted that genes similar to *AHP1* also occur in maize (151). A model was proposed by D'Agostino & Kieber (45), with CKI1 as the receptor, AHP downstream from CKI1, and ARR downstream from AHP. However, a complication is the finding that AHP1 can phosphorylate the receiver domain of CKI1 as well (135). To provide an explanation, the authors speculated that the CKI1 receiver domain may negatively modulate its own signaling pathway through the removal of a phosphate from a previously phosphorylated AHP. The same set of AHP proteins can form stable complexes with B-type ARRs, but does not phosphorylate them (79). Another gene possibly interacting with ARR4 was obtained by a yeast two-hybrid screen (184). This gene (*AtDBP*) had been cloned earlier and encodes a DNA-binding protein (2).

CycD3, encoding a protein involved in the G1—S transition of the cell cycle, may be one of the primary genes induced by cytokinin (148, 165). Transcripts began to accumulate within one hour of cytokinin treatment of cell suspensions and intact seedlings (148). Moreover, tissues overexpressing CycD3 were cytokinin-independent in culture. The inability of cycloheximide to inhibit induction indicates that this is an early response gene, not requiring protein synthesis. Although there is no established connection with the phosphorelay genes described above, regulation through phosphorylation is implicated by the effects of phosphatase and kinase inhibitors (148). Another candidate gene is *cdc2*, a histone H1 kinase involved in G2—M transition with expression induced by cytokinin and auxin (73, 83, 186). As expected, many additional genes are induced or repressed by cytokinins, and in some cases expression was shown to be affected by phosphorylation (for review, see 43, 157). However, for most of these genes either the function is unknown or the lag time before changes in transcription is too long to be considered as early response genes. (See Note Added in Proof, p. 118.)

G-Protein Coupled Receptor

A different type of putative cytokinin receptor, belonging to the class of G-protein coupled receptors (59), was identified by Plakidou-Dymock et al (145) through screening of an *Arabidopsis* EST database for genes with homology to known bacterial G-protein receptors. The deduced amino acid sequence of the gene, *GCR1* (for **G**-protein **c**ytokinin **r**eceptor), contains seven membrane-spanning domains and homology to 7TM G-protein coupled receptors. This protein was assigned a role in cytokinin perception due to the lower sensitivity to cytokinins of *Arabidopsis* transformants containing an antisense *GCR1* construct (145). Binding of this putative receptor to cytokinins and interaction with G-proteins has yet to be shown.

IMPLICATIONS

Significance of Metabolites and Enzymes

The metabolic complexity of natural cytokinins can be reduced substantially if inter-conversions between bases, nucleosides, and nucleotides are considered separately. This seems reasonable since these interchanges are likely adjunct to purine metabolism, as supported by the observation that none of the enzymes involved in the modification of the adenine ring has specificity for cytokinins (34). Mutation of the *APT1* gene of *Arabidopsis* encoding an adenine phosphoribosyltransferase results in male sterility and recalcitrance in tissue culture (66, 123), and the *schizoid* mutant of *Arabidopsis*, having a lesion in a gene with high homology to adenosine kinases, has characteristics indicative of cytokinin overproduction (144). However, it is not known whether the phenotypic alterations are related to a change in cytokinin metabolism or general purine metabolism. Yet, the interconversions between the three forms can have a bearing on cytokinin activity and transport. The free base is usually the most active in bioassays (100, 116, 155, 156, 163), which may be related to rapid uptake and high intrinsic activity (97). Evidence has also been presented that the three forms are transported differentially via the xylem, with the nucleosides being predominant (102). Recently, a family of adenine transporters was discovered in *Arabidopsis* (67). Although they are not specific for cytokinins, their activity is likely to influence the cell-to-cell transport of cytokinin bases as well. Thus, despite the nonspecific nature of the interchanges, the relative proportions of the three forms may directly or indirectly influence cytokinin activity.

Side chain modifications appear to be highly specific. Not only can the enzymes distinguish between cytokinin bases, nucleosides, and nucleotides, but also between saturation, hydroxylation, and steric conformation. The former is illustrated by the fact that zeatin *O*-glycosyltransferases act only on cytokinin bases (49, 112, 113, 177). The latter is demonstrated by the characteristics of zeatin *O*-glycosyltransferases and reductase, with *O*-glycosyltransferases differentiating between *cis*-, *trans*-, and dihydro-zeatin (124) and the reductase recognizing *trans*-zeatin but not *cis*-zeatin or i^6Ade (115). Even though cytokinin oxidases are not as specific, cleaving all cytokinins with unsaturated isoprenoid side chains, the rate of degradation is also dependent on side chain configuration (14, 31). The properties of these enzymes imply that the metabolism of individual cytokinins is precisely regulated by a host of highly specific proteins, many of which yet to be discovered.

Metabolic enzymes and genes are useful tools in dissecting the function of cytokinin metabolites. The levels of enzymes and reaction products can be modulated by manipulating the expression of genes encoding the enzymes. For example, cloning of the *ZOG/ZOX* genes allows more precise determination of the effects of *O*-glycosylation on plant development. The fact that leaf discs of transgenic tobacco (with increased *ZOG1* expression) required significantly higher zeatin concentrations for shoot regeneration (114) confirmed a storage role of *O*-glucosylzeatin. However, in intact plants, increased *O*-glucosylation can also lead to characteristics indicative of higher cytokinin activity, which could not have been predicted from the theoretical consequences of cytokinin sequestering through *O*-glucosylation. Although there are a number of possible explanations for the seemingly opposite effects on detached and intact plants tissues (114), the observations suggest that local cytokinin composition in organs at particular stages of development may be more important than total cytokinins in whole plants.

External factors may influence the expression of metabolic genes and composition of metabolites. In a recent study, zeatin O-glycosyltransferase levels were determined in roots of maize and beans (106) using antibodies specific to the bean enzymes (110). At low temperatures, $10°$ and $4°C$, the amount of antigenic protein was substantially higher than at $25°C$. Thus, low temperatures may induce sequestering of active compound by triggering zeatin O-glycoside formation. If confirmed, this would establish the relationship between a specific metabolic step and an environmental cue. In general, identification of physical and chemical factors influencing the expression of metabolic genes will provide valuable information on the regulation of metabolite levels and plant development.

The function of *cis*-zeatin is unclear. Although it is only weakly active in bioassays (156), *cis*-zeatin and its derivatives can be the predominant cytokinins in some species, such as chickpea (54), or in specific organs, such as male flower buds of *Mercurialis* (51). *cis*-Zeatin and derivatives were also detected in rice roots (82), potato tubers (137, 167), hops (183), wheat (142), and oats (142). It is conceivable that *cis*-zeatin has either a highly specialized function or can serve as a precursor for *trans*-zeatin. For instance, *cis*-isomers produced in roots may be transported to shoots, where light can enhance isomerization to *trans*-isomers (11). Manipulations involving the *cisZOG1* gene of maize (RC Martin, MC Mok, JE Habben & DWS Mok, unpublished results) may be useful to further elucidate the function of *cis*-derivatives, particularly in plant species with substantial amounts of *cis*-zeatin.

The fact that cytokinin oxidase level in whole plants and callus cultures is stimulated by both adenine- and phenylurea-cytokinins (3, 31, 134, 141, 175) indicates that these enzymes are important in the catabolism of excessive cytokinins. Another possible function of oxidases may be the prevention of cytokinin movement into or out of specific tissues or organs. An example may be found in developing seeds where high cytokinin oxidase activity occurs in the seed coat (176), limiting movement of cytokinins to and from developing embryos (102). Now that an oxidase gene from maize has been cloned, determining the distribution of oxidases among endosperm, embryo, aleurone, and pericarp of maize may be an initial step in examining the concept of oxidases as regulators of cytokinin trafficking between tissues.

Cytokinin and cytokinin oxidase activity during grain development have been studied rather extensively, with the ultimate goal of manipulating yield (8, 48, 85, 88, 150). At early embryo development of cereals, there is a narrow period (days) when cytokinin content rises, after which it declines rapidly. This led to the hypothesis that seed fill and the eventual size/yield of the seeds may be related to, and can be manipulated by, maintaining a higher level of cytokinins. However, external application of adenine- or urea-type cytokinins had sporadic effects on yield (8, 78), while transformation with the *ipt* (isopentenyltransferase) gene is beneficial only if expression of the gene could be regulated rather precisely. Since the decline in cytokinin level is accompanied by an increase in cytokinin oxidase, lowering the level of cytokinin oxidases may be a viable alternative. In general, cytokinin genes can conceivably be used to optimize agronomic characteristics.

Biosynthesis

Our knowledge of cytokinin biosynthesis in plants is still very limited. It is generally assumed that i^6Ade and zeatin have a common origin and that the first product of biosynthesis is i^6AMP (16, 35). Although this pathway seems logical, particularly in light of the action of the *ipt* gene of *Agrobacterium tumefaciens* (1, 10), evidence for this pathway in plants is still inconclusive. Only rather crude tobacco extracts were found to contain ipt activity (30). As zeatin-type compounds are predominant in plants, hydroxylation has to be a crucial step in the direct pathway but the general occurrence of this conversion is still uncertain. Incorporation of radiolabeled i^6Ade and i^6Ado into zeatin and its riboside by a microsomal fraction of cauliflower was reported (38). Conversion of exogenous, unlabeled i^6Ade to a product coeluting with zeatin was also observed in *Actinidia* (52), although the product was not further authenticated. On the other hand, callus tissues of *Phaseolus* did not incorporate any significant amount of label from ^{14}C-i^6Ade or ^{14}C-i^6Ado into zeatin or its riboside (28, 131). It is possible that hydroxylation is limited to certain plant species, as supported by a survey (53), accounting for the inconsistent occurrence.

It is also possible that there are other substrates for the direct biosynthesis of zeatin in plants. For example, the formation of ZMP could occur through transfer of a hydroxylated side chain. In fact, this function could also be mediated by the enzyme encoded by the *tzs* gene of *A. tumefaciens*. Expression of this *tzs* in bacteria resulted in the recovery of zeatin in the culture medium (13, 72). The explanation given was that side chain hydroxylation occurred after the formation of i^6AMP/i^6Ado/i^6Ade, through the action of bacterial enzymes. That explanation, however, cannot be reconciled with the observation that *Agrobacterium* without the Ti plasmid secreted only i^6Ade, derived from tRNA (68). Further support in favor of direct transfer of a hydroxylated side chain was recently provided by the dynamics of deuterium in vivo labeling of cytokinins in *ipt*-transformed and wild-type *Arabidopsis* (4). Moreover, transferases could conceivably differ in their relative affinities to isopentenyl and hydroxylated side chains, with plant enzymes preferring the hydroxylated side chains. However, plant transferases are unlikely to have high homology to their bacterial counterparts since extensive probing of plant genomes did not reveal complementary sequences to *ipt/tzs* (12). Nevertheless, the *Arabidopsis* data bank contains a number of candidate genes with low homology to these genes.

For many years, tRNA as a source of cytokinins has been the subject of debate. Measurements of tRNA breakdown indicated that this process can contribute up to 50% of the free cytokinins (9, 108). An often encountered argument against tRNA being a considerable source of cytokinin is the fact that *cis*-zeatin is the major cytokinin in tRNA. However, this problem can potentially be accommodated by the isomerization of *cis*-zeatin to *trans*-zeatin by *cis-trans* isomerases (11). Another objection is the general nature of tRNA breakdown, occurring in all tissues, while cytokinin production is localized in root tips, shoot meristems, and immature seeds (102), and must be highly regulated. Therefore, if tRNAs were a major source of cytokinins, regulatory mechanisms must operate at the level of the metabolism of the released *cis*-zeatin.

The occurrence of *cis*-zeatin as a minor cytokinin constituent could be explained by its origin from tRNA, but its presence as the major component in some plants or plant organs (51, 54, 82) may signify a direct pathway of biosynthesis. The isopentenyl side chain can possibly be hydroxylated to the *cis* configuration or, as proposed above for *trans*-zeatin, a *cis*-hydroxylated side chain is directly transferred to the adenine moiety. The biosynthetic pathway leading to aromatic cytokinins is entirely unknown. To date, no enzymes mediating the conjugation of a benzyl ring to adenine have been identified. It is apparent that the pathway for the biosynthesis of these cytokinins should be substantially distinct from that proposed for the isoprenoid cytokinins, perhaps closer to the metabolism of phenolics (166). A precursor suggested for topolin is the amino acid phenylalanine (185). In the same vein, isoprenoid cytokinins could be derived from compounds related to the amino acid leucine. However, these are theoretical pathways, the confirmation of which will have to come from the identification of the enzymes and genes involved. Nevertheless, the possibility that cytokinins with specific side chain configurations have separate origins, rather than having a common intermediate, must be considered.

Perception

The action of cytokinins at the molecular and the whole plant level is still largely unknown. In addition to putative receptor/signal transduction genes such as *CKI1*, *ARR*, and *GCR1*, proposed cytokinin targets include cell cycle genes and genes affecting shoot meristem formation. Candidate genes related to the cell cycle are *CycD3* and *cdc2* (83). The *knotted* homeobox gene of maize and *Arabidopsis* was also implicated in cytokinin action since transgenic plants overexpressing the *ipt* gene or *kn1* have similar phenotypes (139) and *ipt* transformants have increased mRNA levels of homeobox genes (149). As cytokinins stimulate cell division and formation of meristematic tissues, a link between these events and cytokinin action is expected. However, with the exception of *CycD3* (148), there is no evidence for primary action of these genes and they likely function further downstream from the signal transduction chain.

The study of action/perception will invariably encounter the paradox unique to cytokinins, the apparently indistinguishable biological effects of adenine and phenylurea cytokinins. It has been debated whether the phenylurea derivatives exert direct effect or indirect effect by modifying the biosynthesis and metabolism of endogenous cytokinins. The direct-effect hypothesis is supported by steric modeling studies suggesting that both adenine and urea cytokinins have a conformation capable of binding to the same receptor protein (62, 81). If that is the case, a true cytokinin receptor should display affinity to both types of cytokinins. The report of CBPs with affinity to both types of compounds (138) seems to suggest the occurrence of proteins with epitopes fitting both classes of cytokinins. The induction of the *ARR4* and *ARR5* genes by both adenine and phenylurea cytokinins (17) is also compatible with the direct-action hypothesis. Signal-receiving molecules capable of binding to both types of compounds, however, will also have to conform to the rules for structure-activity relationship of cytokinins, especially regarding the configuration of the N^6-side chain (163). The notion of ligands (cytokinins) with such different chemical structures recognizing the same signal-receiving proteins is challenging. The alternative, i.e. phenylureas acting on endogenous cytokinin metabolism or biosynthesis, is supported by the observations that they are inhibitors of cytokinin oxidases (14, 32) and are able to induce cytokinin-autonomous growth of cultured cells (127). In addition, conversion of cytokinin nucleotides to nucleosides is stimulated by phenylurea cytokinins (28). These properties, coupled with the stability of the phenylureas, are expected to alter the level/action of endogenous cytokinins. Unfortunately, the relative contributions of the direct and indirect effects on cytokinin action cannot easily be determined. Nevertheless, the studies of phenylurea cytokinins indicate quite clearly that in general, the apparent cytokinin activities of chemicals may not necessarily correlate with their affinities to cytokinin receptors since indirect effects and differential stability will influence their efficacy.

FUTURE RESEARCH DIRECTIONS

Cytokinin research based on traditional concepts and approaches will continue to be necessary in updating and confirming earlier findings. Molecular biology coupled with innovative and testable hypotheses will be needed if significant progress is to be made. For example, it may be useful to consider the possibility of independent pathways for the direct biosynthesis of cytokinins with distinct N^6-side chains, rather than continue to pursue a single pathway based on the *Agrobacterium* model. The contribution of the indirect pathway involving tRNA should also be reinvestigated. Parallel pathways may operate in cytokinin biosynthesis, just as for auxin biosynthesis (164), and different pathways may operate in different species. The metabolism of diverse classes of adenine-type cytokinins is likely to be regulated by different sets of genes encoding enzymes with precise recognition based on the configuration of the N^6-side chain. The various metabolites may have unique functions via differential subcellular localization or accumulation in tissues. Therefore, determining the location of enzymes as well as metabolites in tissues and cells will be important. Quantifying cytokinins may be more meaningful if selective measurements are taken of particular tissues at specific stages of development. Determination of changes in cytokinin components associated with defined phenotypic variations should be more useful than data taken on whole plants. Many areas of cytokinin research require attention but the greatest need is the cloning and characterization of additional genes, be they involved in cytokinin biosynthesis, metabolism, or perception/signal transduction. Employing genomics, transgenics, and reverse genetics as routine tools to study cytokinins will be crucial to gene discovery and characterization. Concentrating efforts on model plants extensively used for cytokinin analyses in the past, such as tobacco, beans, and maize, or those with sequenced genomes, such as *Arabidopsis*, should accelerate the pace of progress.

ACKNOWLEDGMENTS

The writing of this review and research conducted in the authors' laboratories are supported by grants from USDA/NRI (9801398), NSF (IBN9981974) and Pioneer Hi-Bred International Inc. This is paper No.11693 of the Oregon Agricultural Experiment Station.

Visit the Annual Reviews home page at www.AnnualReviews.org

LITERATURE CITED

1. Akiyoshi DE, Klee H, Amasino RM, Nester EW, Gordon MP. 1984. T-DNA of *Agrobacterium tumefaciens* encodes an enzyme of cytokinin biosynthesis. *Proc. Natl. Acad. Sci. USA* 81:5994–98

2. Alliotte T, Engler TG, Peleman J, Caplan A, Van Montagu M, et al. 1988. An auxin-regulated gene of *Arabidopsis thaliana* encodes a DNA-binding protein. *Plant Physiol.* 89:743–53

3. Armstrong DJ. 1994. Cytokinin oxidase and the regulation of cytokinin degradation. See Ref. 125a, pp. 139–54

4. Åstot C, Dolezal K, Nordström A, Wang Q, Kunkel T, et al. 2000. An alternative cytokinin biosynthesis pathway. *Proc. Natl. Acad. Sci. USA* 97:14778–83

5. Auer CA. 1997. Cytokinin conjugation: recent advances and patterns in plant evolution. *Plant Growth Regul.* 23:17–32

6. Auer CA, Cohen JD. 1993. Identification of a benzyladenine disaccharide conjugate produced during shoot organogenesis in *Petunia* leaf explants. *Plant Physiol* 102:541–45

7. Banowetz GM. 1994. Immunoanalysis of cytokinins. See Ref. 125a, pp. 305–16

8. Banowetz GM, Ammar K, Chen DD. 1999. Postanthesis temperatures influence cytokinin accumulation and wheat kernel weight. *Plant Cell Environ.* 22:309–16

9. Barnes MF, Tien CL, Gray JS. 1980. Biosynthesis of cytokinins by potato cell cultures. *Phytochemistry* 19:409–12

10. Barry GF, Rogers SG, Fraley RT, Brand L. 1984. Identification of a cloned cytokinin biosynthetic gene. *Proc. Natl. Acad. Sci. USA* 81:4776–80

11. Bassil NV, Mok DWS, Mok MC. 1993. Partial purification of a *cis-trans*-isomerase of zeatin from immature seed of *Phaseolus vulgaris* L. *Plant Physiol.* 102:867–72

12. Beale MH, Sponsel VM. 1993. Future directions in plant hormone research. *J. Plant Growth Regul.* 12:227–35

13. Beaty JS, Powell GK, Lica L, Regier DA, MacDonald EMS, et al. 1986. *Tzs*, a nopaline Ti plasmid gene, from *Agrobacterium tumefaciens* associated with *trans*-zeatin biosynthesis. *Mol. Gen. Genet.* 203:274–80

14. Bilyeu KD, Cole JL, Laskey JG, Riekhof WR, Esparza TJ, et al. 2001. Molecular and biochemical characterization of a cytokinin oxidase from *Zea mays*. *Plant Physiol.* 125:378–86

15. Binns AN. 1994. Cytokinin accumulation and action: biochemical, genetic and molecular approaches. *Ann. Rev. Plant Physiol. Plant Mol. Biol.* 45:173–96

16. Blackwell JR, Horgan R. 1994. Cytokinin biosynthesis by extracts of *Zea mays*. *Phytochemistry* 35:339–42

17. Brandstatter I, Kieber JJ. 1998. Two genes with similarity to bacterial response regulators are rapidly and specifically induced by cytokinin in *Arabidopsis*. *Plant Cell* 10:1009–19

18. Brault M, Caiveau O, Pédron J, Maliney R, Sotta B, et al. 1999. Detection of membrane-bound cytokinin-binding proteins in *Arabidopsis thaliana* cells. *Eur. J. Biochem.* 260:512–19

19. Brault M, Maldiney R. 1999. Mechanisms of cytokinin action. *Plant Physiol. Biochem.* 37:403–12

20. Brault M, Maldiney R, Miginiac E. 1997. Cytokinin-binding proteins. *Physiol. Plant.* 100:520–27

21. Brinegar C. 1994. Cytokinin binding proteins and receptors. See Ref. 125a, pp. 217–32

22. Brinegar C, Shah G, Cooper G. 1996. Photoaffinity labelling of a cytokinin-binding integral membrane protein in plant mitochondria. *Plant Growth Regul.* 18:45–50

23. Brownlee BG, Hall RH, Whitty CD. 1975. 3-Methyl-2-butenal: an enzymatic degradation product of the cytokinin N^6-(Δ^2-isopentenyl)adenine. *Can. J. Biochem.* 53:37–41

24. Brzobohatý B, Moore I, Kristoffersen P, Bakó L, Campos N, et al. 1993. Release of active cytokinin by a β-glucosidase localized to the maize root meristem. *Science* 262:1051–54

25. Burch LR, Horgan R. 1989. The purification of cytokinin oxidase from *Zea mays* kernels. *Phytochemistry* 28:1313–19

26. Burch LR, Stuchbury T. 1987. Activity and distribution of enzymes that interconvert purine bases, ribosides and ribotides in the tomato plant and possible implications for cytokinin metabolism. *Physiol. Plant.* 69:283–88

27. Campos N, Bakó L, Feldwisch J, Schell J, Palme K. 1992. A protein from maize labelled with azido-IAA has novel β-glucosidase activity. *Plant J.* 2:675–84

28. Capelle SC, Mok DWS, Kirchner SC, Mok MC. 1983. Effects of thidiazuron on cytokinin autonomy and the metabolism of N^6-(Δ^2-isopentenyl)[8-^{14}C]adenosine in callus tissues of *Phaseolus lunatus* L. *Plant Physiol.* 73:796–802

29. Chang C, Kwok SF, Bleecker AB, Meyerowitz EM. 1993. *Arabidopsis* ethylene-response gene *ETR1*: similarity of products to two-component regulators. *Science* 262:539–44

30. Chang C, Stewart RC. 1998. The two-component system: regulation of diverse signaling pathways in prokaryotes and eukaryotes. *Plant Physiol.* 117:723–31

31. Chatfield JM, Armstrong DJ. 1986. Regulation of cytokinin oxidase activity in callus tissues of *Phaseolus vulgaris* L. cv. Great Northern. *Plant Physiol.* 80:493–99

32. Chatfield JM, Armstrong DJ. 1987. Cytokinin oxidase from *Phaseolus vulgaris* callus tissues: enhanced *in vitro* activity of the enzyme in the presence of copper-imidazole complexes. *Plant Physiol.* 84:726–31

33. Chaves das Neves HJ, Pais MSS. 1980. A new cytokinin from the fruits of *Zantedeschia aethiopica*. *Tetrahedron Lett.* 21:4387–90

34. Chen C-M. 1997. Cytokinin biosynthesis and interconversions. *Physiol. Plant.* 101:665–73

35. Chen C-M, Ertl JR. 1994. Cytokinin biosynthetic enzymes in plants and slime mold. See Ref. 125a, pp. 81–86

36. Chen C-M, Kristopeit SM. 1981. Metabolism of cytokinin. Dephosphorylation of cytokinin ribonucleotide by 5'-nucleotidases from wheat germ cytosol. *Plant Physiol.* 67:494–98

37. Chen C-M, Kristopeit SM. 1981. Metabolism of cytokinin. Deribosylation of cytokinin ribonucleoside by adenosine nucleosidase from wheat germ cells. *Plant Physiol.* 68:1020–23

38. Chen C-M, Leisner SM. 1984. Modification of cytokinins by cauliflower microsomal enzymes. *Plant Physiol.* 75:442–46

39. Chen C-M, Melitz DK. 1979. Cytokinin biosynthesis in a cell-free system from cytokinin-autotrophic tobacco tissue cultures. *FEBS Lett.* 107:15–20

40. Chen C-M, Melitz DK, Clough FW. 1982. Metabolism of cytokinins: phosphorylation of cytokinin bases by adenine phosphoribosyltransferase from wheat germ. *Arch. Biochem. Biophys.* 214:634–41

41. Chen C-M, Petschow B. 1978. Metabolism of cytokinin. Ribosylation of cytokinin bases by adenosine phosphorylase from wheat germ. *Plant Physiol.* 62:871–74

42. Cicek M, Esen A. 1999. Expression of soluble and catalytically active plant (monocot) β-glucosidases in *E. coli. Biotech. Bioenerg.* 63:392–400

42a. Costacurta A, Vanderleyden J. 1995. Synthesis of phytohormones by plant-associated bacteria. *Crit. Rev. Microbiol.* 21:1–18

43. Crowell DN, Amasino RM. 1994. Cytokinins and plant gene regulation. See Ref. 125a, pp. 233–42

44. D'Agostino IB, Kieber JJ. 1999. Molecular mechanisms of cytokinin action. *Curr. Opin. Plant Biol.* 2:359–64

45. D'Agostino IB, Kieber JJ. 1999. Phosphorelay signal transduction: the emerging family of plant response regulators. *Trends Biochem. Sci.* 24:452–56

46. Deikman J. 1997. Elucidating cytokinin response mechanisms using mutants. *Plant Growth Regul.* 23:33–40

47. Dewitte W, Chiapetta A, Azmi A, Witters E, Strnad M, et al. 1999. Dynamics of cytokinins in apical shoot meristems of a day-neutral tobacco during floral transition and flower formation. *Plant Physiol.* 119:111–21

48. Dietrich JT, Kamínek M, Blevins DG, Reinbott TM, Morris RO. 1995. Changes in cytokinins and cytokinin oxidase in developing maize kernels and the effects of exogenous cytokinin on kernel development. *Plant Physiol. Biochem.* 33:327–36

49. Dixon SC, Martin RC, Mok MC, Shaw G, Mok DWS. 1989. Zeatin glycosylation enzymes in *Phaseolus*: isolation of O-glucosyltransferase from *P. lunatus* and comparison to O-xylosyltransferase from *P. vulgaris. Plant Physiol.* 90:1316–21

50. Duke CC, MacLeod JK, Summons RE, Letham DS, Parker CW. 1978. The structure and synthesis of cytokinin metabolites. II. Lupinic acid and O-β-D-glucopyranosylzeatin from *Lupinus angustifolius. Aust. J. Chem.* 31:1291–301

51. Durand R, Durand B. 1994. Cytokinins and reproductive organogenesis in *Mercurialis.* See Ref. 125a, pp. 295–304

52. Einset JW. 1984. Conversion of N^6–isopentenyladenine to zeatin by *Actinidia* tissues. *Biochem. Biophys. Res. Commun.* 124:470–74

53. Einset JW. 1986. Zeatin biosynthesis from N^6-(Δ^2-isopentenyl)adenine in *Actinidia* and other woody plants. *Proc. Natl. Acad. Sci. USA* 83:972–75

54. Emery RJN, Leport L, Barton JE, Turner NC, Atkins CA. 1998. *cis*-Isomers of cytokinins predominate in chickpea seeds throughout their development. *Plant Physiol.* 117:1515–23

55. Entsch B, Letham DS. 1979. Enzymic glycosylation of the cytokinin, 6–benzylaminopurine. *Plant Sci. Lett.* 14:205–12

56. Entsch B, Parker CW, Letham DS. 1983. An enzyme from lupin seeds forming alanine derivatives of cytokinins. *Phytochemistry* 22:375–81

57. Entsch B, Parker CW, Letham DS, Summons RE. 1979. Preparation and characterization using high-performance liquid chromatography of an enzyme forming glucosides of cytokinins. *Biochim. Biophys. Acta* 570:124–39

58. Ernst D, Schäfer W, Oesterhelt D. 1983. Isolation and identification of a new, naturally occurring cytokinin (6-benzylaminopurine riboside) from an

old anise cell culture (*Pimpinella anisum L.*). *Planta* 159:222–25

59. Estelle M. 1998. Cytokinin action: two receptors better than one? *Curr. Biol.* 8:R539–41

60. Falk A, Rask L. 1995. Expression of a zeatin-*O*-glucoside-degrading β-glucosidase in *Brassica napus*. *Plant Physiol.* 108: 1369–77

61. Faure J-D, Howell SH. 1999. Cytokinin perception and signal transduction. See Ref. 74a, pp. 461–74

62. Fox JE. 1992. Molecular modeling of cytokinins and the CBF-1 receptor. See Ref. 90a, pp. 127–32

63. Frank M, Rupp H-M, Prinsen E, Motyka V, Van Onckelen H, et al. 2000. Hormone autotrophic growth and differentiation identifies mutant lines of *Arabidopsis* with altered cytokinin and auxin content or signaling. *Plant Physiol.* 122:721–29

64. Fujimoto Y, Nagata R, Fukasawa H, Yano K, Azuma M, et al. 1998. Purification and cDNA cloning of cytokinin specific binding protein from mung bean (*Vigna radiata*). *Eur. J. Biochem.* 258:794–802

65. Fusseder A, Ziegler P. 1988. Metabolism and compartmentation of dihydrozeatin exogenously supplied to photoautotrophic suspension cultures of *Chenopodium rubrum*. *Planta* 173:104–9

66. Gaillard C, Moffatt BA, Blacker M, Laloue M. 1998. Male sterility associated with APRT deficiency in *Arabidopsis thaliana* results from a mutation in the gene *APT1*. *Mol. Gen. Genet.* 257:348–53

67. Gillissen B, Bürkle L, André B, Kühn C, Rentsch D, et al. 2000. A new family of high-affinity transporters for adenine, cytosine, and purine derivatives in Arabidopsis. *Plant Cell* 12:291–300

68. Gray J, Gelvin SB, Meilan R, Morris RO. 1996. Transfer RNA is the source of extracellular isopentenyladenine in a Ti-plasmidless strain of *Agrobacterium tumefaciens*. *Plant Physiol.* 110:431–38

68a. Guern J, Péaud-Lenoël C, eds. 1981. *Metabolism and Molecular Activities of Cytokinins*. Berlin: Springer-Verlag

69. Hare PD, van Staden J. 1994. Cytokinin oxidase: biochemical properties and physiological significance. *Physiol. Plant.* 91:128–36

70. Hedden P. 1993. Modern methods for the quantitative analysis of plant hormones. *Annu. Rev. Plant Physiol. Plant Mol. Biol.* 44:107–29

71. Hedden P, Proebsting WM. 1999. Genetic analysis of gibberellin biosynthesis. *Plant Physiol.* 119:365–370

72. Heinemeyer W, Buchmann I, Tonge D, Windass JD, Alt-Moerbe J, et al. 1987. Two *Agrobacterium tumefaciens* genes for cytokinin biosynthesis: Ti plasmid-coded isopentenyltransferases adapted for function in prokaryotic or eukaryotic cells. *Mol. Gen. Genet.* 210:156–64

73. Hemerly AS, Ferreira P, de Almeida Engler J, Van Montagu M, Engler G, et al. 1993. *cdc2a* expression in Arabidopsis is linked with competence for cell division. *Plant Cell* 5:1711–23

74. Hooley R, 1994. Gibberellins: perception, transduction and responses. *Plant Mol. Biol.* 26:1529–55

74a. Hooykaas PJJ, Hall MA, Libbenga KR, eds. 1999. *Biochemistry and Molecular Biology of Plant Hormones*. Amsterdam: Elsevier

75. Horgan R, Hewett EW, Horgan JM, Purse JG, Wareing PF. 1975. A new cytokinin from *Populus x robusta*. *Phytochemistry* 14:1005–8

76. Horgan R, Hewett EW, Purse JG, Wareing PF. 1973. A new cytokinin from *Populus robusta*. *Tetrahedron Lett.* 30:2827–28

77. Houba-Hérin N, Pethe C, d'Alayer J, Laloue M. 1999. Cytokinin oxidase from *Zea mays*: purification, cDNA cloning and expression in moss protoplasts. *Plant J.* 17:615–26

78. Hradecká D, Petr J. 1992. The effect of

cytokinins on the yield of some cereal plants. See Ref. 90a, pp. 245–47

79. Imamura A, Hanaki N, Nakamura A, Suzuki T, Tanaguchi M, et al. 1999. Compilation and characterization of *Arabidopsis thaliana* response regulators implicated in Hisp-Asp phosphorelay signal transduction. *Plant Cell Physiol.* 40:733–42

80. Imamura A, Hanaki N, Umeda H, Nakamura A, Suzuki T, et al. 1998. Response regulators implicated in His-Asp phosphotransfer signaling in *Arabidopsis. Proc. Natl. Acad. Sci. USA* 95:2691–96

80a. Inoue T, Higuchi M, Hashimoto Y, Seki M, Kobayashi M, et al. 2001. Identification of *CRE1* as a cytokinin receptor from *Arabidopsis. Nature* 409:1060–63

81. Iwamura H, Fujita T, Koyama S, Koshimizu K, Kumazawa Z. 1980. Quantitative structure-activity relationship of cytokinin-active adenine and urea derivatives. *Phytochemistry* 19:1309–19

82. Izumi K, Nakagawa S, Kobayashi M, Oshio H, Sakurai A, et al. 1988. Levels of IAA, cytokinins, ABA and ethylene in rice plants as affected by a gibberellin biosynthesis inhibitor, Uniconazole-P. *Plant Cell Physiol.* 29:97–104

83. Jacqmard A, Houssa C, Bernier G. 1994. Regulation of the cell cycle by cytokinins. See Ref. 125a, pp. 197–215

84. Jameson PE. 1994. Cytokinin metabolism and compartmentation. See Ref. 125a, pp. 113–28

85. Jameson PE, McWha JA, Wright GJ. 1982. Cytokinin and changes in their activity during the development of grains of wheat (*Triticum aestivum* L). *Z. Pflanzenphysiol.* 106:27–36

86. Johnson PR, Ecker JR. 1998. The ethyelene gas signal transduction pathway: a molecular perspective. *Annu. Rev. Genet.* 32:227–54

87. Jones RJ, Schreiber BMN. 1997. Role and function of cytokinin oxidase in plants. *Plant Growth Regul.* 23:123–34

88. Jones RJ, Schreiber BM, McNeil K, Brenner ML, Foxon G. 1992. Cytokinin levels and oxidase activity during maize kernel development. See Ref. 90a, pp. 235–39

89. Kakimoto T. 1996. CKI1, a histidine kinase homolog implicated in cytokinin signal transduction. *Science* 274:982–85

90. Kamínek M, Armstrong DJ. 1990. Genotypic variation in cytokinin oxidase from *Phaseolus* callus cultures. *Plant Physiol.* 93:1530–38

90a. Kamínek M, Mok DWS, Zažímalová E, eds. 1992. *Physiology and Biochemistry of Cytokinins in Plants.* The Hague: SPB Academic

91. Kiba T, Taniguchi M, Imamura A, Ueguchi C, Mizuno T, et al. 1999. Differential expression of genes for response regulators in response to cytokinins and nitrate in *Arabidopsis thaliana. Plant Cell Physiol.* 40:767–71

92. Kieber J. 1997. The ethylene response pathway in Arabidopsis. *Annu. Rev. Plant Phys. Plant Mol. Biol.* 48:277–96

93. Kobayashi K, Fukuda M, Igarashi D, Sunaoshi M. 2000. Cytokinin-binding proteins from tobacco callus share homology with osmotin-like protein and an endochitinase. *Plant Cell Physiol.* 41:148–57

94. Kulaeva ON, Karavaiko NN, Selivankina SY, Moshkov IE, Novikova GV. 1996. Cytokinin signalling systems—From a whole plant to the molecular level. *Plant Growth Regul.* 18:29–37

95. Kulaeva ON, Zagranichnaya TK, Brovko FA, Karavaiko NN, Selivankina SY, et al. 1998. A new family of cytokinin receptors from Cereales. *FEBS Lett.* 423:239–42

96. Laloue M, Fox JE. 1989. Cytokinin oxidase from wheat. Partial purification and general properties. *Plant Physiol.* 90:899–906

97. Laloue M, Pethe-Terrine C, Guern J. 1981. Uptake and metabolism of cytokinins in tobacco cells: studies in relation

to the expression of their biological activities. See Ref. 68a, pp. 80–96

98. Lee Y, Sayre LM. 1998. Reaffirmation that metabolism of polyamines by bovine plasma amine oxidase occurs strictly at the primary amino termini. *J. Biol. Chem.* 273:19490–94

99. Lee YH, Mok MC, Mok DWS, Griffin DA, Shaw G. 1985. Cytokinin metabolism in *Phaseolus* embryos. Genetic difference and the occurrence of novel zeatin metabolites. *Plant Physiol.* 77:635–41

100. Leonard NJ, Hecht SM, Skoog F, Schmitz RY. 1969. Cytokinins: synthesis, mass spectra, and biological activity of compounds related to zeatin. *Proc. Natl. Acad. Sci. USA* 63:175–82

101. Letham DS. 1963. Zeatin, a factor inducing cell division isolated from *Zea mays*. *Life Sci.* 8:569–73

102. Letham DS. 1994. Cytokinins as phytohormones—sites of biosynthesis, translocation, and function of translocated cytokinin. See Ref. 125a, pp. 57–80

103. Letham DS, Palni LMS, Tao G-Q, Gollnow BI, Bates CM. 1983. Regulators of cell division in plant tissues XXIX. The activities of cytokinin glucosides and alanine conjugates in cytokinin bioassays. *J. Plant Growth Regul.* 2:103–15

104. Letham DS, Summons RE, Parker CW, MacLeod JK. 1979. Regulators of cell division in plant tissues. XXVII. Identification of an amino-acid conjugate of 6-benzylaminopurine formed in *Phaseolus vulgaris* seeds. *Planta* 146:71–74

105. Letham DS, Zhang R. 1989. Cytokinin translocation and metabolism in lupin species. II. New nucleotide metabolites of cytokinins. *Plant Sci.* 64:161–65

106. Li R, Sosa JL, Zavala ME. 2000. Accumulation of zeatin O-glycosyltransferase in *Phaseolus vulgaris* and *Zea mays* following cold treatment. *J. Plant Growth Regul.* In press

107. Lohrmann J, Buchholz G, Keitel C,

Sweere U, Kircher S, et al. 1999. Differential expression and nuclear localization of response regulator-like proteins from *Arabidopsis thaliana*. *Plant Biol.* 1:495–505

108. Maass H, Klämbt D. 1981. Cytokinin biosynthesis in higher plants. See Ref. 68a, pp. 27–33

109. Martin RC, Cloud KA, Mok MC, Mok DWS. 2000. Substrate specificity and domain analyses of zeatin O-glycosyltransferases. *Plant Growth Regul.* In press

110. Martin RC, Martin RR, Mok MC, Mok DWS. 1990. A monoclonal antibody specific to zeatin O-glycosyltransferases of *Phaseolus*. *Plant Physiol.* 94:1290–94

111. Martin RC, Mok MC, Habben JE, Mok DWS. 2001. A maize cytokinin gene encoding an O-glucosyltransferase specific to cis-zeatin. *Proc. Natl. Acad. Sci. USA.* Submitted

112. Martin RC, Mok MC, Mok DWS. 1999. A gene encoding the cytokinin enzyme zeatin O-xylosyltransferase of *Phaseolus vulgaris*. *Plant Physiol.* 120:553–57

113. Martin RC, Mok MC, Mok DWS. 1999. Isolation of a cytokinin gene, *ZOG1*, encoding zeatin O-glucosyltransferase of *Phaseolus lunatus*. *Proc. Natl. Acad. Sci. USA* 96:284–89

114. Martin RC, Mok DWS, Smets R, Van Onckelen HA, Mok MC. 2001. Development of transgenic tobacco harboring a zeatin O-glucosyltransferase gene from *Phaseolus*. *In Vitro Cell. Dev. Biol.* In press

115. Martin RC, Mok MC, Shaw G, Mok DWS. 1989. An enzyme mediating the conversion of zeatin to dihydrozeatin in *Phaseolus* embryos. *Plant Physiol.* 90:1630–35

116. Matsubara S. 1980. Structure-activity relationships of cytokinins. *Phytochemistry* 19:2239–53

117. McCourt P. 1999. Genetic analysis of hormone signaling. *Annu. Rev. Plant Physiol. Plant Mol. Biol.* 50:219–43

118. McGaw BA, Horgan R. 1983. Cytokinin oxidase from *Zea mays* kernels and *Vinca rosea* crown gall tissue. *Planta* 159:30–37

119. Miller CO, Skoog F, von Saltza MH, Strong M. 1955. Kinetin, a cell division factor from deoxyribonucleic acid. *J. Am. Chem. Soc.* 77:1329–34

120. Mitsui S, Wakasugi T, Sugiura M. 1996. A cytokinin-binding complex from tobacco leaves. *Plant Growth Regul.* 18: 39–43

121. Miyata S, Urao T, Yamaguchi-Shinozaki K, Shinozaki K. 1998. Characterization of genes for two-component phosphorelay mediators with a single Hpt domain in *Arabidopsis thaliana. FEBS Lett.* 437:11–14

122. Moffatt BA, McWhinnie EA, Burkhart WE, Pasternak JJ, Rothstein SJ. 1992. A complete cDNA for adenine phosphoribosyltransferase from *Arabidopsis thaliana. Plant Mol. Biol.* 18:653–62

123. Moffatt BA, Somerville CR. 1988. Positive selection for male-sterile mutants of *Arabidopsis* lacking adenine phosphoribosyltransferase activity. *Plant Physiol.* 86:1150–54

124. Mok DWS, Martin RC, Shan X, Mok MC. 2000. Genes encoding zeatin O-glycosyltransferases. *Plant Growth Regul.* In press

125. Mok DWS, Mok MC. 1987. Metabolism of ^{14}C-zeatin in *Phaseolus* embryos. Occurrence of O-xylosyldihydrozeatin and its ribonucleoside. *Plant Physiol.* 84:596–99

125a. Mok DWS, Mok MC, eds. 1994. *Cytokinins—Chemistry, Activity, and Function.* Boca Raton: CRC Press

126. Mok MC. 1994. Cytokinins and plant development—an overview. See Ref. 125a, pp. 155–66

127. Mok MC, Kim SG, Armstrong DJ, Mok DWS. 1979. Induction of cytokinin autonomy by *N,N'*-diphenylurea in tissue

cultures of *Phaseolus lunatus* L. *Proc. Natl. Acad. Sci. USA* 76:3880–84

128. Mok MC, Martin RC, Mok DWS. 2000. Cytokinins: biosynthesis, metabolism and perception. *In Vitro Cell. Dev. Biol. Plant* 36:102–7

129. Mok MC, Mok DWS. 1985. The metabolism of [^{14}C]-thidiazuron in callus tissues of *Phaseolus lunatus. Physiol. Plant.* 65:427–32

130. Mok MC, Mok DWS, Armstrong DJ, Shudo K, Isogai Y, et al. 1982. Cytokinin activity of *N*-phenyl-*N'*-1,2,3-thiadiazol-5-ylurea (Thidiazuron). *Phytochemistry* 21:1509–11

131. Mok MC, Mok DWS, Dixon SC, Armstrong DJ, Shaw G. 1982. Cytokinin structure-activity relationships and the metabolism of N^6-(Δ^2-isopentenyl)-adenosine-8-^{14}C in *Phaseolus* callus tissues. *Plant Physiol.* 70:173–78

132. Mok MC, Mok DWS, Turner JE, Mujer CV. 1987. Biological and biochemical effects of cytokinin-active phenylurea derivatives in tissue culture systems. *HortScience* 22:1194–97

133. Morris RO, Bilyeu KD, Laskey JG, Cheikh NN. 1999. Isolation of a gene encoding a glycosylated cytokinin oxidase from maize. *Biochem. Biophys. Res. Commun.* 255:328–33

134. Motyka V, Kamínek M. 1992. Characterization of cytokinin oxidase from tobacco and poplar callus cultures. See Ref. 90a, pp. 33–39

135. Nakamura A, Kakimoto T, Imamura A, Suzuki T, Ueguchi C, et al. 1999. Biochemical characterization of a putative cytokinin-responsive His-kinase, CKI1, from *Arabidopsis thaliana. Biosci. Biotechnol. Biochem.* 63:1627–30

136. Nandi SK, Letham DS, Palni LMS, Wong OC, Summons RE. 1989. 6-Benzylaminopurine and its glycosides as naturally occurring cytokinins. *Plant Sci.* 61:189–96

137. Nicander B, Björkman P-O, Tillberg E.

1995. Identification of an N-glucoside of cis-zeatin from potato tuber sprouts. *Plant Physiol* 109:513–16

138. Nogué F, Mornet R, Laloue M. 1996. Specific photoaffinity labelling of a thylakoid membrane protein with an azido-cytokinin agonist. *Plant Growth Regul.* 18:51–58

139. Ori N, Juarez MT, Jackson D, Yamaguchi J, Banowetz GM, et al. 1999. Leaf senescence is delayed in tobacco plants expressing the maize homeobox gene *knotted1* under the control of a senescence-activated promoter. *Plant Cell* 11:1073–80

140. Paces V, Werstiuk E, Hall RH. 1971. Conversion of N^6-(Δ^2-isopentenyl)adenosine to adenosine by enzyme activity in tobacco tissue. *Plant Physiol.* 48:775–78

141. Palmer MV, Palni LMS. 1987. Substrate effects on cytokinin metabolism in soybean callus tissue. *J. Plant Physiol.* 126:365–71

142. Parker CW, Badenoch-Jones J, Letham DS. 1989. Radioimmunoassay for quantifying the cytokinins cis-zeatin and cis-zeatin riboside and its application to xylem sap samples. *J. Plant Growth Regul.* 8:93–105

143. Parkinson JS, Kofoid EC. 1992. Communication modules in bacterial signaling proteins. *Annu. Rev. Genet.* 26:71–112

144. Parsons RL, Behringer FJ, Medford JI. 2000. The *SCHIZOID* gene regulates differentiation and cell division in *Arabidopsis thaliana* shoots. *Planta* 211:34–42

145. Plakidou-Dymock S, Dymock D, Hooley R. 1998. A higher plant seven-membrane receptor that influences sensitivity to cytokinins. *Curr. Biol.* 8:315–24

146. Prinsen E, Kamínek M, van Onckelen HA. 1997. Cytokinin biosynthesis: a black box? *Plant Growth Regul.* 23:3–15

147. Rinaldi AC, Comandini O. 1999. Cytokinin oxidase: new insight into enzyme properties. *Trends Plant Sci.* 4:127–28

148. Riou-Khamlichi C, Huntley R, Jacqmard A, Murray JAH. 1999. Cytokinin activation of *Arabidopsis* cell division through a D-type cyclin. *Science* 283:1541–44

149. Rupp HM, Frank M, Werner T, Strnad M, Schmülling T. 1999. Increased steady state mRNA levels of the *STM* and *KNAT1* homeobox genes in cytokinin overproducing *Arabidopsis thaliana* indicate a role for cytokinins in the shoot apical meristem. *Plant J* 18:557–63

150. Saha S, Nagar PK, Sircar PK. 1986. Cytokinin concentration gradient in the developing grains and upper leaves of rice (*Oryza sativa*) during grain filling. *Can. J. Bot.* 64:2068–72

151. Sakakibara H, Hayakawa A, Deji A, Gawronski SW, Sugiyama T. 1999. Hisp-Asp phosphotransfer possibly involved in the nitrogen signal transduction mediated by cytokinin in maize: molecular cloning of cDNAs for two-component regulatory factors and demonstration of phosphotransfer activity in vitro. *Plant Mol. Biol.* 41:563–73

152. Sakakibara H, Suzuki M, Takei K, Deji A, Taniguchi M, et al. 1998. A response-regulator homologue possibly involved in nitrogen signal transduction mediated by cytokinin in maize. *Plant J.* 14:337–44

153. Sakakibara H, Taniguchi M, Sugiyama T. 2000. His-Asp phosphorelay signaling: a communication avenue between plants and their environment. *Plant Mol. Biol.* 42:273–78

154. Schaller GE, Bleecker AB. 1995. Ethylene-binding sites generated in yeast expressing the *Arabidopsis ETR1* gene. *Science* 270:1809–11

155. Schmitz RY, Skoog F, Hecht SM, Bock RM, Leonard NJ. 1972. Comparison of cytokinin activities of naturally occurring ribonucleosides and corresponding bases. *Phytochemistry* 11:1603–10

156. Schmitz RY, Skoog F, Playtis AJ, Leonard NJ. 1972. Cytokinins: synthesis and biological activity of geometric and position

isomers of zeatin. *Plant Physiol.* 50:702–5

157. Schmülling T, Schäfer S, Romanov G. 1997. Cytokinins as regulators of gene expression. *Physiol. Plant.* 100:505–9

158. Schnorr KM, Gaillard C, Biget E, Nygaard P, Laloue M. 1996. A second form of adenosine phosphoribosyltransferase in *Arabidopsis thaliana* with relative specificity towards cytokinins. *Plant J.* 9:891–98

159. Shantz EM, Steward FC. 1955. The identification of compound A from coconut milk as 1,3-diphenylurea. *J. Am. Chem. Soc.* 77:6351–53

160. Shaw G. 1994. Chemistry of adenine cytokinins. See Ref. 125a, pp. 15–34

161. Shaw G, Wilson DV. 1964. A synthesis of zeatin. *Proc. Chem. Soc.* p. 231

162. Shudo K. 1994. Chemistry of phenylurea cytokinins. See Ref. 125a, pp. 35–42

163. Skoog F, Armstrong DJ. 1970. Cytokinins. *Annu. Rev. Plant. Physiol.* 21:359–84

164. Slovin JP, Bandurski RS, Cohen JD. 1999. Auxin. See Ref. 74a, pp. 115–40

165. Soni R, Carmichael JP, Shah ZH, Murray JAH. 1995. A family of cyclin D homologs from plants differentially controlled by growth regulators and containing the conserved retinoblastoma protein interaction motif. *Plant Cell* 7:85–103

166. Strnad M. 1997. The aromatic cytokinins. *Physiol. Plant.* 101:674–88

167. Suttle JC, Banowetz GM. 2000. Changes in *cis*-zeatin and *cis*-zeatin riboside levels and biological activity during tuber dormancy. *Physiol. Plant.* 109:68–74

168. Suzuki T, Imamura A, Ueguchi C, Mizuno T. 1998. Histidine-containing phosphotransfer (HPt) signal transducers implicated in His-to-Asp phosphorelay in *Arabidopsis*. *Plant Cell Physiol.* 39:1258–68

169. Swain SM, Olszewski NE. 1996. Genetic analysis of gibberellin signal transduction. *Plant Physiol.* 112:11–17

170. Takahashi S, Shudo K, Okamoto T, Yamada K, Isogai Y. 1978. Cytokinin activity of N-phenyl-N′-(4-pyridyl)urea derivatives. *Phytochemistry* 17:1201–7

171. Taller BJ. 1994. Distribution, biosynthesis, and function of cytokinins in tRNA. See Ref. 125a, pp. 101–12

172. Tanaguchi M, Kiba T, Sakakibara H, Ueguchi C, Mizuno T, et al. 1998. Expression of *Arabidopsis* response regulator homologs is induced by cytokinins and nitrate. *FEBS Lett.* 429:259–62

173. Taylor JS, Koshioka M, Pharis RP, Sweet GB. 1984. Changes in cytokinins and gibberellin-like substances in *Pinus radiata* buds during lateral shoot initiation and the characterization of ribosylzeatin and a novel ribosyl zeatin glycoside. *Plant Physiol.* 74:626–31

174. Teller G. 1994. Gas chromatographic-mass spectrometric and related methods for the analysis of cytokinins. See Ref. 125a, pp. 317–23

175. Terrine C, Laloue M. 1980. Kinetics of (N^6-Δ^2-isopentenyl)adenosine degradation in tobacco cells. *Plant Physiol.* 65:1090–95

176. Turner JE, Mok MC, Mok DWS. 1985. Zeatin metabolism in fruits of *Phaseolus*: comparison between embryos, seedcoat, and pod tissues. *Plant Physiol.* 79:321–22

177. Turner JE, Mok DWS, Mok MC, Shaw G. 1987. Isolation and partial purification of an enzyme catalyzing the formation of O-xylosylzeatin in *Phaseolus vulgaris* embryos. *Proc. Natl. Acad. Sci. USA* 84:3714–17

178. Vaňková R. 1999. Cytokinin glycoconjugates—distribution, metabolism and function. In *Advances in Regulation of Plant Growth and Development*, ed. M Strnad, P Peč, E Beck, pp. 67–78. Prague: Peres

179. Vogel JP, Schuerman P, Woeste K, Brandstatter I, Kieber JJ. 1998. Isolation and characterization of Arabidopsis mutants defective in the induction of

ethylene biosynthesis by cytokinin. *Genetics* 149:417–27

180. Von Schwartzenberg C, Kruse S, Reski R, Moffatt B, Laloue M. 1998. Cloning and characterization of an adenosine kinase from *Physcomitrella* involved in cytokinin metabolism. *Plant J.* 13:249–57

181. Wagner BM, Beck E. 1993. Cytokinins in the perennial herb *Urtica dioica* L. as influenced by its nitrogen status. *Planta* 190:511–18

182. Wang TL, Thompson AG, Horgan R. 1977. A cytokinin glucoside from the leaves of *Phaseolus vulgaris* L. *Planta* 135:285–88

183. Watanabe N, Yokota T, Takahashi N. 1981. Variations in the levels of *cis*- and *trans*-ribosylzeatins and other minor cytokinins during development and growth of cones of the hop plant. *Plant Cell Physiol.* 22:489–500

184. Yamada H, Hanaki N, Imamura A, Ueguchi C, Mizuno T. 1998. An *Arabidopsis* protein that interacts with the cytokinin-inducible response regulator, ARR4, implicated in the Hisp-Asp phosphorelay signal transduction. *FEBS Lett.* 436:76–80

185. Zažímalová E, Kamínek M, Brezinová A, Motyka V. 1999. Control of cytokinin biosynthesis and metabolism. See Ref. 74a, pp. 141–60

186. Zhang K, Letham DS, John PC. 1996. Cytokinin controls the cell cycle at mitosis by stimulating the tyrosine dephosphorylation and activation of p34^{cdc2}–like H1 histone kinase. *Planta* 200:2–12

NOTE ADDED IN PROOF

A gene, *CRE1* (cytokinin response 1), encoding a histidine kinase was identified in *Arabidopsis*. When expressed in yeast lacking the endogenous enzyme SLN1, *CRE1* confers a cytokinin dependent growth phenotype, indicative of receptor properties (80a).

Annu. Rev. Plant Physiol. Plant Mol. Biol. 2001. 52:119–37

ONE-CARBON METABOLISM IN HIGHER PLANTS

Andrew D Hanson and Sanja Roje

*Horticultural Sciences Department, University of Florida, Gainesville, Florida 32611;
e-mail: adha@gnv.ifas.ufl.edu*

Key Words   folates, metabolic flux, methyl transfer, one-carbon units,
photorespiration

■ **Abstract**   The metabolism of one-carbon (C_1) units is essential to plants, and
plant C_1 metabolism has novel features not found in other organisms—plus some
enigmas. Despite its centrality, uniqueness, and mystery, plant C_1 biochemistry has
historically been quite poorly explored, in part because its enzymes and intermediates
tend to be labile and low in abundance. Fortunately, the integration of molecular and
genetic approaches with biochemical ones is now driving rapid advances in knowledge
of plant C_1 enzymes and genes. An overview of these advances is presented. There
has also been progress in measuring C_1 metabolite fluxes and pool sizes, although
this remains challenging and there are relatively few data. In the future, combining
reverse genetics with flux and pool size determinations should lead to quantitative understanding of how plant C_1 pathways function. This is a prerequisite for their rational
engineering.

CONTENTS

INTRODUCTION

Reactions involving one-carbon (C_1) units are essential to all organisms (3). In plants, these reactions supply the C_1 units needed to synthesize proteins, nucleic acids, pantothenate, and a great variety of methylated molecules (19). C_1 pathways are particularly active in tissues that produce methylated compounds such as lignin, alkaloids, and betaines because the C_1 demands for these physiologically and economically important secondary metabolites can dwarf those of primary metabolism (Figure 1; see color insert). C_1 transfers are also central to the massive photorespiratory fluxes that occur in C_3 plants (24, 113). It may therefore surprise many readers to learn that much remains to be understood about the enzymes, pathways, and regulatory mechanisms of plant C_1 metabolism. This is largely because C_1 metabolism has been hard to study via classical biochemistry and genetics: Its enzymes may be of low abundance and/or exist as several isoforms, mutants are on the whole lacking, and its key intermediates—C_1 substituted folates, S-adenosylmethionine (AdoMet) and S-adenosyl-homocysteine (AdoHcy)—are labile and hard to quantify. Fortunately, classical approaches to C_1 metabolism can now be complemented by molecular-genetic ones, and progress in analytical biochemistry is facilitating determination of C_1 metabolite pools and fluxes. This review therefore aims to summarize the present status of plant C_1 metabolism, emphasizing advances since a 1997 Cossins & Chen review (19), to illustrate how informative but challenging it is to measure C_1 pool sizes and fluxes, and to point out areas that are still poorly known. Other recent reviews focus on formate metabolism (41), photorespiration (24, 113), methionine metabolism (80), folate synthesis, and compartmentation (80a), and genomics and engineering of C_1 metabolism (35). Earlier work was comprehensively covered by Cossins (17, 18), who has also reviewed the field from a historical perspective (18a). Folate biosynthesis and polyglutamylation have been summarized (18a, 80a) and are not considered here.

OVERVIEW OF C_1 METABOLISM, ENZYMES AND GENES

Plant C_1 metabolism can be conveniently split into four sectors: folate-mediated reactions, a cluster of folate-independent reactions, the activated methyl cycle, and the related S-methylmethionine (SMM) cycle. These reactions and their enzymes are diagrammed in Figure 2 (see color insert), and briefly outlined below. In essence, metabolism of serine, glycine, formate and other molecules generates specific C_1 derivatives of tetrahydrofolate (THF) that are then interconverted between different oxidation states, ranging from 10-formyl-THF (most oxidized) through 5,10-methenyl- and 5,10-methylene- to 5-methyl-THF (most reduced). These interconversions of C_1 substituted folates form the core of C_1 metabolism, from which C_1 units are withdrawn by anabolic reactions. The largest anabolic flux is the use of 5-methyl-THF to convert homocysteine to methionine, which is incorporated into proteins or converted to AdoMet, the donor for methylation

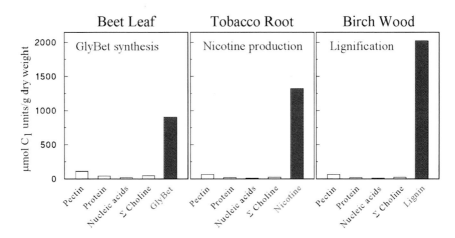

Figure 1 The approximate scale of C_1 demands in plants.
Open bars show the main demands of primary metabolism: synthesis of pectin, protein, nucleic acids and choline moieties, i.e., phosphatidyl-, phosphoryl- and free-choline (Σ Choline). *Red bars* show the massive extra demands associated with the production of three methylated secondary products: glycine betaine (GlyBet) in salinized beet leaves, nicotine in tobacco roots, and lignin in woody tissue of birch. All three are targets for metabolic engineering. Data are calculated from published values (37, 73, 81, 84, 85, 87, 94, 100, 107).

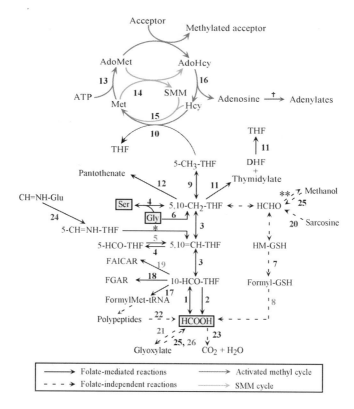

Figure 2 The reactions of plant C_1 metabolism as deduced from biochemical and DNA sequence evidence.

The principal sources of C_1 units are boxed and highlighted in yellow. Enzymes are numbered and listed in Table 1; numbers are color coded as follows. *Black*: enzymes for which there is biochemical evidence in plants and for which corresponding cDNAs have been cloned; *red*, enzymes that are inferred to exist in plants solely on the basis of expressed sequence tags (ESTs) and/or genomic sequences homologous to enzymes from other organisms; light blue, enzymes for which there is only biochemical evidence; *orange*, enzymes for which there is biochemical evidence and for which there are putative ESTs or genomic sequences that have not yet been proven to encode the enzymes. The *asterisk* marks the reaction catalyzed by 5-formimino-THF cyclodeaminase (EC 4.3.1.4), for which there is as yet no biochemical or DNA evidence in plants. The *double asterisk* marks the reduction of formaldehyde to methanol, which has been shown to occur in vivo (55) but for which the enzymatic basis in uncertain. The *dagger* denotes adenosine salvage reactions. Abbreviations: 10-CHO-THF, 10-formyl-THF; 5-CHO-THF, 5-formyl-THF; 5,10=CH-THF, 5,10-methenyl-THF; 5,10-CH$_2$-THF, 5,10-methylene-THF; 5-CH$_3$-THF, 5-methyl-THF; 5-CH=NH-THF, 5-formino-THF; DHF, dihydrofolate; Hcy, homocysteine; Met, methionine; GSH, glutathione; HM-GSH, S-hydroxymethylglutathione; FGAR, formylglycinamide ribonucleotide; FAICAR, formamidoimidazolecarboxamide ribonucleotide; CH=NH-Glu, formiminoglutamate.

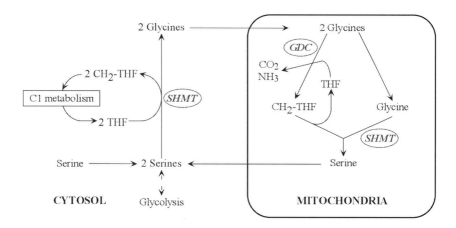

Figure 3 A proposed serine-glycine cycle between the cytosol and the mitochondria, yielding 2 C_1 units in the cytosol, plus 1 CO_2 and 1 NH_3, per serine catabolized. Slightly modified from (63). CH_2-THF, 5,10-methylene-THF.

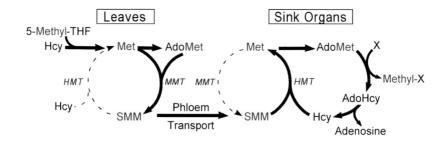

Figure 4 Long-distance transport of methyl groups via movement of SMM in the phloem. *Bold arrows* indicate major fluxes, *dotted arrows* minor ones. SMM is formed in leaves, moves via the phloem to seeds and other sink organs, where it is recycled to methionine (Met). This methionine can be used to produce AdoMet for use in methylation reactions (X → Methyl-X). Hydrolysis of the resulting AdoHcy provides homocysteine, which sustains further conversion of SMM to methionine. The path of the methyl groups is indicated in red.

reactions. Other anabolic reactions are use of 10-formyl-THF to synthesize purines and formylmethionyl-tRNA (for translation initiation in organelles), and use of 5,10-methylene-THF to produce thymidylate and pantothenate. The cluster of folate-independent C_1 reactions is centered on the metabolism of methanol, formaldehyde, and formate. In the activated methyl cycle, the AdoHcy formed after transmethylations is first hydrolyzed to homocysteine and adenosine by Ado-Hcy hydrolase. The homocysteine is then remethylated by 5-methyl-THF to give methionine, and the adenosine is recycled to adenylates. The SMM cycle is unique to plants and seemingly futile: AdoMet is used to methylate methionine to SMM, which serves to methylate homocysteine, thereby regenerating methionine.

Figure 2 and Table 1 summarize which enzymes of C_1 metabolism have been detected in plants and whether they have been cloned, and show enzymes that can be provisionally inferred from DNA sequence data to be present. Table 1 also indicates for each enzyme whether putative Arabidopsis genes have been identified (as of July 2000), and if so how many. The provisional annotation of genes in Table 1 is based on their homology to cDNAs or genes from Arabidopsis or other plant cDNAs, or to cDNAs or genes from other organisms which have been demonstrated to encode the corresponding enzyme (35). From the assembled sequence data, it appears that over half the putative C_1 enzymes are specified by small gene families. Several of these families include genes encoding proteins with well-defined organellar targeting signals, and genes for proteins (putatively cytosolic) that lack such signals. Each of the four sectors of C_1 metabolism will now be discussed in sequence.

FOLATE-MEDIATED C_1 REACTIONS

Serine-Glycine Interconversion

Serine and glycine are both potential sources of C_1 units in plants. They are interconvertible via the action of serine hydroxymethyltransferase (SHMT), which requires THF as cofactor:

$$Serine + THF \leftrightarrow Glycine + 5,10\text{-methylene-THF} + H_2O.$$

The equilibrium constant of this reaction is ≈ 10, so that glycine formation is favored (8). Both biochemical evidence (7) and DNA sequence data (35, 56) show that SHMT is present in cytosol, mitochondria, and plastids, indicating that serine can give rise to C_1 units in all these compartments. Glycine, on the other hand, can yield C_1 units only in the mitochondria, as a result of oxidation by the glycine decarboxylase complex (GDC) (70):

$$Glycine + NAD + THF \rightarrow CO_2 + NADH + NH_3 + 5,10\text{-methylene-THF}.$$

The greatest demand for C_1 units is almost surely in the cytosol, since it is the principal location of THF cofactors (12) and the major, if not sole, site of methionine synthesis (80). Recent ^{13}C NMR studies of fluxes through SHMT and GDC in

TABLE 1 Biochemical and DNA sequence evidence for plant C_1 metabolism enzymes

Enzymes[a]	EC numbers	cDNAs cloned[b]	Arabidopsis genes[c]	Selected references
1. 10-Formyl-THF synthetase	6.3.4.3	+	1p	12, 68, 69, 95
2. 10-Formyl-THF deformylase	3.5.1.10		2x	
3. 5,10-Methylene-THF dehydrogenase/ 5,10-Methenyl-THF cyclohydrolase	1.5.1.5/ 3.5.4.9	+	4p	12, 13, 49
4. Serine hydroxymethyltransferase	2.1.2.1	+	7p	7, 29, 104
5. 5-Formyl-THF cycloligase	6.3.3.2		1x	76
6. Glycine decarboxylase complex				
P-protein	1.4.4.2	+	2p	70
H-protein	—	+	2p	70
T-protein	2.1.2.10	+	1p	70
L-protein	1.8.1.4	+	2p	70
7. Formaldehyde dehydrogenase (GSH)	1.2.1.1	+	1p	54, 91, 114
8. S-Formylglutathione hydrolase	3.1.2.12		1x	106
9. 5,10-Methylene-THF reductase	1.5.1.20	+	2p	82
10. Methionine synthase (B_{12}-independent)	2.1.1.14	+	2p	26, 80, 109
11. Dihydrofolate reductase/ thymidylate synthase	1.5.1.3/ 2.1.1.45	+	3p	53, 67, 111
12. Ketopantoate hydroxymethyltransferase	2.1.2.11		2x	
13. S-Adenosylmethionine synthetase	2.5.1.6	+	3p	89, 109
14. Methionine S-methyltransferase	2.1.1.12	+	1p	10, 43, 64
15. Homocysteine S-methyltransferase	2.1.1.10	+	3p	64, 79
16. S-Adenosylhomocysteine hydrolase	3.3.1.1	+	2p	48, 99
17. Methionyl-tRNA transformylase	2.1.2.9		1x	
18. GAR Transformylase	2.1.2.2	+	1p	5, 88
19. AICAR Transformylase/ IMP cyclohydrolase	2.1.2.3/ 3.5.4.10		1x	5
20. Sarcosine oxidase	1.5.3.1		1x	40
21. Glyoxylate synthetase	—			44, 45
22. Polypeptide deformylase	3.5.1.31		2x	
23. Formate dehydrogenase	1.2.1.2	+		15, 52, 71
24. Glutamate formiminotransferase	2.1.2.5		1x	
25. Catalase (peroxidatic activity)	1.11.1.6	+	3p	36
26. Glyoxylate decarboxylase	—			77

[a]Enzyme numbers 1–26 as in Figure 2. GSH, glutathione; B_{12}, cobalamin; GAR, glycinamide ribonucleotide; AICAR, aminoimidazolecarboxamide ribonucleotide.

[b]Plus indicates that at least one plant cDNA has been demonstrated by a functional assay to encode the corresponding enzyme activity.

[c]Values are the number of sequenced genes (as of July 2000) in the Arabidopsis genome that are highly homologous to Arabidopsis or other plant cDNAs (p), or to cDNAs or genes from other organisms (x), demonstrated to encode the corresponding enzyme. A more detailed table with all Arabidopsis C_1 sequences currently present in GenBank is available in the Annual Reviews Web repository. This table contains a list of annotated proteins with their accession numbers, a list of corresponding genes with either their chromosome-based identification numbers (for genes localized on chromosomes 2 and 4), or their BAC-based identification numbers (for genes localized on chromosomes 1, 3 and 5), and a list of ESTs for which there are as yet no matching genomic sequences.

photosynthetic and nonphotosynthetic tissues have shed light on how these enzymes cooperate in vivo to supply the cytosol with C_1 units (63, 75, 76). These studies support four conclusions, some of which must be qualified, as follows. (*a*) The GDC and SHMT reactions in mitochondria are tightly coupled via a common pool of 5,10-methylene-THF that does not equilibrate with the overall pool. (*b*) Essentially all the 5,10-methylene-THF generated by GDC is probably used for serine synthesis (although its oxidation via 10-formyl-THF and formate to CO_2 cannot be excluded). (*c*) The availability of cytosolic THF (i.e. the rate at which it is liberated by reactions that utilize THF-bound C_1 units) limits the rate of the cytosolic SHMT reaction (at least in the presence of high levels of serine). (*d*) The glycine formed by the cytosolic SHMT reaction is rapidly metabolized via the mitochondrial GDC/SHMT system. Mouillon et al (63) accordingly proposed a serine-glycine cycle (Figure 3; see color insert), one turn of which yields two cytosolic C_1 units, one CO_2, and one NH_3 from the catabolism of one serine. They further proposed that the coupled mitochondrial GDC-SHMT reactions are an obligatory route for glycine catabolism in all plant tissues. If correct, this unifying hypothesis suggests a need to reexamine why mutants lacking mitochondrial GDC or SHMT grow normally under nonphotorespiratory conditions (113); one possibility is that these mutants are leaky. Consistent with the hypothesis of Mouillon et al, victorin, a potent inhibitor of GDC activity, is toxic to nonphotorespiratory tissues as well as to leaves (65).

The power of ^{13}C NMR to probe C_1 fluxes is evident from the studies cited above, but there are some caveats. The insensitivity of NMR necessitates the use of large doses of labeled precursors (e.g. serine, glycine, formate) so that their intracellular pools may expand far beyond the normal range (63); fluxes under these conditions may be abnormal. Furthermore, NMR experiments—especially in vivo ones—often require conditions that preclude normal rates of photosynthesis and photorespiration, so that endogenous C_1 fluxes are depressed (75). This makes it important to validate conclusions using less intrusive methods, such as radiotracer labeling combined with modeling (31, 58, 64).

Formate Activation and Interconversion of C_1-Substituted Folates

Formate Activation   Higher plants contain small pools of formate, and readily incorporate radiotracer formate carbon into serine, methyl groups, and other products of folate metabolism (17). Moreover, recent ^{13}C NMR measurements demonstrated a substantial flux from supplied formate to serine in Arabidopsis (75). Formate can therefore be an important source of C_1 units. It enters folate-mediated C_1 metabolism via ATP-dependent activation to 10-formyl-THF, mediated by 10-formyl-THF synthetase, an enzyme found in cytosol, mitochondria, and chloroplasts (12, 35, 93). This reaction, acting in reverse, has also been considered to be the portal by which formate exits folate-mediated C_1 metabolism. However, a novel possibility suggested by DNA sequence evidence is that plants have

10-formyl-THF deformylase, which could mediate the irreversible hydrolysis of 10-formyl-THF (35).

C₁ Folate Interconversions   10-Formyl-, 5,10-methenyl-, and 5-10-methylene-THF are interconverted by a bifunctional 5,10-methenyl-THF cyclohydrolase/5,10-methylene-THF dehydrogenase; the dehydrogenase activity is NADP-dependent (12, 13, 49). Like 10-formyl-THF synthetase, this enzyme is present in cytosol, mitochondria, and plastids (12, 67). In plants, conversion of 5,10-methylene-THF to 5-methyl-THF is catalyzed by a 5,10-methylene-THF reductase that is NADH-dependent, not NADPH-dependent as in other eukaryotes (82). This difference in coenzyme requirement very probably renders the reaction in plants reversible (82). Another difference from other eukaryotes is that the plant enzyme is not allosterically inhibited by AdoMet (82). The subcellular location of the plant reductase has not been established, but the absence of targeting sequences suggests that it is cytosolic (82).

An important but unexplored C_1 folate interconversion in plants is that of 5-formyl- and 5,10-methenyl-THF. Plants have significant pools of 5-formyl-THF (12, 19), most probably formed as in other organisms via hydrolysis of 5,10-methenyltetrahydrofolate by an SHMT-glycine complex (97). It was also shown recently that Arabidopsis plants can metabolize supplied 5-formyl-THF (76). This presumably occurs via the enzyme 5-formyl-THF cycloligase, for which there appears to be a small gene family encoding cytosolic and organellar proteins (35; S Roje & AD Hanson, unpublished results). In other organisms, 5-formyl-THF is a potent inhibitor of several folate-dependent enzymes including SHMT (32, 97), and may serve as a stable storage form of reduced folates and C_1 units (51). It is noteworthy that 5-formyl-THF dominates the mitochondrial folate pool in pea leaves (12) because this suggests that 5-formyl-THF could regulate the mitochondrial SHMT reaction in planta. More generally, this last point illustrates how important it is to the understanding of plant C_1 metabolism to measure C_1 folate pools. Because these measurements are technically exacting, relatively few have so far been made (19).

FOLATE-INDEPENDENT C_1 REACTIONS

These reactions, centered on methanol, formaldehyde, and formate, are the most obscure sector of plant C_1 metabolism. It is not clear how much flux these reactions normally carry, although there are clues suggesting it can be high. Interest in this sector has recently been stimulated by the finding that plants emit methanol, and by debate about the possible role of applied methanol in promoting plant growth (27, 57).

Methanol, Formaldehyde and Formate Metabolism

Methanol   Leaves contain small pools of methanol (up to about 1 μmol g^{-1} fresh weight) and emit it to the atmosphere (66). The major source of this methanol is probably pectin demethylation (27). Methanol has also been shown to be formed by formaldehyde dismutation or reduction in potato tuber tissue (55). Radiotracer ^{14}C (16) and ^{13}C NMR (33) studies indicate that methanol is metabolized via the route methanol → formaldehyde → formate → CO_2, and that some of the formate and/or formaldehyde formed enters C_1 folate pools, whence label reaches the 3-position of serine and methyl groups. The biochemical basis of the critical methanol → formaldehyde step is unknown; one possibility is H_2O_2-dependent oxidation, mediated by the peroxidatic activity of catalase (36). The methanol → formaldehyde reaction is catalyzed by methanol oxidase in methylotrophic yeasts and by methanol dehydrogenase in methylotrophic bacteria (83), but there is so far no biochemical or DNA sequence evidence that plants have either enzyme.

Formaldehyde   Small pools of formaldehyde (typically 0.1 to 10 μmol g^{-1} fresh weight) can be demonstrated in plants using reagents that form stable formaldehyde adducts (9, 101). Most of the formaldehyde detected in this way does not exist in vivo in the free state but is reversibly bound to endogenous nucleophiles including glutathione (as *S*-hydroxymethylglutathione), arginine (as N^G–hydroxymethylarginines), and asparagine (as a cyclic adduct) (55, 86), as well as to THF (as 5,10-methylene-THF)—although this must be a minor component because THF levels are unlikely to exceed 1 nmol g^{-1} fresh weight (12). These natural adducts form spontaneously and their formation is favored thermodynamically. For example, the equilibrium constants for *S*-hydroxymethylglutathione and 5,10-methylene-THF formation are 670 M^{-1} and 32,000 M^{-1}, respectively (47, 114). Like other organisms, plants have NAD-linked formaldehyde dehydrogenase, which acts on the glutathione adduct and yields the thioester *S*-formylglutathione. This enzyme is constitutively expressed at quite high levels, and has a high affinity for *S*-hydroxymethylglutathione (K_m values of 1.4 to 13 μM) (35, 54, 91, 114). *S*-Formylglutathione hydrolase activity has also been detected in plants (106) and DNA sequence evidence indicates that this, too, is quite highly expressed (35). These two enzymes, coupled with the chemical equilibria mentioned above, may therefore constitute a folate-independent route to oxidize C_1 units from the formaldehyde to the formate level, thus: 5,10-methylene- THF ↔ formaldehyde ↔ *S*-hydroxymethylglutathione → *S*-formylglutathione → formate. Glutathione-independent formaldehyde dehydrogenase activity has also been reported from plants (30). In addition to methanol oxidation and dissociation of 5,10-methyl-ene-THF, formaldehyde could arise, inter alia, from oxidative demethylation reactions (86) or glyoxylate decarboxylation (23, 77). The relative importance of these sources remains conjectural.

Formate   Plants contain small, metabolically active pools of formate (typically 0.1 to 1 μmol g^{-1} fresh weight, although higher values have also been reported) (1, 2, 62, 112). Like methanol, formate can be emitted from leaves to the atmosphere (28a), although emission rates appear to be lower than for methanol. In leaves of C_3 plants in the light, the formate is generally considered to come from glyoxylate formed in photorespiration, via the nonenzymatic, H_2O_2-dependent decarboxylation of glyoxylate, perhaps facilitated by the peroxidatic activity of catalase (11, 36, 112). However, because most of the evidence for this depends on mutants or inhibitors, it is not clear if this is normally the most important route. Nor is it clear how formate is formed in the dark, in nonphotosynthetic tissues, and by C_4 species. Possibilities include oxidation of formaldehyde and cleavage of 10-formyl-THF (see above); the latter is a major source of formate in mitochondria of other eukaryotes (3, 32). There is also evidence from potato tuber chloroplasts for the direct reduction of CO_2 to formate (4). Although supplied formate can give rise to C_1 folates (see above), a quantitatively more important fate is typically oxidation to CO_2 (58, 116) mediated by formate dehydrogenase. Formate dehydrogenase is a mitochondrial matrix enzyme in plants (15, 46); the purified enzyme behaves as a dimer of 42 kDa (52), but in organelles it forms part of a 200-kDa complex that may contain other proteins (46). Formate dehydrogenase is one of the most abundant soluble proteins in mitochondria from non-green tissues, although it is a minor protein in mitochondria from illuminated, unstressed leaves (15, 40, 46). It has also recently been reported in chloroplasts of Arabidopsis, but not pea or tobacco (71). Formate dehydrogenase is notable for being strongly induced in leaves by darkness, C_1-related compounds, and environmental stresses (40, 71) and in roots by formate application, hypoxia, and iron deficiency (93a, 98). These patterns of developmental and environmental regulation imply that there are major metabolic fluxes via formate in certain tissues and conditions.

Glyoxylate Synthesis from Formate

Glyoxylate synthesis from formate has been reported primarily from green potato tubers (78), although in vivo radiolabeling data hint that it may occur also in leaves (116). The enzyme responsible, named glyoxylate synthetase, has been purified from potato tuber chloroplasts and characterized (44, 45). It appears to contain bound THF and to mediate the condensation of two formate molecules to give glyoxylate. This reaction has no precedent in other organisms. It is not known whether the enzyme also mediates the reverse reaction (glyoxylate → 2 formate).

METHIONINE AND THE ACTIVATED METHYL CYCLE

Methionine Synthesis

Although the chloroplast is the site of homocysteine synthesis, homocysteine apparently has to exit the chloroplast to be converted to methionine because methionine synthase seems to be present only in the cytosol (26, 80, 109) and perhaps mitochondria (14, 74). It is noteworthy that homocysteine is now recognized to be potentially cytotoxic at low levels, and that methionine synthesis serves as a defense against this (90, 110). Another defense available to yeast and animal cells is metabolism of homocysteine through the transsulfuration pathway into cysteine.

Since plants lack this capacity (21), they may be especially reliant on methionine synthesis to control their intracellular homocysteine levels. Consistent with this possibility, the homocysteine content of *Lemna* sp. fronds rose 50-fold when cultured with 2 μM methionine (21), which is known to depress methionine synthesis (80). Many precautions are needed to determine homocysteine (105), and there seem to be almost no other data for higher plants.

S-Adenosylmethionine and S-Adenosylhomocysteine Metabolism

There is as yet no evidence that AdoMet synthesis occurs anywhere but the cytosol (35, 89, 109), implying that plastids and mitochondria import AdoMet. The subcellular location of AdoHcy hydrolysis has not yet been established, but a cytosolic location seems probable inasmuch as the AdoHcy hydrolase proteins predicted from the available cDNAs lack targeting sequences (35, 80). If this is the case, then organelles must export AdoHcy for hydrolysis in the cytosol. The equilibrium of the AdoHcy hydrolysis reaction lies far toward the synthesis of AdoHcy [$K_{eq} = 5 \times 10^{-7}$ M (34)], so that for hydrolysis to proceed, the products (homocysteine and adenosine) must be efficiently removed. This is critical because AdoHcy is a strong competitive inhibitor of transmethylation reactions. Hcy can be removed via the action of methionine synthase (see above) or homocysteine *S*-methyltransferase (see below). It is unclear how adenosine is removed. The most direct way would be conversion to AMP by adenosine kinase (and thence to other adenylates), but a two-step pathway involving degradation to adenine followed by ribophosphorylation by adenine phosphoribosyltransferase to give AMP is also a possibility (108). [Deamination of adenosine to inosine by adenosine deaminase seems unlikely because this activity is absent or too low to detect in various species and tissues (20).] Experiments in which *Lemna* fronds were fed [^{14}C]adenosine demonstrated that adenosine is metabolized very fast, but they shed no light on the route(s) because both adenine and adenylates were labeled at the earliest time tested (31). However, Arabidopsis mutants deficient in adenine phosphoribosyltransferase activity do not have a phenotype suggestive of methylation defects (59), whereas mutants deficient in adenosine kinase are compromised in pectin methylation (60). This implies that adenosine kinase may be the more important enzyme for adenosine removal in plants, as appears to be the case in yeast, in which an adenosine kinase-deficient mutant accumulates AdoHcy (42). Two adenosine kinase cDNAs have recently been cloned from Arabidopsis; both appear to encode cytosolic proteins (61).

It is hard to measure AdoMet and AdoHcy levels (25, 115), and there are few published values for plants, some of them discordant. This is a serious gap given how important the AdoMet/AdoHcy ratio is to the activities of methyltransferases, and how crucial these enzymes are to processes ranging from gene expression to secondary metabolism. Interestingly, the most recent and reliable data suggest that AdoMet/AdoHcy ratios in plants can be very high, typically 10 to >300

(22, 25, 28), compared with values of 2 to 10 for rat liver (6, 92). This raises the question of the biochemical causes and consequences of such high ratios; perhaps AdoHcy-mediated inhibition of AdoMet-dependent transmethylation reactions is less prevalent in plants than commonly supposed.

THE *S*-METHYLMETHIONINE CYCLE

The SMM cycle operates within the activated methyl cycle, and in effect short-circuits it (Figure 2) (64). It requires the tandem action of methionine *S*-methyltransferase (MMT) and homocysteine *S*-methyltransferase (HMT). MMT is a cytosolic enzyme that is encoded by a single gene in Arabidopsis and maize (10, 102). Unique to plants, it mediates the reaction:

$$\text{Methionine} + \text{AdoMet} \rightarrow \text{SMM} + \text{AdoHcy}.$$

HMT is probably also cytosolic (79) but is encoded by three or more diverged genes in Arabidopsis and maize (79; P Ranocha, M Tarczynski & AD Hanson, unpublished results). It catalyzes the reaction:

$$\text{SMM} + \text{Homocysteine} \rightarrow 2\,\text{Methionine} + \text{H}^+.$$

AdoMet is also a methyl donor for HMT in vitro, but kinetic considerations indicate that SMM is probably the physiological donor in planta (79). The Arabidopsis HMTs differ markedly in their sensitivity to inhibition by physiological levels of methionine (79). The net result of the MMT and HMT reactions, plus those catalyzed by AdoMet synthetase and AdoHcy hydrolase, is an apparently futile cycle that consumes and then regenerates two methionines while converting ATP to adenosine, PPi, and Pi (64). Flux through the SMM cycle (relative to that through the whole activated methyl cycle) has been estimated only for rapidly growing Lemna fronds (64) and for mature Arabidopsis leaves (SD McNeil, P Ranocha & AD Hanson, unpublished). The data indicate that about 7% (Lemna) and 50% (Arabidopsis) of the AdoMet produced are dissipated via the SMM cycle.

SMM has been found in virtually all higher plant tissues analyzed; levels are usually 10 to 500 nmol g^{-1} fresh weight, which is as high as or higher than methionine and AdoMet levels (10). The SMM is probably present in cytosolic, chloroplastic, and vacuolar pools (50, 103). Mudd & Datko (64) proposed that the SMM cycle serves to prevent a deficiency of methionine created by an overshoot in its conversion to AdoMet. Other hypothetical roles include avoidance of homocysteine toxicity (see above), and ensuring that AdoMet, which is chirally unstable in physiological conditions (38), does not accumulate to high levels and thereby increase the rate of racemization to the inactive *R,S* diastereomer. An established function for the SMM cycle, albeit involving separation of the MMT and HMT reactions in time and space, is in the long-distance transport of methyl groups and reduced sulfur (Figure 4; see color insert). SMM is a major constituent of the phloem sap in wheat and most probably many other species; after synthesis in the leaves, it moves in the phloem to sink organs, where it is reconverted to methionine (10).

ENIGMAS, AND CHALLENGES FOR THE FUTURE

Recent interest in the metabolic engineering of methyl-rich compounds (e.g. lignin, glycine betaine, alkaloids) and of photorespiration has put plant C_1 metabolism in the spotlight (11, 24, 35). Unfortunately, although C_1 metabolism is essential for methylneogenesis and inextricably embedded in photorespiration, we really do not understand enough about it to attempt rational engineering. Here are some areas that particularly need to be explored.

The Matching of C_1 Supply and Demand

It follows from the huge C_1 demands of secondary metabolism (Figure 1), and from the environmental and developmental control of such metabolism, that the C_1 demand varies greatly in plant tissues—and that C_1 supply must vary in step. However, we do not know how plants match C_1 supply with demand. There are many indications that changes in the expression of individual genes are involved (e.g. 26, 48, 72), but whether this is the only—or even the principal—mechanism is undetermined, as is whether plant C_1 genes are regulated globally. Nor is it known whether the gene expression changes are transcriptional responses to signals from C_1 metabolism, for which there is evidence in yeast (39), or whether the genes affecting C_1 supply and demand are governed by the same regulatory genes. The difference between metabolic and genetic mechanisms for coordinating metabolite supply and demand is crucial to metabolic engineering, because systems that simply sense the metabolic demand and respond accordingly are much more tractable. Now that essentially all the genes of plant C_1 metabolism are known (Figure 1), DNA array technology and proteomics can be applied to answer these questions.

The Sizes of C_1 Pools and Fluxes

Our ability to grasp how C_1 metabolism works in planta is crippled by the dearth of measurements of C_1 pools and the fluxes between them. This is as true for C_1 folates as it is for AdoMet, AdoHcy, formaldehyde and formate. Modifying fluxes is a key part of the flux determination process (96), and we now have the capability to do this by antisense, co-suppression, and gene knockouts. By applying these approaches systematically to C_1 metabolism, and combining them with pool size and flux measurements, and with metabolic modeling, it should be possible to solve many long-standing enigmas. Examples are the origins of formaldehyde and formate, the contributions of these compounds to the normal C_1 budget, the physiological significance of 5-formyl-THF, the catabolic route that removes adenosine generated by the activated methyl cycle, and the function of the SMM cycle.

The Uniqueness of Plant C_1 Metabolism

Because plant C_1 metabolism is a small field and animal and microbial C_1 metabolism are large ones, plant C_1 researchers are inevitably much influenced by findings in other organisms, and the paradigms developed from them. These findings are clearly of enormous value to plant research (e.g. in the cloning of many of the enzymes in Figure 2), but the paradigms may not be. This is because C_1 metabolism in plants differs in fundamental ways from that in bacteria, yeast, and mammals: Witness photorespiration, the huge and variable C_1 demand for secondary metabolism, mitochondrial formate dehydrogenase, glyoxylate synthetase, and the SMM cycle, all of which are special to plants. Even the enzymes that plants share with other organisms may have plant-specific functions, for instance, formaldehyde dehydrogenase and S-formylglutathione hydrolase, which seem likely in plants to be metabolizing formaldehyde of endogenous, not environmental, origin. There is thus much novel plant C_1 biochemistry that needs to be elucidated. It will take many investigators many years to do it. Following too closely the footsteps of animal and microbial biochemists can only distract from this exciting and useful task.

ACKNOWLEDGMENTS

We thank many colleagues for sharing unpublished information and ideas, David J Oliver, John King and Barbara Moffatt for illuminating discussions, Michael J Ziemak for preparing the figures, and Yair Shachar-Hill for a critical reading of the manuscript. We gratefully acknowledge research support from the National Science Foundation, the CV Griffin, Sr Foundation, and the Florida Agricultural Experiment Station. Journal Series no. R-07707.

Visit the Annual Reviews home page at www.AnnualReviews.org

LITERATURE CITED

1. Amory AM, Cresswell CF. 1986. Role of formate in the photorespiratory metabolism of *Themeda triandra* Forssk. *J. Plant Physiol.* 124:247–55

2. Amory AM, Ford L, Pammenter NW, Cresswell CF. 1992. The use of 3-amino-1,2,4-triazole to investigate the short-term effects of oxygen toxicity on carbon assimilation by *Pisum sativum* seedlings. *Plant Cell Environ.* 15:655–63

3. Appling DR. 1991. Compartmentation of folate-mediated one-carbon metabolism in eukaryotes. *FASEB J.* 5:2645–51

4. Arora S, Ramaswamy NK, Nair PM. 1985. Partial purification and some properties of a latent CO_2 reductase from green potato tuber chloroplasts. *Eur. J. Biochem.* 153:509–14

5. Atkins CA, Smith PMC, Storer PJ. 1997. Reexamination of the intracellular localization

of de novo purine synthesis in cowpea nodules. *Plant Physiol.* 113:127–35

6. Balaghi M, Horne DW, Wagner C. 1993. Hepatic one-carbon metabolism in early folate-deficiency in rats. *Biochem. J.* 291:145–49

7. Besson V, Neuburger M, Rebeille F, Douce R. 1995. Evidence for three serine hydroxy-methyltransferases in green leaf cells—purification and characterization of the mitochondrial and chloroplastic isoforms. *Plant Physiol. Biochem.* 33:665–73

8. Besson V, Rebeille F, Neuburger M, Douce R, Cossins EA. 1993. Effects of tetrahydrofolate polyglutamates on the kinetic parameters of serine hydroxymethyltransferase and glycine decarboxylase from pea leaf mitochondria. *Biochem. J.* 292:425–30

9. Blunden G, Carpenter BG, Adrian-Romero M, Yang MH, Tyihak E. 1998. Formaldehyde in the plant kingdom. *Acta Biol. Hung.* 49:239–46

10. Bourgis F, Roje S, Nuccio ML, Fisher DB, Tarczynski MC, et al. 1999. *S*-Methylmethionine plays a major role in phloem sulfur transport and is synthesized by a novel type of methyltransferase. *Plant Cell* 11:1465–98

11. Brisson LF, Zelitch I, Havir EA. 1998. Manipulation of catalase levels produces altered photosynthesis in transgenic tobacco plants. *Plant Physiol.* 116:259–69

12. Chen L, Chan SY, Cossins EA. 1997. Distribution of folate derivatives and enzymes for synthesis of 10-formyltetrahydrofolate in cytosolic and mitochondrial fractions of pea leaves. *Plant Physiol.* 115:299–309

13. Chen L, Nargang FE, Cossins EA. 1999. Isolation and sequencing of a plant cDNA encoding a bifunctional methylenetetrahydrofolate dehydrogenase:methenyltetrahydrofolate cyclohydrolase protein. *Pteridines* 10:171–77

14. Clandinin MT, Cossins EA. 1974. Methionine biosynthesis in isolated *Pisum sativum* mitochondria. *Phytochemistry* 13:585–91

15. Colas des Francs-Small C, Ambard-Brett-eville F, Small ID, Remy R. 1993. Identification of a major soluble protein in mitochondria from nonphotosynthetic tissues as NAD-dependent formate dehydrogenase. *Plant Physiol.* 102:1171–77

16. Cossins EA. 1964. The utilization of carbon-1 compounds by plants. I. The metabolism of methanol-^{14}C and its role in amino acid biosynthesis. *Can. J. Biochem.* 42:1793–802

17. Cossins EA. 1980. One-carbon metabolism. In *The Biochemistry of Plants*, ed. PK Stumpf, EE Conn, 2:365–418. New York: Academic

18. Cossins EA. 1987. Folate biochemistry and the metabolism of one-carbon units. In *The Biochemistry of Plants*, ed. PK Stumpf, EE Conn, 11:317–53. New York: Academic

18a. Cossins EA. 2000. The fascinating world of folate and one-carbon metabolism. *Can. J. Bot.* 78:691–708

19. Cossins EA, Chen L. 1997. Folates and one-carbon metabolism in plants and fungi. *Phytochemistry* 45:437–52

20. Dancer JE, Hughes RG, Lindell SD. 1997. Adenosine-5′-phosphate deaminase. A novel herbicide target. *Plant Physiol.* 114:119–29

21. Datko AH, Mudd SH. 1984. Responses of sulfur-containing compounds in *Lemna paucicostata* Hegelm. 6746 to changes in availability of sulfur sources. *Plant Physiol.* 75:474–79

22. Datko AH, Mudd SH, Giovanelli J, Macnicol PK. 1978. Sulfur-containing compounds in *Lemna perpusilla* 6746 grown at a range of sulfate concentrations. *Plant Physiol.* 62:629–35

23. Davies DD, Corbett RJ. 1969. Glyoxylate decarboxylase activity in higher plants [wheat, cucurbits, turnip, pea, *Pelargonium*]. *Phytochemistry* 8:529–42

24. Douce R, Neuburger M. 1999. Biochemical dissection of photorespiration. *Curr. Opin. Plant Biol.* 2:214–22

25. Edwards R. 1995. Determination of *S*-adenosyl-L-methionine and *S*-adenosyl-L-homocysteine in plants. *Phytochem. Anal.* 6:25–30

26. Eichel J, Gonzalez JC, Hotze M, Matthews RG, Schroder J. 1995. Vitamin-B12-independent methionine synthase from a higher plant (*Catharanthus roseus*). Molecular characterization, regulation, heterologous expression, and enzyme properties. *Eur. J. Biochem.* 230:1053–58

27. Fall R, Benson AA. 1996. Leaf methanol—the simplest natural product from plants. *Trends Plant Sci.* 9:296–301

28. Fojtova M, Kovarik A, Votruba I, Holy A. 1998. Evaluation of the impact of *S*-adenosylhomocysteine metabolic pools on cytosine methylation of the tobacco genome. *Eur. J. Biochem.* 252:347–52

28a. Gabriel R, Schafer L, Gerlach C, Rausch T, Kesselmeier J. 1999. Factors controlling the emissions of volatile organic acids from leaves of *Quercus ilex* L. (Holm oak). *Atmos. Environ.* 33:1347–55

29. Gardestrom P, Edwards GE, Henricson D, Ericson I. 1985. The localization of serine hydroxymethyltransferase in leaves of C_3 and C_4 species. *Physiol. Plant.* 64:29–33

30. Giese M, Bauer-Doranth U, Langebartels C, Sandermann H. 1994. Detoxification of formaldehyde by the spider plant (*Chlorophytum comosum* L.) and by soybean (*Glycine max* L.) suspension cultures. *Plant Physiol.* 104:1301–9

31. Giovanelli J, Mudd SH, Datko AH. 1985. Quantitative analysis of pathways of methionine metabolism and their regulation in *Lemna*. *Plant Physiol.* 78:555–60

32. Girgis S, Suh JR, Jolivet J, Stover PJ. 1997. 5-Formyltetrahydrofolate regulates homocysteine remethylation in human neuroblastoma. *J. Biol.Chem.* 272:4729–34

33. Gout E, Aubert S, Bligny R, Rebeille F, Nonomura AR, et al. 2000. Metabolism of methanol in plant cells. Carbon-13

nuclear magnetic resonance studies. *Plant Physiol.* 123:287–96

34. Guranowski A, Pawelkiewicz J. 1977. Adenosylhomocysteinase from yellow lupin seeds. Purification and properties. *Eur. J. Biochem.* 80:517–23

35. Hanson AD, Gage DA, Shachar-Hill Y. 2000. Plant one-carbon metabolism and its engineering. *Trends Plant Sci.* 5:206–13

36. Havir EA, McHale NA. 1990. Purification and characterization of an isozyme of catalase with enhanced-peroxidatic activity from leaves of *Nicotiana sylvestris*. *Arch. Biochem. Biophys.* 283:491–95

37. Hibi N, Higashiguchi S, Hashimoto T, Yamada Y. 1994. Gene expression in tobacco low-nicotine mutants. *Plant Cell* 6:723–35

38. Hoffman JL. 1986. Chromatographic analysis of the chiral and covalent instability of *S*-adenosyl-L-methionine. *Biochemistry* 25:4444–49

39. Hong SP, Piper MD, Sinclair DA, Dawes IW. 1999. Control of expression of one-carbon metabolism genes of *Saccharomyces cerevisiae* is mediated by a tetrahydrofolate-responsive protein binding to a glycine regulatory region including a core 5′-CTTCTT-3′ motif. *J. Biol. Chem.* 274:10523–32

40. Hourton-Cabassa C, Ambard-Bretteville F, Moreau F, de Virville JD, Remy R, Colas des Francs-Small C. 1998. Stress induction of mitochondrial formate dehydrogenase in potato leaves. *Plant Physiol.* 116:627–35

41. Igamberdiev AU, Bykova NV, Kleczcowski LA. 1999. Origins and metabolism of formate in higher plants. *Plant Physiol. Biochem.* 37:503–13

42. Iwashima A, Ogata M, Nosaka K, Nishimura H, Hasegawa T. 1995. Adenosine kinase-deficient mutant of *Saccharomyces cerevisiae*. *FEMS Microbiol. Lett.* 127:23–28

43. James F, Nolte KD, Hanson AD. 1995.

Purification and properties of S-adenosyl-
L-methionine:L-methionine S-methyltran-
sferase from *Wollastonia biflora* leaves. *J.
Biol. Chem.* 270:22344–50

44. Janave MT, Ramaswamy NK, Nair PM.
1993. Purification and characterization
of glyoxylate synthetase from greening
potato-tuber chloroplasts. *Eur. J. Biochem.*
214:889–96

45. Janave MT, Ramaswamy NK, Nair
PM. 1999. Studies on determination of
active site amino acid residues in glyoxylate synthetase from potato tuber chloroplasts. *Plant Physiol. Biochem.* 37:121–
29

46. Jansch L, Kruft V, Schmitz UK, Braun HP.
1996. New insights into the composition,
molecular mass and stoichiometry of the
protein complexes of plant mitochondria.
Plant J. 9:357–68

47. Kallen RG, Jencks WP. 1966. The mechanism of condensation of formaldehyde
with tetrahydofolic acid. *J. Biol. Chem.*
241:5851–63

48. Kawalleck P, Plesch G, Hahlbrock K,
Somssich IE. 1992. Induction by fungal
elicitor of S-adenosyl-L-methionine synthetase and S-adenosyl-L-homocysteine
hydrolase mRNAs in cultured cells and
leaves of *Petroselinum crispum. Proc. Natl.
Acad. Sci. USA* 89:4713–17

49. Kirk CD, Chen LF, Imeson HC, Cossins EA. 1995. A 5,10-methylenetetr-
ahydrofolate dehydrogenase-5,10-methe-
nyltetrahydrofolate cyclohydrolase protein
from *Pisum sativum. Phytochemistry*
39:1309–17

50. Kocsis MG, Nolte KD, Rhodes D,
Shen TL, Gage DA, Hanson AD. 1998.
Dimethyl-sulfoniopropionate biosynthesis
in *Spartina alterniflora*. Evidence that
S-methylmethionine and dimethylsulfo-
niopropylamine are intermediates. *Plant
Physiol.* 117:273–81

51. Kruschwitz HL, McDonald D, Cossins
EA, Schirch V. 1994. 5-Formyltetrahy-
dropteroyl-polyglutamates are the major

folate derivatives in *Neurospora crassa*
conidiospores. *J. Biol. Chem.* 269:28757–
63

52. Li R, Ziola B, King J. 2000. Purification
and characterization of formate dehydrogenase from *Arabidopsis thaliana. J. Plant
Physiol.* In press

53. Luo M, Orsi R, Patrucco E, Pancaldi
S, Cella R. 1997. Multiple transcription start sites of the carrot dihydrofolate
reductase-thymidylate synthase gene, and
sub-cellular localization of the bifunctional
protein. *Plant Mol. Biol.* 33:709–22

54. Martinez MC, Achkor H, Persson B, Fernandez MR, Shafqat J, et al. 1996. Arabidopsis formaldehyde dehydrogenase.
Molecular properties of plant class III alcohol dehydrogenase provide further insights
into the origins, structure and function of
plant class P and liver class I alcohol dehydrogenases. *Eur. J. Biochem.* 241:849–
57

55. Mason RP, Sanders JKM, Gidley MJ. 1986.
NMR visualization of free asparagine
in potato tissue using adduct formation
with [^{13}C]formaldehyde. *Phytochemistry*
25:1567–71

56. McClung CR, Hsu M, Painter JE, Gagne
JM, Karlsberg SD, Salome PA. 2000.
Integrated temporal regulation of the
photorespiratory pathway. Circadian regulation of two arabidopsis genes encoding serine hydroxymethyltransferase.
Plant Physiol. 123:381–92

57. McGiffen ME, Manthey JA. 1996. The role
of methanol in promoting plant growth: a
current evaluation. *HortScience* 31:1092–
96

58. McNeil SD, Nuccio ML, Rhodes D,
Shachar-Hill Y, Hanson AD. 2000. Radiotracer and computer modeling evidence
that phospho-base methylation is the main
route of choline synthesis in tobacco. *Plant
Physiol.* 123:371–80

59. Moffatt B, Somerville C. 1988. Positive
selection for male-sterile mutants of *Arabidopsis* lacking adenine phosphoribosyl

transferase activity. *Plant Physiol.* 86: 1150–54

60. Moffatt BA, Stevens Y, Allen M, Snider J, McCaffrey LM, et al. 2000. Adenosine kinase deficiency is associated with developmental abnormalities and reduced transmethylation. *Plant Physiol.* In press

61. Moffatt BA, Wang L, Allen M, Stevens Y, Qin W, et al. 2000. Adenosine kinase of *Arabidopsis thaliana*:kinetic properties and gene expression *Plant Physiol.* In press

62. Morot-Gaudry JF, Farineau J, Jolivet E. 1979. Effect of leaf position and plant age on photosynthetic carbon metabolism in leaves of 8 and 16 day-old maize seedlings (W64A) with and without the gene *Opaque 2*. *Photosynthetica* 13:365–75

63. Mouillon JM, Aubert S, Bourguignon J, Gout E, Douce R, Rebeille F. 1999. Glycine and serine catabolism in non-photosynthetic higher plant cells: their role in C1 metabolism. *Plant J.* 20:1997–205

64. Mudd SH, Datko AH. 1990. The *S*-methylmethionine cycle in *Lemna paucicostata*. *Plant Physiol.* 93:623–30

65. Navarre DA, Wolpert TJ. 1995. Inhibition of the glycine decarboxylase multienzyme complex by the host-selective toxin victorin. *Plant Cell* 7:463–71

66. Nemecek-Marshall M, MacDonald RC, Franzen JJ, Wojciechowski CL, Fall R. 1995. Methanol emission from leaves—enzymatic detection of gas-phase methanol and relation of methanol fluxes to stomatal conductance and leaf development. *Plant Physiol.* 108:1359–68

67. Neuburger M, Rebeille F, Jourdain A, Nakamura S, Douce R. 1996. Mitochondria are a major site for folate and thymidylate synthesis in plants. *J. Biol. Chem.* 271:9466–72

68. Nour JM, Rabinowitz JC. 1991. Isolation, characterization, and structural organization of 10-formyltetrahydrofolate synthetase from spinach leaves. *J. Biol. Chem.* 266:18363–69

69. Nour JM, Rabinowitz JC. 1992. Isolation

and sequencing of the cDNA coding for spinach 10-formyltetrahydrofolate synthetase. Comparisons with the yeast, mammalian, and bacterial proteins. *J. Biol. Chem.* 267:16292–96

70. Oliver DJ. 1994. The glycine decarboxylase complex from plant mitochondria. *Annu. Rev. Plant Physiol. Plant Mol. Biol.* 45:323–37

71. Olson BJSC, Skavdahl M, Ramberg H, Osterman JC, Markwell J. 2000. Formate dehydrogenase in *Arabidopsis thaliana*:characterization and possible targeting to the chloroplast. *Plant Sci.* In press

72. Peleman J, Boerjan W, Engler G, Seurinck J, Botterman J, et al. 1989. Strong cellular preference in the expression of a housekeeping gene of *Arabidopsis thaliana* encoding *S*-adenosylmethionine synthetase. *Plant Cell* 1:81–93

73. Penning de Vries FWT, Brunsting AHM, Van Laar HH. 1974. Products, requirements and efficiency of biosynthesis:a quantitative approach. *J. Theor. Biol.* 45:339–77

74. Petersen M, Van Der Straeten D, Bauw G. 1995. Full-length cDNA clone from *Coleus blumei* with high similarity to cobalamine-independent methionine synthase. *Plant Physiol.* 109:338

75. Prabhu V, Chatson KB, Abrams GD, King J. 1996. [13]C Nuclear magnetic resonance detection of interactions of serine hydroxymethyltransferase with C_1-tetrahydrofolate synthase and glycine decarboxylase complex activities in Arabidopsis. *Plant Physiol.* 112:207–16

76. Prabhu V, Chatson KB, Lui H, Abrams GD, King J. 1998. Effects of sulfanilamide and methotrexate on ^{13}C fluxes through the glycine decarboxylase/serine hydroxymethyltransferase enzyme system in Arabidopsis. *Plant Physiol.* 116:137–44

77. Prather CW, Sisler EC. 1972. Glycine and glyoxylate decarboxylation in *Nicotiana rustica* roots. *Phytochemistry* 11:1637–47

78. Ramaswamy NK, Sangeeta GJ, Behere

AG, Nair PM. 1983. Glyoxylate synthetase isolated from green potato tuber chloroplasts catalysing the conversion of formate to glyoxylate. *Plant Sci. Lett.* 32:213–20

79. Ranocha P, Bourgis F, Ziemak MJ, Rhodes D, Gage DA, Hanson AD. 2000. Characterization and functional expression of cDNAs encoding methionine-sensitive and -insensitive homocysteine S-methyltransferases from arabidopsis. *J. Biol. Chem.* 275:15962–68

80. Ravanel S, Gakiere B, Job D, Douce R. 1998. The specific features of methionine biosynthesis and metabolism in plants. *Proc. Natl. Acad. Sci. USA* 95:7805–12

80a. Rebeille F, Douce R. 1999. Folate synthesis and compartmentation in higher plants. In *Regulation of Primary Metabolic Pathways in Plants*, ed. NJ Kruger, SA Hill, RG Ratcliffe, pp. 53–99. Dordrecht: Kluwer. 311 pp.

81. Rhodes D, Hanson AD. 1993. Quaternary ammonium and tertiary sulfonium compounds in higher plants. *Annu. Rev. Plant Physiol. Plant Mol. Biol.* 44:357–84

82. Roje S, Wang H, McNeil SD, Raymond RK, Appling DR, et al. 1999. Isolation, characterization, and functional expression of cDNAs encoding NADH-dependent methylenetetrahydrofolate reductase from higher plants. *J. Biol. Chem.* 274:36089–96

83. Rokem JS, Goldberg I. 1991. Oxidation pathways in methylotrophs. *Biotechnology* 18:111–26

84. Roughan PG, Batt RD. 1969. The glycerolipid composition of leaves. *Phytochemistry* 8:363–69

85. Saitoh F, Noma M, Kawashima N. 1985. The alkaloid contents of sixty *Nicotiana* species. *Phytochemistry* 24:477–80

86. Sardi E, Tyihak E. 1994. Simple determination of formaldehyde in dimedone adduct form in biological samples by high performance liquid chromatography. *Biomed. Chromatogr.* 8:313–14

87. Saunders JW, Bush LP. 1979. Nicotine biosynthetic enzyme activities in *Nicotiana tabacum* L. genotypes with different alkaloid levels. *Plant Physiol.* 64:236–40

88. Schnorr KM, Nygaard P, Laloue M. 1994. Molecular characterization of *Arabidopsis thaliana* cDNAs encoding three purine biosynthetic enzymes. *Plant J.* 6:113–21

89. Schroder G, Eichel J, Breinig S, Schroder J. 1997. Three differentially expressed S-adenosyl-methionine synthetases from *Catharanthus roseus*:molecular and functional characterization. *Plant Mol. Biol.* 33:211–22

90. Selhub J. 1999. Homocysteine metabolism. *Annu. Rev. Nutr.* 19:217–46

91. Shafqat J, El-Ahmad M, Danielsson O, Martinez MC, Persson B, et al. 1996. Pea formaldehyde-active class III alcohol dehydrogenase:common derivation of the plant and animal forms but not of the corresponding ethanol-active forms (classes I and P). *Proc. Natl. Acad. Sci. USA* 93:5595–99

92. She QB, Nagao I, Hayakawa T, Tsuge H. 1994. A simple HPLC method for the determination of S-adenosylmethionine and S-adenosylhomocysteine in rat tissues. The effect of vitamin B6 deficiency on these concentrations in rat liver. *Biochem. Biophys. Res. Commun.* 205:1748–54

93. Shingles R, Woodrow L, Grodzinski B. 1984. Effects of glycolate pathway intermediates on glycine decarboxylation and serine synthesis in pea (*Pisum sativum* L.). *Plant Physiol.* 74:705–10

93a. Shiraishi T, Fukusaki E, Kobayashi A. 2000. Formate dehydrogenase in rice plant:growth stimulation effect of formate in rice plant. *J. BioSci. Bioeng.* 89:241–46

94. Sjostrom E. 1981. *Wood Chemistry.* New York: Academic. 223 pp.

95. Skavdahl M, Olson BJSC, Markwell J, Osterman JC. 1999. Nucleotide sequence of a cDNA encoding 10-formyltetrahydrofolate synthetase from Arabidopsis. *Plant Physiol.* 121:312

96. Stephanopoulos G. 1999. Metabolic fluxes and metabolic engineering. *Metab. Eng.* 1:1–11

97. Stover P, Schirch V. 1993. The metabolic role of leucovorin. *Trends Biochem. Sci.* 18:102–6

98. Suzuki K, Itai R, Suzuki K, Nakanishi H, Nishizawa NK, et al. 1998. Formate dehydrogenase, an enzyme of anaerobic metabolism, is induced by iron deficiency in barley roots. *Plant Physiol.* 116:725–32

99. Tanaka H, Masuta C, Kataoka J, Kuwata S, Koiwai A, Noma M. 1996. Inducible expression by plant hormones of *S*-adenosyl-L-homocysteine hydrolase gene from *Nicotiana tabacum* during early newer bud formation in vitro. *Plant Sci.* 113:167–74

100. Thakur BR, Singh RK, Handa AK. 1997. Chemistry and uses of pectin—a review. *Crit. Rev. Food Sci. Nutr.* 37:47–73

101. Trezl L, Hullan L, Szarvas T, Csiba A, Szende B. 1998. Determination of endogenous formaldehyde in plants (fruits) bound to L-arginine and its relation to the folate cycle, photosynthesis and apoptosis. *Acta Biol. Hung.* 49:253–63

102. Trossat C, Nolte KD, Hanson AD. 1996. Evidence that the pathway of dimethylsulfoniopropionate biosynthesis begins in the cytosol and ends in the chloroplast. *Plant Physiol.* 111:965–73

103. Trossat C, Rathinasabapathi B, Weretilnyk EA, Shen TL, Huang ZH, et al. 1998. Salinity promotes accumulation of 3-dimethylsulfoniopropionate and its precursor *S*-methylmethionine in chloroplasts. *Plant Physiol.* 116:165–71

104. Turner S, Ireland R, Morgan C, Rawsthorne S. 1992. Identification and localization of multiple forms of serine hydroxymethyltransferase in pea (*Pisum sativum*) and characterization of a cDNA encoding a mitochondrial isoform. *J. Biol. Chem.* 267:13528–34

105. Ueland PM, Refsum H, Stabler SP, Malinow MR, Andersson A, Allen RH. 1993. Total homocysteine in plasma or serum:methods and clinical applications. *Clin. Chem.* 39:1764–79

106. Uotila L, Koivusalo M. 1979. Purification of formaldehyde and formate dehydrogenases from pea seeds by affinity chromatography and *S*-formylglutathione as the intermediate of formaldehyde metabolism. *Arch. Biochem. Biophys.* 196:33–45

107. Verma DC, Dougall DK. 1978. DNA, RNA and protein content of tissue during growth and embryogenesis in wild-carrot suspension cultures. *In Vitro* 14:183–91

108. von Schwartzenberg K, Kruse S, Reski R, Moffatt B, Laloue M. 1998. Cloning and characterization of an adenosine kinase from *Physcomitrella* involved in cytokinin metabolism. *Plant J.* 13:249–57

109. Wallsgrove RM, Lea PJ, Miflin BJ. 1983. Intracellular localization of aspartate kinase and the enzymes of threonine and methionine biosynthesis in green leaves. *Plant Physiol.* 71:780–84

110. Wang H, Yoshizumi M, Lai K, Tsai JC, Perrella MA, et al. 1997. Inhibition of growth and p21[ras] methylation in vascular endothelial cells by homocysteine but not cysteine. *J. Biol. Chem.* 272:25380–85

111. Wang M, Ratnam S, Freisheim JH. 1995. Cloning, nucleotide sequence and expression of the bifunctional dihydrofolate reductase-thymidylate synthase from *Glycine max. Biochim. Biophys. Acta* 1261:3325–36

112. Wingler A, Lea PJ, Leegood RC. 1999. Photorespiratory metabolism of glyoxylate and formate in glycine-accumulating mutants of barley and *Amaranthus edulis*. *Planta* 207:518–26

113. Wingler A, Lea PJ, Quick WP, Leegood RC. 2000. Photorespiration—metabolic

pathways and their role in stress protection. *Proc. R. Soc. London Ser. B.* In press

114. Wippermann U, Fliegmann J, Bauw G, Langebartels C, Maier K, Sandermann H. 1999. Maize glutathione-dependent formaldehyde dehydrogenase:protein sequence and catalytic properties. *Planta* 208:12–18

115. Wise C, Fullerton F. 1995. Analytical procedure for determination of S-adenosylmethionine, S-adenosylhomocysteine and S-adenosylethionine in same isocratic HPLC run, with a procedure for preparation and analysis of the analog S-adenosylhomocysteine sulfoxide. *J. Liq. Chromatogr.* 18:2005–17

116. Zemlyanukhin AA, Makeev AM, Raikhinshtein MV. 1972. Metabolism of formic acid and related compounds in maize seedlings. *Sov. Plant Physiol.* 19:473–79

Annu. Rev. Plant Physiol. Plant Mol. Biol. 2001. 52:139–62

CIRCADIAN RHYTHMS IN PLANTS

C Robertson McClung

Department of Biological Sciences, Dartmouth College, Hanover, New Hampshire
03755-3576; e-mail: mcclung@dartmouth.edu

Key Words biological clocks, cryptochrome, flowering time, photoperiodism, phytochrome

■ **Abstract** Circadian rhythms, endogenous rhythms with periods of approximately 24 h, are widespread in nature. Although plants have provided many examples of rhythmic outputs and our understanding of photoreceptors of circadian input pathways is well advanced, studies with plants have lagged in the identification of components of the central circadian oscillator. Nonetheless, genetic and molecular biological studies, primarily in Arabidopsis, have begun to identify the components of plant circadian systems at an accelerating pace. There also is accumulating evidence that plants and other organisms house multiple circadian clocks both in different tissues and, quite probably, within individual cells, providing unanticipated complexity in circadian systems.

CONTENTS

1040-2519/01/0601-0139$14.00

DEDICATION

This review is dedicated to the memory of Richard C Crain (1951–1998), Dartmouth Class of 1973, a pioneer in the study of inositol phospholipids in plant signal transduction and an enthusiastic advocate of second messenger and circadian rhythms research.

INTRODUCTION

It is often opined that death and taxes are the only two inescapable aspects of the human existence, but Ernest Hemingway correctly noted that "The Sun Also Rises" (50). Indeed, the daily rotation of the earth on its axis has meant that biological evolution has occurred in an environment that changes drastically every day. It should come as no surprise that, since much of an organism's biochemistry, physiology, and behavior is temporally organized with respect to the environmental oscillation of day and night, most organisms express diurnal rhythms. It is less obvious that many of these rhythms should persist in the absence of environmental time cues (e.g. light:dark or temperature cycles). However, organisms from cyanobacteria to humans endogenously measure time and temporally regulate aspects of their biology. This review focuses on recent advances in our understanding of the molecular bases of plant circadian rhythms.

Circadian rhythms are defined by three fundamental parameters: periodicity, entrainability, and temperature compensation. Although daily environmental changes drive diurnal rhythms, a true circadian rhythm persists in the absence of environmental time cues with a free-running period of approximately 24 h (Figure 1; see color insert). Environmental time information from the daily rotation of the Earth on its axis, such as light:dark and temperature cycles, entrains the oscillation to precisely 24 h. Experimentally, one can entrain circadian oscillations to non-24 h periods with imposed environmental cycles. An intriguing characteristic of circadian rhythms is that the period of the rhythm is temperature-compensated and remains relatively constant over a range of physiological temperatures, in sharp contrast to the temperature dependence of most biochemical processes.

The earliest known account of a circadian rhythm dates from the fourth century BC, when Androsthenes, in descriptions of the marches of Alexander the Great, described diurnal leaf movements of the tamarind tree (101). The endogenous nature of leaf movement rhythms was experimentally demonstrated in the eighteenth century (24, 28). The deviation of the endogenous period from exactly 24 h was first described for the free-running period of leaf movements in the nineteenth century (23). Now, at the dawn of the twenty-first century, we are finally unraveling the molecular details of plant circadian systems.

A BASIC MODEL OF THE PLANT CIRCADIAN SYSTEM

Formally, one can divide the circadian system into three conceptual parts: input pathways that entrain the clock, the central oscillator (clock), and output pathways to generate overt rhythms (Figure 2; see color insert). I first address the output pathways in order to introduce the assays that feature in the analysis of plant clocks. Then I discuss input pathways and consider the central oscillator and the exciting recent progress in elucidating the oscillator mechanism in plants.

RHYTHMIC OUTPUTS

One of the attractions of plants as model clock systems is the myriad rhythmic outputs, or "hands" of the clock. The clock times (gates) different overt rhythms to distinct times of day (phase angle). I do not attempt an exhaustive survey as plant rhythmic processes have been reviewed in detail (89, 94, 139, 148).

Movement and Growth Rhythms

These include the classic system of pulvinar leaf movements, in which cells in the extensor and flexor regions of the pulvinus swell in antiphase (180° out of phase) to drive a circadian oscillation in leaf position (32). Swelling is driven by volume changes resulting from ion fluxes (69). This provides an excellent system in which to study the roles of second messengers including calcium and phosphoinositides (43, 93).

There are also rhythms that reflect growth rate, chiefly cell elongation. For example, inflorescence stems of Arabidopsis (66) exhibit a circadian oscillation in elongation rate that is correlated with the level of indole-3-acetic acid (IAA) in rosette leaves, although IAA levels in the inflorescence stem do not oscillate. Decapitation of the inflorescence stem abolishes elongation but application of IAA to the decapitated stem restores rhythmic elongation, implicating a rhythm either in polar transport of IAA or in the ability to elongate in response to IAA and excluding rhythmic synthesis of IAA in the shoot apex (65). Inhibition of IAA polar transport blocks elongation, but this does not distinguish between either rhythmic IAA transport or sensitivity as critical for the overt rhythm in elongation rate. Arabidopsis also exhibits a circadian rhythm in the rate of hypocotyl elongation (27). Although defective inhibition of hypocotyl elongation has been a staple of screens for photoperception mutants, the hypocotyl elongation defect may also result from a primary dysfunction in the circadian system with a resulting failure to impose a daily period of growth arrest (27).

There is also a circadian rhythm in the elongation rate of the abaxial and adaxial cells of the petiole that confers an oscillation in position of cotyledons and leaves (32). Leaf movements of individual seedlings are easily monitored by video imaging, providing the basis of a search for natural alleles that contribute quantitatively (quantitative trait loci, or QTLs) to period length in Arabidopsis (147).

Stomatal Aperture, Gas Exchange and CO_2 Assimilation

Circadian rhythms in stomatal aperture are well documented (157) and are correlated with a circadian rearrangement of guard cell cytoskeleton (40). In beans there is circadian control of Calvin cycle reactions in addition to control of stomatal aperture and gas exchange (51). Arabidopsis exhibits a circadian rhythm in the rate of CO_2 assimilation (EV Kearns & CR McClung, unpublished), but circadian regulation of the Calvin cycle has not been investigated. Circadian rhythms of CO_2 assimilation in Crassulacean Acid Metabolism (CAM) have been extremely well studied, and the molecular mechanism is understood in considerable detail (111). There is a rhythm in the transport of malate across the tonoplast (111). In addition, flux through PEP carboxylase (PEPc) is regulated by reversible phosphorylation; at night PEPc is phosphorylated and less sensitive to inhibition by malate. Although second messengers typically regulate kinases, PEPc kinase from *Kalanchoë fedtschenkoi* is unusual in that it lacks regulatory domains. The circadian oscillation in PEPc kinase activity stems purely from a rhythm in protein abundance that requires de novo protein synthesis, which reflects a circadian oscillation in transcript accumulation (47, 48).

Hormone Production and Responsiveness

In addition to the circadian oscillations in auxin levels and transport/sensitivity described above (65, 66), ethylene production exhibits circadian rhythmicity in a number of species (34, 56). In sorghum there are underlying rhythms in mRNA abundance for the *SbACO2* gene encoding 1-aminocyclopropane-1-carboxylic acid (ACC) oxidase and in ACC oxidase activity (35). It is possible, although not established, that the diurnal oscillation demonstrated in gibberellic acid levels in sorghum is truly circadian (36). It is likely that more hormones will exhibit circadian rhythms in production. More interesting and challenging is the potential rhythmicity of hormonal responsiveness. Components of the biosynthetic machinery, of the perception and signaling mechanisms, or of the response pathways could be targets of circadian regulation.

Calcium

Ca^{2+} plays a critical role in guard cell signaling (79, 136) and so is suspected in the circadian regulation of stomatal aperture and gas exchange. Because Ca^{2+} is a ubiquitous second messenger in plant signaling pathways (132) and has been implicated in red and blue light signal transduction (6, 7, 39, 87), it is possible that Ca^{2+} plays a role in the entrainment of the circadian oscillator as well as in the regulation of clock-controlled gene expression. Indeed, external application of either Ca^{2+} or a Ca^{2+} ionophore phase shifts the leaflet movement rhythm of *Robinia pseudoacacia* (43). Intriguingly, free cytosolic and possibly chloroplastic Ca^{2+} levels, monitored by aequorin luminescence, oscillate with a circadian rhythm in tobacco and Arabidopsis (62). The light to dark transition stimulates a spike in chloroplast stromal Ca^{2+} levels (62), although whether this signals the circadian clock is not known.

Rhythms in Gene Expression

The list of plant clock-controlled genes (*CCGs*; see 33, 94, 139) has expanded considerably since Kloppstech's (71) original observation of a circadian oscillation in mRNA abundance of a chlorophyll *a/b* binding protein gene (*LHCB* or *CAB*). This list continues to grow (75, 95) and it seems likely that microarray analysis should soon identify most genes showing circadian oscillations in mRNA abundance. Initial estimates suggest that from 5% to 6% of Arabidopsis genes are rhythmically expressed (46a). This is a far cry from the apparent universality of circadian regulation of transcription in the cyanobacterium *Synechococcus* (85), but suggests that there are between ~1250 and 1500 Arabidopsis *CCGs*, based on a current estimate of ~25,000 Arabidopsis genes (154). Of course, the biological material used to generate the hybridization probes limits the detection of oscillating transcripts to those that are regulated in those tissues at the developmental stage under the specific growth conditions sampled, and it will take many iterations to exhaustively sample all possible developmental stages and environmental conditions. Nor will these initial experiments identify genes whose induction or repression in response to environmental or biological stimuli is gated by the clock.

Although most genes exhibiting circadian oscillations are nuclear, a number of *Chlamydomonas* plastid transcripts show circadian oscillations (55, 129) that are correlated with a circadian oscillation in DNA supercoiling in the plastid genome (130). The plastid-encoded *psbD* gene oscillates robustly in wheat (107). This oscillation, as well as light regulation, is dependent on an atypical -35 promoter element and it is hypothesized that transcription of this gene requires a plastid-encoded RNA polymerase and a nuclear-encoded sigma factor that itself is a CCG (107). Consistent with this hypothesis, transcription of nuclear-encoded sigma factor genes is circadian in Arabidopsis and wheat (67, 102). This echoes the clock regulation of a *Synechococcus* sigma factor (153) and, moreover, offers a mechanism for temporal coordination between the nuclear and plastid genomes.

Circadian oscillation of *LHCB* mRNA abundance is widespread, if not universal, among angiosperms (33, 116), although not gymnosperms (11). Both nuclear run-on experiments and transcriptional gene fusions establish a transcriptional component to this regulation in several angiosperms (33, 116). Typical reporters are unsuitable for circadian studies. Even though mRNA abundance oscillates in response to clock-gated transcription, the reporter activity (e.g. β-glucuronidase or chloramphenicol acetyltransferase) is too stable to allow turnover within a circadian cycle, and the accumulation of reporter activity obscures the underlying rhythm in transcription. Luciferase (LUC) protein is stable and accumulates over time, but LUC activity (light production) is unstable; activity over time requires translation of new LUC protein and provides a reliable assessment of *LUC* transcription (99). The measurement of LUC activity is nondestructive and quantitative and allows both temporal and spatial resolution of gene expression in real time in vivo.

Minimal nuclear promoters sufficient to confer maximal circadian transcription at a mid-morning phase have been identified for several *LHCB* genes (33, 116), tomato *LHCA* genes (68), and the Arabidopsis *RCA* gene (86). Of course, the rates of maximal transcription of different genes occur at distinct circadian phases (times of day) and a number of different phase angle markers are available (Figure 1). For example, mRNA abundance of the *CAT2* and *CAT3* catalase genes of Arabidopsis peaks at dawn and dusk, respectively (162). We have defined a minimal *CAT3* promoter sufficient to confer evening-specific circadian transcription (TP Michael & CR McClung, unpublished; see Figure 1). Evening-specific promoters have also been defined for the Arabidopsis genes encoding a glycine-rich RNA-binding protein (*ATGRP7/CCR2*) and a germin-like protein (*AtGER3*) (142–144). As is discussed below, many genes implicated in the input and central oscillator mechanisms are themselves *CCGs*. It will soon be possible to target the expression of one's favorite gene to a particular time of day with the same precision that sets of tissue- and cell type–specific promoters afford for spatial expression.

In vivo functional analysis of progressively truncated *LHCB1*1* (*CAB2*) promoter fragments fused to luciferase defined a 36-bp region sufficient to confer circadian transcription. In vitro analysis of DNA binding by electrophoretic mobility shift assays and DNA footprinting identified binding sites for multiple complexes in this short fragment (16, 33). The *CIRCADIAN CLOCK ASSOCIATED 1* (*CCA1*) gene that had been previously implicated in phytochrome regulation (155) encodes a single Myb domain protein that shows circadian binding to an element (consensus AAa/cAATCT) within the functionally defined region of the *LHCB1*1* promoter (156). This CCA1-binding element is also found in the functionally defined minimal *LHCA* and *RCA* promoters (68, 86), although the functional importance of CCA1 binding to the circadian transcription of *LHCA* or *RCA* has not yet been established. Curiously, sequences closely related to the CCA1-binding consensus are also found in the functionally defined minimal evening-specific *AtGRP7/CCR2* (142) and *CAT3* promoters (TP Michael & CR McClung, unpublished). Again, the functional significance of these elements has not been established, but that CCA1 binding sites are in promoters that are transcribed nearly 180° out of phase suggests that the mechanism by which the phase of transcription is determined will not necessarily be the simple solution of a series of phase-specific transcriptional activators.

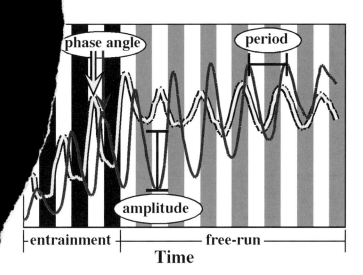

Figure 1 Characteristics of circadian rhythms illustrated using the circadian oscillation in luciferase activity of Arabidopsis seedlings carrying either a *CAB2::LUC* transgene (yellow) or a *CAT3::LUC* transgene (orange). Under entraining conditions (12 h light:12 h dark, indicated by the white and black bars, respectively) the rhythms exhibit 24 h periods. The peak in luciferase activity for each rhythm maintains constant phase relationship with dawn. The peak in *CAB2::LUC* activity occurs ~4 6 h after dawn whereas the peak in *CAT3::LUC* activity occurs ~10 12 hours after dawn. The amplitude of the rhythm is defined as one half of the peak to trough difference. Both rhythms persist when the seedlings are released into continuous conditions (constant dim light), although the period lengthens to reveal the endogenous free-running period of ~25 h. This results in the peaks in luciferase activity shifting with respect to subjective dawn as defined by the entraining 12:12 light:dark cycle (indicated by the gray and white bars, respectively).

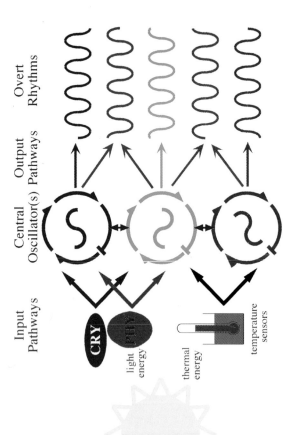

Figure 2 A simple (linear) conceptual model of a simple circadian system consisting of a set of input (entrainment) pathways, multiple central oscillators, and sets of output pathways. Entraining stimuli include light, mediated through phytochromes (PHY) and cryptochromes (C... perature, and imbibition (not shown). Although the input pathways are drawn as discrete linear pathways, there are cryptochromes as well as interaction among them and their downstream signaling pathways. Each central oscill... ing positive and negative components that yields a self-sustaining oscillation with a period of approximat... cate possible coupling between the oscillators. Multiple output pathways are drawn as each rece... Although not indicated, different oscillators may drive separate rhythms with distinct perio... interaction among them is not known, although some cross talk among output pathw... oscillators whereas others may receive input from more than one oscillator.

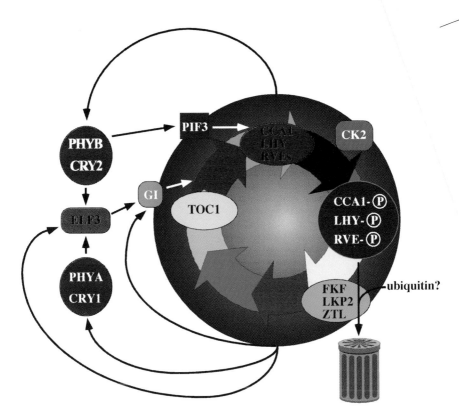

Figure 3 A speculative model of an Arabidopsis circadian clock. Light input via phytochromes and cryptochromes (PHYA/CRY1 and PHYB/CRY2 complexes are shown, although other configurations are likely to occur) is mediated through ELF3 and GI, or through PIF3. PHYA-PIF3 and PHYB-PIF3 interactions are known to occur. PIF3 binds to CCA1 and LHY promoters and possibly to other targets in the clock. The pathway downstream of GI is not known. Although the input pathways are drawn as discrete linear pathways, there may be interaction among them. For simplicity, a single central oscillator is illustrated with a number of putative oscillator components indicated. CCA1/LHY/RVE and FKF/LKP2/ZTL are clustered, although there is no evidence that they form molecular complexes. Components on the internal circular arrows oscillate in mRNA or protein abundance. *FKF* but not *ZTL* mRNA oscillates, so FKF is indicated closest to the circular arrows. CCA1 and LHY are phosphorylated by CK2, which may make them substrates for the F-box proteins (ZTL, FKF and LKP2) and target them for ubiquitination and degradation by the proteasome (trash can). Output pathways emanate from the oscillator to input components known to be regulated by the clock at transcriptional, mRNA abundance or protein abundance levels.

Not all regulation of gene expression is transcriptional. In addition to the oscillation in phosphorylation and dephosphorylation of PEPc in CAM plants (111), sucrose phosphate synthase activity in tomato is regulated circadianly by a protein phosphatase (63). The rhythm in nitrate reductase (NR) mRNA abundance in Arabidopsis reflects posttranscriptional control, as shown by the failure to detect transcriptional oscillations in nuclear run-on experiments (117). In tomato, the circadian oscillation in NR mRNA is blocked by a protein phosphatase inhibitor, although the precise targets of phosphorylation and dephosphorylation remain unknown (64).

ENTRAINMENT (INPUT)

Circadian rhythms persist in the absence of external time cues but are entrainable to the environment. It has long been clear that clock response to environmental stimuli varies over the circadian cycle. A plot of the magnitude of the phase shift resulting from the application of a given stimulus at a series of discrete times spanning a circadian cycle yields the phase response curve (PRC), a powerful tool with which to study the circadian oscillator (59, 60).

Light

Although many environmental parameters provide stimulus to the clock, the most potent and best-characterized entraining stimulus in plants is light. Light perception in plants has been studied and reviewed in detail (17, 26, 82, 105, 108). The Arabidopsis genome includes five phytochrome genes (*PHYA-PHYE*) and two cryptochrome genes (*CRY1* and *CRY2*). There are other blue light receptors, including phototropin (NPH1) and possibly zeaxanthin, thought to be the stomatal blue light receptor (10).

Period length is inversely related to light intensity (parametric, or continuous, entrainment) in plants and animals that are active in the light (3). In Arabidopsis, PHYA and PHYB as well as CRY1 and CRY2 contribute to the establishment of period length (100, 139a). PHYB is important at high intensities of red light whereas PHYA functions at low intensities (139a). CRY1 functions at high intensities of blue light and both PHYA and CRY1 function at low intensities (139a). Double mutant studies also demonstrate a role for CRY2 in the establishment of period, although that role is redundantly specified by CRY1 (PF Devlin & SA Kay, personal communication). PHYA and CRY1 interact at the molecular level and CRY1 can be phosphorylated by PHYA (2). Direct interaction between PHYB and CRY2 in vivo has been established by Fluorescence Resonance Energy Transfer (91a).

Red light pulses (nonparametric, or discrete, entrainment) phase shift clock-controlled gene expression by a very low fluence PHYA response (73, 104). Far red light pulses phase shift in a PHYA-dependent fashion (160). A bacteriophytochrome, CikA, provides light input to the cyanobacterial clock, and *cikA* mutants show dramatic alterations in phase angle of multiple gene expression rhythms (135). Similarly, novel alleles of Arabidopsis PHYB and CRY1 do not affect the period but instead alter the phase angle of multiple rhythms, indicating that PHYB and CRY1 contribute to the establishment of circadian phase as well as period (PA Salomé & CR McClung, unpublished). Light phase response curves are available for a number of angiosperms (60). Two types of light phase response curves have recently been generated in Arabidopsis. High-intensity red light pulses given upon a dim red background shift the phase of *LHCB::LUC* transcription (S Panda & SA Kay, personal communication). *AtGRP7/CCR2* transcription oscillates in extended dark without damping (144), which has allowed the generation of a phase response curve for pulses of red, blue, or white light over a dark background (S Panda & SA Kay, personal communication).

One mechanism by which the sensitivity of the oscillator to light might vary over the circadian cycle would be clock regulation of components of the light input pathway. Indeed, *PHYB* expression (both mRNA accumulation and transcription, as monitored with *PHYB::LUC* fusions) is rhythmic in tobacco and Arabidopsis, although it is important to note that bulk PHYB protein abundance does not oscillate (9). Recently, this result has been extended to other photoreceptors: In Arabidopsis, expression of *PHYA*, *PHYC*, and *CRY1* shows robust circadian oscillations at both mRNA abundance and transcriptional levels. Expression of *CRY2* is not rhythmic whereas *PHYD* and *PHYE* expression is, at most, weakly rhythmic (L Kozma-Bognár & F Nagy, personal communication). That the clock may regulate its own sensitivity to entraining stimuli complicates use of the PRC to probe the state of the oscillator.

The understanding of the downstream signaling pathways from PHY and CRY is incomplete. Various signaling intermediates (e.g. cGMP and Ca^{2+}-calmodulin) and phosphorylation are implicated (10, 26, 82), and a number of signaling components downstream from the photoreceptors have been identified (10, 26, 82). In particular, red-illuminated PHYB (PfrB) interacts with PIF3, a bHLH protein that binds directly to the G box in a number of phytochrome-regulated promoters (91), which establishes that light signaling pathways can be unexpectedly short. This is relevant to light input to circadian clocks because the targets of PIF3 include the promoters of *CCA1* and *LATE ELONGATED HYPOCOTYL (LHY)* (91), two putative oscillator components (see below). The plant G box (CACGTG) is related to the animal E box (CANNTG) targeted by heterodimeric transcription factors of Drosophila and mammalian central oscillators (29, 46). However, the binding of PIF3 to G boxes of light and clock-regulated promoters is likely to represent only part of a complicated signaling network entailing multiple pathways and targets. For example, it has recently been established that PHYA and PHYB signaling target distinct regions of the Arabidopsis *LHCB1*2* promoter (160). Similarly, phytochrome and circadian regulation target distinct elements of the tomato *LHCA3* gene (120).

The timing of flowering in many species is regulated by photoperiod as well as by light quality and vernalization (81, 138). Bünning (14) hypothesized that circadian timekeeping was essential for photoperiodic time measurement and many mutations that affect circadian rhythms in gene expression and leaf movement also affect flowering timing (81, 138). Conversely, flowering timing mutants constitute a reservoir of potential circadian clock mutants. Null mutations of *FLOWER-ING LOCUS C*, in the autonomous flowering pathway, confer early flowering and shorten the circadian period in leaf movement (147). Two mutations in the Arabidopsis photoperiodic pathway, *early flowering 3 (elf3)* and the late flowering *gigantea (gi)*, confer defects in the circadian timing and define components of the light input pathway.

elf3 loss-of-function alleles yield early flowering, hypocotyl elongation, and conditional arrhythmicity in continuous light (53). *ELF3* is a *CCG* encoding a nuclear protein that contains a glutamine-rich motif, suggesting it is a transcription factor; both mRNA and protein abundance oscillate (84). Genetic experiments suggest substantial redundancy in ELF3 and PHYB function (123). Interestingly, ELF3 interacts with PHYB in the yeast two-hybrid assay (21) and plays a key role in the regulation of light input to the clock (95a).

GI is a *CCG* whose transcript abundance oscillates with a circadian rhythm that is altered in a number of mutants affected in clock function, including *elf3*. *gi* mutants are altered in leaf movement and gene expression rhythms of *GI* itself and of other *CCGs*, including *LHCB, LHY*, and *CCA1* (38, 114). In *gi-2*, a null allele, the period of leaf movement is shortened but the period of gene expression rhythms gradually lengthens (114). The period shortening effect of *gi-1* on gene expression rhythms is less severe in extended dark than in continuous light, and the extension of period length seen in light of decreasing fluence is less pronounced in *gi-1* than in wild type. Collectively, these data are consistent with GI acting in light input rather than in a central oscillator (114). *gi* was independently identified on the basis of a defect in inhibition of hypocotyl elongation in red but not in far red light, which implicates GI in PHYB signaling (54). GI is localized to the nucleoplasm, which is consistent with a role in early PHYB signaling and in the transcriptional regulation of *CCGs*, although the GI sequence lacks any motifs that might suggest it is a transcription factor (54). However, the effects of loss of GI function on hypocotyl elongation are the same as seen in *phyB* loss of function, which suggests that GI is a positive mediator of PHYB signaling yet *gi* mutants are late flowering, which is opposite to the early flowering phenotype of *phyB* null alleles. This may suggest that GI plays different roles at different developmental stages or may simply indicate our incomplete knowledge of the signaling pathways leading to the hypocotyl and flowering responses (54).

Temperature

Although the circadian oscillator is temperature compensated, temperature pulses or temperature steps are potent entraining stimuli. Temperature pulse PRCs have been generated for several plants (60). Temperature cycles entrain Arabidopsis rhythms in *LHCB* (141) and *CAT3* transcription (TP Michael & CR McClung, unpublished). Curiously, the temperature step associated with release from stratification at 4°C to growth at 22°C was ineffective in phase resetting in Arabidopsis

(163), suggesting a refractory period before temperature is capable of entraining the Arabidopsis oscillator. This is quite similar to observations that a light-insensitive circadian oscillator is detected shortly after germination of tobacco and Arabidopsis (72, 73).

Imbibition and Others

Although germinating seedlings are refractory to temperature and light input, the timing of imbibition (hydration) of the dried seed serves as a novel entraining stimulus synchronizing the clocks within populations of Arabidopsis seedlings (163). Other entraining stimuli that have been used to generate PRCs in various plants include abscisic acid, cAMP, and various antimetabolites and amino acid analogs (60).

THE OSCILLATOR: A Negative Feedback Loop

Genetic and molecular biological analyses in a variety of systems suggest that the central oscillator is a negative feedback loop (29, 57, 161) or, as emerging evidence from eukaryotic systems indicates, two interlocked feedback loops (42, 80, 137). Rhythmic transcription of key clock genes is inhibited by the nuclear (in eukaryotes) accumulation of the protein products of these genes (29, 94). For example, in Neurospora, FREQUENCY (FRQ) negatively autoregulates by preventing its own transcriptional activation by the WHITE COLLAR (WC-1/WC-2) heterodimer. However, FRQ also positively regulates rhythmic WC-1 translation from nonoscillating *WC-1* mRNA (80). Protein stability, phosphorylation, ubiquitination, and degradation via the proteasome also play roles in the intertwined negative feedback loops (29, 57, 94).

This leaves the clear expectation that the plant clock will emerge as a negative feedback loop or, more likely, interlocked loops, although this model almost certainly represents an oversimplification (57, 78, 96, 125). There is a great deal of conservation among the components of the fly and mammalian clocks (29) but the PAS domain, a protein-protein interaction domain (149), is the only element that has been found in all clock systems. Happily, a growing number of putative components of plant clocks have recently been identified. No clear picture has yet emerged, but it is apparent that many of the themes of other clock systems are conserved in plants (Figure 3; see color insert). At present, two myb transcription factors, CCA1 and LHY, and a pseudo response regulator, TOC1, are strong candidates as canonical clock components of interlocked feedback loops, although the molecular details of these loops remain unknown.

Single Myb Domain DNA-Binding Proteins

CCA1 and LHY are closely related single Myb domain DNA-binding proteins (134, 155, 156). Additional members of this family, termed REVEILLE (RVE), have been identified, and a single Myb domain related to that of CCA1 has been identified in an Arabidopsis pseudo response regulator, APRR2 (90). *CCA1, LHY* (134, 156), and at least some *RVEs* (CR Andersson & SA Kay, personal communication) are *CCGs* and oscillate at both mRNA and protein levels. CCA1 binds in circadian fashion to a short element of the *LHCB1*1* (*CAB2*) promoter sufficient to confer phytochrome responsiveness and circadian transcription. Overexpression of CCA1 or LHY or several RVEs results in elongated hypocotyls, late flowering, and abolishes several circadian rhythms, including *LHCB* transcription and leaf movement. Consistent with roles as components of negative feedback loops, both CCA1 and LHY negatively autoregulate, although the mechanism is unknown (134, 156). CCA1 loss of function shortens the circadian period of several *CCGs* but does not confer arrhythmicity, suggesting that there is redundancy of CCA1-specified clock functions (45). Thus CCA1/LHY/RVE may represent components of the central oscillator as well as components of the output pathway by which the clock regulates transcription (134, 156). That PIF3 binds to the *CCA1* and *LHY* promoters provides a mechanism for phytochrome input into the clock (91).

CCA1 DNA binding is affected by phosphorylation by casein kinase II (CK2) (145), which also phosphorylates LHY in vitro (146). Phosphorylation by casein kinase I is critical in Drosophila and mammalian clocks (29, 88, 161), and autophosphorylation of the cyanobacterial clock protein, KaiC, is essential for rhythmicity (57). Overexpression of the regulatory CKB3 subunit increases CK2 activity, which would be presumed to enhance CCA1 activity. However, CKB3 overexpression results in period shortening and early flowering, similar to that seen in plants with reduced CCA1 activity (146). This apparent inconsistency probably indicates our incomplete understanding of the role of CCA1/LHY/RVE proteins in the circadian system. For example, promoters transcribed at different phases (e.g. *LHCB* versus *CAT3* or *AtGRP7/CCR2*) contain very similar CCA1 binding targets. The specification of circadian phase may entail differential binding by different members of this family of proteins at distinct circadian phases. Alternatively, phase specification may involve differential modification (quite likely by phosphorylation but other modifications are possible) of family members at distinct circadian phases. There may also be different interacting partners recruited to the promoters that modulate CCA1/LHY/RVE function. Finally, it has long been known that Drosophila Krüppel, for example, can act either as an activator or as a repressor of transcription when present at different concentrations (133). Clearly, a great deal remains to be learned about CCA1, LHY, and their relatives.

TOC Genes

A genetic screen on the basis of alterations in rhythmic expression of a *CAB2* (*LHCB*)::*LUC* transgene in Arabidopsis has identified a series of *timing of CAB* (*toc*) mutations that disrupt clock function (97). *toc1-1* shortens the period of multiple rhythms, including *LHCB* transcription, leaf movement, and stomatal conductance, and results in early flowering (141). Interestingly, the early flowering phenotype of *toc1* is rescued in 21 h light:dark cycles that mimic the shortened *toc1* period (144). The period-shortening effect of *toc1-1* is independent of light intensity and is seen in extended darkness, which argues that TOC1 does not act in light input. *TOC1* mRNA abundance oscillates in continuous light, peaking late in the day; the period of this oscillation is shortened by the *toc1-1* mutation, indicating that TOC1 feeds back to control its own oscillation (144). Collectively, these data suggest that TOC1 is likely to be a component of an oscillator, although it is curious that *TOC1* mRNA oscillations damp rapidly in extended darkness (144), yet a number of gene expression rhythms, including *AtGRP7/CCR2* (76, 144) and *CAT3* (164; TP Michael & CR McClung, unpublished), persist robustly in the dark.

TOC1 encodes an Arabidopsis pseudo-response regulator (APRR1) (90, 144), which implicates signal transduction through two-component systems (128) in clock function. Typically, a sensor histidine kinase responds to an environmental stimulus, autophosphorylates, and transfers the phosphate to a response regulator, which then effects a response. However, TOC1, like other APRRs, lacks the invariant phosphor-accepting Asp residue and is unlikely to function in the conventional His-Asp relay (90, 144). Nonetheless, this suggests a mechanistic link to cyanobacterial clocks (57, 61), in which the sensory histidine kinase, SasA, interacts with the oscillator component KaiC (58).

TOC1 also has a carboxy-terminal motif seen in the CONSTANS family of transcriptional activators (121) and an acidic region often found in transcriptional activators. TOC1/APRR1 interacts with a PIF3-like protein (90), which suggests a mechanism by which the clock might regulate acute induction by light or gate its sensitivity to light input (98, 163). Moreover, TOC1/APRR1 was also identified as an ABSCISIC ACID INSENSITIVE 3-interacting protein (77), which might indicate an interaction of the clock with abscisic acid (ABA) as an input or provide clock regulation of ABA responses.

The gene identified by a second of these *toc* mutants, *ZEITLUPE* (*ZTL*, identified as *toc7*), has recently been cloned (70a, 140) and is a member of a three-gene family including *FKF* (*FLAVIN-BINDING KELCH REPEAT F-BOX*) (109) and *LKP2* (*LOV DOMAIN KELCH PROTEIN*). *ztl* mutants exhibit lengthened period length (140) whereas *fkf* mutants exhibit altered waveform in *CCA1* and *LHCB* mRNA oscillations (109). Both mutants flower late. *FKF* but not *ZTL* mRNA abundance oscillates with an evening-specific maximum. These proteins have an amino-terminal PAS (also called LOV, for light oxygen voltage) domain most similar to those of NPH1, the phototropism blue light receptor (19), an unusual phytochrome from a fern (112) and Neurospora WC-1 (4). In NPH1, this domain binds the flavin chromophore (20), suggesting that these proteins may serve as photoreceptors or on a light input pathway. This is supported by the fluence rate dependence of the *ztl* phenotype (140).

ZTL, FKF, and LKP2 also contain multiple kelch repeats, which define a propeller-like structure that functions in protein-protein interaction (1). A significant clue to the function of these three proteins is that they each contain an F-box, a domain that recruits target proteins to E3 ubiquitination complexes (115).

Although a role in ubiquitination has not been functionally established for ZTL, FKF, or LKP2, such evidence has been collected for other plant F-box proteins that function in flower development (UFO; 131) and auxin responses (TIR; 44). That the ZTL/FKF/LKP2 proteins are involved in the light-regulated ubiquitination and degradation of critical clock proteins is an attractive hypothesis. For example, Drosophila TIM is degraded in the light by an ubiquitin-proteasome mechanism; TIM degradation is correlated with changes in phosphorylation (106), which is required for substrate recognition by F-box proteins (22). As described above, Arabidopsis CCA1 is phosphorylated by CK2, a serine-threonine kinase (145, 146). Is phosphorylation and degradation of CCA1, LHY or another key target part of the circadian oscillation (Figure 3) and might this explain the phenotypic results (short period and late flowering) of CKB3 overexpression?

WHEN DOES TIMING BEGIN?

The circadian clock regulates multiple outputs throughout plant growth and development. How early in development can one demonstrate clock activity? In mammals, the circadian clock starts to function during late fetal and early postnatal life and is entrained by maternal signals (124). In zebrafish, mRNA abundance of the clock gene *Per3* exhibits circadian oscillations throughout embryonic development (as early as 40 h postfertilization), although rhythmic expression of an output gene, *Rev-erbα*, exhibits a developmental delay (25). In plants, a circadian rhythm has been detected in the respiration rate of dry onion seeds in continuous dark (13), although we have been unable to detect similar rhythms in Arabidopsis (EV Kearns & CR McClung, unpublished). However, a variety of studies confirm that a circadian clock is functioning upon germination. For example, circadian oscillations have been detected in transcription and mRNA abundance of a number of genes in both etiolated and light-grown seedlings (33), and as little as a single light pulse is sufficient to induce circadian oscillations of *LHCB* mRNA abundance in etiolated seedlings (33). Moreover, light inducibility of *LHCB* and *CAT2* in etiolated Arabidopsis seedlings is gated by the clock (98, 163). As mentioned above, imbibition entrains Arabidopsis seedlings, although it is not known whether it initiates clock function or synchronizes oscillators that were functioning embryonically (163). Nonetheless, this means that the circadian clock is running from the time of imbibition. Interestingly, temperature steps capable of entraining the clocks of older plants (76, 141) have no effect in these young seedlings (163). It is well established that seed germination of many species is affected by light treatment mediated through phytochrome. Thus, one of the critical sensory transduction systems that provides input to the clock is functional in the seed. However, phytochrome-regulated expression of *LHCB* genes in Arabidopsis seedlings is preceded by a period in which expression is light independent (12). *LHCB* genes in very young tobacco seedlings are regulated by two circadian rhythms with distinct phases of maximal transcription and mRNA accumulation, only one of which is phytochrome responsive (72, 73). The light-independent oscillation is expressed from germination, and short light pulses from 12 to 44 h after sowing induce a second oscillation without affecting the first light-independent oscillation. Repeated red light pulses given 60 h after sowing synchronize the two rhythms, but earlier pulses that induced the second oscillation fail to synchronize the two oscillations. Apparently, the light-insensitive clock of very young seedlings either acquires light-responsiveness during development or is supplanted by the light-responsive clock that becomes active after germination (73).

HOW MANY CLOCKS?

Considerable evidence supports the existence of multiple oscillators in multicellular plants. Most of the evidence takes the form of multiple rhythms running with different periods (internal desynchronization), which was demonstrated in *Phaseolus coccineus* (92) and *Chenopodium rubrum* (70) in the 1970s. In *Phaseolus vulgaris*, rhythms in CO_2 assimilation and stomatal aperture exhibit a different period from the rhythm in leaf movement (52). Similarly, in Arabidopsis the free-running periods in leaf movement and *LHCB* (*CAB*) expression are different, although both are shortened by the *toc1-1* mutation (97). Moreover, the *gi-2* mutation shortens the period in leaf movement but lengthens the period in gene expression (114). In extended darkness, the period of *LHCB* transcription lengthens to ~30 h whereas the oscillations in *AtGRP7/CCR2* and *AtGRP8/CCR1* (15, 144), and *CAT3* (164; TP Michael & CR McClung, unpublished) mRNA abundance and transcription retain 24 h periods, again suggesting that they are driven by distinct oscillators. Tobacco seedlings exhibit rhythms in cytosolic Ca^{2+} and *LHCB* transcription with different periods (127). In each case, it is difficult to establish that these two rhythms are expressed in the same cells, but it is nonetheless clear that the rhythms are responding to distinct circadian oscillators. Although these data indicate that distinct oscillators drive the rhythms with different periods, they cannot distinguish between the presence of two distinct molecular oscillators within a single cell or a single oscillator that exhibits organ- or cell type–specific differences in period. The demonstration of two oscillators within a single cell is not simple, but has been achieved in the dinoflagellate, *Gonyaulax polyedra* (103, 126). First, these authors established in long time courses that two distinct rhythms with different periods actually showed phase crossings (126) and second, they showed that the two rhythms could be independently reset by a single stimulus (103).

A recent study has unambiguously demonstrated that explants of different organs retain rhythmicity in *LHCB*, *CHS*, and *PHYB* transcription in culture, establishing firmly the existence of multiple self-sustaining and entrainable circadian oscillators (150). Furthermore, the two cotyledons of intact Arabidopsis and tobacco seedlings could be entrained to novel phases that are antiphase to one another and, in tobacco, distinct from the initial phase retained by the shoot apex, indicating that the clocks were not coupled. Similar results were obtained with two primary tobacco leaves or with roots versus aerial tissues of Arabidopsis. Collectively, these experiments argue compellingly for autonomy of the clocks of different organs and tissues.

The circadian rhythms of cyanobacteria and of unicellular eukaryotes, such as *Chlamydomonas* and *Gonyaulax*, make it clear that a circadian clock (or clocks) can exist within a single cell and several mammalian cell types retain a functional circadian oscillator in culture (5, 30, 151). Thus, we can assume that every cell in a multicellular plant potentially contains a clock. Are these clocks coordinated or are they cell-autonomous? Thain et al (150) showed that distal and proximal areas of a single primary tobacco leaf could be entrained to distinct phases! This suggests that clock autonomy at all levels of the circadian system, from photoperception through gene expression output rhythms, exists at a cellular level. However, the authors note that short-range signaling like that induced by phytochrome (8) remains to be addressed. Nonetheless, there quite clearly is no systemic phototransduction signal that coordinates the plant circadian system on an organismal scale. This contrasts sharply with the situation in animals, where a central neural oscillator (e.g. the mammalian suprachiasmatic nucleus or the ventral lateral brain neurons of Drosophila) regulates behavioral rhythms (29). In recent years, it has become clear that peripheral tissues of a variety of animals, including Drosophila, iguanas, and zebrafish, contain multiple additional clocks that can be independently entrained in culture (41, 119, 152, 158). In vivo, these peripheral clocks are probably entrained by coupling pathways from the central neural oscillator (159).

ARE CIRCADIAN CLOCKS OF ADAPTIVE SIGNIFICANCE?

Why are circadian rhythms ubiquitous? Is adaptive fitness enhanced by the synchronization of an organism's internal clock with the diurnal cycle imposed by its environment? The "escape from light" hypothesis (118) posits advantage in phasing sunlight-sensitive cellular events to the night. Cell division in unicellular organisms is frequently gated to the dawn, with DNA replication occurring in the preceding night (31). The adaptive fitness of aspects of circadian biology such as dawn anticipation has been addressed by recent studies with cyanobacteria (113) and green algae (110).

Mutants of the cyanobacterium *Synechococcus elongatus* PCC 7942 with alterations in period length have been identified on the basis of the rhythmic expression of a photosynthetic gene fused to bacterial luciferase (74). Strains with wild type (25 h), short (23 h), or long (30 h) period grow at essentially the same rate in pure culture in either continuous light or in light:dark cycles. However, when these strains are mixed and competed against each other in light:dark cycles of 22, 24, or 30 h, in each case the strain whose period most closely matches that of the imposed cycle rapidly eliminates the competitor (113). Although the mechanism of this fitness enhancement in *Synechococcus* remains poorly understood (61), the "escape from light" hypothesis has received strong support from recent studies with the green alga *Chlamydomonas*. *Chlamydomonas* exhibits circadian rhythms in cell division and in sensitivity to UV irradiation (110). Maximal UV sensitivity occurs at the end of the day and beginning of the night, coincident with DNA division. This is entirely consistent with the idea that circadian clocks evolved under selective pressure to time DNA replication to the night. The widespread role of cryptochrome in circadian systems of mammals, flies, and plants is also consistent with this reasoning. Cryptochromes are related to and probably evolved from DNA photolyases, which play a critical role in the repair of UV-induced DNA damage (18). Although it remains speculative, it seems plausible that an ancestral protein that contributed to the daily repair of UV-induced DNA damage was recruited into the circadian system.

CONCLUDING REMARKS

The study of plant circadian clocks has matured in recent years and a great deal of progress has been made, particularly in the identification of molecular components. The next and more difficult phase will be to assemble the components into a coherent molecular model. Obviously, the relatively simple models of the circadian system presented in Figures 2 and 3 are inadequate. Some clock functions are redundantly specified, as shown by the loss-of-function *cca1* and *lhy* alleles. In addition, there are likely to be many interconnections among both input and output pathways. We now have good evidence that some genes encoding light input pathway components are themselves *CCGs* whose abundance and, probably, activity are modulated over the circadian cycle; outputs can feed back to affect input to the clock. Components can play multiple roles on input and output pathways, and perhaps in the central oscillator(s). Moreover, we do not yet have reliable criteria with which to unambiguously assign molecules to roles as input, output, or oscillator components (37, 96, 125). Indeed, even the concept of a single central oscillator is inadequate, as it is certain that a single cell can contain two self-sustaining circadian oscillators (103, 126) as well as non-self-sustaining oscillators (49), and there is good evidence in plants as well as in animals for tissue- and cell-specific oscillators that can run independently (150). We can anticipate this breakneck pace of advancement in our understanding of plant clocks will continue; the timing could not be better.

ACKNOWLEDGMENTS

I thank many colleagues for sharing unpublished information and apologize to those whose work could not be cited due to space limitations. I particularly thank Todd Michael, Patrice Salomé, Tom Jack, and Mary Lou Guerinot for helpful discussion. Work in my lab is supported by grants from the National Science Foundation (MCB 9723482 and IBN-9817603).

Visit the Annual Reviews home page at www.AnnualReviews.org

LITERATURE CITED

1. Adams J, Kelso R, Cooley L. 2000. The kelch repeat superfamily of proteins: propellers of cell function. *Trends Cell Biol.* 10:17–24
2. Ahmad M, Jarillo JA, Smirnova O, Cashmore AR. 1998. The CRY1 blue light photoreceptor of *Arabidopsis* interacts with phytochrome A in vitro. *Mol. Cell* 1:939–48
3. Aschoff J. 1960. Exogenous and endogenous components in circadian rhythms. *Cold Spring Harbor Symp. Quant. Biol.* XXV:11–28
4. Ballario P, Macino G. 1997. White collar proteins: PASsing the light signal in *Neurospora crassa*. *Trends Microbiol.* 5:458–62
5. Balsalobre A, Damiola F, Schibler U. 1998. A serum shock induces circadian gene expression in mammalian tissue culture cells. *Cell* 93:929–37
6. Barnes SA, McGrath RB, Chua N-H. 1997. Light signal transduction in plants. *Trends Cell Biol.* 7:21–26
7. Baum G, Long JC, Jenkins GI, Trewavas AJ. 1999. Stimulation of the blue light phototropic receptor NPH1 causes a transient increase in cytosolic Ca^{2+}. *Proc. Natl. Acad. Sci. USA* 96:13554–59
8. Bischoff F, Millar AJ, Kay SA, Furuya M. 1997. Phytochrome-induced intercellular signalling activates cab::luciferase gene expression. *Plant J.* 12:839–49
9. Bognár LK, Hall A, Ádám É, Thain SC, Nagy F, Millar AJ. 1999. The circadian clock controls the expression pattern of the circadian input photoreceptor, phytochrome B. *Proc. Natl. Acad. Sci. USA* 96:14652–57
10. Briggs WR, Huala E. 1999. Blue-light photoreceptors in higher plants. *Annu. Rev. Cell Dev. Biol.* 15:33–62
11. Brinker M, Jäschke K, Klaff P, Wissel K,

Menzel H, et al. 2000. Different *Lhc* mRNA stabilities and diurnal/circadian mRNA accumulation patterns in angiosperm and gymnosperm plant species. *Plant Mol. Biol.* In press
12. Brusslan JA, Tobin EM. 1992. Light-independent developmental regulation of *cab* gene expression in *Arabidopsis thaliana* seedlings. *Proc. Natl. Acad. Sci. USA* 89:7791–95
13. Bryant TR. 1972. Gas exchange in dry seeds: circadian rhythmicity in the absence of DNA replication, transcription, and translation. *Science* 178:634–36
14. Bünning E. 1936. Die endogene Tagesrhythmik als Grundlage der photoperiodischen Reaktion. *Ber. Dtsch. Bot. Ges.* 54:590–607
15. Carpenter CD, Kreps JA, Simon AE. 1994. Genes encoding glycine-rich *Arabidopsis thaliana* proteins with RNA-binding motifs are influenced by cold treatment and an endogenous circadian rhythm. *Plant Physiol.* 104:1015–25
16. Carré IA, Kay SA. 1995. Multiple DNA-protein complexes at a circadian-regulated promoter element. *Plant Cell* 7:2039–51
17. Casal JJ. 2000. Phytochromes, cryptochromes, phototropin: photoreceptor interactions in plants. *Photochem. Photobiol.* 71:1–11
18. Cashmore AR, Jarillo JA, Wu Y-J, Liu D. 1999. Cryptochromes: blue light receptors for plants and animals. *Science* 284:760–65
19. Christie JM, Reymond P, Powell GK, Bernasconi P, Raibekas AA, et al. 1998. *Arabidopsis* NPH1: a flavoprotein with the properties of a photoreceptor for phototropism. *Science* 282:1698–701
20. Christie JM, Salomon M, Nozue K, Wada M, Briggs WR. 1999. LOV (light, oxygen, or voltage) domains of the blue-light

photoreceptor phototropin (nph1): binding sites for the chromophore flavin mononucleotide. *Proc. Natl. Acad. Sci. USA* 96: 8779–83

21. Covington MF, Liu XL, Kay SA, Wagner DR. 2000. *ELF3 gates input to the circadian clock. Int. Conf. Arabidopsis Res., 11th*, Abstr. 428

22. Craig KL, Tyers M. 1999. The F-box: a new motif for ubiquitin dependent proteolysis in cell cycle regulation and signal transduction. *Prog. Biophys. Mol. Biol.* 72: 299–328

23. de Candolle AP. 1832. *Physiologie Vegetale*. Paris: Bechet Jeune

24. de Mairan J. 1729. Observation botanique. *Hist. Acad. R. Sci.* 35–36

25. Delaunay F, Thisse C, Marchand O, Laudet V, Thisse B. 2000. An inherited functional circadian clock in zebrafish embryos. *Science* 289:297–300

26. Deng X-W, Quail PH. 1999. Signalling in light-controlled development. *Semin. Cell Dev. Biol* 10:121–29

27. Dowson-Day MJ, Millar AJ. 1999. Circadian dysfunction causes aberrant hypocotyl elongation patterns in Arabidopsis. *Plant J.* 17:63–71

28. Duhamel duMonceau HL. 1759. *La Physique des Arbres*. Paris: Guerin & Delatour

29. Dunlap JC. 1999. Molecular bases for circadian clocks. *Cell* 96:271–90

30. Earnest DJ, Liang F-Q, Ratcliff M, Cassone VM. 1999. Immortal time: circadian clock properties of rat suprachiasmatic cell lines. *Science* 283:693–95

31. Edmunds LN. 1988. *Cellular and Molecular Bases of Biological Clocks*. New York: Springer-Verlag

32. Engelmann W, Johnsson A. 1998. Rhythms in organ movement. See Ref. 89, pp. 35–50

33. Fejes E, Nagy F. 1998. Molecular analysis of circadian clock-regulated gene expression in plants: features of the 'output' pathways. See Ref. 89, pp. 99–118

34. Finlayson SA, Lee I-J, Morgan PW. 1998. Phytochrome B and the regulation of circa-

dian ethylene production in sorghum. *Plant Physiol.* 116:17–25

35. Finlayson SA, Lee I-J, Mullet JE, Morgan PW. 1999. The mechanism of rhythmic ethylene production in sorghum. The role of phytochrome B and simulated shading. *Plant Physiol.* 119:1083–89

36. Foster KR, Morgan PW. 1995. Genetic regulation of development in *Sorghum bicolor*. IX. The ma_3^R allele disrupts diurnal control of gibberellin biosynthesis. *Plant Physiol.* 108:337–43

37. Foster RG, Lucas RJ. 1999. Clocks, criteria and critical genes. *Nat. Genet.* 22:217–19

38. Fowler S, Lee K, Onouchi H, Samach A, Richardson K, et al. 1999. *GIGANTEA*: a circadian clock-controlled gene that regulates photoperiodic flowering in *Arabidopsis* and encodes a protein with several membrane-spanning domains. *EMBO J.* 18:4679–88

39. Frohnmeyer H, Bowler C, Zhu J-K, Yamagata H, Schäfer E, Chua N-H. 1998. Different roles for calcium and calmodulin in phytochrome and UV-regulated expression of chalcone synthase. *Plant J.* 13:763–72

40. Fukuda M, Hasezawa S, Asai N, Nakajima N, Kondo N. 1998. Dynamic organization of microtubules in guard cells of *Vicia faba* L. with diurnal cycle. *Plant Cell Physiol.* 39:80–86

41. Giebultowicz JM, Stanewsky R, Hall JC, Hege DM. 2000. Transplanted Drosophila excretory tubules maintain circadian clock cycling out of phase with the host. *Curr. Biol* 10:107–10

42. Glossop NRJ, Lyons LC, Hardin PE. 1999. Interlocked feedback loops within the *Drosophila* circadian oscillator. *Science* 286:766–68

43. Gómez LA, Simón E. 1995. Circadian rhythm of *Robinia pseudoacacia* leaflet movements: role of calcium and phytochrome. *Photochem. Photobiol.* 61:210–15

44. Gray WM, Estelle M. 2000. Function of the ubiquitin-proteasome pathway in auxin response. *Trends Biochem. Sci.* 25:133–38

45. Green RM, Tobin EM. 1999. Loss of the circadian clock-associated protein 1 in *Arabidopsis* results in altered clock-regulated gene expression. *Proc. Natl. Acad. Sci. USA* 96:4176–79

46. Hao H, Glossop NRJ, Lyons L, Qiu J, Morrish B, et al. 1999. The 69 bp circadian regulatory sequence (CRS) mediates *per*-like developmental, spatial, and circadian expression and behavioral rescue in *Drosophila. J. Neurosci.* 19:987–94

46a. Harmer SL, Hogenesch JB, Straume M, Chang H-S, Han B, et al. 2000. Orchestrated transcription of key pathways in Arabidopsis by the circadian clock. *Science.* In press

47. Hartwell J, Gill A, Nimmo GA, Wilkins MB, Jenkins GI, Nimmo HG. 1999. Phosphoenolpyruvate carboxylase kinase is a novel protein kinase regulated at the level of expression. *Plant J.* 20:333–42

48. Hartwell J, Smith LH, Wilkins MB, Jenkins GI, Nimmo HG. 1996. Higher plant phosphoenolpyruvate carboxylase kinase is regulated at the level of translatable mRNA in response to light or a circadian rhythm. *Plant J.* 10:1071–78

49. Heintzen C, Nater M, Apel K, Staiger D. 1997. AtGRP7, a nuclear RNA-binding protein as a component of a circadian-regulated negative feedback loop in *Arabidopsis thaliana. Proc. Natl. Acad. Sci. USA* 94:8515–20

50. Hemingway E. 1926. *The Sun Also Rises.* New York: Scribner's

51. Hennessey TL, Field CB. 1991. Oscillations in carbon assimilation and stomatal conductance under constant conditions. *Plant Physiol.* 96:831–36

52. Hennessey TL, Field CB. 1992. Evidence of multiple circadian oscillators in bean plants. *J. Biol. Rhythms* 7:105–13

53. Hicks KA, Millar AJ, Carré IA, Somers DE, Straume M, et al. 1996. Conditional circadian dysfunction of the *Arabidopsis early-flowering 3* mutant. *Science* 274:790–92

54. Huq E, Tepperman JM, Quail PH. 2000. GIGANTEA is a nuclear protein involved in phytochrome signaling in *Arabidopsis. Proc. Natl. Acad. Sci. USA* 97:9654–58

55. Hwang S, Kawazoe R, Herrin DL. 1996. Transcription of *tufA* and other chloroplast-encoded genes is controlled by a circadian clock in *Chlamydomonas. Proc. Natl. Acad. Sci. USA* 93:996–1000

56. Ievinsh G, Kreicbergs O. 1992. Endogenous rhythmicity of ethylene production in growing intact cereal seedlings. *Plant Physiol.* 100:1389–91

57. Iwasaki H, Kondo T. 2000. The current state and problems of circadian clock studies in cyanobacteria. *Plant Cell Physiol.* 41:1013–20

58. Iwasaki H, Williams SB, Kitayama Y, Ishiura M, Golden SS, Kondo T. 2000. A KaiC-interacting sensory histidine kinase, SasA, necessary to sustain robust circadian oscillation in cyanobacteria. *Cell* 101:223–33

59. Johnson CH. 1999. Forty years of PRCs–What have we learned? *Chronobiol. Int.* 16:711–43

60. Johnson CH. 2000. *PRC Atlas.* http://johnsonlab. biology. vanderbilt. edu/prcatlas/prcatlas.html

61. Johnson CH, Golden SS. 1999. Circadian programs in cyanobacteria: adaptiveness and mechanism. *Annu. Rev. Microbiol.* 53:389–409

62. Johnson CH, Knight MR, Kondo T, Masson P, Sedbrook J, et al. 1995. Circadian oscillations of cytosolic and chloroplastic free calcium in plants. *Science* 269:1863–65

63. Jones TL, Ort DR. 1997. Circadian regulation of sucrose phosphate synthase activity in tomato by protein phosphatase activity. *Plant Physiol.* 113:1167–75

64. Jones TL, Tucker DE, Ort DR. 1998. Chilling delays circadian pattern of sucrose phosphate synthase and nitrate reductase activity in tomato. *Plant Physiol.* 118:149–58

65. Jouve L, Gaspar T, Kevers C, Greppin H, Agosti RD. 1999. Involvement of indole-3-acetic acid in the circadian growth of the first internode of *Arabidopsis*. *Planta* 209:136–42

66. Jouve L, Greppin H, Agosti RD. 1998. *Arabidopsis thaliana* floral stem elongation: evidence for an endogenous circadian rhythm. *Plant Physiol. Biochem.* 36:469–72

67. Kanamaru K, Fujiwara M, Seki M, Katagiri T, Nakamura M, et al. 1999. Plastidic RNA polymerase sigma factors in Arabidopsis. *Plant Cell Physiol.* 40:832–42

68. Kellmann J-W, Hoffrogge R, Piechulla B. 1999. Transcriptional regulation of oscillating steady-state *Lhc* mRNA levels: characterization of two *Lhca* promoter fragments in transgenic tobacco plants. *Biol. Rhythm Res.* 30:264–71

69. Kim HY, Coté GG, Crain RC. 1993. Potassium channels in *Samanea saman* protoplasts controlled by phytochrome and the biological clock. *Science* 260:960–62

70. King RW. 1975. Multiple circadian rhythms regulate photoperiodic flowering responses in *Chenopodium rubrum*. *Can. J. Bot.* 53:2631–38

70a. Kiyosue T, Wada M. 2000. LKP1 (LOV kelch protein 1): a factor involved in the regulation of flowering time in *Arabidopsis*. *Plant J.* 23:807–15

71. Kloppstech K. 1985. Diurnal and circadian rhythmicity in the expression of light-induced nuclear messenger RNAs. *Planta* 165:502–6

72. Kolar C, Ádám É, Schäfer E, Nagy F. 1995. Expression of tobacco genes for light-harvesting chlorophyll a/b binding proteins of photosystem II is controlled by two circadian oscillators in a developmentally regulated fashion. *Proc. Natl. Acad. Sci. USA* 92:2174–78

73. Kolar C, Fejes E, Ádám É, Schäfer E, Kay S, Nagy F. 1998. Transcription of *Arabidopsis* and wheat *Cab* genes in single tobacco transgenic seedlings exhibits

independent rhythms in a developmentally regulated fashion. *Plant J.* 13:563–69

74. Kondo T, Tsinoremas NF, Golden SS, Johnson CH, Kutsuna S, Ishiura M. 1994. Circadian clock mutants of cyanobacteria. *Science* 266:1233–36

75. Kreps JA, Muramatsu T, Furuya M, Kay SA. 2000. Fluorescent differential display identifies circadian clock-regulated genes in *Arabidopsis thaliana*. *J. Biol. Rhythms* 15:208–17

76. Kreps JA, Simon AE. 1997. Environmental and genetic effects on circadian clock-regulated gene-expression in *Arabidopsis thaliana*. *Plant Cell* 9:297–304

77. Kurup S, Jones HD, Holdsworth MJ. 2000. Interactions of the developmental regulator ABI3 with proteins identified from developing Arabidopsis seeds. *Plant J.* 21:143–55

78. Lakin-Thomas PL. 2000. Circadian rhythms new functions for old clock genes? *Trends Genet.* 16:135–42

79. Leckie CP, McAinsh MR, Montgomery L, Priestley AJ, Staxen I, et al. 1998. Second messengers in guard cells. *J. Exp. Bot.* 49:339–49

80. Lee K, Loros JJ, Dunlap JC. 2000. Interconnected feedback loops in the *Neurospora* circadian system. *Science* 289:107–10

81. Lin C. 2000. Photoreceptors and regulation of flowering time. *Plant Physiol.* 123:39–50

82. Lin C. 2000. Plant blue-light receptors. *Trends Plant Sci.* 5:337–42

83. Deleted in proof

84. Liu XL, Covington MF, Fankhauser C, Chory J, Wagner DR. 2000. *ELF3* encodes a circadian-regulated nuclear protein that functions in an *Arabidopsis PHYB* signal transduction pathway. *Int. Conf. Arabidopsis Res., 11th*, Abstr. 317

85. Liu Y, Tsinoremas NF, Johnson CH, Golden SS, Ishiura M, Kondo T. 1995. Circadian orchestration of gene expression in cyanobacteria. *Genes Dev.* 9:1469–78

86. Liu Z, Taub CC, McClung CR. 1996. Identification of an *Arabidopsis* Rubisco Activase (*RCA*) minimal promoter regulated by phytochrome and the circadian clock. *Plant Physiol.* 112:43–51

87. Long JC, Jenkins GI. 1998. Involvement of plasma membrane redox activity and calcium homeostasis in the UV-B and UV-A/blue light induction of gene expression in Arabidopsis. *Plant Cell* 10:2077–86

88. Lowrey PL, Shimomura K, Antoch MP, Yamazaki S, Zemenides PD, et al. 2000. Positional syntenic cloning and functional characterization of the mammalian circadian mutation *tau*. *Science* 288:483–91

89. Lumsden PJ, Millar AJ, eds. 1998. *Biological Rhythms and Photoperiodism in Plants.* Oxford: Bios Sci. Publ. 284 pp.

90. Makino S, Kiba T, Imamura A, Hanaki N, Nakamura A, et al. 2000. Genes encoding pseudo-response regulators: insight into His-to-Asp phosphorelay and circadian rhythm in *Arabidopsis thaliana*. *Plant Cell Physiol.* 41:791–803

91. Martínez-García JF, Huq E, Quail PH. 2000. Direct targeting of light signals to a promoter element-bound transcription factor. *Science* 288:859–63

91a. Más P, Devlin PF, Panda S, Kay SA. 2000. Functional interaction of phytochrome B and cryptochrome 2. *Nature* 408:207–11

92. Mayer W, Sadleder D. 1972. Different light intensity dependence of the free-running periods as the cause of internal desynchronization of circadian rhythms in *Phaseolus coccineus. Planta* 108:173–78

93. Mayer W-E, Hohloch C, Kalkuhl A. 1997. Extensor protoplasts of the *Phaseolus* pulvinus: light-induced swelling may require extracellular Ca^{2+} influx, dark-induced shrinking inositol 1,4,5 triphosphate-induced Ca^{2+} mobilization. *J. Exp. Bot.* 48:219–28

94. McClung CR. 2000. Plant circadian clocks: a millennial view. *Physiol. Plant.* 109:359–71

95. McClung CR, Hsu M, Painter JE, Gagne JM, Karlsberg SD, Salomé PA. 2000. Integrated temporal regulation of the photorespiratory pathway: circadian regulation of two Arabidopsis genes encoding serine hydroxymethyltransferase. *Plant Physiol.* 123:381–92

95a. McWatters HG, Bastow RM, Hall A, Millar AJ. 2000. The *ELF3 zeitnehmer* regulates light signalling to the circadian clock. *Nature* 408:716–20

96. Merrow M, Brunner M, Roenneberg T. 1999. Assignment of circadian function for the Neurospora clock gene *frequency. Nature* 399:584–86

97. Millar AJ, Carré IA, Strayer CA, Chua N-H, Kay SA. 1995. Circadian clock mutants in *Arabidopsis* identified by luciferase imaging. *Science* 267:1161–63

98. Millar AJ, Kay SA. 1996. Integration of circadian and phototransduction pathways in the network controlling *CAB* gene transcription in *Arabidopsis. Proc. Natl. Acad. Sci. USA* 93:15491–96

99. Millar AJ, Short SR, Chua N-H, Kay SA. 1992. A novel circadian phenotype based on firefly luciferase expression in transgenic plants. *Plant Cell* 4:1075–87

100. Millar AJ, Straume M, Chory J, Chua N-H, Kay SA. 1995. The regulation of circadian period by phototransduction pathways in *Arabidopsis. Science* 267:1163–66

101. Moore-Ede MC, Sulzman FM, Fuller CA. 1982. *The Clocks That Time Us: Physiology of the Circadian Timing System.* Cambridge, MA: Harv. Univ. Press

102. Morikawa K, Ito S, Tsunoyama Y, Nakahira Y, Shiina T, Toyoshima Y. 1999. Circadian-regulated expression of a nuclear-encoded plastid σ factor gene (*sigA*) in wheat seedlings. *FEBS Lett.* 451:275–78

103. Morse D, Hastings JW, Roenneberg T. 1994. Different phase responses of the two circadian oscillators in *Gonyaulax. J. Biol. Rhythms* 9:263–74

104. Nagy F, Fejes E, Wehmeyer B, Dallman G, Schafer E. 1993. The circadian oscillator is regulated by a very low fluence response of phytochrome in wheat. *Proc. Natl. Acad. Sci. USA* 90:6290–94

105. Nagy F, Schafer E. 2000. Nuclear and cytosolic events of light-induced, phytochrome-regulated signaling in higher plants. *EMBO J.* 19:157–63

106. Naidoo N, Song W, Hunter-Ensor M, Sehgal A. 1999. A role for the proteasome in the light response of the Timeless clock protein. *Science* 285:1737–41

107. Nakahira Y, Baba K, Yoneda A, Shiina T, Toyoshima Y. 1998. Circadian-regulated transcription of the *psbD* light-responsive promoter in wheat chloroplasts. *Plant Physiol.* 118:1079–88

108. Neff MM, Fankhauser C, Chory J. 2000. Light: an indicator of time and place. *Genes Dev.* 14:257–71

109. Nelson DC, Lasswell J, Rogg LE, Cohen MA, Bartel B. 2000. *FKF1*, a clock-controlled gene that regulates the transition to flowering in *Arabidopsis*. *Cell* 101:331–40

110. Nikaido SS, Johnson CH. 2000. Daily and circadian variation in survival from ultraviolet radiation in *Chlamydomonas reinhardtii*. *Photochem. Photobiol.* 71:758–65

111. Nimmo HG. 2000. The regulation of phosphoenolpyruvate carboxylase in CAM plants. *Trends Plant Sci.* 5:75–80

112. Nozue K, Kanegae T, Imaizumi T, Fukuda S, Okamoto H, et al. 1998. A phytochrome from the fern *Adiantum* with features of the putative photoreceptor NPH1. *Proc. Natl. Acad. Sci. USA* 95:15826–30

113. Ouyang Y, Andersson CR, Kondo T, Golden SS, Johnson CH. 1998. Resonating circadian clocks enhance fitness in cyanobacteria. *Proc. Natl. Acad. Sci. USA* 95:8660–64

114. Park DH, Somers DE, Kim YS, Choy YH, Lim HK, et al. 1999. Control of circadian rhythms and photoperiodic flowering by the *Arabidopsis GIGANTEA* gene. *Science* 285:1579–82

115. Patton EE, Willems AR, Tyers M. 1998. Combinatorial control in ubiquitin-dependent proteolysis: Don't Skp the F-box hypothesis. *Trends Genet.* 14:236–43

116. Piechulla B. 1999. Circadian expression of the light-harvesting complex protein genes in plants. *Chronobiol. Intl.* 16:115–28

117. Pilgrim ML, Caspar T, Quail PH, McClung CR. 1993. Circadian and light regulated expression of nitrate reductase in *Arabidopsis*. *Plant Mol. Biol.* 23:349–64

118. Pittendrigh CS. 1993. Temporal organization: reflections of a Darwinian clock-watcher. *Annu. Rev. Physiol.* 55:17–54

119. Plautz JD, Kaneko M, Hall JC, Kay SA. 1997. Independent photoreceptive circadian clocks throughout *Drosophila*. *Science* 278:1632–35

120. Pott MB, Kellman JW, Piechulla B. 2000. Circadian and phytochrome control act at different promoter regions of the tomato *Lhca3* gene. *J. Plant Physiol.* 157:449–52

121. Putterill J, Robson F, Lee K, Simon R, Coupland G. 1995. The *CONSTANS* gene of *Arabidopsis* promotes flowering and encodes a protein showing similarities to zinc finger transcription factors. *Cell* 80:847–57

122. Deleted in proof

123. Reed JW, Nagpal P, Bastow RM, Solomon KS, Dowson-Day MJ, et al. 2000. Independent action of ELF3 and phyB to control hypocotyl elongation and flowering time. *Plant Physiol.* 122:1149–60

124. Reppert SM. 1995. Interaction between the circadian clocks of mother and fetus. In *Circadian Clocks and Their Adjustment, CIBA Found. Symp. Vol. 183*, ed. DJ Chadwick, K Ackrill, pp. 198–211. Chichester, UK: Wiley

125. Roenneberg T, Merrow M. 1998. Molecular circadian oscillators: an alternative hypothesis. *J. Biol. Rhythms* 13:167–79

126. Roenneberg T, Morse D. 1993. Two circadian oscillators in one cell. *Nature* 362:362–64

127. Sai J, Johnson CH. 1999. Different circadian oscillators control Ca^{2+} fluxes and *Lhcb* gene expression. *Proc. Natl. Acad. Sci. USA* 96:11659–63

128. Sakakibara H, Taniguchi M, Sugiyama T. 2000. His-Asp phosphorelay signaling: a communication avenue between plants and their environment. *Plant Mol. Biol.* 42:273–78

129. Salvador ML, Klein U, Bogorad L. 1993. Light-regulated and endogenous fluctuations of chloroplast transcript levels in *Chlamydomonas*. Regulation by transcription and RNA degradation. *Plant J.* 3:213–19

130. Salvador ML, Klein U, Bogorad L. 1998. Endogenous fluctuations of DNA topology in the chloroplast of *Chlamydomonas reinhardtii*. *Mol. Cell. Biol.* 18:7235–42

131. Samach A, Klenz JE, Kohalmi SE, Risseeuw E, Haughn GW, Crosby WL. 1999. The *UNUSUAL FLORAL ORGANS* gene of *Arabidopsis thaliana* is an F-box protein required for normal patterning and growth in the floral meristem. *Plant J.* 20:433–45

132. Sanders D, Brownlee C, Harper JF. 1999. Communicating with calcium. *Plant Cell* 11:691–706

133. Sauer F, Jäckle H. 1991. Concentration-dependent transcriptional activation or repression by *Krüppel* from a single binding site. *Nature* 353:563–66

134. Schaffer R, Ramsay N, Samach A, Corden S, Putterill J, et al. 1998. *LATE ELONGATED HYPOCOTYL*, an Arabidopsis gene encoding a MYB transcription factor, regulates circadian rhythmicity and photoperiodic responses. *Cell* 93:1219–29

135. Schmitz O, Katayama M, Williams SB, Kondo T, Golden SS. 2000. CikA, a bacteriophytochrome that resets the cyanobacterial circadian clock. *Science* 289:765–68

136. Schroeder J. 2001. Guard cell signal transduction. *Annu. Rev. Plant Physiol. Plant Mol. Biol.* 52 In press

137. Shearman LP, Sriram S, Weaver DR, Maywood ES, Chaves I, et al. 2000. Interacting molecular loops in the mammalian circadian clock. *Science* 288:1013–19

138. Simpson GG, Gendall AR, Dean C. 1999. When to switch to flowering. *Annu. Rev. Cell Dev. Biol.* 15:519–50

139. Somers D. 1999. The physiology and molecular bases of the plant circadian clock. *Plant Physiol.* 121:9–19

139a. Somers DE, Devlin P, Kay SA. 1998. Phytochromes and cryptochromes in the entrainment of the *Arabidopsis* circadian clock. *Science* 282:1488–90

140. Somers DE, Schultz TF, Milnamow M, Kay SA. 2000. ZEITLUPE encodes a novel clock-associated PAS protein from Arabidopsis. *Cell* 101:319–29

141. Somers DE, Webb AAR, Pearson M, Kay SA. 1998. The short-period mutant, *toc1-1*, alters circadian clock regulation of multiple outputs throughout development in *Arabidopsis thaliana*. *Development* 125:485–94

142. Staiger D, Apel K. 1999. Circadian clock-regulated expression of an RNA-binding protein in *Arabidopsis*: characterisation of a minimal promoter element. *Mol. Gen. Genet.* 261:811–19

143. Staiger D, Apel K, Trepp G. 1999. The *Atger3* promoter confers circadian clock-regulated transcription with peak expression at the beginnning of night. *Plant Mol. Biol.* 40:873–82

144. Strayer C, Oyama T, Schultz TF, Raman R, Somers DE, et al. 2000. Cloning of the *Arabidopsis* clock gene *TOC1*, an autoregulatory response regulator homolog. *Science* 289:768–71

145. Sugano S, Andronis C, Green RM, Wang Z-Y, Tobin EM. 1998. Protein

kinase CK2 interacts with and phospho-rylates the *Arabidopsis* circadian clock-associated 1 protein. *Proc. Natl. Acad. Sci. USA* 95:11020–25

146. Sugano S, Andronis C, Ong MS, Green RM, Tobin EM. 1999. The protein kinase CK2 is involved in regulation of circadian rhythms in Arabidopsis. *Proc. Natl. Acad. Sci. USA* 96:12362–66

147. Swarup K, Alonso-Blanco C, Lynn JR, Michaels SD, Amasino RM, et al. 1999. Natural allelic variation identifies new genes in the Arabidopsis circadian system. *Plant J.* 20:67–77

148. Sweeney BM. 1987. *Rhythmic Phenomena in Plants.* New York: Academic

149. Taylor BL, Zhulin IB. 1999. PAS domains: internal sensors of oxygen, redox potential, and light. *Microbiol. Mol. Biol. Rev.* 63:479–506

150. Thain SC, Hall A, Millar AJ. 2000. Functional independence of multiple circadian clocks that regulate plant gene expression. *Curr. Biol.* 10:951–56

151. Tosini G, Menaker M. 1996. Circadian rhythms in cultured mammalian retina. *Science* 272:419–21

152. Tosini G, Menaker M. 1998. Multioscillatory circadian organization in a vertebrate, *Iguana iguana. J. Neurosci.* 18:1105–14

153. Tsinoremas NF, Ishiura M, Kondo T, Andersson CR, Tanaka K, et al. 1996. A sigma factor that modifies the circadian expression of a subset of genes in cyanobacteria. *EMBO J.* 15:2488–95

154. Wambutt R, Murphy G, Volckaert G, Pohl T, Dusterhoft A, et al. 2000. Progress in *Arabidopsis* genome sequencing and functional genomics. *J. Biotechnol.* 78:281–92

155. Wang Z-Y, Kenigsbuch D, Sun L, Harel E, Ong MS, Tobin EM. 1997. A Myb-related transcription factor is involved in the phytochrome regulation of an Arabidopsis *Lhcb* gene. *Plant Cell* 9:491–507

156. Wang Z-Y, Tobin EM. 1998. Constitutive expression of the *CIRCADIAN CLOCK ASSOCIATED 1 (CCA1)* gene disrupts circadian rhythms and suppresses its own expression. *Cell* 93:1207–17

157. Webb AAR. 1998. Stomatal rhythms. See Ref. 89, pp. 69–79

158. Whitmore D, Foulkes NS, Sassone-Corsi P. 2000. Light acts directly on organs and cells in culture to set the vertebrate circadian clock. *Nature* 404:87–91

159. Yamazaki S, Numano R, Abe M, Hida A, Takahashi R, et al. 2000. Resetting central and peripheral circadian oscillators in transgenic rats. *Science* 288:682–85

160. Yanovsky MJ, Izaguirre M, Wagmaister JA, Gatz C, Jackson SD, et al. 2000. Phytochrome A resets the circadian clock and delays tuber formation under long days in potato. *Plant J.* 23:223–32

161. Young MW. 1998. The molecular control of circadian behavioral rhythms and their entrainment in *Drosophila. Annu. Rev. Biochem.* 67:135–52

162. Zhong HH, McClung CR. 1996. The circadian clock gates expression of two *Arabidopsis* catalase genes to distinct and opposite circadian phases. *Mol. Gen. Genet.* 251:196–203

163. Zhong HH, Painter JE, Salomé PA, Straume M, McClung CR. 1998. Imbibition, but not release from stratification, sets the circadian clock in Arabidopsis seedlings. *Plant Cell* 10:2005–17

164. Zhong HH, Resnick AS, Straume M, McClung CR. 1997. Effects of synergistic signaling by phytochrome A and cryptochrome 1 on circadian clock-regulated catalase expression. *Plant Cell* 9:947–55

Annu. Rev. Plant Physiol. Plant Mol. Biol. 2001. 52:163–210

Macronutrient Utilization by Photosynthetic Eukaryotes and the Fabric of Interactions

Arthur Grossman
Department of Plant Biology, The Carnegie Institution of Washington
260 Panama Street, Stanford, California 94305; e-mail: arthur@andrew2.stanford.edu

Hideki Takahashi
RIKEN Plant Science Center, 2-l Hirosawa, Wako, Saitama 351-0198, Japan;
e-mail: hideki@postman.riken.go.jp

Key Words   nitrogen, phosphorus, sulfur, starvation, light

■ **Abstract**   Organisms acclimate to a continually fluctuating nutrient environment. Acclimation involves responses specific for the limiting nutrient as well as responses that are more general and occur when an organism experiences different stress conditions. Specific responses enable organisms to efficiently scavenge the limiting nutrient and may involve the induction of high-affinity transport systems and the synthesis of hydrolytic enzymes that facilitate the release of the nutrient from extracellular organic molecules or from internal reserves. General responses include changes in cell division rates and global alterations in metabolic activities. In photosynthetic organisms there must be precise regulation of photosynthetic activity since when severe nutrient limitation prevents continued cell growth, excitation of photosynthetic pigments could result in the formation of reactive oxygen species, which can severely damage structural and functional features of the cell. This review focuses on ways that photosynthetic eukaryotes assimilate the macronutrients nitrogen, sulfur, and phosphorus, and the mechanisms that govern assimilatory activities. Also discussed are molecular responses to macronutrient limitation and the elicitation of those responses through integration of environmental and cellular cues.

CONTENTS

INTRODUCTION

This review focuses on acquisition and assimilation of the macronutrients nitrogen (N), sulfur (S) and phosphorus (P) by plants and algae (primarily *Chlamydomonas reinhardtii*; designated Chlamydomonas throughout) and responses of these organisms to macronutrient deprivation. This version of the text has been abstracted, with a complete version of the text available at http://www.annualreviews.org/pubs/supmat/supmat.asp.

Organisms grown in medium limiting for a particular nutrient exhibit responses specific for the limiting nutrient and more general responses elicited by a variety of different stress conditions. Nutrient-specific responses include the biosynthesis of transport systems for the limiting nutrient and induction of hydrolytic activities that enable cells to access alternative sources of the limiting nutrient. Table 1 lists transporters of Chlamydomonas and vascular plants that function in the transport of ammonium (NH_4^+), nitrate (NO_3^-), nitrite (NO_2^-) and sulfate (SO_4^{2-}). Phosphate (Pi) transporters were excluded because they have not been extensively enough characterized. General responses to nutrient limitation include changes in the morphology of the organism (316, 333, 334), cessation of cell division (47), accumulation of polysaccharides (11, 276), reduced photosynthetic activities (47, 207, 325), and modification of metabolic processes to satisfy the demands of a reduced nutrient environment (61, 168, 291). Some responses may result from changes in metabolism that occur because depriving cells of nutrients retards growth and limits the utilization of reductant and chemical bond energy. A dramatic slowing of anabolic processes leads to a reduced need for ATP and NADPH generated by photosynthetic electron transport. Hence, even when nutrient-deprived plants and algae are grown in moderate or low light, photosynthetic electron carriers will tend to be fully reduced. The redox potential of the cell will increase as a consequence of hyperreduction of the plastoquinone pool (and other photosynthetic electron carriers), although some of this redox pressure may be relieved by elevated starch synthesis. This increase in intracellular redox potential will have a global effect on cellular metabolism and gene expression (66, 308). Additionally, with a decreased demand for reductant during nutrient limitation, the cell would tend to accumulate high potential electrons and excited chlorophyll molecules that could interact with oxygen, creating reactive oxygen species. These species could cause extensive cell damage and also function as regulatory signals that alter metabolic activities.

Finally, responses to a changing nutrient environment are integrated with other environmental conditions and the developmental stage of the organism. Most results described in this review are from experimentation in which conditions were engineered to insure that levels of a specific element limited the growth of the organism, a more static condition than is found in nature.

NITROGEN

Nitrogen in the Environment

All organisms require an abundance of N for the synthesis of proteins and nucleic acids. N limits the growth of organisms in a number of different ecosystems and is especially critical in marine ecosystems. N (P or S) limitation can profoundly influence the morphology and physiology of plants. Plants deprived of N develop an elevated root:shoot ratio relative to unstarved plants with shortened lateral branches whereas an excess of NO_3^- inhibits root growth and leads to a decrease in the root:shoot ratio (260, 334). Internal levels of nitrogenous metabolites and/or the N:C ratio may serve as a systemic signal that influences root development (260).

Plants and algae actively transport and utilize both NH_4^+ and NO_3^-, although the concentration of NH_4^+ in the soil is generally much lower than that of NO_3^- (170). However, relative to the utilization of NO_3^- or NO_2^-, the assimilation of NH_4^+ is metabolically inexpensive since it does not have to be reduced prior to incorporation into amino acids and nitrogenous bases.

Ammonium Transport

Generally, administration of NH_4^+ to plants as a sole source of N leads to stunted growth. Diminution of shoot biomass is the consequence of a reduction in both the number and size of leaf cells (316). Co-addition of NH_4^+ and NO_3^- eliminate stunting, suggesting that the growth phenotype resulted from a lack of NO_3^- rather than NH_4^+ toxicity. The growth defect has also been correlated with a dramatic reduction in the level of cytokinins in the xylem and an increase in the level of abscissic acid (210, 316). These results suggest that NO_3^- strongly influences plant hormone levels and may be required for cytokinin biosynthesis or transport of cytokinins from the root, its site of synthesis, to leaves. In contrast, Chlamydomonas readily grows with NH_4^+ as its sole N source.

TABLE 1 Characteristics of ammonium, nitrate, nitrite and sulfate transporters

Species	Gene	Affinity	Localization	Response	Reference
Ammonium Transporters					
Arabidopsis	*AtAmt1;1*	High	Root	-N (up)	91, 233
				Gln (down)	
			Leaf	Const.	
Arabidopsis	*AtAmt1;2*	High	Root	Nitrate (down)	91
Arabidopsis	*AtAmt1;3*	High	Root	Light (up)	91, 314
				Sucrose (up)	
Arabidopsis	*AtAmt2*	N.D.	Root	-N (up)	273
			Leaf	Const.	
Tomato	*LeAmt1;1*	N.D.	Root (rh)	-N (up)	146, 315
			Leaf	Const.	
Tomato	*LeAmt1;2*	N.D.	Root (rh)	Nitrate (up)	315
				Ammonia (up)	
			Leaf	Nitrate (up)	
				Light (up)	
				CO_2 (down)	
Tomato	*LeAmt1;3*	N.D.	Leaf	Nitrate (up)	315
				Light (down)	
				CO_2 (down)	

Group 1 Nitrate Transporters

Arabidopsis	*AtNrt1;1*	Low/High	Root (ep, co, en)	Nitrate (up) Light (up) Low pH (up) Sucrose (up) -N (down)	77, 151, 300, 322
Brassica	*BnNrt1;2*	Low	Root	Nitrate (up)	337
Tomato	*LeNrt1;2*	N.D.	Root (rh)	Nitrate (up)	146
Arabidopsis	*AtNrt1;2*	Low	Root	Const.	39, 157
Rice	*OsNrt1;1*	Low	Root (ep, rh)	Const.	156
Tomato	*LeNrt1;1*	N.D.	Root	Const.	146

Group 2 Nitrate Transporters

Arabidopsis	*AtNrt2;1*	High	Root	-N (up) Nitrate (up) Light (up) Sucrose (up) Ammonia (down) Gln (down)	77, 151, 322, 340
Arabidopsis	*AtNrt2;2*	N.D.	Root	N.D.	340
Tobacco	*NpNrt2;1*	N.D.	Root (ep, en)	Nitrate (up) Ammonia(down) Gln (down)	135, 220

(Continued)

TABLE 1 *(Continued)*

Species	Gene	Affinity	Localization	Response	Reference
Soybean	*GmNrt2*	N.D.	Root	-N (up)	1
				Nitrate (up)	
				Ammonia (down)	
Barley	*HvNrt2;1*	N.D.	Root	Nitrate (up)	297
Barley	*HvNrt2;2*	N.D.	Root	Nitrate (up)	297
Algal Nitrate and Nitrite Transporters					
Chlamydomonas	*Nrt2;1*	High (nitrate/nitrite)		Nitrate (up)	89, 217
				Ammonia (down)	
Chlamydomonas	*Nrt2;2*	High (Nitrate)		Nitrate(up)	89, 217
				Ammonia (down)	
Chlamydomonas	*Nrt2;3*	High (nitrite)		Nitrite (up)	238
		Low (nitrate)		CO_2 (up)	
				Ammonia (down)	
Chlamydomonas	*Nar1*	High (nitrite)	Chloroplast	Nitrate (up)	239 (*a*)
				Ammonia (down)	
Group 1 Sulfate Transporters					
Arabidopsis	*Sultr1;1*	High	Root (ep, co, rh)	-S (up)	284
Arabidopsis	*Sultr1;2*	High	Root (co)	-S (up)	(*b*)
Barley	*Hvst1*	High	Root	-S (up)	271, 310
				GSH (down)	
Stylosanthes	*Shst1*	High	Root	-S (up)	270
Stylosanthes	*Shst2*	High	Root	-S (up)	270
Maize	*Zmst1*	N.D.	Root	-S (up)	21
				Cys (down)	

Group 2 Sulfate Transporters

Arabidopsis	Sultr2;1	Low	Root (pc, xp)	-S (up) GSH (down)	144, 284, 285
			Leaf (ph, xp)	-S (down)	
Arabidopsis	Sultr2;2	Low	Root (ph)	const.	284
			Leaf (vbs)	-S (up)	
Stylosanthes	Shst3	Low	Root	-S (up)	270
			Leaf	-S (down)	

Group 3 Sulfate Transporters

Arabidopsis	Sultr3;1	N.D.	Leaf	Const.	284
Arabidopsis	Sultr3;2	N.D.	Leaf	Const.	284
Arabidopsis	Sultr3;3	N.D.	Leaf	Const.	284

Chloroplast and Algal Sulfate Transporters

Arabidopsis	Sultr4;1	N.D.	Chloroplast	-S (up)	283, 284
Chlamydomonas		N.D.	N.D.	-S (up)	(c)

(a) A putative chloroplast nitrite transporter from cucumber that is not related to Chlamydomonas *Nar1* is in the database (accession no. Z69370). (b) Accession no. AB042322 (H Takahashi, unpublished data). (c) J Davies (personal communication).
There are several additional sequences encoding ammonium, nitrate, and sulfate transporters in the Arabidopsis genome; *AtAmt1;4* (accession no. AL035353), *AtAmt1;5* (accession no. AP000382); *AtNrt2;3* and *AtNrt2;4* (accession no. AB015472); *Sultr1;3* (accession no. AC069252), *Sultr3;4* (accession no. AB012247), *Sultr4;2* (accession no. AP002047).
up, up-regulation; down, down-regulation; const, constitutive expression; N.D., not determined. co, cortex; en, endodermis; ep, epidermis; pc, pericycle; ph, phloem; rh, root hair; vbs, vascular bundle sheath; xp, xylem parenchyma.

Use of Ammonium by Chlamydomonas   Chlamydomonas has at least two NH_4^+ carriers (84); the gene for neither has been cloned. Mutants defective for NH_4^+ transport were selected for resistance to methylammonium and the lesions mapped to two nuclear loci. One locus defines a constitutively expressed, low-affinity NH_4^+ transporter with a high maximum uptake velocity whereas the other defines an NH_4^+-repressible, high-affinity NH_4^+ transporter with a low maximum uptake velocity. The low-affinity system functions under N-replete conditions whereas the high-affinity system is important when the concentration of NH_4^+ in the environment becomes limiting.

Use of Ammonium by Plants   Plants also have several NH_4^+ transporters. Six potential isoforms of NH_4^+ transporters have been identified in Arabidopsis (91, 192, 314, 315). The first gene encoding a plant high-affinity NH_4^+ transporter ($K_m = 0.5 \mu M$) was designated *AtAmt1;1* (192). *AtAmt1;1* mRNA accumulates in Arabidopsis leaves, roots, and seedlings (91), increases in abundance during N starvation, and declines as the glutamine concentration in roots rises (91, 192, 233). These characteristics suggest that AtAmt1;1 facilitates efficient NH_4^+ transport when Arabidopsis experiences low NH_4^+ conditions. The uptake of NH_4^+ by roots correlates with an increase in the level of *AtAmt1;1* mRNA and a decrease in the concentration of glutamine (233). Furthermore, when the conversion of NH_4^+ to glutamine is blocked by administration of methionine sulfoximine, high levels of NH_4^+ are unable to suppress accumulation of *AtAmt1;1* mRNA. Therefore, a metabolite derived from NH_4^+, and not NH_4^+ itself, serves to control *AtAmt1;1* mRNA levels. NH_4^+ may also have a direct effect on uptake activity. There are strong interactions between NH_4^+ assimilation and the generation of carbon (C) skeletons, which are critical for NH_4^+ assimilation.

In contrast to AtAmt1;1, the AtAmt1;2 and AtAmt1;3 transporters are root specific and have low affinities for NH_4^+ ($K_m = 30$–$35 \mu M$) (91). Two other putative NH_4^+ transporter genes present on the Arabidopsis genome are *AtAmt1;4* and *AtAmt1;5*. The tissue specificity and N dependence of expression of these genes have not been characterized. A sixth putative NH_4^+ transporter is encoded by *AtAmt2;1*. This gene is expressed in both roots and leaves and is unique in that it encodes a protein that is only distantly related to the other plant NH_4^+ transporters (273).

Genes encoding NH_4^+ transporters have also been isolated and characterized in tomato. Two of these genes, *LeAmt1;1* and *LeAmt1;2*, are preferentially expressed in root hairs (146, 315). The mRNA level of *LeAmt1;1* dramatically increases when tomato plants are starved for N, similar to the expression pattern of *AtAmt1;1*, and like AtAmt1;1, the LeAmt1;1 transporter may be critical for the uptake of NH_4^+ by roots when the soil is depleted for NH_4^+. In contrast, the level of *LeAmt1;2* mRNA is highest when plants are experiencing N-replete growth (315).

The rate of influx of NH_4^+ into Arabidopsis roots shows a diurnal rhythm with a maximum that occurs toward the end of the light period (91). There is a sharp decline in influx soon after the dark period begins. The *AtAmt1;1, AtAmt1;2,* and

AtAmt1;3 genes all show diurnal patterns of expression, although peak levels of *AtAmt1;3* mRNA best correspond to the peak of NH_4^+ uptake (91). The influx of NH_4^+ toward the end of the light period may be influenced by increased availability of sugars (91, 314), suggesting a link between NH_4^+ uptake, expression of *AtAmt1;3*, and C metabolism.

Nitrate and Nitrite Transport NO_3^- is the major source of inorganic N in the soil and serves as a substrate for N assimilation. The concentration of NO_3^- in the cytoplasm of a plant cell is maintained at a relatively constant level (179), although considerable quantities can be stored in vacuoles and only mobilized when N becomes limiting (304). NO_3^- can also be transported out of roots into the rhizosphere by a passive efflux system that is saturable and both NO_3^- selective (99) and inducible (7). Nearly all studies on NO_3^- transport concern the movement of NO_3^- from the soil solution into cells or the plant body.

Nitrate and Nitrite Transport by Chlamydomonas   Chlamydomonas synthesizes several transport systems that are specifically involved in acquisition of NO_3^- and NO_2^-. At least six genes encoding polypeptides that function in NO_3^-/NO_2^- assimilation are clustered on the Chlamydomonas genome (218, 219). This locus includes two regions for systems (System I and II) that transport NO_3^- and NO_2^- into cells. There are at least two additional genes encoding NO_3^-/NO_2^- transport systems (Systems III and IV) at different chromosomal locations. The accumulation of transcripts from these loci is repressed by NH_4^+, whereas the transcripts are most abundant when cells are exposed to NO_3^-. System I is encoded by the *Nrt2;1/Nar2* genes. This system catalyzes high-affinity transport of both NO_3^- (High Affinity Nitrate Transport or HANT) and NO_2^- (High Affinity Nitrite Transport or HANiT). System II is encoded by *Nrt2;2/Nar2* and exhibits monospecific HANT activity. Although the *Nar2* gene product is required for the activity of both of these systems, its function is not known. It may be a structural element that associates with the Nrt2;1 and Nrt2;2 polypeptides (89, 217), a hypothesis supported by the finding that electrogenic NO_3^- transport into *Xenopus* oocytes occurs only when the oocytes harbor both the Nrt2;1 and Nar2 polypeptides (336). System III, encoded by *Nrt2;3*, exhibits both HANiT and low-affinity NO_3^- transport or [LANT] activities (238). The *Nrt2;3* gene is clustered with *Nar5*, a gene of unknown function that, like the transporter genes, is regulated by the N status of the environment. System IV exhibits both HANT and HANiT activities and is probably encoded by *Nrt2;4* (238). *Nar1*, a separate gene, encodes an integral membrane protein involved in the transport of NO_2^- into chloroplasts (239), the site of NO_2^- reduction.

Nitrate and Nitrite Transport by Plants   Energy-dependent transporters in vascular plants move NO_3^- across the plasma membrane of root epidermal and cortical cells. Subsequently, NO_3^- is reduced, stored in the vacuole, or transported symplastically across the Casparian strip through the endodermal cell layer to reach the stele (39). Inside the vascular tissue, NO_3^- is taken up by xylem parenchyma cells and loaded into xylem vessels, where it is routed to the leaves. Loading of NO_3^- into the xylem requires an efflux system that transports the anion out of xylem parenchyma cells. Following transport, NO_3^- is unloaded from the xylem and loaded into leaf mesophyll cells. Most reduction of NO_3^- to NO_2^- is thought to occur in the cytoplasm of leaf cells, while further reduction and assimilation occurs primarily in leaf cell chloroplasts. However, a considerable amount of NO_3^- assimilation can occur in plant roots, especially the roots of woody plants. Following reduction of NO_3^- to NH_4^+, GS catalyzes its incorporation into glutamine and the ferredoxin-dependent glutamate synthetase or glutamine:2-oxoglutarate aminotransferase (GOGAT) catalyzes the transamination of an amino group from glutamine to 2-oxoglutarate to form two molecules of glutamate. Glutamate is used for the synthesis of aspartate and alanine, and glutamate and aspartate then serve as amino donors for the biosynthesis of other amino acids and various N-containing compounds.

NO_3^- uptake by plant roots is driven by a proton motive force (39) and probably mediated by $2H^+/1NO_3^-$ symport (175). Low- and high-affinity NO_3^- uptake systems are associated with plant roots. Low-affinity NO_3^- transport systems (LATS; $K_m > 0.5$ mM) are constitutively expressed and serve as the major transport activity when the NO_3^- concentration in the environment is in the millimolar range. Low-affinity NO_3^- transporters have been placed in the NRT1 class (82). High-affinity NO_3^- transporters (HATS; 200 μM $> K_m > 5$ μM) operate at micromolar concentrations of NO_3^-. The high-affinity NO_3^- transporters are in the NRT2 class. The HATS and LATS polypeptides are predicted to be integral to membranes with 12 transmembrane helices separated into two groups of six helices by a hydrophilic region; they are members of the major facilitator superfamily of transport proteins (205). HATS have been divided into two categories, cHATS and iHATS, that respond differently to environmental NO_3^- concentrations. cHATS are constitutively expressed at a high level, although they can be upregulated in the presence of NO_3^- (5, 138). High-level expression of the iHATs requires NO_3^- (6, 137).

Several genes on plant genomes encode NO_3^- transporters (82); barley has 7-10 putative NO_3^- transporters (297). NO_3^- transporters have been identified by analyses of NO_3^- transport mutants (300, 320), functional complementation of yeast transport mutants (299), homologies of deduced protein sequences to known NO_3^- transporters (146), patterns of expression of putative transport genes with respect to N conditions, and activity of specific transporters in *Xenopus* oocytes (156, 180, 336). Mutants defective for NO_3^- transport and reduction have been generated by selecting for strains resistant to ClO_3^- (reviewed in 38); this selection identified the *chl1* mutant of Arabidopsis (300). A T-DNA tagged allele of *chl1* facilitated the cloning of the gene, designated *AtNrt1;1*. *AtNrt1;1* is NO_3^--inducible and expressed in the epidermis, cortex, and endodermis of Arabidopsis roots (115, 300). The *AtNrt1;1* product is a LATS (115, 296) that, under certain conditions, exhibits HATS activity (157, 322), suggesting that AtNrt1;1 is a dual function transporter operating at both low and high substrate levels. NO_3^- uptake experiments using the *chl1* mutant have suggested the existence of an additional constitutive LATS activity that is likely encoded by *AtNrt1;2* (157). Expression studies in *Xenopus* oocytes have confirmed that *AtNrt1;2* encodes a LATS.

Genes that are putative *AtNrt1* homologs have been cloned from a number of organisms. *OsNrt1;1*, the *AtNrt1;2* homolog from rice, encodes a LATS component that is constitutively expressed in root epidermal cells and root hairs (156). *BnNrt1;2* is an *AtNrt1;1* homolog from *Brassica napus* that displays NO_3^--induced transcript accumulation and LATS activity upon expression in *Xenopus* oocytes (337). In tomato, the *LeNrt1;2* gene may encode a polypeptide that functions similarly to *AtNrt1;1* since it is preferentially expressed in root hairs and up-regulated by NO_3^- (146). In contrast, *LeNrt1;1* encodes a transporter that is constitutively expressed and not exclusively localized to root hairs (146).

The members of the plant *Nrt2* gene family encode high-affinity NO_3^- transporters of the cHAT or iHAT type (82). Expression of genes encoding iHATs is often susceptible to negative feedback regulation through products of N assimilation (128). Key metabolites involved in this control are the amino acids glutamine and asparagine (187, 203). At least four *Nrt2* genes have been identified on the Arabidopsis genome. *AtNrt2;1* and *AtNrt2;2* are contiguous in a tail-to-tail configuration at the top of chromosome 1 (340) whereas *AtNrt2;3* and *AtNrt2;4* are 4 kbp apart in a head-to-tail configuration at the top of chromosome V (GenBank Accession number AB015472) (82). The *Chl8* gene of Arabidopsis probably encodes a cHAT (320), although there is no sequence information that clearly establishes it as a member of the NRT2 family. Antisense suppression of *AtNrt2;1* expression has provided direct evidence that this gene encodes a high-affinity NO_3^- transporter (82). Based on spatial distribution of transcripts of *NpNrt2;1*, a homolog of *AtNrt2;1* in *Nicotiana plumbaginifolia*, the gene is expressed in root epidermal and endodermal cells (135). The physiological functions of the different *Nrt2* genes of Arabidopsis are unknown.

Regulation of Transport NO_3^- assimilation is controlled by both N and C metabolites. Addition of NH_4^+ to plants suppresses the assimilation of NO_3^- (82, 275, 276). Tobacco transformants with elevated expression of nitrate reductase (NR), which can lead to an increase in the glutamine concentration in the cell, have depressed rates of NO_3^- uptake relative to wild-type cells (93). This is strong evidence that NO_3^- uptake is controlled by downstream products of NO_3^- assimilation. Furthermore, either the addition of exogenous sugars or conditions that elevate CO_2 fixation strongly affect NO_3^- uptake (see below).

NO_3^- stimulates the accumulation of *AtNrt1;1* and *AtNrt2;1* mRNA (77, 151). An Arabidopsis mutant lacking NR accumulates high levels of both NO_3^- and *AtNrt1;1* and *AtNrt2;1* transcripts. This is probably a consequence of an inability of the mutant to synthesize reduced N metabolites that feedback to suppress expression of the NO_3^- transport genes. Accumulation of NH_4^+ and glutamine causes repression of the *AtNrt2;1* in Arabidopsis (340) and its homologs in *N.*

plumbaginifolia (220) and soybean (1). An increase in root *AtNrt2;1* mRNA abundance correlates with the rate of high-affinity NO_3^- uptake in plants exposed to low N conditions. Induction of *AtNrt2;1* mRNA by N limitation may be a consequence of release from feedback control by reduced N metabolites. Expression of both *AtNrt1;1* and *AtNrt2;1* genes are diurnally regulated with expression peaking just prior to the dark period and declining as plants enter the dark period (151). Exogenous sucrose prevents the decline in mRNA during the dark period (151), suggesting that C metabolite levels are critical for controlling NO_3^- uptake and that the circadian pattern of expression of the NO_3^- transport genes may be a consequence of changes in the cellular concentrations of C and N metabolites.

Transport of Other Nitrogen Sources

In addition to assimilating NH_4^+, NO_3^-, and NO_2^-, Chlamydomonas can utilize N from urea, certain nitrogenous bases, and amino acids. Purines can support the growth of Chlamydomonas in the absences of other N sources (212). Chlamydomonas also has transporters specific for urea and arginine (129). Although Chlamydomonas cannot rapidly take up other amino acids, it synthesizes an extracellular L-amino acid oxidase in response to N limitation (211, 301) that catalyzes the deamination of amino acids and the release of NH_4^+.

Plant roots possess active uptake systems for amino acids. These systems may supply plants with N in soils that contain high concentrations of organic matter. Genes encoding these amino acid permeases (designated *Aap*) in Arabidopsis have been cloned (78). Most of these transporters have broad substrate specificities (78, 81) and the tissue specificity of some may reflect a function in moving amino acids between plant tissue types (78, 81). Aap3 is exclusively in Arabidopsis roots (81), and it probably facilitates the uptake and retrieval of amino acids from the soil. The precise roles of the amino acid permeases in plant nutrition and development are still relatively unexplored. Other transporters that move small oligopeptides across membranes are also present in plants (237), but their role in N metabolism is not clear.

Nitrate and Nitrite Reduction

The conversion of NO_3^- to NO_2^- is performed by NR, and of NO_2^- to NH_4^+ by nitrite reductase (NiR). NR is cytosolic, mainly located in root epidermal and cortical cells (70) and leaf mesophyll cells (307) and highly regulated (69, 116, 216). NiR is chloroplast localized and encoded in the nuclear genome (80).

Most reducing equivalents used for the reduction of NO_3^- to NH_4^+ are derived directly from photosynthetic electron transport. Reduced ferredoxin (Fd) is the electron donor that fuels the catalytic activity of NiR. In nonphotosynthetic tissue, NADPH derived from the oxidative pentose phosphate pathway (121, 235) can be used to generate NH_4^+ from NO_3^-. Reducing equivalents are transferred from NADPH to Fd via Fd-NADPH oxidoreductase (FNR). NO_3^- induces expression of Fd (174), FNR (2, 240), and the 6-phosphogluconate dehydrogenase genes; the latter is an integral component of the oxidative pentose phosphate pathway (235).

Chlamydomonas Nitrate and Nitrite Reductase   The NO_3^-/NO_2^- assimilation gene cluster of Chlamydomonas contains the structural genes encoding NR and NiR. The *Nia1* gene encodes NR (74). Mutants have been isolated that are defective in the NR structural gene (74) or in genes required for producing a functional molybdopterin cofactor (reviewed in 72). NiR of Chlamydomonas, encoded by *Nii1*, has both a siroheme and [Fe_4S_4] cluster that function as redox centers (25).

NH_4^+ and NO_3^- are key regulatory molecules that control the transcriptional activity of genes encoding the NO_3^-/NO_2^- transporters, NR and NiR. Several posttranscriptional processes also govern NO_3^-/NO_2^- assimilation. NH_4^+ addition to NO_3^--grown cells triggers a rapid decrease in NR activity, which reflects both enzyme inactivation (83) and inhibition of de novo synthesis (71, 101). Inactivated NR is more rapidly degraded than the active enzyme (83). Analyses of a Chlamydomonas strain expressing *Nia1* from the *cabII-1* gene promoter also suggest posttranscriptional control (188). Furthermore, constitutive expression of NR results in altered regulation of the NO_3^-/NO_2^- transporters, supporting the idea that N metabolites downstream of NR regulate the acquisition of NO_3^- and NO_2^- (188).

Light is another environmental cue involved in controlling NO_3^- assimilation and the uptake of a number of anions (3, 223). Blue light activates NR (3, 126), and in the green alga *Monorhapidium braunii* it is required for the biosynthesis of NiR (221). Recently it was shown that blue light is needed for the biosynthesis of the NO_2^- transport system in Chlamydomonas and that protein synthesis inhibitors block the stimulatory effect of blue light (222).

Several mutants of Chlamydomonas devoid of NR activity have been isolated. These mutants fall into three categories; (*a*) those defective in *Nia1*; (*b*) those that cannot synthesize a functional molybdopterin cofactor; and (*c*) those that are aberrant for *Nit2*. *Nit2* encodes a polypeptide that acts as a positive regulator for the NO_3^- assimilation genes (73). A *Nit2* gene of Chlamydomonas was identified in a mutant strain in which the gene was tagged by the transposon *Gulliver* (262). The *Nit2* transcript is high in N-free medium and downregulated by NH_4^+. Other loci involved in the control of NO_3^-/NO_2^- assimilation are *NRG1*, *NRG2* (214), and *FAR1* (335). Mutants in the *Nrg* and *Far1* genes are defective in NH_4^+ repression of NO_3^- transport.

Nitrate and Nitrite Reductase in Plants   Arabidopsis has two genes that encode NR, *Nia1* and *Nia2* (323). These genes are responsive to light, levels of N metabolites, and hormones. Light can act to regulate expression of the *Nia* genes as a consequence of direct absorption by a photoreceptor or by altering the rate of photosynthesis and levels of C metabolites in the cell. However, there are significant differences in the way in which *Nia1* and *Nia2* are controlled with respect to the kinetics of induction by light and in their expression levels in the absence of NO_3^- and following administration of cytokinin (27, 155). *Nia1* and *Nia2* are both induced by light, but the induction of the latter is more rapid than that of the former. While both genes are positively regulated by NO_3^-, especially in the presence of sucrose, the induction of the *Nia1* gene is stronger (155). Administration of cytokinins to Arabidopsis seedlings triggers an increase in the transcription of *Nia1* but not of *Nia2* (332).

Nia expression is controlled by the cellular concentrations of N metabolites. *Nia* transcripts are low when plants are exposed to high NH_4^+ or glutamine and are induced by NO_3^- (29, 30, 258). In plants maintained on a day-night cycle, *Nia* transcripts are high toward the end of the night, remain high as plants are exposed to light, and decline after 1 or 2 h in the light (NR protein levels remain high for approximately 4 h into the light period). The decline in mRNA continues throughout the entire light period but increases gradually during the subsequent dark period (87, 92, 259). The decline in NR protein levels during the second half of the light period exhibits a slight lag with respect to the decline in transcript levels, which suggests that the levels of NR protein are controlled, at least in part, by mRNA abundance. Furthermore, the protein remaining at the end of the light period is rapidly inactivated when the lights are extinguished; most of the decline in NR activity is not reversed until initiation of the next light period. Daily changes in N metabolite levels in plants maintained on a light-dark cycle correlate with the observed pattern of *Nia* expression. The decline in *Nia* mRNA during the light period parallels a decline in NO_3^- and an accumulation of glutamine in leaves (259). Conversely, the accumulation of *Nia* mRNA during the dark period coincides with an increase in NO_3^- and a decrease in glutamine. The level of *Nii* mRNA is coordinated in a similar manner (112).

As suggested above, posttranscriptional processes (in addition to transcriptional control) modulate NR activity (116, 117, 259). When leaves are placed in the dark, NR activity declines. Dark inactivation of NR is reversed in plants that are either starved for NO_3^- or that express NR at a reduced level (258). The inability to inactivate the enzyme in the dark in NO_3^--starved plants or in plants genetically modified for reduced NR or NiR synthesis (259, 306) correlates with decreased glutamine and NH_4^+ levels, suggesting a marked influence of N metabolites on posttranscriptional regulation of NR. In support of this view, NR activation is diminished in detached leaves that are fed glutamine (184, 259). Additionally, posttranslational control of NR activity is observed in plants that are constitutively expressing *Nia* from the CaMV 35S promoter (75, 311) and is dependent upon the amino terminus of the NR protein (196). Dark inactivation is a consequence of phosphorylation of serine-543 (9) catalyzed by a calcium-dependent or Snf1-related protein kinase (55, 56, 277). Phospho-NR activity is inhibited by binding 14-3-3 polypeptide (8, 183).

Sugar levels can strongly influence N assimilation. When Arabidopsis is maintained in the dark there is little expression of *Nia* (29) and other genes involved in N assimilation (275, 276), but administration of sucrose to dark-grown plants can mimic light induction (29). The mechanism by which sucrose causes activation of N assimilation genes is not understood, although it has been suggested that hexokinase function is required for sensing and responding to sugars (119). Furthermore, C skeletons, and more specifically organic acids, are required for the assimilation of NH_4^+, and certain organic acids such as 2-oxoglutarate stimulate expression of genes involved in N acquisition and utilization. Conversely, high levels of available N favor elevated expression of genes encoding enzymes required for the synthesis of organic acids, including the genes for PEP carboxylase, pyruvate kinase, citrate synthase, and NADP-isocitrate dehydrogenase (258).

Light activation of N assimilation genes is only partly a consequence of increased sugar levels, and sugars do not mimic light with respect to the elevation of *Nii* mRNA in *N. plumbaginifolia* (312). Both *Nia* and *Nii* mRNA levels in etiolated seedlings increase in response to red (14, 177, 226) and blue (177) light, and phytochrome has been implicated in light control (14, 226). Furthermore, constitutive photomorphogenesis mutants that are defective in red light–mediated de-etiolation exhibited derepression of *Nia2* (but not *Nia1* and *Nii*) in the dark, along with many other light-regulated genes, including *RbcS* and *Lhc* (52). These results suggest that *Nia2*, *Lhc*, and *RbcS* expression is influenced by a similar light-dependent regulatory pathway and that a different pathway modulates *Nia1* and *Nii* activities.

The accumulation of active NR and NiR in plants is coordinated. Like *Nia* genes, *Nii* genes are regulated by the levels of N metabolite, sugars, and light (10, 190, 312). Light-induced accumulation of NiR activity in mustard seedlings required NO_3^- (266), and NR mutants have elevated levels of *Nii* mRNA and NiR activity. Furthermore, the expression of *Nii* genes exhibits a diurnal rhythm (312) that might reflect fluctuations in the levels of the C metabolites. Four *Nii* genes have been identified in tobacco. The *Nii1* and *Nii2* genes exhibit leaf- and root-specific expression, respectively (136). As with NR, posttranscriptional regulation is important for controlling levels of active NiR (41).

Glutamine Synthetase

The main route of NH_4^+ assimilation into organic compounds is through the GS/GOGAT system (141). GS catalyzes amination of glutamate to form glutamine and GOGAT facilitates reductive amination of 2-oxoglutarate using the amide of glutamine as the N donor. There are distinct GS isoenzymes in vascular plants. GS1 resides in the cytoplasm of leaf cells and cells of nonphotosynthetic tissue. GS2 is encoded by a single gene in most plants and is located in plastids (102, 167). The cytoplasmic and chloroplast isoforms of GS of Chlamydomonas are similar to the GS enzymes of vascular plants (28). The genes encoding different GS isoforms are also developmentally and temporally regulated (64, 154, 256).

Several plants harbor a number of different genes encoding GS1 (209, 317); many of these genes exhibit tissue-specific expression and are developmentally regulated. A specific *GS1* gene is expressed in nodules of leguminous plants where high levels of NH_4^+ may be generated and converted into organic molecules (110, 241). GS1 is also important during the senescence of leaves in which protein N must be remobilized and exported to plant sinks (208). Maize root GS1 is encoded by five distinct genes with different expression patterns within the root tissue (154). GS_{1-3} and GS_{1-4} are constitutive and expressed throughout the root. GS_{1-2} is predominantly expressed in vascular tissue, while the transcripts from GS_{1-1} and GS_{1-5} are present in cortical tissue. GS1 of the root cortex is likely to be involved in the assimilation of external NH_4^+ (279). Furthermore, specific upregulation of GS_{1-1} and GS_{1-5} occurs upon administration of NH_4^+ whereas high NH_4^+ levels depress the activities of GS_{1-3} and GS_{1-4} (253). Interestingly, transgenic plants impaired for expression of GS1 in phloem companion cells exhibited a marked reduction in proline levels under conditions in which the plants were forced to assimilate high levels of NH_4^+. The plants were also more sensitive to water stress conditions (23). These results suggest that the phloem-associated GS1 isoform may control proline synthesis for both N storage and as an osmoticum to protect plants from conditions that lead to desiccation.

The plastid-localized GS2 isoform is predominantly expressed in leaf mesophyll cells and functions in primary assimilation of N (64) and recapture of NH_4^+ generated by photorespiration (64, 176, 274). GS2 mutants of barley cannot reassimilate NH_4^+ released from the photorespiratory pathway even though they synthesized cytosolic GS1 isoforms (319). Transgenic tobacco seedlings overexpressing GS2 also exhibited reduced levels of free leaf NH_4^+ and an increase in the pool of some amino acids (including glutamine and glutamate), although protein levels did not increase. Finally, the transgenic seedlings exhibited an increase in biomass, suggesting that the levels of GS2 protein may be limiting to biomass production (178). Expression of GS2 is regulated by several factors including light, sucrose concentrations, and the levels of NO_3^- and amino acids (40, 64, 199). Although addition of NO_3^- can stimulate GS2 expression, there is also a dramatic induction of GS2 mRNA by light; this induction is mediated in part by light-induced changes in C metabolite levels and in part by phytochrome (199). The GS1 genes are also upregulated by light, but the increase in abundance is primarily a consequence of changes in C metabolite levels. In addition to influencing levels of GS transcripts, sucrose may modulate GS enzyme activity (176, 199). Amino acids such as glutamine, glutamate, asparagine, and aspartate antagonize the sucrose-stimulated increases in GS mRNA and enzyme activity. In general, it appears that metabolic regulation of GS expression in plants reflects the relative abundance of C skeletons and amino acids. These regulatory features are similar to those associated with both the uptake and reduction of NO_3^-. Furthermore, posttranscriptional processes control tobacco GS2 (178).

Glutamine:2-Oxoglutarate Aminotransferase

Chlamydomonas and vascular plants have two classes of the iron sulfur protein glutamate synthase or GOGAT. The reductant used by one form of GOGAT is NADH whereas the other uses reduced Fd (88, 169). The Fd-GOGAT is plastid-localized (147, 267) and often accounts for over 90% of GOGAT activity in leaves and over 60% in roots (274, 281).

Expression of the Fd-GOGAT genes is controlled by NO_3^- (252) and light (15, 251, 287). In Arabidopsis there are two distinct Fd-GOGAT genes, Glu1 and

Glu2. *Glu1* mRNA is prevalent in leaves and increases in the light or upon administration of sucrose whereas *Glu2* mRNA is most abundant in roots and exhibits constitutive expression (36, 141). The *gls1* mutant of Arabidopsis contains less than 5% of the Fd-GOGAT activity. This mutant exhibits a conditional lethal phenotype, dying under conditions that enhance photorespiration (274). The *Glu1* gene and the *gls1* mutant map to the same region of chromosome 5 (*Glu2* maps to a different location) (36). Furthermore, although the *gls1* mutant is rescued from lethality under conditions of high CO_2 (e.g. 1% CO_2), it is still somewhat chlorotic relative to wild-type Arabidopsis plants (36). These results suggest that the leaf-specific *Glu1* Fd-GOGAT is important for the primary assimilation of NH_4^+ and recapture of NH_4^+ generated by photorespiration (36, 255). The root-specific Fd-GOGAT encoded by *Glu2* is likely to function in primary N assimilation and re-assimilation of catabolically generated NH_4^+.

There are also a number of distinct NADH-GOGAT isoforms. In rice, the root isoforms have been localized to the apical meristem, the central cylinder, and the primordia of secondary roots, and their levels strongly increase in epidermal and exodermal cells following administration of NH_4^+ (118). Furthermore, NADH-GOGAT and GS1 are coordinately regulated (107, 118). These enzymes, mostly in roots, function in primary assimilation of NH_4^+ generated from soil NO_3^- and NH_4^+ (197) and re-assimilation of NH_4^+ released during seed germination and amino acid catabolism (288). The NADH-GOGAT is also important for the assimilation of NH_4^+ produced as a consequence of N_2 fixation in root nodules (263, 303).

Additional Regulatory Considerations

Little is known about regulatory proteins that control N metabolism in plants. GS activity in bacteria is regulated at posttranscriptional/posttranslational levels by the PII protein (120). A nuclear-encoded, chloroplast-localized PII homolog, designated GLB1, was isolated from Arabidopsis (114). GLB1 lacks the conserved tryrosine-51 that is uridylylated in bacterial PII (this modification is important for controlling PII activity), but GLB1 mRNA increases in plants exposed to sucrose and decreases in plants exposed to glutamine, asparagine, and aspartate. These characteristics of GLB1 expression suggest that it plays a role in regulating N metabolism in plants.

The transcriptional regulator Nit2 controls expression of N assimilation genes in Chlamydomonas (262) and fungi (171). This protein binds to GATA elements in the promoters of N-regulated genes (327). The promoter of the spinach *Nii* gene contains GATA elements that could bind the zinc finger domain of the *Neurospora crassa* NIT2 protein (227). A cDNA encoding a GATA-1 zinc finger protein with homology to NIT2 has been identified in tobacco (43), but its role in the control of N metabolism is not known.

NO_3^- control of gene activity is not understood at a mechanistic level. Two distinct regulatory pathways appear to control the expression of the N and C assimilation genes. Induction of genes for N assimilation enzymes by NO_3^- may involve calcium and protein phosphorylation. In contrast, induction of the *PEP* carboxylase gene (and other genes encoding enzymes of the C4 dicarboxylic acid cycle) by NO_3^- requires synthesis and accumulation of cytokinin in roots (278, 280). One regulatory element induced in maize by both NO_3^- and cytokinin is ZmRR1; this protein is similar to response regulators of two component regulatory systems (254). The Arabidopsis homologs, *ARR3 – ARR7*, show elevated transcript levels in response to NO_3^- and cytokinin treatments (286). More detailed biochemical investigations should reveal the roles of these regulatory elements in N metabolism and the relationships of cytokinin to this process.

SULFUR

Sulfur in the Environment

S is an essential element present in proteins, lipids, intermediary metabolites, molecules involved in photoprotection, electron carriers, and redox controllers. Sulfur can be limiting in the environment and may limit plant productivity in certain agricultural settings.

There is no specific S storage compound within cells, so plant growth is dependent on external S sources. The majority of S taken up from the soil solution by microorganisms and plants is the SO_4^{2-} anion. Assimilation of SO_4^{2-} involves reduction to sulfide and the subsequent synthesis of cysteine and methionine. SO_4^{2-} in soils is often covalently bonded to organic molecules. The two main classes of organic S compounds that occur in soils are SO_4^{2-} esters and sulfonates. Furthermore, plants and microorganisms release a variety of organic compounds containing S (e.g. proteins, lipids, polysaccharides) when they die.

Sulfate Utilization by Chlamydomonas

Arylsulfatase   Many soil organisms access the S bonded to organic molecules through the synthesis and secretion of sulfatases and sulfonatases. Chlamydomonas synthesizes a prominent, extracellular arylsulfatase (Ars) in response to S limitation (264). This arylsulfatase has been purified to homogeneity and characterized, and the *Ars* gene has been cloned (50, 51). Expression of the *Ars* gene is positively controlled by the Sac1 protein during S starvation and repressed by the Sac3 protein during S-replete growth (47–49). The Ars protein is tightly associated with the Chlamydomonas cell wall and is synthesized as a preprotein with a signal sequence that is cleaved during export from the cell (51). The extracellular location of Ars allows it to hydrolyze soluble SO_4^{2-} esters in the medium, thereby releasing free SO_4^{2-} for assimilation by the cell. No *Ars* gene has been identified to date in vascular plants.

Sulfate Transport and Assimilation SO_4^{2-} is taken up by plants and microorganisms by specific transport systems and is either used for direct sulfation of compounds or is assimilated following reduction and incorporation into cysteine (153, 247, 272). Eukaryotic organisms have multiple transport systems for SO_4^{2-} uptake. Generally, systems capable of high-affinity SO_4^{2-} uptake increase when S levels in the environment drop and the cells are deprived of S (32, 106, 145, 328).

When Chlamydomonas is starved for S there is a dramatic increase in the V_{max} and decrease in the K_m for SO_4^{2-} transport (328). Recently a gene for an inducible SO_4^{2-} transporter, probably with high affinity for its substrate, has been isolated from Chlamydomonas. This gene is activated during S-limited growth and controlled by Sac1, although it is not clear if it is located on the plasma membrane or chloroplast envelope (J Davies, personal communication).

Sulfate Utilization by Plants

Sulfate Transport   Genes encoding high-affinity SO_4^{2-} transporters have been isolated from *Stylosanthes hamata* (270), *Arabidopsis thaliana* (284, 285), and barley (271, 310). Levels of transcripts for these transporters increase in plant roots following S starvation. Arabidopsis has multiple genes encoding SO_4^{2-} transporters; these genes have been designated *Sultr*, with the Sultr1 group representing high-affinity transporters and the Sultr2 group representing transporters with a lower affinity for SO_4^{2-}. Expression of *Sultr1;1* was noted in root hairs as well as in epidermal and cortical cells of roots (284) whereas *Sultr1;2* expression was primarily in the root cortex (Accession number AB042322; H Takahashi, unpublished data). These data suggest that high-affinity transporters are synthesized in the outer cell layers of roots and help maximize SO_4^{2-} uptake under starvation conditions.

Once taken up by roots, SO_4^{2-} is translocated symplastically through endodermal cells to the stele. Inside the stele, SO_4^{2-} is transferred to xylem parenchyma cells, either by moving symplastically or by re-absorption of SO_4^{2-} that leaks into the intracellular space. The SO_4^{2-} is exported from xylem parenchyma cells and loaded into xylem vessels for distribution to various plant tissues. Two low-affinity Arabidopsis transporters probably play roles in the internal translocation of SO_4^{2-} from roots to leaves. The Sultr2;1 low-affinity transporter ($K_m \sim 0.4$ mM) is located in the pericycle and xylem parenchyma cells of the root stele, and in phloem and xylem parenchyma cells of leaf veins (284, 285). Under conditions of S limitation, expression of *Sultr2;1* increases in roots and declines in leaves. This transporter may function to re-absorb SO_4^{2-} that leaks from vascular tissue into the intercellular space. Upregulation of *Sultr2;1* in roots during S starvation would partly contribute to maintaining efficient transfer of SO_4^{2-} to leaves. The Sultr2;2 transporter is expressed in the root phloem and leaf bundle sheath cells; it has an even lower affinity for SO_4^{2-} ($K_m > 1.2$ mM) (284) than Sultr2;1. This transporter is probably responsible for distributing SO_4^{2-} from the vascular bundle to palisade and mesophyll cells. *Sultr2;2* mRNA levels in leaves increase when plants experience low SO_4^{2-} condition, whereas leaf *Sultr2;1* mRNA declines under the same conditions. The coordinated expression of these two low-affinity transporters may optimize the distribution of SO_4^{2-} in leaf tissue when the plants are limited for S.

Once inside the cells of leaves, SO_4^{2-} is either transported into chloroplasts for assimilation or stored in vacuoles. Sultr4;1 is a unique SO_4^{2-} transporter isoform that is localized to Arabidopsis chloroplasts (283). The mRNA for *Sultr4;1* accumulates to high levels in leaves of S-starved plants (285). This transporter is likely involved in the uptake of SO_4^{2-} by chloroplasts, the major site of reductive assimilation. Vacuolar influx and efflux of SO_4^{2-} requires specific transporters on the tonoplast membrane; the genes and proteins involved in vacuolar transport have not been identified.

Sulfate Reduction   Once SO_4^{2-} enters cells it is activated by ATP sulfurylase to form adenosine 5'-phosphosulfate (APS). ATP sulfurylase isoforms in plants are located either in plastids or in the cytosol (166, 265). The cDNAs for these isoforms were first isolated from potato (130). In Arabidopsis there appear to be at least three plastidic and one putative cytosolic ATP sulfurylase (105, 152, 162). The APS generated by ATP sulfurylase can serve as a substrate for SO_4^{2-} reduction or can be phosphorylated by APS kinase to yield 3'-phosphoadenosine 5'-phosphosulfate (PAPS) (4, 149). PAPS is the substrate of various sulfotransferases to catalyze the sulfation of a range of metabolites including flavanols, choline, and glucosides (305).

The SO_4^{2-} of APS is reduced to sulfite by the plastid-localized APS sulfotransferase (243), also called APS reductase (104, 268). The reductant used by the enzyme is probably reduced glutathione (215); a domain of the enzyme resembles a glutathione-dependent reductase (18). mRNA for APS sulfotransferase accumulates during S starvation, suggesting that a key juncture for controlling assimilatory processes occurs at the point at which APS interacts with either APS kinase or APS sulfotransferase (104, 285). Interestingly, mRNAs encoding ATP sulfurylase and APS sulfotransferase accumulate upon exposure of plants to cadmium. This increase in expression may allow for the efficient synthesis of phytochelatin (148). The SO_3^{2-} generated in the APS sulfotransferase reaction is reduced to sulfide by plastid sulfite reductase. A gene encoding sulfite reductase has recently been identified (22). Electrons used for SO_3^{2-} reduction are donated by reduced ferredoxin (329).

Cysteine Synthesis   Cysteine is synthesized from sulfide and O-acetylserine (OAS) in a reaction catalyzed by O-acetylserine(thiol)lyase, which is present in the cytosol, plastids, and mitochondria (166). cDNA clones encoding different isoforms of O-acetylserine(thiol)lyase have been isolated from various plants (96, 109, 249). The mRNA for the cytosolic isoform of the Arabidopsis enzyme was highest in trichomes under normal growth conditions (96), and it accumulated in leaves and shoots following salt stress (13). The induction of the gene under high salt conditions may allow for the synthesis of the osmoprotectant 3-dimethylsulfoniopropionate (131). Furthermore, overexpression of O-acetylserine(thiol)lyase in transgenic tobacco increased the tolerance of the plant to H_2S gas and sulfite (248, 331), probably because these potentially toxic compounds could be more rapidly assimilated.

Serine acetyltransferase, which catalyzes the formation of OAS, is localized in the cytosol, chloroplasts, and mitochondria (245). The activity of cytosolic serine acetyltransferase is inhibited at micromolar concentrations of cysteine, suggesting stringent feedback control (194, 250). Furthermore, the level of plastid serine acetyltransferase mRNA increases upon S starvation (283). Serine acetyltransferase is associated with O-acetylserine(thiol)lyase in the cysteine synthase complex (20). The complex is inefficient in synthesizing cysteine (58) and free O-acetylserine(thiol)lyase appears to be responsible for cysteine synthesis. Overexpression of the serine acetyltransferase gene in tobacco chloroplasts increased both cysteine and GSH levels, and the plants were more tolerant to oxidative stress (19).

Methionine Synthesis   Methionine is synthesized from cysteine and O-phosphohomoserine (OPH) through the three consecutive reactions catalyzed by cystathionine γ-synthase, cystathionine β-lyase, and methionine synthase (230). Cystathionine γ-synthase, localized to chloroplasts, catalyzes cystathionine formation (228, 229). Its activity is controlled by the availability of OPH and S-adenosylmethionine. OPH, which is generated from aspartate, can serve as substrates for both cystathionine γ-synthase and threonine synthase. The relative activities of these enzymes are controlled by the S status of cells. Threonine synthase is most active during S-replete growth when the levels of S-adenosylmethionine are high (42). However, when S-adenosylmethionine levels drop, threonine synthase activity declines and a greater proportion of the OPH is converted to methionine via cystathionine γ-synthase (229). The gene encoding cystathionine γ-synthase has been cloned from Arabidopsis (127). Antisense suppression of cystathionine γ-synthase levels was lethal in homozygous transgenic plants, indicating that cystathionine synthesis in chloroplasts is a dominant pathway (and perhaps the only pathway) for methionine synthesis (230). Interestingly, recent work with Arabidopsis has demonstrated that cystathionine γ-synthase mRNA is controlled at the level of stability and that this stability is governed by a sequence present in the first exon of the gene. This *cis*-acting destabilization of the mRNA is triggered either by methionine or a methionine metabolite (31).

In plants and bacteria, α,β-elimination of cystathionine by cystathionine β-lyase generates homocysteine; the enzyme activity is present in plant cell chloroplasts (57, 318). The gene encoding cystathionine β-lyase appears to be represented as a single copy on the Arabidopsis genome (232). The native recombinant cystathionine β-lyase is a tetramer of four identical 46-kDa subunits, each associated with one molecule of pyridoxal 5'-phosphate. The physicochemical properties of the plant enzyme are similar to those reported for bacterial enzymes (57, 231).

Methionine synthase catalyzes the methylation of homocysteine to generate methionine. Methionine synthase genes of plants and algae encode cobalamin-independent enzymes with no presequences characteristic of transit peptides

(85, 140). The level of methionine synthase mRNA increases several fold in Chlamydomonas gametes activated by fertilization (140), which may be important for adhesion-induced processes that accompany fertilization.

Glutathione Synthesis   GSH and GSSH, reduced and oxidized forms of glutathione, respectively, are readily interchangeable. This tripeptide (γ-Glu-Cys-Gly) is the dominant non-protein thiol in plants (236) and can play a role in regulating the uptake of SO_4^{2-} by plant roots (108, 143). It is also a substrate for GSH-S-transferases, which are important for detoxification of xenobiotics (142, 168), and is the precursor of phytochelatins, peptides that enable plant cells to cope with heavy metals in the environment (98, 261). GSH is an abundant antioxidant in cells and supports redox buffering (139). The synthesis of GSH occurs in plastids by a two-step reaction catalyzed by γ-glutamylcysteine synthetase and GSH synthetase; genes encoding both have been isolated from Arabidopsis (234).

Exposure of plants to cadmium induces phytochelatin synthesis. This heavy metal chelator is synthesized from GSH by phytochelatin synthase and consists of repetitions of the γ-glutamylcysteine dipeptide that terminates with a glycine (33, 34). Mutants defective in phytochelatin synthesis are sensitive to heavy metals (35) whereas overexpression of γ-glutamylcysteine synthetase or GSH synthetase in *Brassica juncea* allowed increased cadmium tolerance (338, 339).

Regulation

In general, high concentrations of cysteine and glutathione repress S assimilation activities while S starvation results in increased activities of key enzymes in the assimilatory pathway. Administration of high concentrations of cysteine and glutathione to plant roots leads to lowered steady-state levels of mRNAs for the SO_4^{2-} transporter, ATP sulfurylase, and APS sulfotransferase (21, 144). Glutathione, which is readily transported through the phloem sap, may be a signaling molecule that represses the activity of genes encoding key enzymes in the S assimilation pathway (144). Plant roots subjected to exogenous OAS exhibit an increase in accumulation of mRNA encoding the SO_4^{2-} transporter (271) and APS sulfotransferase (133). Limited evidence derived from studies of plant systems suggests that, as in bacteria, a number of the S starvation responses are linked to the concentration of OAS.

Recently, specific proteins involved in the regulation of Chlamydomonas to S deprivation have been identified. Most responses of Chlamydomonas to S limitation require the Sac1 protein. A *sac1* mutant of Chlamydomonas exhibited abnormal SO_4^{2-} uptake and was unable to synthesize extracellular arylsulfatase, as well as other extracellular proteins, in response to S deprivation. The inability of the *sac1* strain to properly respond to S limitation is reflected in the rapid decline in viability of mutant cells following exposure to S deprivation (47). This decline in viability reflects an inability of the mutant to modify metabolic processes, such as photosynthesis, as the alga experiences sulfur limitation.

Interestingly, the *Sac1* gene product is predicted to be a polypeptide with similarity to ion transporters (46; J Davies & AR Grossman, unpublished). The deduced polypeptide sequence of Sac1 and the phenotype of the *sac1* mutant display some similarities with the sequence of Snf3 of yeast and the phenotype of the *snf3* mutant, respectively. Snf3 is a yeast regulatory protein that governs the expression of genes involved in hexose utilization (201, 202). The similarity between Sac1 and Snf3 raises the possibility that polypeptides whose original function was to bind and transport various substrates into cells may have evolved into regulatory elements.

Another mutant, *sac3*, was selected for low-level constitutive Ars activity. In addition, SO_4^{2-} transport could not be activated to the same extent as in wild-type cells (49). These results suggest that *Sac3* encodes a negative regulator of *Ars* gene activity and a positive regulator of gene(s) encoding the SO_4^{2-} transport system. *Sac3* encodes a putative serine-threonine kinase; the exact mechanism by which this kinase modulates the transcription of genes in both a positive and negative sense requires additional analyses.

PHOSPHATE

Phosphate in the Environment

The prevalent form of available P in the environment is Pi, which is a major component of nucleic acids, phospholipids, and intermediary metabolites. P occurs both in the intracellular and extracellular environment as the free Pi anion, precipitated Pi salts, Pi esters such as phytates, and more rarely as phosphonates; much of the P in soil is not readily available to plants. Crop yields are often limited by Pi availability and, as a consequence, high levels of Pi are important components of commercial fertilizers. A considerable proportion of this supplementary Pi is leached from agricultural fields and deposited into nearby lakes and rivers, triggering rapid algal blooms that cause eutrophication and fish kills.

Phosphatases and Phosphate Transport in Chlamydomonas

Phosphatases   Yeast has served as a model system for elucidating how P conditions modulate gene expression, primarily through the analysis of phosphatase activities (see the complete version of the text at http://www.annualreviews.org/pubs/supmat/supmat.asp). Less is known for Chlamydomonas and vascular plants. Chlamydomonas does synthesize a number of phosphatases during P limitation. Two Chlamydomonas acid phosphatases are constitutively expressed, although their levels increase when the cells are limited for P (172, 173). There is also a neutral phosphatase and two alkaline phosphatases that accumulate upon P starvation (163, 164). Mutants that exhibit aberrant expression of the various phosphatases have been isolated (164, 165, 172). Subcellular locations of some phosphatases have been determined; one of the acid phosphatases is in the vacuole, the second may be associated with the cell wall, while the neutral and alkaline phosphatases are extracellular and probably associated with the cell wall (173, 206).

Quisel et al (224) have identified and characterized phosphatases that accumulate in the periplasmic space upon exposure of Chlamydomonas to P limitation. The majority of periplasmic phosphatase activity behaves like a 5′ nucleotidase and has a monomeric molecular mass of approximately 190 kDa. A second periplasmic phosphatase (10% of the total) has a molecular mass of approximately 73 kDa and can slowly hydrolyze IMP and AMP. The third periplasmic species (<5% of the total) can be resolved from the other two activities by column chromotography (224), although the polypeptide responsible for this activity has not been identified. Other genes that are activated during P starvation encode enolase, pyruvate-formate lyase, and two ribosomal proteins; some of the genes may also be induced under other growth-limiting conditions (63).

Phosphate Transport   Pi transport into Chlamydomonas cells has recently been characterized (269). Upon P starvation the V_{max} for Pi transport increases by a factor of 10 to 20. Furthermore, both a low- and high-affinity kinetic component can be distinguished. The K_m for low-affinity transport was between 10 and 20 μM Pi and that of the high-affinity transporter was between 0.1 and 0.5 μM. Low-affinity transport dominates when cells are maintained on complete medium. After 24 h of P starvation, Pi uptake is essentially all via the high-affinity system.

Phosphatatases and Phosphate Transport in Plants

Several visual changes occur when plants are limited for P. Older leaves experiencing P limitation exhibit an overall slowing of growth, increased root-to-shoot ratio, decreased production of lateral roots, increased length and density of root hairs, and they accumulate anthocyanin (170). Biochemical changes observed in plants starved for P include an increase in the fixed C storage reserves and elevated levels of lipids and phenolics and the production of phosphatases (76, 94, 95). Roots of some P-starved plants exude organic acids such as malate and citrate (113). Increased rhizosphere acidity may mobilize soil Pi, facilitating uptake in the immediate vicinity of the root.

Phosphatases and Rnases   Phosphate starvation causes increased accumulation of intracellular and/or extracellular acid phosphatase (APase). This response has been noted for many plants (e.g. 62, 298; see the expanded article for additional references at http://www.annualreviews.org/pubs/supmat/supmat.asp). These phosphatases probably serve the same purpose in plants as they do in bacteria, yeasts, and algae: They increase the level of available Pi by hydrolyzing Pi-esters in the soil. Intracellular phosphatases may also increase during P limitation and help mobilize internal Pi stores.

Phosphatases have been characterized to some extent from different plant species (95, 103, 193, 204). Goldstein et al (94) demonstrated that P starvation resulted in an increase in the APase activity secreted from tomato seedlings and that the activity was associated with a 57-kDa extracellular protein. Duff et al (59, 60) resolved two acid phosphatases (APases) from *B. nigra*. One of these enzymes was vacuolar and had significant specificity for PEP (59). Little is known about genes encoding plant APases. An APase gene from nematode-resistant tomato (324) has been isolated; the sequence of this APase is unlike that of any other characterized from nonplant tissue. However, it shows some sequence similarity to soybean vegetative storage proteins (53, 246), which appear to be capable of hydrolyzing Pi from several different substrates, but are most effective on short chain polyphosphates (53).

In addition to the production of phosphatases, plants produce other hydrolytic enzymes that help scavenge Pi from intracellular or extracellular sources. In tomato, four RNases induced upon P starvation have been characterized (122, 160, 161). Three of these RNases are vacuolar and probably function in the release of Pi from cellular RNA. Nürnberger et al (195) identified a periplasmic RNase of tomato that was specifically synthesized during P limitation and presumed to be important for releasing ribonucleotides from RNA in the soil.

RNase genes of Arabidopsis have also been characterized (reviewed in 97). The genes encoding S-like ribonucleases, including RNS1 and RNS2, are strongly induced in Arabidopsis during P starvation. These RNases are part of the T-2 ribonuclease family, which includes members that also function in gametophytic self-incompatibility in plants (191). Recently, antisense constructs were used to suppress expression of RNS1 and RNS2 of Arabidopsis (12). The transgenic plants with reduced levels of RNases showed increased anthocyanin accumulation, which is often induced by Pi stress.

Phosphate Transport   Several studies have demonstrated that P limitation can elevate the V_{max} for Pi uptake via an increase in high-affinity transport (see http://www.annualreviews.org/pubs/supmat/supmat.asp). The uptake of Pi by plants is metabolically driven, and the Pi concentration in the xylem sap can be 400 times that of the soil solution. The main form of Pi transported into plants is $H_2PO_4^-$, which becomes prominent in acid soils. Only recently have a number of different genes encoding Pi transport proteins of plants been isolated and characterized (see 225). Like the NO_3^- and SO_4^{2-} transporters, the Pi transporters have 12 membrane-spanning helices. Transcripts for high-affinity Pi transporters often preferentially accumulate in root tissue (44, 159), and the genes are often induced when plants are starved for P (150, 159, 185, 186). Recently, antibodies were used to demonstrate that in addition to the LePT1 (high-affinity transporter in tomato) transcript, the LePT1 protein rapidly increases in the plasma membrane of tomato root cells following P starvation (186). High-affinity Pi transporters have also been shown to be present in leaves, tubers, stems, and flowers (150, 159); they may function to distribute Pi within the plant tissue. This is supported by the phenotype of the *pho1* mutant, which is defective in loading Pi into the xylem (213), and the *pho2* mutant, which may have aberrant phloem transport (54). Pi transporters are also associated with plant mitochondria (282) and plastids (79), and specific plant Pi transporters may interface with mycorrhizal fungi and facilitate the transfer of nutrients from the fungus to the plant (242).

There are reports of six high-affinity Pi transporters (AtPT1-AtPT6) in Arabidopsis (159, 182, 272), and sequence information suggests the existence of an additional three (*AtPT7–AtPT9*; BAC F9H16.16, Accession numbers AC015450, AC007551) (225). None of the nine *PT* genes are allelic with genes altered in the *pho1* and *pho2* mutants (225). Recently, a gene encoding a low-affinity transporter, *Pht2;1*, was also isolated from Arabidopsis (45). This transporter appears to be a Pi:H^+ symporter with 12 membrane-spanning helices. It is constitutively expressed in Arabidopsis leaves and may function in the allocation of Pi within shoots.

The distinct location of the individual Pi transporters in plants reflects the need of the plant to balance Pi levels within its tissue and suggests that control of transport activities may be complex and strongly linked to physiological conditions. This Pi homeostasis is also controlled by Pi efflux from the cell and the flux of Pi in and out of the vacuole; these processes maintain a relatively constant concentration of Pi within the cytoplasm (181). The transporters on tonoplast membranes have yet to be identified.

Phosphorus Limitation and Metabolism

P limitation causes modification of various metabolic pathways. In P-starved Arabidopsis the levels of phospholipids decline whereas levels of sulfolipids increase; this increase was also reflected by an increase in expression of at least one gene important for sulfolipid biosynthesis (68). Furthermore, the *pho1* mutant (213) of Arabidopsis also showed decreased levels of phospholipids and increased levels of sulfolipids. These data suggest that one compensatory response for phospholipid deficiency is elevation of sulfolipid production, perhaps to help preserve the anionic character of plant thylakoid membranes (68).

There are also significant modifications with respect to activities associated with the glycolytic pathway. PEP phosphatase (the PEP-specific, vacuolar APase), which catalyzes the formation of pyruvate and Pi from PEP, increases in specific activity during P deprivation in both *Brassica nigra* (60) and *Selenastrum minutum* (90, 290); it generates pyruvate, effectively substituting for pyruvate kinase. Although the reaction is metabolically wasteful (ATP is generated by the pyruvate kinase reaction but not by PEP phosphatase), it would eliminate the need for phosphorylated adenylates, which would be limiting during P deprivation, in the conversion of PEP to pyruvate. This may increase the capacity of the cell to synthesize key glycolytic intermediates during P-limited growth.

Other enzymes have also been identified that might serve bypass functions described. PEP carboxylase, which catalyzes the carboxylation of PEP to form malate and Pi, also increases in *B. nigra* during P limitation (61). If coupled with malate dehydrogenase and the NAD malic enzyme, it offers an alternate route for the formation of pyruvate. The levels of phosphofructophosphatase (PFP) and the nonphosphorylating, NADP-dependent glyceraldehyde-3-phosphate dehydrogenase (nonphosphorylating NADP-G3PDH) were elevated 20-fold during Pi-deprivation, whereas the level of the phosphorylation-dependent NAD glyceraldehyde-3-phosphate dehydrogenase (phosphorylating NAD-G3PDH) decreased by a factor of six (61, 289). The PFP reaction can substitute for the phosphofructokinase reaction while the nonphosphorylating NADP-G3PDH reaction can substitute for the coupled phosphorylating NAD-G3PDH/phosphoglycerate kinase reactions. Both PFP and nonphosphorylating NADP-G3PDH reduce the Pi pressure by circumventing the need for adenylates and Pi as substrates in glycolysis. Some of these reactions (PFP, PEP phosphatase, and PEPC) may also promote Pi-recycling by releasing Pi from P-esters, and add to the flexibility of the plant's metabolic machinery.

Although many bypass reactions offer some conservation of P and promote recycling of Pi, it is uncertain whether they significantly affect Pi availability for plant metabolism. Furthermore, some bypass reactions still require pyrophosphate as the high-energy Pi donor. An alternative interpretation of the data might be that during P deprivation the cells must lower the pool of adenylates (perhaps to limit certain metabolic processes). The decrease in adenylates may severely slow the flux of metabolites through glycolysis. To sustain glycolysis at a rate needed for cell maintenance, specific steps of the glycolytic pathway are changed, making the pathway less sensitive to decreased adenylate levels.

Regulation

Control of the P deprivation responses may reflect a variety of regulatory mechanisms that operate at different levels. It is likely to include cellular responses, responses elicited by long-distance communication between different tissue types, and responses triggered by changes in metabolite pools, redox levels, and growth rates. For most responses, it is likely that the internal Pi supply is the dominant regulatory factor. This is supported by results of split root experiments in which one half of the tomato root system was placed in P-sufficient medium and the other in medium devoid of P. Transcripts encoding the Pi transporters LePT1 and LePT2 remained low (not induced) on the side of the root exposed to medium devoid of Pi (158), suggesting that internal pools of Pi control acclimation responses.

Recently, a regulatory element involved in acclimation to P limitation has been isolated. The Chlamydomonas mutant *psr1* (phosphate starvation response) (326) is unable to induce the specific responses to P starvation. The mutant was complemented and the *Psr1* gene identified (326). The Psr1 protein contains domains characteristic of transcription regulators; the region from residues 187 to 245 has similarity to Cca1, an Arabidopsis transcription factor responsible for phytochrome-mediated regulation of the light-harvesting genes (321). This DNA binding domain is distantly related to the DNA binding domain of myb proteins.

Psr1 also contains three stretches rich in glutamine and a helix-loop-helix structure that are characteristic of eukaryotic transcription factors.

During P limitation, the levels of both *Psr1* transcript and protein increase. Immunocytochemical experiments have localized the Psr1 polypeptide to the nucleus (326); the level of Psr1 in the nucleus paralleled the increase in whole-cell Psr1 polypeptide during P-limited growth. The sequence of Psr1, its location in the cell, and the phenotype of the *psr1* mutant all suggest that the Psr1 protein functions as a regulator of cellular transcription that enables Chlamydomonas to acclimate to P-limited growth.

Interestingly, although Psr1 resembles proteins deduced from plant cDNA sequences, it does not resemble any protein encoded by the yeast genome. This raises the possibility that Pi metabolism in Chlamydomonas and possibly in vascular plants is regulated in a different way from that of nonphotosynthetic eukaryotes.

GENERAL RESPONSES TO NUTRIENT LIMITATION

Cell Division

Nutrient deprivation prevents cell cycle progression, a phenomenon examined in some detail in yeast. Both the cAMP-dependent (26, 294) and MAP kinase (37, 123) pathways control cell division during nutrient-limited growth. Specific regulators of S metabolism (292) are also involved in controlling cell cycle progression by modulating the degradation of components that influence the activity of cyclin-dependent kinases (125).

Cell Cycle/Cell Division/Elongation   Little is known about cell cycle control in eukaryotic algae or vascular plants, although a few intriguing observations have been reported. A *mat3* mutant of Chlamydomonas, which is aberrant for cell cycle control, is defective in a gene encoding a MAP kinase (J Uhman & U Goodenough, personal communication). Characterization of the root meristem-less *rml1* mutant suggests that cell division in Arabidopsis is partly associated with the control of S metabolism (309). The *rml1* mutant is unable to establish an active postembryonic meristem in the root apex and exhibits no cell division in roots (cell division continues in shoots). The *Rml1* gene encodes γ-glutamylcysteine synthetase, which catalyzes the first step of GSH synthesis. Addition of GSH rescues the phenotype of the mutant, suggesting a link between root meristem function and GSH levels.

Photosynthesis

Regulation of photosynthetic electron transport is a critical aspect of tailoring the metabolism of the cell to nutrient availability. Starvation of Chlamydomonas for S or P results in a decrease in O_2 evolution that correlates with a decline in electron flow through photosystem II (325). This decline in electron transport is a consequence of both a loss of reaction center activity and the formation of Q_B nonreducing centers (100), which are more resistant to photoinhibition and may function to dissipate excess absorbed light energy (189). Nutrient-limited Chlamydomonas cells also dissipate energy by nonphotchemical quenching of chlorophyll fluorescence (325), and are mostly in state 2, in which the majority of the antennae complexes of the photosynthetic apparatus are directing energy to photosystem I (86, 302). This results in a decreased yield of O_2 evolution at subsaturating light levels, which can be beneficial to nutrient-deprived organisms because it decreases the production of NADPH, favors ATP generation through cyclic electron flow, and allows cells to more effectively dissipate excess absorbed excitation energy.

Photosynthetic electron transport also declines when Chlamydomonas is deprived of N (207), although much of this reduction is due to the loss of the cytochrome b_6f complex. Furthermore, N-limited Chlamydomonas cells tend to be in state 2, resulting in a reduced ratio of photosystem II to photosystem I activity at subsaturating light levels (17). Similar to S- and P-starved Chlamydomonas cells, N-limited *Dunaliella tertiolectra*, and *Thalassiosira weissflogii* exhibit diminished photosytem II activity and retardation of electron flow from Q_A to Q_B.

Overall, these results suggest that profound changes in functional aspects of the photosynthetic apparatus occur when algae and plants are starved for nutrients. Effectors that generate these changes are not known although they may be sensitive to redox levels, oxidative stress, and/or changes in the pool of cellular metabolites. It will be important to determine the ways in which these signals interface with the metabolic machinery of the cell and how such signals might elicit senescence and cell death, modulate various developmental processes, and trigger changes in rates of turnover and synthesis of proteins, nucleic acids, and lipids.

CONCLUDING REMARKS

Many lessons are being learned from the analysis of nutrient utilization and the acclimation of plants to nutrient deprivation. The process of nutrient acquisition and assimilation is dynamic and is continually modulated with changing environmental conditions. Internal and external cues determine the details of nutrient management, and such cues may be perceived directly by the plant or indirectly sensed as changes in cellular redox conditions and/or metabolite pools. Phytochrome and blue light photoreceptors participate in controlling nutrient level-responsive genes, while C metabolites generated by photosynthesis clearly integrate into regulatory circuits that control N utilization.

Only now are we beginning to identify regulatory elements that govern specific responses of photosynthetic organisms to their environment. The identification of such regulatory elements in simple algal systems is stimulating reverse genetic approaches that may unmask regulators in vascular plants. However, the different cell and tissue types that occur in a vascular plant will necessitate specific allocation of nutrients to different plant organs and tissues, and this allocation will be controlled by both the developmental stage of the plant (including an influence of plant growth regulators) and environmental conditions. The control of nutrient allocation will require strategies for systemic communication among plant tissues and controlled synthesis of activities tailored to function in specific tissue/cell types and that respond to particular regulatory signals.

Researchers have begun to define processes critical for acquiring, assimilating, and distributing nutrients within plants. However, we will only develop a holistic understanding of the effects of nutrient conditions on plants by elucidating the integration of nutrient availability with other environmental cues, and with both the growth potential and the developmental stage of the plant.

ACKNOWLEDGMENTS

The authors would like to thank the National Science Foundation (Grants IBN9727836 and MCB9976765 to ARG) and USDA (Grants 97-35301-4575, 98-35301-6445, and 93-37100-9100) for continued support of our work on the acquisition and utilization of nutrients by photosynthetic organisms. HT was supported by a postdoctoral research fellowship (No. 6067) from the Japan Society for the Promotion of Science. We would also like to thank the National Science Foundation for fostering genome-wide studies of Chlamydomonas (MCB9975765). Unpublished information included in the text was generously provided by Dr John Davies and Dr Emilio Fernández. Finally, we thank Mark Stitt for informed and stimulating discussions. Because of the scope of this review and the limitations of the authors, we were unable to include the results of a considerable body of work from noteworthy manuscripts; we apologize to those whose work we have neglected. This is a Carnegie Institution Publication Number 1459.

Visit the Annual Reviews home page at www.AnnualReviews.org

LITERATURE CITED

1. Amarasinghe BHRR, deBruxelles GL, Braddon M, Onyeocha I, Forde BG, Udvardi MK. 1998. Regulation of *GmNRT2* expression and nitrate transport activity in roots of soybean (*Glycine max*). *Planta* 206:44–52

2. Aoki H, Ida S. 1994. Nucleotide sequence of a rice root ferredoxin-NADP$^+$ reductase cDNA and its induction by nitrate. *Biochim. Biophys. Acta* 1183:553–56

3. Aparicio PJ, Quiñones MA. 1991. Blue light, a positive switch signal for nitrate and nitrite uptake by the green alga *Monoraphidium braunii*. *Plant Physiol.* 95:374–78

4. Arz HE, Gisselmann G, Schiffmann S, Schwenn JD. 1994. A cDNA for adenylyl sulfate (APS) kinase from *Arabidopsis thaliana. Biochim. Biophys. Acta* 1218:447–52

5. Aslam M, Travis RL, Huffaker RC. 1992. A comparative kinetics and reciprocal inhibition of nitrate and nitrite uptake in roots of uninduced and induced barley (*Hordeum vulgare* L) seedlings. *Plant Physiol.* 99:1124–33

6. Aslam M, Travis RL, Huffaker RC. 1993. Comparative induction of nitrate and nitrite

uptake and reduction systems by ambient nitrate and nitrite in intact roots of barley (*Hordeum vulgare* L) seedlings. *Plant Physiol.* 102:811–19

7. Aslam M, Travis RL, Rains DW. 1996. Evidence for substrate induction of a nitrate efflux system in barley roots. *Plant Physiol.* 112:1167–75

8. Bachmann M, Huber JL, Liao P-C, Gage DA, Huber S. 1996. The inhibitor of phosphorylated nitrate reductase from spinach (*Spinachia oleracea*) is a 14-3-3 protein. *FEBS Lett.* 387:127–31

9. Bachmann M, Shiraishi N, Campbell WH, Yoo B-C, Harmon AC, Huber SC. 1996. Identification of Ser-543 as the major regulatory phosphorylation site in spinach leaf nitrate reductase. *Plant Cell* 8:505–17

10. Back E, Dunne W, Schneiderbauer A, de Framond A, Rastogi R, Rothstein SJ. 1991. Isolation of spinach nitrite reductase gene promoter which confers nitrate inducibility on GUS gene expression in tobacco. *Plant Mol Biol.* 17:9–18

11. Ball S. 1998. Regulation of starch biosynthesis. See Ref. 240a, pp. 549–67

12. Bariola PA, MacIntosh GC, Green PJ. 1999. Regulation of S-like ribonuclease levels in Arabidopsis. Antisense inhibition of RNS1 or RNS2 elevates anthocyanin accumulation. *Plant Physiol.* 119:331–42

13. Barroso C, Romero LC, Cejudo FJ, Vega JM, Gotor C. 1999. Salt-specific regulation of the cytosolic O-acetylserine (thiol)lyase gene from *Arabidopsis thaliana* is dependent on abscisic acid. *Plant Mol. Biol.* 40:729–36

14. Becker TW, Foyer C, Caboche M. 1992. Light-regulated expression of nitrate reductase and nitrite reductase genes in tomato and in the phytochrome-deficient *aurea* mutant of tomato. *Planta* 188:39–47

15. Becker TW, Nef-Campa C, Zehnacker C, Hirel B. 1993. Implication of the phytochrome in light regulation of the tomato

gene(s) encoding ferredoxin-dependent glutamate synthase. *Plant Physiol. Biochem.* 31:725–9

16. Deleted in proof

17. Berges JA, Charlebois DO, Mauzerall DC, Falkowski PG. 1996. Differential effects of nitrogen limitation on photosynthetic efficiency of photosystem I and II in microalgae. *Plant Physiol.* 110:689–96

18. Bick JA, Åslund F, Chen Y, Leustek T. 1998. Glutaredoxin function for the carboxyl terminal domain of the plant-type 5-adenylylsulfate reductase. *Proc. Natl. Acad. Sci. USA* 95:8404–9

19. Blaszczyk A, Brodzik R, Sirko A. 1999. Increased resistance to oxidative stress in transgenic tobacco plants overexpressing bacterial serine acetyltransferase. *Plant J.* 20:237–43

20. Bogdanova N, Hell R. 1997. Cysteine synthesis in plants: protein-protein interactions of serine acetyltransferase from *Arabidopsis thaliana*. *Plant J.* 11:251–62

21. Bolchi A, Petrucco S, Tenca P, Foroni C, Ottonello S. 1999. Coordinate modulation of maize sulfate permease and ATP sulfurylase mRNAs in response to variations in sulfur nutritional status: stereospecific down-regulation by L-cysteine. *Plant Mol. Biol.* 39:527–37

22. Bork C, Schwenn JD, Hell R. 1998. Isolation and characterization of a gene for assimilatory sulfite reductase from *Arabidopsis thaliana*. *Gene* 212:147–53

23. Brugière N, Dubois F, Limami AM, Lelandais M, Roux Y, et al. 1999. Glutamine synthetase in the phloem plays a major role in controlling proline production. *Plant Cell* 11:1995–2011

24. Deleted in proof

25. Campbell W, Kinghorn JR. 1990. Functional domains of assimilatory nitrate reductases and nitrite reductases. *Trends Biochem. Sci.* 15:315–19

26. Cannon JF, Tachell K. 1987. Characterization of *Saccharomyces cerevisiae* genes

encoding subunits of cyclic AMP-dependent protein kinase. *Mol. Cell. Biol.* 7:2653–63

27. Chen CM, Jin G, Andersen BR, Ertl JR. 1993. Modulation of plant gene expression by cytokinins. *Aust. J. Plant Physiol.* 20:609–19

28. Chen Q, Silflow CD. 1996. Isolation and characterization of glutamine synthetase genes in *Chlamydomonas reinhardtii*. *Plant Physiol.* 112:987–96

29. Cheng C-L, Acedo GN, Cristinsin M, Conkling MA. 1992. Sucrose mimics the light induction of Arabidopsis nitrate reductase gene transcription. *Proc. Natl. Acad. Sci. USA* 89:1861–64

30. Cheng C-L, Acedo GN, Dewdney J, Goodman HM, Conkling MA. 1991. Differential expression of the two *Arabidopsis* nitrate reductase genes. *Plant Physiol.* 96:275–79

31. Chiba Y, Ishikawa M, Kijima F, Tyson RH, Kim J, et al. 1999. Evidence for autoregulation of cystathionine γ-synthase mRNA stability in *Arabidopsis*. *Science* 286:1371–74

32. Clarkson D, Smith F, Van den Berg P. 1983. Regulation of sulfate transport in a tropical legume, *Macroptilium atropurpurum* cv. *Sirato*. *J. Exp. Bot.* 34:1463–83

33. Cobbett CS. 2000. Phytochelatins and their roles in heavy metal detoxification. *Plant Physiol.* 123:825–32

34. Cobbett CS. 1999. A family of phytochelatin synthase genes from plant, fungal and animal species. *Trends Plant Sci.* 4:335–37

35. Cobbett CS, May MJ, Howden R, Rolls B. 1998. The glutathione-deficient, cadmium-sensitive mutant, *cad2-1*, of *Arabidopsis thaliana* is deficient in γ-glutamylcysteine synthetase. *Plant J.* 16:73–78

36. Coschigano KT, Melo-Oliveira R, Lim J, Coruzzi GM. 1998. Arabidopsis *gls* mutants and distinct Fd-GOGAT genes: implication for photorespiration and primary nitrogen assimilation. *Plant Cell* 10:741–52

37. Costigan C, Snyder M. 1994. SLK1, a yeast homolog of MAP kinase activators, has a RAS/cAMP-independent role in nutrient sensing. *Mol. Gen. Genet.* 243:286–96

38. Crawford NM, Arst HN. 1993. The molecular genetics of nitrate assimilation in fungi and plants. *Annu. Rev. Genet.* 27:115–46

39. Crawford NM, Glass ADM. 1998. Molecular and physiological aspects of nitrate uptake in plants. *Trends Plant Sci.* 3:389–95

40. Cren M, Hirel B. 1999. Glutamine synthetase in higher plants: regulation of gene and protein expression from the organ to the cell. *Plant Cell Physiol.* 40:1187–93

41. Crete P, Caboche M, Meyer C. 1997. Nitrite reductase expression is regulated at the post-transcriptional level by the nitrogen source in *Nicotiana plumbaginifolia* and *Arabidopsis thaliana*. *Plant J.* 11:625–34

42. Curien G, Job D, Douce R, Dumas R. 1998. Allosteric activation of Arabidopsis threonine synthase by S-adenosylmethionine. *Biochem.* 37:13212–21

43. Daniel-Vedele F, Caboche M. 1993. A tobacco cDNA clone encoding a GATA-1 zinc finger protein homologous to regulators of nitrogen metabolism in fungi. *Mol. Gen. Genet.* 240:365–73

44. Daram P, Brunner S, Persson BL, Amrhein N, Bucher M. 1998. Functional analysis and cell-specific expression of a phosphate transporter from tomato. *Planta* 206:225–33

45. Daram P, Brunner S, Rausch C, Steiner C, Amrhein N, Bucher M. 1999. Pht2;1 encodes a low-affinity phosphate transporter from Arabidopsis. *Plant Cell* 11:2153–66

46. Davies J, Grossman AR. 1998. Responses to deficiencies in macronutrients. See Ref. 240a, pp. 613–35

47. Davies J, Yildiz F, Grossman AR. 1996. Sac1, a putative regulator that is critical for survival of *Chlamydomonas reinhardtii* during sulfur deprivation. *EMBO J.* 15:2150–59

48. Davies J, Yildiz F, Grossman AR. 1994.

Mutants of *Chlamydomonas* with aberrant responses to sulfur deprivation. *Plant Cell* 6:53–63

49. Davies J, Yildiz F, Grossman AR. 1999. Sac3, an SNF1-like serine/threonine kinase that positively and negatively regulates the responses of Chlamydomonas to sulfur limitation. *Plant Cell* 11:1179–90

50. de Hostos EL, Schilling J, Grossman AR. 1989. Structure and expression of the gene encoding the periplasmic arylsulfatase of *Chlamydomonas reinhardtii*. *Mol. Gen. Genet.* 218:229–39

51. de Hostos EL, Togasaki RK, Grossman AR. 1988. Purification and biosynthesis of a derepressible periplasmic arylsulfatase from *Chlamydomonas reinhardtii*. *J. Cell Biol.* 106:9–37

51a. de Kok LJ, Stulen I, Rennenberg H, Brunold C, Rauser WE, eds. 1993. *Sulfur Nutrition and Sulfur Assimilation in Higher Plants*. The Hague: SPB Acad.

52. Deng X-W, Casper T, Quail PH. 1991. *cop1*: a regulatory locus involved in light-controlled development and gene expression in *Arabidopsis*. *Genes Dev.* 5:1172–82

53. DeWald DB, Mason HS, Mullet JE. 1992. The soybean vegetative storage proteins VSP-α and VSP-β are acid phosphatases active on polyphosphates. *J. Biol. Chem.* 267:15958–64

54. Dong B, Rengel Z, Delhaize E. 1998. Uptake and translocation of phosphate by *pho2* mutant and wild-type seedlings of *Arabidopsis thaliana*. *Planta* 205:251–56

55. Douglas P, Moorhead G, Hong Y, Morrice N, MacKintosh C. 1998. Purification of a nitrate reductase kinase from *Spinachia oleracea* leaves, and its identification as a calmodulin-domain protein kinase. *Planta* 206:435–42

56. Douglas P, Pigaglio E, Ferrer A, Halford NG, MacKintosh C. 1997. Three spinach leaf nitrate reductase-3-hydroxy-3-methylglutaryl-CoA reductase kinases that are regulated by reversible phosphorylation and/or Ca^{2+} ions. *Biochem. J.* 325:101–9

57. Droux M, Ravanel S, Douce R. 1995. Methionine biosynthesis in higher plants. I. Purification and characterization of cystathionine β-lyase from spinach chloroplasts. *Arch. Biochem. Biophys.* 316:585–95

58. Droux M, Ruffet M-L, Douce R, Job D. 1998. Interactions between serine acetyltransferase and *O*-acetylserine (thiol) lyase in higher plants. *Eur. J. Biochem.* 255:235–45

59. Duff SMG, Lefebvre DD, Plaxton WC. 1989. Purification and characterization of a phosphoenolpyruvate phosphatase from *Brassica nigra* suspension cells. *Plant Physiol.* 90:734–41

60. Duff SMG, Lefebvre DD, Plaxton WC. 1991. Purification, characterization and subcellular localization of an acid phosphatase from *Brassica nigra* suspension cells. Comparison with phospho*enol* pyruvate phosphatase. *Arch. Biochem. Biophys.* 286:226–32

61. Duff SMG, Moorhead GBB, Lefebvre DD, Plaxton WC. 1989. Phosphate starvation inducible "bypasses" of adenylate and phosphate dependent glycolytic enzymes in *Brassica nigra* suspension cells. *Plant Physiol.* 90:1275–78

62. Duff SMG, Plaxton WC, Lefebvre DD. 1991. Phosphate-starvation response in plant cells: de novo synthesis and degradation of acid phosphatase. *Proc. Natl. Acad. Sci. USA* 88:9538–42

63. Dumont F, Joris B, Gumusboga A, Bruyninx M, Loppes R. 1993. Isolation and characterization of cDNA sequences controlled by inorganic phosphate in *Chlamydomonas reinhardtii*. *Plant Sci.* 89:55–67

64. Edwards JW, Coruzzi GM. 1989. Photorespiration and light act in concert to regulate the expression of the nuclear gene

for chloroplast glutamine synthetase. *Plant Cell* 1:241–48

65. Deleted in proof

66. Escoubas JM, Lomas M, LaRoche J, Falkowski PG. 1995. Light intensity regulation of *cab* gene transcription is signaled by the redox state of the plastoquinone pool. *Proc. Natl. Acad. Sci. USA* 92:10237–41

67. Espinoza FH, Ogas J, Herskowitz I, Morgan DO. 1994. Cell cycle control by a complex of the cyclin HCS26 (PCL1) and the kinase PHO85. *Science* 266:1388–91

68. Essigmann B, Guler S, Narang RA, Linke D, Benning C. 1998. Phosphate availability affects the thylakoid lipid composition and the expression of SQD1, a gene required for sulfolipid biosynthesis in *Arabidopsis thaliana*. *Proc. Natl. Acad. Sci. USA* 95:1950–55

69. Faure J-D, Vincentz M, Kronenberger J, Caboche M. 1991. Co-regulated expression of nitrate and nitrite reductases. *Plant J.* 1:107–13

70. Fedorova E, Greenwood JS, Oaks A. 1994. In situ localization of nitrate reductase in maize roots. *Planta* 194:279–86

71. Fernández E, Cárdenas J. 1989. Genetic and regulatory aspects of nitrate assimilation in algae. In *Molecular and Genetic Aspects of Nitrate Assimilation*, ed. JL Ray, JR Kinghorn, pp. 101–24. Oxford: Oxford Univ. Press

72. Fernández E, Galván A, Quesada A. 1998. Nitrogen assimilation and its regulation. See Ref. 240a, pp. 637–59

73. Fernández E, Matagne RF. 1986. In vivo complementation analysis of nitrate reductase deficient mutants in *Chlamydomonas reinhardtii*. *Curr. Genet.* 10:397–403

74. Fernández E, Schnell R, Ranum LPW, Hussey SC, Silflow CD, Lefebvre PA. 1989. Isolation and characterization of the nitrate reductase structural gene of *Chlamydomonas reinhardtii*. *Proc. Natl. Acad. Sci. USA* 86:6449–53

75. Ferrario S, Valadier MH, Morotgaudry JF,

Foyer CH. 1995. Effects of constitutive expression of nitrate reductase in transgenic *Nicotiana plumbaginifolia* L in response to varying nitrogen supply. *Planta* 196:288–94

76. Fife CA, Newcomb W, Lefebvre DD. 1990. The effect of phosphate deprivation on protein synthesis and carbon storage reserves in *Brassica nigra* suspension cells. *Can. J. Bot.* 68:1840–47

77. Filleur S, Daniel-Vedele F. 1999. Expression analysis of a high-affinity nitrate transporter isolated from *Arabidopsis thaliana* by differential display. *Planta* 207:461–69

78. Fischer WN, Andre B, Rentsch D, Krolkiewicz S, Tegeder M, et al. 1998. Amino acid transport in plants. *Trend Plant Sci.* 3:188–95

79. Fischer K, Kammerer B, Gutensohn M, Arbinger B, Weber A, et al. 1997. A new class of plastidic phosphate translocators: a putative link between primary and secondary metabolism by the phospho*enol*pyruvate/phosphate antiporter. *Plant Cell* 9:453–62

80. Fischer P, Klein U. 1988. Localization of nitrogen-assimilating enzymes in the chloroplast of *Chlamydomonas reinhardtii*. *Plant Physiol.* 88:947–52

81. Fischer WM, Kwart M, Hummel S, Frommer WB. 1995. Substrate specificity and expression profile of amino-acid transporters (AAPS) in Arabidopsis. *J. Biol. Chem.* 270:16315–20

82. Forde BG. 2000. Nitrate transporters in plants: structure, function and regulation. *Biochim. Biophys. Acta* 1465:219–35

83. Franco AR, Cárdenas J, Fernández E. 1987. Involvement of reversible inactivation in the regulation of nitrate reductase enzyme levels in *Chlamydomonas reinhardtii*. *Plant Physiol.* 84:665–69

84. Franco AR, Cárdenas J, Fernández E. 1988. Two different carriers transport both ammonium and methylammonium in *Chlamydomonas reinhardtii*. *J. Biol. Chem.* 263:14039–43

85. Gakiere B, Job D, Douce R, Ravanel S, 1999, Characterization of the cDNA and gene for a cytosolic cobalamin-independent methionine synthase in *Arabidopsis thaliana* (accession no. U97200). *Plant Physiol.* 120:1206

86. Gal A, Zer H, Ohad I. 1997. Redox-controlled thylakoid protein phosphorylation. News and views. *Physiol. Plant.* 100:869–85

87. Galangau F, Daniel-Vedele F, Moureaux T, Dorbe MF, Leydecker MT, Caboche M. 1988. Expression of leaf nitrate reductase genes from tomato and tobacco in relation to light-dark regimes and nitrate supply. *Plant Physiol.* 88:383–88

88. Galván F, Márquez AJ, Vega JM. 1984. Purification and molecular properties of ferredoxin-glutamate synthase from *Chlamyomonas reinhardtii. Planta* 162:180–87

89. Galván A, Quesada A, Fernández E. 1996. Nitrate and nitrite are transported by different specific transport systems and by a bispecific transporter in *Chlamydomonas reinhardtii. J. Biol. Chem.* 271:2088–92

90. Gauthier DA, Turpin DH. 1994. Inorganic phosphate (Pi) enhancement of dark respiration in the Pi limited green alga *Selenastrum minutum. Plant Physiol.* 104:629–37

91. Gazzarrini S, Lejay L, Gojon A, Ninnemann O, Frommer WB, von Wirén N. 1999. Three functional transporters for constitutive, diurnally regulated, and starvation-induced uptake of ammonium into Arabidopsis roots. *Plant Cell* 11:937–47

92. Geiger M, Walch-Liu P, Engels C, Harnecker J, Schulze ED, et al. 1998. Enhanced carbon dioxide leads to a modified diurnal rhythm of nitrate reductase activity in older plants, and a large stimulation of nitrate reductase activity and higher levels of amino acids in young tobacco plants. *Plant Cell Environ.* 21:253–68

93. Gojon A, Dapoigny L, Lejay L, Tillard P, Rufty TW. 1998. Effects of genetic modification of nitrate reductase expression on $(NO_3{}^-)$-N-15 uptake and reduction in *Nicotiana* plants. *Plant Cell Environ.* 21:43–53

94. Goldstein AH, Baertlein DA, McDaniel RG. 1988. Phosphate starvation inducible metabolism in *Lycopersicon esculentum*. I. Excretion of acid phosphatase by tomato plants and suspension-cultured cells. *Plant Physiol.* 87:711–15

95. Goldstein AH, Danon A, Baertlein DA, McDaniel RG. 1988. Phosphate starvation inducible metabolism in *Lycopersicon esculentum*. II. Characterization of the phosphate starvation inducible-excreted acid phosphatase. *Plant Physiol.* 87:716–20

96. Gotor C, Cejudo FJ, Barroso C. 1997. Tissue-specific expression of *AtCys-3A*, a gene encoding the cytosolic isoform of *O*-acetylserine (thiol)lyase in *Arabidopsis. Plant J.* 11:347–52

97. Green PJ. 1994. The ribonucleases of higher plants. *Annu. Rev. Plant Physiol. Plant Mol. Biol.* 45:421–45

98. Grill E, Loffler S, Winnacker EL, Zenk MH. 1989. Phytochelatins, the heavy-metal-binding peptides of plants, are synthesized from glutathione by a specific γ-glutamylcysteine dipeptidyl transpeptidase (phytochelatin synthetase). *Proc. Natl. Acad. Sci. USA* 86:6838–42

99. Grouzis JP, Pouliquin P, Rigaud J, Grignon C, Gibrat R. 1997. In vitro study of passive nitrate transport by native and reconstituted plasma membrane vesicles from corn root cells. *Biochim. Biophys. Acta* 1325:329–42

100. Guenther JE, Nemson JA, Melis A. 1990. Development of photosystem II in dark grown *Chlamydomonas reinhardtii*. A light-dependent conversion of PSII, QB-nonreducing centers to the PSII, QB-reducing form. *Photosynth. Res.* 24:35–46

101. Guerrero MG, Vega JM, Losada M. 1981. The assimilatory nitrate reducing system

and its regulation. *Annu. Rev. Plant Physiol.* 32:169–204

102. Guiz C, Hirel B, Shedlofsky G, Gadal P. 1979. Occurrence and influence of light on the relative proportions of 2 glutamine synthetases in rice leaves. *Plant Sci. Lett.* 15:271–77

103. Guthrie RE, McLachlan KD, De Marco DG. 1991. Acid phosphatases associated with phosphorus deficiency in wheat: partial purification and properties. *Aust. J. Plant Physiol.* 18:615–26

104. Gutierrez-Marcos J, Roberts M, Campbell E, Wray J. 1996. Three members of a novel small gene-family from *Arabidopsis thaliana* able to complement functionally an *Escherichia coli* mutant defective in PAPS reductase activity encode proteins with a thioredoxin-like domain and "APS reductase" activity. *Proc. Natl. Acad. Sci. USA* 93:13377–82

105. Hatzfeld Y, Lee S, Lee M, Leustek T, Saito K. 2000. Functional characterization of a gene encoding a fourth ATP sulfurylase isoform from *Arabidopsis thaliana*. *Gene* 248:51–58

106. Hawkesford MJ, Davidian J-C, Grignon C. 1993. Sulphate/proton cotransport in plasma-membrane vesicles isolated from roots of *Brassica napus* L.: increased transport in membranes isolated from sulphur-starved plants. *Planta* 190:297–304

107. Hayakawa T, Hopkins L, Peat LJ, Yamaya T, Tobin AK. 1999. Quantitative intercellular localization of NADH-dependent glutamate synthase protein in different types of root cells in rice plants. *Plant Physiol.* 119:409–16

108. Herschbach C, Rennenberg H. 1994. Influence of glutathione (GSH) on net uptake of sulfate and sulfate transport in tobacco plants. *J. Exp. Bot.* 45:1069–76

109. Hesse H, Lipke J, Altmann T, Hofgen R. 1999. Molecular cloning and expression analysis of mitochondrial and plastidic isoforms of cysteine synthase (*O*-acetylserine(thiol)lyase) from *Arabidopsis thaliana*. *Amino Acids* 16:113–31

110. Hirel B, Bouet C, King B, Layzell B, Jacobs F, Verma DPS. 1987. Glutamine synthetase genes are regulated by ammonia provided externally or by symbiotic nitrogen fixation. *EMBO J.* 6:1167–71

111. Hirst K, Fisher F, McAndrew PC, Goding CR. 1994. The transcription factor, the Cdk, its cyclin and their regulator: directing the transcriptional response to a nutritional signal. *EMBO J.* 13:5410–20

112. Hoff T, Truong HN, Caboche M. 1994. The use of mutants and trangenic plants to study nitrate assimilation. *Plant Cell Environ.* 17:489–506

113. Hoffland E, Vandenboogaard R, Nelemans J, Findenegg G. 1992. Biosynthesis and root exudation of citric and malic acids in phosphate starved rape plants. *New Phytol.* 122:675–80

114. Hsieh M-H, Lam H-M, van de Loo FJ, Coruzzi GM. 1998. A PII-like protein in Arabidopsis: putative role in nitrogen sensing. *Proc. Natl. Acad. Sci. USA* 95:13965–70

115. Huang N-C, Chiang C-S, Crawford NM, Tsay Y-F. 1996. *CHL1* encodes a component of the low-affinity nitrate uptake system in Arabidopsis and shows cell type-specific expression in roots. *Plant Cell* 8:2183–91

116. Huber SC, Bachmann M, Huber JL. 1996. Post-translational regulation of nitrate reductase activity: a role for Ca^{2+} and 14-3-3 proteins. *Trends Plant Sci.* 1:432–38

117. Huber JL, Redinbaugh MG, Huber SC, Campbell WH. 1994. Regulation of maize leaf nitrate reductase activity involves both gene expression and protein phosphorylation. *Plant Physiol.* 106:1667–74

118. Ishiyama K, Hayakawa T, Yamaya T. 1998. Expression of NADH-dependent glutamate synthase protein in the epidermis of rice roots in response to the supply of ammonium ions. *Planta* 204:288–94

119. Jang J-C, Leon P, Zhou L, Sheen J. 1997.

Hexokinase as a sugar sensor in higher plants. *Plant Cell* 9:5–19

120. Jiang P, Peliska JA, Ninfa AJ. 1998. Enzymological characterisation of the signal-transducing uridyltransferase/uridyl-removing enzyme of *Escherichia coli* and its interaction with the PII protein. *Biochemistry* 37:12782–94

121. Jin T, Huppe HC, Turpin DH. 1998. In vitro reconstitution of electron transport from glucose-6–phosphate and NADPH to nitrite. *Plant Physiol.* 117:303–9

122. Jost W, Bak H, Glund K, Terpstra P, Beintema JJ. 1991. Amino acid sequence of an extracellular, phosphate-starvation-induced ribonuclease from cultured tomato (*Lycopersicon esculentum*) cells. *Eur. J. Biochem.* 198:1–6

123. Kaffman A, Herskowitz I, Tjian R, O'Shea EK. 1994. Phosphorylation of the transcription factor PHO4 by a cyclin-CDK complex, PHO80–PHO85. *Science* 263:1153–56

124. Deleted in proof

125. Kaiser P, Sia RA, Bardes EG, Lew DJ, Reed SI. 1998. Cdc34 and the F-box protein Met30 are required for degradation of the Cdk-inhibitory kinase Swe1. *Genes Dev.* 12:2587–97

126. Kamiya A. 1988. Blue light-induced in vivo absorbance changes and in vitro activation of nitrate reductase in nitrate-starved *Chlorella* mutant. *Plant Cell Physiol.* 29:489–96

127. Kim J, Leustek T. 1996. Cloning and analysis of the gene for cystathionine γ-synthase from *Arabidopsis thaliana*. *Plant Mol. Biol.* 32:1117–24

128. King BJ, Siddiqi MY, Ruth TJ, Warner RL, Glass ADM. 1993. Feedback-regulation of nitrate influx in barley roots by nitrate, nitrite and ammonium. *Plant Physiol.* 102:1279–86

129. Kirk DL, Kirk MM. 1978. Carrier-mediated uptake of arginine and urea by *Chlamydomonas reinhardtii*. *Plant Physiol.* 61:556–60

130. Klonus D, Hofgen R, Willmitzer L, Riesmeier JW. 1994. Isolation and characterization of two cDNA clones encoding ATP-sulfurylases from potato by complementation of a yeast mutant. *Plant J.* 6:105–12

131. Kocsis MG, Hanson AD. 2000. Biochemical evidence for two novel enzymes in the biosynthesis of 3-dimethylsulfoniopropionate *in Spartina alterniflora*. *Plant Physiol.* 123:1153–61

132. Deleted in proof

133. Koprivova A, Suter M, den Camp RO, Brunold C, Kopriva S. 2000. Regulation of sulfate assimilation by nitrogen in Arabidopsis. *Plant Physiol.* 122:737–46

134. Kozaki A, Takeba G. 1996. Photorespiration protects C3 plants from photooxidation. *Nature* 384:557–60

135. Krapp A, Fraisier V, Scheible W-R, Quesada A, Gojon A, et al. 1998. Expression studies of *Nrt2:1Np*, a putative high-affinity nitrate transporter: evidence for its role in nitrate uptake. *Plant J.* 14:723–31

136. Kronenberger J, Lepingle A, Caboche M, Vaucheret H. 1993. Cloning and expression of distinct nitrite reductases in tobacco leaves and roots. *Mol. Gen. Genet.* 236:203–8

137. Kronzucker HJ, Glass ADM, Siddiqi MY. 1995. Nitrate induction in spruce: an approach using compartmental analysis. *Planta* 196:683–90

138. Kronzucker HJ, Siddiqi MY, Glass ADM. 1995. Kinetics of NO_3^- influx in spruce. *Plant Physiol.* 109:319–26

139. Kunert KJ, Foyer C. 1993. Thiol/disulfide exchange in plants. See Ref. 51a, pp. 139–51

140. Kurvari V, Qian F, Snell WJ. 1995. Increased transcript levels of a methionine synthase during adhesion-induced activation of *Chlamydomonas reinhardtii* gametes. *Plant Mol. Biol.* 29:1235–52

141. Lam H-M, Coschigano KT, Oliveira IC, Melo-Oliveira R, Coruzzi GM. 1996. The

molecular genetics of nitrogen assimilation into amino acids in higher plants. *Annu. Rev. Plant Physiol. Plant Mol. Biol.* 47:569–93

142. Lamoureux GL, Rusness DG. 1993. Glutathione in the metabolism and detoxification of xenobiotics in plants. See Ref. 51a, pp. 221–37

143. Lappartient AG, Touraine B. 1996. Demand-driven control of root ATP sulfurylase activity and SO_4^{2-} uptake in intact canola: the role of phloem-translocated glutathione. *Plant Physiol.* 111:147–57

144. Lappartient AG, Vidmar JJ, Leustek T, Glass ADM, Touraine B. 1999. Interorgan signaling in plants: regulation of ATP sulfurylase and sulfate transporter genes expression in roots mediated by phloem-translocated compound. *Plant J.* 18:89–95

145. Lass B, Ullrich-Eberius CI. 1984. Evidence for proton/sulfate cotransport and its kinetics in *Lemna gibba* G1. *Planta* 161:53–60

146. Lauter F-R, Ninnemann O, Bucher M, Riesmeier JW, Frommer WB. 1996. Preferential expression of an ammonium transporter and of two putative nitrate transporters in root hairs of tomato. *Proc. Natl. Acad. Sci. USA* 93:8139–44

147. Lea PJ, Robinson SA, Stewart GR. 1990. The enzymology and metabolism of glutamine, glutamate and asparagine. In *The Biochemistry of Plants*, ed. BJ Miflin, PJ Lea, 16:121–59. New York: Academic

148. Lee S, Leustek T. 1999. The effect of cadmium on sulfate assimilation enzymes in *Brassica juncea. Plant Sci.* 141:201–7

149. Lee S, Leustek T. 1998. APS kinase from *Arabidopsis thaliana*: genomic organization, expression, and kinetic analysis of the recombinant enzyme. *Biochem. Biophys. Res. Commun.* 247:171–75

150. Leggewie G, Willmitzer L, Riesmeier JW. 1997. Two cDNAs from potato are able to complement a phosphate uptake-deficient

yeast mutant: identification of phosphate transporters from higher plants. *Plant Cell* 9:381–92

151. Lejay L, Tillard P, Lepetit M, Olive FD, Filleur S, et al. 1999. Molecular and functional regulation of two NO_3^- uptake systems by N- and C- status of Arabidopsis plants. *Plant J.* 18:509–19

152. Leustek T, Murillo M, Cervantes M. 1994. Cloning of a cDNA encoding ATP sulfurylase from *Arabidopsis thaliana* by functional expression in *Saccharomyces cerevisiae. Plant Physiol.* 105:897–902

153. Leustek T, Saito K. 1999. Sulfate transport and assimilation in plants. *Plant Physiol.* 120:637–43

154. Li MG, Villemur R, Hussey PJ, Silflow CD, Gantt JS, Snustad DP. 1993. Differential expression of 6 glutamine synthetase genes in *Zea mays. Plant Mol. Biol.* 23:401–7

155. Lin Y, Cheng C-L. 1997. A chlorate-resistant mutant defective in the regulation of nitrate reductase gene expression in Arabidopsis defines a new *HY locus. Plant Cell* 9:21–35

156. Lin C-M, Koh S, Stacey G, Yu S-M, Lin T-Y, Tsay Y-F. 2000. Cloning and functional characterization of a constitutively expressed nitrate transporter gene, *OsNRT1*, from rice. *Plant Physiol.* 122:379–88

157. Liu K-H, Huang C-Y, Tsay Y-F. 1999. CHL1 is a dual-affinity nitrate transporter of Arabidopsis involved in multiple phases of nitrate uptake. *Plant Cell* 11:865–74

158. Liu C, Muchhal US, Mukatira U, Kononowicz AK, Raghothama KG. 1998. Tomato phosphate transporter genes are differentially regulated in plant tissues by phosphorus. *Plant Physiol.* 116:91–99

159. Liu H, Trieu AT, Blaylock LA, Harrison MJ. 1998. Cloning and characterization of two phosphate transporters from *Medicago truncatula* roots: regulation in response to phosphate and to colonization by

arbuscular mycorrhizal (AM) fungi. *Mol. Plant-Microbe Interact.* 11:14–22

160. Löffler A, Abel S, Jost W, Glund K. 1992. Phosphate-regulated induction of intracellular ribonucleases in cultured tomato (*Lycopersicon esculentum*) cells. *Plant Physiol.* 98:1472–78

161. Löffler A, Glund K, Irie M. 1993. Amino acid sequence of an intracellular, phosphate-starvation inducible ribonuclease from cultured tomato (*Lycopersicon esculentum*) cells. *Eur. J. Biochem.* 214:627–33

162. Logan HM, Cathala N, Grignon C, Davidian J-C. 1996. Cloning of a cDNA encoded by a member of the *Arabidopsis thaliana* ATP sulfurylase multigene family: expression studies in yeast and in relation to plant sulfur nutrition. *J. Biol. Chem.* 271:12227–33

163. Loppes R. 1976. Genes involved in the regulation of the neutral phosphatase in *Chlamydomonas reinhardtii. Mol. Gen. Genet.* 148:315–21

164. Loppes R, Braipson J, Matagne RF, Sassen A, Ledoux L. 1977. Regulation of the neutral phosphatase in *Chlamydomonas reinhardtii*: an immunogenetic study of wild-type and mutant strains. *Biochem. Genetics* 15:1147–57

165. Loppes R, Matagne RF. 1973. Acid phosphatase mutants in *Chlamydomonas*: isolation and characterization by biochemical, electrophoretic and genetic analysis. *Genetics* 75:593–604

166. Lunn JE, Droux M, Martin J, Douce R. 1990. Localization of ATP sulfurylase and O-acetyl(thiol)lyase in spinach leaves. *Plant Physiol.* 94:1345–52

167. Mann AF, Fentem PA, Stewart GR. 1979. Identification of 2 forms of glutamine synthetase in barley (*Hordeum vulgare*). *Biochem. Biophys. Res. Commun.* 88:515–21

168. Marrs KA. 1996. The functions and regulation of glutathione S-transferases in

plants. *Annu. Rev. Plant Physiol. Plant Mol. Biol.* 47:127–58

169. Márquez AG, Galván F, Vega JM. 1984. Purification and characterization of the NADH-glutamate synthase from *Chlamydomonas reinhardtii. Plant Sci. Lett.* 34:305–14

170. Marschner H. 1995. *Mineral Nutrition of Higher Plants.* San Diego: Academic

171. Marzluf GA. 1997. Genetic regulation of nitrogen metabolism in the fungi. *Microbiol. Mol. Biol. Rev.* 61:17–32

172. Matagne RF, Loppes R. 1975. Isolation and study of mutants lacking a derepressible phosphatase in *Chlamydomonas reinhardtii. Genetics* 80:239–50

173. Matagne RF, Loppes R, Deltour R. 1976. Phosphatases of *Chlamydomonas reinhardtii*: biochemical and cytochemical approach with specific mutants. *J. Bacteriol.* 126:937–950

174. Matsumura T, Sakakibara H, Nakano R, Kimata Y, Sugiyama T, Hase T. 1997. A nitrate-inducible ferredoxin in maize roots. Genomic organization and differential expression of two nonphotosynthetic ferredoxin isoproteins. *Plant Physiol.* 114:653–60

175. Meharg AA, Blatt MR. 1995. NO_3^- transport across the plasma membrane of *Arabidopsis thaliana* root hairs: kinetic control by pH and membrane voltage. *J. Membr. Biol.* 145:49–66

176. Melo-Oliveira R, Oliveira IC, Coruzzi GM. 1996. Arabidopsis mutant analysis and gene regulation define a nonredundant role for glutamate dehydrogenase in nitrogen assimilation. *Proc. Natl. Acad. Sci. USA* 93:4718–23

177. Melzer JM, Kleinhofs A, Warner RL. 1989. Nitrate reductase regulation: effect of nitrate and light on nitrate reductase messenger RNA accumulation. *Mol. Gen. Genet.* 217:341–46

178. Migge A, Carrayol E, Hirel B, Becker TW. 2000. Leaf-specific overexpression of plastidic glutamine synthetase

stimulates the growth of transgenic tobacco seedlings. *Planta* 210:252–60

179. Miller AJ, Smith SJ. 1996. Nitrate transport and compartmentation in cereal roots. *J. Exp. Bot.* 47:843–54

180. Miller AJ, Zhou JJ. 2000. *Xenopus* oocytes as an expression system for plant transporters. *Biochim. Biophys. Acta* 1465:343–358

181. Mimura T. 1999. Regulation of phosphate transport and homeostasis in plant cells. *Int. Rev. Cytol.* 191:149–200

182. Mitsukawa N, Okumura S, Shirano Y, Sato S, Kato T, et al. 1997. Overexpression of an *Arabidopsis thaliana* high-affinity phosphate transporter gene in tobacco cultured cells enhances cell growth under phosphate-limited conditions. *Proc. Natl. Acad. Sci. USA* 94:7098–102

183. Moorhead G, Douglas P, Morrice N, Scarabel M, Aitken A, MacKintosh C. 1996. Phosphorylated nitrate reductase from spinach leaves inhibited by 14-3-3 proteins and activated by fusicoccin. *Curr. Biol.* 6:1104–13

184. Morcuende R, Krapp A, Hurry V, Stitt M. 1998. Sucrose-feeding leads to increased rates of nitrate assimilation, increased rates of α-oxoglutarate synthesis, and increased synthesis of a wide spectrum of amino acids in tobacco leaves. *Planta* 206:394–409

185. Muchhal US, Pardo JM, Raghothama KG. 1996. Phosphate transporters from the higher plant *Arabidopsis thaliana*. *Proc. Natl. Acad. Sci. USA* 93:10519–23

186. Muchhal US, Raghothama KG. 1999. Transcriptional regulation of plant phosphate transporters. *Proc. Natl. Acad. Sci. USA* 96:5868–72

187. Muller B, Touraine B. 1992. Inhibition of NO_3^- uptake by various phloem-translocated amino acids in soybean seedlings. *J. Exp. Bot.* 43:617–23

188. Navarro MT, Prieto R, Fernández E, Galván A. 1996. Constitutive expression of nitrate reductase changes the regulation of nitrate and nitrite transporters in *Chlamydomonas reinhardtii*. *Plant J.* 9:819–27

189. Neale PJ, Melis A. 1990. Activation of a reserve pool of photosystem II in *Chlamydomonas reinhardtii* counteracts photoinhibition. *Plant Physiol.* 92:1196–204

190. Neininger A, Bichler J, Schneiderbauer A, Mohr H. 1993. Response of a nitrite reductase 3.1-kilobase upstream regulatory sequence from spinach to nitrate and light in transgenic tobacco. *Planta* 189:440–42

191. Newbigin E. 1996. The evolution of self-incompatibility: a molecular voyeur's perspective. *Sex. Plant Reprod.* 9:357–61

192. Ninnemann O, Jauniaux JC, Frommer WB. 1994. Identification of a high affinity ammonium transporter from plants. *EMBO J.* 13:3464–71

193. Ninomiya Y, Ueki K, Sato S. 1977. Chromatographic separation of extracellular acid phosphatase of tobacco cells cultured under Pi supplied and omitted conditions. *Plant Cell Physiol.* 18:413–20

194. Noji M, Inoue K, Kimura N, Gouda A, Saito K. 1998. Isoform-dependent differences in feedback regulation and subcellular localization of serine acetyltransferase involved in cysteine biosynthesis from *Arabidopsis thaliana*. *J. Biol. Chem.* 273:32739–745

195. Nürnberger T, Abel S, Jost W, Glund K. 1990. Induction of an extracellular ribonuclease in cultured tomato cells upon phosphate starvation. *Plant Physiol.* 92:970–76

196. Nussaume L, Vincente M, Meyer C, Boutin JP, Caboche M. 1995. Posttranscriptional regulation of nitrate reductase by light is abolished by an N-terminal deletion. *Plant Cell* 7:611–21

197. Oaks A. 1992. A re-evaluation of nitrogen assimilation in roots. *BioScience* 42:103–11

198. Deleted in proof

199. Oliveira IC, Coruzzi GM. 1999. Carbon and amino acids reciprocally modulate

the expression of glutamine synthetase in *Arabidopsis. Plant Physiol.* 121:301–9

200. Deleted in proof

201. Ozcan S, Dover J, Johnston M. 1998. Glucose sensing and signaling by two glucose receptors in the yeast *Saccharomyces cerevisiae. EMBO J.* 17:2566–73

202. Ozcan S, Dover J, Rosenwald AG, Wolf S, Johnston M. 1996. Two glucose transporters in *Saccharomyces cerevisiae* are glucose sensors that generate a signal for induction of gene expression. *Proc. Natl. Acad. Sci. USA* 93:12428–32

203. Padgett PE, Leonard RT. 1996. Free amino acid levels and the regulation of nitrate uptake in maize cell suspension cultures. *J. Exp. Bot.* 47:871–83

204. Panara F, Pasqualini S, Antonielli M. 1990. Multiple forms of barley root acid phosphatase: purification and some characteristics of the major cytoplasmic isozyme. *Biochim. Biophys. Acta.* 1037: 73–80

205. Pao SS, Paulsen IT, Saier MH. 1998. Major facilitator superfamily. *Microbiol. Mol. Biol. Rev.* 62:1–34

206. Patni NJ, Dhawale SW, Aaronson S. 1977. Extracellular phosphatases of *Chlamydomonas reinhardtii* and their regulation. *J. Bacteriol.* 130:205–11

207. Peltier G, Schmidt GW. 1991. Chlororespiration: an adaptation to nitrogen deficiency in *Chlamydomonas reinhardtii. Proc. Natl. Acad. Sci. USA* 88:4791–95

208. Perez-Rodriguez J, Valpuesta V. 1996. Expression of glutamine synthetase genes during natural senescence of tomato leaves. *Physiol. Plant.* 97:576–82

209. Peterman TK, Goodman HM. 1991. The glutamine synthetase gene family of *Arabidopsis thaliana*: light-regulation and differential expression in leaves, roots, and seeds. *Mol. Gen. Genet.* 230:145–54

210. Peuke AD, Jeschke WD, Hartung W. 1998. Foliar application of nitrate or ammonium as sole nitrogen supply in *Ricinus communis*: II. The flows of cations, chloride and abscisic acid. *New Phytol.* 140:625–36

211. Piedras P, Pineda AM, Muñoz J, Cárdenas J. 1992. Purification and characterization of an L-amino acid oxidase from *Chlamydomonas reinhardtii. Planta* 188:13–18

212. Pineda M, Cárdenas J. 1996. Transport and assimilation of purines in *Chlamydomonas reinhardtii. Sci. Mar.* 60:195–201

213. Poirier Y, Thoma S, Somerville C, Schiefelbein J. 1991. A mutant in Arabidopsis deficient in xylem loading of phosphate. *Plant Physiol.* 97:1087–93

214. Prieto R, Dubus A, Galván A, Fernández E. 1996. Isolation and characterization of two new negative regulatory mutants for nitrate assimilation in *Chlamydomonas reinhardtii* obtained by insertional mutagenesis. *Mol. Gen. Genet.* 251:461–71

215. Prior A, Uhrig JF, Heins L, Wiesmann A, Lilliq CH, et al. 1999. Structural and kinetic properties of adenylylsulfate reductase from *Catheranthus roseus* cell cultures. *Biochim. Biophys. Acta* 1430: 25–38

216. Quesada AA, Fernández E. 1994. Expression of nitrate assimilation related genes in *Chlamydomonas reinhardtii. Plant Mol. Biol.* 24:185–94

217. Quesada AA, Galván A, Fernández E. 1994. Indentification of nitrate transporter genes in *Chlamydomonas reinhardtii. Plant J.* 5:407–19

218. Quesada A, Galván A, Schnell RA, Lefebvre PA. 1993. Nitrate assimilation-related loci are clustered in *Chlamydomonas reinhardtii. Mol. Gen. Genet.* 240:387–94

219. Quesada A, Gomez I, Fernández E. 1998. Clustering of the nitrite reductase gene and a light-regulated gene with nitrate assimilation loci in *Chlamydomonas reinhardtii. Planta* 206:259–65

220. Quesada A, Krapp A, Trueman LJ, Daniel-Vedele F, Fernández E, et al.

1997. PCR-identification of a *Nicotiana plumbaginifolia* cDNA homologous to the high-affinity nitrate transporters of the *crnA* family. *Plant Mol. Biol.* 34:265–74

221. Quiñones MA, Aparicio P. 1990. Flavin type action spectrum of nitrate utilization by *Monoraphidium braunii*. *Photochem. Photobiol.* 51:689–92

222. Quiñones MA, Galván A, Fernández E, Aparicio PJ. 1999. Blue-light requirement for the biosynthesis of an NO_2^- transport system in the *Chlamydomonas reinhardtii* nitrate transport mutant S10. *Plant Cell Environ.* 22:1169–75

223. Quiñones MA, Giráldez N, Witt FG, Aparicio PJ. 1997. Blue light-dependent monovalent anion uptake. *Physiol Plant.* 100:45–52

224. Quisel J, Wykoff D, Grossman AR. 1996. Biochemical characterization of the extracellular phosphatases produced by phosphorus-deprived *Chlamydomonas reinhardtii*. *Plant Physiol.* 111:839–48

225. Raghothama KG. 2000. Phosphate transport and signaling. *Curr. Opin. Plant Biol.* 3:182–87

226. Rajasekhar VK, Gowri G, Campbell WH. 1988. Phytochrome-mediated light regulation of nitrate reductase expression in squash cotyledons. *Plant Physiol.* 88:242–44

227. Rastogi R, Bate NJ, Sivanskar S, Rothstein SJ. 1997. Footprinting of the spinach nitrite reductase gene promoter reveals the preservation of nitrate regulatory elements between fungi and higher plants. *Plant Mol. Biol.* 34:465–76

228. Ravanel S, Droux M, Douce R. 1995. Methionine biosynthesis in higher plants. I. Purification and characterization of cystathionine γ-synthase from spinach chloroplasts. *Arch. Biochem. Biophys.* 316:572–84

229. Ravanel S, Gakiere B, Job D, Douce R. 1998. Cystathionine γ-synthase from *Arabidopsis thaliana*: purification and biochemical characterization of the rec-

ombinant enzyme overexpressed in *Escherichia coli. Biochem. J.* 331:639–48

230. Ravanel S, Gakiere B, Job D, Douce R. 1998. The specific features of methionine biosynthesis and metabolism in plants. *Proc. Natl. Acad. Sci. USA* 95:7805–12

231. Ravanel S, Job D, Douce R. 1996. Purification and properties of cystathionine β-lyase from *Arabidopsis thaliana* overexpressed in *Escherichia coli. Biochem. J.* 320:383–92

232. Ravanel S, Ruffet ML, Douce R. 1995. Cloning of an *Arabidopsis thaliana* cDNA encoding cystathionine β-lyase by functional complementation in *Escherichia coli. Plant Mol. Biol.* 29:875–82

233. Rawat SR, Silim SN, Kronzucker HJ, Siddiqi MY, Glass ADM. 1999. *AtAMT1* gene expression and NH_4^+ uptake in roots of *Arabidopsis thaliana*: evidence for regulation by root glutamine levels. *Plant J.* 19:143–52

234. Rawlins MR, Leaver CJ, May MJ. 1995. Characterization of an *Arabidopsis thaliana* cDNA encoding glutathione synthetase. *FEBS Lett.* 376:81–86

235. Redinbaugh MG, Campbell WH. 1998. Nitrate regulation of the oxidative pentose phosphate pathway in maize (*Zea mays* L.) root plastids: induction of 6-phosphogluconate dehydrogenase activity, protein and transcript levels. *Plant Sci.* 134:129–40

236. Rennenberg H. 1982. Glutathione metabolism and possible biological role in higher plants. *Phytochem.* 21:2771–81

237. Rentsch D, Boorer KJ, Frommer WB. 1998. Structure and function of plasma membrane amino acid, oligopeptide and sucrose transporters from higher plants. *J. Membr. Biol.* 162:177–90

238. Rexach J, Montero B, Férnandez E, Galván A. 1999. Differential regulation of the high affinity nitrite transport systems III and IV in *Chlamydomonas reinhardtii. J. Biol. Chem.* 39:27801–6

239. Rexach J, Férnandez E, Galván A. 2000. The *Chlamydomonas reinhardtii Nar1* gene encodes a chloroplast membrane protein involved in nitrite transport. *Plant Cell.* 12:1441–53

240. Ritchie SW, Redinbaugh MG, Shiraishi N, Vrba JM, Campbell WH. 1994. Identification of a maize root transcript expressed in the primary response to nitrate: characterization of a cDNA with homology to ferredoxin-NADP$^+$ oxidoreductase. *Plant Mol. Biol.* 26:679–90

240a. Rochaix J-D, Goldschmidt-Clermont M, Merchant S, eds. 1998. *The Molecular Biology of Chloroplasts and Mitochondria in Chlamydomonas.* Dordrecht: Kluwer

241. Roche D, Temple SJ, Sengupta-Gopalan C. 1993. Two classes of differentially regulated glutamine synthetase genes are expressed in the soybean nodule: a nodule-specific and constitutively expressed class. *Plant Mol. Biol.* 22:971–83

242. Rosewarne GM, Barker SJ, Smith SE, Smith FA, Schachtman DP. 1999. A *Lycopersicon esculentum* phosphate transporter (LePT1) involved in phosphorus uptake from a vesicular-arbuscular mycorrhizal fungus. *New Phytol.* 144:507–16

243. Rotte C. 1998. *Subcellular localization of sulfur assimilation enzymes in Arabidopsis thaliana (L.) HEYNH.* Diplomarbeit thesis. Carl von Ossietzky Univ. Oldenburg, Oldenburg, Germany

244. Deleted in proof

245. Ruffet M-L, Lebrun M, Droux M, Douce R. 1995. Subcellular localization of serine acetyltransferase from *Pisum sativum* and characterization of an *Arabidopsis thaliana* putative cytosolic isoform. *Eur. J. Biochem.* 227:500–9

246. Sadka A, DeWald DB, May GD, Park WD, Mullet JE. 1994. Phosphate modulates transcription of soybean VSPB and other sugar-inducible genes. *Plant Cell* 6:737–49

247. Saito K. 2000. Regulation of sulfate transport and synthesis of sulfur-containing amino acids. *Curr. Opin. Plant. Biol.* 3:188–95

248. Saito K, Kurosawa M, Tatsuguchi K, Takagi Y, Murakoshi I. 1994. Modulation of cysteine biosynthesis in chloroplasts of transgenic tobacco overexpressing cysteine synthase [*O*-acetylserine(thiol)-lyase]. *Plant Physiol.* 106:887–95

249. Saito K, Tatsugushi K, Takagi Y, Murakoshi I. 1994. Isolation and characterization of cDNA that encodes a putative mitochondrion-localizing isoform of cysteine synthase (*O*-acetylserine(thiol)lyase) from *Spinacia oleracea. J. Biol. Chem.* 269:28187–92

250. Saito K, Yokoyama H, Noji M, Murakoshi I. 1995. Molecular cloning and characterization of a plant serine acetyltransferase playing a regulatory role in cysteine biosynthesis from watermelon. *J. Biol. Chem.* 270:16321–26

251. Sakakibara H, Kawabata S, Hase T, Sugiyama T. 1992. Differential effect of nitrate and light on the expression of glutamine synthetases and ferredoxin-dependent glutamate synthase in maize. *Plant Cell Physiol.* 33:1193–98

252. Sakakibara H, Kobayashi K, Deji A, Sugiyama T. 1997. Partial characterization of the signaling pathway for the nitrate-dependent expression of genes for nitrogen-assimilatory enzymes using detached maize leaves. *Plant Cell Physiol.* 38:837–43

253. Sakakibara H, Shimizu H, Hase T, Yamazaki Y, Takao T, et al. 1996. Molecular identification and characterization of cytosolic isoforms of glutamine synthetase in maize roots. *J. Biol. Chem.* 271:29561–8

254. Sakakibara H, Suzuki M, Takei K, Deji A, Taniguchi M, Sugiyama T. 1998. A response-regulator homologue possibly

involved in nitrogen signal transduction mediated by cytokinin in maize. *Plant J.* 14:337–44

255. Sakakibara H, Watanabe M, Hase T, Sugiyama T. 1991. Molecular cloning and characterization of complementary DNA encoding for ferredoxin-dependent glutamate synthase in maize leaf. *J. Biol. Chem.* 266:2028–35

256. Sakamoto A, Takeba G, Tanaka K. 1990. Synthesis de novo of glutamine synthetase in the embryonic axis, closely related to the germination of lettuce seeds. *Plant Cell Physiol.* 31:677–82

257. Deleted in proof

258. Scheible W-R, Gonzalez-Fontes A, Lauerer M, Muller-Rober B, Caboche M, Stitt M. 1997. Nitrate acts as a signal to induce organic acid metabolism and repress starch metabolism in tobacco. *Plant Cell* 9:783–98

259. Scheible W-R, Gonzalez-Fontes A, Morcuende R, Lauerer M, Geiger M, et al. 1997. Tobacco mutants with a decreased number of functional *nia* genes compensate by modifying the diurnal regulation of transcription, post-translational modification and turn over of nitrate reductase. *Planta* 203:304–19

260. Scheible WR, Lauerer M, Schulze ED, Caboche M, Stitt M. 1997. Accumulation of nitrate in the shoot acts as a signal to regulate shoot-root allocation in tobacco. *Plant J.* 11:671–91

261. Scheller HV, Huang B, Hatch E, Goldsbrough PB. 1987. Phytochelatin synthesis and glutathione levels in response to heavy metals in tomato cells. *Plant Physiol.* 85:1031–35

262. Schnell RA, Lefebvre PA. 1993. Isolation of the regulatory gene *NIT2* by transposon tagging. *Genetics* 134:737–47

263. Schoenbeck MA, Temple SJ, Trepp GB, Blumenthal JM, Samac DA, et al. 2000. Decreased NADH glutamate synthase activity in nodules and flowers of alfalfa (*Medicago sativa* L.) transformed with an antisense glutamate synthase transgene. *J. Exp. Bot.* 51:29–39

264. Schreiner O, Lien T, Knutsen G. 1975. The capacity for arylsulfatase synthesis in synchronized cultures of *Chlamydomonas reinhardtii. Biochim. Biophys. Acta* 384:180–93

265. Schürmann P, Brunold C. 1980. Formation of cysteine from adenosine 5-phosphosulfate (APS) in extracts from spinach chloroplasts. *Z. Pflanzenphysiol.* 100:257–68

266. Schuster C, Mohr H. 1990. Appearance of nitrite reductase mRNA in mustard seedling cotyledons is regulated by phytochrome. *Planta* 181:327–34

267. Sechley KA, Yamaya T, Oaks A. 1992. Compartmentation of nitrogen assimilation in higher plants. *Int. Rev. Cytol.* 134:85–63

268. Setya A, Murillo M, Leustek T. 1996. Sulfate reduction in higher plants: molecular evidence for a novel 5′-adenylylsulfate reductase. *Proc. Natl. Acad. Sci. USA* 93:13383–88

269. Shimogawara K, Wykoff D, Grossman AR, Usuda H. 1999. Isolation and characterization of mutants of *Chlamydomonas reinhardtii* unable to acclimate to phosphate limitation. *Plant Physiol.* 120:685–93

270. Smith FW, Ealing PM, Hawkesford MJ, Clarkson DT. 1995. Plant members of a family of sulfate transporters reveal functional subtypes. *Proc. Natl. Acad. Sci. USA* 92:9373–77

271. Smith FW, Hawkesford MJ, Ealing PM, Clarkson DT, Vanden Berg PJ, et al. 1997. Regulation of expression of a cDNA from barley roots encoding a high affinity sulphate transporter. *Plant J.* 12:875–84

272. Smith FW, Rae AL, Hawkesford MJ. 2000. Molecular mechanisms of phosphate and sulphate transport in plants. *Biochim. Biophys. Acta* 1465:236–45

273. Sohlenkamp C, Shelden M, Howitt S,

Udvardi M. 2000. Characterization of *Arabidopsis* AtAMT2, a novel ammonium transporter in plants. *FEBS Lett.* 467:273–78

274. Somerville CR, Ogren WL. 1980. Inhibition of photosynthesis in Arabidopsis mutants lacking leaf glutamate synthase activity. *Nature* 286:257–59

275. Stitt M. 1999. Nitrate regulation of metabolism and growth. *Curr. Opin. Plant. Biol.* 2:178–86

276. Stitt M, Krapp A. 1999. The interaction between elevated carbon dioxide and nitrogen nutrition: the physiological and molecular background. *Plant Cell Environ.* 22:583–621

277. Sugden C, Donaghy PG, Halford NG, Hardie DG. 1999. Two SNF1-related protein kinases from spinach leaf phosphorylate and inactivate 3-hydroxy-3-methylglutaryl-coenzyme A reductase, nitrate reductase, and sucrose phosphate synthase in vitro. *Plant Physiol.* 120:257–74

278. Sugiharto B, Suzuki I, Burnell JN, Sugiyama T. 1992. Glutamine induces the N-dependent accumulation of mRNAs encoding phospho*enol*pyruvate carboxylase and carbonic anhydrase in detached maize leaf tissue. *Plant Physiol.* 100:2066–70

279. Sukanya R, Li M-G, Snustad DP. 1994. Root- and shoot-specific responses of individual glutamine synthetase genes of maize to nitrate and ammonia. *Plant Mol. Biol.* 26:1935–46

280. Suzuki I, Cretin C, Omata T, Sugiyama T. 1994. Transcriptional and posttranscriptional regulation of nitrogen-responding expression of phospho*enol*pyruvate carboxylase gene in maize. *Plant Physiol.* 105:1223–29

281. Suzuki A, Rothstein S. 1997. Structure and regulation of ferredoxin-dependent glutamate synthase from *Arabidopsis thaliana*: cloning of cDNA, expression in different tissues of wild-type and *gltS* mutant strains, and light induction. *Eur. J. Biochem.* 243:708–18

282. Takabatake R, Hata S, Taniguchi M, Kouchi H, Sugiyama T, Izui K. 1999. Isolation and characterization of cDNAs encoding mitochondrial phosphate transporters in soybean, maize, rice, and Arabidopsis. *Plant Mol. Biol.* 40:479–86

283. Takahashi H, Asanuma W, Saito K. 1999. Cloning of an Arabidopsis cDNA encoding a chloroplast localizing sulfate transporter isoform. *J. Exp. Bot.* 50:1713–24

284. Takahashi H, Watanabe-Takahashi A, Smith FW, Blake-Kalff M, Hawkesford MJ, Saito K. 2000. The roles of three functional sulphate transporters involved in uptake and translocation of sulphate in *Arabidopsis thaliana*. *Plant J.* 23:171–82

285. Takahashi H, Yamazaki M, Sasakura N, Watanabe A, Leustek T, et al. 1997. Regulation of sulfur assimilation in higher plants: a sulfate transporter induced in sulfate-starved roots plays a central role in *Arabidopsis thaliana*. *Proc. Natl. Acad. Sci. USA* 94:11102–7

286. Taniguchi M, Kiba T, Sakakibara H, Ueguchi C, Mizuno T, Sugiyama T. 1998. Expression of Arabidopsis response regulator homologs is induced by cytokinins and nitrate. *FEBS Lett.* 429:258–62

287. Teller S, Schmidt KH, Appenroth KJ. 1996. Ferredoxin-dependent but not NADH-dependent glutamate synthase is regulated by phytochrome and a blue/UV-A light receptor in turions of *Spirodela polyrhiza*. *Plant Physiol. Biochem.* 34:713–19

288. Temple SJ, Vance CP, Gantt JS. 1998. Glutamate synthase and nitrogen assimilation. *Trends Plant Sci.* 3:51–56

289. Theodorou ME, Cornel FA, Duff SMG, Plaxton WC. 1992. Phosphate starvation inducible synthesis of the α-subunit of the pyrophosphate-dependent phosphofructokinase in black mustard suspension cells. *J. Biol. Chem.* 267:21901–5

290. Theodorou ME, Elrifi IR, Turpin DH, Plaxton WC. 1991. Effects of phosphorus limitation on respiratory metabolism in the green alga *Selenastrum minutum*. *Plant Physiol.* 95:1089–95

291. Theodorou ME, Plaxton WC. 1993. Metabolic adaptation of plant respiration to nutritional phosphate deprivation. *Plant Physiol.* 101:339–44

292. Thomas D, Kuras L, Barbey R, Cherest H, Blaiseau PL, Surdin-Kerjan Y. 1995. Transcriptional inhibitor that responds to S-adenosylmethionine is an essential protein with WD40 repeats. *Mol. Cell. Biol.* 15:6526–34

293. Deleted in proof

294. Toda T, Cameron S, Sass P, Zoller M, Scott JD, et al. 1987. Cloning and characterization of *BCY1*, a locus encoding a regulatory subunit of the cyclic AMP-dependent protein kinase in *Saccharomyces cerevisiae*. *Mol. Cell. Biol.* 7:1371–77

295. Deleted in proof

296. Touraine B, Glass ADM. 1997. NO_3^- and ClO_3^- fluxes in the *chl1-5* mutant of *Arabidopsis thaliana*: Does the *CHL1-5* gene encode a low-affinity NO_3^- transporter? *Plant Physiol.* 114:137–44

297. Trueman LJ, Richardson A, Forde BG. 1996. Molecular cloning of higher plant homologues of the high-affinity nitrate transporters of *Chlamydomonas reinhardtii* and *Aspergillus nidulans*. *Gene* 175:223–31

298. Trull MC, Guiltinan MJ, Lynch JP, Deikman J. 1997. The responses of wild-type and ABA mutant of *Arabidopsis thaliana* to phosphorus starvation. *Plant Cell Environ.* 20:85–92

299. Truong HN, Caboche M, Daniel-Vedele F. 1997. Sequence and characterization of two *Arabidopsis thaliana* cDNAs isolated by functional complementation of a yeast *gln3 gdh1* mutant. *FEBS Lett.* 410:213–18

300. Tsay Y-F, Schroeder JI, Feldmann KA, Crawford NM. 1993. The herbicide sensitivity gene *CHL1* of Arabidopsis encodes a nitrate-inducible nitrate transporter. *Cell* 72:705–13

301. Vallon O, Bulte L, Kuras R, Olive J, Wollman F-A. 1993. Extensive accumulation of an extracellular L-amino-acid oxidase during gametogenesis of *Chlamydomonas reinhardtii*. *Eur. J. Biochem.* 215:351–60

302. Vallon O, Bulte L, Dainese P, Olive J, Bassi R, Wollman F-A. 1991. Lateral redistribution of cytochrome b_6f complexes along thylakoid membranes upon state transitions. *Proc. Natl. Acad. Sci. USA* 88:8262–66

303. Vance CP, Miller SS, Gregerson RG, Samac DA, Robinson DL, Gantt JS. 1995. Alfalfa NADH-dependent glutamate synthase: structure of the gene and importance in symbiotic N_2 fixation. *Plant J.* 8:345–58

304. van der Leij M, Smith SJ, Miller AJ. 1998. Remobilisation of vacuolar stored nitrate in barley root cells. *Planta* 205:64–72

305. Varin L, Marsolais F, Richard M, Rouleau M. 1997. Biochemistry and molecular biology of plant sulfotransferases. *FASEB J.* 11:517–25

306. Vaucheret H, Kronenberger J, Lepingle A, Boutin J-P, Caboche M. 1992. Inhibition of tobacco nitrite reductase activity by expression of antisense RNA. *Plant J.* 2:559–69

307. Vaughn KC, Campbell WH. 1988. Immunological localization of nitrate reductase in maize leaves. *Plant Physiol.* 88:1354–67

308. Vener AV, Vankan PJM, Gal A, Andersson B, Ohad I. 1995. Activation-deactivation cycle of redox-controlled thylakoid protein phosphorylation: role of plastoquinol bound to the reduced cytochrome bf complex. *J. Biol. Chem.* 270:25225–32

309. Vernoux T, Wilson RC, Seeley KA, Reichheld J-P, Muroy S, et al. 2000. The *ROOT MERISTEMLESS1/CADMIUM*

SENSITIVE2 gene defines a glutathione-dependent pathway involved in initiation and maintenance of cell division during postembryonic root development. *Plant Cell* 12:97–109

310. Vidmar JJ, Schjoerring JK, Touraine B, Glass ADM. 1999. Regulation of the *hvst1* gene encoding a high-affinity sulfate transporter from *Hordeum vulgare*. *Plant Mol. Biol.* 40:883–92

311. Vincentz M, Caboche M. 1991. Constitutive expression of nitrate reductase allows normal growth and development of *Nicotiana plumbaginifolia* plants. *EMBO J.* 10:1027–35

312. Vincentz M, Moureaux T, Leydecker MT, Vaucheret H, Caboche M. 1993. Regulation of nitrate and nitrite reductase expression in *Nicotiana plumbaginifolia* leaves by nitrogen and carbon metabolites. *Plant J.* 3:315–24

313. Deleted in proof

314. von Wirén N, Gazzarrini S, Gojon A, Frommer WB. 2000. The molecular physiology of ammonium uptake and retrieval. *Curr. Opin. Plant. Biol.* 3:254–61

315. von Wirén N, Lauter FR, Ninnemann O, Gillisen B, Walch-Liu P, et al. 2000. Differential regulation of three functional ammonium transporter genes by nitrogen in root hairs and by light in leaves of tomato. *Plant J.* 21:167–75

316. Walch-Liu P, Neumann G, Bangerth F, Engels C. 2000. Rapid effects of nitrogen form on leaf morphogenesis in tobacco. *J. Exp. Bot.* 51:227–37

317. Walker EL, Coruzzi GM. 1989. Developmentally regulated expression of the gene family for cytosolic glutamine synthetase in *Pisum sativum*. *Plant Physiol.* 91:702–8

318. Wallsgrove RM, Lea PJ, Miflin BJ. 1983. Intracellular localization of aspartate kinase and the enzymes of threonine and methionine biosynthesis in green leaves. *Plant Physiol.* 71:780–84

319. Wallsgrove RM, Turner JC, Hall NP, Kendall AC, Bright SWJ. 1987. Barley mutants lacking chloroplast glutamine synthetase—biochemical and genetic analysis. *Plant Physiol.* 83:155–58

320. Wang R, Crawford NM. 1996. Genetic identification of a gene involved in constitutive, high-affinity nitrate transport in higher plants. *Proc. Natl. Acad. Sci. USA* 93:9297–301

321. Wang ZY, Kenigsbuch D, Sun L, Harel E, Ong MS, Tobin EM. 1997. A Myb-related transcription factor is involved in the phytochrome regulation of an Arabidopsis *Lhcb* gene. *Plant Cell* 9:491–507

322. Wang R, Liu D, Crawford NM. 1998. The *Arabidopsis* CHL1 protein plays a major role in high-affinity nitrate uptake. *Proc. Natl. Acad. Sci. USA* 95:15134–39

323. Wilkinson JQ, Crawford NM. 1993. Identification and characterization of a chlorate-resistance mutant of *Arabidopsis thaliana* with mutations in both nitrate reductase structural genes *NIA1* and *NIA2*. *Mol. Gen. Genet.* 239:289–97

324. Williamson VM, Colwell G. 1991. Acid phosphatase-1 from nematode resistant tomato. Isolation and characterization of its gene. *Plant Physiol.* 97:139–46

325. Wykoff DD, Davies JP, Grossman AR. 1998. The regulation of photosynthetic electron transport during nutrient deprivation in *Chlamydomonas reinhardtii*. *Plant Physiol.* 117:129–39

326. Wykoff DD, Grossman AR, Weeks DP, Usuda H, Shimogawara K. 1999. Psr1, a nuclear localized protein that regulates phosphorus metabolism in Chlamydomonas. *Proc. Natl. Acad. Sci. USA* 96:15336–41

327. Xiao XD, Marzluf GA. 1996. Identification of the native NIT2 major nitrogen regulatory protein in nuclear extracts of *Neurospora crassa*. *Genetica* 97:153–63

328. Yildiz FH, Davies JP, Grossman AR.

1994. Characterization of sulfate transport in *Chlamydomonas reinhardtii* during sulfur-limited and sulfur-sufficient growth. *Plant Physiol.* 104:981–87

329. Yonekura-Sakakibara K, Onda Y, Ashikari T, Tanaka Y, Kusumi T, Hase T. 2000. Analysis of reductant supply systems for ferredoxin-dependent sulfite reductase in photosynthetic and non-photosynthetic organs of maize. *Plant Physiol.* 122:887–94

330. Deleted in proof

331. Youssefian S, Nakamura M, Sano H. 1993. Tobacco plants transformed with the *O*-acetylserine(thiol)lyase gene of wheat are resistant to toxic levels of hydrogen sulphide gas. *Plant J.* 4:759–69

332. Yu X, Sukumaran S, Marton L. 1998. Differential expression of the Arabidopsis *Nia1* and *Nia2* genes. *Plant Physiol.* 116:1091–96

333. Zhang H, Forde BG. 1998. An *Arabidopsis* MADS box gene that controls nutrient-induced changes in root architecture. *Science* 279:407–9

334. Zhang H, Jennings A, Barlow PW, Forde BG. 1999. Dual pathways for regulation of root branching by nitrate. *Proc. Natl. Acad. Sci. USA* 96:6529–34

335. Zhang D, Lefebvre PA. 1997. *FAR1*, a new negative regulatory locus required for the repression of the nitrate reductase gene in *Chlamydomonas reinhardtii*. *Genetics* 146:121–33

336. Zhou JJ, Fernández E, Galván A, Miller AJ. 2000. A high affinity nitrate transport system from Chlamydomonas requires two gene products. *FEBS Lett.* 466:225–27

337. Zhou JJ, Theodoulou FL, Muldin I, Ingemarsson B, Miller AJ. 1998. Cloning and functional characterization of a *Brassica napus* transporter that is able to transport nitrate and histidine. *J. Biol. Chem.* 15:12017–23

338. Zhu YL, Pilon-Smits EAH, Jouanin L, Terry N. 1999. Overexpression of glutathione synthase in Indian mustard enhances cadmium accumulation and tolerance. *Plant Physiol.* 119:73–79

339. Zhu YL, Pilon-Smits EAH, Tarun AS, Weber SU, Jouanin L, Terry N. 1999. Cadmium tolerance and accumulation in Indian mustard is enhanced by overexpressing γ-glutamylcysteine synthetase. *Plant Physiol.* 121:1169–78

340. Zhuo D, Okamoto M, Vidmar JJ, Glass ADM. 1999. Regulation of a putative high-affinity nitrate transporter (*Nrt2;1At*) in roots of *Arabidopsis thaliana*. *Plant J.* 17:563–68

Annu. Rev. Plant Physiol. Plant Mol. Biol. 2001. 52:211–31

PLANT PHOSPHOLIPASES

Xuemin Wang

*Department of Biochemistry, Kansas State University, Willard Hall, Manhattan,
Kansas 66506; e-mail: wangs@ksu.edu*

Key Words   lipid messengers, signal transduction, lipid hydrolysis, membranes,
stress response

■ **Abstract**   Phospholipases are a diverse series of enzymes that hydrolyze phospholipids. Multiple forms of phospholipases D, C, and A have been characterized in plants. These enzymes are involved in a broad range of functions in cellular regulation, lipid metabolism, and membrane remodeling. In recent years, increasing attention has been paid to the many roles of phospholipases in signal transduction. This review highlights recent developments in the understanding of biochemical, molecular biological, and functional aspects of various phospholipases in plants.

CONTENTS

INTRODUCTION

Phospholipases constitute a diverse series of enzymes that can be classified into
phospholipases D (PLD), C (PLC), A_2 (PLA_2), A_1 (PLA_1), and B (PLB) according

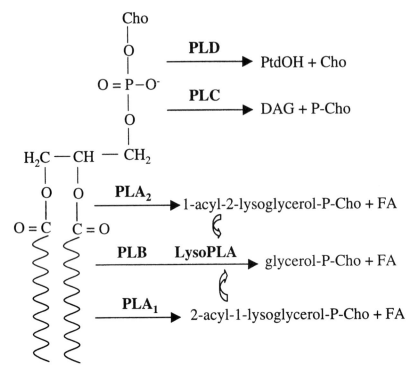

Figure 1 Hydrolysis of PtdCho by PLD, PLC, PLA$_2$, PLA$_1$, PLB, and lysoPLA and the respective reaction products. Note that the arrow lines for PLD, PLC, and PLA$_2$ indicate their site of hydrolysis, but those for PLB, lysoPLA, and PLA$_1$ do not. PLA$_1$ hydrolyzes the sn-1 acylester bond, whereas lysoPLA removes the last fatty acid from lysophospholipids that can be produced by PLA$_2$ and PLA$_1$, as marked by the curved arrows. PLB sequentially removes two fatty acids from phospholipids, and its final reaction products are the same as those of lysoPLA. Cho, choline; P-Cho, phosphocholine; FA, fatty acid.

to their sites of hydrolysis on phospholipids (Figure 1). Each class is divided further into subfamilies based on sequences, biochemical properties, or a combination of both. A closely related class of enzymes comprises lysophospholipases (lysoPLAs), which hydrolyze the products of PLAs (Figure 1); some phospholipases also exhibit this activity. Phospholipids provide the backbone for biomembranes, serve as rich sources of signaling messengers, and occupy important junctions in lipid metabolism. The activities of phospholipases not only affect the structure and stability of cellular membranes, but they also regulate many cellular functions. The past two decades have brought rapid growth in knowledge about the role of phospholipases in cell regulation and signaling processes, particularly in animal systems (2, 42, 64, 98). Activation of phospholipases often is an initial step in generating lipid and lipid-derived second messengers. In the past several years, significant advances have been made toward understanding

PLD, PLC, and PLA_2 in plants. Several reviews covering various aspects of plant phospholipases and phospholipids in cellular regulation have appeared recently (5, 11, 49, 82, 94, 95). This article is not intended to cover exhaustively all literature in the field, but to highlight recent developments in the knowledge of molecular biology, biochemistry, and cellular functions of plant phospholipases.

PHOSPHOLIPASE D

Subfamilies

PLD cleaves the terminal phosphodiesteric bond of phospholipids to phosphatidic acid (PtdOH) and water-soluble free head groups (Figure 1). Based on the requirements for Ca^{2+} and lipids of in vitro assays, PLDs can be grouped into three classes: (*a*) the conventional PLD that is most active at millimolar levels of Ca^{2+} (20 to 100 mM), (*b*) the polyphosphoinositide (PI)-dependent PLD that is most active at micromolar levels of Ca^{2+}, and (*c*) the phosphatidylinositol (PtdIn)-specific PLD that is Ca^{2+}-independent (reviewed in 95). The conventional PLD is the most prevalent and best studied class in plants and has been purified to apparent homogeneity from several plant sources (95 and references therein). The PI-dependent PLD was characterized recently in *Arabidopsis* (58). The PtdIn-specific PLD was identified in suspension cells of *Catharanthus roseus* (99).

A cDNA for the conventional PLD was isolated initially from castor bean (97); this cloning revealed the first primary structure of an intracellular PLD. PLD has subsequently been cloned from a number of plants (95), animals (21), and fungi (68) and found to constitute a supergene family (42). Taking into account the similarities of deduced amino acid sequence, gene architecture, and biochemical properties, PLDs in *Arabidopsis* are divided into five groups, PLDα, β, γ, δ, and ε. Three PLDγs (γ1, γ2, and γ3) are located close together on chromosome IV (95). Most of the PLDs cloned from other plant species belong to the PLDα group, and multiple PLDαs have been cloned from cabbage (34, 54), *Craterostiga plantagineum* (16), and rice (47). The PLDα gene product is responsible for the conventional PLD activity (97), and PLDβ and γ possess the newly identified PI-dependent PLD activity (62). PLDβ-like genes also have been cloned from cotton (10) and rice (D McGee & J Leach, personal communication). None of the cloned PLDs exhibits the PtdIn-specific PLD activity.

Catalysis and Substrate Specificity

The PLDs cloned from eukaryotes all contain two HxKxxxD motifs, which constitute two active-site regions necessary for PLD activity (101). The motif also was observed in some phospholipid-synthesizing enzymes, bacterial phosphatidylserine (PtdSer) synthase and cardiolipin synthase, endonucleases, and other proteins of unknown functions in pathogenic viruses and bacteria (61). The presence of the HxKxxxD motif is used to define the PLD superfamily. Recently, crystal structures have been determined for a 16-kDa endonuclease member of the PLD superfamily (84) and a 54-kDa bacterial PLD (41). Such structural information provides valuable insights into the mode of action of PLD catalysis. The enzymes of the PLD superfamily use the conserved histidine for nucleophilic attack on the substrate phosphorus. PLD hydrolyzes phospholipids at the P-O rather than the C-O bond via a two-step Ping-Pong reaction mechanism involving a phosphatidy-lated enzyme intermediate (84).

Most plant PLDs have broad substrate specificity (1, 55), but different groups of PLDs exhibit varied abilities to hydrolyze different phospholipids (55). PLDα, β, and γ all utilize phosphatidylcholine (PtdCho), phosphatidylethanolamine (PtdEtn), and phosphatidylglycerol (PtdGro) as substrates, but the substrate presentation and Ca^{2+} levels required for PLDβ and γ are strikingly different from those for PLDα (55). In addition, PLDβ and γ use PtdSer and N-acylphosphatidy-lethanolamine (NAPtdEtn) as substrates. Although PLDβ and γ hydrolyze the same substrates, PLDγ, but not PLDβ, prefers ethanolamine-containing lipids, PtdEtn and NAPtdEtn, to other lipids. None of these cloned PLDs uses phosphatidylinositol (PtdIn), phosphatidylinositol 4,5-bisphosphate (PtdInP$_2$), or cardiolipin as a substrate. In contrast, the Ca^{2+}-independent PLD from $C.\ roseus$ hydrolyzes PtdIn, but not PtdCho, PtdEtn, or PtdGro (99). This PLD also was reported to lack the transphosphatidylation activity characteristic for all other PLDs (55, 95). The varied substrate specificities and preferences suggest that activation of different PLDs may result in selective hydrolysis of membrane phospholipids.

Regulation and Activation

The activities of PLD are affected by a number of factors, including Ca^{2+} (95, 104), PIs (58, 62), substrate lipid composition (55), pH changes (56), and mastoparan, a tetradecapeptide G-protein activator (16, 48, 90). PLDs bind Ca^{2+} and phosphatidylinositol 4,5-bisphosphate (PtdInP$_2$) (58, 104); significant progress has been made toward understanding how Ca^{2+} regulates PLD. Sequence analysis indicates that plant PLDs contain a Ca^{2+}/phospholipid-binding fold, called the C2 domain, at the N terminus (57). The C2 domains of PLDα and β have been demonstrated to bind Ca^{2+}, and this binding causes conformational changes of the proteins (104). They also display distinctive thermodynamics of binding, with the PLDβ C2 having a higher affinity for Ca^{2+}. In addition, the Ca^{2+} requirement of PLDα is influenced strongly by pH and substrate lipid composition (56). PLDα is active at near-physiological, micromolar Ca^{2+} concentrations at an acidic pH of 4.5–5.0 in the presence of mixed lipid vesicles. In contrast, PLDβ and α are most active around neutral pH, and their Ca^{2+} requirements are independent of pH.

Intracellular translocation between cytosol and membranes has been proposed as one important mechanism of PLD activation (95). Indeed, PLD associated with microsomal membranes are correlated with stress-induced activation of PLD-mediated hydrolysis (72, 93), and membrane-associated PLD from *C. plantagineum* was activated within minutes during dehydration (16). The relative distribution of PLD between the soluble and membrane fractions changes during development and in response to stress (72, 93). Study of the Ca^{2+} and C2 domain interaction showed that Ca^{2+} binding increases the affinity of the C2 domains for membrane phospholipids (104). This indicates that the C2 domain in PLDs is responsible for mediating a Ca^{2+}-dependent intracellular translocation between cytosol and membranes. The increased association with membranes of preexisting PLD in the cell may represent a rapid and early step in PLD activation in stress responses (93). In addition, gene expression also plays a role in regulating the cellular levels of some PLD isoforms as described below.

Cellular Functions

PLD-catalyzed hydrolysis of phospholipids has been observed during seed germination, aging, and senescence and under a broad spectrum of stress conditions, including freezing, drought, wounding, pathogen infection, nutrient deficiency, and air pollution (5, 16, 95, 103). Most of the early studies linked the increase in PLD activity to lipid catabolism and membrane degradation. Owing to recent advances in the manipulation and analysis of PLD genes, proteins, and reaction products, a clearer picture has emerged of the cellular functions of PLD in plants. Specifically, PLD play pivotal roles in plant response to stresses, and one way in which they do so is through mediating the action and production of the stress-related hormones, abscisic acid (ABA) (15, 29, 65), jasmonic acid (93), and ethylene (39, 71). In particular, evidence is strong for the role of PLD in the ABA signaling pathway. Addition of PtdOH to protoplasts of barley aleurone and *Vicia faba* guard cells partially mimics the effect of ABA (29, 65). In guard cells, ABA activates PLD, and PA triggers signaling events that lead to closure of the inward K^+ channel and stomatal aperture. Activity and gene expression of PLD also increase in tissues treated with ABA and in plants under a water deficit (16, 50, 102). The role of PLD in ABA action was indicated initially by the finding that genetic suppression of PLDα in *Arabidopsis* decreased the rate of ABA-promoted senescence in detached leaves (15). Further studies using PLDα-depleted and PLDα-overexpressing plants showed that PLD play a crucial role in controlling plant water loss by regulating stomatal closure induced by ABA and water deficit (Y Sang & X Wang, unpublished data). The expression and activities of the other PLDs are not altered in the PLDα-abrogated plants. These results identify the role of PLDα and also indicate that the other PLDs cannot compensate for the loss of PLDα.

Results of gene expression studies suggest that PLD isoforms may have different roles in stress responses. The expression of PLDβ, γ1, and γ2 genes increases in wounded *Arabidopsis* leaves, whereas PLDα is activated by increased association of the preexisting enzyme with membranes (93). The relative levels of expression of different PLDs also differ in *Arabidopsis* exposed to low temperature, heavy metals, salts, drought, and the stress-related hormones ABA and jasmonic acid (96). In addition, the various PLDs give distinct temporal responses for a given stressor. Of the two α class PLDs in *C. plantagineum*, CpPLD1 is constitutive, as is the PLDα characterized in other plant species, whereas CpPLD2 is induced by dehydration (16). Such expression patterns suggest that different PLDs may act in different steps in response to a specific stress; the constitutively expressed PLDs such as PLDα are likely to be activated first to initiate or prime signaling and metabolic events that may involve the stress-induced isoforms.

Studies have begun to address the question of how PLDs carry out their cellular functions, particularly in animal and yeast systems. In yeast, PLD is required for the late phases of meiosis and sporulation (68); its function in these processes may result from a role in membrane trafficking (100). In mammalian cells, PLD function is important for various processes, including vesicular trafficking, secretion, mitogenesis, oxidative burst, and cytoskeletal rearrangement (reviewed in 42). Activation of PLD produces messengers activating various enzymes such as protein kinases, lipid kinases, phosphatases, and phospholipases. PtdOH can stimulate protein kinases, including Ca^{2+}-dependent and -independent kinases, such as protein kinase C, mitogen-activated protein kinases, and Raf-kinases (42). A PtdOH-specific protein kinase mediating the activation of NADPH oxidase also has been identified in mammalian cells (91). In plants, a protein kinase activated by PtdOH in response to wounding has been found (Y Lee, personal communication), but the role of PLD in elicitor-induced reactive oxygen production is uncertain (86). PtdOH also stimulates PI-5 kinase, PLC, and PLA$_2$ (Figure 2; see color insert), which are involved in signaling cascades. A recent study also suggests that PLD activation may promote degradation of the translation factor eEF1A (63). In addition, PtdOH can be phosphorylated to diacylglycerol (DAG) pyrophosphate, dephosphorylated to DAG, or deacylated to generate lysoPtdOH and free fatty acids (Figure 2). Such metabolism may attenuate the PtdOH effect or generate new lipid mediators in a signaling cascade (94). The head group released by PLD also may have regulatory functions, and the formation of *N*-acylethanolamine by PLD has been implicated in plant responses to fungal elicitation (5, 89). Furthermore, some cellular roles of PtdOH may result from its effect on membrane properties and configuration (8), rather than its direct effect on proteins, because of its non-bilayer-forming property. Thus, diverse targets may underlie the various effects of PLD in cell function.

PHOSPHOLIPASE C

Subfamilies

PLC hydrolyzes the glycerophosphate ester linkage of phospholipids to DAG and phosphorylated head groups (Figure 1). According to substrate specificity and cellular function, PLCs in plants can be divided into three groups: (*a*) the PI-PLC that hydrolyzes phosphoinositides, (*b*) the nonspecific-PLC (also referred to as PtdCho-PLC) that acts on the common phospholipid PtdCho and some other phospholipids,

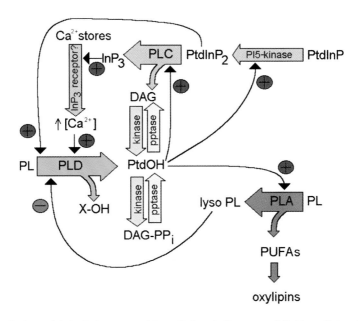

Figure 2 A model depicting networking of phospholipases and lipid mediators in plant cells. PLC produces DAG and InP_3 that increases the level of cytoplasmic Ca^{2+} (81). Ca^{2+} and $PtdInP_2$ both stimulate the activity of PLD (95, 104). The activation of PLD generates PtdOH, which enhances the activities of PLC, PLA, and PI5-kinase, based on mammalian studies (42). The role of PLD on PLA activity and oxylipin synthesis is indicated also by the effect of PLD-suppression on wound-induced accumulation of jasmonic acid (93). LysoPtdEtn, a potential PLA product, inhibits PLD activity (71). Kinases and phosphatases involved in the interconversion of DAG, PtdOH, and $DAG-PP_i$ have been characterized in plants (49). $\oplus$ denotes stimulation, and — denotes inhibition. $DAG-PP_i$, DAG-pyrophosphate; InP_3, inositol 1,4,5-trisphosphate; lysoPL, lysophospholipids; PI5-kinase, phosphatidylinositol 4-phosophate 5-kinase; PL, phospholipid; PPtase, phospholipid phosphatase; PUFAs, polyunsaturated fatty acids; X-OH, free head group.

and (c) the glycosylphosphatidylinositol (GPI)-PLC that hydrolyzes GPI-anchors on proteins.

The PtdCho-hydrolyzing PLC has been found in particulate or soluble preparations of various plant species and tissues (7, 32, 69, 83). However, detecting the PLC activity in plants requires caution because of the relatively high activity of PLD and the possible interconversion of PLD and PLC products by phosphatases and kinases (Figure 2). The identification and understanding of PtdCho-PLC function in plants, as well as in animals, has been hindered by the lack of molecular information on this enzyme. On the other hand, multiple PLCs that use PtdCho as a substrate have been cloned and characterized from gram-positive and gram-negative bacteria (reviewed in 88). An *Arabidopsis* cDNA with significant sequence similarity to the gram-negative bacterial PLC has been isolated, and the protein is localized in plastids (D Ling & X Wang, unpublished data). In addition, the *Arabidopsis* Genome Project has revealed six *Arabidopsis* genes that show sequence similarities to bacterial PLCs, but the catalytic identities of these putative proteins await experimental verification.

The GPI-PLC cleaves the terminal lipid that links GPI-anchored proteins to the plasma membrane. GPI-anchored proteins are extracellular and function as enzymes, such as phosphatases or nitrate reductase, to recruit nutrients, as receptors to interact with extracellular ligands, or as matrix proteins, such as arabinogalactan proteins (reviewed in 87). GPI-PLC has been characterized in animals and microorganisms (66). A GPI-PLC was purified partially from peanut seeds; it cleaved solubilized GPI-anchor, but paradoxically did not act on membrane-bound GPI (4). A recent structural analysis of the lipid moiety of a GPI-anchored arabinogalactan has raised the possibility of the presence of a GPI-PLD in plants (53). Extracellular GPI-PLD occurs in animal blood serum (66 and references therein), but no GPI-PLD activity has been characterized in plants.

Compared with the other PLCs, the group of PI-PLCs is better understood. The PI-PLCs in animal systems comprise at least ten different isoenzymes, which are divided into three classes, PLCβ, γ, and δ, based on the sequence homology and mechanisms of activation (reviewed in 64, 98). Multiple PLCs have been cloned from plants, such as *Arabidopsis*, soybean, tobacco, and potato (22, 25, 26, 35). Similar to yeast and mold PI-PLCs, the domain structure, size, and overall sequence similarity of plant PI-PLCs characterized so far are related more closely to mammalian PLCδ than to the other PI-PLCs (reviewed in 49). Plant PI-PLCs all contain domains X ($\sim$170 amino acids) and Y ($\sim$260 amino acids) that are necessary for the phosphoesterase activity, followed by a Ca^{2+}-dependent phospholipid binding a C2 domain toward the C terminus, but lack a pleckstrin homology domain. The presence of N-terminal EF-hand motifs was reported for PI-PLCs from soybean and *Arabidopsis*, but not from potato (35).

Catalysis and Regulation

Determination of the three-dimensional structure of a mammalian PI-PLCδ1 has given insights into the catalysis of PI-PLCs (12). A two-step mechanism, tether and fix, has been proposed (12, 64). The PH domain of PI-PLCδ1 binds PtdInP$_2$, and this binding tethers the enzyme to a membrane. In the presence of Ca^{2+}, the C2 domain fixes the catalytic domain in the correct orientation. Another Ca^{2+} ion resides at the active site and, together with two His residues, mediates catalysis. The conservation of the C2 domain and the two His residues indicates that the catalytic mechanism of plant PI-PLCs may be the same as that of mammalian PI-PLCs, but the lack of the PH domain in plant PI-PLCs suggests that some other regions or mechanisms are involved in the initial interaction with membranes. This notion is consistent with a recent kinetic analysis of PtdInP$_2$ hydrolysis, which indicates that plant PI-PLC binds lipid vesicles via a single binding site (24). It may first bind noncatalytically to PtdInP$_2$ at the same site where catalysis occurs (24). This is in contrast to mammalian PLCs that show multiple binding sites for the interface and subsequent binding of the lipid substrate at the interface.

Ca^{2+} is required for plant PI-PLC activities (24), and, as described above, it may regulate the PI-PLC via dual functions, catalysis and membrane binding (24). The cloned PI-PLCs prefer PtdIn(4,5)P$_2$ as a substrate at physiological concentrations of Ca^{2+} (μM), but PtdIn is the preferred substrate at millimolar levels of Ca^{2+} (35). This decreased specificity toward PtdIn(4,5)P$_2$ as Ca^{2+} levels increase resembles that of mammalian PI-PLCs. Both membrane-associated and soluble PI-PLCs have been found in plant extracts; the former hydrolyzes PtdIn(4,5)P$_2$ and requires micromolar concentrations of Ca^{2+}, whereas the latter acts primarily on PtdIn in the presence of millimolar Ca^{2+} (49 and references therein). Expression of an epitope-tagged PI-PLC in transgenic tobacco indicates that both the membrane and soluble PLC activities can be derived from the same PI-PLC (77). Activity of PI-PLC also is modulated by other cations such as Mg^{2+} and Al^{3+}. Al^{3+} inhibits PtdInP$_2$ hydrolysis (35), and the effect of Mg^{2+} on PI-PLC varies with the enzyme source. It stimulates PI-PLC activity associated with plant membranes (9), but not the *E. coli*-expressed potato PLC (35). These varied substrate specificities and cation effects indicate that the cellular activity of PI-PLC is modulated by subcellular location, association with other cellular factors, and membrane environments, a property shared by other lipolytic enzymes (24, 55, 92, 95).

The G proteins are important regulators of mammalian PI-PLCs, and their effects differ on the three classes of PI-PLCs (reviewed in 64, 98). PLCβs are activated by the α subunit of heterotrimeric G$_q$ proteins, whereas PLCγs are activated by protein receptor-linked or nonreceptor tyrosine kinases. The activation of PLCδs is understood less than that of the other classes, and PLCδ1 may be activated by the G$_h\alpha$ subunit and also by the small G protein RhoA. The regulation of plant PI-PLC by G proteins has been suggested mostly based on studies using mastoparan (6, 49). When used at concentrations above 10 μM, however, mastoparan may activate PI-PLC via permeabilizing the plasma membrane that induces Ca^{2+} influx, rather than via G-protein activation. A recent study showed that mastoparan stimulated PI-PLC activity without permeabilizing *Chlamydomonas* cells, and, interestingly, the level of mastoparan required for activating PI-PLC was tenfold higher than that for activating PLD (90).

The cellular levels of PI-PLC isoforms are regulated at the level of gene expression (26, 35). Multiple PI-PLCs are expressed in most tissues, and the relative levels of different isoforms can vary among tissues (35). In addition, different PI-PLCs are expressed differentially under various stress conditions. For example, in a drought treatment, the leaf transcript level of potato PLC1 decreased, whereas that of PLC2 increased, and the level of PLC3 did not change. In *Arabidopsis*, drought and low temperature increased the mRNA levels of AtPLC1S, but the AtPLC2 gene was expressed constitutively (26). These different patterns of expression suggest that different *cis* and/or *trans* factors may regulate the expression levels of PI-PLC isoforms and raise the possibility that individual PI-PLCs may serve particular functions.

Cellular Functions

PI-PLC-mediated signaling has been proposed to be important in the plant response to various stimuli, including osmotic stress, ABA, light, gravity, pathogen attack, and pollination (5, 40, 49, 60, 77, 81 and references therein). A recent report suggests that PI-PLC plays a role in the signaling cascade leading to the light-dependent phosphorylation of C4 phosphoenolpyruvate carboxylase, a process that activates this enzyme that concentrates CO_2 for C4 photosynthesis (9). The best-known function of PI-PLC in animal systems is its hydrolysis of PtdIn $(4,5)P_2$ to produce the cellular messengers, inositol 1,4,5-trisphosphate (InP_3) and DAG (64, 98) (Figure 2). InP_3 binds to a receptor and mediates Ca^{2+} release to the cytoplasm, whereas DAG activates protein kinase C (PKC). Many components in the animal PI-PLC cascade have been identified in plant cells; these include the occurrence of $PtdInP_2$, stimulus-induced production of InP_3 and DAG, InP_3-induced Ca^{2+} release, and PI-kinases involved in the production of $PtdInP_2$ (reviewed in 11, 49, 82). Compared with animal cells, the level of $PtdInP_2$ in plants is quite low, ranging from 0.05 to 0.5% of total phospholipids, depending on the types of plants and cells. However, little is known about the plant InP_3 receptor and DAG-activated protein kinase, and the immediate targets of InP_3 and DAG remain elusive in plants.

Strong evidence exists to support the involvement of the PI-PLC-mediated signaling in Ca^{2+} mobilization and oscillation in plants. One such process that has received considerable attention is the osmotic regulation of guard cells (2, 81 and references therein). InP_3 was reported to increase in ABA-treated guard cell protoplasts, to promote an increase in cytoplasmic Ca^{2+}, and to attenuate the inward K^+ channel of the plasma membrane. Inhibition of PI-PLC by U-73122 also inhibited ABA-promoted Ca^{2+} oscillation and stomatal closure. The InP_3-mediated Ca^{2+} oscillations have been proposed also to regulate pollen tube growth (17). In response to gravity, InP_3 levels increased transiently on the lower side of bent maize pulvini (60), and the levels of InP_3 have been suggested also to oscillate in the early phase of gravistimulation (82). The InP_3 fluctuations, which may result from a cascade effect of activation of PLC and the rate of

InP$_3$ metabolism, may regulate the oscillations and changes of cytoplasmic Ca^{2+} concentrations.

In addition, the activity of PI-PLC decreases the levels of PtdIn(4,5)P$_2$ in membranes, and the decrease itself could be an important signal in cell regulation (reviewed in 64, 82). PtdIn(4,5)P$_2$ is an activator of PLD and a substrate for PI-3 kinase. It also serves as a membrane-attachment site for various proteins with pleckstrin homology domains and is required for membrane-trafficking events. Furthermore, PtdIn(4,5)P$_2$ modulates cytoskeletal dynamics by interacting with many actin-binding proteins, including profilin, gelsolin, cofilin, and actinin. PI-PLC also is affected by actin-depolymerizing factors. Two classes of maize profilin, an actin monomer binding protein, displayed different abilities to inhibit PI-PLC (37), which, in turn, may influence the levels of PtdInP$_2$ that affect cytoskeletal organization. Thus, the levels and locations of PtdInP$_2$ in the cell are regulated dynamically, and the activity of PI-PLC may play an important role in the regulation.

PHOSPHOLIPASE A$_2$

Subfamilies

PLA$_2$ hydrolyzes the sn-2 acylester bond of phospholipids to free fatty acids and 1-acyl-2-lysophospholipids (Figure 1). Based on sequence data, PLA$_2$s from animals are classified into 10 groups, which can be simplified into three major types based on their biological properties: (*a*) the secretory, low-molecular-weight PLA$_2$ (sPLA$_2$), (*b*) the cytosolic Ca^{2+}-dependent PLA$_2$ (cPLA$_2$), and (*c*) the intracellular Ca^{2+}-independent PLA$_2$ (iPLA$_2$) (3). The presence of PLA$_2$ in plants had been presumed for some time, and its activity has been associated with various physiological processes (reviewed in 49, 74). Only recently have sPLA$_2$-like PLA$_2$s been purified and cloned in plants (33, 79, 80), and intracellular, iPLA$_2$-like PLA$_2$s also have been reported in plants (31, 36, 45, 76). A database search in July 2000 revealed one iPLA$_2$-like gene sequence in *Arabidopsis*, but no cPLA$_2$-like sequence has been found yet in plants.

The sPLA$_2$-like PLA$_2$ was purified first from elm seed endosperm and has a low molecular weight of 14 kDa. It requires millimolar levels of Ca^{2+} for optimal activity and exhibits specificity toward the sn-2 acyl group (79). Two cDNAs corresponding to the PLA$_2$ were cloned from rice and one similar cDNA was isolated from developing carnation flowers (33, 80). Sequence analysis revealed that they possess several disulfide bonds and contain putative signal peptides for secretion (33, 80). All these data indicate that these PLA$_2$s resemble animal sPLA$_2$.

The intracellular PLA$_2$s reported to date show sequence similarities to patatin, a group of closely related, vacuolar storage proteins in potato tubers that possess acyl hydrolase activity (28 and references therein). These PLA$_2$s include a membrane-associated enzyme from broad bean leaves (31), a latex allergen (Hev b 7) (36), a protein associated with cucumber lipid bodies (45), and a potato cytosolic enzyme induced by a late blight fungus (76). The sizes of these proteins range from 40 to 48 kDa. The purified enzyme from broad bean was inhibited by inhibitors of mammalian iPLA$_2$ and cPLA$_2$ (ETYA and an arachidonyl trifluoromethyl ketone AACOCF3), but not by inhibitors of sPLA$_2$. It prefers 2-linolenoyl-PtdCho to 2-linoleoyl-PtdCho and has a lysoPLA activity, but no PLA$_1$ activity. This enzyme is stimulated by calmodulin, but not by Ca^{2+}, and, thus, is suggested to be an iPLA$_2$-like PLA$_2$ (31).

Identification and Catalytic Mechanisms

The identity of PLA$_2$ in plants has been a common subject of confusion because of the overlapping specificities of PLA$_2$ and nonspecific acyl hydrolases, which are very active in some plant tissues (reviewed in 28). The acyl hydrolases remove fatty acids at the sn-1 and -2 positions from several classes of lipids, including glycolipids, sulfolipids, monoacylglycerols, and DAG, in addition to phospholipids, but they are inactive on triacylglycerols. Thus, these enzymes have the combined capacities of PLA$_2$, PLA$_1$, PLB, lysoPLA, and galactolipases. One example of such proteins is patatin, which has been shown to have acyl-hydrolyzing activities toward various glycerolipids (28 and references therein). As discussed earlier, patatin-like proteins from several plant sources recently have been reported to exhibit PLA$_2$ activity. Depending on their sources, these enzymes also display other lipolytic activities, such as PLA$_1$, monoacylglycerol esterase, and/or lysoPLA (31, 36, 45, 76). However, the substrate specificities of the established mammalian cPLA$_2$ and iPLA$_2$ also are not absolute (92 and references therein). For example, cPLA$_2$ displays lysoPLA activities, and iPLA$_2$ also exhibits PLA$_1$, lysoPLA, transacylase, and platelet-activating factor acetylhydrolase activities. The relative level of these activities depends strongly on substrate presentation (43). Thus, establishing the identity of a PLA$_2$ requires careful characterization that takes into account its substrate specificity and preferences, sequence and structural similarities with known PLA$_2$s, and, most important, the lipolytic activity in vivo. Enzymes with sequences related to the patatin family may act as PLAs to release free fatty acids and lysophospholipids involved in various plant responses.

The broad substrate specificity may be related to the catalytic mechanism shared by many acyl-hydrolyzing enzymes. The cPLA$_2$ and iPLA$_2$ have been proposed to function as serine hydrolases, with the active Ser residue located in the middle of the consensus sequence GxSxG (3, 92 and references therein). This sequence also is found in PLA$_1$, PLB, and lysoPLA, as well as many lipases. Both cPLA$_2$ and iPLA$_2$ hydrolyze the ester bond via an acyl-enzyme intermediate. Although Ca^{2+} does not participate directly in the catalysis, cPLA$_2$ needs Ca^{2+} to associate with membranes (3). In contrast, Ca^{2+} has a direct role in the catalysis of sPLA$_2$, whose catalytic mechanism is different from that of the other PLA$_2$s. Ca^{2+} binds to a conserved Ca^{2+} binding loop of sPLA$_2$ and stabilizes the transition-state intermediate. The sPLA$_2$ catalysis does not involve the formation of the classical acyl-enzyme intermediate of the serine hydrolases. Instead, sPLA$_2$s use an His residue, aided by an Asp, to polarize an H_2O, which then attacks the carbonyl group. The low-molecular-weight PLA_2s of plants conserve the His and Asp in the catalytic site and other residues in Ca^{2+} binding (80) and, thus, may use the same catalytic mechanism as $sPLA_2$s.

Cellular Functions

One extensively studied function of PLA_2 in cell regulation is the release of arachidonic acid, a rate-limiting step in the eicosanoid pathway in animal systems (3). An analogous process in plants is the octadecanoid pathway that uses linolenic acid to produce jasmonic acid and related compounds (52, 70 and references therein) (Figure 2). These oxylipins regulate many cellular processes, such as wound and defense responses. Evidence was provided recently for the presence of a wound/systemin-inducible PLA_2 activity. Wounding promoted systemic accumulation of lysoPtdCho and lysoPtEtn in several plant species (38). Systemin and oligosaccharide elicitors, which induce jasmonic acid synthesis, also increase a PLA_2-like activity without wounding. The animal PLA_2 inhibitors manoalide and AACOCF3 both decreased systemin-induced formation of lysoPtdCho (52). The activation of PLA2 may be mediated by a wound-inducible cell surface receptor to release polyunsaturated fatty acids for oxylipin synthesis (70).

The activities of PLA_2 are important in other cellular processes, such as lipid metabolism (5, 45), plant-pathogen interactions (49, 67, 76), and auxin-stimulated growth (59, 74). A PLA-like activity preferentially removes uncommon fatty acids, such as ricinoleic and vernolic acids, from PtdCho, and this activity might channel these fatty acids to triacylglycerols (5, 78). A patatin-related PLA_2 in cucumber is localized in lipid bodies and may be involved in lipid catabolism and mobilization during seed germination and seedling growth (45). In pathogen-infected or elicitor-treated cells, activation of PLA_2 may be involved in reactive oxygen generation and alkaloid production (5, 49, 67, 76). In auxin-stimulated growth, PLA-released fatty acids may carry out second messenger functions, particularly in cell elongation, whereas lysoPtdCho and lysoPtEtn may have functions different from those of free fatty acids in auxin and stress responses (59). The $iPLA_2$ inhibitor HELSS inhibited the auxin-induced elongation of zucchini hypocotyls and maize coleoptils, but the PLA_2 inhibitor AACOCF3, which inhibits systemin-inducible PLA, was not effective (59). These results suggest that wounding and auxin signaling may involve different types of PLA_2, but little is known about the molecular nature of these PLA activities.

PHOSPHOLIPASES A_1 AND B; LYSOPHOSPHOLIPASES

PLA_1 hydrolyzes the sn-1 acylester bond of phospholipids to free fatty acids and 2-acyl-1-lysophospholipids. PLB sequentially removes two fatty acids from phospholipids and thus has both PLA and lysoPLA activities (Figure 1). Multiple PLA_1s and PLBs have been identified and cloned from animals and yeast (46, 51), but their functions are not as well understood as those of PLA_2. Simultaneous inactivation of the three *PLB* genes in yeast resulted in total loss of PLB activity in vitro, but no apparent growth defect occurred (46). Two forms of PtdSer-specific PLA_1 have been identified in mammalian cells, and their activities are important in controlling the levels of PtdSer and lysoPtdSer that are involved in the metastatic process in tumor cells (51). A PLA_1 activity was found in the tonoplasts of *Acer pseudoplatanus* cells (85). Although few reports deal directly with PLB in plants, several plant proteins possess PLB-like activities, such as the purified PLA_2 from broad bean (31) and the ricin B chain from castor bean (23).

PLBs, and some PLA_1s, $cPLA_2$s, and $iPLA_2$s, also possess lysoPLA activity, which removes the last fatty acid from lysophospholipids (Figure 1). Together with some transacylases and acyl transferases, these are grouped as large lyso-PLAs in animal cells (92). In addition, two types of small lysoPLAs, I and II, with molecular weights of about 25 kDa, have been identified in mammalian cells (92). Lysophospholipids are found in low concentrations in biological membranes and have many cellular functions, such as signal transduction and vesicular trafficking in mammalian cells (92 and references therein). LysoPtdCho modulates multiple gene expression, promotes secretion of growth factors, and induces cell adhesion. Receptors specific for lysoPtdOH, the simplest naturally occurring lysophospholipid, have been cloned and identified as G protein–coupled receptors (20). The formation of lysoPtdOH and PtdOH occurs specifically at the neck of budding synaptic vesicles and is required for membrane budding (75). Lysophospholipids in plants are produced in response to stress cues, as discussed earlier, and modulate a number of enzyme activities (5, 49, 59, 74 and references therein). LysoPtdCho may interact directly with plant plasma membrane H^+-ATPase to stimulate proton pumping (19). LysoPtdEtn retards senescence, possibly through inhibition of PLD (71) (Figure 2). Thus, lysophospholipases are potentially important in regulating the levels of lysophospholipids and serve a major function in lipid signaling cascades and lipid metabolism (92).

Early studies reported the presence of acidic and basic lysoPLA activities in germinating barley seeds, and these activities may be involved in lipid mobilization (18, 44). Database searches in July 2000 revealed multiple *Arabidopsis* and rice genes that encode proteins of 310–330 amino acids with sequence similarities to small animal lysoPLAs (X Wang, unpublished data). The catalytic mechanism of mammalian small lysoPLAs resembles the classical serine hydrolases (92). The deduced plant proteins contain the GXSXG and catalytic triad Ser-Asp-His consensus sequences, although the lipolytic activity of these gene products remains to be identified. Related to the catalytic mechanism of serine hydrolases are two recently identified genes, EDS1 and PAD4; EDS1 is an essential component of R gene–mediated disease resistance in *Arabidopsis* (14) and PAD4 is important for salicylic acid signaling (30). But the identity of these defense-related genes as lipolytic enzymes has not been established. Nevertheless, the occurrence of multiple lysoPLA-like genes in the plant genomes and the functional revelation of putative lipolytic enzymes warrant further study of these enzymes.

NETWORK OF PHOSPHOLIPASES
IN CELLULAR FUNCTION

It is increasingly clear that multiple lipid signaling enzymes often form complex networks that mediate a specific cellular response. The involvement of PLC, PLD, and PLA in stomatal movement presents an example for such interaction (Figure 2). Evidence has indicated that both PI-PLC and PLD are involved in mediating stomatal closure (29, 81), whereas the activity of PLA may stimulate stomatal opening (5 and references therein). PI-PLC releases InP$_3$ that promotes oscillations and increases in cytoplasmic Ca^{2+} (81). The increase in Ca^{2+} may enhance PLD association with membranes, resulting in PLD activation (95, 104). On the other hand, PLD-derived PA may activate PtdInP-5 kinase, producing the PI-PLC substrate PtdInP$_2$, as shown in animal systems (42). PtdInP$_2$ is a required activator for PLDs, and activations of PLD and PtdInP-5 kinase have been proposed to form a positive feedback loop that leads to rapid generation of PtdOH and PtdInP$_2$, which are involved in vesicular trafficking and cytoskeletal dynamics in animal systems (42). Active membrane trafficking and cytoskeletal rearrangements have been suggested to occur in stomatal movement (13, 27). Using U73122 to inhibit PI-PLC and 1-butanol to attenuate PtdOH formation by PLD, a recent study indicated that PLC and PLD act on the same pathway in ABA-induced stomatal closure (29). On the other hand, lysophospholipids inhibit PLD activity (71) and, thus, the activation of PLA that promotes stomatal opening also may, in turn, down-regulate PLD (Figure 2). But the effect of PLA activation on PLD/PLC or vice versa has not been tested directly.

Another interplay among the lipid-signaling enzymes occurs in wound-induced lipid hydrolysis and oxylipin production. Activation of PLA has been suggested to release linolenic acid for the synthesis of jasmonic acid and related oxylipins (52). However, in studies where the temporal patterns were analyzed, increases in PtdOH preceded those of other lipid metabolites such as DAG, free fatty acids, peroxidized fatty acids, or lysophospholipids (38, 73). The activation of PLD may generate PtdOH, stimulating other lipolytic activities such as PLA, as shown in mammalian systems (42) (Figure 2). A recent study showed that antisense suppression of PLDα in *Arabidopsis* resulted in decreases in wound-induced accumulation of linolenic acid and jasmonic acid (93), providing evidence that activation of PLD modulates wound induction of jasmonic acid.

CONCLUDING REMARKS

Over the past several years, significant advances have been made toward understanding the biochemistry and molecular biology of PLD, PLC, and PLA$_2$. These enzymes have been connected with various facets of cellular processes, particularly responses to hormones and abiotic and biotic stresses. Based on the available information, the functions of phospholipases as a whole may be considered in three categories: (*a*) cell regulation, such as signal transduction, vesicular trafficking, and cytoskeletal dynamics; (*b*) lipid catabolism, such as membrane lipid degradation during cell differentiation, senescence, aging, and stress injuries and removal of undesirable lipids from membranes; and (*c*) membrane remodeling, such as changing acyl and head group compositions of membrane lipids during growth and development and in response to stresses. One underexplored, important area is the detailed molecular and cellular mechanisms by which phospholipases mediate these cellular functions in plants. Little is known about the cellular activators and targets of PLD, PLC, and PLAs. Understanding the mechanisms in which phospholipases are involved will require identification and knowledge of the molecules that interact with phospholipases and the reactions or processes that lie directly downstream of these enzymes and their reaction products.

PLD, PI-PLC, and PLA_2 have been demonstrated to have multiple isoforms, and the same is anticipated for other classes of plant phospholipases. This raises important questions about what roles particular phospholipase isoforms play in plant growth and development and how the properties of a specific isoform are exploited in the cell. The locations and timing of expression and activation are likely to be keys to determining the function of each isoform, and deciphering these questions requires approaches directed toward specific isoenzymes. Genetic depletion of a PLDα represents the first alteration of a specific phospholipase isoform in plants; this manipulation has improved understanding of the PLD family (58, 95). Genetic manipulations, including suppression, point and insertional mutagenesis, and overexpression in plant cells, should be forthcoming for other phospholipases and specific isoforms. Future studies should capitalize on the vast information on phospholipase-like genes revealed by the genomic sequencing and the approaches of functional genomics, proteinomics, and metabolomics. Results should shed light on the diverse cellular roles of phospholipases in plants.

ACKNOWLEDGMENTS

I thank Dr R Welti for critically reading the manuscript, Drs W Boss and B Drobak for discussion on PI-PLC, and Drs T Munnik and Y Lee for sharing unpublished data. Work in the author's laboratory is supported by grants from the US National Science Foundation and US Department of Agriculture and this is contribution 01-59-J of the Kansas Agricultural Experiment Station.

Visit the Annual Reviews home page at www.AnnualReviews.org

LITERATURE CITED

1. Abousalham A, Nari J, Teissere M, Ferte N, Noat G, Verger R. 1997. Study of fatty acid specificity of sunflower phospholipase D using detergent/phospholipid micelles. *Eur. J. Biochem.* 248:374–79

2. Assmann SM, Shimazaki K. 1999. The

multisensory guard cell. Stomatal response to blue light and abscisic acid. *Plant Physiol.* 119:809–15

3. Balsinde J, Balboa MA, Insel PA, Dennis EA. 1999. Regulation and inhibition of phospholipase A2. *Annu. Rev. Pharmacol. Toxicol.* 39:175–89

4. Butikofer P, Brodbeck U. 1993. Partial purification and characterization of a (glycosyl) inositol phospholipid-specific phospholipase C from peanut. *J. Biol. Chem.* 268:17794–802

5. Chapman KD. 1998. Phospholipase activity during plant growth and development and in response to environmental stress. *Trends Plant Sci.* 11:419–26

6. Cho MH, Tan Z, Erneux C, Shears SB, Boss WF. 1995. The effects of mastoparan on the carrot cell plasma membrane polyphosphoinositide phospholipase C. *Plant Physiol.* 107:845–56

7. Chrastil J, Parrish FW. 1987. Phospholipases C and D in rice grains. *J. Agric. Food Chem.* 35:624–27

8. Cornell RB, Arnold RS. 1996. Modulation of the activities of enzymes of membrane lipid metabolism by non-bilayer-forming lipids. *Chem. Phys. Lipids* 81:215–27

9. Coursol S, Giglioli N, Vidal J, Pierre J-N. 2000. An increase in phosphoinositide specific phospholipase C activity precedes induction of C4 phosphoenolpyruvate carboxylase phosphorylation in illuminated and NH_4Cl-treated protoplasts from *Digitaria sanguinalis. Plant J.* 23:497–506

10. Cui X, Brown RM Jr. 1999. Molecular cloning of a phospholipase D gene from cotton fibers (accession no. AF159139). *Plant Physiol.* 120:1207

11. Drobak BK, Dewey RE, Boss WF. 1999. Phosphoinositide kinase and the synthesis of polyphosphoinositide in higher plant cells. *Int. Rev. Cytol.* 189:95–130

12. Essen LO, Perisic O, Cheung R, Katan M, Williams RL. 1996. Crystal structure of a mammalian phosphoinositide-specific phospholipase Cδ. *Nature* 380:595–602

13. Eun SO, Lee Y. 1997. Actin filaments of guard cells are reorganized in response to light and abscisic acid. *Plant Physiol.* 115:1491–98

14. Falk A, Feys BJ, Frost LN, Jones JD, Daniels MJ, Parker JE. 1999. EDS1, an essential component of R gene-mediated disease resistance in *Arabidopsis* has homology with eukaryotic lipases. *Proc. Natl. Acad Sci. USA* 96:3292–97

15. Fan L, Zheng S, Wang X. 1997. Antisense suppression of phospholipase Dα retards abscisic acid- and ethylene-promoted senescence of postharvest *Arabidopsis* leaves. *Plant Cell* 9:2916–19

16. Frank W, Munnik T, Kerkmann K, Salamini F, Bartels D. 2000. Water deficit triggers phospholipase D activity in the resurrection plant *Craterostigma plantagineum. Plant Cell* 12:111–24

17. Franklin-Tong VE, Drobak BK, Allan AC, Watkins PAC, Trewavas AJ. 1996. Growth of pollen tubes of *Papaver rhoeas* is regulated by a slow-moving calcium wave propagated by inositol 1,4,5-trisphosphate. *Plant Cell* 8:1305–21

18. Fujikura Y, Baisted D. 1985. Purification and characterization of a basic lysophospholipase in germinating barley. *Arch. Biochem. Biophys.* 243:570–78

19. Gomes E, Venema K, Simon-Plas F, Milat ML, Palmgren MG, Blein JP. 1996. Activation of the plant plasma membrane H^+-ATPase. Is there a direct interaction between lysophosphatidylcholine and the C-terminal part of the enzyme? *FEBS Lett.* 398:48–52

20. Guo Z, Liliom K, Fischer DJ, Bathurst IC, Tomei LD, et al. 1996. Molecular cloning of a high-affinity receptor for the growth factor-like lipid mediator lysophosphatidic acid from *Xenopus* oocytes. *Proc. Natl. Acad. Sci. USA* 93:14367–72

21. Hammond SM, Alshuller YM, Sung T, Rudge SA, Rose K, et al. 1995. Human ADP-ribosylation factor-activated phosphatidylcholine-specific phospholipase D

defines a new and highly conserved gene family *J. Biol. Chem.* 270:29640–43

22. Hartweck LM, Llewellyn DJ, Dennis ES. 1997. The *Arabidopsis thaliana* genome has multiple divergent forms of phosphoinositol-specific phospholipase C1. *Gene* 202:151–56

23. Helmy M, Lombard S, Pieroni G. 1999. Ricin RCA60: evidence of its phospholipase activity. *Biochem. Biophys. Res. Commun.* 258:252–55

24. Hernández-Sotomayor SMT, Santos-Briones CDL, Muñoz-Sánchez JA, Loyola-Vargas VM. 1999. Kinetic analysis of phospholipase C from *Catharanthus roseus* transformed roots using different assays. *Plant Physiol.* 120:1075–82

25. Hirayama T, Mitsukawa N, Shibata D, Shinozaki K. 1997. AtPLC2, a gene encoding phosphoinositide-specific phospholipase C, is constitutively expressed in vegetative and floral tissues in *Arabidopsis thaliana*. *Plant Mol. Biol.* 34:175–80

26. Hirayama T, Ohto C, Mizoguchi T, Shinozaki K. 1995. A gene encoding a phosphatidylinositol-specific phospholipase C is induced by dehydration and salt stress in *Arabidopsis thaliana*. *Proc. Natl. Acad. Sci. USA* 92:3903–7

27. Homann U, Thiel G. 1999. Unitary exocytic and endocytotic events in guard-cell protoplasts during osmotically driven volume changes. *FEBS Lett.* 460:495–99

28. Huang AHC. 1993. Lipases. In *Lipid Metabolism in Plants*, ed. TS Moore, pp. 473–503. Boca Raton, FL: CRC Press

29. Jacob T, Ritchie S, Assmann SM, Gilroy S. 1999. Abscisic acid signal transduction in guard cells is mediated by phospholipase D activity. *Proc. Natl. Acad. Sci. USA* 96:12192–97

30. Jirage D, Tootle TL, Reuber TL, Frost LN, Feys BJ, et al. 1999. *Arabidopsis thaliana* PAD4 encodes a lipase-like gene that is important for salicylic acid signaling. *Proc. Natl. Acad. Sci. USA* 96:13583–88

31. Jung KM, Kim DK. 2000. Purification and characterization of a membrane-associated 48-kilodalton phospholipase A2 in leaves of broad bean. *Plant Physiol.* 123:1057–68

32. Kates M. 1955. Hydrolysis of lecithin by plant plastid enzymes. *Can. J. Biochem. Physiol.* 33:575

33. Kim JY, Chung YS, Ok SH, Lee SG, Chung WI, et al. 1999. Characterization of the full-length sequences of phospholipase A2 induced during flower development. *Biochim. Biophys. Acta* 1489:389–92

34. Kim DU, Roh TY, Lee J, Noh JY, Jang YJ, et al. 1999. Molecular cloning and functional expression of a phospholipase D from cabbage (*Brassica oleracea* var. *capitata*). *Biochim. Biophys. Acta.* 1437:409–14

35. Kopka J, Pical C, Gray JE, Muller-Rober B. 1998. Molecular and enzymatic characterization of three phosphoinositide-specific phospholipase C isoforms from potato. *Plant Physiol.* 116:239–50

36. Kostyal DA, Hickey VL, Noti JD, Sussman GL, Beezhold DH. 1998. Cloning and characterization of a latex allergen (Hev b 7): homology to patatin, a plant PLA2. *Clin. Exp. Immunol.* 112:355–62

37. Kovar DR, Drobak BK, Staiger CJ. 2000. Maize profilin isoforms are functionally distinct. *Plant Cell* 12:583–98

38. Lee S, Suh S, Kim S, Crain RC, Kwak JM, et al. 1997. Systemic elevation of phosphatidic acid and lysophospholipid levels in wounded plants. *Plant J.* 12:547–56

39. Lee SH, Chae TK, Kim SH, Shin SH, Cho BH, et al. 1998. Ethylene-mediated phospholipid catabolism pathway in glucose-starved carrot suspension cells. *Plant Physiol.* 116:223–29

40. Legendre L, Yueh YG, Crain R, Haddock N, Heinstein PF, Low PS. 1993. Phospholipase C activation during elicitation of the oxidative burst in cultured plant cells. *J. Biol. Chem.* 268:24559–63

41. Leiros I, Secundo F, Zambonelli C, Servi S, Hough E. 2000. The first crystal structure

of a phospholipase D. *Struct. Fold Des.* 8:855–67

42. Liscovitch M, Czarny M, Fiucci G, Tang X. 2000. Phospholipase D: molecular and cell biology of a novel gene family. *Biochem. J.* 345:401–15

43. Loo RW, Conde-Frieboes K, Reynolds LJ, Dennis E. 1997. Activation, inhibition, and regiospecificity of the lysophospholipase activity of the 85-kDa group IV cytosolic phospholipase A2. *J. Biol. Chem.* 272:19214–19

44. Lundgard R, Baisted D. 1986. Secretion of a lipolytic protein aggregate by barley aleurone and its dissociation by starch endosperm. *Arch. Biochem. Biophys.* 249:447–54

45. May C, Preisig-Muller R, Hohne M, Gnau P, Kindl H. 1998. A phospholipase A2 is transiently synthesized during seed germination and localized to lipid bodies. *Biochim. Biophys. Acta* 1393:267–76

46. Merkel O, Fido M, Mayr JA, Pruger H, Raab F, et al. 1999. Characterization and function in vivo of two novel phospholipases B/lysophospholipases from *Saccharomyces cerevisiae. J. Biol. Chem.* 274:28121–27

47. Morioka S, Ueki J, Komari T. 1997. Characterization of two distinctive genomic clones (accession nos. AB001919 and AB001920) for phospholipase D from rice (PGR 97-076). *Plant Physiol.* 114:396

48. Munnik T, Arisz SA, de Vrije T, Musgrave A. 1995. G-protein activation stimulates phospholipase D signaling in plants. *Plant Cell* 7:2187–210

49. Munnik T, Irvine RF, Musgrave AP. 1998. Phospholipid signalling in plants. *Biochim. Biophys. Acta* 1389:222–72

50. Munnik T, Meijer HJ, Ter Riet B, Hirt H, Frank W, et al. 2000. Hyperosmotic stress stimulates phospholipase D activity and elevates the levels of phosphatidic acid and diacylglycerol pyrophosphate. *Plant J.* 22:147–54

51. Nagai Y, Aoki J, Sato T, Amano K, Matsuda Y, et al. 1999. An alternative splicing form of phosphatidylserine-specific phospholipase A1 that exhibits lysophosphatidylserine-specific lysophospholipase activity in humans. *J. Biol. Chem.* 274:11053–59

52. Narvaez-Vasquez J, Florin-Christensen J, Ryan CA. 1999. Positional specificity of a phospholipase A activity induced by wounding, systemin, and oligosaccharide elicitors in tomato leaves. *Plant Cell* 11:2249–60

53. Oxley D, Bacic A. 1999. Structure of the glycosylphosphatidylinositol anchor of an arabinogalactan protein from *Pyrus communis* suspension-cultured cells. *Proc. Natl. Acad. Sci. USA* 96:14246–51

54. Pannenberg P, Mansfeld J, Ulbrich-Hofmann R. 1998. Identification of two isoenzymes (accession nos. AF09044 and 09045) of phospholipase D from cabbage (*Brassica oleracea* var. *capitata*). *Plant Physiol.* 118:1102

55. Pappan K, Austin-Brown S, Chapman KD, Wang X. 1998. Substrate selectivities and lipid modulation of phospholipase Dα, β, and γ from plants. *Arch. Biochem. Biophys.* 353:131–40

56. Pappan K, Wang X. 1999. Plant phospholipase Dα is an acidic phospholipase active at near-physiological Ca^{2+} concentrations. *Arch. Biochem. Biophys.* 368:347–53

57. Pappan K, Qin W, Dyer JH, Zheng L, Wang X. 1997. Molecular cloning and functional analysis of polyphosphoinositide-dependent phospholipase D, PLDβ, from *Arabidopsis. J. Biol. Chem.* 272:7055–61

58. Pappan K, Zheng S, Wang X. 1997. Identification and characterization of a novel phospholipase D that requires polyphosphoinositide and submicromolar calcium for activity in *Arabidopsis. J. Biol. Chem.* 272:7048–54

59. Paul RU, Holk A, Scherer GF. 1998. Fatty acids and lysophospholipids as potential second messengers in auxin action. Rapid activation of a phospholipase A2 activity

by auxin in suspension-cultured parsley and soybean cells. *Plant J.* 16:601–11

60. Perera IY, Heilmann I, Boss WF. 1999. Transient and sustained increases in inositol 1,4,5-trisphosphate precede the differential growth response in ravistimulated maize pulvini. *Proc. Natl. Acad. Sci. USA* 96:5838–43

61. Ponting CP, Kerr ID. 1996. A novel family of phospholipase D homologues that includes phospholipid synthases and putative endonucleases: identification of duplicated repeats and potential active site residues. *Protein Sci.* 5:914–22

62. Qin W, Pappan K, Wang X. 1997. Molecular heterogeneity of phospholipase D(PLD): cloning of PLDγ and regulation of plant PLDα, β, and γ by polyphosphoinositides and calcium. *J. Biol. Chem.* 272:28267–73

63. Ransom-Hodgkins WD, Brglez I, Wang X, Boss WF. 2000. Calcium-regulated proteolysis of eEF1A. *Plant Physiol.* 122:957–65

64. Rhee SG, Bae YS. 1997. Regulation of phosphoinositide-specific phospholipase C isozymes. *J. Biol. Chem.* 272:15045–48

65. Ritchie SM, Gilroy S. 1998. Abscisic acid signal transduction in the barley aleurone is mediated by phospholipase D activity. *Proc. Natl. Acad. Sci. USA* 95:2697–702

66. Roberts MF. 1996. Phospholipases: structural and functional motifs for working at an interface. *FASEB J.* 10:1159–72

67. Roos W, Dordschbal B, Steighardt J, Hieke M, Weiss D, Saalbach G. 1999. A redox-dependent, G-protein-coupled phospholipase A of the plasma membrane is involved in the elicitation of alkaloid biosynthesis in *Eschscholtzia californica*. *Biochim. Biophys. Acta* 1448:390–402

68. Rose K, Rudge SA, Frohman MA, Morris AJ, Engebrecht J. 1995. Phospholipase D signaling is essential for meiosis. *Proc. Natl. Acad. Sci. USA* 92:12151–55

69. Rouet-Mayer MA, Valentova O, Simond-Cote E, Daussan J, Thevenot C. 1995. Critical analysis of phospholipid hydrolyzing activities in ripening tomato fruits. Study by spectrofluorimetry and high-performance liquid chromatography. *Lipids* 30:739–46

70. Ryan CA. 2000. The systemin signaling pathway: differential activation of plant defensive genes. *Biochim. Biophys. Acta* 1477:112–21

71. Ryu SB, Karlsson BH, Ozgen M, Palta JP. 1997. Inhibition of phospholipase D by lysophosphatidylethanolamine, a lipid-derived senescence retardant. *Proc. Natl. Acad. Sci. USA* 94:12717–21

72. Ryu SB, Wang X. 1996. Activation of phospholipase D and the possible mechanism of activation in wound-induced lipid hydrolysis in castor bean leaves. *Biochim. Biophys. Acta* 1303:243–50

73. Ryu BS, Wang X. 1998. Increase in free linolenic and linoleic acids associated with phospholipase D-mediated hydrolysis of phospholipids in wounded castor bean leaves. *Biochim. Biophys. Acta* 1393:193–202

74. Scherer GF. 1995. The functional relationship of plant lipid-derived second messengers and plant lipid-activated protein kinase. *Biochem. Soc. Trans.* 23:871–75

75. Schmidt A, Wolde M, Thiele C, Fest W, Kratzin H, et al. 1999. Endophilin I mediates synaptic vesicle formation by transfer of arachidonate to lysophosphatidic acid. *Nature* 401:133–41

76. Senda K, Yoshioka H, Doke N, Kawakita K. 1996. A cytosolic phospholipase A2 from potato tissues appears to be patatin. *Plant Cell Physiol.* 37:347–53

77. Shi J, Gonzales RA, Bhattacharyya MK. 1995. Characterization of a plasma membrane-associated phopshinositide-specific phospholipase C from soybean. *Plant J.* 8:381–90

78. Stahl U, Banas A, Stymne S. 1995. Plant microsomal acyl hydrolases have selectivities for uncommon fatty acids. *Plant Physiol.* 107:953–62

79. Stahl U, Ek B, Stymne S. 1998. Purification and characterization of a low-molecular-weight phospholipase A2 from developing seeds of elm. *Plant Physiol.* 117:197–205

80. Stahl U, Lee M, Sjodahl S, Archer D, Cellini F, et al. 1999. Plant low-molecular-weight phospholipase A2S (PLA2s) are structurally related to the animal secretory PLA2s and are present as a family of isoforms in rice (*Oryza sativa*). *Plant Mol. Biol.* 41:481–90

81. Staxen I, Pical C, Montgomery LT, Gray JE, Hetherington AM, McAinsh MR. 1999. Abscisic acid induces oscillations in guard-cell cytosolic free calcium that involve phosphoinositide-specific phospholipase C. *Proc. Natl. Acad. Sci. USA* 96:1779–84

82. Stevenson JM, Perera IY, Heilmann I, Persson S, Boss WF. 2000. Inositol signaling and plant growth. *Trends Plant Sci.* 5:252–58

83. Strauss H, Leibovitz-Ben Gershon Z, Heller M. 1976. Enzymatic hydrolysis of 1-monoacyl-SN-glycerol-3-phosphoryl-choline (1-lysolecithin) by phospholipases from peanut seeds. *Lipids* 11:442–48

84. Stuckey JA, Dixon JE. 1999. Crystal structure of a phospholipase D family member. *Nat. Struct. Biol.* 6:278–84

85. Tavernier E, Pugin A. 1995. Phospholipase activities associated with the tonoplast from *Acer pseudoplatanus* cells: identification of a phospholipase A1 activity. *Biochim. Biophys. Acta* 1233:118–22

86. Taylor AT, Low SP. 1997. Phospholipase D involvement in the plant oxidative burst. *Biochem. Biophys. Res. Commun.* 237:10–15

87. Thompson GA, Okuyama H. 2000. Lipid-linked proteins of plants. *Prog. Lipid Res.* 39:19–39

88. Titball RW. 1998. Bacterial phospholipases. *J. Appl. Microbiol. Symp. Suppl.* 84:127S–37S

89. Tripathy S, Venables BJ, Chapman KD. 1999. N-Acylethanolamines in signal transduction of elicitor perception. Attenuation of alkalinization response and activation of defense gene expression. *Plant Physiol.* 121:1299–308

90. Van Himbergen JAJ, ter Riet B, Meijer HJG, van den Ende H, Musgrave A, Munnik T. 1999. Mastoparan analogues stimulate phospholipase C and phospholipase D-activity in *Chlamydomonas*: a comparative study. *J. Exp. Bot.* 50:1735–42

91. Waite KA, Wallin R, Qualliotine-Mann D, McPhail LC. 1997. Phosphatidic acid-mediated phosphorylation of the NADPH oxidase component p47-phox. Evidence that phosphatidic acid may activate a novel protein kinase. *J. Biol. Chem.* 272:15569–78

92. Wang A, Dennis EA. 1999. Mammalian lysophospholipases. *Biochim. Biophys. Acta* 1439:1–16

93. Wang C, Zien C, Afitlhile M, Welti R, Hildebrand DF, Wang X. 2000. Involvement of phospholipase D in wound-induced accumulation of jasmonic acid in *Arabidopsis*. *Plant Cell* 12:

94. Wang X. 1999. The role of phospholipase D in signaling cascade. *Plant Physiol.* 120:645–51

95. Wang X. 2000. Multiple forms of phospholipase D in plants: the gene family, catalytic and regulatory properties, and cellular functions. *Prog. Lipid Res.* 39:109–49

96. Wang X, Wang C, Sang Y, Zheng L, Qin C. 2000. Determining functions of multiple phospholipase Ds in stress response of *Arabidopsis*. *Biochem. Soc. Trans.* 28:000–00

97. Wang X, Xu L, Zheng L. 1994. Cloning and expression of phosphatidylcholine-hydrolyzing phospholipase D from *Ricinus communis* L. *J. Biol. Chem.* 269:20312–17

98. Williams RL. 1999. Mammalian phosphoinositide-specific phospholipase C. *Biochim. Biophys. Acta* 1441:255–67

99. Wissing JB, Grabo P, Kornak B. 1996.

Purification and characterization of multiple forms of phosphatidylinositol-specific phospholipases D from suspension cultured *Catharanthus roseus* cells. *Plant Sci.* 117:17–31

100. Xie Z, Fang M, Rivas MP, Faulkner AJ, Sternweis PC, et al. 1998. Phospholipase D activity is required for suppression of yeast phosphatidylinositol transfer protein defects. *Proc. Natl. Acad. Sci. USA* 95:12346–51

101. Xie Z, Ho WT, Exton JH. 2000. Association of the N- and C-terminal domains of phospholipase D: contribution of the conserved HKD motifs to the interaction and the requirement of the association for

Ser/Thr phosphorylation of the enzyme. *J. Biol. Chem.* 275:24962–69

102. Xu L, Zheng S, Zheng L, Wang X. 1997. Promoter analysis and expression of a phospholipase D gene from castor bean. *Plant Physiol.* 115:387–95

103. Young S, Wang X, Leach JE. 1996. Changes in the plasma membrane distribution of rice phospholipase D during resistant interactions with *Xanthomonas oryzae* pv *oryzae*. *Plant Cell* 8:1079–90

104. Zheng L, Krishnamoorthi R, Zolkiewski M, Wang X. 2000. Distinct Ca^{2+} binding properties of novel C2 domains of plant phospholipase $D\alpha$ and β. *J. Biol. Chem.* 275:19700–6

Annu. Rev. Plant Physiol. Plant Mol. Biol. 2001. 52:233–67

ENDOSPERM DEVELOPMENT: Cellularization and Cell Fate Specification

Odd-Arne Olsen

*Department of Chemistry and Biotechnology, Agricultural University of Norway,
P.O. Box 5051, N-1432 Aas, Norway; e-mail: odd-arne.olsen@ikb.nlh.no*

Key Words microtubular cytoskeleton, cereals, *Arabidopsis*, cell cycle, aleurone

■ **Abstract** The endosperm develops from the central cell of the megagametophyte after introduction of the second male gamete into the diploid central cell. Of the three forms of endosperm in angiosperms, the nuclear type is prevalent in economically important species, including the cereals. Landmarks in nuclear endosperm development are the coenocytic, cellularization, differentiation, and maturation stages. The differentiated endosperm contains four major cell types: starchy endosperm, aleurone, transfer cells, and the cells of the embryo surrounding region. Recent research has demonstrated that the first two phases of endosperm occur via mechanisms that are conserved among all groups of angiosperms, involving directed nuclear migration during the coenocytic stage and anticlinal cell wall deposition by cytoplasmic phragmoplasts formed in interzones between radial microtubular systems emanating from nuclear membranes. Complete cellularization of the endosperm coenocyte is achieved through centripetal growth of cell files, extending to the center of the endosperm cavity. Key points in cell cycle control and control of the MT (microtubular) cytoskeletal apparatus central to endosperm development are discussed. Specification of cell fates in the cereal endosperm appears to occur via positional signaling; cells in peripheral positions, except over the main vascular tissues, assume aleurone cell fate. Cells over the main vascular tissue become transfer cells and all interior cells become starchy endosperm cells. Studies in maize have implicated Crinkly4, a protein receptor kinase-like molecule, in aleurone cell fate specification.

CONTENTS

INTRODUCTION

A little over a century ago, endosperm was recognized as an independent genetic entity, the result of a second fertilization event that is typical for angiosperms (67, 127). Following the discovery of double fertilization, two hypotheses, which still persist today, were proposed for the evolutionary origin of the angiosperm endosperm [reviewed in (59, 60)]. In one, the endosperm was hypothesized to originate as an alturistic twin embryo, which evolved into a nourishing endosperm for the surviving embryo, whereas in the second, the endosperm was viewed as a continued development of the megagametophyte triggered by fertilization. In early accounts of endosperm development, dating back to the late nineteenth century (19, 82, 96, 175) and in subsequent work (92, 114, 149), the processes involved in subdivision of the multinucleate endosperm into cellular compartments were unclear. These processes have remained elusive until recently. Endosperm cellularization is the topic of the first part of this review. Based on studies using immunohistochemical methods, it is now known that cellularization of the endosperm coenocyte is mediated through a tightly orchestrated interplay between the machinery controlling progression through the cell cycle and the microtubular cytoskeleton, integrating all known plant cytoskeletal components, and four mechanisms of cell wall deposition, into the sequence of events leading to endosperm cellularization. Far from being an oddity in the plant kingdom, this mode of cellularization is an integral part of the cell life cycle, occurring during pollen, megagametophyte, and endosperm development (23). In the meristematic cell, the far better understood part of the plant cell life cycle, cytokinesis is mediated by interzonal phragmoplasts (71, 163, 166). Although endosperm appears to use the same basic machinery for cytokinesis and progression through the cell cycle, the controls of these processes differ from those in meristematic cells.

   The second topic of this review is the specification of the developmental fate of the four endosperm cell types, the embryo surrounding region, the transfer cells, the aleurone layer, and the starchy endosperm. Each of these cell types has a characteristic temporal and spatial developmental profile. For aleurone cells, recent data strongly suggest that cell fate specification occurs via positional signaling.

   Because of the simple overall organization of nuclear endosperm, this system provides a unique opportunity to study the integration and coordination of genetic subprograms into a unit specifying the body plan of an "organism." This review discusses steps in endosperm development that may account for its unique developmental pathway, and describes how these controlling steps are integrated temporally as well as spatially. Several approaches to improve our understanding of these controls are also discussed. For earlier reviews of endosperm development, the reader is referred to (7, 11, 47, 110, 138, 140).

OVERVIEW OF ENDOSPERM CELLULARIZATION

The model presented in this section is based on data from dicot and monocot species, and represents a highly conserved mode of nuclear endosperm cellularization. The data underlying the model are discussed in the following sections. The fate of the endosperm varies in different species. In the grasses, including the cereals, the endosperm is persistent and contains four major cell types (see below). In some dicots, e.g. *Arabidopsis*, the endosperm is nonpersistent, and only one cell type is retained in mature seeds.

The endosperm develops from the fertilized central cell of the megagametophyte or embryo sac, which is positioned within the mass of nucellar parenchyma cells (Figure 1*a*). At the time of fertilization, the embryo sac, which contains both the central cell and the egg cell, constitutes only a small portion of the grain. The central cell is an ellipsoid structure that fills up most of the embryo sac, with its diploid nucleus positioned proximally in a cytoplasm surrounding a large central vacuole (Figure 2*a*; see color insert). Shortly after fertilization, repeated rounds

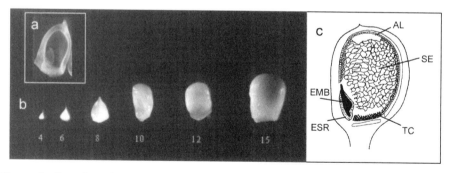

Figure 1   Overview of endosperm development in maize. (*a*) The endosperm develops from the fertilized triploid central cell which is positioned within the megagametophyte or embryo sac. The embryo sac is embedded in a large body of nucellus parenchyma cells, which is enclosed in the integuments of the grain. For details of the central cell, please see Figure 2. (*b*) In maize, expansion of the endosperm occurs rapidly after fertilization, as demonstrated by the relative size of the dissected endosperm from the interval between 4 and 15 DAP (days after pollination). (*c*) Diagram of longitudinal section of 15 DAP maize grain consisting of the aleurone layer (AL), the starchy endosperm (SE), the transfer cell region (TC), and the embryo surrounding region (ESR) around the basal part of the embryo (EMB).

of mitosis, but no cell wall formation or cytokinesis, take place, leading to the endosperm coenocyte (Figure 2b). Cellularization of the coenocyte is initiated by the formation of a radial microtubular system (RMS) from the envelope of all nuclei (Figure 2c). After the formation of cytoplasmic phragmoplasts in the interzones between opposing RMSs, cell walls are deposited around each nucleus forming alveoli, which are tube-like structures (Figure 2d). Mitotic divisions of nuclei within alveoli, followed by cell wall formation, lead to one peripheral layer of cells, and a new layer of alveoli (Figure 2e). Repeated rounds of the same cycle of events lead to cell files that eventually completely invade the central vacuole (Figure 2f). The cellularization process occurs during the first few days after fertilization. In maize, the cellularization process is completed at the end of day 4 after pollination (Figure 1b). The rapid expansion of the endosperm during the interval 4 to 15 days after pollination (DAP) (Figure 1b) is attributable to both cell division and cell expansion. The fully developed endosperm consists of four major cell types, the starchy endosperm, the aleurone layer, the transfer cells, and the embryo surrounding region (Figure 1c). Details of the formation of the endosperm coenocyte are shown in Figures 3 and 4, and the cellularization process is shown in Figures 5 to 7. A model for endosperm cell fate specification in cereals is presented in Figure 8 (Figure 8; see color insert). The pattern of cell division in starchy endosperm and aleurone cells is presented in Figures 7 and 9, respectively. Table 1 summarizes the main events in endosperm development.

THE ENDOSPERM COENOCYTE

Mitotic Divisions and Suppression of Phragmoplast Function

Shortly after fertilization, the central cell nucleus (Figure 2a, see color insert) divides without the formation of cell walls. The microtubular (MT) cytoskeleton typical for endosperm coenocyte mitosis in barley (27) is illustrated in Figure 3, which shows two neighboring endosperm coenocyte nuclei (Figure 3a). The dividing nuclei display metaphase/anaphase spindles (Figure 3b): teleophase spindles at the poles and interzonal MT connecting the two poles (Figure 3c), assembly of interzonal phragmoplast (Figure 3d), and structurally complete phragmoplasts between condensating complements of chromosomes (Figure 3e). Up to this stage, the mitosis of the endosperm coenocyte is identical to that of meristematic cells. In contrast to meristematic cells, however, where the phragmoplast facilitates the assembly of the cell wall in the interzone between its two parallel MT discs (arrow, Figure 3e), no cell plate forms in the barley endosperm coenocyte mitosis. After completion of the division cycle, the phragmoplast remains only as traces of condensed MT material on the nuclear membranes (Figure 3f). In a similar study in wheat, deposition of a short-lived cell plate has been reported, but it fails to extend to a complete cell wall, suggesting that the transient phragmoplast structure is partly functional (172). At least for the small grains, therefore, formation of the

TABLE 1   Summary of events in endosperm cellularization and cell differentiation

Stage/event	Cell cycle	Cytoskeletal events	Cell fate specification
Coenocytic stage	Repeated rounds of mitosis; Figure 2b	Suppression of interzonal phragmoplast formation; Figure 3 Nuclear migration; Figure 4	Specification of T-cell fate; Figure 8a (green cytoplasm)
Alveolar stage	Cell cycle arrest, mitotic hiatus	RMS formation; Figure 2c and 5a–c Cell wall deposition by cytoplasmic phragmoplasts leading to alveolus formation; Figure 2d, 5d and e	
Completion of endosperm cellularization	Release of cell cycle arrest and synchronous mitosis of alveolar nuclei; Figure 6 Continued mitosis in the inner cell layers; Figure 2f	Deposition of periclinal cell walls by interzonal phragmoplasts; Figure 2e and 6e–g Repeated rounds of RMS and alveolus formation leads to the cellular endosperm; Figure 2f and 7b	Specification of aleurone and starchy endosperm cell fates; Figure 8c (blue and red cells)
Formation of Starchy endosperm cells	Continued mitosis in inner cell; Figure 8c (red cells)	Interzonal phragmoplast deposit cell walls at random planes; Figure 7c, d	
Formation of aleurone cells	Release of mitotic arrest in peripheral cell layer; Figure 8c (blue cells)	PPBs and interzonal phragmoplasts deposit cel walls at anticlinal (or periclinal) planes; Figure 9	

endosperm coenocyte is mediated through an inhibition of phragmoplast function, but not phragmoplast assembly.

A second example of a nonfunctional phragmoplast, supporting the presence of a checkpoint for overriding cell plate formation, is evident in orchids that produce pollen with no set arrangement of tetrads. Following meiosis I, a phragmoplast develops in the interzone, but no wall is deposited (20). Interestingly, a coenocytic stage also occurs in the development of embryo sacs, from which the central cell develops (5). Thus, suppression of cytokinesis is an important phenomenon in the

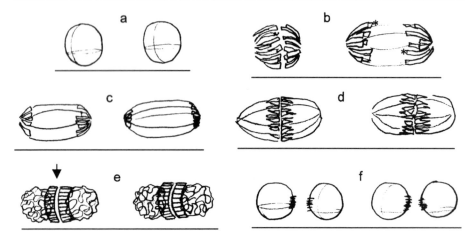

Figure 3   Mitosis without cytokinesis in the endosperm coenocyte. (*a*) Two interphase endosperm coenocyte nuclei from a stage between those depicted in Figure 2*a* and *b*. The line below the nuclei represents the central cell wall, and the central vacuole is oriented on top of the nuclei. (*b*) Mitotic spindles separating the two diploid sets of chromosomes. The two nuclei are at slightly different stages; the nucleus to the left is in late metaphase, the one to the right in anaphase. For simplicity, the chromosomes (the asterisks indicates centromere attachment points) are not drawn. (*c*) Both dividing nuclei have MT arrays typical of telophase. Note the MTs connecting the two poles. (*d*) Initiation of phragmoplast assembly in the interzone between separating groups of chromosomes, and (*e*) phragmoplasts between the two sets of condensing complements of chromosome sets. In contrast to phragmoplasts in meristematic cells, no cell plate is formed between the separating nuclei. Instead, the phragmoplasts degenerate, leaving traces of condensed MTs on the nuclear membranes of the four daughter nuclei (*f*).

plant life cycle, and insight into the stage at which cytokinesis is blocked in the different systems may also yield valuable information about the control points in the meristematic mitotic cycle.

What is the mechanism controlling the suppression of phragmoplast function in nuclear endosperm? Rapidly accumulating evidence points to a link between the dynamics of MT formation and regulators of the cell cycle. Thus, Cdc-2-like kinases and mitotic cyclins, associating to form the complexes that regulate cell cycle progression, have been localized in phragmoplasts as well as in spindles and preprophase bands, suggesting a role for Cdc-cyclins in the regulation or function of these structures [reviewed in (163)]. In maize cells, cyclins II and III are associated with the postmitotic spindle, such as those depicted in Figure 3*c* and *d*, possibly reflecting kinase-mediated regulation [reviewed in (145)]. Recent work also suggests a role for MAP kinases in cytokinesis. The two closely related MAP kinases NTF6 (32) and MMK3 (14) from tobacco and alfalfa, respectively, are specifically activated during M-phase. Here they reach peak activity during cytokinesis, when they are present in the cell plate, suggesting that they regulate the activity of protein(s) involved in cell plate formation. Further evidence for the

involvement of MAP kinases in the regulation of cytokinesis comes from a study of MAP-KKK, which is presumed to act upstream of MAPK in kinase cascades (4). MAP-KKK kinases were also found to be associated with cytokinesis (4). Finally, the most direct evidence for a link between MAP kinases and phragmoplast formation was seen in tobacco, where NPK1 seems to interact directly with a phragmoplast-localized kinesin-like protein (111).

Based on the observation that phragmoplast initiation, and even partial cell plate deposition, occurs in syncytial endosperm, regulation of one or more steps of phragmoplast function downstream of phragmoplast initiations seem likely control points to regulate endosperm coenocyte formation. Systematic probing of molecules associated with phragmoplasts in meristematic cells in syncytial endosperm is one way to search for mechanisms involved in phragmoplast suppression. Genetically, this problem may be addressed by a search for mutants that lack a coenocytic stage because of a defect in phragmoplast suppression.

In addition to specific control points discussed here, recent studies suggest the existence of an overriding control of endosperm development acting on endosperm chromatin structure. This conclusion is based on the *Arabidopsis* "maternal-effect" mutants *fie* (fertilization independent) (137), *fis* (fertilization-independent seeds) (37), and *Medea* [(66); reviewed in (147). The products of two of these genes have similarity to Polycomb group proteins, which regulate gene expression through epigenetic silencing (146). In *Drosophila*, these genes play a role in maintaining established patterns of gene expression. Establishment or maintenance of patterns of endosperm gene expression, including suppression of phragmoplast formation, may therefore also be the function of these genes in plants. Interestingly, polycomb-like genes may provide insight into the mechanisms underlying the requirement for a 1:2 ratio between maternally and paternally derived genomes for normal endosperm development (106, 158).

Nuclear Migration

In maize, the initial endosperm coenocyte mitoses occur at predictable planes, followed by migration of the daughter nuclei to restricted domains of the coenocyte cytoplasm. After fertilization, the first mitosis occurs in a plane perpendicular to the longitudinal axis of the embryo sac (Figure 4*a* and *b*, see color insert), and the next two at alternate planes (Figure 4*c* and *d*). At the eight-nuclear stage, the nuclei form a ring in the proximal cytoplasm around the embryo (Figure 4*e*), before migrating to discrete and separate longitudinal sectors of the peripheral cytoplasm of the central cell (Figure 4*f*). This interpretation of the orientation of mitotic planes and the pattern of nuclear migration is based on direct observations of the early division planes and on revertant sectors of mutants with different marker genes (45, 119, 180). In *Arabidopsis*, nuclear migration occurs in the direction from the micropylar to to the chalazal chambers (24). A second example of a plant system where positioning of nuclei in a syncytium precedes differentiation is the eight-celled *Polygonum*-type megagametophyte of cereals and

Arabidopsis (151), in which the two mitotic nuclei of the functional megaspore migrate to opposite poles of the cell. The fate of the cells derived from these two nuclei are widely different, and are possibly determined by developmental cues deposited in a polarized cytoplasm. In this system, the antipodals develop in the chalazal end, the synergids in the micropylar end, and the egg and the central cell between these two extreme positions.

Attention to improving our understanding of the underlying controls of this stage of endosperm development should focus on the mechanism involved in nuclear migration, and its functional significance, if any. In *Drosophila*, compartmentalization (i.e. a common genetic control of cells in a parasegment that prevents cells from mixing with their neighbors and controls their subsequent development) plays an important role in the development of segments in the fly body [(150) and references therein]. Although cell-lineage studies demonstrate a predictable spatial order in the migration of the endosperm nuclei in the ceonocyte, the borders between domains do not reflect obvious developmental patterns in the mature endosperm. A more likely possibility, therefore, is that nuclear positioning plays a role in the differentiation of the endosperm coenocyte (23). As described below, the nuclei in the proximal end of the endosperm coenocyte already assume transfer cell fate at the coenocytic stage, indicating the presence of particular developmental cues in this portion of the central cell cytoplasm. Also, in the young *Arabidopsis* endosperm, a developmental gradient exists. The structure referred to as the chalazal cyst, which is located in the opposite (proximal) end of the horseshoe-shaped central cell, possibly plays a role in nutrient uptake (24). Deposition of nuclei in the distal cytoplasm, through nuclear migration, may therefore be a way to ensure differentiation of the chalazal cyst, and hence provide access to maternal nutrients.

In the cereals, possible approaches to dissect these processes include studies of the maize *indeterminate1* mutant, in which abnormal microtubular behavior results in irregular positioning of megametophyte nuclei (75), as well studies of mutants with an uneven distribution of endosperm cells in the endosperm cavity (O-A Olsen, unpublished). A more direct approach is the study of *Arabidopsis* mutants in which disruption of cytoskeletal organization appears to cause a failure of endosperm nuclei to migrate to the chalazal end of the seed. Such mutants include *pilz* (118) and *titan-1* (109).

Cell Cycle Arrest at the End of the Coenocytic Stage

After the period of mitotic divisions and nuclear migration leading to formation of the endosperm coenocyte, as depicted in Figure 2*b*, mitosis in barley ceases at 3 DAP and resumes 2 days later. During this mitotic hiatus, the endosperm coenocyte prepares for celullarization by a series of remarkable rearrangements of the MT cytoskeleton. Direct observations of a similar mitotic hiatus have not been made in other species, most likely because the cellularization process is much more rapid in species such as wheat, maize, and *Arabidopsis*. In these species, cellularization takes only 3 to 4 days, compared with 6 days in barley. It is therefore assumed that a similar mitotic hiatus occurs in other species as well. The variation in the final

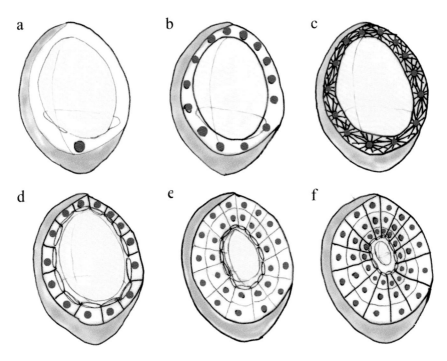

Figure 2 Diagrammatic overview of the endosperm cellularization process. (*a*) In the central cell, the fertilized triploid nucleus (orange) is situated in the proximal end of a cytoplasm which surrounds a large central vacuole (yellow). (*b*) Mitotic divisions occur without cell wall formation and leads to a multinucleate cell with a large central vacuole; the endosperm coenocyte. (*c*) Endosperm cellularization is initiated by the formation of RMS (radial microtubular systems) at the surface of the endosperm nuclei. (*d*) Cell wall formation is facilitated by interaction between RMSs from each nucleus forming the cytoplasmic phragmoplast, and each nucleus becomes surrounded by a tube-like wall structure (alveolus) with its open end towards the central vacuole. (*e*) Continued growth of alveoli towards the central vacuole, and periclinal cell divisions with wall formation between the daughter nuclei within the alveoli, leads to two cell layers, one complete layer in the periphery, and a new layer of alveoli internally. (*f*) After one repetition of the alveolation process and a mitotic division, two layers of peripheral cells are formed, the new layer of alveoli extending almost to the center of the central vacuole. After further centripetal growth of the cell files, the central vacuole is completely closed. Please note that the figure has not been drawn to scale, and only one layer of endosperm cells is shown.

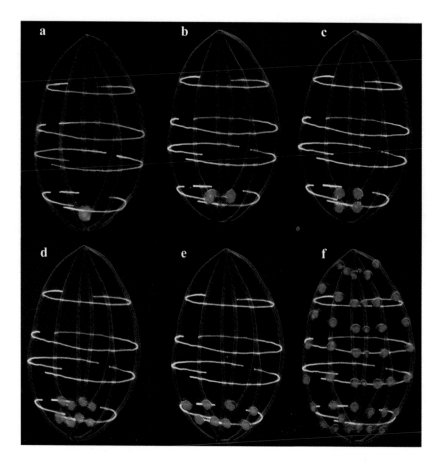

Figure 4 The first mitotic divisions in the endosperm coenocyte in maize occur at predictable planes. Diagrammatic representation of the first mitotic division in the cytoplasm of the central cell, the endosperm coenocyte. Only the nuclei and the cytoplasm of the central cell and the endosperm coenocyte of Figure 2 *a* and *b* are shown. (*a* and *b*) The first division. (*c* and *d*) Second and third divisions. (*e*) The eight nuclei are positioned in the periphery of the basal cytoplasm. (*f*) Each of the eight nuclei gives rise to a population of cells that migrate to a proximal-distal sector of the endosperm cytoplasm corresponding to one eighth of the surface of the coenocyte. After cellularization in the centripetal direction (toward the center), these nuclei will form a part of the endosperm with a shape similar to a segment of an orange.

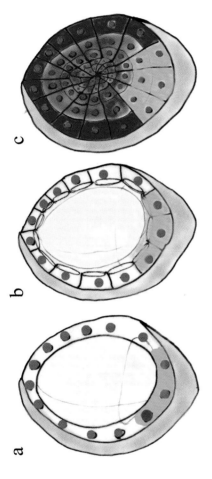

Figure 8 A model for endosperm cell fate specification. The endosperm in (*a*) and (*b*) correspond to those of Figure 2*b* and *d*, respectively, (*c*) to a stage later than Figure 2*f*. (*a*) A transfer cell specific transcript (green) is detectable in the basal endosperm at the coenocytic stage, indicating that cell fate specification has already taken place. (*b*) nuclei in the basal region of the endosperm coenocyte give rise to alveoli with transfer cell identity. (*c*) After completion of endosperm cellularization, the peripheral cell layer (blue) assumes aleurone cell fate, the interior cells assume starchy endosperm cell fate (red). In the cell files of the basal endosperm, the lower cells assume transfer cell fate (green), and the upper cells assume starchy endosperm cell fate (red).

number of nuclei in different species also suggests that the mitotic arrest point is under genetic control. In maize, cellularization is initiated after eight or nine rounds of nuclear divisions (180); *Astelaria* and many legume species produce many nuclei before cellularization, whereas *Helianthus* cellularization begins when fewer than ten free nuclei are present in the endosperm coenocyte (57).

In plants, arrest after mitosis can occur in either G1 or in G2 [for an overview see (48, 79, 83)]. Of these, the best studied checkpoint is the G1, which has been documented in yeast, flies, and mammals as well as in plants. In mammalian cells, retinoblastoma protein (Rb) and its relatives prevent cells from progressing to S phase by inactivating E2F transcription factors that activate the transcription of S phase–specific genes. Inactivation of Rb by phosphorylation in late G1 releases genes under E2F control from repression and the cells become ready for S-phase entry (102). In plants, homologues of most of the key players in the Rb pathway, including Rb itself, have been identified, and most show structural and functional similarities to their animal counterparts (65). Similarly, in animal cells, control of Rb activity may occur through CycDs, the transcription of some types of CycD being inducible during cell-cycle entry by mitogens. Recently, E2F transcription factors were also identified in wheat and tobacco, both of which were shown to interact with maize Rb1 and tobacco Rb, respectively, in yeast two-hybrid assays (148). CDK activity requires activating phosphorylation by CDK-activating kinase (176). In addition, four CDK inhibitor (CKI) protein genes are reported in plants, but only one, ICK1, has been characterized biochemically (181). ICK1, which interacts with both CDK-a (cdc2a) and cyclin CycD3, is an inhibitor of plant cdc2-like kinases in vitro. Its C-terminal consensus sequence resembles part of the CDK2-binding domain of the mammalian CKI p27Kip1 (181).

It is not known whether the nuclei of the endosperm coenocyte are arrested in the G1 or in G2 stages of the cell cycle. In light of the cell cycle research summarized above, and assuming that cell cycle arrest occurs in G1, one possibility is that control involves Rb. This would be similar to maize leaf development, where lateral cells in the shoot apical meristem exit the cell cycle in G1 (69). This event is correlated with Rb expression and loss of cell division activity. Analysis of DNA contents as well as expression and activity analysis of Rb at the early phase of endosperm development is one approach to studying the mechanisms underlying this step in endosperm development. Analyses of mutants arrested at the syncytial stage in *Arabidopsis* and barley (16) also represent attractive material for such studies.

ENDOSPERM CELLULARIZATION

Radial Microtubular Systems (RMS) and Alveolus Formation

The process leading to subdivision of the endosperm coenocyte into cellular compartments is initiated by the formation of RMS emanating from the membrane of each endosperm nucleus (Figures 2c and 5a). RMS in developing nuclear endosperm are well documented, and have been observed in the endosperm

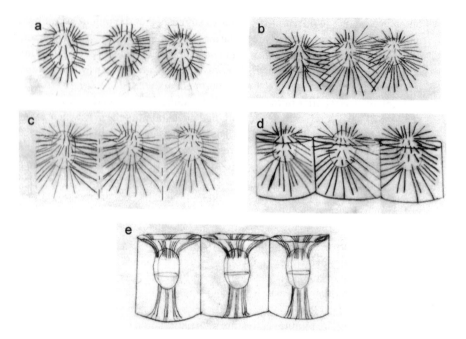

Figure 5   Formation of RMS (radial microtubular systems) and initiation of anticlinal cell wall formation. Illustrations of the process leading to the formation of the partly cellularized endosperm in Figure 2*d* from the endosperm coenocyte in Figure 2*b*. (*a*) RMS forms at the nuclear membranes. Orientation is the same as in Figure 3. (*b*) RMSs extend and initially overlap, but soon form cytoplasmic phragmoplasts that deposit anticlinal cell walls (*dotted line*) (*c*). Partial anticlinal cell wall are formed around each nucleus (*d*). (*e*) Walls extend centripetally (toward the central vacuole) aided by adventitious phragmoplasts formed by a canopy of MT arrays extending from the upper pole of endosperm nuclei.

coenocyte in a number of species, including wheat (172, 177), *Arabidopsis* (24, 144, 183), *Ranunculus sceleratus* (186), barley (27), rice (26), *Phaseolus vulgaris* (185), *Brassica napus* (178), and *Myrsine laetevirens* (143). In addition, extensive studies of extruded *Haemanthus* endosperm have contributed to a greater understanding of the mitotic apparatus as well as MT arrays similar to those of the early cereal endosperm [see for instance (2, 161) and references therein].

Initially, in barley, the MTs of neighboring RMSs overlap (Figure 5*b*), but interzones soon form between individual RMSs (Figure 5*c*), marking out a nucleocytoplasmic domain for each nucleus (22). Arrays of microtubuli, assumed to have the same polarity (plus ends), were termed cytoplasmic phragmoplasts by Brown and coworkers (27), based on the observation that cellularization of the endosperm coenocyte is initiated by deposition of anticlinal walls in these RMS interzones. For a reason not yet fully understood, the anticlinal walls are first visible in the light microscope close to the former central cell wall. Soon these walls surround each nucleus, forming an alveolus, or a tube-like wall structure (Figures 2*d* and 5*d*). The pattern of cytoplasmic phragmoplast development seen in the cereals closely resembles those of the cytoplasmic phragmoplast that form in isolated bits of coenocytic endosperm of *Haemanthus* (2). As the alveolus extends centripetally (toward the central vacuole), the MT arrays in barley and rice undergo dramatic reshaping, assuming a tree-like shape with MTs anchoring the elongated nucleus to the central cell wall, and sending a canopy of microtubules up toward the central vacuole near the upper end of the alveolus (Figure 5*e*). MTs in the canopy from opposing NCDs function to deposit the walls of the leading edge as the alveolus extends toward the center of the central vacuole. These structures were termed adventitious phragmoplasts in barley (27).

The mechanisms involved in cell wall initiation between non-sister nuclei in nuclear endosperm have been debated extensively [reviewed in (47, 87, 138)]. These walls represent an exception to the default mechanism for cell wall formation in meristematic cells of somatic tissue, where interzonal phragmoplasts facilitate formation of the wall leading to cytokinesis or cell division. In the early literature addressing this problem in the cereals, the initial anticlinal walls were described as extensions of wall pegs protruding from the embryo sac or central cell wall (116, 117, 124, 125). Similar descriptions of so-called free-growing walls in the absence of interzonal phragmoplasts were also given for nuclear endosperm of dicot plants, for instance in soybean (35, 51), *Ranunculus sceleratus* L (39), and *Papaver somniferum* L (13). This mode of cellularization may resemble the cellularization process in *Drosophila* embryos, where membrane material is deposited in a process involving syntaxin, leading to the centripetally growing furrows that result in the cellular blastoderm (30). In 1982, Fineran and co-workers proposed a solution to the problem of initial cell wall formation in nuclear endosperm, namely, that these walls are formed by normal cytokinesis (56). Although a similar mode of anticlinal cell wall formation was also reported for *Ranunculus sceleratus* L (186), few other reports support this mode of cellularization in early nuclear endosperm.

Observations by light and transmission electron microscopy of the MT arrays in early wheat endosperm led van Lammeren to conclude: "It is likely that the radiating microtubular arrays function in the formation of phragmoplasts, independent of nuclear divisions" (177). The dynamics of these structures was clarified in 1994 by Brown et al using confocal microscopy in three-dimensional reconstructions of the nuclei and the cytoskeletal arrays in developing barley endosperm (27). These reconstructions form the basis for the model shown in Figure 5, in which the initial anticlinal walls form in RMS interzones, termed cytoplasmic phragmoplasts (27). Using similar techniques, cytoplasmic phragmoplasts have been implicated in the cellularization process in rice (25, 28), maize (RC Brown, BE Lemmon & O-A Olsen, unpublished), and *Arabidopsis* (24, 115). Recently, high-pressure freezing/freeze-substitution techniques were used to study initial cell formation in *Arabidopsis* endosperm, confirming that initial cell plates form in RMS interzones (144).

Is the cytoplasmic phragmoplast in endosperm cell wall formation unique to nuclear endosperm? As reviewed in (23), several observations suggest that the cytoplasmic phragmoplast represents an integral part of the plant life cycle. In addition to endosperm, RMS plays a central role in sporogenesis in lower plants, microsporogenesis of heterosporous plants, male and female gametophyte development in gymnosperms and angiosperms, and embryogenesis of gymnosperms. One example of NCD-mediated wall formation and secondary phragmoplast is found in orchids that have no fixed arrangement of tetrads, mentioned above (20). Following meiosis I, a phragmoplast develops in the division interzone, but no wall is deposited. After meiosis II, two interzonal phragmoplasts form between pairs of sister nuclei simultaneous with the formation of radial microtubules on the surface of all nuclei, interacting to form a secondary (cytoplasmic) phragmoplast among non-sister nuclei in the same way as in the coenocytic endosperm. Confirming the similar nature of the two types of structures, the interzonal and the secondary phragmoplasts become indistinguishable, depositing cell walls that subdivide the four spores into approximately equal volumes at the end of meiosis. A second example of formation of MT structures with phragmoplast function occurs during meiosis of *Selaginella* and *Marattiales*. Here, a raft of vesicles accumulates at the interface of the opposing microtubule arrays resulting in a phragmoplast-like structure known as the procytokinetic plate (PCP) (21).

The role and occurrence of cytoplasmic phragmoplasts support the earlier suggestion by Bajer & Mole-Bajer (3) that plant MTs posses an inherent property that causes opposing arrays of MTs to function in cell wall assembly. Other lines of evidence also support the functional similarity between interzonal and cytoplasmic phragmoplasts, including the data of Endle et al (52), who demonstrated that a novel population of short actin filaments continuously assembles in the phragmoplast at the growing cell plate in both interzonal phragmoplasts and in cytoplasmic phragmoplasts in endosperm syncytia. Also, plant polypeptides that share antigenic epitopes with human vinculin are revealed within the forming cell plate of both systems, suggesting their recruitment during cytokinesis-associated actin assembly. These vinculin-like antigens may participate in membrane/F-actin anchorage of protein complexes involved in cell wall assembly. Further evidence for the functional similarity between cytoplasmic phragmoplasts and interzonal phragmoplasts is that the Knolle protein, a cytokinesis-specific syntaxin functioning in vesicle fusion leading to cell plate growth in *Arabidopsis*, is also expressed in both types of phragmoplast (118). Although functional similarities exist between interzonal and cytoplasmic or phragmoplasts, structural as well as compositional differences can also be found. The differences involve the mechanisms of fusion of the cell plate–forming vesicles, the lack of terminal fucose residues on the trisaccharide side chains of xyloglucans, as well as the persistence of callose in endosperm cell walls (28, 143).

In plants, the mechanisms involved in MT polymerization have remained elusive, in part because of the lack of centrosomes, which function as microtubule organizing centers (MTOC) in animal cells. Currently, two alternative scenarios are envisioned [reviewed in (33)]. First, multiple nucleation sites are suggested to be responsible for the assembly and organization of the various microtuble arrays. Second, microtubule nucleation and organization may take place at one site, the nuclear surface, and the MTs are translocated from here to the different sites where they function. Several lines of experimentation have established that plant nuclei can assemble microtubules, including microinjection of fluorescent brain tubulin into living higher plant cells (99, 160, 168, 169), and the incorporation of reporter tubulin into lysed endosperm cells (179). Interestingly, Mizuno incubated nuclear particles from tobaco BY-2 cells with bovine brain tubulin and obtained aster-figures similar to the RMS of endosperm nuclei (121). In addition, antigenic determinants of the pericentriolar material of isolated animal centrosomes have been detected on the plant nuclear surface at the site where MTs are anchored (38). γ-tubulin, a universal component of MTOCs and an MT minus end marker (136), is detectable at plant nuclear surfaces in preparations with high numbers of nuclear-associated MTs (108). A close association between the MTOCs of nuclear surfaces and the nuclear matrix was recently demonstrated using an antibody directed against calf thymus centrosomes that recognized an antigen on plant nuclear surfaces (64, 168, 169). Electron micrographs of nuclear pore complexes have shown cytoplasmic as well as nuclear fibrils connected to several pore complexes, and these peripheral stuctures are thought to connect nucleo-cytoplasmic and cytoplasmic cytoskeletal elements (72).

What causes the remarkable MTOC activity on nuclear membranes in RMS formation? Assuming that nuclear surfaces represent the principal MTOC activity in plant cells, one possibility is that RMS formation results from a block in the translocation of MT to other locations in the cells, a view that is compatible with the lack of other MT cytoskeletal components in endosperm coenocytes during RMS formation. Alternatively, the RMS assembly could be caused by a change in the rate of MT initiation and/or depolymerization.

The machinery involved in regulation of plant MT polymerization is unknown, but it is generally assumed to be similar to that in animal cells, where centrosome activity is thought to be cell cycle–regulated by cyclin-dependent protein kinases [see for instance (29)]. In tobacco BY-2 cells, DNA replication must be completed before the pre-prophase band (PPB) is formed (145), again suggesting a link between the machinery that controls progression through the cell cycle and the dynamics of the MT cytoskeleton. Mutants perturbed in the assembly and function of the MT cytoskeleton in endosperm alveolation should yield valuable insights into the components involved in this process. Indications that at least some components of the MTOC apparatus function in more than one context come from a study of the Arabidopsis *PILZ* mutants, which affect the MT cytoskeleton (118). Defects are seen in these mutants in both the formation of mitotic spindles and the radial MT systems of endosperm nuclei. These studies also demonstrate the existence of context-specific components, because development of the gametophyte is unaffected in these mutants (118). If sufficient material of in vitro fertilized central cells can be produced, this system should yield valuable insight into the early steps in endosperm cellularization (95).

Release of Mitotic Block and Cell File Development

Following the completion of alveolus formation in barley, a synchronous round of mitosis is initiated in all alveolar nuclei (Figures 2*d* and 6), wherein the plane of division is periclinal (i.e. oriented in parallel to the former central cell wall) (Figure 6*b*). The cytoskeletal arrays are the same as those in the endosperm coenocyte, except that the phragmoplast is functional, depositing a cell wall perpendicular to the former central cell wall (Figure 6*g*). The formation of these periclinal cell walls results in a layer of complete cells in the periphery of the developing endosperm, and an inner layer of alveoli with their openings toward the central vacuole (Figures 2*e* and 7*a*). The same process is subsequently reiterated several times, leading to cell files converging toward the center of the central vacuole from

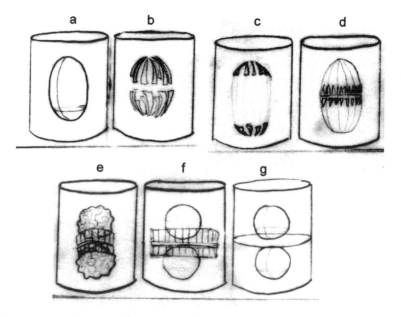

Figure 6 Periclinal division in endosperm alveoli. Mitotic division of a nucleus in the endosperm alveoli depicted in Figure 2*d*. This mitotic division gives rise to the two endosperm cell layers shown in Figure 2*e*. (*a*) Endosperm alveolus. (*b* and *c*) Mitotic spindles in metaphase and anaphase, in periclinal orientation, respectively. Chromosomes are not shown. (*d–f*) A functional interzonal phragmoplast is formed in the mitotic interzone between the separating daughter nuclei, depositing a periclinal endosperm cell wall that separates the outer cell layer from the second layer of alveoli (*g*).

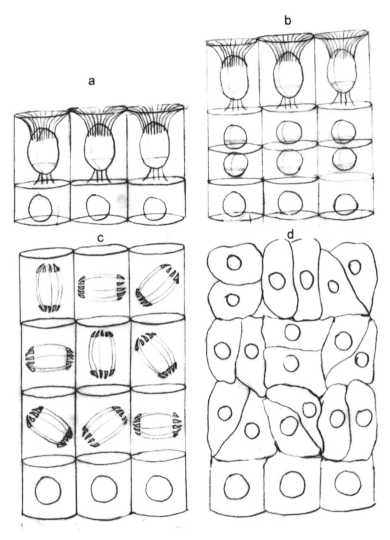

Figure 7   Endosperm cell file development. Development of three cell files extending from the periphery of the endosperm (*down*) towards the central vacuole (*up*) as depicted in Figure 2e and f. (*a*) Development of the second layer of alveoli from the upper cell of Figure 6g. (*b*) Continued centripetal growth toward the central vacuole after three rounds of mitotic divisions. (*c*) Mitosis in starchy endosperm cells lacking PPBs are at random division planes. (*d*) Starchy endosperm cells resulting from the random division planes in (*c*). After two rounds of divisions, the cell file pattern is lost.

all sides (Figures 2*f* and 7*b*), eventually completely invading it. This event marks the end of the endosperm cellularization phase.

What is the mechanism involved in the release of cell cycle arrest following the mitotic hiatus? Although direct experimental data are lacking, one possibility is that hormones play a role at this checkpoint, in particular cytokinin, which peaks early in endosperm development. In many species, cytokinin levels start to rise after fertilization when rapid cell divisions are occurring [for a review, see (122)]. For instance, in barley, cytokinin activity starts to rise around the time of cell divisions in the alveoli, lasting for a few days and coinciding with the most rapid period of mitotic activity in the endosperm. In plants, the link between auxin and cytokinin and cell division is now well established (48), and auxin alone has been shown to increase the level of cyclin dependent kinase (CDK) protein in cultured tobacco cells and stem pith explants. However, the addition of cytokinin is required to activate this kinase (84). Somewhat confusingly, both hormones have been associated with progression through the G1-S and the G2-M control points. One example of this is seen in root pericycle cells, which are arrested in G2 phase and normally assume divisions at an appropriate distance from the apical meristem at a critical ratio of auxin to cytokinin. Arrest of pericycle cells at the hormonal checkpoint is indicated by a rapid increase in p34cdc2 activity in root tissue during the induction of lateral root meristems by auxin (84), consistent with the presence of p34cdc2 awaiting activation by tyrosine dephosphorylation (189). Recently, CycD3 has been shown to be induced by cytokinin in both cultured cells and intact plants, a finding that supports the proposed role for this hormone in the G1-S transition. Evidence came from overexpression of CycD3 in stable *Arabidopsis* transformants, where it was found to remove the requirement for exogenous cytokinin during callus initiation and growth from leaf pieces (152). A model for the action of cytokinin in the G1-S transition has been proposed in which cytokinin- and sucrose-induced D-type cyclins bind to CDK-a to form inactive heterodimers. Phosphorylation of Rb by CDK-a complexes releases the transcription factor E2F, which is the active molecule required to enter S phase. The phosphorylation of plant CDK-a by CAK and the presence of Rb-E2F complexes on the promoters of S-phase genes remain to be demonstrated for plants, and are inferred from the mammalian G1-S model (48). The existence of several plant-specific CDKs, which are unique among CDKs in showing cell-cycle regulation of expression, suggests control mechanisms yet to be explored (48). If cytokinin plays a role in stimulating mitotic activity after the mitotic hiatus, the response may be mediated by cycD3. One way to test this hypothesis is to overexpress or transcriptionally silence the cydD3 in endosperm at the syncytial stage. If this hypothesis is correct, inactivation could block progression into mitosis. Conversely, ectopic expression of cycD3 could eliminate the mitotic hiatus.

What determines the periclinal plane of cell division in the first alveolar mitosis? One likely possibility is that the axis is set by space constraints in combination with the lack of PPBs in this round of mitosis. Barley mutants displaying alternative division planes in alveolar mitosis (138) should be suitable objects for the study of this step in endosperm cellularization.

ENDOSPERM CELL FATE SPECIFICATION AND DIFFERENTIATION

The differentiated endosperm contains four tissues or cell types: the embryo surrounding region, transfer cells, the starchy endosperm, and the aleurone layer (Figure 1c). Based on current insight, the underlying genetic programs for endosperm cellularization (described above) and cell fate specification (described below) probably originated as independent genetic programs, which have been integrated during the course of evolution. For simplicity, endosperm cellularization has been described first, serving as a structural basis for the discussion of endosperm cell fate specification to follow. However, cellularization and differentiation are closely integrated processes, both temporally and spatially. In the following text, cell fate specifications of the four endosperm cell types are described in the order in which they are believed to occur.

The Embryo Surrounding Region

The embryo surrounding region represents the cells that line the cavity of the endosperm in which the embryo develops (Figure 1c). In maize, these cells are identifiable by their dense cytoplasmic contents (94, 157) as well as by the cell-specific expression of three different *Esr* (embryo surrounding region) transcripts (142). The function of the embryo surrounding region is unknown, but may include a role in embryo nutrition or in establishing a physical barrier between the embryo and the endosperm during seed development. In spontaneously occurring embryoless endosperms, *Esr* expression is lacking, suggesting a dependence of *Esr* on signaling from the embryo (142). On the other hand, the observation that the endosperm of embryoless mutants form a normal size embryo cavity suggests that the endosperm has an intrinsic program for formation of this structure (70).

The mechanism underlying cell fate specification of the embryo surrounding region is unknown. Based on the observation in maize that cell walls appear to be forming in the endosperm coenocyte around the embryo during the coenocytic stage (RC Brown, BE Lemmon & O-A Olsen, unpublished), the embryo surrounding region may form through a mechanism that permits a functional phragmoplast to form near the embryo. Also in barley, cellularization occurs early in the immediate vicinity of the embryo (53). Further studies are needed to confirm whether these cells represent precursors of the embryo surrounding region. Studies involving transgenic maize lines expressing the GUS reporter in this region under the control of *Esr* promoters (15) should contribute insight into the molecular mechanisms underlying differentiation of this region of the endosperm.

Transfer Cells

Transfer cells develop over the main vascular tissue of the maternal plant (Figure 1c), where they facilitate transport of photosynthate (e.g. sucrose) into the endosperm. In cereals, endosperm transfer cells are characterized by prominent secondary wall ingrowths. At a young stage of the grain, these cells possess an extensive and complex endomembrane system (43, 182). In maize, two to three cell layers of endosperm cells have cell wall ingrowths in a gradient decreasing toward the interior of the endosperm (62, 157). In barley, the transfer cell-specific transcript *END1* appears in the endosperm coenocyte over the maternal vascular tissue (49) (Figure 8a; green cells; see color insert). The nuclei in this region give rise to the transfer cells (Figure 8b and c). *END1* transcript is also present in fully developed grains (49). A second group of transfer cell-specific transcripts, consisting of four *Bet* genes, are found in maize (76, 78). The function of these two groups of genes are yet to be identified, but a weak similarity between *BETL1* and *3* and plant defensins suggests a role in plant defense (76). The soluble acid invertase *Incw2* from maize also represents a molecular marker for the endosperm transfer cell layer (171).

What determines transfer cell fate? The restricted expression of the *END1* transcript in endosperm coenocyte nuclei over the vascular tissue (Figure 8a) hints at the presence of a localized factor that activates *END1* transcription. Polarized transcription in a plant coenocyte has not been reported to date, but is known to occur at the syncytial stage during *Drosphila* embryogenesis and could suggest a mechanism for END1 transcriptional control. In this system, at the syncytial blastoderm stage, the maternally derived anterior or head-specific transcript *bicoid* is anchored to the MT cytoskeleton at the anterior end (135). From this site, the bicoid protein diffuses in a gradient toward the posterior end, with high concentrations activating head-specific genes by binding to the promoter upstream region of head-specific genes. Alternatively, *END1* transcription could be activated through a mechanism similar to the localized nuclear import of DORSAL protein in response to localized activation of the TOLL receptor in the specification of ventral cell fate in the syncytial blasdoderm in Drosophila (9). Recently, the promoter upstream regions of the *BETL-2, 3*, and *4* genes were used in electrophoretic mobility shift assays to detect common DNA binding activity from endosperm extracts (76, 77). This approach, in combination with studies of maize mutants such as *rgf1* (reduced grain filling) (113) and a maize mutant recently isolated in our laboratories that lacks differentiated transfer cells (O-A Olsen, V Meeley & SE Nichols, unpublished), should lead to improved insight into the mechanism underlying transfer function and differentiation.

Aleurone Cells

The aleurone layer covers the entire perimeter of the endosperm except for the transfer cell region (Figure 1c). In maize (180) and wheat (31), there is one cell layer; in rice, one to several layers (74); and in barley, three layers (85). In maize, the aleurone layer consists of an estimated 250,000 cells (180), whereas barley grains have around 100,000 aleurone cells (97). The aleurone cell cytoplasm is dense and granular owing to the presence of many aleurone grains, small vacuoles with inclusion bodies (31). Aleurone cells contain lytic vacuoles and protein storage vacuoles (170), both of which may contain two major types of inclusion bodies (80)—the globoid bodies, which contain a crystalline matrix of phytin, protein, and lipid, and protein-carbohydrate bodies. Lipid droplets surround the aleurone grains (85, 98, 123). The endoplasmic reticulum of these cells is well developed, and a large number of mitochondria are also observable (85). Mature aleurone cells appear cuboidal in section and contain anthocyanins, which are responsible for the colorful grains of corn (131). In barley, the aleurone cells are highly polyploid (90).

The earliest molecular marker for aleurone cells is the barley *Ltp2* transcript, which is present shortly after the onset of visible aleurone cell differentiation (88). Other aleurone marker genes include *Ltp1* (107, 126a, 159a), *B22E* (93), *pZE40* (164), *ole-1* and *ole-2* (1), and *per-1* (165). Using a transient assay, Leah and colleagues identified putative enhancer elements in the barley *chi33* gene involved in aleurone cell-specific gene expression (103). In maize, *C1* represents an aleurone-specific marker (131). Future studies of the mechanisms involved in the cell specific regulation of these genes should yield valuable information about aleurone cell differentiation.

Toward the end of seed maturation, a specialized developmental program confers desiccation tolerance to the aleurone cells, allowing them to survive the maturation process (73, 89, 100, 128, 153). After imbibition, the function of the aleurone cells is to produce cell wall degrading, proteolytic, and hydrolytic enzymes to convert the storage proteins and starch granules of the starchy endosperm into sugars and amino acids for the growing embryo. Production of these enzymes is initiated by de novo transcription upon gibberellic acid stimulation from the imbibed embryo (86). At the end of the germination phase, aleurone cells undergo programmed cell death (12).

When is the fate of aleurone cells specified during endosperm development? The first sign of aleurone cell differentiation using immunohistochemical methods is observable in the peripheral layer of cells after completion of the cellularization process (Figure 8c; blue cells). These cells are derived from the peripheral daughters of the first periclinal division of the alveolar nuclei. The exact time for the onset of aleurone cell fate specification is unclear, but the first manifestation of a difference in the fate of this cell layer comes from barley, in which the MT cytoskeletal cycle is regulated differently from interior starchy endosperm cell layers (Figure 8c; red cells). In these peripheral cells, for the first time during endosperm development, the full complement of cytoskeletal arrays of meristematic cells is displayed, including hoop-like cortical arrays (Figure 9a), PPB (120), which guides the division plane for cell wall deposition by the pharagmoplast (Figure 9b), the mitotic spindle apparatus (Figure 9c), and functional phragmoplasts (Figure 9d), which deposit cell walls in the anticlinal plane predetermined by the PPB (Figure 9e, anticlinal division plane). One argument for considering this MT cytoskeletal cycle of arrays as part of the aleurone cell program is the importance of the cell division plane in the onotogeny of the aleurone layer. As the grain grows because of the expansion of the starchy endosperm cells (Figure 1b), anticlinal divisions such as those in Figure 9 are essential for surface area of the aleurone to expand. In maize, an estimated 17 rounds of anticlinal divisions are needed to create the surface of the mature aleurone layer of mature grains (104), which could be achieved through a control mechanism involving the PPB (145). It is therefore tempting to suggest that the rate of anticlinal (and periclinal) cell divisons in the aleurone layer is directly linked to the expansion of the grain via a mechanism that is yet to be determined. The distribution between anticlinal and periclinal divisions in the aleurone layer is unknown, but Kiesselbach reported that in maize, a shift to exclusive anticlinal divisions occurs about 20 days after pollination (92). Genetic evidence for the existence of a control of periclinal division

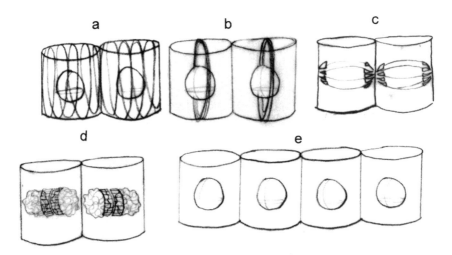

Figure 9   The MT cytoskeletal cycle of aleurone initials. (a) Two neighboring aleurone cell initials with hoop-like cortical arrays. (b) The future division plane is determined by anticlinally oriented PPBs. (c) Mitotic spindle axis. (d) Interzonal phragmoplast oriented in the anticlinal plane predicted by the PPBs. Note that the steps involving phragmoplast formation have been omitted from this figure. (e) The resulting four aleurone daughter cells. Anticlinal divisions in the aleurone expand the surface of the aleurone layer.

rates comes from the maize mutant *xc1* (extra cell layers), which possesses extra leaf epidermis cell layers as well as aleurone layers in the endosperm because of aberrant periclinal divisions (91).

Using light or electron microscopy, typical features of aleurone cell differentiation such as numerous small vacuoles and a dense cytoplasm can be observed in the outermost cell layer in barley at 8 DAP (17), only 2 days after introduction of the meristematic division cycle. Subsequently, the second and third layers differentiate into aleurone cells. In maize, wheat, and rice, which complete the cellularization process 2 days earlier than barley, the morphology of the peripheral cell layer is at first indistinguishable from internal cells (27, 98, 123, 149, 157). In maize, Randolph reported that the first sign of aleurone cell differentiation occurs as a reorientation of cell division planes from random to mostly anticlinal and as the appearance of cuboidal cells (149). Similarly, in wheat, the first indication of aleurone differentiation is the appearance of cuboidal cells in the periphery (123). Following a change in cell shape around 10 DAP, vacuoles accumulate and the cytoplasm becomes dense (98, 123, 157), similar to barley and rice (17, 25). Confocal microscopy analysis is needed to determine whether the meristematic MT cycle is introduced in these species as well.

What determines aleurone cell fate? Based on current insight, aleurone cell fate is thought to be determined by positional information deposited in the periphery of the endosperm close to the former central cell wall (139). This is in contrast to the view of aleurone cells as a separate cell lineage from the starchy endosperm (8, 45, 104, 149). Recently, this model was supported and expanded by the Becraft laboratory in a lineage analysis in maize using *Ds*-induced chromosome breakage to uncover the waxy (*wx*) starchy endosperm marker and the aleurone anthocyanin marker *C1* (6, 7). The result of this analysis showed that the aleurone does not form a separate lineage from the starchy endosperm. Furthermore, studies of revertant sectors from a mutable allele of *dek1* in maize, which entirely lacks aleurone cells (130), suggest that positional cues are required throughout endosperm development to maintain aleurone cell fate. In these studies, following a somatic mutation in the *dek1* gene, aleurone cells converted to starchy endosperm cells. Conversely, somatic reversion of a mutant *dek1* gene to wild type converted aleurone cells to starchy endosperm cells even late in grain development. These data show that neither aleurone nor starchy endosperm cell fates are terminally determined states of differentiation, and are in agreement with earlier descriptions of periclinal divisions in wheat aleurone where the interior daughter cells dedifferentiated and converted to starchy endosperm (123).

What is the molecular basis for the interpretation of the positional information? In the proposed model (139), the positional information is "read" by a signal transduction pathway that starts with the Crinkly4 protein kinase-like receptor on the surface of endosperm cells (8). The *Crinkly4* gene encodes a protein receptor kinase-like molecule with similarity to tumor necrosis factor receptors (TNFRs), prototypes of a large family of cell surface receptors that are critical for lymphocyte development and function in mammals [(36) and references therein]. The ligand for TNFRs, tumor necrosis factor (TNF-α), is an important effector cytokine for immune responses and inflammation. Homotrimeric TNF-α is thought to recruit three receptor chains into a complex that juxtaposes the cytoplasmic domains. The extracellular domain of both TNFRs contain three cysteine-rich domains that characterize the TNFR superfamily and a less conserved, membrane proximal, fourth cysteine-rich domain (81). The ligand binding pocket for TNF-α is mainly formed by the second and the third cysteine-rich domains, whereas the first cysteine-rich domain mediates ligand-independent assembly of the receptor trimers interacting with the ligand (36). Interestingly, Crinkly4 bears resemblance to TNFR in the second and the third cysteine-rich domains.

The positional information believed to define aleurone cell fate is likely to represent a ligand binding to and activating the Crinkly4 receptor, and could exist at threshold concentration only in the periphery of the endosperm. In maize and other species with only one layer of aleurone cells, the gradient of the ligand is believed to decline more rapidly toward the interior than in barley, which has three layers of aleurone cells. Alternatively, three layers of aleurone cells could be achieved through a higher sensitivity of the receptor to ligand binding (139).

The *crinkly4* grain phenotype is most easily seen as patches of white on the surface of purple kernels (167). These white patches come from the lack of aleurone cells, as starchy endosperm cells are positioned in the periphery of the endosperm. In addition to aleurone cell differentiation, homozygous *crinkly4* plants have crinkly leaves, demonstrating that this receptor-like kinase also functions in leaf differentiation. In addition to studies of Crinkly4 and its proposed ligand, ongoing efforts in several laboratories to clone the *dek-1* gene, the second gene in maize known to abolish aleurone cell identity (134), should help to elucidate the mechanism establishing and maintaining aleurone cell identity. Mutants with multiple aleurone layers may also be expected to reveal gene functions involved in interpreting the positional information leading to aleurone cell fate specification (129, 184).

In addition to maize mutants that either lack or have multiple layers of aleurone, mutants in which aleurone cell differentiation is disrupted have also been reported. *cp2* (collapsed) -*o12* mutants have thin-walled, flattened aleurone cells with numerous vacuoles; *pfc* (paleface) mutants have unusually rounded cells and sporadically more than one cell layer (6), and *Dap* (dappled) mutants show abnormalities in aleurone cell morphology (63, 167). Also, mutants in the *etched* loci are affected in aleurone cell development (132, 154). Several maize mutant lines have also been reported that show color mosaicism, but no effect on aleurone cell morphology. The coloration patterns of these mutants are interpreted to reflect processes that function to organize and coordinate endosperm development (6). Interestingly, these patterns differ from the clonal patterns of endosperm development, which originates from the directed migration of endosperm coenocyte nuclei (Figure 4; see above). Recently, our laboratory carried out a microscopy screen of the Pioneer TUSC collection (10), identifying many maize mutants perturbed in aleurone cell differentiation, revealing mutants that entirely lack aleurone cells, contain only patches of aleurone cells, defective aleurone cell mophology, multiple layers of aleurone cells that are either well organized or completely unorganized with respect to plane of cell division (O-A Olsen, SE Lid, B Meeley & SE Nichols, unpublished). Allelism tests are under way to establish whether this collection represents new mutant variation in aleurone cell fate determination or differentiation. Endosperm mutants affected in aleurone cell differentiation have also been reported in barley (16), but the progress of these studies has been hampered by the lack of a facility to clone the underlying mutant genes.

The aleurone system represents an interesting system to advance our knowledge of fate determination in plants. The study of signal transduction pathways in plants is still in its infancy, and except for the brassinosteriod system (68) and the clavata1 receptor and its proposed ligand clavata3 (18, 174), there are few concrete examples of such signal transductions pathways. The maize aleurone, with its richness of mutants and repertoire of molecular techniques, could potentially expand our knowledge in this area.

Starchy Endosperm Cells

The starchy endosperm represents the largest body of cell mass in the endosperm and consists of an estimated 80,000 to 90,000 cells in barley (44, 97), and 60,000 in wheat (40). The bulk of the starchy endosperm is starch, synthesized within amyloplasts by the four enzymes, ADP-glucose pyrophosphorylase (AGPase), starch synthases (SS), branching enzymes (BE), and debranching enzymes [reviewed in (162)]. Of these, the wheat SS1 gene (105) and the major isoform of barley AGPase (50) are preferentially expressed in early starchy endosperm cells, representing the earliest known molecular markers for this tissue. The second major cell-specific component of starchy endosperm cells are prolamin storage proteins (126, 159). The basis for the tissue-specific expression of prolamin storage proteins rests on two common promoter motifs: the P-box (prolamin-box) (58), for which protein factors have been identified (179a); and a binding site 20 bp downstream of the P-box in the 22-kDa zein gene promoter, which binds the basic leucine zipper protein Opaque2, an endosperm specific transcriptional activator of zein gene expression (179a). In barley, the starchy endosperm-specific barley leucine Zipper1 (BLZ2) protein, dimerizing in vitro with the ubiquitously expressed Blz1 gene, binds specifically to the GCN4-like motif in a 43-bp oligonucleotide derived from the promoter region of a *Hor-2* gene, which also includes the P-box (141). Similar in vitro studies in wheat of the bi-factorial endosperm box region of the wheat prolamin *LMWG-1D1* gene demonstrated that transcriptional activation by bZIP transcription factor SPA is dependent on the binding activity of the nuclear protein ESBFI (46). These transcriptional activators, which lead to prolamin gene expression around 10 DAP, are valuable tools in understanding what underlies starchy endosperm cell differentiation. Following the phase of cellularization and cell fate specification, starchy endosperm cells undergo endoreduplication [reviewed in

(101)]. Toward the end of the grain-filling period, the starchy endosperm cells die, involving a process that resembles programmed cell death in animal cells (188).

The first starchy endosperm cells are the inner part of the cell files at endosperm closure, which are all derived from the interior daughter cells of the first periclinal division in the endosperm alveoli (Figure 8c; red cells). In contrast to the aleurone cell initials, which display the full MT cytoskeletal arrays of meristematic cells, the starchy endosperm cells develop cortical microtubules, but lack PPBs (27, 42). Presumably, as a result of a lack of PPBs combined with less spatial constraint than endosperm alveoli, starchy endosperm cell walls mediated by interzonal phragmoplast are deposited in random planes (Figure 7c). Consequently, after one or two rounds of cell divisions, the cell file pattern is lost (Figure 7d). An additional source of starchy endosperm cells is the inner daughter cells of aleurone cells, which divide periclinally and subsequently redifferentiate to become starchy endosperm cells (see discussion above). The outer layer of the starchy endosperm has smaller cells and a different concentration of storage proteins (110); most, if not all, of these cells may be derived from periclinal division of aleurone cells.

Several mutants that lack PPB have been described. Similar to starchy endosperm cells, these mutants orient division planes randomly, and cell plate deposition is mediated by interzonal phragmoplasts in the default plane, which is perpendicular to the axis of the mitotic spindle [reviewed in (145)]. Such mutants include the *Arabidopsis fass* and *toneau* (173) and the maize mutants *dsc1* and *dsc2* (discordia) (61) and *tan1* (tangled) (41). One interpretation of the *tan1* phenotype is that the so-called actin depleted zone, which forms in the area surrounding the narrowing MT in the phragmoplast, is defective, permitting phragmoplast fusion to occur anywhere on the inner surface of the cells (166).

Little is known about the steps involved in PPB formation or its regulation. However, the fact that the progenitors of daughter cells of the first periclinal division in the endosperm turns on the full meristematic MT cytoskeletal cycle, whereas the other daughter cells suppress PPB formation, demonstrates that plant cells can regulate PPB formation. Whether the control mechanism in endosperm involves the same genes that are affected in the mutants listed above remains to be determined. Probing for the expression of these mutant genes in aleurone and starchy endosperm cells should shed light on this question and possibly identify the mechanisms involved in the regulation of PPB formation in plants.

Several collections of mutants with defects in the starchy endosperm have been described, and are broadly referred to as *dek* (defective kernel) mutants (132, 155). In most cases, the developmental lesion in these mutants has not been identified. One exception is the *Dsc1* (discolored) gene, which has been cloned (156). The *Dsc1* mRNA is detected specifically in kernels 5–7 DAP, but its function is yet to be determined. In addition to these maize collections, barley shrunken endosperm mutants similar to the maize *dek* mutants as well as barley mutants with defective or reduced endosperm that are maternally inherited have been reported (16, 54, 55).

Little is known about the mechanisms involved in starchy endosperm cell fate specification, in part because of the lack of cereal mutants that directly affect starchy endosperm fate specification. In particular, mutants with aleurone cells, but no starchy endosperm, would be useful in addressing the question of starchy endosperm cell fate specification. Potentially, such mutants could be present in extreme *deks* such as the *emp* (empty pericarp) mutants (155). Alternative strategies, currently under way in many laboratories, include identification of early starchy endosperm markers through functional genomics and proteomics based on tissues from young, dissected endosperm.

Does *Arabidopsis* represent a useful model system to elucidate endosperm cell fate specification? More data on *Arabidopsis* endosperm development are needed to fully answer this question. Clearly, the cell contents differ markedly between the persistent peripheral cell layer of the *Arabidopsis* endosperm and the cereal aleurone. Also, the contents of the nonpersistent inner cell mass of *Arabidopsis* are different from the persistent cereal starchy endosperm. However, based on the high degree of conservation of the cellularization process between *Arabidopsis* and the cereal endosperm, as well as the similarity in the ontogeny of the two main endosperm cell types, studies of *Arabidopsis* may well contribute valuable information on starchy endosperm as well as aleurone cell fate specification, provided effective screens for relevant mutants can be designed.

SUMMARY AND FUTURE DIRECTIONS

Nuclear endosperm offers the opportunity to study the identity and integration of components of a developmental program specifying an entire plant body plan. There appear to be few regulatory steps required for endosperm formation, and these consist of control points in highly conserved plant cell processes (Table 1). The first step in endosperm development is coenocyte formation, which results from a suppression of interzonal phragmoplast function. During the ensuing mitotic arrest, cellularization of the coenocyte is initiated by RMS formation and cell wall deposition by cytoplasmic phragmoplasts in a cycle of events that is also applied in microsporogenesis and megagemetophyte cellularization. The underlying basis for these events is the ability of nuclear surfaces to act as MTOCs, which in endosperm coenocytes are regulated in a way that leads to an accumulation of MTs forming the RMS. The second feature is cell wall deposition by cytoplasmic phragmoplasts, which appear to be functionally similar to interzonal phragmoplasts. Positional information in the basal part of the endosperm coenocyte may be involved in the specification of transfer cell fate. Following the formation of the first layer of alveoli, mitosis resumes, and periclinal cell wall deposition is mediated for the first time in endosperm development by a functional interzonal phragmoplast. The MT cytoskeletal cycle is different in the two daughter nuclei resulting from this periclinal division; the peripheral (aleurone) daughter cells use a cycle typical of meristematic cells, including PPBs and interzonal phragmoplast, whereas the inner (starchy endosperm) daughters lacks PPBs. As a result, the cell division plane is strictly controlled in aleurone cells (predominantly anticlinal), whereas division planes in starchy endosperm cells are randomly oriented. Aleurone cell fate specification occurs via positional signaling, and involves the Crinkly4 receptor-like kinase.

From the data summarized above, the endosperm body plan likely results from the regulation of conserved plant processes rather than involving a process not applied by meristematic cells. The study of the key regulatory mechanisms in endosperm development outlined above should therefore yield valuable insight into processes such as cell cycle regulation, the regulation of MT cytoskeletal structure and function, as well as mechanisms in cell fate specification. Important progress in endosperm research has been achieved by the use of the two most potent experimental plant systems available, *Arabidopsis* and maize. Much excitement lies ahead in endosperm research.

ACKNOWLEDGMENTS

Kaisa Stenberg Olsen is gratefully acknowledged for Figures 2–9, and Donald S Robertson for valuable suggestions and discussions. Roy Brown, Betty E Lemmon, Brian Larkins, and Phil Becraft are acknowledged for providing preprints of their manuscripts. Thanks are also due to Stein Erik Lid for inspiring discussions.

Visit the Annual Reviews home page at www.AnnualReviews.org

LITERATURE CITED

1. Aalen RB. 1995. The transcripts encoding two oleosin isoforms are both present in the aleurone and in the embryo of barley (*Hordeum vulgare* L.) seeds. *Plant Mol. Biol.* 28:583–88

2. Bajer A, Mole-Bajer J. 1982. Asters, poles and transport properties within spindlelike microtubule arrays. *Cold Spring Harbor Symp. Quant. Biol.* 46:263–83

3. Bajer AS, Mole-Bajer J. 1986. Reorganization of microtubules in endosperm cells and cell fragments of the higher plant *Haemanthus* in vivo. *J. Cell Biol.* 102:263–81

4. Banno H, Hirano K, Nakamura T, Irie K, Nomoto S, et al. 1993. NPK1, a tobacco gene that encodes a protein with a domain homologous to yeast BCK1, STE1 and Byr2 protein kinases. *Mol. Cell. Biol.* 13:4745–52

5. Battaglia E. 1991. Embryological questions: 16. Unreduced embryo sacs and related problems in angiosperms (apomixis, cyclo-sis, cellularization). *Atti Soc Toscana Sci. Nat. Pisa Mem. P.V. Ser. A*, pp. 1–134

6. Becraft PW, Asuncion-Crabb Y. 2000. Positional cues specify and maintain aleurone cell fate in maize edosperm development. *Development* 127:4039–48

7. Becraft PW, Brown RC, Lemmon BE, Olsen O-A, Opsahl-Ferstad HG. 2000. Endosperm development. In *Current Trends in the Embryology of Angiosperms*, ed. SS Bhojwani, pp. 353–74. Dordrecht, The Netherlands: Kluwer Academic

8. Becraft PW, Stinard PS, McCarty D. 1996. CRINKLY4: A TNFR-like receptor kinase involved in maize epidermal differentiation. *Science* 273:1406–9

9. Belvin MP, Anderson KV. 1996. A conserved signaling pathway: the *Drosophila* toll-dorsal pathway. *Annu. Rev. Cell Dev. Biol.* 12:393–416

10. Bensen RJ, Johal GS, Crane VC, Tossberg JT, Schnabel PS, et al. 1995. Cloning and

characterization of the maize *An1* gene. *Plant Cell* 7:75–84

11. Berger F. 1999. Endosperm development. *Curr. Opin. Plant Biol.* 2:28–32

12. Bethke PC, Lonsdale JE, Fath A, Jones RL. 1999. Hormonally regulated programmed cell death in barley aleurone cells. *Plant Cell* 11:1033–46

13. Bhandari NN, Bhargava M, Chitralekha P. 1986. Cellularization of free-nuclear endosperm of *Papaver somniferum* L. *Phytomorphology* 36:357–66

14. Bögre L, Calderini O, Binarova P, Mattauch M, Till S, et al. 1999. A MAP kinase is activated late in plant mitosis and becomes localized to the plane of cell division. *Plant Cell* 11:101–13

15. Bonello J-F, Opsahl-Ferstad H-G, Perez P, Dumas C, Rogowsky PM. 2000. *Esr* genes show different levels of expression in the same region of maize endosperm. *Gene* 246:219–27

16. Bosnes M, Harris E, Aigeltinger L, Olsen O-A. 1987. Morphology and ultrastructure of 11 barley shrunken endosperm mutants. *Theor. Appl. Genet.* 74:177–87

17. Bosnes M, Weideman F, Olsen O-A. 1992. Endosperm differentiation in barley wild-type and sex mutants. *Plant J.* 2:661–74

18. Brand U, Fletcher JC, Hobe M, Meyerowitz EM, Simon R. 2000. Dependence of stem cell fate in *Arabidopsis* on a feedback loop regulated by CLV3 activity. *Science* 289:617–19

19. Brenchley WE. 1909. On the strength and development of the grain of wheat (*Triticum vulgare* L.). *Curr. Opin. Plant Biol.* 23:117–24

20. Brown RC, Lemmon BE. 1991. The cytokinetic apparatus in meiosis: control of division plane in the absence of a preprophase band of microtubules. In *The Cytoskeletal Basis of Plant Growth and Form*, ed. CW Loyd, pp. 259–73. London: Academic

21. Brown RC, Lemmon BE. 1991. Plastid polarity and meiotic spindle development in

microsporogenesis of *Selaginella*. *Protoplasma* 161:168–80

22. Brown RC, Lemmon BE. 1992. Cytoplasmic domain: a model for spatial control of cytokinesis in reproductive cells of plants. *EMSA Bull.* 22:48–53

23. Brown RC, Lemmon BE. 1999. *The Cytoskeleton and Spatial Control of Cytokinesis in the Plant Life Cycle. Protoplasma.* In press

24. Brown RC, Lemmon BE, Nguyen H, Olsen O-A. 1999. Development of endosperm in *Arabidopsis thaliana. Sex. Plant Reprod.* 12:32–42

25. Brown RC, Lemmon BE, Olsen O-A. 1996. Development of the endosperm in rice (*Oryza sativa* L.): cellularization. *J. Plant Res.* 109:301–13

26. Brown RC, Lemmon BE, Olsen O-A. 1996. Polarization predicts the pattern of cellularization in cereal endosperm. *Protoplasma* 192:168–77

27. Brown RC, Lemon BE, Olsen O-A. 1994. Endosperm development in barley: microtubule involvement in the morphogenetic pathway. *Plant Cell* 6:1241–52

28. Brown RC, Lemmon BE, Stone BA, Olsen O-A. 1997. Cell wall $(1\rightarrow3)$ and $(1\rightarrow3, 1\rightarrow4)$ β-glucans during early grain development in rice (*Oryza sativa* L.). *Planta* 202:414–26

29. Buendia B, Draetta G, Karsenti E. 1992. Regulation of the microtubule nucleating activity of centrosomes in *Xenopus* egg extracts: role of cyclin A-associated protein kinase. *J. Cell Biol.* 116:1431–42

30. Burgess RW, Deitcher DL, Schwartz TL. 1997. The synaptic protein syntaxin1 is required for cellularization of *Drosophila* embryos. *J. Cell Biol.* 138:861–75

31. Buttrose M. 1963. Ultrastructure of the developing aleurone cells of wheat grain. *Aust. J. Biol. Sci.* 16:768–74

32. Calderini O, Bögre L, Vicente O, Binarova P, Herble-Bors E, Wilson C. 1998. A cell cycle regulated MAP kinase with a possible

role in cytokinesis in tobacco cells. *J. Cell Sci.* 111:3091–100

33. Canaday J, Stoppin-Mellet V, Mutterer J, Lambert A-M, Schmit A-C. 2000. Higher plant cells: gamma-tubulin and microtubule nucleation in the absence of centrosomes. *Microsc. Res. Tech.* 49:487–95

34. Deleted in proof

35. Chamberlin MA, Horner HT, Palmer RG. 1994. Early endosperm, embryo, and ovule development in *Glycine max* (L). Merr. *Int. J. Plant Sci.* 155:421–36

36. Chan FK-M, Chun HJ, Zheng L, Siegel RM, Bui KL, Lenardo MJ. 2000. A domain in TNF receptors that mediates ligand-independent receptor assembly and signaling. *Science* 288:2351–54

37. Chaudhury AM, Ming L, Miller C, Craig S, Dennis ES, Peacock WJ. 1997. Fertilization-independent seed development in *Arabidopsis thaliana*. *Proc. Natl. Acad. Sci. USA* 94:4223–28

38. Chevrier V, Komesli S, Schmit A-C, Vantard M, Lambert AM, Job D. 1992. A monoclonal antibody raised against mammalian centrosomes and screened by recognition of plant microtubule organizing centers identifies a pericentriolar component in different cell types. *J. Cell Sci.* 101:823–35

39. Chitralekha P, Bhandari NN. 1993. Cellularization of free-nuclear endosperm in *Ranunculus sceleratus* L. *Phytomorphology* 43:165–83

40. Chojecki AJS, Bayliss MW, Gale MD. 1986. Cell production and DNA accumulation in the wheat endosperm, and their association with grain weight. *Ann. Bot.* 58:809–18

41. Cleary AL, Smith LG. 1998. The *Tangled1* gene is required for spatial control of cytoskeletal arrays associated with cell divisions during maize leaf development. *Plant Cell* 10:1875–88

42. Clore AM, Dannenhoffer JM, Larkins BA. 1996. Characterization of the cytoskeleton of maize endosperm cells. *Microsc. Res. Tech.* 33:89

43. Cochrane MP, Duffus CM. 1980. The nucellar projection and modified aleurone in the crease region of developing caryopses of barley (*Hordeum vulgare* var. *distichum*). *Protoplasma* 103:361–76

44. Cochrane MP, Duffus CM. 1983. Endosperm cell number in cultivars of barley differing in grain weight. *Ann. Appl. Biol.* 102:177–82

45. Coe EH Jr. 1978. The aleurone tissue of maize as a genetic tool. In *Maize Breeding and Genetics*, ed. DB Walden, pp. 447–59. New York: Wiley & Sons

46. Conlan RS, Hammond-Kosack M, Bevan M. 1999. Transcription activation mediated by the bZIP factor SPA on the endosperm box is modulated by ESBF-1 in vitro. *Plant J.* 19:173–81

47. DeManson DA. 1997. Endosperm structure and development. See Ref. 101a, pp. 73–115

48. den Boer BGW, Murray JAH. 2000. Triggering the cell cycle in plants. *Trends Cell Biol.* 10:245–50

49. Doan DNP, Linnestad C, Olsen O-A. 1996. Isolation of molecular markers from the barley endosperm coenocyte and the surrounding nucellus cell layers. *Plant Mol. Biol.* 31:877–86

50. Doan DNP, Rudi H, Olsen O-A. 1999. The allosterically unregulated isoform of ADP-glucose pyrophosphorylase from barley endosperm is the most likely source of ADP-glucose incorporated into endosperm starch. *Plant Physiol.* 121:965–75

51. Dute RR, Peterson CM. 1992. Early endosperm development in ovules of soybean, *Glycine max* (L.) Merr. (Fabaceae). *Ann. Bot.* 69:263–71

52. Endle MC, Stoppin V, Lambert AM, Schmit AC. 1998. The growing cell plate of higher plants is a site of both actin assembly and vinculin-like antigen recruitment. *Eur. J. Cell Biol.* 77:10–18

53. Engell K. 1989. Embryology of barley: time course and analysis of controlled fertilization and early embryo formation based on serial sections. *Nord. J. Bot.* 9:265–80

54. Felker FC, Peterson DM, Nelson OE. 1985. Anatomy of immature grains of eight maternal-effect-shrunken-endosperm barley mutants. *Am. J. Bot.* 72:248–56

55. Felker FC, Peterson DM, Nelson OE. 1987. Early grain development of the seg2 maternal-effect shrunken-endosperm mutant of barley. *Can. J. Bot.* 65:943–48

56. Fineran BA, Wild DJC, Ingerfeld M. 1982. Initial wall formation in the endosperm of wheat, *Triticum aestivum*: a reevaluation. *Can. J. Bot.* 60:1776–95

57. Floyd SK, Lerner VT, Friedman WE. 1999. A developmental and evolutionary analysis of embryology in *Platanus* (Platanaceae), a basal, eudicot. *Am. J. Bot.* 86:1523–31

58. Foerde BG, Heyworth A, Pywell J, Kreiss M. 1985. Nucelotide sequence of a *B1* hordein gene and the identification of possible upstream regulatory sequences in endosperm storage protein genes from barley, wheat and maize. *Nucleic Acids Res.* 13:7327–39

59. Friedman WE. 1994. The evolution of embryogeny in seed plants and the developmental origin and early history of endosperm. *Am. J. Bot.* 81:1468–86

60. Friedman WE. 1998. The evolution of double fertilization and endosperm: an "historical" perspective. *Sex. Plant Reprod.* 11:6–16

61. Gallagher K, Smith LG. 1999. discordia mutations specifically misorient asymmetric cell divisions during development of the maize leaf epidermis. *Development* 126:4623–33

62. Gao R, Dong S, Fan J, Hu C. 1998. Relationship between development of endosperm transfer cells and grain mass in maize. *Biol. Plant. Prague* 41:539–46

63. Gavazzi G, Dolfini S, Allegra D, Castiglioni P, Todesco G, Hoxha M. 1997.

Dap (defective aleurone pigmentation) mutations affect maize aleurone development. *Mol. Gen. Genet.* 256:223–30

64. Gindullis F, Meier I. 1999. Matric attachment region binding protein MFP1 is localized in discrete domains at the nuclear envelope. *Plant Cell* 11:1117–28

65. Grafi G, Larkins B. 1995. Endoreduplication in maize endosperm: involvement of M phase–promoting factor inhibition and induction of S-phase related kinases. *Science* 269:1262–64

66. Grossniklaus U, Vielle-Calzada J-P, Hoeppner MA, Gagliano WB. 1998. Maternal control of embryogenesis by MEDEA, a *polycomb*-group gene in *Arabidopsis*. *Science* 280:446–50

67. Guignard L. 1901. La double fècondation dans le mais. *J. Bot.* 15:37–50

68. He Z, Wang ZY, Li J, Zhu Q, Lamb C, et al. 2000. Perception of brassinosteroids by the extracellular domain of the receptor kinase BRI1. *Science* 288:2360–63

69. Healy S, Freeman D, Lavender P, de Jager S, Greenwood J, et al. 1998. The maize retinoblastoma protein homologue ZmRb-1 is regulated during leaf development and displays conserved interactions with G1/S regulators and plant cyclin D (CycD) proteins. *Plant Mol. Biol.* 37:155–69

70. Heckel T, Werner K, Sheridan WF, Dumas C, Rogowsky PM. 1999. Novel phenotypes and developmental arrest in early *embryo specific* mutants of maize. *Planta* 210:1–8

71. Heese M, Mayer U, Jürgens G. 1998. Cytokinesis in flowering plants: cellular process and developmental integration. *Curr. Opin. Plant Biol.* 1:486–91

72. Heese-Peck A, Raikhel NV. 1998. The nuclear pore complex. *Plant Mol. Biol.* 38:145–62

73. Hoecker U, Vasil IK, McCarty DR. 1995. Integrated control of seed maturation and germination programs by activator and repressor functions of *Viviparous-1* of maize. *Genes Dev.* 9:2459–69

74. Hoshikawa K. 1993. Anthesis, fertilization and development of caryopsis. In *Science of the Rice Plant I: Morphology*, ed. T Matsuo, K Hoshikawa, pp. 339–76. Tokyo: Nobunkyo

75. Huang Bing-Q, Sheridan WF. 1996. Embryo sac development in the maize *indeterminate gametophyte 1* mutant: abnormal nuclear behavior and defective microtubule organization. *Plant Cell* 8:1391–407

76. Hueros G, Gomez E, Cheik N, Edwards J, Weldon M, et al. 1999. Identification of a promoter sequence from the *BETL-1* gene cluster able to confer transfer-cell specific expression in transgenic maize. *Plant Physiol.* 121:1143–52

77. Hueros G, Royo J, Maitz M, Salamini F, Thompson RD. 1999. Evidence for factors regulating transfer cell-specific expression in maize endosperm. *Plant Mol. Biol.* 41:403–14

78. Hueros G, Varotto S, Salamini F, Thompson Richard D. 1995. Molecular characterization of *BET1*, a gene expressed in the endosperm transfer cells of maize. *Plant Cell* 7:747–57

79. Inze D, Gutierrez C, Chua N-H. 1999. Trends in plant cell cycle research. *Plant Cell* 11:991–94

80. Jakobsen JV, Knox RB, Pyliotis NA. 1971. The structure and composition of aleurone grains in the barley aleurone layer. *Planta* 101:189–209

81. Jiang Y, Woronicz JD, Liu W, Goeddel DV. 1999. Prevention of constitutive TNF receptor 1 signaling by silencer of death domains. *Science* 283:543–46

82. Johannsen W. 1884. Om frøviden og dens utvikling hos byg (On the endosperm and its development in barley). *Medd. Carlsberg Lab. 1883–1884 (Copenhagen, Denmark)* II:103–33

83. John PCL. 1996. The plant cell cycle: conserved and unique features in mitotic control. *Progr. Cell Cycle Res.* 2:59–72

84. John PCL, Zhang K, Dong C, Diederich L, Wightman F. 1993. p34cdc2 related protein in control of cell cycle progression, the switch between division and differentiation in tissue development, and stimulation of division by auxin and cytokinin. *Aust. J. Plant Physiol.* 20:503–26

85. Jones RL. 1969. The fine structure of barley aleurone cells. *Planta* 85:359–75

86. Jones RL, Jacobsen JV. 1991. Regulation of synthesis and transport of secreted proteins in cereal aleurone. *Int. Rev. Cytol.* 126:49–88

87. Jürgens G. 2000. Cytokinesis: the art of partitioning. *Plant Cell* 12:827–9

88. Kalla R, Shimamoto K, Potter R, Nielsen PS, Linnestad C, Olsen O-A. 1994. The promoter of the barley aleurone-specific gene encoding a putative 7 kDa lipid transfer protein confers aleurone-specifc gene expression in transgenic rice. *Plant J.* 6:849–60

89. Kao CY, Cocciolone SM, Vasil IK, McCarty DR. 1996. Localization and interaction of the cis-acting element for abscisic acid, *Viviparous 1*, and light activation of the *C1* gene of maize. *Plant Cell* 8:1171–79

90. Keown AC, Taiz L, Jones RL. 1977. The nuclear content of developing barley aleurone cells. *Am. J. Bot.* 64:1248–53

91. Kessler SA, Sinha NR. 2000. *Characterization of xc1 (extra cell layers), a mutation affecting plane of cell division during maize development.* Presented at Annu. Meet. Am Soc. Plant Physiol., Plant Biol., July 15–19, San Diego. Abstr. 131

92. Kiesselbach TA. 1949. The structure and reproduction of corn. *Res. Bull. Univ. Neb. Coll. Agric.* 161. 96 pp.

93. Klemsdal SS, Hughes W, Lønneborg A, Aalen RB, Olsen O-A. 1991. Primary structure of a novel barley gene differentially expressed in immature aleurone layers. *Mol. Gen. Genet.* 228:9–16

94. Kowles RV, Phillips RL. 1988. Endosperm development in maize. *Int. Rev. Cytol.* 112:97–136

95. Kranz E, von Wiegen P, Quader H, Lörz H.

1998. Endosperm development after fusion of isolated, single maize sperm and central cells in vitro. *Plant Cell* 10:511–24

96. Kuwada Y. 1909. On the development of pollen and the embryo sac, and the formation of the endosperm etc of *Oryza sativa* L. *Bot. Mag.* 23:334–43

97. Kvaale A, Olsen OA. 1986. Rates of cell division in developing barley (*Hordeum vulgare* var. *distichum* cultivar Bomi) endosperms. *Ann. Bot.* 57:829–34

98. Kyle DJ, Styles ED. 1977. Development of aleurone and sub-aleurone layers in maize. *Planta* 137:185–93

99. Lambert AM. 1993. Microtubular-organizing centers in higher plants. *Curr. Opin. Cell Biol.* 5:116–22

100. Lane BG. 1991. Cellular desiccation and hydration: developmentally regulated proteins, and the maturation and germination of seed embryos. *FASEB J.* 5:2893–901

101. Larkins BA, Dilkes BP, Dante RA, Coelho CM, Woo Y, Liu Y. 2000. Understanding the hows and whys of endoreduplicaton. *J. Exp. Bot.* In press

101a. Larkins BA, Vasil IK, eds. 1997. *Cellular and Molecular Biology of Plant Seed Development.* Dordrecht, The Netherlands: Kluwer

102. Lavia P, Jansen-Durr P. 1999. EF2 target genes and cells-cycle checkpoint control. *BioEssays* 21:221–30

103. Leah R, Skriver K, Knudsen S, Ruud-Hansen J, Raikhel NV, Mundy J. 1994. Identification of an enhancer/silencer sequence directing the aleurone specific expression of a barley chitinase gene. *Plant J.* 6:579–89

104. Levy AA, Walbot V. 1990. Regulation of the timing of transposable element excision during maize endosperm development. *Science* 248:1534–37

105. Li ZY, Chu XS, Mouille G, Yan LL, Kosar Hashemi B, et al. 1999. The localization and expression of the class II starch synthases of wheat. *Plant Physiol.* 120:1147–55

106. Lin BY. 1982. Association of endosperm reduction with parental imprinting in maize. *Genetics* 100:475–86

107. Linnestad C, Lønneborg A, Kalla R, Olsen O-A. 1991. The promoter of a lipid transfer protein gene is expressed in barley aleurone cells contains similar Myc and Myb recognition sites as the maize *Bz-McC* allele. *Plant Physiol.* 97:841–43

108. Liu B, Joshi HC, Wilson TJ, Silflow CD, Palevitz BA, Snustad DP. 1994. γ-Tubulin in *Arabidopsis*: gene sequence, immunoblot, and immunofluorescent studies. *Plant Cell* 6:303–14

109. Liu CM, Meinke DW. 1998. The *titan* mutants of *Arabidopsis* are disrupted in mitosis and cell cycle control during seed development. *Plant J.* 16:21–31

110. Lopes MA, Larkins BA. 1993. Endosperm origin, development, and function. *Plant Cell* 5:1383–99

111. Machida Y, Nakashima M, Morikiyo K, Banno H, Ishikawa M, et al. 1998. MAPKKK-related protein kinase NPK1: regulation of the M phase plant cycle. *J. Plant Cell Res.* 111:243–46

112. Deleted in proof

113. Maitz M, Santandrea G, Zhang Z, Lal S, Hannah C, et al. 2000. *rgf1*, a mutation reducing grain filing in maize through effects on basal endosperm and pedicel development. *Plant J.* 23:29–42

114. Mangelsdorf PC. 1926. The genetics and morphology of some endosperm characters in corn. *Conn. Exp. Stn. Bull.* 279:513–614

115. Mansfield SG, Briarty LG. 1990. Endosperm cellularization in *Arabidopsis thaliana* L. *Arabidopsis Inform. Serv.* 27:65–72

116. Mares DJ, Norstog K, Stone BA. 1975. Early stages in development of wheat endosperm I. The change from free nuclear to cellular endosperm. *Aust. J. Bot.* 23:311–26

117. Mares DJ, Stone BA, Jeffrey C, Norstog K. 1977. Early stages in the development of wheat endoseprm II. Ultrastructural observations on cell wall formation. *Aust. J. Bot.* 25:599–613

118. Mayer U, Herzog U, Berger F, Inzé D, Jürgens G. 1999. Mutations in the *PILZ* group genes disrupt the microtubule cytoskeleton and uncouple cell cycle progression from cell division in *Arabidopsis* embryo and endosperm. *Eur. J. Cell Biol.* 78:100–8

119. McClintock B. 1978. Development of the maize endosperm as revealed by clones. In *The Clonal Basis of Development*, ed. S Subtelny, I Sussex, pp. 217–37. New York: Academic

120. Mineyuki Y. 1999. The preprophase band of microtubules: its function as a cytokinetic apparatus in higher plants. *Int. Rev. Cytol.* 187:1–49

121. Mizuno K. 1993. Microtubule nucleation sites on nuclei of higher plant cells. *Protoplasma* 173:77–85

122. Morris RO. 1997. Hormonal regulation of seed development. See Ref. 101a, pp. 117–49

123. Morrison IN, Kuo J, O'Brian TP. 1975. Histochemistry and fine structure of developing aleurone cells. *Planta* 123:105–16

124. Morrison IN, O'Brian TP. 1976. Cytokinesis in the developing wheat grain: division with and without a phragmoplast. *Planta* 130:57–67

125. Morrison IN, O'Brian TP, Kuo J. 1978. Initial cellularization and differentiation of the aleurone cells in the ventral region of the developing wheat grain. *Planta* 140:19–30

126. Muentz K. 1998. Deposition of storage proteins. *Plant Mol. Biol.* 38:77–99

126a. Munday J, Rogers JC. 1986. Selective expression of a probable amylase/protease inhibitor in barley (*Hordeum vulgare*) aleurone cells: comparison to the barley amylase/subtilisin inhibitor. *Planta* 169:51–63

127. Nawaschin S. 1898. Resulte eine Revison der Befruchtungsvorgange bei *Lilium martagon* und *Ritillaria tenella*. *Bull. Acad. Imp. Sci. St. Petersburg* 9:377–82

128. Neill SJ, Horgan R, Parry AD. 1986. The carotenoid and abscisic acid content of *Viviparous* kernels and seedlings of *Zea mays*. *Planta* 169:87–96

129. Nelson OE, Chang MT. 1974. Effect of multiple aleurone layers on the protein and amino acid content of maize endosperm. *Crop Sci.* 14:374–76

130. Neuffer MG. 1995. Chromosome breaking sites for genetic analysis in maize. *Maydica* 40:99–116

131. Neuffer MG, Coe EH, Wessler SR. 1997. *Mutants of Maize.* Cold Spring Harbor, NY: Cold Spring Harbor Lab. Press. 468 pp.

132. Neuffer MG, Sheridan WF. 1980. Defective kernel mutants of maize. I. Genetic and lethality studies. *Genetics* 95:292–944

133. Deleted in proof

134. Neuffer MG, Sheridan W, Bendbow E. 1978. Rescue of lethal defective kernel mutants by genetic manipulation. *Maize Genet. Coop. Newsl.* 52:84–88

135. Nusslein-Volhardt C. 1996. Gradients that organize embryo development. *Sci. Am.* Aug.:54–61

136. Oakley BR. 1992. γ-tubulin: the microtubule organizer. *Trends Cell Biol.* 2:1–5

137. Ohad N, Margossian L, Hsu Y-C, Williams C, Repetti P, Fischer RL. 1996. A mutation that allows endosperm development without fertilization. *Proc. Natl. Acad. Sci. USA* 93:5319–24

138. Olsen O-A, Brown R, Lemon BE. 1995. Pattern and process of wall formation in developing endosperm. *BioEssays* 17:803–12

139. Olsen O-A, Lemmon BE, Brown RC. 1998. A model for aleurone cell development. *Trends Plant Sci.* 3:168–69

140. Olsen O-A, Linnestad C, Nichols SE. 1999. Developmental biology of the cereal endosperm. *Trends Plant Sci.* 4:253–57

141. Onate L, Vicente-Carbajosa J, Lara P, Diaz I, Carbonero P. 1999. Barley BLZ2, a seed-specific bZIP protein that interacts with BLZ1 in vivo and activates transcription from the GCN4-like motif of B-hordein promoters in barley endosperm. *J. Biol. Chem.* 274:9175–82

142. Opsahl-Ferstad HG, Le Deunff E, Dumas C, Rogowsky PM. 1997. *ZmEsr*, a novel endosperm-specific gene expressed in a restricted region around the maize embryo. *Plant J.* 12:235–46

143. Otegui M, Lima C, Maldonado S, deLederkremer RM. 1999. Development of the endosperm of *Myrsine laetevirens* (Myrsinaceae). I. Cellularization and deposition of cell-wall storage carbohydrates. *Int. J. Plant Sci.* 160:491–500

144. Otegui M, Staehelin LA. 2000. Synctial-type cell plates: a novel kind of cell plate involved in endosperm cellularization of *Arabidopsis. Plant Cell* 12:933–47

145. Pickett-Heaps JD, Gunning BES, Brown RC, Lemmon BE, Cleary AL. 1999. The cytoplast concept in dividing plant cells: cytoplasmic domains and the evolution of spatially organized cell division. *Am. J. Bot.* 86:153–72

146. Pirrotta V. 1998. Polycombing the genome: PcG, trxG, and chromatin silencing. *Cell* 93:333–36

147. Preuss D. 1999. Chromatin silencing and Arabidopsis development: a role for polycomb proteins. *Plant Cell* 11:765–67

148. Ramirez-Parra E, Xie Q, Boniotti MB, Gutierrez C. 1999. The cloning of plant E2F, a retinoblastoma-binding protein, reveals unique and conserved features with animal G(1)/S regulators. *Nucleic Acids Res.* 27:3527–33

149. Randolph LF. 1936. Developmental morphology of the caryopsis in maize. *J. Agric. Res.* 53:881–916

150. Rauskolb C, Correia T, Irvine KD. 1999. Fringe-dependent separation of dorsal and ventral cells in the Drosophila wing. *Nature* 401:476–80

151. Reiser L, Fischer RL. 1993. The ovule and the embryo sac. *Plant Cell* 5:1291–301

152. Riou-Khamlichi C, Huntley R, Jacqmard A, Murray JA. 1999. Cytokinin activation of *Arabidopsis* cell division through a D-type cyclin. *Science* 283:1541–44

153. Robichaud CS, Sussex IM. 1986. The response of *viviparous-1* and wild-type embryos of *Zea mays* to culture in the presence of abscisic acid. *J. Plant Physiol.* 126:235–42

154. Scanlon MJ, James MG, Stinard PS, Myers AM, Robertson DS. 1994. Characterization of ten new mutations of the maize *Etched*-1 locus. *Maydica* 39:301–8

155. Scanlon MJ, Stinard PS, James MG, Myers AM, Robertson DS. 1994. Genetic analysis of 63 mutations affecting maize kernel development isolated from *mutator* stocks. *Genetics* 136:281–94

156. Scanlon MJ, Myers AM. 1998. Phenotypic analysis and molecular cloning of *discolored-1* (*dsc1*), a maize gene required for early kernel development. *Plant Mol. Biol.* 37:483–93

157. Schel JHN, Kieft H, Van Lammeren AAM. 1984. Interactions between embryo and endosperm during early developmental stages of maize caryopses (*Zea mays*). *Can. J. Bot.* 62:2842–53

158. Scott RJ, Spielman M, Bailey J, Dickenson HG. 1998. Parent-of-origin effects on seed development in *Arabidopsis thaliana. Development* 125:3329–41

159. Shewry PR, Napier JA, Tatham AS. 1995. Seed storage proteins: structures and biosynthesis. *Plant Cell* 7:945–56

159a. Skriver K, Leah R, Muller-Uri F, Olsen FL, Mundy J. 1992. Structure and expression of the barley lipid transfer protein gene Ltp1. *Plant Mol. Biol.* 18:585–89

160. Shibaoka H, Nagai R. 1994. The plant cytoskeleton. *Curr. Opin. Cell Biol.* 6:10–15

161. Smirnova EA, Bajer AS. 1998. Early stages of spindle formation and independence of chromosome and microtubule cycles in *Haemanthus* endosperm. *Cell Motil. Cytoskel.* 40:22–37

162. Smith AM. 1999. Making starch. *Curr. Opin. Plant Biol.* 2:223–29

163. Smith LG. 1999. Divide and conquer: cytokinesis in plant cells. *Curr. Opin. Plant Biol.* 2:447–53

164. Smith LM, Handley J, Li Y, Martin H, Donovan L, Bowles DJ. 1992. Temporal and spatial regulation of a novel gene in barley embryos. *Plant Mol. Biol.* 20:255–66

165. Stacy RA, Nordeng TW, Culianez-Macia FA, Aalen RB. 1999. The dormancy-related peroxiredoxin anti-oxidant, PER1, is localized to the nucleus of barley embryo and aleurone cells. *Plant J.* 19:1–8

166. Staehelin LA, Hepler PK. 1996. Cytokinesis in higher plants. *Cell* 84:821–24

167. Stinard P, Robertson D. 1987. Dappled: a putative Mu-induced aleurone developmental mutant. *Maize Genet. Coop. Newsl.* 61:7–9

168. Stoppin V, Lambert AM, Vantard M. 1996. Plant microtubule associated proteins (MAPs) affect microtubule nucleation and growth at plant nuclei and mammalian centrosomes. *Eur. J. Cell Biol.* 69:11–23

169. Stoppin V, Vantard M, Schmit A-C, Lambert AM. 1994. Isolated plant nuclei nucleate microtubule assembly: The nuclear surface in higher plants has centrosome-like activity. *Plant Cell* 6:1099–106

170. Swanson SJ, Bethke PC, Jones RL. 1998. Barley aleurone cells contain two types of vacuoles. Characterization of lytic organelles by use of fluorescent probes. *Plant Cell* 10:685–98

171. Taliercio EW, Kim J-Y, Mahe A, Shanker S, Choi J, et al. 1999. Isolation, characterization and expression analyses of two cell wall invertase genes in maize. *J. Plant Physiol.* 155:197–204

172. Tian G-W, You R-L, Guo F-L, Wang X-C. 1998. Microtubular cytoskeleton of free endosperm nuclei during division in wheat. *Cytol. Tokyo* 63:427–33

173. Traas JA, Bellini C, Nacry P, Kronenburger J, Bouchez D, Cabouche M. 1995. Normal differentiation patterns in plants lacking microtubular preprophase bands. *Nature* 375:676–77

174. Trotochaud AE, Jeong S, Clark SE. 2000. Clavata3, a multimeric ligand for the Clavata1 receptor kinase. *Science* 289:613–17

175. True RH. 1893. On the development of the caryopsis. *Bot. Gaz.* 18:212–26

176. Umeda M, Bhalerao RP, Schell J, Uchimiya H, Koncz C. 1998. A distinct cyclin-dependent kinase-activating kinase of *Arabidopsis thaliana*. *Proc. Natl. Acad. Sci. USA* 95:5021–26

177. Van Lammeren AAM. 1988. Structure and function of the microtubular cytoskeleton during endosperm development in wheat: an immunofluorescence study. *Protoplasma* 146:18–27

178. Van Lammeren AAM, Kieft H, Ma F, Van Veenendaal WLH. 1996. Light microscopical study of endosperm formation in *Brassica napus* L. *Acta Soc. Bot. Polon.* 65:267–72

179. Vantard M, Lambert AM, De Mey J, Picquot P, Van Eldik LJ. 1985. Characterization and immunocytochemical distribution of calmodulin in higher plant endosperm cells: localization in the mitotic apparatus. *J. Cell Biol.* 101:488–99

179a. Vincente-Carbajosa VJ, Moose SP, Parsons RL, Schmidt RJ. 1997. A maize zinc-finger protein binds the prolamin box in zein gene promoters and interacts with the basic leucine zipper transcriptional activator Opaque2. *Proc. Natl. Acad. Sci. USA* 94:7685–90

180. Walbot V. 1994. Overview of key steps

in aleurone development. In *The Maize Handbook*, ed. M Freeling, V Walbot, pp. 78–80. New York: Springer-Verlag

181. Wang H, Qi Q, Schorr P, Cutler AJ, Crosby WL, Fowke LC. 1998. ICK1, a cyclin-dependent protein kinase inhibitor from *Arabidopsis thaliana* interacts with both Cdc2a and CycD3, and its expression is induced by abscisic acid. *Plant J.* 15:501–10

182. Wang HL, Offler CE, Patrick JW. 1995. The cellular pathway of photosynthate transfer in the developing wheat grain. II. A structural analysis and histochemical studies of the pathway from the crease phloem to the endosperm cavity. *Plant Cell Environ.* 18:373–88

183. Webb MC, Gunning BES. 1991. The microtubular cytoskeleton during development of the zygote, proembryo and free-nuclear endosperm in *Arabidopsis thaliana* (L.) Heynh. *Planta* 184:187–95

184. Wolf MJ, Cutler HC, Zuber MS, Khoo U. 1972. Maize with multilayer aleurone of high protein content. *Crop. Sci.* 12:440–42

185. XuHan X, Van Lammeren AAM. 1994. Microtubular configurations during endosperm development in *Phaseolus vulgaris*. *Can. J. Bot.* 72:1489–95

186. XuHan X, Van Lammeren AAM. 1993. Microtubular configurations during the cellularization of coenocytic endosperm in *Ranunculus sceleratus* L. *Sex. Plant Reprod.* 6:127–32

187. Deleted in proof

188. Young TE, Gallie DR, DeMason DA. 1997. Ethylene-mediated programmed cell death during maize endosperm development of wild type and shrunken2 genotypes. *Plant Physiol.* 115:737–51

189. Zhang K, Letham DS, John PC. 1996. Cytokinin controls the cell cycle at mitosis by stimulating the tyrosine dephosphorylation and activation of p34cdc2-like H1 histone kinase. *Planta* 200:2–12

Annu. Rev. Plant Physiol. Plant Mol. Biol. 2001. 52:269–95

MECHANISTIC FEATURES OF THE MO-CONTAINING NITROGENASE

Jason Christiansen and Dennis R Dean

Department of Biochemistry, Virginia Polytechnic Institute and State University, Blacksburg, Virginia 24061; e-mail: jasonc@vt.edu and deandr@vt.edu

Lance C Seefeldt

Department of Chemistry and Biochemistry, Utah State University, Logan, Utah 84332; e-mail: seefeldt@cc.usu.edu

Key Words nitrogenase, nucleotides, metalloenzyme, hydrolysis, redox proteins

■ **Abstract** Nitrogenase is the complex metalloenzyme responsible for biological dinitrogen reduction. This reaction represents the single largest contributor to the reductive portion of the global nitrogen cycle. Recent developments in understanding the mechanism of the Mo-based nitrogenase are reviewed. Topics include how nucleotide binding and hydrolysis are coupled to electron transfer and substrate reduction, how electrons are accumulated and transferred within the MoFe-protein, and how substrates bind and are reduced at the active site metal cluster.

CONTENTS

1040-2519/01/0601-0269$14.00

269

INTRODUCTION AND OVERVIEW

Biological nitrogen fixation (the reduction of molecular N_2 to NH_3) represents the most significant contributor to the global nitrogen cycle (35). Only a select group of microorganisms, commonly referred to as diazotrophs, are able to catalyze nitrogen fixation. Diazotrophs are widely distributed among and restricted to the Archaea and Bacteria. Among those that have been extensively studied are nitrogenases from *Azotobacter vinelandii* (an obligate aerobe), *Clostridium pasteurianum* (an obligate anaerobe), *Klebsiella pneumoniae* (a facultative anaerobe), *Rhodospirillum rubrum* (a photosynthetic bacterium), *Anabaena sp.* 7120 (a heterocyst-forming cyanobacterium), and *Bradyrhizobium japonicum* (a symbiotic bacterium). Although free-living diazotrophs significantly contribute to global nitrogen cycle flux, they have little direct agronomic relevance. From the agronomic perspective, symbiotic nitrogen fixers are very important. These organisms invade leguminous plants, such as pea and alfalfa, inducing the formation of specialized structures, called root nodules. In this symbiotic association, the root nodule contains differentiated bacteria specializing in nitrogen fixation with the consequent delivery of fixed nitrogen to the plant host. The establishment of such symbioses, and the capacity of the endosymbiont for effective nitrogen fixation, is critical for plant productivity. Thus, the biochemical mechanism of nitrogen fixation has attracted broad interest, ranging from bioinorganic chemists to plant physiologists.

Nitrogen fixation is catalyzed by a metalloenzyme called nitrogenase and the reaction is usually depicted as shown in Equation 1.

$$N_2 + 8\,H^+ + 16\,MgATP + 8e^- \rightarrow 2\,NH_3 + H_2 + 16\,MgADP + 16\,Pi \qquad 1.$$

Four classes of nitrogenases have been characterized (32, 44). Three classes share many similarities, differing in part by the heterometal atom contained in the active site metal cluster (Mo, V, or Fe). The fourth class is a superoxide-dependent nitrogenase recently isolated from *Streptomyces thermoautotrophicus* (44), which is distinct from the other nitrogenase classes. The Mo-dependent nitrogenases are the best studied and most widely distributed (10, 33), and are the focus of this review. The primary sequence, as well as the three-dimensional structure of the three Mo-dependent enzymes whose structures have been solved, are highly conserved. Thus, mechanistic insights gained from analysis of Mo-dependent nitrogenase from free-living organisms is applicable to the nitrogenases from the agronomically relevant rhizobia and fundamentally to the V- and Fe-dependent classes as well.

Mo-dependent nitrogenases consist of two component proteins named the Fe protein (or component II or dinitrogenase reductase) and the MoFe protein (or component I or dinitrogenase) (12). The Fe protein is a homodimeric protein ($\sim$64 kDa) with a single [4Fe-4S] cluster bridged between its two subunits (36, 42, 45). The Fe protein also contains two nucleotide-binding sites, one on each subunit

(36). The MoFe protein is an $\alpha_2\beta_2$ tetramer ($\sim$250 kDa) that contains two pairs of novel metalloclusters called the P- (or [8Fe-7S]) cluster and the iron-molybdenum-cofactor (FeMo-cofactor) (3–5, 15, 26, 52, 53). Each $\alpha\beta$ dimer of the MoFe protein contains one P-cluster and one FeMo-cofactor and is believed to function as an independent catalytic unit together with one Fe protein. X-ray structures have been presented for the Fe protein and MoFe protein from *Azotobacter vinelandii* (36, 52, 99), and for MoFe proteins from *Clostridium pasteurianum* (4–6, 54, 99) and *Klebsiella pneumoniae* (74). In addition, X-ray structures have also been reported for the *A. vinelandii* Fe protein-MoFe protein complex stabilized in two different ways (89, 98). Figure 1 (see color insert) illustrates the overall organization of one catalytic unit of nitrogenase (one Fe protein bound to an $\alpha\beta$-unit of the MoFe protein), along with models for the relative positions of the three metal cluster types.

During catalysis, the Fe protein serves as a specific reductant of the MoFe protein, which in turn provides the site for substrate reduction. An Fe protein, with two MgATP molecules bound, transiently associates with one $\alpha\beta$-unit of the MoFe protein. During this association, the two MgATP molecules are hydrolyzed to MgADP and P_i, an event that is coupled to the transfer of one electron from the Fe protein $[4Fe-4S]^{1+}$ cluster into the MoFe protein. Recently, it has been demonstrated that the Fe protein [4Fe-4S] cluster can be reduced to an all ferrous $[4Fe-4S]^0$ state in vitro (1, 2, 121), and that from this state two electrons can be transferred to the MoFe protein concomitant with the hydrolysis of 2 MgATP molecules (34). The physiological relevance of the all-ferrous state of the Fe protein is not yet known. The P-clusters are thought to act as intermediate electron acceptors (13, 68, 71, 83) before passing the electrons on to the FeMo-cofactor where substrates bind and are reduced (77, 80, 81, 106, 107). Following electron transfer, the oxidized Fe protein, with MgADP bound, dissociates from the MoFe protein in what is thought to be the overall reaction rate-limiting step (31, 38, 90). The Fe protein is reduced by small, electron transfer proteins in vivo (e.g. ferredoxin, flavodoxin) or by electron transfer mediators in vitro. Because all substrates reduced by nitrogenase require two or more electrons, this cycle must be repeated multiple times for substrate reduction to occur. Although many challenges remain in understanding the mechanism of this complex metalloenzyme, three of the most significant questions are:

1. How is ATP binding and hydrolysis linked to electron transfer and substrate reduction?

2. What are the properties of the P-clusters and what roles do they play in electron transfer from the Fe protein to the FeMo-cofactor?

3. How does the MoFe protein control binding and reduction of substrates at the active site FeMo-cofactor?

In this review, we present recent advances aimed at addressing each of these open questions.

ROLES FOR NUCLEOTIDES AND THE FE PROTEIN

Complex Roles in Catalysis

On first glance, the Fe protein might appear to serve simply as a reductant of the MoFe protein. However, the participation of the Fe protein in the nitrogenase mechanism is much more intimate, constituting a complex interplay between the Fe protein, nucleotides, and the MoFe protein that regulates inter- and intraprotein electron transfer and, perhaps, substrate access and reduction. The Fe protein and nucleotides also participate in the biosynthesis of the FeMo-cofactor and the insertion of this cofactor into an apo-MoFe protein (70, 91). These latter roles for the Fe protein and nucleotides are not discussed further here, rather we focus on their roles in the nitrogenase substrate reduction mechanism.

The complex nature of the interactions of the Fe protein and nucleotides in the nitrogenase reaction is most apparent from the fact that the Fe protein is the only known reductant that will support substrate reduction catalyzed by the MoFe protein. The metal clusters of the MoFe protein (P-cluster and FeMo-cofactor) are accessible to small electron transfer mediators, as evidenced by an ability to remove electrons from the resting state of the MoFe protein, or to add electrons to oxidized states of the MoFe protein (120). But despite this accessibility, no mediator has been found to support substrate reduction or electron transfer to the as-isolated form of the MoFe protein. Driving force is clearly not the limiting factor for these reactions, as mediators with midpoint potentials more negative than that of the Fe protein have been examined. This leads to the inescapable conclusion that the Fe protein contributes more to the overall reaction than just electrons. Further, the absolute requirement for MgATP hydrolysis to support substrate reduction points to fundamental roles for nucleotides in controlling the reaction.

Nucleotides appear to participate at several steps in the nitrogenase mechanism. For example, binding of nucleotides to the Fe protein alters the properties of the Fe protein and the electronic properties of its associated [4Fe-4S] cluster (16, 40, 59, 65, 66, 76, 80, 94, 95, 107, 109, 113, 118, 125). Nucleotide binding also promotes formation of the Fe protein-MoFe protein complex. Once the Fe protein, with a MgATP bound to each subunit, associates with the MoFe protein, the hydrolysis of ATP is initiated. In the absence of the MoFe protein, the Fe protein does not hydrolyze MgATP at appreciable rates. The energy from the hydrolysis of ATP is ultimately harnessed to accomplish electron transfer and substrate reduction. The details of how these events are coupled are not well understood and remain among the outstanding questions regarding the nitrogenase mechanism. Although the exact order of ATP hydrolysis and electron transfer has not been unequivocally established (29, 30, 115), clearly these two events are intimately linked. Competent catalytic electron transfer absolutely requires the hydrolysis of MgATP. Finally, MgATP hydrolysis is utilized to signal the dissociation of the Fe protein from the MoFe protein at the end of the reaction cycle (58).

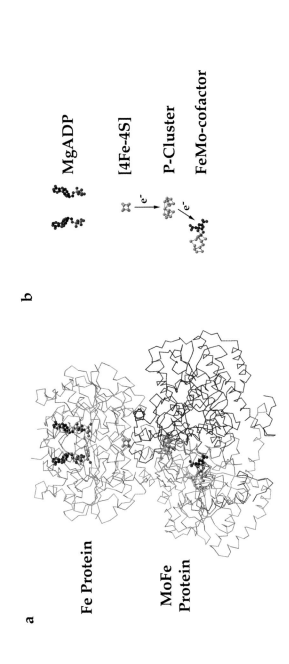

MgADP

[4Fe-4S]

P-Cluster

FeMo-cofactor

Fe Protein

MoFe
Protein

a

b

Figure 1 Nitrogenase proteins and metal clusters. (*Panel a*) The structure of one catalytic unit of nitrogenase is shown with a single, homodimeric Fe protein (green) and an αβ-dimer of the MoFe protein (α subunit in cyan and β subunit in red). (*Panel b*) With the polypeptide chains removed, the relative positions of the two bound MgADP molecules, the Fe protein [4Fe-4S] cluster, the MoFe protein P-cluster and FeMo-cofactor are easily visualized. The direction of electron flow between the clusters is indicated by arrows. Figures were generated using Molscript (56) and Raster3D (75) from the coordinates for the ADP-AlF$_4^-$ nitrogenase complex (98). Atom colors are carbon in black, nitrogen in blue, oxygen in red, phosphorous in dark green, sulfur in yellow, molybdenum in purple, and iron in light green.

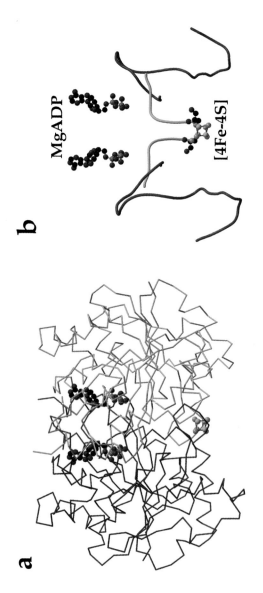

Figure 2 Nitrogenase Fe protein structure. (*Panel a*) The overall structure of the homodimeric Fe protein shows the relative positions of the two bound MgADP molecules (*top center*), the [4Fe-4S] cluster (cubane structure at the bottom), and the MoFe protein docking surface (*bottom*). (*Panel b*) The positions of the putative Fe protein switch I (magenta) and switch II (cyan) are shown relative to the two bound MgADP molecules and the [4Fe-4S] cluster. Atom colors are as described in Figure 1.

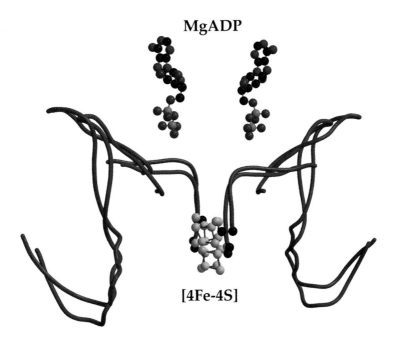

Figure 3 Conformational changes in the Fe protein switches. An overlay of the Fe protein switches I and II for the Fe protein in the absence of any bound nucleotides (*red*) and when bound to MgADP-AlF$_4^-$ in complex with the MoFe protein (*blue*) is shown.

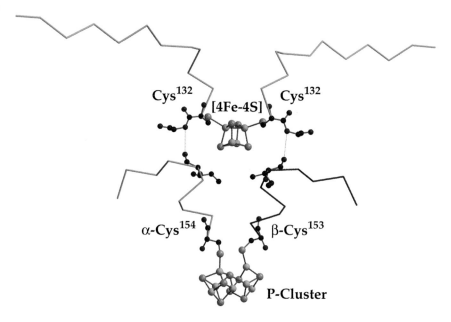

Figure 4 Postulated electron transfer pathways from the Fe protein [4Fe-4S] cluster to the MoFe protein P-cluster are shown. The dashed line indicates a likely hydrogen bond. The α-carbon trace for switch II (*green*) in the Fe protein, and the probable electron transfer paths (*blue* and *red*) in the MoFe protein are shown.

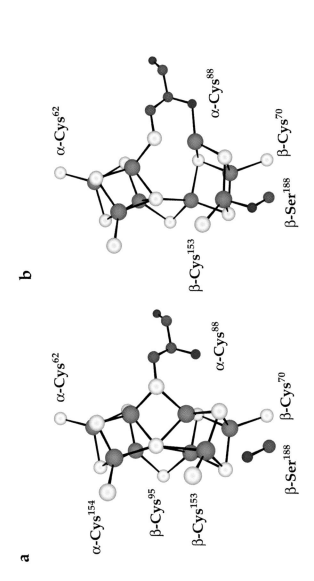

Figure 5 P-cluster models. The two different reported structures of the P-cluster in the reduced (*panel a*) and oxidized (*panel b*) states. Note the change in ligation of the α-Cys88 and β-Ser188 residues.

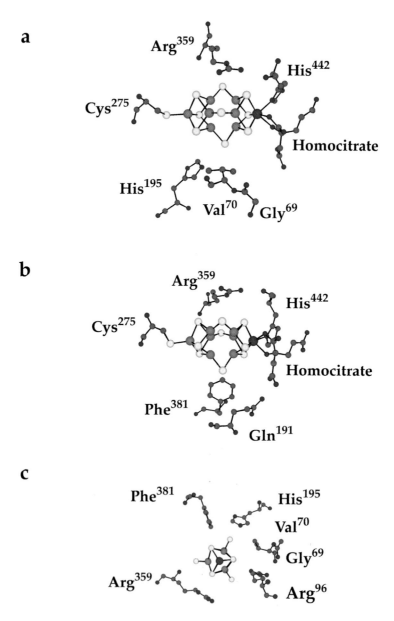

Figure 6 FeMo-cofactor views. (*Panels a* and *b*) Two orientations of the FeMo-cofactor showing the location of homocitrate and the α-subunit ligands (Cys[275] and His[442]). Also shown are several approaching α-subunit amino acid residues. (*Panel c*) Another view of the FeMo-cofactor looking down the long axis, with the homocitrate and protein ligands removed for clarity.

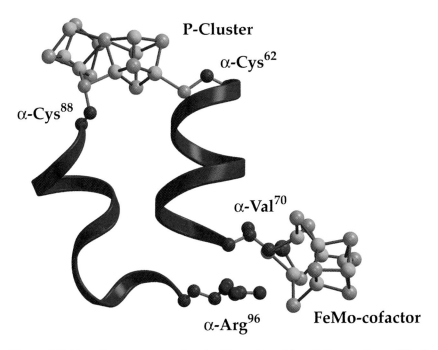

Figure 8 FeMoco-P cluster connection. An illustration of the relative positions of the P-cluster and FeMo-cofactor in the MoFe protein. Two of the residues that directly approach one [Fe-S] face of the FeMo-cofactor (α-Val^{70} and α-Arg^{96}) are connected to the P-cluster through short peptide stretches which may act as communication pathways.

An examination of the structure of the Fe protein reveals that the nucleotide binding sites are located approximately 15 Å away from the Fe protein [4Fe-4S] cluster and the docking interface with the MoFe protein (Figure 2; see color insert). This architecture for the Fe protein demands that nucleotides exert their effects on the nitrogenase catalytic cycle from a distance through protein conformational changes (46, 103, 112). Such a mechanism of long-range nucleotide signal transduction is not unique to the Fe protein; it is found in many members of the larger family of nucleotide utilizing proteins (e.g. myosin, ras p21, recA, etc) (119). The unique feature of nitrogenase is that a nucleotide signal is communicated over long distances to control electron transfer and substrate reduction. So, how are nucleotide signals communicated over long range to affect the nitrogenase mechanism? A comparison of the Fe protein amino acid sequence (93) and tertiary structure (36) with other members of the nucleotide-utilizing family of proteins (49, 55, 110) reveals common motifs. Two amino acid stretches in the Fe protein have been observed to be homologous to amino acid stretches in the GTP binding Ras P21 protein. Both of these stretches have been observed to undergo substantial conformational changes reflecting the nucleotide bound status of the protein (8, 117). These regions have been termed switch I and switch II in Ras P21, and these designations are used here (Figure 2).

Switch II as a Nucleotide Transduction Pathway

Switch II in the Fe protein originates in the nucleotide phosphate-binding region (Asp[125]) and proceeds to a Cys ligand to the [4Fe-4S] cluster (Cys[132]). In this review, all amino acid numbering is for the *Azotobacter vinelandii* nitrogenase unless otherwise specified. Given that the Fe protein is a homodimer, each nucleotide binding site is connected through switch II to a ligand of the [4Fe-4S] cluster, accounting for two of the four ligands to the cluster. Two lines of evidence support a role for switch II in nucleotide signal transduction. First, the properties of Fe proteins with amino acids substitutions within switch II support a model where this region of the Fe protein communicates from the nucleotide binding site to the [4Fe-4S] cluster (97, 122). Second, comparison of the X-ray structures of the Fe protein alone (36, 99) to Fe protein with bound MgADP-AlF$_4^-$ complexed with the MoFe protein (98) reveals substantial movement in the switch II motif (Figure 3; see color insert). This observation suggests that the presence of the bound nucleotide is, in part, communicated as changes in switch II, which is, in turn, communicated to the [4Fe-4S] cluster. A caveat to this conclusion is that the relative contributions from nucleotide binding and Fe protein-MoFe protein complex formation to the observed changes in switch II are not known. Recently, the structure of the Fe protein has been solved with MgADP bound (48a), allowing conformational changes resulting from nucleotide binding to be examined in the absence of protein-protein complex formation. In this case, clear changes in switch II are observed and ascribable to MgADP binding. This leads to a working model where the switch II motif in the Fe protein provides a means for communication between the nucleotide binding site and the [4Fe-4S] cluster site.

This switch motif could also be involved in communicating nucleotide status into the MoFe protein to alter properties within the MoFe protein and as a way to control electron transfer between the Fe protein and the MoFe protein. Recent work has shown that one function of MgATP in the nitrogenase reaction is to accelerate electron transfer from the Fe protein to the MoFe protein (14). Calculations from electron transfer (Marcus) theory (24, 72, 78) using parameters measured for nitrogenase (60, 61) suggest that this rate acceleration cannot be accounted for solely by changes in either distance between the [4Fe-4S] cluster and the P-cluster or the driving force (ΔE_m) between the electron donor and acceptor. This leaves the pathway of electron transfer as the likely variable that is modified by nucleotides. Examination of the structure of the Fe protein-MoFe protein complex reveals two probable electron transfer pathways (47), each originating at the [4Fe-4S] cluster of the Fe protein with a through space jump to two short protein stretches in the MoFe protein leading to ligands to the P-cluster (Figure 4; see color insert). It is easy to envision how nucleotide-induced protein conformational changes propagated through switch II could alter these proposed electron transfer pathways, thereby altering the rate of electron transfer or the reversibility of electron transfer. This working model remains to be tested. The ability to make site-specifically modified Fe or MoFe proteins, to measure midpoint potentials of the individual metal centers, and to establish X-ray structures for Fe protein-MoFe protein complexes, offers a clear path for future studies to establish how nucleotides control electron transfer in the nitrogenase reaction.

Switch I and Complex Association

An important aspect of the nitrogenase mechanism is the transient association of the two component proteins (38). The weight of evidence suggests that following each electron transfer event, the Fe protein must dissociate from the MoFe protein following electron transfer (115), and that this step is rate limiting in the overall reaction (38, 114). However, kinetic evidence suggests that, under special conditions, the Fe protein and MoFe protein might not dissociate following each electron transfer event (29). It appears that one function of MgATP hydrolysis is to act as a timing mechanism to control the association of the Fe protein with the MoFe protein. In this model, the MgATP bound form of the Fe protein would have higher affinity for binding to the MoFe protein. Either electron transfer from the Fe protein into the MoFe protein and/or MgATP hydrolysis to MgADP and P_i signals dissociation of the Fe protein from the MoFe protein (67). Given the architecture of the Fe protein, the nucleotide bound state must be communicated to the MoFe protein-docking interface via protein conformational changes. The switch I motif in the Fe protein offers an attractive means for communication between the nucleotide binding site and the MoFe protein docking interface (46, 58). This putative switch runs from Asp^{39}, interacting with the Mg^{2+} bound to the nucleotide, to residues in the 50 to 60 region. These latter residues form a series of interactions with partner residues on the MoFe protein, accounting for many of the interactions between these two proteins in the complex (98). Thus, it seems reasonable to suggest that nucleotide binding is communicated through changes in switch I to alter the interactions between the two protein partners. Two lines of evidence support this model for a role of switch I. First, altering Asp^{39} at the terminus of this switch I to Asn^{39} interfered with the attainment of the MgADP bound conformation. Importantly, this resulted in an Fe protein that failed to dissociate from the MoFe protein following electron transfer, suggesting a role for switch I in communicating the signal to dissociate (58). Second, a comparison of the X-ray structure of the Fe proteins either in the absence of bound nucleotides (36, 99), in the presence of MgADP (48a), or in the $MgADP-AlF_4^-$ stabilized complex with the MoFe protein (98), reveals significant changes in the switch I motif. These results, taken together, point to a role for switch I in nucleotide signal transduction controlling the association between the two component proteins. Again, this model should be testable by using a combination of amino acid substitution and X-ray crystallography.

Roles for the MoFe Protein in MgATP Hydrolysis and Electron Transfer   Because the MoFe protein is necessary for MgATP hydrolysis to occur on the Fe protein, component protein-protein interactions must result in a signal that is transmitted from the MoFe protein docking surface to the nucleotide-binding site within the Fe protein. Inspection of the Fe protein-MoFe protein complex structure (98) suggests possible interactions that might be responsible for activating the MgATP hydrolysis event. Among the many interactions, the pseudosymmetrically related α-Phe^{125} and β-Phe^{125} residues on the MoFe protein are especially intriguing. Although the side chains of these residues do not appear to directly interact with Fe protein residues, the backbone carbonyl atoms from pseudosymmetrically related residues at positions 123 and 124 in both the α- and β-subunits appear to form hydrogen bonds to the Fe protein [4Fe-4S] cluster-coordinating residues Cys^{97}. Thus, it was considered that movement of the bulky α-Phe^{125} and β-Phe^{125} side chains during early component protein interaction events could be communicated through switch II to ultimately elicit MgATP hydrolysis and intercomponent electron transfer. This possibility was tested by substitution of these residues, both separately or in combination, by alanine (18). The altered singly substituted MoFe proteins retained about half the normal catalytic activity. In contrast, the doubly substituted MoFe protein lost all catalytic activity, was unable to elicit MgATP hydrolysis, and could not form a stable complex with the Fe protein under any condition tested. These results are consistent with the possibility that α-Phe^{125} and β-Phe^{125} are involved in triggering MgATP hydrolysis and electron transfer, but do not prove that is the case.

The interactions between the Fe protein Arg^{100} residues with either or both of the MoFe protein α-Glu^{120} or β-Glu^{120} residues also appear to be important. The Fe protein Arg[100] residue has been implicated in Fe protein-MoFe protein interactions being the site of ADP-ribosylation in some photosynthetic organisms (69). In addition, substitution of this residue by histidine results in the severe uncoupling of MgATP hydrolysis from electron transfer (123). For this altered Fe protein, MgATP hydrolysis occurs at a relatively high rate although effective substrate reduction does not occur. Substitution of either MoFe protein α-Glu[120] or β-Glu[120] by glutamine partially reverses the effect of the Fe protein His[100] substitution (VL Cash & DR Dean, unpublished results). Many additional interactions between the Fe protein and the MoFe protein are apparent and remain to be examined by amino acid substitutions.

P-CLUSTERS AND ELECTRON TRANSFER

The [8Fe-7S] P-cluster is located $\sim$10 Å below the surface of the MoFe protein and bridges the dimeric interface between the MoFe protein α- and β-subunits (47). As can be seen in Figure 1, the P-cluster is situated between the Fe protein [4Fe-4S] cluster and the active site FeMo-cofactor. In the crystallographically determined MgADP-AlF$_4$$^-$-Fe protein-MoFe protein complex shown in Figure 1, the P-cluster is located almost equidistant from both the Fe protein [4Fe-4S] cluster and FeMo-cofactor (98). An important aspect of nitrogenase research is understanding how the P-cluster communicates with the Fe protein during intercomponent electron transfer and also how it promotes electron transfer to FeMo-cofactor.

Structural Features

Originally, the P-cluster was thought to be a [4Fe-4S]-like cubane, of which there were two pairs in each MoFe protein heterotetramer [for an earlier review, see (79)]. Subsequently, spectroscopic (41) and early crystallographic studies (5) showed that the P-cluster was a larger, more complex structure. Now, further crystallographic refinement has shown that the P-cluster has a unique structure consisting of a [4Fe-4S] fragment bridged by two cysteine residues to a [4Fe-3S] fragment (4, 74, 84). This structure can also be thought of as consisting of two individual [4Fe-4S] cubes joined together at a common, hexacoordinate sulfur (Figure 5; see color insert). The cluster is covalently attached to the MoFe protein by two terminal cysteine residues from each subunit (α-Cys[62], α-Cys[154], β-Cys[70], and β-Cys[153]) and two bridging cysteines, one from each subunit (α-Cys[88] and β-Cys[95]) (53).

Crystallographic studies have also shown that the P-cluster undergoes dramatic structural changes and ligand rearrangement upon oxidation (74, 84). When MoFe protein in the as-isolated dithionite-reduced state is oxidized, certain Fe atoms in the fragment of the P-cluster, located primarily within the β-subunit of the MoFe protein, separate and move away from the central S atom. This rearrangement results in a P-cluster consisting of one [4Fe-4S] fragment residing predominantly in the α-subunit, which has undergone relatively small changes, and an expanded

[4Fe-3S] fragment contained predominantly within the β-subunit. Thus, upon oxidation of the P-cluster, the central S atom goes from hexacoordinate to tetracoordinate, by only binding to a single Fe within the [4Fe-3S] fragment. To complete the coordination of the two Fe atoms that were previously bound to this central sulfur atom, β-Ser[188] forms an alkoxide ligand to the iron atom also coordinated to the peptide by β-Cys[153]. The second Fe atom, which is still ligated to bridging ligand α-Cys[88], now forms a bond with a backbone amide, also provided by α-Cys[88].

Electronic Features

In the resting, dithionite-reduced state of the MoFe protein, the P-clusters are in a $S = 0$, diamagnetic state, denoted P^N (124). Mössbauer studies have shown that in this state all of the iron atoms are essentially ferrous (111). These same studies have also indicated the possible presence of some ferric character in this diamagnetic state, although there is no direct experimental evidence to show that the P-clusters can be reduced below the P^N state. However, three more oxidized states of the P-cluster have been studied and are readily observed using EPR spectroscopy. As shown in Scheme 1, these states are denoted P^{1+}, P^{2+}, and P^{3+}, where the superscript denotes the number of electrons removed from the individual cluster starting at the P^N state. States above P^{3+} have been observed, but these states are irreversible and, therefore, unlikely to participate in nitrogenase activity.

$$P^N \leftrightarrow P^{1+} \leftrightarrow P^{2+} \leftrightarrow P^{3+}. \hspace{3cm} \text{Scheme 1.}$$

When the MoFe protein is treated with the dye oxidants thionin or indigodisulfonate (IDS) the P-cluster is oxidized to the P^{2+} state (120). This spin state is considered to be $S \geq 3$ and exhibits an absorption shaped signal at g $\sim$12 that can be observed using parallel mode EPR (although it is also visible in perpendicular mode EPR, and was originally reported in this mode) (39, 86, 111). When the MoFe protein is stirred over a mixture containing solid thionin, the P-clusters can be oxidized by one more electron above the P^{2+} state to the P^{3+} state (40). This state is a $S = 7/2$, $S = 1/2$ mixed spin state, and provided the original evidence indicating that the P-clusters must consist of a more complex arrangement than the individual [4Fe-4S] cluster previously suggested. Finally, there is the singly oxidized P-cluster state, P^{1+}. This state was originally observed during redox titrations of the higher oxidation states of the P-cluster, and the midpoint potential reported for the P^N/P^{1+} couple was identical to that reported for the P^{1+}/P^{2+} couple (86). By performing controlled stoichiometric oxidations of the P-cluster, Tittsworth & Hales characterized P^{1+} as a $S = 1/2$ and $S = 5/2$ mixed spin state that is distinct from the higher oxidation states (116). The reason for the mixed spin state nature of P^{1+} is still unclear. In the original characterization two possibilities were suggested. The mixture could arise from a distribution of conformational differences in the P-cluster upon oxidation or the electron could be removed from different halves of the P-cluster, giving rise to a distribution of $S = 1/2$ and $S = 5/2$ spin states, depending on which half the electron was removed from. A recent high-resolution crystallographic study of MoFe protein isolated from *K. pneumoniae* in different redox states lends support to the first suggestion (74). This study proposes a model of the P-cluster in an oxidation state that is intermediate between the resting, dithionite-reduced state and the P^{2+} oxidized form. This intermediate model can be described by a superposition of two models, both with interactions observed in the oxidized model: one with a population of the P-clusters with an Fe atom possessing the serinate ligand from β-Ser[188] and the others with an Fe atom possessing the backbone-amide ligand provided by α-Cys[88]. The presence of these two different conformers may well be responsible for the mixed spin state observed in the EPR of the P^{1+} state.

The Role of the P-Cluster

The P-cluster is the first biological example of a [Fe-S] cluster that naturally has serine and amide ligands (from the peptide backbone), together with a complement of cysteine ligands. The protonatable nature of these two exchangeable ligands implies that changes in the local pH could have an effect on the structural rearrangement and hence on the redox states observable using EPR spectroscopy. As stated above, it was originally reported that the midpoint potentials for the P^{N}/P^{1+} and P^{1+}/P^{2+} redox couples were identical, at -309 mV. This degeneracy would help to explain the early difficulties encountered in attempting to characterize the P^{1+} state. However, Lanzilotta and co-workers found that by performing EPR-monitored redox titrations at different pH values, a pH dependence could be observed for the P^{1+}/P^{2+} redox couple (the P^{N}/P^{1+} redox couple did not demonstrate any pH dependence) (57). These results showed that by poising the pH and potential of the MoFe protein, one could readily optimize the amount of P^{1+} or P^{2+} signal observed. Furthermore, the observed change in potential with pH was -53 mV/pH unit, indicating a single protonation event associated with each electron transfer event. These experiments indicated that the structural changes that occur in the P-cluster upon oxidation could be linked to a proton transfer event. To examine this possibility, the β-Ser[188] residue was substituted by glycine. Glycine is not protonatable and also will not act as a ligand to the P-cluster. Examination of the altered MoFe protein showed that the pH dependence of the P^{1+}/P^{2+} redox couple was unchanged, thus indicating that β-Ser[188] is not the protonatable ligand observed in unaltered MoFe protein (57). In the recent crystallographic studies of the *K. pneumoniae* nitrogenase MoFe protein, it was suggested that β-Ser[92] (β-Ser[90] in *K. pneumoniae*) might be responsible for the observed pH dependence. To test this possibility, amino acid substitutions were placed at this position but no change in pH dependence was observed (J Christiansen, LC Seefeldt & DR Dean, unpublished results). These results indirectly implicate the backbone amide from α-Cys[88] as the protonatable ligand; however, there is no direct evidence for this possibility so other changes in the local P-cluster environment have not been ruled out as the source of pH dependence. Experiments involving substitutions for the α-Cys[88] position would not be informative because the binding interaction to

Fe is through a backbone amide, which will be relatively invariant with different side-chain substitutions.

Although the β-Ser^{188} residue does not appear to play a direct role in the electron-proton transfer mechanism described above, it is involved in the structural changes observed for the P-cluster upon oxidation. Because β-Ser^{188} is only ligated to the oxidized form of the P-cluster (see Figure 5), we hypothesized that substitution by cysteine might result in trapping a more oxidized form of the P-cluster. Isolation and characterization of the β-Cys^{188} MoFe protein indicates that this prediction was correct (13). In the resting, dithionite-reduced state, the β-Cys^{188} MoFe protein exhibits a $S = 1/2$, $S = 5/2$ mixed spin type EPR signal (13). The two observed signals are similar to those previously reported for the unaltered MoFe protein in the P^{1+} oxidation state (116). The $S = 1/2$ component of this signal exhibits a midpoint potential (in the oxidative direction) ~90 mV more negative than any previously reported P-cluster midpoint potential. The midpoint potential was also observed to decrease significantly when titrated in the reductive direction, although owing to protein instability at very low potentials, an accurate measure of the midpoint potential was not possible. These titrations showed that, along with the more negative midpoint potential, the P-cluster of the β-Cys^{188} MoFe protein could be reversibly reduced or oxidized by one electron. When the pH was varied during these titrations, the oxidizing redox couple was seen to be pH dependent, analogous to the P^{1+}/P^{2+} redox couple in the unaltered MoFe protein. It was further verified that these signals arise from the P-cluster because an apo-form of the β-Cys^{188} MoFe protein, which does not contain FeMo-cofactor, exhibits the same $S = 1/2$ and $S = 5/2$ EPR signals as observed with the intact MoFe protein. Although the above two reports indicate that interaction with the β-Ser^{188} residue is not absolutely required for full activity, the same is not true for the β-Cys^{153} ligand to the same P-cluster Fe atom. It has been shown that substitution of β-Cys^{153} by serine resulted in a MoFe protein that still exhibits ~50% of enzymatic activity. However, if the cysteine residue was substituted by alanine or deleted altogether, the resulting strains were incapable of supporting diazotrophic growth (73).

The above reports have helped to shed some light on the behavior of the P-cluster in various redox states. However, the exact role of the P-cluster during catalysis is still not well understood. Although the P-cluster is ideally positioned to act as an intermediate electron acceptor and electron mediator between the Fe protein and the active site FeMo-cofactor, a major pitfall of nitrogenase research has been the difficulty in obtaining direct evidence for this pathway. Using stopped-flow spectrophotometry and EPR, Lowe and co-workers showed that there is a [Fe-S] cluster oxidation event that occurs in the MoFe protein only after sufficient electrons have accumulated to begin the process of dinitrogen reduction (68). This result implies that the P-cluster can act as an electron capacitor, accumulating sufficient reducing equivalents and then discharging them at a specified time for substrate reduction. However, the experiment was not able to definitively assign the oxidation event to the P-clusters. Another report suggesting the involvement of the P-clusters in catalysis involved the use of an altered MoFe protein (82). In this study, a tyrosine residue on a helix located between the P-cluster and FeMo-cofactor, β-Tyr^{98}, was substituted by histidine (83). Here, it was observed that the interaction of the altered MoFe protein with the Fe protein was unaffected, but that the substitution caused an apparent impairment in electron transfer from the P-cluster to the FeMo-cofactor. Stopped-flow and kinetic data indicated that two electrons accumulated on the P-cluster prior to their delivery to FeMo-cofactor. However, a conflict arises in that there is currently no evidence showing that the P-cluster can be reduced lower than the P^N state. Finally, the β-Cys^{188} substituted MoFe protein described above was used to examine the P-cluster under turnover conditions (13). Because this MoFe protein has a P-cluster that is paramagnetic in the resting state, there is a signal that can be monitored during enzymatic turnover. When the β-Cys^{188} MoFe protein is placed under turnover conditions and monitored with EPR, the $S = 1/2, S = 5/2$ mixed spin state signals disappear. More importantly, upon cessation of turnover (i.e. exhaustion of MgATP) the signals return to their full intensity. This result provides some of the first direct evidence that the P-cluster is directly involved in the transfer of electrons during nitrogenase catalytic activity.

Although there is mounting evidence that the P-cluster is directly involved in the transfer of electrons from the Fe protein to the FeMo-cofactor, several questions remain: What are the relevant redox states of the cluster during catalytic activity? Although several oxidized forms have been characterized, it is not clear which of these states are accessed during turnover. It is also still unclear how a cluster that contains only ferrous iron in the as-isolated state is able to accumulate and mediate electron transfer from the Fe protein. Could there be a state more reduced than P^N, and if so, what spectroscopic signature will it have? Could it be that the P-clusters act only as simple intermediaries of electron transfer, cycling only between two oxidation states? Do electrons donated to the P-cluster simply displace electrons to the active site, thus making an intermediate oxidation state only a very transient event? Or is the P-cluster's role more complex? Does it act to accumulate electrons and release them during specific reduction events, acting as electron capacitors? And finally, what are the electron transfer pathways in and out of the P-cluster? If the P-cluster is to play a role in the complex mechanism of nitrogen fixation, it almost certainly must be in some form of communication with the Fe protein as the electron donor and the FeMo-cofactor as the ultimate electron acceptor.

SUBSTRATE BINDING AND REDUCTION

FeMo-Cofactor Structure

Although there is convincing evidence that substrate binding and reduction occurs at the FeMo-cofactor site of nitrogenase (43, 64, 101, 102, 106), exactly where and how substrate becomes bound to the FeMo-cofactor and is subsequently reduced during catalysis remains among the most intriguing, and as yet unanswered, questions in bioinorganic chemistry. As shown in Figure 1, the FeMo-cofactor is contained entirely within the MoFe protein α-subunit. It is constructed from S-bridged [4Fe-3S] and [3Fe-3S-Mo] subfragments that are geometrically analogous to pieces derived from cuboidal clusters (Figures 1, 6). An organic constituent, homocitrate, is coordinated to the Mo atom through its 2-hydroxy and 2-carboxyl groups (15). Opposite ends of the FeMo-cofactor are covalently attached to the MoFe protein α-subunit through α-Cys^{275}, coordinated to an Fe atom at one end of the molecule, and α-His^{442}, which is coordinated to the antipodal Mo atom. FeMo-cofactor also interacts with the MoFe protein through a number of direct and water-bridged hydrogen bonds (4, 47).

Prior to the availability of a structural model for FeMo-cofactor, many investigators believed that where and how substrates and inhibitors might interact with FeMo-cofactor would be self-evident once such a model became available. This prediction, however, was not fulfilled, and a variety of mutually exclusive models for substrate binding have been proposed. These models, none of which has been fully established by experimental evidence, fall into two dominant categories. The first involves binding of substrate to one of the three structurally analogous [4Fe-4S] faces of FeMo-cofactor (23, 105). A variation of this model is location of the substrate-binding site within the [6Fe-3S] cage of the central waist portion of FeMo-cofactor (15). Available information that supports an Fe-based site in substrate binding and activation includes the fact that the six Fe atoms that compose the "waist" region of FeMo-cofactor are coordinately unsaturated and in unusually close proximity to each other. These features have been proposed to contribute to the possible reactivity of substrate toward one or more of the Fe atoms contained within the metal-sulfur core of FeMo-cofactor (104). Supporting this proposal has been recent analysis of nitrogenase freeze-trapped during turnover with the substrates C_2H_2 and CS_2 or the inhibitor CO. Using ENDOR spectroscopy in conjunction with isotopically labeled substrates ($^{13}CS_2$, $^{13}C_2H_2$, or ^{13}CO), insights into the nature of bound intermediates have been obtained (21, 62, 63, 87, 96). In the case of CO, which is the best studied of the three molecules examined, the studies have uniquely pointed to the involvement of CO-Fe interactions (21, 62, 87). An argument against the involvement of a specific [4Fe-4S] face during substrate binding is that each of three faces is tightly packed within the MoFe protein by amino acid side chains that provide the first shell of noncovalent interactions with FeMo-cofactor (see Figure 6; see color insert). Thus, there is no obvious access site for substrate to any of the three [4Fe-4S] faces.

The second dominant model for substrate binding involves the Mo atom. This model has historical origins in the "Chatt" cycle that was proposed many years ago and describes a possible pathway for binding and sequential reduction of dinitrogen at the Mo site (85). This model finds some support in Mo-based chemistry and by the fact that the Mo atom is in close proximity to a pool of water molecules situated between FeMo-cofactor and the P-cluster. These water molecules are attractive candidates for providing the source of protons necessary for substrate reduction and perhaps in providing a pathway for electron and proton transfer between the Mo atom and the P-cluster. An argument against the direct involvement of Mo in substrate binding is that it is coordinately saturated in the resting state. Also, inspection of the structural model indicates that there does not appear to be adequate space for substrate access to the Mo site. An interesting suggestion that circumvents these problems is that the 2-carboxylate group of homocitrate might act as a tethered leaving group whose movement serves to provide both substrate access and a means for electron and proton shuttling.

The models for substrate binding suggested so far, based primarily on theoretical and chemical considerations of the isolated FeMo-cofactor structure, are provocative and could provide a rational basis for development of a chemical system for dinitrogen reduction. Nevertheless, it seems unlikely that characterization of the chemical reactivity of isolated FeMo-cofactor will necessarily provide a definitive answer in the short term about where and how substrate is bound during catalysis. The chemical synthesis of FeMo-cofactor has not yet been achieved. Thus, analysis of the chemical reactivity of isolated FeMo-cofactor under different conditions is limited because material used for such analyses is scarce as it must be isolated from the purified protein. Also amino acid substitution studies discussed below have shown that the polypeptide is an active participant in the catalytic process. It is clear from many studies that one or more electrons must be accumulated within the MoFe protein before substrate can be bound to the active site (10). In this regard, an interesting feature of both dominant models for substrate binding is that they appear to demand rearrangement of the FeMo-cofactor itself, and/or an alteration in its interaction with the polypeptide matrix. An obvious conjecture that emerges is that an important role of the FeMo-cofactor protein environment is to promote formation and stabilization of an FeMo-cofactor form that is competent for substrate interaction. Thus, from the mechanistic view, the value of theoretical models for substrate binding is that they should provide a basis for predicting how and which changes within the FeMo-cofactor environment might impact the structure and reactivity of the catalytic site. It should then be possible to test such predictions by amino acid substitution studies and kinetic methods.

Amino Acid Substitution Studies

Amino acid substitution approaches were developed in order to probe and alter the catalytic features of nitrogenase as an avenue to gain mechanistic insight even before a structural model was available (27, 37, 50, 101, 102). These studies were remarkably successful in predicting those residues that provide the coordinating ligands to the P-cluster and FeMo-cofactor, as well as in predicting some features of the noncovalent interactions between FeMo-cofactor and certain MoFe protein amino acid residues. However, even now with a structural model in hand, studies of this sort have provided very little mechanistic insight. One aspect of catalysis for which amino acid substitution studies have provided information is the nature of the interaction among nitrogenase substrates and inhibitors and recent results along these lines are described below.

In addition to its natural substrate, dinitrogen, nitrogenase is able to reduce a variety of other substrates. This topic has been reviewed previously (9, 11) and therefore a comprehensive description of the interaction among all nitrogenase substrates and inhibitors is not described here. Instead, we describe the interaction among the substrates: dinitrogen, acetylene, protons, and the effect of the inhibitor CO as they relate to amino acid substitution studies. The interaction among nitrogenase substrates and inhibitors is very complex and not yet fully understood. Some of the salient features with respect to substrate reduction are as follows. (*a*) The rate at which electrons and protons are delivered to substrates is referred to as flux. Flux can be controlled by adjusting the ratio of the Fe protein to the MoFe protein in in vitro assays. High flux refers to a high ratio of Fe protein to the MoFe protein whereas low flux refers to a low ratio. (*b*) Flux is independent of the substrate that is being reduced. (*c*) Under optimal catalytic conditions the reduction of one molecule of dinitrogen, which requires six electrons and six protons, involves the obligate reduction of two protons to yield one molecule of H_2. (*d*) Nitrogenase is able to reduce acetylene by two electrons and two protons to yield ethylene (28, 100). Unlike dinitrogen, acetylene is theoretically able to completely suppress the reduction of protons (92). (*e*) Dinitrogen is a weak competitive inhibitor of acetylene reduction but acetylene is an effective noncompetitive inhibitor of dinitrogen reduction (28, 48, 92). (*f*) In the absence of any other substrate, nitrogenase diverts all electron flow towards proton reduction. (*g*) CO is not a substrate but is a powerful noncompetitive inhibitor of the reduction of dinitrogen and acetylene (48). In the presence of CO, all electron flow is diverted to proton reduction regardless of whether any other substrate is present. (*h*) Hydrogen gas is a competitive inhibitor of dinitrogen reduction but does not inhibit the reduction of any other nitrogenase substrate (48). These observations, made almost three decades ago, raise a number of fundamental questions, most of which have not yet been answered. For example, does the apparently obligate evolution of one H_2 molecule for each dinitrogen reduction event, but not other reduction activities, mean that a protonated form of FeMo-cofactor is necessary for the activation of dinitrogen binding but not the binding of other substrates?

The fact that there are a variety of different, mutually inhibitory, nitrogenase substrates raises the question of whether these substrates compete for occupancy of the same site or bind to different sites and merely compete for the available electrons. Amino acid substitutions have provided some insight on this issue. In the crystallographic model, the epsilon-nitrogen atom of the imidazole ring of α-His[195] provides a NH-S hydrogen bond to one of the three sulfide ions that bridge the FeMo-cofactor subclusters. Substitution of this residue by glutamine results in an altered MoFe protein that does not appreciably reduce dinitrogen ($<1\%$ activity) but still remains capable of reducing protons and acetylene at near wild-type rates (51). Determination of the X-ray structure of the altered MoFe protein reveals that the NH-S hydrogen bond normally provided by α-His[195] is replaced by a similar interaction with the glutamine side chain and that the global structure of the altered protein is otherwise unperturbed (108). The interesting feature of the

α-Gln^{195} protein is that, even though it is not reduced, dinitrogen remains an inhibitor of both proton and acetylene reduction. Our interpretation of these results is that acetylene, protons, and dinitrogen must occupy the same or closely overlapping binding sites within the MoFe protein. Another insight provided by characterization of the α-Gln^{195} MoFe protein is that electron capture by the substrate during turnover appears to play an important role in controlling the direction of electron flow during nitrogenase catalysis. This suggestion is supported by the observation that, even though the altered protein cannot reduce dinitrogen, the presence of dinitrogen uncouples MgATP hydrolysis from substrate reduction (51). In other words, the presence of dinitrogen inhibits the rate of proton reduction for the altered α-Gln^{195} MoFe protein but does not inhibit the rate of MgATP hydrolysis. An interpretation of this result is that, once the MoFe protein becomes saturated with electrons that cannot be captured by substrate, the two component proteins retain their ability to associate and effect MgATP hydrolysis but are unable to achieve productive intercomponent electron transfer. The possibility that electron flow is ultimately controlled by the substrate acting as an electron sink is also supported by the observation that MoFe protein lacking FeMo-cofactor (i.e. apo-MoFe protein) is unable to reduce any substrate but is able to stimulate Fe protein-dependent MgATP hydrolysis (19).

Because it was possible to isolate an altered nitrogenase able to reduce acetylene and protons, but not dinitrogen, we wondered whether it would be possible to isolate an altered nitrogenase that is affected in its ability to reduce acetylene but is able to reduce dinitrogen normally. The rationale for searching for such an altered protein was based on the following. The effect of any amino acid substitution on substrate reduction catalyzed by the MoFe protein could arise from: (*a*) a perturbation in proton or electron delivery to the active site (flux effects), (*b*) an inability of the enzyme to achieve the appropriate redox state, or (*c*) alteration in a particular substrate's ability to access the active site. Thus, because the reduction of dinitrogen is more demanding than reduction of acetylene in terms of both flux and redox state, an altered MoFe protein that is defective in acetylene reduction but not dinitrogen reduction must be specifically able to discriminate between the binding of acetylene and dinitrogen. It follows then that an amino acid substitution leading to such discrimination should provide an indication of the physical location of the substrate reduction site. In order to obtain an altered MoFe protein that was affected in acetylene reduction, but not dinitrogen reduction, a mutant strain that could continue to fix dinitrogen when grown in the presence of acetylene (a powerful inhibitor of physiological dinitrogen reduction) was isolated. This mutant strain produces an altered MoFe protein for which the α-Gly^{69} residue is substituted by serine (17). As expected, the altered MoFe protein was normal for dinitrogen reduction but was severely impaired for acetylene reduction. Biochemical characterization of the α-Ser^{69} substituted MoFe protein led to three interesting observations. First, the α-Ser^{69} substitution results in a 20-fold increase in K_m for acetylene reduction. Second, acetylene was converted from a noncompetitive to a competetive inhibitor of dinitrogen reduction. Third, CO was converted from a noncompetitive inhibitor of the reduction of all substrates, except protons, to a competetive inhibitor (20). One interpretation of these results is that in the normal enzyme there are two acetylene-binding and two CO-binding sites that are catalytically relevant but only one dinitrogen reduction site. These sites have been designated as site 1 and site 2. Site 1 is proposed to be a high-affinity acetylene-binding site to which both acetylene and CO bind but dinitrogen does not bind. Site 2 is a low-affinity acetylene-binding site to which both CO and dinitrogen also bind.

Speculations on the Nature of the Substrate Reduction Site

What is the relationship between site 1 and site 2 within the MoFe protein? One possibility is that they represent two physically independent sites. The other possibility is that they represent essentially the same entity but at different oxidation states within the enzyme and that dinitrogen can access one state but not the other. This possibility is shown schematically in Figure 7. It seems unlikely that site 1 and site 2 represent completely different physical locations for the following reasons: First, if there were two completely independent binding sites then dinitrogen should be a noncompetitive inhibitor of acetylene reduction. However, dinitrogen is a weak, competitive inhibitor of acetylene reduction (92). Second, for the altered α-Gln^{195} MoFe protein, dinitrogen remains a competitive inhibitor for acetylene

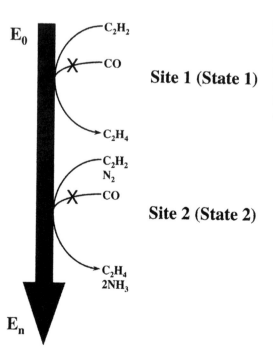

Figure 7   Nitrogenase catalytic states. Illustration of the two site/state model described in the text. The arrow indicates progressively more reduced states of the MoFe protein, with more oxidized forms at the top.

reduction even though dinitrogen cannot be reduced (51). Thus, as mentioned above, dinitrogen does not exert its inhibitory effect on acetylene reduction by competing for reducing equivalents but by preventing the binding of acetylene to the active site. In contrast, a model where acetylene (or CO) is able to access a more oxidized form of the MoFe protein than does dinitrogen is consistent with all of the available information. For example, as originally proposed by Davis and colleagues (25, 64), the noncompetitive nature of acetylene with respect to dini-trogen reduction can be considered a special case of noncompetitive inhibition. Here, acetylene acts as a noncompetitive inhibitor by binding to the enzyme at a redox state that is not yet sufficiently reduced for dinitrogen to bind. In this way acetylene effectively lowers the pool of available active sites and thereby exhibits a noncompetitive pattern for inhibition of dinitrogen reduction. In contrast, as shown in Figure 7, binding of dinitrogen will be a competitive inhibitor of acetylene bind-ing but only when the enzyme reaches a sufficiently reduced state to accommodate dinitrogen reduction. In this model, binding and reduction of acetylene at the more oxidized state(s) unavailable to dinitrogen binding is not affected by dinitrogen. Consequently, dinitrogen is only a very weak inhibitor that exhibits a competitive pattern of inhibition of acetylene reduction. The two-state model is also consis-tent with what is observed for the altered α-Ser^{69} MoFe protein. In this case, it is suggested that the more oxidized state to which acetylene and CO are able to bind in the unaltered enzyme is no longer accessible. This situation results in the mutually competitive pattern for all substrates and inhibitors that is experimentally observed for the α-Ser^{69} MoFe protein.

Speculations on the Location of the Substrate Binding Site

The ability to isolate an altered MoFe protein that is affected in acetylene reduc-tion but not dinitrogen reduction also impacts our consideration of structural dyna-mics that might occur at the active site during catalysis. If the two-state model is correct, then it should not be possible to isolate an altered MoFe protein unable to bind substrates at a relatively oxidized state but capable of binding substrates at a more reduced state, unless there are structural constraints that differentiate acces-sibility to these two states. In other words, it appears that the α-Ser^{69} substitution prevents the access of substrates to the active site at one oxidation state but not another, which must mean that there is a structural rearrangement either in the FeMo-cofactor or its polypeptide environment as a consequence of changes in redox state. Inspection of the MoFe protein structure (88) and the position of the α-Gly^{69} residue provide some basis for speculation on how this might occur. The α-Gly^{69} residue is located on a short helix that spans from the P-cluster coordinat-ing residue α-Cys^{62} to the α-Val^{70} residue (Figure 8; see color insert). The α-Val^{70} residue is one of two residues, the other being α-Arg^{96}, that cap one of the three structurally identical [4Fe-4S] faces within the central region of the FeMo-cofactor structure. In the *A. vinelandii* structure, the α-Arg^{96} residue is putatively hydrogen-bonded to a bridging sulfide within FeMo-cofactor and is also connected to the

P-cluster through a short sequence ending in the bridging P-cluster ligand provided by α-Cys[88]. α-Cys[88] is the same residue that participates in the redox-dependent structural rearrangement that occurs within the P-cluster. It is easy, therefore, to envision that redox-dependent structural changes that occur within the P-cluster could be directly communicated to the FeMo-cofactor through either or both α-Val[70] and α-Arg[96]. Such movement could be facilitated by the location of glycine residues that immediately precede both α-Val[70] and α-Arg[96]. We have proposed that movement of either or both α-Val[70] and α-Arg[96] could be involved in opening a site for substrate binding. Our interpretation of the kinetic consequences of substituting α-Gly[69] by serine is that this substitution restricts the redox-dependent movement of α-Val[70], thereby preventing substrate access at the more oxidized states. The effect of the α-Ser[69] substitution is thought to arise from restricted flexibility of the short helix, rather than as a consequence of the substituting side chain, because substitution by cysteine, proline, glutamate, or aspartate at this position all result in the same effect as substitution by serine. A simplistic inference that emerges from this model is that the [4Fe-4S] face approached by α-Val[70], α-Arg[96], and α-His[195] provides the site of substrate binding, and we favor this model. However, two other issues must be considered before direct participation of the Mo atom in substrate binding can be dismissed. First, if there is a redox-dependent rearrangement in the FeMo-cofactor polypeptide environment, or perhaps even the FeMo-cofactor structure, there is no way to anticipate whether Mo becomes accessible upon such rearrangement. Second, both α-Val[70] and α-Arg[96] are in relatively close proximity to the Mo atom and therefore any movement of their side chains could impact substrate accessibility to the Mo atom, as well as the previously proposed movement of the 2-carboxylate group of homocitrate. Finally, we need to keep in mind the suggestion that partially reduced substrates might shuttle from an Fe site to the Mo site (22).

SUMMARY AND FUTURE PROSPECTS

Nitrogenase represents one of the most complex nucleotide switch-dependent enzyme systems. This remarkable enzyme uses the binding and hydrolysis of MgATP at one end of an electron delivery protein, the Fe protein, to time and control substrate binding and reduction events that occur more than 30 Å away within the MoFe protein. These events are initiated by nucleotide-induced conformational changes within the Fe protein that lead to association of the two protein partners. Subsequent to complex formation, intercomponent electron transfer and MoFe protein-induced MgATP hydrolysis occur, ultimately leading to component protein dissociation. Multiple rounds of these events ensure that the multiple electrons necessary for substrate reduction become accumulated within the MoFe protein. It now seems likely, although not yet proven, that interaction of the component proteins also leads to conformational changes within the MoFe protein, and perhaps both of its associated metalloclusters, so that electron accumulation and substrate accessibility are facilitated. The structural dynamics of this process, as well as the details of substrate binding, remain challenging issues that continue to be debated and explored by a combination of genetic, biophysical, and kinetic approaches.

ACKNOWLEDGMENTS

The authors thank the National Science Foundation (MCB 9722937 to LCS and MCB 9630127 to DRD) and the National Institutes of Health (R01-GM59087) for support of their work on nitrogenase.

Visit the Annual Reviews home page at www.AnnualReviews.org

LITERATURE CITED

1. Angove HC, Uyoo SJ, Burgess BK, Munck E. 1997. Mossbauer and EPR evidence for an all-ferrous Fe_4-S_4 cluster with $S = 4$ in the Fe protein of nitrogenase. *J. Am. Chem. Soc.* 119:8730–31

2. Angove HC, Yoo SJ, Munck E, Burgess BK. 1998. An all-ferrous state of the Fe protein of nitrogenase—interaction with nucleotides and electron transfer to the MoFe protein. *J. Biol. Chem.* 273:26330–37

3. Bolin JT, Campobasso N, Muchmore SW, Minor W, Morgan TV, Mortenson LE. 1993. Structure of the nitrogenase MoFe protein: spatial distribution of the intrinsic metal atoms determined by X-ray anomalous scattering. In *New Horizons in Nitrogen Fixation*, ed. R Palacios, J Mora, WE Newton, pp. 89–94. Dordrecht: Kluwer

4. Bolin JT, Campobasso N, Muchmore SW, Morgan TV, Mortenson LE. 1993. The stucture and environment of the metal clusters in the nitrogenase MoFe protein from *Clostridium pasteurianum*. See Ref. 109a, pp. 186–95

5. Bolin JT, Ronco AE, Morgan TV, Mortenson LE, Xuong NH. 1993. The unusual metal clusters of nitrogenase: structural features revealed by x-ray anomalous diffraction studies of the MoFe protein from *Clostridium pasteurianum*. *Proc. Natl. Acad. Sci. USA* 90:1078–82

6. Bolin JT, Ronco AE, Mortenson LE, Morgan TV, Williamson M, Xuong NH. 1990.

Structure of the nitrogenase MoFe protein: spatial distribution of the intrinsic metal atoms determined by X-ray anomalous scattering. In *Nitrogen Fixation: Achievements and Objectives*, ed. PM Gresshoff, LE Roth, G Stacey, WE Newton, pp. 117–22. New York: Chapman & Hall

7. Brill WJ. 1977. Biological nitrogen fixation. *Sci. Am.* 236:68–81

8. Brunger AT, Milburn MV, Tong L, DeVos AM, Jancarik J, et al. 1990. Crystal structure of an active form of RAS protein, a complex of a GTP analog and the HRAS p21 catalytic domain. *Proc. Natl. Acad. Sci. USA* 87:4849–53

9. Burgess BK. 1985. Substrate reactions of nitrogenase. See Ref. 108a, pp. 161–220

10. Burgess BK, Lowe DJ. 1996. The mechanism of molybdenum nitrogenase. *Chem. Rev.* 96:2983–3011

11. Burris RH. 1979. Inhibition. In *A Treatise on Dinitrogen Fixation, Sections I and II: Inorganic and Physical Chemistry and Biochemistry*, ed. RWF Hardy, F Bottemely, RC Burns, pp. 569–604. New York: Wiley & Sons

12. Burris RH. 1991. Nitrogenase. *J. Biol. Chem.* 266:9339–42

13. Chan JM, Christiansen J, Dean DR, Seefeldt LC. 1999. Spectroscopic evidence for changes in the redox state of the nitrogenase P-cluster during turnover. *Biochemistry* 38:5779–85

14. Chan JM, Ryle MJ, Seefeldt LC. 1999. Evidence that MgATP accelerates primary electron transfer in a *Clostridium pasteurianum* Fe protein–*Azotobacter vinelandii* MoFe protein nitrogenase tight complex. *J. Biol. Chem.* 274:17593–98

15. Chan MK, Kim J, Rees DC. 1993. The nitrogenase FeMo-cofactor and P-cluster pair: 2.2 Å resolution structures. *Science* 260:792–94

16. Chen L, Gavini N, Tsuruta H, Eliezer D, Burgess BK, et al. 1994. MgATP-induced conformational changes in the iron protein from *Azotobacter vinelandii*, as studied by small-angle X-ray scattering. *J. Biol. Chem.* 269:3290–94

17. Christiansen J, Cash VL, Seefeldt LC, Dean DR. 2000. Isolation and characterization of an acetylene-resistant nitrogenase. *J. Biol. Chem.* 275:11459–64

18. Christiansen J, Chan JM, Seefeldt LC, Dean DR. 2000. The role of the MoFe protein α-125^{Phe} and β-125^{Phe} residues in *Azotobacter vinelandii* MoFe protein–Fe protein interaction. *J. Inorg. Biochem.* 80:195–204

19. Christiansen J, Goodwin PJ, Lanzilotta WN, Seefeldt LC, Dean DR. 1998. Catalytic and biophysical properties of a nitrogenase apo-MoFe protein produced by a *nifB*-deletion mutant of *Azotobacter vinelandii*. *Biochemistry* 37:12611–23

20. Christiansen J, Seefeldt LC, Dean DR. 2000. Competitive substrate and inhibitor interactions at the physiologically relevant active site of nitrogenase. *J. Biol. Chem.* 275:36104–7

21. Christie PD, Lee HI, Cameron LM, Hales BJ, Orme-Johnson WH, Hoffman BM. 1996. Identification of the CO-binding cluster in nitrogenase MoFe protein by ENDOR of ^{57}Fe isotopomers. *J. Am. Chem. Soc.* 118:8707–9

21a. Cole JA, Ferguson S, eds. 1988. *The Nitrogen and Sulfur Cycles*. Cambridge, MA: Univ. Press

22. Coucouvanis D. 1996. Functional analogs for the reduction of certain nitrogenase substrates. Are multiple sites within the Fe/Mo/S active center involved in the 6 e-reduction of N_2? *J. Biol. Inorg. Chem.* 1:594–600

23. Dance IG. 1994. The binding and reduciton of dinitrogen at an Fe_4 face of the FeMo cluster of nitrgenase. *Aust. J. Chem.* 47:979–90

24. Davidson VL. 1996. Unraveling the kinetic complexity of interprotein electron transfer reactions. *Biochemistry* 35:14035–39

25. Davis LC, Wang Y-L. 1980. In vivo and in vitro kinetics of nitrogenase. *J. Bacteriol.* 141:1230–38

26. Dean DR, Bolin JT, Zheng L. 1993. Nitrogenase metallclusters: structures, organization, and synthesis. *J. Bacteriol.* 175:6737–44

27. Dean DR, Setterquist RA, Brigle KE, Scott DJ, Laird NF, Newton WE. 1990. Evidence that conserved residues Cys-62 and Cys-154 within the *Azotobacter vinelandii* nitrogenase MoFe protein α-subunit are essential for nitrogenase activity but conserved residues His-38 and Cys-88 are not. *Mol. Microbiol.* 4:1505–12

28. Dilworth MJ. 1966. Acetylene reduction by nitrogen-fixing preparations from *Clostridium pasteurianum*. *Biochim. Biophys. Acta* 127:285–94

29. Duyvis MG, Wassink H, Haaker H. 1998. Nitrogenase of *Azotobacter vinelandii*: kinetic analysis of the Fe protein redox cycle. *Biochemistry* 37:17345–54

30. Duyvis MG, Wassink H, Haaker H. 1994. Pre-steady-state MgATP-dependent proton production and electron transfer by nitrgenase from *Azotobacter vinelandii*. *Eur. J. Biochem.* 225:881–90

31. Duyvis MG, Wassink H, Haaker H. 1996. Formation and characterization of a transition state complex of *Azotobacter vinelandii* nitrogenase. *FEBS Lett.* 380:233–36

32. Eady RR. 1996. Structure-function relationships of alternative nitrogenases. *Chem. Rev.* 96:3013–30

33. Eady RR, Robson RL, Smith BE. 1988. Alternative and conventional nitrogenases. See Ref. 21a, pp. 363–82

34. Erickson JA, Nyborg AC, Johnson JL, Truscott SM, Gunn A, et al. 1999. Enhanced efficiency of ATP hydrolysis during nitrogenase catalysis utilizing reductants that form the all-ferrous redox state of the Fe protein. *Biochemistry* 38:14279–85

35. Ferguson SJ. 1988. The redox reactions of the nitrogen and sulphur cycles. See Ref. 21a, pp. 1–30

36. Georgiadis MM, Komiya H, Chakrabarti P, Woo D, Kornuc JJ, Rees DC. 1992. Crystallographic structure of the nitrogenase iron protein from *Azotobacter vinelandii*. *Science* 257:1653–59

37. Govezensky D, Zamir A. 1989. Structure-function relationship in the a subunit of *Klebsiella pneumoniae* nitrogenase MoFe protein from analysis of *nifD* mutants. *J. Bacteriol.* 171:5729–35

38. Hageman RV, Burris RH. 1978. Nitrogenase and nitrogenase reductase associate and dissociate with each catalytic cycle. *Proc. Natl. Acad. Sci. USA* 75:2699–702

39. Hagen WR. 1992. EPR spectroscopy of iron-sulfur proteins. In *Advances in Inorganic Chemistry: Iron-Sulfur Proteins*, ed. AG Sykes, R Cammack, pp. 165–222. New York: Academic

40. Hagen WR, Eady RR, Dunham WR, Haaker H. 1985. A novel $S = 3/2$ EPR signal associated with native Fe proteins of nitrogenase. *FEBS Lett.* 189:250–54

41. Hagen WR, Wassink H, Eady RR, Smith BE, Haaker H. 1987. Quantitative EPR of an $S = 7/2$ system in thionine-oxidized MoFe proteins of nitrogenase. A redefinition of the P-cluster concept. *Eur. J. Biochem.* 169:457–65

42. Hausinger RP, Howard JB. 1983. Thiol reactivity of the nitrogenase Fe-protein from *Azotobacter vinelandii*. *J. Biol. Chem.* 258:3486–92

43. Hawkes TR, McLean PA, Smith BE. 1984. Nitrogenase from *nifV* mutants of *Klebsiella pneumoniae* contains an altered form of the iron-molybdenum cofactor. *Biochem. J.* 217:317–21

44. Hofmann-Findeklee C, Gadkari D, Meyer O. 2000. Superoxide-dependent nitrogen fixation. In *Nitrogen Fixation: From Molecules to Crop Productivity*, ed. FO Pedrosa, M Hungaria, MG Yates, WE Newton, pp. 23–30. Boston: Kluwer

45. Howard JB, Davis R, Moldenhauer B, Cash VL, Dean D. 1989. Fe-S cluster ligands are the only cysteines required for nitrogenase Fe-protein activities. *J. Biol. Chem.* 264:11270–74

46. Howard JB, Rees DC. 1994. Nitrogenase: a nucleotide-dependent molecular switch. *Annu. Rev. Biochem.* 63:235–64

47. Howard JB, Rees DC. 1996. Structural basis of biological nitrogen fixation. *Chem. Rev.* 96:2965–82

48. Hwang JC, Chen CH, Burris RH. 1973. Inhibition of nitrogenase-catalyzed reductions. *Biochim. Biophys. Acta* 292:256–70

48a. Jang SB, Seefeldt LC, Peters JW. 2000. Insights into nucleotide signal transduction in nitrogenase: structure of an iron protein with MgADP bound. *Biochemistry* 39:14745–52

49. Jurnak F. 1985. Structure of the GDP domain of EF-Tu and location of the amino acids homologous to ras oncogene proteins. *Science* 230:32–36

50. Kent HM, Ioannidis I, Gormal C, Smith BE, Buck M. 1989. Site-Directed mutagenesis of the *Klebsiella pneumonia* nitrogenase. *Biochem. J.* 264:257–64

51. Kim CH, Newton WE, Dean DR. 1995. Role of the MoFe protein alpha-subunit histidine-195 residue in FeMo-cofactor binding and nitrogenase catalysis. *Biochemistry* 34:2798–808

52. Kim J, Rees DC. 1992. Crystallographic

structure and functional implications of the nitrogenase molybdenum iron protein from *Azotobacter vinelandii. Nature* 360:553–60

53. Kim J, Rees DC. 1992. Structural models for the metal centers in the nitrogenase molybdenum-iron protein. *Science* 257:1677–82

54. Kim J, Woo D, Rees DC. 1993. X-ray crystal structure of the nitrogenase molybdenum-iron protein from *Clostridium pasteurianum* at 3.0-Å resolution. *Biochemistry* 32:7104–15

55. Koonin EV. 1993. A superfamily of AT-Pases with diverse functions containing either classical or deviant ATP-binding motifs. *J. Mol. Biol.* 229:1165–74

56. Kraulis PJ. 1991. MOLSCRIPT: a program to produce both detailed and schematic plots of protein structures. *J. Appl. Crystallogr.* 24:946–50

57. Lanzilotta WN, Christiansen J, Dean DR, Seefeldt LC. 1998. Evidence for coupled electron and proton transfer in the [8Fe-7S] cluster of nitrogenase. *Biochemistry* 37:11376–84

58. Lanzilotta WN, Fisher K, Seefeldt LC. 1997. Evidence for electron transfer-dependent formation of a nitrogenase iron protein-molybdenum-iron protein tight complex: the role of aspartate 39. *J. Biol. Chem.* 272:4157–65

59. Lanzilotta WN, Holz RC, Seefeldt LC. 1995. Proton NMR investigation of the $[4Fe-4S]^{1+}$ cluster environment of nitrogenase iron protein from *Azotobacter vinelandii*: Defining nucleotide-induced conformational changes. *Biochemistry* 34:15646–53

60. Lanzilotta WN, Parker VD, Seefeldt LC. 1998. Electron transfer in nitrogenase analyzed by Marcus theory: evidence for gating by MgATP. *Biochemistry* 37:399–407

61. Lanzilotta WN, Seefeldt LC. 1997. Changes in the midpoint potentials of the nitrogenase metal centers as a result of iron protein-molybdenum-iron protein com-

plex formation. *Biochemistry* 36:12976–83

62. Lee HI, Cameron LM, Hales BJ, Hoffman BM. 1997. CO binding to the FeMo cofactor of CO-inhibited nitrogenase:^{13}CO and ^{1}H Q-band ENDOR investigation. *J. Am. Chem. Soc.* 119:10121–26

63. Lee HI, Sorlie M, Christiansen J, Song R, Dean DR, et al. 2000. Characterization of an intermediate in the reduction of acetylene by nitrogenase α-Gln195 MoFe protein by Q-band EPR and ^{13}C, ^{1}H ENDOR. *J. Am. Chem. Soc.* 122:5582–87

64. Liang J, Burris RH. 1988. Interactions among N_2, N_2O, and C_2H_2 as substrates and inhibitors of nitrogenase from *Azotobacter vinelandii. Biochemistry* 27:6726–32

65. Lindahl PA, Gorelick NJ, Münck E, Orme-Johnson WH. 1987. EPR and Mössbauer studies of nucleotide-bound nitrogenase iron protein from *Azotobacter vinelandii. J. Biol. Chem.* 262:14945–53

66. Ljones T, Burris RH. 1978. Nitrogenase: the reaction between the Fe protein and bathophenanthrolinedisulfonate as a probe for interactions with MgATP. *Biochemistry* 17:1866–72

67. Lowe DJ, Ashby GA, Brune M, Knights H, Webb MR, Thorneley RNF. 1995. ATP hydrolysis and energy transduction by nitrogenase. In *Nitrogen Fixation: Fundamentals and Applications*, ed. IA Tikhonovich, NA Provorov, VI Romanov, WE Newton, pp. 103–8. Boston: Kluwer

68. Lowe DJ, Fisher K, Thorneley RNF. 1993. *Klebsiella pneumoniae* nitrogenase: pre-steady state absorbance changes show that redox changes occur in the MoFe protein that depend on substrate and component protein ratio; a role for P-centres in reducing nitrogen? *Biochem. J.* 292:93–98

69. Lowery RG, Saari LL, Ludden PW. 1986. Reversible regulation of the nitrogenase iron protein from *Rhodospirillum rubrum* by ADP-ribosylation in vitro. *J. Bacteriol.* 166:513–18

70. Ludden PW, Shah WK, Roberts GP, Homer

M, Allen R, et al. 1993. Biosynthesis of the iron-molybdenum cofactor of nitrogenase. See Ref. 109a, pp. 196–215

71. Ma L, Brosius MA, Burgess BK. 1996. Construction of a form of the MoFe protein of nitrogenase that accepts electrons from the Fe protein but does not reduce substrate. *J. Biol. Chem.* 271:10528–32

72. Marcus RA, Sutin N. 1985. Electron transfers in chemistry and biology. *Biochim. Biophys. Acta* 811:265–322

73. May HD, Dean DR, Newton WE. 1991. Altered nitrogenase MoFe proteins from *Azotobacter vinelandii*. *Biochem. J.* 277:457–64

74. Mayer SM, Lawson DM, Gormal CA, Roe SM, Smith BE. 1999. New insights into structure-function relationships in nitrogenase: a 1.6 Å resolution X-ray crystallographic study of *Klebsiella pneumoniae* MoFe-protein. *J. Mol. Biol.* 292:871–91

75. Merritt EA, Murphy MEP. 1994. Raster 3D version 2.0: a program for photorealistic molecular graphics. *Acta Crystallogr.* D50:869–73

76. Meyer J, Gaillard J, Moulis JM. 1988. Hydrogen-1 nuclear magnetic resonance of the nitrogenase iron protein (Cp2) from *Clostridium pasteurianum*. *Biochemistry* 27:6150–56

77. Mortenson LE, Zumft WG, Palmer G. 1973. Electron resonance studies on nitrogenase. 3. Function of magnesium adenosine 5-triphosphate and adenosine 5-diphosphate in catalysis by nitrogenase. *Biochim. Biophys. Acta* 292:422–35

78. Moser CC, Dutton PL. 1996. Outline of theory of protein electron transfer. In *Protein Electron Transfer*, ed. DS Bendall, pp. 1–21. Herndon, VA: BIOS Sci.

79. Orme-Johnson WH. 1985. Molecular basis of biological nitrogen fixation. *Annu. Rev. Biophys. Biophys. Chem.* 14:419–59

80. Orme-Johnson WH, Hamilton WD, Jones TL, Tso MYW, Burris RH, et al. 1972. Electron paramagnetic resonance of nitrogenase and nitrogenase components from *Clostridium pasteurianum* W5 and *Azotobacter vinelandii* OP. *Proc. Natl. Acad. Sci. USA* 69:3142–45

81. Orme-Johnson WH, Münck E. 1980. On the prosthetic groups of nitrogenase. In *Molybdenum and Molybdenum Containing Enzymes*, ed. MP Coughlan, pp. 427–38. Oxford: Pergamon

82. Peters JW, Fisher K, Dean DR. 1995. Nitrogenase structure and function: a biochemical-genetic perspective. *Annu. Rev. Microbiol.* 49:335–66

83. Peters JW, Fisher K, Newton WE, Dean DR. 1995. Involvement of the P cluster in intramolecular electron transfer within the nitrogenase MoFe protein. *J. Biol. Chem.* 270:27007–13

84. Peters JW, Stowell MHB, Soltis SM, Finnegan MG, Johnson MK, Rees DC. 1997. Redox-dependent structural changes in the nitrogenase P-cluster. *Biochemistry* 36:1181–87

85. Pickett CJ. 1996. The Chatt cycle and the mechanism of enzymic reduction of molecular nitrogen. *J. Biol. Inorg. Chem.* 1:601–6

86. Pierik AJ, Wassink H, Haaker H, Hagen WR. 1993. Redox properties and EPR spectroscopy of the P-clusters of *Azotobacter vinelandii* MoFe protein. *Eur. J. Biochem.* 212:51–61

87. Pollock CR, Lee H-I, Cameron LM, DeRose VJ, Hales BJ, et al. 1995. Investigation of CO bound to inhibited forms of nitrogenase MoFe protein by ^{13}C ENDOR. *J. Am. Chem. Soc.* 117:8686–87

88. Rees DC, Chan MK, Kim J. 1993. Structure and function of nitrogenase. *Adv. Inorg. Chem.* 40:89–119

89. Rees DC, Schindelin H, Kisker C, Schlessman J, Peters JW, et al. 1998. Complex structures of nitrogenase. In *Biological Nitrogen Fixation for the 21st Century*, ed. C Elmerich, A Kondorosi, WE Newton, pp. 11–16. Boston: Kluwer

90. Renner KA, Howard JB. 1996. Aluminum fluoride inhibition of nitrogenase: stabilization of a nucleotide-Fe-protein-MoFe

protein complex. *Biochemistry* 35:5353–58

91. Ribbe MW, Bursey EH, Burgess BK. 2000. Identification of an Fe protein residue (Glu 146) of *Azotobacter vinelandii* nitrogenase that is specifically involved in FeMo cofactor insertion. *J. Biol. Chem.* 275:17631–38

92. Rivera-Ortiz JM, Burris RH. 1975. Interactions among substrates and inhibitors of nitrogenase. *J. Bacteriol.* 123:537–45

93. Robson RL. 1984. Identification of possible adenine nucleotide binding sites in nitrogenase Fe- and MoFe-proteins by amino acid sequence comparison. *FEBS Lett.* 173:394–98

94. Ryle MJ, Lanzilotta WN, Mortenson LE, Watt GD, Seefeldt LC. 1995. Evidence for a central role of lysine 15 of *Azotobacter vinelandii* nitrogenase iron protein in nucleotide binding and protein conformational changes. *J. Biol. Chem.* 270:13112–17

95. Ryle MJ, Lanzilotta WN, Seefeldt LC, Scarrow RC, Jensen GM. 1996. Circular dichroism and X-ray spectroscopies of *Azotobacter vinelandii* nitrogenase iron protein: MgATP and MgADP induced protein conformational changes affecting the [4Fe-4S] cluster and characterization of a [2Fe-2S] form. *J. Biol. Chem.* 271:1551–57

96. Ryle MJ, Lee HI, Seefeldt LC, Hoffman BM. 2000. Nitrogenase reduction of carbon disulfide: freeze-quench EPR and ENDOR evidence for three sequential intermediates with cluster-bound carbon moieties. *Biochemistry* 39:1114–19

97. Ryle MJ, Seefeldt LC. 1996. Elucidation of a MgATP signal transduction pathway in the nitrogenase iron protein: formation of a conformation resembling the MgATP-bound state by protein engineering. *Biochemistry* 35:4766–75

98. Schindelin H, Kisker C, Schlessman JL, Howard JB, Rees DC. 1997. Structure of ADP-AlF$_4^-$ stabilized nitrogenase

complex and its implications for signal transduction. *Nature* 387:370–76

99. Schlessman JL, Woo D, Joshua-Tor L, Howard JB, Rees DC. 1998. Conformational variability in structures of the nitrogenase iron proteins from *Azotobacter vinelandii* and *Clostridium pasteurianum*. *J. Mol. Biol.* 280:669–85

100. Schöllhorn R, Burris RH. 1967. Acetylene as a competitive inhibitor of N$_2$ fixation. *Biochemistry* 58:213–16

101. Scott DJ, Dean DR, Newton WE. 1992. Nitrogenase-catalyzed ethane production and CO-sensitive hydrogen evolution from MoFe proteins having amino acid substitutions in an α-subunit FeMo cofactor-binding domain. *J. Biol. Chem.* 267:20002–10

102. Scott DJ, May HD, Newton WE, Brigle KE, Dean DR. 1990. Role for the nitrogenase MoFe protein α-subunit in FeMo-cofactor binding and catalysis. *Nature* 343:188–90

103. Seefeldt LC, Dean DR. 1997. Role of nucleotides in nitrogenase catalysis. *Acc. Chem. Res.* 30:260–66

104. Sellmann D. 1999. On the function of FeMo cofactor and competitive catalysts: chemical principles, structural blueprints, and the relevance of iron sulfur complexes for N$_2$ fixation. *Coord. Chem. Rev.* 190:607–27

105. Sellmann D, Sutter J. 1996. Elementary reactions, structure-function relationships, and the potential relevance of low molecular weight metal-sulfur ligand complexes to biological N$_2$ fixation. *J. Biol. Inorg. Chem.* 1:587–93

106. Shah VK, Brill WJ. 1977. Isolation of an iron-molybdenum cofactor from nitrogenase. *Proc. Natl. Acad. Sci. USA* 74:3249–53

107. Smith BE, Lowe DJ, Bray RC. 1973. Studies by electron paramagnetic resonance on the catalytic mechanism of nitrogenase of *Klebsiella pneumoniae*. *Biochem. J.* 135:331–41

108. Sørlie M, Christiansen J, Lemon BJ, Peters JW, Dean DR, Hales BJ. 2000. Mechanistic features and structure of the nitrogenase α-195Gln MoFe protein. *J. Am. Chem. Soc.* In press

108a. Spiro TG, ed. 1985. *Metal Ions in Biology: Molybdenum Enzyme.* New York: Wiley

109. Stephens PJ, McKenna CE, Smith BE, Nguyen HT, McKenna MC, et al. 1979. Circular dichroism and magnetic circular dichroism of nitrogenase proteins. *Proc. Natl. Acad. Sci. USA* 76:2585–89

109a. Stiefel EI, Coucouvanis D, Newton WE, eds. 1993. *Molybdenum Enzymes, Cofactors and Model Systems.* Washington, DC: Am. Chem. Soc.

110. Story RM, Steitz TA. 1992. Structure of the recA protein-ADP complex. *Nature* 355:374–76

111. Surerus KK, Hendrich MP, Christie PD, Rottgardt D, Orme-Johnson WH, Münck E. 1992. Mössbauer and integer-spin EPR of the oxidized P-clusters of nitrogenase: P^{ox} is a non-kramers system with a nearly degenerate ground doublet. *J. Am. Chem. Soc.* 114:8579–90

112. Thorneley RNF. 1992. Nitrogenase of *Klebsiella pneumoniae*: a MgATP hydrolysing energy transduction system with similarities to actomyosin and p21 ras. *Philos. Trans. R. Soc. London Ser. B* 336:73–82

113. Thorneley RNF, Ashby GA. 1989. Oxidation of nitrogenase iron protein by dioxygen without inactivation could contribute to high respiration rates of *Azotobacter* species and facilitate nitrogen fixation in other aerobic environments. *Biochem. J.* 261:181–87

114. Thorneley RNF, Lowe DJ. 1983. Nitrogenase of *Klebsiella pneumoniae*. *Biochem. J.* 215:393–403

115. Thorneley RNF, Lowe DJ. 1985. Kinetics and mechanisms of the nitrogenase enzyme system. See Ref. 108a, pp. 221–84

116. Tittsworth RC, Hales BJ. 1993. Detection of EPR signals assigned to the 1–equiv-oxidized P-clusters of the nitrogenase MoFe protein from *Azotobacter vinelandii*. *J. Am. Chem. Soc.* 115:9763–67

117. Tong L, DeVos AM, Milburn MV, Kim SH. 1991. Crystal structures at 2.2 Å resolution of the catalytic domains of normal ras protein and an oncogenic mutant complexed with GDP. *J. Mol. Biol.* 217:503–16

118. Walker GA, Mortenson LE. 1974. Effect of magnesium adenosine 5'-triphosphate on the accessibility of the iron of clostridial azoferredoxin, a component of nitrogenase. *Biochemistry* 13:2382–88

119. Walker JE, Saraste M, Runswick MJ, Gay NJ. 1982. Distantly related sequences in the α- and β-subunits of ATP synthase, myosin, kinases and other ATP-requiring enzymes and a common nucleotide binding fold. *EMBO J.* 1:945–51

120. Watt GD, Burns A, Lough S, Tennent DL. 1980. Redox and spectroscopic properties of oxidized MoFe protein from *Azotobacter vinelandii. Biochemistry* 19:4926–32

121. Watt GD, Reddy KRN. 1994. Formation of an all ferrous Fe_4S_4 cluster in the iron protein component of *Azotobacter vinelandii* nitrogenase. *J. Inorgan. Biochem.* 53:281–94

122. Wolle D, Dean DR, Howard JB. 1992. Nucleotide iron-sulfur cluster signal transduction in the nitrogenase iron-protein: the role of Asp125. *Science* 258:992–95

123. Wolle D, Kim C, Dean D, Howard JB. 1992. Ionic interactions in the nitrogenase complex: Properties of Fe-protein containing substitutions for Arg-100. *J. Biol. Chem.* 267:3667–73

124. Zimmermann R, Münck E, Brill WJ, Shah VK, Henzl MT, et al. 1978. Nitrogenase X: Mössbauer and EPR studies on

reversibly oxidized MoFe protein from *Azotobacter vinelandii* OP: nature of the iron centers. *Biochim. Biophys. Acta* 537:185–207

125. Zumft WG, Palmer G, Mortenson LE. 1973. Electron paramagnetic resonance studies on nitrogenase II. Interaction of adenosine 5-triphosphate with azoferredoxin. *Biochim. Biophys. Acta* 292:413–21

Annu. Rev. Plant Physiol. Plant Mol. Biol. 2001. 52:297–314

MOLECULAR ENGINEERING OF C_4 PHOTOSYNTHESIS

Makoto Matsuoka
BioScience Center, Nagoya University, Chikusa, Nagoya 464-8601, Japan; e-mail: j45751a@nucc.cc.nagoya-u.ac.jp

Robert T Furbank
CSIRO Plant Industry, G.P.O. Box 1600, Canberra ACT 2601, Australia; e-mail: furbank@pi.csiro.au

Hiroshi Fukayama and Mitsue Miyao
Laboratory of Photosynthesis, National Institute of Agrobiological Resources, Kannondai, Tsukuba 305-8602, Japan; e-mail: mmiyao@abr.affrc.go.jp

Key Words C_3 plants, C_4 plants, carbon metabolism, evolution, transgenic plants

■ **Abstract** The majority of terrestrial plants, including many important crops such as rice, wheat, soybean, and potato, are classified as C_3 plants that assimilate atmospheric CO_2 directly through the C_3 photosynthetic pathway. C_4 plants such as maize and sugarcane evolved from C_3 plants, acquiring the C_4 photosynthetic pathway to achieve high photosynthetic performance and high water- and nitrogen-use efficiencies. The recent application of recombinant DNA technology has made considerable progress in the molecular engineering of C_4 photosynthesis over the past several years. It has deepened our understanding of the mechanism of C_4 photosynthesis and provided valuable information as to the evolution of the C_4 photosynthetic genes. It also has enabled us to express enzymes involved in the C_4 pathway at high levels and in desired locations in the leaves of C_3 plants for engineering of primary carbon metabolism.

CONTENTS

1040-2519/01/0601-0297$14.00

INTRODUCTION

The majority of terrestrial plants, including many important crops such as rice, wheat, barley, soybean, and potato, assimilate atmospheric CO_2 directly through the C_3 photosynthetic pathway, also known as the Calvin cycle, and these are classified as C_3 plants. The enzyme of primary CO_2 fixation in this pathway, ribulose 1,5-bisphosphate carboxylase/oxygenase (Rubisco), reacts not only with CO_2 but also with O_2, leading to photorespiration, which essentially wastes assimilated carbon. Under current atmospheric conditions, potential photosynthesis in C_3 plants is suppressed by oxygen by as much as 40%. The extent of suppression further increases under stress conditions such as drought, high light, and high temperature, through a decline of the CO_2 concentration inside leaves due to closure of stomata. C_4 plants such as maize, sorghum, and sugarcane have evolved a novel biochemical mechanism to overcome photorespiration. In addition to the C_3 pathway, they use the C_4 photosynthetic cycle to elevate the CO_2 concentration at the site of Rubisco and thus suppress its oxygenase activity. This mechanism enables C_4 plants to achieve elevated photosynthetic capacity particularly at higher temperatures, of up to twice as high as that of C_3 plants, in addition to higher water- and nitrogen-use efficiencies (for reviews of C_4 photosynthesis, see 17, 22, 40a). Consequently, it has long been postulated that the transfer of C_4 traits to C_3 plants could improve the photosynthetic performance of C_3 species.

Leaves of C_4 plants have two types of photosynthetic cells, the mesophyll cell (MC) and bundle sheath cell (BSC). While all the photosynthetic enzymes are confined in MCs in C_3 plants, they are localized in MCs and/or BSCs in C_4 plants (Table 1). In addition, C_4 plants show extensive venation, with a ring of BSCs surrounding each vein and an outer ring of MCs surrounding the bundle sheath. This unique leaf structure, known as Kranz anatomy, and the cell-specific compartmentalization of enzymes are essential for operation of the C_4 pathway.

The initial fixation of CO_2 in the C_4 pathway occurs in the MC cytosol by phospho*enol*pyruvate carboxylase (PEPC) to form the C_4 acid oxaloacetate (OAA). OAA is either reduced to malate by NADP-malate dehydrogenase (NADP-MDH) or transaminated to aspartate by aspartate aminotransferase (AspAT). The resultant C_4 acid is transported to the BSCs and then decarboxylated to release CO_2 in the vicinity of Rubisco. The decarboxylation reaction is catalyzed by one or more of the three enzymes, namely, NADP-malic enzyme (NADP-ME), NAD-malic enzyme (NAD-ME), and phospho*enol*pyruvate carboxykinase (PEP-CK), and C_4 plants are classified into three subtypes depending on the major decarboxylation enzyme. A C_3 acid generated by the decarboxylation is shuttled back to MCs to regenerate the primary CO_2 acceptor phospho*enol*pyruvate (PEP) by pyruvate,orthophosphate dikinase (PPDK) in the MC chloroplasts.

TABLE 1   Location of major photosynthetic enzymes in leaves of C$_4$ plants

Enzyme	Gene	C$_4$ subtype(s)	Location	Function
Rubisco (C$_3$)	*rbc*	All	BSC, Chlt	Net CO$_2$ fixation
PEPC (C$_4$)	*Ppc*	All	MC, Cyt	Initial CO$_2$ (HCO$_3^-$) fixation
PPDK (C$_4$)	*Pdk*	All	MC, Chlt	Regeneration of PEP
NADP-MDH (C$_4$)	*mdh*	NADP-ME	MC, Chlt	OAA → malate
NADP-ME (C$_4$)	*Me*	NADP-ME	BSC, Chlt	Decarboxylation of malate
NAD-ME (C$_4$)		NAD-ME (PEP-CK)	BSC, Mit	Decarboxylation of malate
AspAT (C$_4$)		NAD-ME PEP-CK	MC, Cyt; BSC, Mit	OAA → asparate (MC) Asparate → OAA (BSC)
PEP-CK (C$_4$)		PEP-CK (NADP-ME)	BSC, Cyt	Decarboxylation of OAA
CA (C$_4$)		All	MC, Cyt	CO$_2$ → HCO$_3^-$

Enzymes mentioned in this article are listed. MC, mesophyll cells; BSC, bundle sheath cells; Cyt, cytosol; Chlt, chloroplasts; Mit, mitochondria.

The enzymes involved in the C$_4$ pathway (C$_4$ enzymes) had previously been considered to be specific for C$_4$ plants, since the activities of homologues are low in C$_3$ plants and their kinetic properties are usually different from those of C$_4$ enzymes. However, recent comparative studies have revealed that C$_3$ plants have at least two different types of genes, one encoding enzymes of "housekeeping" function and the other very similar to the C$_4$ photosynthetic genes in C$_4$ plants, although expression of the latter is very low or even undetectable in C$_3$ plants. Based on this finding, it is postulated that the C$_4$-specific genes evolved from a set of preexisting counterpart genes in ancestral C$_3$ plants, with some modifications in expression patterns in leaves and kinetic properties of enzymes (33, 40).

The recent application of recombinant DNA technology to plant metabolism has considerably advanced our understanding of the regulation of photosynthesis (18). By altering the levels and properties of key enzymes in photosynthesis in transgenic C$_4$ plants, we are now able to deepen our understanding of the mechanism of C$_4$ photosynthesis. Cell-specific expression of C$_4$ photosynthetic genes can also be probed using reporter gene constructs in transgenic plants (9, 33). Our understanding of the evolution of photosynthetic carbon metabolism can be advanced by examining the consequences of the transfer of C$_4$-specific genes to transgenic C$_3$ plants. Lastly, a great challenge is to use these techniques and C$_4$ genes to alter carbon metabolism of C$_3$ crop plants to answer fundamental questions concerning agronomic performance and to improve crop productivity. Here we review progress in these key areas of C$_4$ photosynthesis research.

METABOLIC ENGINEERING OF C_4 ENZYMES IN C_4 PLANTS

The capacity to alter photosynthesis in transgenic plants with a high degree of precision has provided a powerful tool for studying rate-limiting processes in photosynthesis and carbon partitioning in vivo (see 18). This technology, using the C_4 dicot *Flaveria bidentis* (8) along with the isolation of C_4 mutants of *Amaranthus edulis* requiring high CO_2 for growth (see 10), has allowed the analysis of control points in the C_4 pathway in intact plants. In this section we review the contribution of these approaches to our understanding of C_4 metabolism and mechanism.

Rate-Limiting Reactions in C_4 Photosynthesis

One of the great challenges in plant biochemistry has been to transfer the vast amount of knowledge on enzyme kinetics in vitro to the control of flux through metabolic pathways in vivo. Using antisense, cosuppression, ectopic overexpression, and the mutational approach described above, we now have a relatively clear picture of the role individual enzymes play in controlling photosynthetic flux in C_4 plants. Table 2 summarizes this work by presenting control coefficients (C_j) for the individual enzymes examined so far. These coefficients were mostly determined at saturating light and ambient CO_2. The significance of control coefficients has been reviewed elsewhere (1) but a C_j of one indicates that flux is fully controlled at this step in the pathway, whereas a value of zero indicates no control over flux.

The results summarized in Table 2 indicate that the bulk of control in C_4 photosynthesis lies with the three enzymes Rubisco, PPDK, and PEPC. Experiments where expression of the gene encoding the small subunit of Rubisco (*rbcS*) was reduced by antisense in *Flaveria* indicate that at high light, a control coefficient of 0.5 to 0.6 is likely for this enzyme (15, 16). This result was somewhat surprising as it has been suggested that the high CO_2 concentration in BSCs has allowed C_4 plants to reduce the amount of Rubisco in BSCs, relative to that in C_3 plants (one

TABLE 2   Control coefficients (C_j) for photosynthetic enzymes in C_4 plants determined by measuring CO_2 assimilation under saturating illumination and ambient CO_2

Enzyme	C_4 species	Technique	C_j	References
Rubisco	*F. bidentis*	Antisense RNA	0.5–0.6	15, 16
PPDK	*F. bidentis*	Antisense RNA	0.2–0.4	15
PEPC	*A. edulis*	Mutation	0.35	2, 10
NAD-ME	*A. edulis*	Mutation	~0	11
NADP-MDH	*F. bidentis*	Cosuppression	~0	47

third to one quarter of C_3 levels), without affecting photosynthesis, resulting in greater nitrogen-use efficiency (41). It appears that this evolutionary optimization of Rubisco level has poised nitrogen investment in this protein to the minimum effective level in wild-type plants. As with C_3 plants, it would be instructive to elevate Rubisco levels in transgenic C_4 plants; however, the overexpression of the chloroplast-encoded large subunit of Rubisco currently provides a technical barrier to these experiments.

Control of photosynthesis by PPDK and PEPC is more difficult to assess. Both these enzymes are subject to complex regulation by reversible protein phosphorylation and in the case of PEPC, mutants have been shown to increase the enzyme activation state in response to decreased enzyme levels (10). In the case of PEPC, a control coefficient of 0.35 was calculated for *Amaranthus* mutants at saturating light and ambient CO_2 (2). A similar value was found for PPDK in transgenic *Flaveria* containing an antisense gene construct targeted to this enzyme (15). The fact that the C_j values for these three enzymes sum to greater than one may be due to the different growth conditions used in each case or possibly interspecific or decarboxylation-type variations in enzyme levels.

Two of the enzymes in C_4 photosynthesis examined thus far appear to exert little or no control over photosynthetic flux in vivo: NADP-MDH (47) and NAD-ME (11). In the case of NADP-MDH, transgenic *Flaveria* containing antisense or cosuppression constructs showed no effect of reduced enzyme level until plants contained less than 10% of wild-type levels of the protein (47). Even after it is taken into account that these plants showed increased enzyme activation state to compensate for reduced enzyme levels, Cj for this thioredoxin-regulated enzyme was effectively zero under all conditions examined (47). Similarly, in heterozygous *Amaranthus* mutants with an approximately 50% reduction in NAD-ME activity, no effect on photosynthesis could be detected, indicating that this enzyme effectively exerts no control over photosynthetic flux (11).

Although the experiments described above in which high control coefficients are observed indicate where control of flux in C_4 photosynthesis lies, the observations that several "key enzymes" appear to have no regulatory role are equally intriguing. NADP-MDH is highly regulated by light through the thioredoxin-mediated reduction of multiple disulfide bridges (see 17). NAD-ME activity is also regulated, in this case allosterically, by a number of metabolites including adenylates (14). Yet modulation of these enzymes, apart from a crude on/off mechanism, could have no effect on photosynthetic flux in vivo. These observations are important in that they should engender a degree of caution when espousing the importance of a key enzyme in regulation of any metabolic pathway and raise the question as to why sophisticated mechanisms of enzyme regulation are necessary for such enzymes. One possible explanation lies in the evolutionary origins of C_4 photosynthesis. There is not a single enzyme in the C_4 pathway that does not have a homologue in C_3 plants, leading to the hypothesis that the genes encoding these proteins have been recruited for the C_4 process [see Introduction; (9, 33)]. The presence in C_4 plants of these housekeeping enzymes at levels up to 100-fold higher than those found in C_3 leaf cells, often still in their original C_3 compartment, could play havoc with all manner of pathways of secondary metabolism (see 15). It is tempting to postulate that regulation of these nonlimiting enzymes preserves flux through minor pathways by conserving metabolites from the massive flood of carbon through C_4 photosynthesis.

Transgenic C_4 Plants and the CO_2 Pump

A long-standing focus of interest in C_4 photosynthesis has been the CO_2 concentrating mechanism and the barrier to CO_2 diffusion afforded by the bundle sheath/mesophyll interface (see 49). This aspect of the C_4 mechanism is particularly pertinent to the introduction of C_4 traits into C_3 plants that lack the Kranz leaf anatomy common to terrestrial C_4 plants. It has long been postulated that the relative levels of the enzymes of the CO_2 pump in MCs and the enzymes of the Calvin cycle in BSCs, along with the permeability characteristics of BSCs, largely determine the efficiency with which C_4 photosynthesis operates (49). Transgenic plants with altered PEPC/Rubisco ratios (45, 50) or altered bundle sheath inorganic carbon composition (35) provide the opportunity to test these hypotheses.

If the content of Rubisco in a C_4 leaf is progressively reduced without a commensurate effect on PEPC levels (as is the case in the transgenic *Flaveria* discussed above), one would intuitively expect the bundle sheath CO_2 concentration to rise. This would result in an increase in leakage of CO_2 from the bundle sheath and a decline in photosynthetic efficiency per net CO_2 fixed. This is, in fact, what is observed when the Rubisco antisense *Flaveria* transgenics are analyzed using carbon isotope discrimination (50) or chlorophyll fluorescence and gas exchange (45). Carbon isotope discrimination allows the calculation of a leakiness parameter known as ϕ, which is the fraction of CO_2 generated in C_4 acid decarboxylation that subsequently leaks out of the bundle sheath (see 49). In transgenic *Flaveria* with a 40% reduction in Rubisco, this leakiness parameter increased by 50%. The increased ATP required to support this CO_2 leakage was also evident in the quantum efficiency of the photosystems where plants with a 70% reduction in Rubisco content required approximately 28 quanta per CO_2 fixed compared with 17 for wild-type leaves at saturating light in air (45).

It has been postulated that an important requirement of the CO_2 concentrating mechanism of C_4 photosynthesis is the lack of equilibration of CO_2 and bicarbonate in BSCs (29). This hypothesis is supported by the lack of appreciable carbonic anhydrase (CA) activity in BSCs of any C_4 plant (6). Theoretically, by reducing the bicarbonate content of the bundle sheath inorganic carbon pool, the concentration of CO_2 (the active species for fixation by Rubisco) is optimized and leakage of bicarbonate to MCs through plasmodesmata minimized (29). This hypothesis has been tested and the energetic ramifications assessed by ectopically expressing CA from tobacco in BSCs of *Flaveria* (35). Transgenic plants with two- to fivefold increases in CA activity in BSCs showed similar increases in leakiness to the Rubisco antisense transgenic plants discussed above and an approximately 20%

decrease in light-saturated photosynthesis (35). These experiments indicate the importance of seemingly minor aspects of biochemical specialization of the C$_4$ pathway in determining the efficiency of the process.

MOLECULAR ENGINEERING OF C$_4$ ENZYMES IN C$_3$ PLANTS

How to Overproduce C$_4$ Enzymes in the Leaves of C$_3$ Plants

Previously, attempts have been made to transfer C$_4$ traits to C$_3$ plants by conventional hybridization between C$_3$ and C$_4$ plants (4). However, this approach was available only in several plant genera such as *Panicum, Moricandia, Brassica, Atriplex,* and *Flaveria.* Moreover, most C$_3$-C$_4$ hybrids showed infertility due to abnormal chromosome pairing and/or genetic barriers. Recent developments in plant genetic engineering have enabled us to introduce the desired genes encoding C$_4$ enzymes into C$_3$ plants. In the past several years a variety of "C$_4$ transgenic" C$_3$ plants have been produced (Table 3).

Enzymes Located in the Mesophyll Cells of C$_4$ Plants   The first attempt of this kind used a chimeric gene construct containing a cDNA of the maize C$_4$-specific PEPC (*Ppc* cDNA) fused to the 5′- and 3′-flanking sequences of the chlorophyll *a/b* binding protein gene (*Cab*) from *Nicotiana plumbaginifolia* (25). The introduction of this chimeric gene into tobacco increased the PEPC activity in the leaves to 2.2-fold that of nontransformants, but the levels of transcripts and protein in these transformants were far below those in maize. Similarly, the expression of a cDNA for the C$_4$ enzyme under the control of strong promoters such as *Cab, rbcS,* and *Cauliflower mosaic virus* 35S promoters led to only two- to fivefold increases in the activity of PEPC (20, 31), PPDK (12, 27, 44), and NADP-MDH (19). In these transformants, the level of the enzyme protein was low and only detectable by immunoblotting. The expression of bacterial *Ppc* genes from either *Escherichia coli* or *Corynebacterium glutamicum* under the control of the 35S promoter increased the enzyme activity of transgenic potato leaves but the extent of increase was less than several fold, a value almost comparable to that obtained with the higher plant *Ppc* cDNA under the control of the 35S promoter (20).

To raise the expression level of the C$_4$ enzymes, sequences that have enhancer-like effects were included in the introduced gene (20, 28). Gehlen et al (20) examined the effects of the 5′-untranslated region (UTR) of the chalcone synthase gene from parsley, and found that the expression of the *Ppc* gene from *C. glutamicum* under the control of the 35S promoter was enhanced by its presence. The highest expression level, however, was still only fivefold that of nontransformants in terms of PEPC activity. Thus, conventional strategies to express foreign genes in transgenic plants did not dramatically increase the activity of C$_4$ enzymes in the leaves of C$_3$ plants.

TABLE 3   Increase in activities of C_4 enzymes in the leaves of transgenic C_3 plants

C_4 enzyme (Location in C_4 plants)	Host C_3 plant	Introduced construct	Highest activity[a] (Increase in fold)	References
PEPC (MC)	Tobacco	*Nicotiana Cab* prom::maize C_4 cDNA::*Nicotiana Cab* terminator	2.2	25
		35S prom::maize C_4 cDNA	2.4	31
	Potato	35S prom::5′UTR::*Corynebacterium* gene	5.4	20
	Rice	Intact maize C_4 gene	110	32
PPDK (MC)	Tobacco	35S prom::*Mesembryanthemum* FL CAM cDNA	1.6	44
	Arabidopsis	*Arabidopsis rbcS* prom::maize C_4 cDNA	2.4	27
		35S prom::maize C_4 cDNA	4.0	27
	Potato	Enhanced 35S prom::maize C_4 cDNA	5.4	28
	Rice	Rice *Cab* prom::maize FL C_4 cDNA	5	13
		Maize *Pdk* prom::maize FL C_4 cDNA	5	13
		Intact maize C_4 gene	40	13
NADP-MDH (MC)	Tobacco	35S prom::*Sorghum* FL C_4 cDNA	3	19
AspAT (MC)	Tobacco	35S prom::C_4 *Panicum* cDNA	3.1	43
	Rice	Intact C_4 *Panicum* gene	20	—[b]
AspAT (BSC)	Tobacco	35S prom::C_4 *Panicum* cDNA	3.5	43
NADP-ME (BSC)	Potato	35S prom::C_3 *Flaveria* cDNA	7.1	34
	Rice	Rice *Cab* prom::rice FL C_3 cDNA	5	48
		Rice *Cab* prom::maize FL C_4 cDNA	30	48
			70	46
PEP-CK (BSC)	Rice	Maize *Ppc* prom::*Urochloa* C_4 cDNA	0.5[c]	45a
		Maize *Pdk* prom::*Urochloa* C_4 cDNA	0.5[c]	45a

[a]Highest enzyme activities among the primary transgenic plants are listed.

[b]M Nomura & M Matsuoka, unpublished observation.

[c]Highest activities of the secondary transgenic plants relative to the activity of *Urochloa* leaves are presented.

MC, mesophyll cells; BSC, bundle sheath cells; prom, promoter; FL, full-length.

Another approach has been used to introduce the intact gene of C$_4$ enzymes from C$_4$ plants into C$_3$ plants. Our previous studies have demonstrated that the promoters for maize C$_4$-specific genes such as *Ppc* and *Pdk* can drive high-level expression of a reporter gene in transgenic rice plants in an organ-specific, MC-specific, and light-dependent manner as in maize (38–40). These results suggest that the rice plant possesses the regulatory factors necessary for high-level expression of C$_4$-specific genes, and they imply that the introduction of the intact maize gene would lead to high-level expression of C$_4$ enzymes in rice leaves. As expected, the introduction of the intact maize C$_4$-specific *Ppc* gene containing all exons and introns and its own promoter and terminator sequences led to high-level expression of the PEPC protein in the leaves of transgenic rice plants (32). The majority (85%) of the transgenic rice plants showed PEPC activity in the leaves 2- to 30-fold that of nontransformants, whereas the remaining showed activity 30- to 110-fold that of nontransformants, or 1- to 3-fold that of maize leaves. The level of the PEPC protein accounted for 12% of total leaf soluble protein at most. In these transgenic rice plants, the levels of transcripts and protein and the PEPC activity in the leaves all correlated well with the copy number of the introduced gene. The levels of transcripts per copy of the maize C$_4$-specific *Ppc* gene were also comparable in both maize and transgenic rice plants (32). These observations suggest that the maize C$_4$-specific *Ppc* gene behaves in a qualitatively and also quantitatively similar way in both maize and transgenic rice plants. The introduction of the intact maize gene was also effective in expressing another C$_4$ enzyme, PPDK, in rice leaves. The introduction of the intact maize C$_4$-specific *Pdk* gene increased the PPDK activity in rice leaves up to 40-fold that of nontransformants or about half of the activity in maize (12). In a homozygous transgenic line, the PPDK protein accounted for 35% of total leaf soluble protein or 16% of total leaf nitrogen (12), much above the levels of foreign protein in transgenic C$_3$ plants reported previously.

Such high-level expression of the C$_4$ enzymes in rice leaves could not be solely ascribed to the transcriptional activity of the maize gene, since the expression of a chimeric gene containing the full-length cDNA for the maize C$_4$-specific PPDK under the control of either the promoter of the maize C$_4$-specific *Pdk* or the rice *Cab* promoter increased the PPDK activity only up to several fold (12). It is suggested that one or more of the introns or the terminator sequence of the maize gene, or a combination of both, leads to high-level expression of the C$_4$ enzyme by increasing the stability of the transcript (12).

Maize and rice both belong to the Gramineae. Our recent study indicated that the introduction of the intact gene from other C$_4$ gramineous plants could also lead to high-level expression of a C$_4$ enzyme in transgenic rice plants. The activity of the cytosolic form of AspAT in rice leaves was increased to reach 20-fold that of nontransformants by introduction of the intact gene from *Panicum miliaceum* (M Nomura & M Matsuoka, unpublished observations). *P. miliaceum* is classified in the NAD-ME subtype of C$_4$ plants, whereas maize is in the NADP-ME subtype. Thus, the intact genes from C$_4$ gramineous plants, irrespective of the C$_4$ subtype, will likely lead to high-level expression of the C$_4$ enzymes in MCs of C$_3$ gramineous plants.

This strategy, however, has some limitation in that transgenes from phylogenetically closely related plants have to be used to achieve high-level expression of the C_4 enzyme in C_3 plants. The intact maize C_4-specific *Ppc* gene was not expressed at high levels in tobacco leaves, because of incorrect transcription initiation (25). Not only incorrect initiation and termination of transcription but also incorrect splicing could occur when genes from monocots are introduced into dicots (see 21). Thus, phylogenetic distance may hamper the expression of genes from C_4 plants in the leaves of C_3 plants.

Enzymes Located in the Bundle Sheath Cells of C_4 Plants   Unlike the C_4 enzymes located in MCs of C_4 plants, those located in BSCs can be expressed at high levels in MCs of C_3 plants by the introduction of a chimeric gene containing the full-length cDNA for the C_4 enzyme fused to the *Cab* promoter, which directs mesophyll-specific expression in C_3 plants (42). The expression of the maize C_4-specific NADP-ME cDNA under the control of the rice *Cab* promoter increased the activity of NADP-ME in rice leaves to 30- or 70-fold that of nontransformants (46, 48). The level of the NADP-ME protein was also increased to several percent of total leaf soluble protein (46, 48). Such high-level expression was unique to the cDNA for the C_4-specific NADP-ME, and expression of the cDNA for the C_3-specific isoform increased the activity only several fold (34, 48). The *Flaveria* C_4-specific *Me* gene has a regulatory sequence in the 3′UTR that enhances its expression (37), and this sequence increases expression of a reporter gene when combined with heterologous promoters in the leaves of both C_4 *Flaveria* and tobacco (S Ali & WC Taylor, unpublished information). The maize C_4-specific *Me* gene may therefore contain such an enhancer element for high-level expression whereas the C_3-specific gene does not. The expression of a cDNA of the C_4-specific PEP-CK of *Urochloa panicoides* under the control of the maize C_4-specific *Ppc* or *Pdk* promoter was also effective in increasing the activity of PEP-CK in MCs of rice leaves (45a).

Recently, expression of the intact gene for C_4 enzymes located in BSCs of C_4 plants in C_3 plants has also been addressed. When the intact gene for the mitochondrial AspAT of *Panicum miliaceum*, which is located in BSCs, was introduced into rice, high AspAT activity was detected in vascular tissues and BSCs of transgenic rice plants (M Nomura & M Matsuoka, unpublished observations). Similar results were observed with the PEP-CK gene from *Zoysia japonica* and β-glucuronidase activity under the control of the PEP-CK promoter, which was selectively detected in vascular tissues and BSCs (M Nomura & M Matsuoka, unpublished information). These results demonstrate that the C_4-specific genes for the BSC enzymes can retain their property of cell-specific expression even in a C_3 plant, rice, and they therefore suggest that C_3 plants have a regulatory mechanism for gene expression of the BSC-specific C_4 genes at their correct site. This fact is interesting in terms of evolutionary aspects of C_4 photosynthesis, but it also indicates that the strategy to introduce intact C_4-specific genes is not applicable to building the C_4 pathway solely in MCs of C_3 plants.

Physiological Impacts of Overproduction of C$_4$ Enzymes in C$_3$ Plants

PEPC   At present, there are four independent reports of transgenic C$_3$ plants that overproduce PEPC in the MC cytosol (Table 3): two independent reports of transgenic tobacco plants expressing the maize C$_4$-specific PEPC gene (25, 31), transgenic potato expressing a bacterial PEPC gene from *C. glutamicum* (20), and transgenic rice expressing the maize C$_4$-specific PEPC gene (32). In the former three cases, PEPC activities in the leaves of 2- to 5-fold greater than wild-type levels were reported, whereas in the latter, activities up to 110-fold greater than wild-type were observed. In general, PEPC from either higher plants or bacteria undergoes regulation by various metabolite effectors, being inhibited by malate, aspartate, and glutamate (see 17). Since concentrations of these inhibitors are high in the MC cytoplasm of C$_3$ plants, about 1 mM for malate and around 40 mM for aspartate and glutamate (24), the PEPC activities of the transformants in vivo would be lower than maximum extractable activities, especially when measured in the presence of activators. Plant PEPC is also regulated by phosphorylation at a specific serine residue near the N terminus that reduces sensitivity to these inhibitors (see 17). The maize PEPC in transgenic rice leaves remained in its dephosphorylated and less active form during illumination (13).

All the transformants analyzed to date show a higher level of malate (23, 25, 31) or OAA (13) in the leaves compared with wild-types, an indication that the foreign PEPC is at least active in the leaves of these transformants. The level of malate/OAA in these transformants, however, did not exceed twofold that of wild-type, irrespective of the expression level of PEPC in the C$_3$ leaves. This is consistent with the notion that PEPC is not fully active in these plants. It is also likely that malate and OAA produced by the action of PEPC are metabolized inside the cell or translocated from the leaves. The endogenous PEPC in MCs of C$_3$ plants has an anaplerotic function that replenishes the tricarboxylic acid (TCA) cycle with organic acids to meet the demands of carbon skeletons for amino acid synthesis (7). Thus, levels of organic acids other than malate and oxaloacetic acid, as well as foliar amino acids, would be predicted to increase in the transformants. At present, only a slight increase in the level of amino acids has been reported in transgenic potato (23).

Effects of overexpression of PEPC on photosynthesis are controversial. At temperatures optimal for plant growth, practically no difference in the rate of CO$_2$ assimilation and the CO$_2$ compensation point (Γ) was observed in transgenic tobacco expressing the maize PEPC gene (25, 31). Activities of PEPC were only about twofold higher than in wild-type plants in these experiments. In transgenic rice plants expressing the maize PEPC gene, the rate of CO$_2$ assimilation was also not altered significantly, but the O$_2$ inhibition of net CO$_2$ assimilation was mitigated with increasing activity of PEPC (32). However, this effect appears not to have resulted from the fixation of CO$_2$ for photosynthesis by the maize PEPC. The initial CO$_2$ fixation product, determined by ^{14}CO$_2$ labeling experiments with transgenic rice plants having a 50-fold elevation in PEPC activity, was exclusively the C_3 compound 3-phosphoglycerate (13). In addition, overexpression of C_4 PEPC in transgenic rice leaves suppressed CO_2 assimilation at 2% O_2 to a greater extent than that at 21% O_2, probably through limitation of inorganic phosphate (Pi) for the Calvin cycle reactions (13). The major increase in PEPC activity may lead to depletion of Pi in the cytosol, through a stimulation of glycolysis that would suppresses sucrose synthesis. These collective reactions consume one Pi molecule and release four Pi molecules, respectively.

Changes in the photosynthetic characteristics at optimal temperatures have been reported only in transgenic potato expressing the bacterial PEPC (23). In this case, it was reported that the CO_2 compensation point independent of respiration (Γ^*), measured according to Brooks & Farquhar (3), decreased by about 16% in the transformants with fivefold activity, as compared with wild-type plants (23). The authors argue that the decrease in Γ^* resulted from the increase in CO_2 concentration in the vicinity of Rubisco by decarboxylation of organic acids produced by PEPC and/or through its anaplerotic function (23). Determination of the initial CO_2 fixation products and quantification of flux through PEPC in these potato transformants is awaited.

Significant changes in the photosynthetic characteristics in PEPC transformants have thus far been observed mostly at supraoptimal temperatures. In wild-type plants, the rate of CO_2 assimilation in air declines with increasing temperature, whereas in PEPC-overexpressing transformants, it remains unchanged or becomes even greater at higher temperatures in transgenic tobacco (31) and potato (34). This phenomenon is not yet fully understood, but it might be possible that PEPC participates in the initial CO_2 fixation for photosynthesis (despite the absence of elevated levels of the other enzymes necessary for a C_4 cycle) or that it acts to increase the CO_2 concentration in the vicinity of Rubisco under conditions in which the oxygenation reaction of Rubisco proceeds much faster that its carboxylation reaction, as proposed previously (23, 34).

PPDK   There are four reports of transgenic C_3 plants that express PPDK in the MC chloroplast (Table 3): transgenic *Arabidopsis* (27), potato (28), rice (12) expressing the maize C_4-specific PPDK gene, and transgenic tobacco expressing a PPDK gene from the CAM plant *Mesembryanthemum crystallinum* (44). In all cases, no changes in photosynthetic characteristics were observed in these transformants, even in the transgenic rice with PPDK activity 40-fold higher than wild-type levels (12). A modest increase in the $\delta^{13}C$ value was reported in the transgenic potato but this difference was marginal in significance (28). Some changes in the level and composition of free amino acids were also reported in the transgenic tobacco (44). In general, the overall PPDK reaction is freely reversible, depending on concentrations of substrates, activators, and inactivators (5). This is probably the case in MCs of C_3 plants, in which the activity of inorganic pyrophosphatase and adenylate kinase is low (22) and could be the reason why the overexpression of PPDK does not result in significant effects on carbon metabolism in C_3 leaves.

The expression of chloroplast-targeted PPDK increased the number of seeds per seed capsule and the weight of each seed capsule by about 40% and 20%, respectively, in transgenic tobacco, with about a 1.5-fold increase in activity of PPDK in the leaves (44). These effects were not observed in transgenic tobacco plants that express PPDK in the cytosol (44). The mechanism of the increase in seed yield by PPDK is obscure at present. One possibility is that overexpression of PPDK in the chloroplast enhances photosynthesis in organs surrounding seeds. In seed pods of C$_3$ dicots and spikelets of C$_3$ monocots, enzyme activities associated with the C$_4$ pathway are high and C$_4$-like photosynthesis is operative, contributing significantly to grain filling (see 26, 30). Thus, it is possible that overexpression of PPDK in the chloroplast enhances C$_4$-like photosynthesis in organs such as hulls and ears to raise the yield of seeds and grains.

NADP-ME   There are four reports of transgenic C$_3$ plants that express NADP-ME in the MC chloroplast (Table 3): two sets of transgenic rice plants expressing the maize C$_4$-specific isoform (46, 48), transgenic rice expressing the rice C$_3$-specific isoform (48), and transgenic potato expressing the C$_3$-specfic isoform of *Flaveria pringlei* (34). The transformants expressing the C$_3$-specific isoform with activities up to several fold higher than wild-type levels did not show any detectable differences in their growth and photosynthesis (34, 48), whereas those overexpressing the maize C$_4$-specific isoform showed serious stunting and leaf photobleaching, due to increased photoinhibition of photosynthesis under natural light conditions (46, 48). It is proposed that the maize C$_4$ NADP-ME in the chloroplasts acts to increase the NADPH/NADP ratio and to suppress photorespiration, rendering photosynthesis more susceptible to photoinhibition (46, 48). Such detrimental effects of the maize enzyme might imply significant flexibility of carbon metabolism in MCs of C$_3$ plants, especially in terms of transport of metabolites between the cytosol and the chloroplast stroma.

PEP-CK   There is only one report of transgenic rice plants that express the C$_4$-specific PEP-CK of *U. panicoides* in the MC chloroplast (45a) (Table 3). Although this enzyme is located in the BSC cytosol of *U. panicoides*, the introduced construct was designed so that the enzyme was targeted to the MC chloroplasts in transgenic rice leaves. The expression of chloroplast-targeted PEP-CK showed significant alterations of carbon metabolism in rice leaves (45a). In ^{14}CO$_2$ pulse-chase experiments of transgenic rice with PEP-CK activity comparable to that in *U. panicoides*, about 20% of the radioactivity was incorporated in the C$_4$ compounds, malate, OAA, and aspartate. Feeding of ^{14}C-labeled malate also increased the incorporation of the radioactivity into sucrose. It is unclear whether the introduced PEP-CK together with endogenous PEPC could drive a C$_4$-like pathway in MCs of rice leaves as proposed previously, since the CO$_2$ compensation point was unchanged in transgenic rice plants (45a).

FUTURE PERSPECTIVES

There has been considerable progress in recent years in the molecular engineering of C_4 photosynthesis. The technology to express the C_4 enzymes at high levels and in the desired locations in the leaves of C_3 species is becoming well established, and it is now possible to produce transgenic C_3 plants that express at least a set of key enzymes of the C_4 pathway. Thus, we have just reached the starting point in introducing the basic biochemical elements of the C_4 pathway into C_3 plants. Apart from the goal of installation of a complete C_4 pathway into C_3 plants, some transgenic C_3 plants that overproduce a single C_4 enzyme show alterations in carbon metabolism. These plants are also proving to be useful tools in probing the "housekeeping" function(s) of the C_4-like enzymes in C_3 plants and the evolution of the C_4 photosynthetic genes. Experiments with transgenic plants have reinforced the fact that the C_4 mechanism is a finely tuned metabolic "machine" where both a high degree of precision in gene expression and structural morphology work together to concentrate CO_2 efficiently at the site of Rubisco. Work with transgenic C_4 *Flaveria* and also transgenic C_3 plants shows that relatively small changes in leaf biochemistry, induced by transgene action, can have major deleterious effects on photosynthetic competence. In light of these observations, some important questions must be answered in the quest to introduce the C_4 pathway in C_3 crop plants. First, can we deliver the degree of precision required to coexpress the necessary genes at the correct levels and ratios in the correct compartments? For the primary enzymes of the C_4 pathway these preliminary results are promising but correct posttranslational regulation of the introduced, heterologous enzymes, fine-tuning of the levels of ancillary enzymes (such as CA, adenylate kinase, and pyrophosphatase) and metabolite transporters must also be addressed. Most important, can we create an efficient CO_2 concentrating mechanism in a plant lacking Kranz leaf anatomy, a morphological feature independently arrived at several times through the convergent evolution of C_4 plants? Would the metabolic cost of establishing a CO_2 concentrating mechanism without an effective barrier to CO_2 diffusion outweigh the advantages? In connection with this key issue, there are good examples of higher plant CO_2 concentrating mechanisms without Kranz anatomy, namely, the submersed aquatic macrophytes (SAMs) such as *Hydrilla verticillata*, in which an intracellular C_4-like pathway is induced in response to a decline of ambient CO_2 concentration (see 36). It remains to be seen, however, whether this process is a highly efficient addition to the C_3 process or a low-efficiency survival mechanism in SAM species. Studies on the mechanisms of induction of a C_4-like pathway in SAM plants may help us to understand how to introduce an effective C_4-like mechanism to MCs of C_3 plants. However, a conclusive answer as to the performance of an artificially introduced C_4 pathway in C_3 crops can only be obtained by the generation and comprehensive analysis of transgenic crop plants such as those described here and those currently being produced.

ACKNOWLEDGMENTS

The authors are grateful to Drs RE Häusler, HJ Hirsch, H Honda, RC Leegood, WC Taylor, and S Toki for providing unpublished information and to Ms Hiroko Tsuchida for her assistance in preparing the manuscript. Work in the authors' laboratories was supported by a PROBRAIN grant from the Bio-Oriented Technology Research Advancement Institution (BRAIN) of Japan and from the Australia/Japan Bilateral Science Agreement.

Visit the Annual Reviews home page at www.AnnualReviews.org

LITERATURE CITED

1. ap Rees T, Hill SA. 1994. Metabolic control analysis of plant metabolism. *Plant Cell Environ.* 17:587–99
2. Bailey KJ, Battistelli A, Dever LV, Lea PJ, Leegood RC. 2000. Control of C_4 photosynthesis: effects of reduced activities of phosphoenolpyruvate carboxylase on CO_2 assimilation in *Amaranthus edulis* L. *J. Exp. Bot.* 51:339–46
3. Brooks A, Farquhar GD. 1985. Effect of temperature on the CO_2/O_2 specificity of ribulose-1,5-bisphoshate carboxylase/oxygenase and the rate of respiration in the light. Estimates from gas-exchange measurements on spinach. *Planta* 165:397–406
4. Brown RH, Bouton JH. 1993. Physiology and genetics of interspecific hybrids between photosynthetic types. *Annu. Rev. Plant Physiol. Plant Mol. Biol.* 44:435–56
5. Burnell JN, Hatch MD. 1985. Light-dark modulation of leaf pyruvate, Pi dikinase. *Trends Biochem. Sci.* 10:288–91
6. Burnell JN, Hatch MD. 1988. Low bundle sheath carbonic anhydrase is apparently essential for effective C_4 pathway operation. *Plant Physiol.* 86:1252–56
7. Champigny M-L, Foyer C. 1992. Nitrate activation of cytosolic protein kinases diverts photosynthetic carbon from sucrose to amino acid biosynthesis. Basis for a new concept. *Plant Physiol.* 100:7–12
8. Chitty JA, Furbank RT, Marshall JS, Chen Z, Taylor WC. 1994. Genetic transformation of the C_4 plant, *Flaveria bidentis. Plant J.* 6:949–56
9. Dengler NG, Taylor WC. 2000. Developmental aspects of C_4 photosynthesis. In *Advances in Photosynthesis, Vol. 9, Photosynthesis: Physiology and Metabolism*, ed. RC Leegood, TD Sharkey, S von Caemmerer, pp. 471–95. Dordrecht: Kluwer. 624 pp.
10. Dever LV, Bailey KJ, Leegood RC, Lea PJ. 1997. Control of photosynthesis in *Amaranthus edulis* mutants with reduced amounts of PEP carboxylase. *Aust. J. Plant Physiol.* 24:469–76
11. Dever LV, Pearson M, Ireland RJ, Leegood RC, Lea PJ. 1998. The isolation and characterisation of a mutant of the C_4 plant *Amaranthus edulis* deficient in NAD-malic enzyme activity. *Planta* 206:649–56
12. Fukayama H, Agarie S, Nomura M, Tsuchida H, Ku MSB, et al. 1999. High-level expression of maize C_4–specific pyruvate, Pi dikinase and its light activation in transgenic rice plants. *Plant Cell Physiol.* 40:s116 (Abstr.)
13. Fukayama H, Imanari E, Tsuchida H, Izui K, Matsuoka M, et al. 2000. *In vivo* activity of maize phospho*enol*pyruvate carboxylase in transgenic rice plants. *Plant Cell Physiol.* 41:s112 (Abstr.)
14. Furbank RT, Agostino A, Hatch MD. 1991. Regulation of C_4 photosynthesis: modulation of mitochondrial NAD-malic enzyme by adenylates. *Arch. Biochem. Biophys.* 289:376–81

15. Furbank RT, Chitty JA, Jenkins CLD, Taylor WC, Trevanion SJ, et al. 1997. Genetic manipulation of key photosynthetic enzymes in the C_4 plant *Flaveria bidentis*. *Aust. J. Plant Physiol.* 24:477–85

16. Furbank RT, Chitty JA, von Caemmerer S, Jenkins CLD. 1996. Antisense RNA inhibition of *rbcS* gene expression reduces Rubisco level and photosynthesis in the C_4 plant *Flaveria bidentis*. *Plant Physiol.* 111:725–34

17. Furbank RT, Hatch MD, Jenkins CLD. 2000. C_4 photosynthesis: mechanism and regulation. See Ref. 9, pp. 435–57

18. Furbank RT, Taylor WC. 1995. Regulation of photosynthesis in C_3 and C_4 plants: a molecular approach. *Plant Cell* 7:797–807

19. Gallardo F, Miginiac-Maslow M, Sangwan R, Decottignies P, Keryer E, et al. 1995. Monocotyledonous C_4 NADP$^+$-malate dehydrogenase is efficiently synthesized, targeted to chloroplasts and processed to an active form in transgenic plants of the C3 dicotyledon tobacco. *Planta* 197:324–32

20. Gehlen J, Panstruga R, Smets H, Merkelbach S, Kleines M, et al. 1996. Effects of altered phospho*enol*pyruvate carboxylase activities on transgenic C3 plant *Solanum tuberosum*. *Plant Mol. Biol.* 32:831–48

21. Goodall GJ, Filipowicz W. 1991. Different effects of intron nucleotide composition and secondary structure on pre-mRNA splicing in monocot and dicot plants. *EMBO J.* 10:2635–44

22. Hatch MD. 1987. C_4 photosynthesis: a unique blend of modified biochemistry, anatomy and ultrastructure. *Biochim. Biophys. Acta* 895:81–106

23. Häusler RE, Kleines M, Uhrig H, Hirsch H-J, Smets H. 1999. Overexpression of phospho*enol*pyruvate carboxylase from *Corynebacterium glutamicum* lowers the CO_2 compensation point (Γ^*) and enhances dark and light respiration in transgenic potato. *J. Exp. Bot.* 336:1231–42

24. Heineke D, Riens B, Grosse H, Hoferichter P, Peter U, et al. 1991. Redox transfer across the inner chloroplast envelope membrane. *Plant Physiol.* 95:1131–37

25. Hudspeth RL, Grula JW, Dai Z, Edwards GE, Ku MSB. 1992. Expression of maize phospho*enol*pyruvate carboxylase in transgenic tobacco. *Plant Physiol.* 98:458–64

26. Imaizumi N, Samejima M, Ishihara K. 1997. Characteristics of photosynthetic carbon metabolism of spikelets in rice. *Photosynth. Res.* 52:75–82

27. Ishimaru K, Ichikawa H, Matsuoka M, Ohsugi R. 1997. Analysis of a C_4 maize pyruvate, orthophosphate dikinase expressed in C_3 transgenic *Arabidopsis* plants. *Plant Sci.* 129:57–64

28. Ishimaru K, Ohkawa Y, Ishige T, Tobias DJ, Ohsugi R. 1998. Elevated pyruvate, orthophosphate dikinase (PPDK) activity alters carbon metabolism in C_3 transgenic potatoes with a C_4 maize PPDK gene. *Physiol. Plant.* 103:340–46

29. Jenkins CLD, Furbank RT, Hatch MD. 1989. Mechanism of C_4 photosynthesis. A model describing the inorganic carbon pool in bundle sheath cells. *Plant Physiol.* 91:1372–81

30. King SP, Badger MR, Furbank RT. 1998. CO_2 refixation characteristics of developing canola seeds and silique wall. *Aust. J. Plant Physiol.* 25:377–86

31. Kogami H, Shono M, Koike T, Yanagisawa S, Izui K, et al. 1994. Molecular and physiological evaluation of transgenic tobacco plants expressing a maize phospho*enol*pyruvate carboxylase gene under the control of the cauliflower mosaic virus 35S promoter. *Transgenic Res.* 3:287–96

32. Ku MSB, Agarie S, Nomura M, Fukayama H, Tsuchida H, et al. 1999. High-level expression of maize phospho*enol*pyruvate carboxylase in transgenic rice plants. *Nat. Biotechnol.* 17:76–80

33. Ku MSB, Kano-Murakami Y, Matsuoka M. 1996. Evolution and expression of C_4 photosynthesis genes. *Plant Physiol.* 111:949–57

34. Lipka V, Häusler RE, Rademacher T, Li J,

Hirsch H-J, et al. 1999. *Solanum tuberosum* double transgenic expressing phosphoenolpyruvate carboxylase and NADP-malic enzyme display reduced electron requirement for CO$_2$ fixation. *Plant Sci.* 144:93–105

35. Ludwig M, von Caemmerer S, Price GD, Badger MR, Furbank RT. 1998. Expression of tobacco carbonic anhydrase in the C$_4$ dicot *Flaveria bidentis* leads to increased leakiness of the bundle sheath and a defective CO$_2$–concentrating mechanism. *Plant Physiol.* 117:1071–81

36. Magnin NC, Cooley BA, Reiskind JB, Bowes G. 1997. Regulation and localization of key enzymes during the induction of Kranz-less, C$_4$–type photosynthesis in *Hydrilla verticillata*. *Plant Physiol.* 115:1681–89

37. Marshall JS, Stubbs JD, Chitty JA, Surin B, Taylor WC. 1997. Expression of the C$_4$ *Me1* gene from *Flaveria bidentis* requires an interaction between 5′ and 3′ sequences. *Plant Cell* 9:1515–25

38. Matsuoka M, Kyozuka J, Shimamoto K, Kano-Murakami Y. 1994. The promoters of two carboxylases in a C$_4$ plant (maize) direct cell-specific, light-regulated expression in a C$_3$ plant (rice). *Plant J.* 6:311–19

39. Matsuoka M, Tada Y, Fujimura T, Kano-Murakami Y. 1993. Tissue-specific light-regulated expression directed by the promoter of a C4 gene, maize pyruvate, orthophosphate dikinase, in a C3 plant, rice. *Proc. Natl. Acad. Sci. USA* 90:9586–90

40. Nomura M, Sentoku N, Nishimura A, Lin J-H, Honda C, et al. 2000. The evolution of C$_4$ plants: acquisition of *cis*-regulatory sequences in the promoter of C$_4$-type pyruvate, orthophosphate dikinase gene. *Plant J.* 22:211–21

40a. Sage RF, Monson RK, eds. 1999. *Plant Biology.* San Diego: Academic. 596 pp.

41. Sage RF, Pearcy RW. 2000. The physio-logical ecology of C$_4$ photosynthesis. See Ref. 9, pp. 497–532

42. Sakamoto M, Sanada Y, Tagiri A, Murakami T, Ohashi Y, et al. 1991. Structure and characterization of a gene for light-harvesting Chl a/b binding protein from rice. *Plant Cell Physiol.* 32:385–93

43. Sentoku N, Taniguchi M, Sugiyama T, Ishimaru K, Ohsugi R, et al. 2000. Analysis of transgenic tobacco plants expressing *Panicum miliaceum* aspartate aminotransferase genes. *Plant Cell Rep.* 19:598–603

44. Sheriff A, Meyer H, Riedel E, Schmitt JM, Lapke C. 1998. The influence of plant pyruvate, orthophosphate dikinase on a C$_3$ plant with respect to the intracellular location of the enzyme. *Plant Sci.* 136:43–57

45. Siebke K, von Caemmerer S, Badger M, Furbank RT. 1997. Expressing an *rbcS* antisense gene in transgenic *Flaveria bidentis* leads to an increased quantum requirement for CO$_2$ fixed in photosystems I and II. *Plant Physiol.* 115:1163–74

45a. Suzuki S, Murai N, Burnell JN, Arai M. 2000. Changes in photosynthetic carbon flow in transgenic rice plants that express C4-type phospho*enol*pyruvate carboxykinase from *Urochloa panicoides*. *Plant Physiol.* 124:163–72

46. Takeuchi Y, Akagi H, Kamasawa N, Osumi M, Honda H. 2000. Aberrant chloroplasts in transgenic rice plants expressing a high level of maize NADP-dependent malic enzyme. *Planta* 211:265–74

47. Trevanion SJ, Furbank RT, Ashton AR. 1997. NADP-malate dehydrogenase in the C$_4$ plant *Flaveria bidentis*. Cosense suppression of activity in mesophyll and bundle-sheath cells and consequences for photosynthesis. *Plant Physiol.* 113:1153–65

48. Tsuchida H, Tamai T, Fukayama H, Agarie S, Nomura M, et al. 2000. High level expression of C$_4$-specific NADP-malic

enzyme in leaves and impairment of pho-toautotrophic growth of C_3 plant rice. *Plant Cell Physiol.* In press

49. von Caemmerer S, Furbank RT. 1999. Modeling C_4 photosynthesis. See Ref. 40a, pp. 173–211

50. von Caemmerer S, Millgate A, Farqu-har GD, Furbank RT. 1997. Reduction of ribulose-1,5-bisphosphate carboxylase/oxygenase by antisense RNA in the C_4 plant *Flaveria bidentis* leads to reduced assimilation rates and increased carbon isotope discrimination. *Plant Physiol.* 113:469–77

Annu. Rev. Plant Physiol. Plant Mol. Biol. 2001. 52:315–33

THE PLASTID DIVISION MACHINE

Katherine W Osteryoung and Rosemary S McAndrew

Department of Plant Biology, Michigan State University, East Lansing, Michigan 48824;
e-mail: osteryou@msu.edu, smithr72@msu.edu

Key Words chloroplast, FtsZ, MinD, bacterial cell division, organelle fission, *Arabidopsis*

■ **Abstract** Plastid division is essential for the maintenance of plastid populations in cells undergoing division and for the accumulation of large chloroplast numbers in photosynthetic tissues. Although the mechanisms mediating plastid division are poorly understood, ultrastructural studies imply this process is accomplished by a dynamic macromolecular machine organized into ring structures at the plastid midpoint. A key component of the engine that powers this machine is the motor-like protein FtsZ, a cytoskeletal GTPase of endosymbiotic origin that forms a ring at the plastid division site, similar to the function of its prokaryotic relatives in bacterial cytokinesis. This review considers the phylogenetic distribution and structural properties of two recently identified plant FtsZ protein families in the context of their distinct roles in plastid division and describes current evidence regarding factors that govern their placement at the division site. Because of their evolutionary and mechanistic relationship, the process of bacterial cell division provides a valuable, though incomplete, paradigm for understanding plastid division in plants.

CONTENTS

INTRODUCTION

It is perhaps premature given the sparse state of our knowledge to refer to the protein components that make up the plastid division complex as a "machine." Nevertheless, plastid division, like other cellular processes involving remodeling of organelles, is clearly orchestrated by a macromolecular complex composed of numerous proteins that coordinate the mechanical activity required to constrict the plastid. This review focuses specifically on the molecules that are known or postulated to make up the plastid division apparatus in photosynthetic eukaryotes. Because only a few components of the divison complex have been identified to date, their functions are emphasized. However, information from other systems, most prominently bacteria, is included in the context of its potential relevance to understanding plastid division. For literature related to the developmental and regulatory aspects of plastid division, the reader is referred to other reviews (9, 48–50, 85a–88).

MORPHOLOGICAL ASPECTS OF PLASTID DIVISION

A brief discussion of the morphological and ultrastructural changes that accompany progression through a plastid division cycle is in order at the outset because functional analysis of the protein participants must be interpreted within the context of what is actually observed. More detailed treatments of this subject can be found in the following references: (46, 47, 51, 86, 121). Most of the information derived from light microscopy has concentrated on observations of green chloroplasts because they are easily viewed, but ultrastructural evidence and recent molecular and genetic data suggest that the division process and associated machinery are likely to be similar for all plastid types.

At the level of light microscopy, the first visible indication that chloroplast division has commenced is the formation of a constriction located at the plastid midpoint, perpendicular to the longitudinal axis (48, 51). In land plants, division is accompanied by a lengthening and narrowing of the chloroplast, and at late stages a narrow, twisted isthmus joining the two daughter plastids is sometimes observed. At the ultrastructural level, formation of the central constriction is frequently associated with the appearance of an electron-dense annular structure termed the plastid dividing (PD) ring (11–13, 23, 38, 39, 45, 47, 51, 64, 67, 68, 79, 80, 86, 114). Such structures have been described in chloroplasts from diverse plant and algal taxa, as well as in amyloplasts and proplastids from various tissues (tabulated in 47). In the red algae *Cyanidioschyzon merolae* and *Cyanidium caldarium*, in which the ultrastructure of plastid division has been investigated in detail, the PD ring is visible early in the division process and becomes thicker as the constriction narrows, but in land plants the PD ring does not become visible until constriction is well under way. In many electron micrographs, the PD ring can be resolved into two concentric rings, one associated with the stromal surface of the inner envelope membrane and the other associated with the cytosolic surface of the outer envelope membrane. More recent work has revealed a third electron-dense component of the PD ring localized in the intermembrane space in *C. merolae* (66). In some studies, thin filaments encircling the constriction have also been described (13, 47, 79, 116). It is generally assumed that the PD ring functions in the division process by constricting the membranes, but the molecular composition of these rings and how they function remains to be established.

EVOLUTIONARY ORIGIN OF THE DIVISION APPARATUS

Like many plastid-associated processes, plastid division has its evolutionary origin in the cyanobacterial endosymbiont that gave rise to chloroplasts (82). The possibility that the plastid division apparatus might have components in common with those involved in prokaryotic cell division was recognized by Possingham & Lawrence (86) and more recently by Suzuki et al (114). The latter investigators specifically suggested a possible relationship between the PD rings in *C. merolae* and the bacterial cell division protein FtsZ, an essential cytoskeletal component of the bacterial cell division apparatus that forms a contractile ring during cytokinesis (described below). This relationship was confirmed with the discovery of a nuclear gene from *Arabidopsis thaliana* that encoded a protein with over 40% amino acid identity to many bacterial FtsZ proteins and over 50% identity to the cyanobacterial FtsZs. The further demonstration that the *Arabidopsis* FtsZ protein was synthesized as a precursor and posttranslationally targeted to the chloroplast by virtue of a cleavable chloroplast transit peptide strongly suggested its involvement in chloroplast division (84).

A definitive role for plant FtsZ proteins in plastid division was subsequently confirmed in the moss *Physcomitrella patens* and in *Arabidopsis*. In the moss, homologous recombination was used to create a knockout mutation in one of two *FtsZ* genes present in this organism (111). Instead of having multiple chloroplasts as in wild-type plants, cells in the deletion mutants appeared to contain only a single "macrochloroplast" in every tissue examined, consistent with a defect in plastid division. In *Arabidopsis*, an antisense approach was employed to generate transgenic plants in which accumulation of AtFtsZ1-1 (formerly called cpFtsZ), the chloroplast-targeted FtsZ protein described above, was greatly reduced (83, 110). In this case as well, cells from mesophyll tissue, instead of containing the wild-type complement of approximately 100 chloroplasts (Figure 1*A*; see color insert), contained as few as one very large chloroplast (Figure 1*B*; see color insert). These studies demonstrated an essential role for *FtsZ* genes in plastid division in both nonvascular and vascular land plants, indicating that a portion of the prokaryotic cell division apparatus was recruited during the evolution of chloroplasts from their cyanobacterial ancestors to function in plastid division. Subsequent studies described later in this review have revealed that this conservation extends to other prokaryotic cell division genes as well.

FTSZ FUNCTION IN PLASTID DIVISION

Bacterial FtsZ

A brief overview of the structure and function of bacterial FtsZ is important for understanding how its eukaryotic counterparts might function in plastid division. The reader is also referred to other recent reviews (7, 25, 58, 62, 76, 104). *FtsZ*, like numerous other genes involved in bacterial cell division, was identified genetically in a screen for temperature-sensitive mutants of *Escherichia coli* that formed long filaments at the restrictive temperature due to defects in cell division, and hence they were termed *fts* mutants (filamentation temperature-sensitive) (59). The protein is encoded by an ancient and highly conserved gene found in most prokaryotes, usually in a single copy. FtsZ is now known to be a structural homologue and very likely the evolutionary precursor of the eukaryotic tubulins (26, 30, 54, 77). Like tubulin, FtsZ is a self-polymerizing, filament-forming GTPase (8, 15, 28, 72–74, 99, 101, 123), and it functions during bacterial cell division by assembling into a ring structure at the division site on the interior surface of the cytoplasmic membrane (5). Mutant analysis has shown that FtsZ ring assembly is required for the subsequent midcell localization of all other components of the cell division apparatus (1, 62). The FtsZ ring remains associated with the leading edge of the division septum throughout cytokinesis, then it disassembles immediately following cell separation before rapidly reassembling at the center of the newly formed daughter cells (1, 5, 19, 113). The in vivo structure of the FtsZ ring and how it effects bacterial cytokinesis are not yet known, but recent data suggest that GTP hydrolysis triggered by FtsZ polymerization may generate the force and induce the curvature necessary for constriction (55).

Phylogenetic Distribution of *FtsZ* Genes

Genes encoding FtsZ have been identified in nearly all prokaryotes, including archaeal species, cyanobacteria, and the wall-less mycoplasmas as well as in diverse eukaryotes, including unicellular algae and other protists, moss, and vascular plants (reviewed recently in 2, 33). Most of the eukaryotic *FtsZ* genes identified to date are related to those in cyanobacteria and are presumed to be involved in chloroplast division. Recently, a role for FtsZs in mitochondrial division has also been uncovered in the chromophyte algae and in red algae, which, in addition to their cyanobacterial-like FtsZs, contain *FtsZ* genes closely related to those of the α-proteobacterial ancestors of mitochondria (3, 115). However, *FtsZ* genes have not been found in fungi or animals, organisms in which mitochondrial division is apparently accomplished by another self-assembling GTPase, dynamin (27, 81).

Evolutionary and Functional Diversity Among Plant FtsZ Proteins

A significant number of FtsZ sequences from land plants have been submitted to the gene databases in the past few years. In phylogenetic analyses, these proteins,

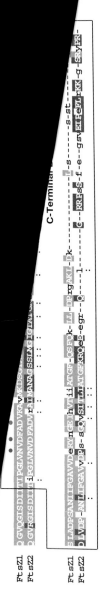

C-Terminal

```
FtsZ1   QGVQGISDIITPGLVNVDFADVKAVVKDSG...
FtsZ2   QGKGISDIIIPGLVNVDFADVFIMANAGSSIVGILAV...

FtsZ1   SLADPSANIIFGAVVDERKNGEIRNVIIIAGF-QSIQk-IM-DPrgAKI-Dk------------s------s-st-----
FtsZ2   DIVDE-ANIIFGAVVDPs-sQVSTIIIAGFKRQEa-egr--Q------l--@--RRIsS-f-e-gsvEIEeIL-KK-g-SEVER-
```

Figure 4 Comparison of FtsZ1 and FtsZ2 proteins from higher plants. Each sequence shown is a consensus derived from several full-length FtsZ1 or FtsZ2 sequences using the Clustal W program (117) at the Biology WorkBench 3.2 website (http://workbench.sdsc.edu). Sequences used to generate the FtsZ1 consensus were from *Arabidopsis thaliana* (U39877), *Tagetes erecta* (AF251346) and *Nicotiana tabacum* (AJ133453, AJ271749, and AF205858). Sequences used to generate the FtsZ2 consensus were from *A. thaliana* (AF089738 and CAB89236), *G. lutea* (AAF23771), *N. tabacum* (AJ271750), and *Lilium longiflorum* (AB042101). The highly variable extreme amino termini are not included in the alignment. The N-terminal and C-terminal domains are enclosed in boxes. Residues identical in FtsZ1 and FtsZ2 are highlighted in gray. Residues in FtsZ1 that differ from FtsZ2, and vice versa, are highlighted in green and blue, respectively. Similar residues, underscored by a colon, were as specified by the default setting of the Boxshade program at the Biology WorkBench 3.2 website. Upper case letters indicate residues that are identical in all FtsZ1 or FtsZ2 family members indicated above. Lower case letters indicate amino acids that are similar within FtsZ1 or FtsZ2 family, but not identical. Residues that are not similar and not conserved within protein family are indicated by a dash. Thick black lines above the alignment show residues known to contact the guanine nucleotide in *M. jannaschii* FtsZ (53) that are also conserved in the plant FtsZ sequences. Red diamonds indicate residues essential for GTPase activity in bacterial FtsZ, and a change in one of these specific to FtsZ1 is circled in black (26). Red dots indicate "synergy" residues that do not contact GTP, but are required for the regulation of GTP hydrolysis in the bacterial protein. The "tubulin signature motif" is underscored by a double black line. The "C-terminal core domain" sequence (60), specific to FtsZ2, is enclosed by a red box. Further details are provided in the text.

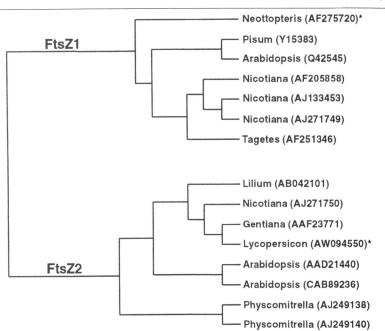

Figure 2 Phylogenetic analysis of FtsZ proteins from land plants performed using Clustal W (117) at the Biology WorkBench 3.2 website (http://workbench.sdsc.edu). The tree was rooted with a cyanobacterial sequence (accession P45482; not shown). Accession numbers are shown in parentheses. Asterisks indicate partial sequences.

all encoded in the nucleus, fall into two major groups that have been designated the FtsZ1 and FtsZ2 families (83) (Figure 2). Expressed sequence tag collections suggest that both families are represented in most angiosperms and are encoded by small gene families. *Arabidopsis* has one *FtsZ1* and two *FtsZ2* genes; but multiple *FtsZ1* genes are present in tobacco, and a partial sequence from a fern groups with the FtsZ1 family (note *Neottopteris* in Figure 2), suggesting that *FtsZ1* and *FtsZ2* genes are present in all vascular plants. The only two FtsZ sequences currently available from a nonvascular plant are from *Physcomitrella*, and both of these fall into the FtsZ2 family.

The *FtsZ1* and *FtsZ2* gene products are more closely related to the cyanobacterial FtsZs than to those in other prokaryotes, consistent with an endosymbiotic origin in both cases, yet they differ in their overall sequence relatedness and in their predicted subcellular localizations. All members of the FtsZ1 family for which full-length sequences are available are predicted by the program TargetP (24) to contain cleavable chloroplast transit peptides at their amino-terminal ends that target them to the stromal compartment (Table 1). These predictions have been verified in in vitro chloroplast import assays for *Arabidopsis* AtFtsZ1-1 (84) and for an FtsZ1 family member from *Pisum sativum* (32). In contrast, most members of the FtsZ2 family are not predicted by TargetP to bear chloroplast transit peptides, at least not in flowering plants. Consistent with the low TargetP score

TABLE 1   TargetP predictions for the presence of an N-terminal chloroplast transit peptide for all full-length FtsZ sequences from land plants currently represented in the public databases

Organism	Accession number	Family grouping	TargetP[a] score[b]	Chloroplast import assay results	Reference number
Arabidopsis thaliana	Q43545	FtsZ1	.974	Imported	83, 84
Nicotiana tabacum	AJ133453	FtsZ1	.934	NPD[c]	—
Nicotiana tabacum	AJ271749	FtsZ1	.916	NPD	—
Nicotiana tabacum	AF205858	FtsZ1	.968	NPD	—
Pisum sativum	Y15383	FtsZ1	.945	Imported	32
Tagetes erecta	AF2513460	FtsZ1	.938	NPD	69
Arabidopsis thaliana	AAD21440	FtsZ2	.161[d]	Not imported[d]	83
Arabidopsis thaliana	CAB89236	FtsZ2	.374	NPD	83
Gentiana lutea	AAF23771	FtsZ2	.555	NPD	—
Nicotiana tabacum	AJ271750	FtsZ2	.131	NPD	—
Lilium longiflorum	AB042101	FtsZ2	.712	NPD	—
Physcomitrella patens	AJ249140	FtsZ2	.782	Imported	43a
Physcomitrella patens	AJ249138	FtsZ2	.871	Imported	43a, 111

[a](24); http://www.cbs.dtu.dk/services/TargetP/

[b]Calculated using N-terminal 130 amino acids of predicted open reading frame.

[c]No published data.

[d]Based on predicted open reading frame.

of 0.161 calculated for AtFsZ2-1, an *Arabidopsis* FtsZ2 family member (Table 1, accession number AAD21440), this protein failed to undergo import into isolated chloroplasts under the same conditions in which AtFtsZ1-1 was imported (83). However, the higher TargetP score for an FtsZ2 protein from *Lilium longiflorum* suggest that some higher plant FtsZ2 family members could be imported into the chloroplast, as recently noted for the two FtsZ proteins from *Physcomitrella* (43a) (Table 1). This ambiguity underscores the limitations of the available computational resources for predicting the presence or absence of chloroplast transit peptides, and it emphasizes the need for verifying the localization predictions experimentally, particularly in cases where the scores are equivocal. A further caveat to use of TargetP and related programs is that the input sequences used in the analyses are often taken from the open reading frames (ORFs) identified by gene prediction programs, which may not accurately predict the true translational initiation sites. For example, recent database submissions have revealed that the ORF predicted from the genomic and cDNA sequences of *AtFtsZ2-1* (Table 1, accession number AAD21440) is shorter at its 5′ end than the ORFs predicted for several other *FtsZ2* genes. However, inspection of the *AtFtsZ2-1* gene sequence reveals a second potential in-frame start codon 243 nucleotides (81 codons)

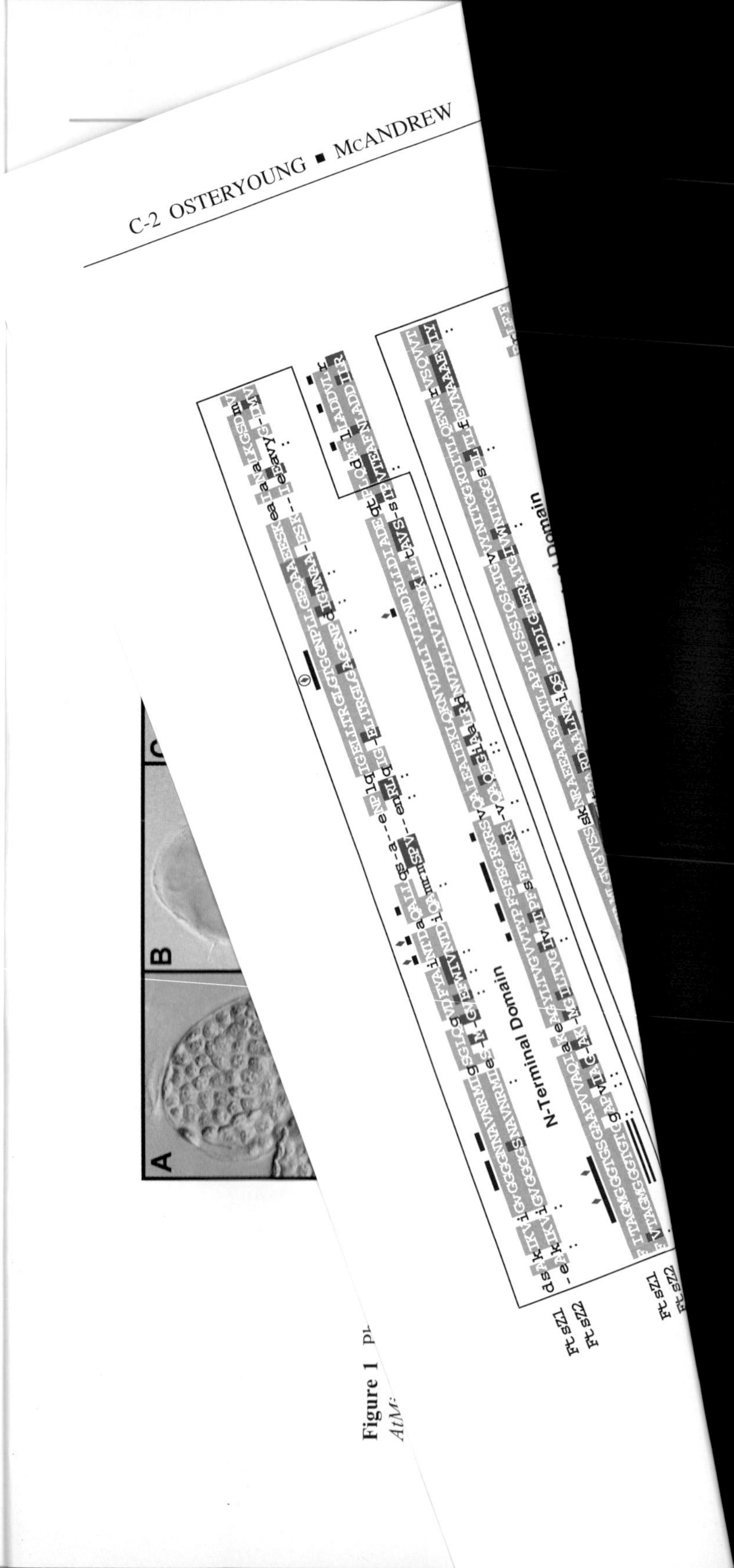

Figure 1

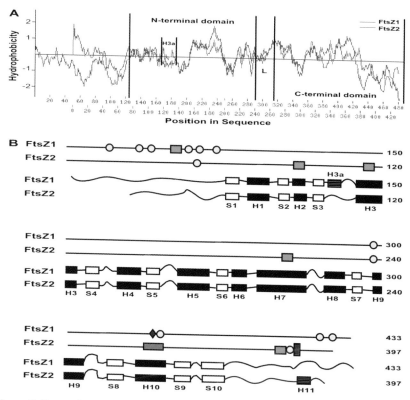

Figure 5 Comparison of structural properties and sequence motifs predicted for FtsZ1 and FtsZ2 proteins from higher plants. (*A*) Hydropathy profiles of FtsZ1 from *Arabidopsis* (U39877) (red) and FtsZ2 from *Gentiana lutea* (AAF23771) (blue), were determined using the Kyte-Doolittle x-1 method at the Weizmann Institute Bioinformatics website (http://bioinfo.weizmann.ac.il/). Regions described in the text containing the N-terminal and C-terminal domains, and the linker region connecting them (L), are separated by vertical black lines. The difference in hydrophobicity from FtsZ2 seen in the helical region H3a of FtsZ1 also is shown. (*B*) Alignment between FtsZ1 and FtsZ2 consensus sequences (described in legend to Figure 4) showing predicted motifs and secondary structural features. Numbers at the right of each line indicate the approximate residue numbers within the FtsZ1 and FtsZ2 proteins. The top two lines in the alignment indicate various phosphorylation sites predicted for FtsZ1 or FtsZ2 proteins that are conserved within each family. Included are those recognized by protein kinase C (yellow ovals), cGMP-dependent kinases (red box), casein kinase II (red diamond), tyrosine-dependent kinase (blue box), and those that may be phosphorylated by either cGMP-, cAMP-, or calmodulin-dependent kinases (green boxes). Predictions were made using the programs PPSEARCH (http://expasy.cbr.nrc.ca, and http://www.ebi.ac.uk), PhosphoBase (44) and NetPhos 2.0 (http://www.cbs.dtu.dk). Consensus sites were included in the figure only if they were indicated by all three programs, were conserved in all members of the FtsZ1 or FtsZ2 family listed in Figure 4, and received a NetPhos 2.0 score of at least 0.9. Secondary structural predictions made by

Figure 5 *continued*

PSIPRED (http://globin.bio.warwick.ac.uk) are shown in the bottom two lines of the alignment. Regions predicted to be non-structured random coils, or loops, are indicated by wavy black lines; α-helices or β-strands that are conserved in each protein family are indicated by black or white boxes and labeled H or S, respectively. Hatched boxes indicate two helices, H3a and H11, that are found only in FtsZ1 or FtsZ2 proteins, respectively. The strands and helices, more fully described in the text, are numbered according to their relative positions in the primary sequences of FtsZ1 or FtsZ2.

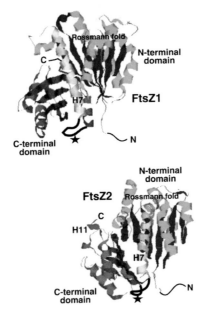

Figure 6 Comparison of hypothetical three-dimensional structures of FtsZ1 and FtsZ2. Ribbon diagrams of FtsZ1 (*top*) and FtsZ2 (*bottom*) were modeled using the program RasMol 2.6 from structural coordinates determined by the Swiss-Model protein modeling server (34, 85) (http://www.expasy.ch/) using the AtFtsZ1-1 (U39877) and AtFtsZ2-1 (AF089738) protein sequences, respectively, and the crystal structure of FtsZ from *Methanococcus jannaschii* (ID1FSZ) (54). α-Helices and β-strands of the N-terminal domain are green and blue, respectively, and those of the C-terminal domain are orange and red. The N- and C-terminal ends, and the central helices connecting the two domains (yellow) are labeled N, C, and H7, respectively; the helix containing the "C-terminal core domain" (60) in the FtsZ2 structure (light blue) is labeled H11. The Rossmann fold GTP-binding structures in the N-terminal domains of FtsZ1 and FtsZ2 are composed of alternating β-strands (S1-S6 in Figure 5B) and α-helices (H1-H5 in Figure 5B), which together form parallel β-sheets (53, 103). The loops in the C-terminal domains contain the "synergy" residues (stars). The FtsZ2 structure is shown from a slightly different angle than that of FtsZ1 to emphasize the presence of the C-terminal core domain, which is not found in FtsZ1 proteins. Otherwise, the structures are nearly superimposable. The figure is further described in the text.

upstream of the predicted start site that corresponds closely to the position of the predicted start codon for a second *Arabidopsis FtsZ2* gene, *AtFtsZ2-2* (Table 1, accession number CAB89263). This suggests the possibility of misidentified or perhaps multiple translational initiation sites among *FtsZ2* genes. Analysis of the longer *AtFtsZ2-1* ORF by TargetP changes the chloroplast targeting score from 0.161 to a more ambiguous 0.555 and suggests that the corresponding polypeptide might be imported into chloroplasts if tested in an in vitro import assay, contrary to the results obtained using the shorter ORF (Table 1) (83). In addition, targeting prediction programs may be less reliable for proteins from taxonomic groups that are not well represented in the datasets used in their construction. Nevertheless, these programs have been invaluable for revealing a potentially important distinction between FtsZ1 and FtsZ2 proteins in flowering plants, though whether both groups are represented in all land plants, and if so whether the apparent correlation between family grouping and presence or absence of a transit peptide will apply in all cases, remains unknown.

Although the localization predictions suggest that many FtsZ2 proteins are not targeted to the stromal compartment, an essential role for them in plastid division was established by the finding that *Arabidopsis* plants expressing an *AtFtsZ2-1* antisense transgene exhibited defects in chloroplast division identical to those observed in the *AtFtsZ1-1* antisense plants (83) (Figure 1*C*; see color insert). The demonstration that AtFtsZ1-1 protein levels were unaffected in the *AtFtsZ2-1* antisense plants and vice versa (110) confirmed that FtsZ1 and FtsZ2 proteins, though postulated to be localized in different subcellular compartments, each played essential but functionally distinct roles in plastid division.

Proposed Functions of FtsZ1 and FtsZ2

A consistent feature of recent models depicting the macromolecular configuration of the plastid division apparatus is inclusion of the stromal and cytosolic PD rings observed in ultrastructural studies (47, 65, 79). Osteryoung et al (83) incorporated the results of the AtFtsZ1-1 and AtFtsZ2-1 chloroplast import and antisense experiments described above into these models by postulating that, in higher plants, FtsZ1 and FtsZ2 proteins are components of the stromal and cytosolic PD rings, respectively, functioning together on the two envelope surfaces to constrict the organelle. In partial support of this model, recent immunofluorescence localization studies have confirmed that FtsZ1 and FtsZ2 proteins colocalize to rings at the plastid midpoint in *Arabidopsis* and other plants (Figure 3; see color insert) (S Vitha, RS McAndrew, & KW Osteryoung, submitted). Based on the combination of targeting predictions and in vitro chloroplast import experiments (32, 84), it can be reasonably concluded that the FtsZ1-containing ring is localized inside the chloroplast, though whether it represents the same structure as the stromal PD ring remains to be established. However, higher resolution techniques are needed to determine precisely where with respect to the envelope membranes the FtsZ2-containing ring is situated. Though its proposed localization on the cytosolic surface of the outer envelope is consistent with the position of the cytosolic PD ring, these two rings may represent distinct structures, and the FtsZ2 ring may be positioned along with FtsZ1 inside the stromal compartment. If this were true, it would suggest the possibility that FtsZ1 and FtsZ2 form heterodimers in vivo, as do α- and β-tubulin (78). Alternatively, FtsZ2 could be localized in the intermembrane space, a possibility suggested by the recent description of a third PD ring positioned between the envelope membranes in the red alga *C. merolae* (66). Complicating this issue further is the fact that it has not yet been determined whether there is functional overlap between AtFtsZ2-1 and AtFtsZ2-2. The arrangement of the FtsZ1 and FtsZ2 rings remains a major outstanding issue with important implications for understanding how the plastid division complex as a whole is organized and how its component proteins function together to achieve organelle constriction.

COMPARISON BETWEEN PLANT FTSZ1 AND FTSZ2 PROTEINS

Although the predicted presence or absence of a chloroplast transit peptide in higher plant FtsZ proteins is correlated with their assignment to the FtsZ1 or FtsZ2 family, respectively, the phylogenetic analyses responsible for these assignments (Figure 2) are based on sequence alignments that exclude the amino-terminal portions of the proteins, which are highly variable and thus phylogenetically uninformative. It is therefore instructive to consider structural properties in addition to the transit peptides that distinguish FtsZ1 and FtsZ2 proteins from one another. This is best accomplished by comparing the plant proteins with their well-studied bacterial counterparts.

Structural Domains

In general, plant FtsZ proteins share most of the structural features common to the bacterial proteins (26, 53, 54). These features are highlighted in Figures 4, 5, and 6 (see color inserts), which represent the primary (excluding the extreme amino-terminal end), secondary, and tertiary structures, respectively, of FtsZ1 and FtsZ2. All FtsZs can be divided into two major structural domains: a highly conserved N-terminal domain and a less well-conserved C-terminal domain. The N-terminal domain forms a Rossmann fold (53, 103), typical of the GTPase domain of Ras and other G-proteins. This structure contains the "tubulin signature motif," GGGTG(T/S)G, required for GTP binding in FtsZs and tubulins (15, 25, 56, 73, 99) (note double underline in Figure 4) as well as residues that contact the guanine nucleotide (black bars) and are essential for GTP-hydrolysis (red diamonds) (120). These residues are completely conserved in the plant sequences with one exception. In FtsZ1 proteins, an alanine residue essential for GTP-binding and hydrolysis in the bacterial proteins has been replaced by a threonine residue (circled red diamond). This may be important for its function in the chloroplast stroma, as just prior to this substitution there is a helical structure (H3a) (Figure 5B) not present in FtsZ2 proteins that corresponds to the only region in the N-terminal domain in which FtsZ1 and FtsZ2 differ significantly in their hydrophobicity (Figure 5A). Otherwise, the secondary (Figure 5B) and tertiary (Figure 6) structures of the N-terminal domains in FtsZ1, FtsZ2, and the bacterial FtsZ proteins (26, 53) are nearly identical. In addition, there is a stretch of amino acids at the amino-terminal end of *E. coli* FtsZ, protruding from the otherwise globular structure, that forms a small helix and is required for FtsZ ring assembly in vivo (120). This helix is not evident in the plant structures (Figure 5B), but the residues at the amino-terminal ends of the FtsZ1 and FtsZ2 proteins are also predicted to protrude (Figure 6) and may be involved in assembly of the chloroplast FtsZ rings in plants.

The C-terminal domain of FtsZ is more variable among proteins from different organisms and appears to play a more regulatory role. However, some conserved features can be distinguished. Among these are three highly conserved "synergy" residues that regulate GTP hydrolysis and are essential for cell division in *E. coli*, although the C-terminal domain is dispensable for GTPase activity and FtsZ polymerization per se (120). These synergy residues are completely conserved in the plant FtsZ1 and FtsZ2 families (Figure 4, red dots; Figure 6, stars; see color inserts). Also present in the C-terminal domain are loop structures that have been implicated in the binding of calcium (53), which is thought to stabilize FtsZ polymer networks formed in vitro (29, 75, 109, 113, 123). Similar loop structures are predicted in FtsZ1 and FtsZ2, and they may participate in the assembly of plant FtsZs into multimers, which has been reported for an FtsZ1 protein from pea (32). The carboxyl end of the C-terminal domain contains a high proportion of hydrophilic residues exposed at the surface of the protein (Figure 5A; see color insert), and it resembles the microtubule-associated protein (MAP) binding regions of tubulin (20). Within this region is a small, highly conserved sequence, D/E-I/V-P-X-F/Y-L, termed the C-terminal core domain (60), which is required for direct interactions between FtsZ and two other essential cell division proteins in *E. coli*, ZipA and FtsA (21, 37, 52, 60, 70, 71, 120, 122). ZipA is an integral membrane protein with homology to MAPs that stabilizes the FtsZ ring structure and may be involved in anchoring it to the bacterial cell membrane (35–37, 98). FtsA is a peripheral membrane protein related to the actin/HSP70 superfamily of ATPases and also functions in part to support the FtsZ ring structure (4, 35, 61, 106). Interestingly, the C-terminal core domain and associated secondary structure are conserved in the plant FtsZ2 proteins (Figure 4, red box; Figure 5B, H11; Figure 6, H11), but they are missing from FtsZ1. This suggests that proteins similar to ZipA and/or FtsA may interact specifically with FtsZ2, and it reveals a structural distinction between the two protein families that may be relevant to their distinct functions in plastid division.

The N-terminal and C-terminal domains are connected and clearly delimited by a long central helix (Figure 5B, H7; Figure 6, H7). In bacteria, this helix contains additional residues that contact the guanine nucleotide (53). The linker helix and associated GTP-binding residues are also conserved in both FtsZ1 and FtsZ2 (Figure 4, black bars in unboxed region). The presence in both plant proteins of all structural elements required for FtsZ activity in bacteria implies that the FtsZ1 and FtsZ2 proteins catalyze similar reactions even though they have distinct functions and may be localized in different subcellular compartments.

Posttranslational Modification Motifs

Posttranslational modifications of FtsZ proteins have not been documented so far, but they occur for tubulins. In animal systems, phosphorylation by various kinases mediates tubulin assembly and stability, microtubule localization, and binding of tubulin and microtubules to other proteins such as MAPs (61a). Related modifications of tubulins also occur in higher plants (108a). Analysis of FtsZ1 and FtsZ2 for posttranslational modification consensus motifs using various online resources reveals a number of potential phosphorylation sites that are unique to, but conserved within, each family (Figure 5B). For example, FtsZ2 proteins share one tyrosine kinase recognition site (Figure 5B, blue box) and one cGMP-dependent kinase recognition site (red box) that are not present in FtsZ1 proteins. Likewise, FtsZ1 proteins may be uniquely phosphorylated by casein kinase II (Figure 5B, red diamond). Although the consensus phosphorylation sites indicated in Figure 5B are derived primarily from studies of kinases from nonplant systems, kinases with comparable activities exist in plants (34a, 52a, 114a, 119a). Other kinds of modifications that are not easily predicted are also possible, such as palmitoylation, which mediates attachment of tubulin to membranes (10, 124). Although the predicted posttranslational modifications shown in Figure 5B would have to be tested experimentally to determine whether they occur in vivo, they nevertheless provide potential clues to mechanisms that may be important for regulating FtsZ1 and FtsZ2 function.

PLACEMENT OF THE PLASTID DIVISION MACHINERY

The many images of intact, dividing plastids present in the literature, whether obtained by conventional light microscopy (51, 68, 92, 100, 102), three-dimensional reconstruction (31, 67), or scanning electron microscopy (12, 65), invariably show the constriction positioned near the center of the organelle, perpendicular to the longitudinal axis. This implies the existence of a mechanism for ensuring proper placement of the division machinery. Recent data have revealed that this process also has a prokaryotic origin, having evolved from the mechanism controlling the site of cell division in many bacteria.

Selection of the Cell Division Site in Bacteria

In *E. coli*, placement of the FtsZ ring is governed by the *minB* operon, which encodes three gene products: MinC, MinD, and MinE (reviewed in 57, 104, 105, 112). Genetic analysis has shown that the activities of these proteins exhibit a complicated pattern of interdependency. In wild-type cells, MinC acts as a division inhibitor by suppressing formation of the FtsZ ring at all sites except the cell center (6, 17, 18) in part by destabilizing FtsZ polymerization at inappropriate sites (41). This activity is dependent on MinD, which is thought to form a heterodimer with MinC (42). Localization studies in *E. coli* that are based on fusions to green fluorescent protein have revealed that MinD is associated with the cell membrane but only on one side of the cell at a time. MinD oscillates between the two cell poles with a periodicity of less than one minute and is thought to carry along as cargo the MinC division inhibitor, which exhibits a similar membrane association and oscillatory behavior (40, 95, 96). The oscillation of MinD requires MinE, which localizes to a ring at the midcell independently of FtsZ and in turn requires MinD for its activity (97). The MinE ring prevents MinCD from acting at the cell center, thereby allowing FtsZ ring assembly, and hence cell division, only at that position. The *min* locus is so-named because mutations in *minC* or *minD* allow the FtsZ ring to assemble at aberrant sites near the cell poles, resulting in the formation of mini-cells that lack chromosomes and cannot expand (16). Mutations in *minE*, on the other hand, permit MinCD to act ectopically at the midcell, thereby preventing FtsZ ring assembly at all sites and resulting in the formation of bacterial filaments. The mechanisms responsible for this complex situation are not yet fully understood.

Genes encoding MinC, MinD, and MinE are also found in numerous other prokaryotes, including the cyanobacterium *Synechocystis* PCC6803 (43). MinE is absent in *Bacillus subtilis*, however, and exclusion of the MinCD inhibitor from the cell center is accomplished by a different protein (104).

Role of MinD in Plastid Division Site Selection

That placement of the plastid division machinery in photosynthetic eukaryotes is mediated by a mechanism related to that in bacteria was strongly suggested by the discovery that homologues of MinD and MinE are encoded in the plastid genomes of the unicellular algae *Chlorella vulgaris* (119) and *Guillardia theta* (22). MinD is also encoded in the plastid genomes of the algae *Nephroselmis olivacea* (118) and *Prototheca wickerhamii* (accession number CAB53105) as well as the nuclear genomes of diverse higher plants, including *Arabidopsis*, rice, and marigold (14, 69). The MinD proteins from *Arabidopsis* and marigold bear cleavable chloroplast transit peptides that direct their import into isolated chloroplasts (14; J Froehlich & KW Osteryoung, unpublished results). *MinC* genes have not been identified in any photosynthetic eukaryote.

A role for MinD in positioning of the chloroplast division apparatus has recently been confirmed. Using an antisense approach, Colletti et al (14) demonstrated that reduced expression of *AtMinD1*, which encodes the chloroplast-targeted MinD homologue from *Arabidopsis*, yielded plants that had asymmetrically constricted plastids, indicating misplacement of the division apparatus and an abnormally high degree of heterogeneity in chloroplast size and number, resembling the bacterial minicell phenotype (Figure 1*D*; see color insert). Similar phenotypes have been described in the *Arabidopsis* mutant *arc11* (63), which may be allelic with *AtMinD1* (14). The antisense phenotypes also had implications for the order in which components of the plastid division apparatus are assembled. The asymmetric constriction suggested that reduced levels of plastid-targeted MinD allows misplacement of the plastid-localized FtsZ1 ring, which in turn leads to misplacement of other division components and hence to asymmetric division. Therefore, these results suggested that placement of the entire plastid division apparatus is normally determined from inside the chloroplast by the position of the FtsZ1 ring (14).

ADDITIONAL COMPONENTS OF THE PLASTID DIVISION APPARATUS

Currently, *FtsZ*, *MinD*, and *MinE* are the only obvious homologues of bacterial cell division genes known to exist in photosynthetic eukaryotes, and a role for *MinE* in plastid division has yet to be demonstrated. Because the functions of most of the other bacterial cell division proteins are unknown, they provide few clues regarding the likelihood that functional counterparts might participate in plastid division. However, at least nine proteins localize to the division septum in *E. coli* (62, 104), and the plastid division apparatus is likely to be at least as complex (82).

One potentially rich source of new plastid division genes is represented by the *Arabidopsis arc* mutants (accumulation and replication of chloroplasts). These mutants, which exhibit various abnormalities in chloroplast number and size, define at least 11 loci that are important in the control of plastid division and expansion in plants (63, 87, 89–91, 93). The *arc6* mutation, which causes drastically reduced numbers of enlarged chloroplasts and proplastids (93, 94) resembling those in plants expressing the *AtFtsZ1-1* and *AtFtsZ2-1* antisense transgenes (83; see also Figure 1*B* & 1*C*, see color inserts), is not allelic with any of the FtsZ genes in *Arabidopsis* (KA Pyke, personal communication) and may represent a regulatory step in plastid division (63). In most of the other *arc* mutants, the nature of the affected locus is not obvious and could be either structural or regulatory. The phenotype of *arc5*, however, in which the chloroplasts fail to separate completely and remain permanently constricted (102), strongly suggests that the *ARC5* gene product is a late-acting structural component of the division machinery. Cloning of this and other *arc* loci should reveal additional plastid division proteins and provide new insights as to how plastid division in plants is regulated.

Other approaches likely to yield new plastid division components include identification of proteins that interact directly with plant FtsZ proteins and proteomics-based strategies that rely on isolation of plastid division complexes. Progress toward the latter goal is represented by the recent isolation of intact chloroplasts from synchronized cultures of *C. merolae* to which PD rings remain visibly attached (65).

FUTURE CHALLENGES

As molecular dissection of the plastid division machinery moves forward, many of the questions alluded to throughout this review will begin to find answers. These include: (*a*) What is the composition of the plastid division apparatus? (*b*) How and in what order are its component parts assembled? (*c*) How are they topologically organized? (*d*) What are their biochemical activities and how do they affect constriction of the two envelope membranes? (*e*) How are these activities coordinated? (*f*) How is the division site specified and recognized? Because of the evolutionary relationship between plastid and prokaryotic cell division, bacterial models will no doubt continue to inform investigation of these questions, though the finding that multiple FtsZ genes participate in plastid division already suggests some fundamental differences between the plastid and bacterial cell division processes (82). It will also be of interest to learn whether there are differences between the plastid division machineries in algae and land plants that might shed light on the evolutionary steps that gave rise to the FtsZ1 and FtsZ2 gene families during land plant evolution (33).

Related questions that remain largely unexplored include the following: (*a*) Do active mechanisms exist for controlling plastid DNA segregation and thylakoid membrane partitioning to daughter plastids during division? The former possibility has been suggested by the discovery of a plastid DNA binding protein associated with the envelope membranes (107, 108). (*b*) Is there an active mechanism governing plastid segregation during cell division? The fact that aplastidic cells are not observed (except in guard cells) (94) suggests this may be the case. (*c*) How is total plastid compartment volume perceived and regulated? That such processes exist is implied by the finding that decreases in plastid number are almost always compensated for by corresponding increases in plastid size and vice versa (87, 90). (*d*) How are plastid division and expansion integrated into the plant's developmental program? A full understanding of plastid division will ultimately require investigation of all these issues.

Visit the Annual Reviews home page at www.AnnualReviews.org

LITERATURE CITED

1. Addinall SG, Bi E, Lutkenhaus J. 1996. FtsZ ring formation in *fts* mutants. *J. Bacteriol.* 178:3877–84
2. Beech PL, Gilson PR. 2000. FtsZ and organelle division in protists. *Protist* 151:11–16
3. Beech PL, Nheu T, Schultz T, Herbert S, Lithgow T, et al. 2000. Mitochondrial FtsZ in a chromophyte alga. *Science* 287:1276–79
4. Begg K, Nikolaichik Y, Crossland N, Donachie WD. 1998. Roles of FtsA and FtsZ in activation of division sites. *J. Bacteriol.* 180:881–84
5. Bi E, Lutkenhaus J. 1991. *FtsZ* ring structure associated with division in *Escherichia coli. Nature* 354:161–64
6. Bi E, Lutkenhaus J. 1993. Cell division inhibitors SulA and MinCD prevent formation of the FtsZ ring. *J. Bacteriol.* 175:1118–25

6a. Boffey SA, Lloyd D, eds. 1988. *Division and Segregation of Organelles.* Cambridge, UK: Cambridge Univ. Press
7. Bramhill D. 1997. Bacterial cell division. *Annu. Rev. Cell Dev. Biol.* 13:395–424
8. Bramhill D, Thompson CM. 1994. GTP-dependent polymerization of *Escherichia coli* FtsZ protein to form tubules. *Proc. Natl. Acad. Sci. USA* 91:5813–17
9. Butterfass T. 1988. Nuclear control of plastid division. See Ref. 6a, pp. 21–38
10. Caron JM. 1997. Posttranslational modification of tubulin by palmitoylation: I. In vivo and cell-free studies. *Mol. Biol. Cell* 8:621–36
11. Chaly N, Possingham JV. 1981. Structure of constricted proplastids in meristematic plant tissues. *Biol. Cell* 41:203–9

12. Chaly N, Possingham JV, Thomson WW. 1980. Chloroplast division in spinach leaves examined by scanning electron microscopy and freeze-etching. *J. Cell Sci.* 46:87–96

13. Chida Y, Ueda K. 1991. Division of chloroplasts in a green alga, *Trebouxia potteri*. *Ann. Bot.* 67:435–42

14. Colletti KS, Tattersall EA, Pyke KA, Froelich JE, Stokes KD, Osteryoung KW. 2000. A homologue of the bacterial cell division site-determining factor MinD mediates placement of the chloroplast division apparatus. *Curr. Biol.* 10:507–16

15. de Boer P, Crossley R, Rothfield L. 1992. The essential bacterial cell-division protein *FtsZ* is a GTPase. *Nature* 359:254–56

16. de Boer PAJ, Crossley RE, Rothfield LI. 1988. Isolation and properties of *minB*, a complex genetic locus involved in correct placement of the division site in *Escherichia coli*. *J. Bacteriol.* 170:2106–12

17. de Boer PAJ, Crossley RE, Rothfield LI. 1989. A division inhibitor and a topological specificity factor coded for by the minicell locus determine proper placement of the division septum in *E. coli*. *Cell* 56:641–49

18. de Boer PAJ, Crossley RE, Rothfield LI. 1992. Roles of MinC and MinD in the site-specific septation block mediated by the MinCDE system of *Escherichia coli*. *J. Bacteriol.* 174:63–70

19. Den Blaauwen T, Buddelmeijer N, Aarsman ME, Hameete CM, Nanninga N. 1999. Timing of FtsZ assembly in *Escherichia coli*. *J. Bacteriol.* 181:5167–75

20. Desai A, Mitchison TJ. 1998. Tubulin and FtsZ structures: functional and therapeutic implications. *BioEssays* 20:523–27

21. Din N, Quardokus EM, Sackett MJ, Brun YV. 1998. Dominant C-terminal deletions of FtsZ that affect its ability to localize in *Caulobacter* and its interaction with FtsA. *Mol. Microbiol.* 27:1051–63

22. Douglas SE, Penny SL. 1999. The plastid genome of the cryptophyte alga, *Guillardia theta*: complete sequence and conserved synteny groups confirm its common ancestry with red algae. *J. Mol. Evol.* 48:236–44

23. Duckett JG, Ligrone R. 1993. Plastid-dividing rings in ferns. *Ann. Bot.* 72:619–27

24. Emanuelsson O, Nielsen H, Brunak S, von Heijne G. 2000. Predicting subcellular localization of proteins based on their N-terminal amino acid sequence. *J. Mol. Biol.* 300:1005–16

25. Erickson HP. 1997. FtsZ, a tubulin homologue in prokaryote cell division. *Trends Cell Biol.* 7:362–67

26. Erickson HP. 1998 Atomic structures of tubulin and FtsZ. *Trends Cell Biol.* 8:133–37

27. Erickson HP. 2000. Dynamin and FtsZ: missing links in mitochondrial and bacterial division. *J. Cell Biol.* 148:1103–5

28. Erickson HP, Stoffler D. 1996. Protofilaments and rings, two conformations of the tubulin family conserved from bacterial FtsZ to α/β and γ tubulin. *J. Cell Biol.* 135:5–8

29. Erickson HP, Taylor DW, Taylor KA, Bramhill D. 1996. Bacterial cell division protein FtsZ assembles into protofilament sheets and minirings, structural homologs of tubulin polymers. *Proc. Natl. Acad. Sci. USA* 93:519–23

30. Faguy DM, Doolittle WF. 1998. Cytoskeletal proteins: the evolution of cell division. *Curr. Biol.* 8:R338–41

31. Gaffal KP, Arnold CG, Friedrichs GJ, Gemple W. 1995. Morphodynamical changes of the chloroplast of *Chlamydomonas reinhardtii* during the 1st round of division. *Arch. Protistenkd.* 145:10–23

32. Gaikwad A, Babbarwal V, Pant V, Mukherjee SK. 2000. Pea chloroplast FtsZ can form multimers and correct the thermosensitive defect of an *Escherichia coli ftsZ* mutant. *Mol. Gen. Genet.* 263:213–21

33. Gilson PR, Beech PL. 2000. Cell division protein FtsZ: running rings around bacteria, chloroplasts and mitochondria. *Res. Microbiol.* In press

34. Guex N, Peitsch MC. 1997. SWISS-MODEL and the Swiss-PdbViewer: an environment for comparative protein modeling. *Electrophoresis* 18:2714–23

34a. Guillén G, Valdlés-López V, Noguez R, Olivares J, Rodriguez-Zapata LC, et al. 1999. Profilin in *Phaseolus vulgaris* is encoded by two genes (only one expressed in root nodules) but multiple isoforms are generated *in vivo* by phosphorylation on tyrosine residues. *Plant J.* 19:497–508

35. Hale CA, de Boer PAJ. 1999. Recruitment of ZipA to the septal ring of *Escherichia coli* is dependent on FtsZ and independent of FtsA. *J. Bacteriol.* 181:167–76

36. Hale CA, de Boer PAJ. 1997. Direct binding of FtsZ to ZipA, an essential component of the septal ring structure that mediates cell division in *E. coli. Cell* 88:175–85

37. Hale CA, Rhee AC, de Boer PA. 2000. ZipA-induced bundling of FtsZ polymers mediated by an interaction between C-terminal domains. *J. Bacteriol.* 182:5153–66

38. Hashimoto H. 1986. Double ring structure around the constricting neck of dividing plastids of *Avena sativa. Protoplasma* 135:166–72

39. Hashimoto H, Possingham JV. 1989. Division and DNA distribution in ribosome-deficient plastids of the barley mutant "albostrians." *Protoplasma* 149:20–23

40. Hu Z, Lutkenhaus J. 1999. Topological regulation of cell division in *Escherichia coli* involves rapid pole to pole oscillation of the division inhibitor MinC under the control of MinD and MinE. *Mol. Microbiol.* 34:82–90

41. Hu Z, Mukherjee A, Pichoff S, Lutkenhaus J. 1999. The MinC component of the division site selection system in *Escherichia coli* interacts with FtsZ to prevent polymerization. *Proc. Natl. Acad. Sci. USA* 96:14819–24

42. Huang J, Cao C, Lutkenhaus J. 1996. Interaction between FtsZ and inhibitors of cell division. *J. Bacteriol.* 178:5080–85

43. Kaneko T, Sato S, Kotani H, Tanaka A, Asamizu E, et al. 1996. Sequence analysis of the genome of the unicellular cyanobacterium *Synechocystis* sp. strain PCC6803. II. Sequence determination of the entire genome and assignment of potential protein-coding regions. *DNA Res.* 3:109–36

43a. Kiessling J, Kruse S, Rensing SA, Harter K, Decker EL, Reski R. 2000. Visualization of a cytoskeleton-like FtsZ network in chloroplasts. *J. Cell Biol.* 151:945–50

44. Kreegipuu A, Blom N, Brunak S. 1999. PhosphoBase, a database of phosphorylation sites: release 2.0. *Nucleic Acids Res.* 27:237–39

45. Kuroiwa T. 1989. The nuclei of cellular organelles and the formation of daughter organelles by the "plastid-dividing ring". *Bot. Mag.* 102:291–329

46. Kuroiwa T. 1991. The replication, differentiation, and inheritance of plastids with emphasis on the concept of organelle nuclei. *Int. Rev. Cytol.* 128:1–62

47. Kuroiwa T, Kuroiwa H, Sakai A, Takahashi H, Toda K, Itoh R. 1998. The division apparatus of plastids and mitochondria. *Int. Rev. Cytol.* 181:1–41

48. Leech RM. 1976. The replication of plastids in higher plants. In *Cell Division in Higher Plants*, ed. MM Yeoman, pp. 135–59. London: Academic

49. Leech RM. 1986. Stability and plasticity during chloroplast development. In *Plasticity in Plants*, Vol. 40, ed. JW Jennings, AJ Trewavas, pp. 121–53. Cambridge, UK: Cambridge Univ. Press

50. Leech RM, Pyke KA. 1988. Chloroplast division in higher plants with particular reference to wheat. See Ref. 6a, pp. 39–62

51. Leech RM, Thomson WW, Platt-Aloia KA. 1981. Observations on the mechanism of chloroplast division in higher plants. *New Phytol.* 87:1–9

52. Liu Z, Mukherjee A, Lutkenhaus J. 1999. Recruitment of ZipA to the division site by interaction with FtsZ. *Mol. Microbiol.* 31:1853–61

52a. Loog M, Toomik R, Sak K, Muszynska G, Jarv J, Ek P. 2000. Peptide phosphorylation by calcium-dependent protein kinase from maize seedlings. *Eur. J. Biochem.* 267:337–43

53. Löwe J. 1998. Crystal structure determination of FtsZ from *Methanococcus jannaschii. J. Struct. Biol.* 124:235–43

54. Löwe J, Amos LA. 1998. Crystal structure of the bacterial cell-division protein FtsZ. *Nature* 391:203–6

55. Lu C, Reedy M, Erickson HP. 2000. Straight and curved conformations of FtsZ are regulated by GTP hydrolysis. *J. Bacteriol.* 182:164–70

56. Lutkenhaus J. 1993. FtsZ ring in bacterial cytokinesis. *Mol. Microbiol.* 9:403–9

57. Lutkenhaus J. 1998. The regulation of bacterial cell division: a time and place for it. *Curr. Opin. Microbiol.* 1:210–15

58. Lutkenhaus J, Addinall SG. 1997. Bacterial cell division and the Z ring. *Annu. Rev. Biochem.* 66:93–116

59. Lutkenhaus J, Wolf-Watz H, Donachie WD. 1980. Organization of genes in the *ftsZ-envA* region of the *Escherichia coli* genes map and identification of a new *fts* locus (*ftsZ*). *J. Bacteriol.* 142:615–20

60. Ma XL, Margolin W. 1999. Genetic and functional analyses of the conserved C-terminal core domain of *Escherichia coli* FtsZ. *J. Bacteriol.* 181:7531–44

61. Ma XL, Sun Q, Wang R, Singh G, Jonietz EL, Margolin W. 1997. Interactions between heterologous FtsA and FtsZ proteins at the FtsZ ring. *J. Bacteriol.* 179:6788–97

61a. MacRae TH. 1997. Tubulin post-translational modifications—enzymes and their mechanisms of action. *Eur. J. Biochem.* 244:265–78

62. Margolin W. 1998. A green light for the bacterial cytoskeleton. *Trends Microbiol.* 6:233–38

63. Marrison JL, Rutherford SM, Robertson EJ, Lister C, Dean C, Leech RM. 1999. The distinctive roles of five different *ARC* genes in the chloroplast division process in *Arabidopsis. Plant J.* 18:651–62

64. Mita T, Kuroiwa T. 1988. Division of plastids by a plastid-dividing ring in *Cyanidium caldarium. Protoplasma* 1(Suppl.):133–52

65. Miyagishima S, Itoh R, Aita S, Kuroiwa H, Kuroiwa T. 1999. Isolation of dividing chloroplasts with intact plastid-dividing rings from a synchronous culture of the unicellular red alga *Cyanidioschyzon merolae. Planta* 209:371–75

66. Miyagishima S, Itoh R, Toda K, Takahashi H, Kuroiwa H, Kuroiwa T. 1998. Identification of a triple ring structure involved in plastid division in the primitive red alga *Cyanidioschyzon merolae. J. Electron Microsc.* 47:269–72

67. Miyagishima S, Itoh R, Toda K, Takahashi H, Kuroiwa H, Kuroiwa T. 1998. Orderly formation of the double ring structures for plastid and mitochondrial division in the unicellular red alga *Cyanidioschyzon merolae. Planta* 206:551–60

68. Modrusan Z, Wrischer M. 1990. Studies on chloroplast division in young leaf tissues of some higher plants. *Protoplasma* 154:1–7

69. Moehs CP, Tian L, Osteryoung KW, DellaPenna D. 2001. Analysis of carotenoid biosynthetic gene expression during marigold petal development. *Plant Mol. Biol.* In press

70. Mosyak L, Zhang Y, Glasfeld E, Haney S, Stahl M, et al. 2000. The bacterial cell-division protein ZipA and its interaction with an FtsZ fragment revealed by X-ray crystallography. *EMBO J.* 19:3179–91

71. Moy FJ, Glasfeld E, Mosyak L, Powers R. 2000. Solution structure of ZipA, a crucial component of *Escherichia coli* cell division. *Biochemistry* 39:9146–56

72. Mukherjee A, Dai K, Lutkenhaus J. 1993. *Escherichia coli* cell division protein FtsZ is a guanine nucleotide binding protein. *Proc. Natl. Acad. Sci. USA* 90:1053–57

73. Mukherjee A, Lutkenhaus J. 1994. Guanine nucleotide-dependent assembly of FtsZ into filaments. *J. Bacteriol.* 176:2754–58

74. Mukherjee A, Lutkenhaus J. 1998. Dynamic assembly of FtsZ regulated by GTP hydrolysis. *EMBO J.* 17:462–69

75. Mukherjee A, Lutkenhaus J. 1999. Analysis of FtsZ assembly by light scattering and determination of the role of divalent metal cations. *J. Bacteriol.* 181:823–32

76. Nanninga N. 1998. Morphogenesis of *Escherichia coli*. *Microbiol. Mol. Biol. Rev.* 62:110–29

77. Nogales E, Downing KH, Amos LA, Löwe J. 1998. Tubulin and FtsZ form a distinct family of GTPases. *Nat. Struct. Biol.* 5:451–58

78. Nogales E, Wolf SG, Downing KH. 1998. Structure of the α/β tubulin dimer by electron crystallography. *Nature* 391:199–203

79. Ogawa S, Ueda K, Noguchi T. 1994. Division apparatus of the chloroplast in *Nannochloris bacillaris* (Chlorophyta). *J. Phycol.* 31:132–37

80. Oross JW, Possingham JV. 1989. Ultrastructural features of the constricted region of dividing plastids. *Protoplasma* 150:131–38

81. Osteryoung KW. 2000. Organelle fission: crossing the evolutionary divide. *Plant Physiol.* 123:1213–16

82. Osteryoung KW, Pyke KA. 1998. Plastid division: evidence for a prokaryotically derived mechanism. *Curr. Opin. Plant Biol.* 1:475–79

83. Osteryoung KW, Stokes KD, Rutherford SM, Percival AL, Lee WY. 1998. Chloroplast division in higher plants requires members of two functionally divergent gene families with homology to bacterial *ftsZ*. *Plant Cell* 10:1991–2004

84. Osteryoung KW, Vierling E. 1995. Conserved cell and organelle division. *Nature* 376:473–74

85. Peitsch MC. 1996. ProMod and Swiss-Model: Internet-based tools for automated comparative protein modelling. *Biochem. Soc. Trans.* 24:274–79

85a. Possingham JV, Hashimoto H, Oross J. 1988. Factors that influence plastid division in higher plants. See Ref. 6a, pp. 1–20

86. Possingham JV, Lawrence ME. 1983. Controls to plastid division. *Int. Rev. Cytol.* 84:1–56

87. Pyke KA. 1997. The genetic control of plastid division in higher plants. *Am. J. Bot.* 84:1017–27

88. Pyke KA. 1999. Plastid division and development. *Plant Cell* 11:549–56

89. Pyke KA, Leech RM. 1991. Rapid image analysis screening procedure for identifying chloroplast number mutants in mesophyll cells of *Arabidopsis thaliana* (L.) Heynh. *Plant Physiol.* 96:1193–95

90. Pyke KA, Leech RM. 1992. Chloroplast division and expansion is radically altered by nuclear mutations in *Arabidopsis thaliana*. *Plant Physiol.* 99:1005–8

91. Pyke KA, Leech RM. 1994. A genetic analysis of chloroplast division and expansion in *Arabidopsis thaliana*. *Plant Physiol.* 104:201–7

92. Pyke KA, Page AM. 1998. Plastid ontogeny during petal development in *Arabidopsis*. *Plant Physiol.* 116:797–803

93. Pyke KA, Rutherford SM, Robertson EJ, Leech RM. 1994. *arc6*, a fertile *Arabidopsis* mutant with only two mesophyll cell chloroplasts. *Plant Physiol.* 106:1169–77

94. Pyke KA, Rutherford SM, Robertson EJ, Leech RM. 1994. *arc6*, an extreme chloroplast division mutant of *Arabidopsis* also alters proplastid proliferation and morphology in shoot and root apices. *J. Cell. Sci.* 108:2937–44

95. Raskin DM, de Boer PAJ. 1999. MinDE-dependent pole-to-pole oscillation of division inhibitor MinC in *Escherichia coli*. *J. Bacteriol.* 181:6419–24

96. Raskin DM, de Boer PAJ. 1999. Rapid pole-to-pole oscillation of a protein required for directing division to the middle of *Escherichia coli*. *Proc. Natl. Acad. Sci. USA* 96:4971–76

97. Raskin DM, de Boer PAJ. 1997. The MinE ring: an FtsZ-independent cell structure required for selection of the correct division site in *Escherichia coli*. *Cell* 91:685–94

98. RayChaudhuri D. 1999. ZipA is a MAP-Tau homolog and is essential for structural integrity of the cytokinetic FtsZ ring during bacterial cell division. *EMBO J.* 18:2372–83

99. RayChaudhuri D, Park JT. 1992. *Escherichia coli* cell-division gene ftsZ encodes a novel GTP-binding protein. *Nature* 359:251–54

100. Ridley SM, Leech RM. 1970. Division of chloroplasts in an artificial environment. *Nature* 227:463–65

101. Rivas G, Lopez A, Mingorance J, Ferrandiz MJ, Zorrilla S, et al. 2000. Magnesium-induced linear self-association of the FtsZ bacterial cell division protein monomer. The primary steps for FtsZ assembly. *J. Biol. Chem.* 275:11740–49

102. Robertson EJ, Rutherford SM, Leech RM. 1996. Characterization of chloroplast division using the *Arabidopsis* mutant *arc5*. *Plant Physiol.* 112:149–59

103. Rossmann MG, Moras D, Olsen KW. 1974. Chemical and biological evolution of nucleotide-binding protein. *Nature* 250:194–99

104. Rothfield L, Justice S, Gracía-Lara J. 1999. Bacterial cell division. *Annu. Rev. Genet.* 33:423–48

105. Rothfield LI, Justice SS. 1997. Bacterial cell division: the cycle of the ring. *Cell* 88:581–84

106. Sánchez M, Valencia A, Ferrandiz MJ, Sander C, Vicente M. 1994. Correlation between the structure and biochemical activities of FtsA, an essential cell division protein of the actin family. *EMBO J.* 13:4919–25

107. Sato N, Albrieux C, Joyard J, Douce R, Kuroiwa T. 1993. Detection and characterization of a plastid envelope DNA-binding protein which may anchor plastid nucleoids. *EMBO J.* 12:555–61

108. Sato N, Ohshima K, Watanabe A, Ohta N, Nishiyama Y, et al. 1998. Molecular characterization of the PEND protein, a novel bZIP protein present in the envelope membrane that is the site of nucleoid replication in developing plastids. *Plant Cell* 10:859–72

108a. Smertenko AP, Lawrence SL, Hussey PJ. 1998. Immunological homologues of the *Arabidopsis thaliana* β1 tubulin are polyglutamylated in *Nicotiana tabacum*. *Protoplasma* 203:138–43

109. Sossong TM Jr, Brigham-Burke MR, Hensley P, Pearce KH Jr. 1999. Self-activation of guanosine triphosphatase activity by oligomerization of the bacterial cell division protein FtsZ. *Biochemistry* 38:14843–50

110. Stokes KD, McAndrew RS, Figueroa R, Vitha S, Osteryoung KW. 2000. Chloroplast division and morphology are differentially affected by overexpression of *FtsZ1* and *FtsZ2* genes in *Arabidopsis*. *Plant Physiol.* 124:1668–77

111. Strepp R, Scholz S, Kruse S, Speth V, Reski R. 1998. Plant nuclear gene knockout reveals a role in plastid division for the homolog of the bacterial cell division protein FtsZ, an ancestral tubulin. *Proc. Natl. Acad. Sci. USA* 95:4368–73

112. Sullivan SM, Maddock JR. 2000. Bacterial division: finding the dividing line. *Curr. Biol.* 10:R249–52

113. Sun Q, Margolin W. 1998. FtsZ dynamics during the division cycle of

live *Escherichia coli* cells. *J. Bacteriol.* 180:2050–56

114. Suzuki K, Ehara T, Osafune T, Kuroiwa H, Kawano S, Kuroiwa T. 1994. Behavior of mitochondria, chloroplasts and their nuclei during the mitotic cycle in the ultramicroalga *Cyanidioschyzon merolae. J. Cell Biol.* 63:280–88

114a. Szczegielniak J, Liwosz A, Jurkowski I, Loog M, Dobrowolska G, et al. 2000. Calcium-dependent protein kinase from maize seedlings activated by phospholipids. *Eur. J. Biochem.* 267:3818–27

115. Takahara M, Takahashi H, Matsunaga S, Miyagishima S, Takano S, et al. 2000. A putative mitochondrial *ftsZ* gene is present in the unicellular primitive red alga *Cyanidioschyzon merolae. Mol. Gen. Genet.* 7:245–51

116. Tewinkel M, Volkmann D. 1987. Observations on dividing plastids in the protonema of the moss *Funaria hygrometrica* Sibth.: arrangement of microtubules and filaments. *Planta* 172:309–20

117. Thompson JD, Higgins DG, Gibson TJ. 1994. CLUSTAL W: improving the sensitivity of progressive multiple sequence alignment through sequence weighting, position-specific gap penalties and weight matrix choice. *Nucleic Acids Res.* 22:4673–80

118. Turmel M, Otis C, Lemieux C. 1999. The complete chloroplast DNA sequence of the green alga *Nephroselmis olivacea*: insights into the architecture of ancestral chloroplast genomes. *Proc. Natl. Acad. Sci. USA* 96:10248–53

119. Wakasugi T, Nagai T, Kapoor M, Sugita M, Ito M, et al. 1997. Complete nucleotide sequence of the chloroplast genome from the green alga *Chlorella vulgaris*: the existence of genes possibly involved in chloroplast division. *Proc. Natl. Acad. Sci. USA* 94:5967–72

119a. Walden R. 1998. The alphabet soup of plant intracellular signalling: enter cyclic nucleotides. *Curr. Opin. Plant Biol.* 1:419–23

120. Wang X, Huang J, Mukherjee A, Cao C, Lutkenhaus J. 1997. Analysis of the interaction of FtsZ with itself, GTP, and FtsA. *J. Bacteriol.* 179:5551–59

121. Whatley JM. 1988. Mechanisms and morphology of plastid division. See Ref. 6a, pp. 63–84

122. Yan K, Pearce KH, Payne DJ. 2000. A conserved residue at the extreme C terminus of FtsZ is critical for the FtsA-FtsZ interaction in *Staphylococcus aureus. Biochem. Biophys. Res. Commun.* 270:387–92

123. Yu XC, Margolin W. 1997. Ca^{2+}-mediated GTP-dependent dynamic assembly of bacterial cell division protein FtsZ into asters and polymer networks *in vitro. EMBO J.* 16:5455–63

124. Zambito AM, Wolff J. 1997. Palmitoylation of tubulin. *Biochem. Biophys. Res. Commun.* 239:650–54

NOTE ADDED IN PROOF

Recent experiments based on cDNAs for the longer *AtFtsZ2-1* ORF referred to on page 321, as well as for *AtFtsZ2-2*, show both gene products are translocated into isolated chloroplasts and processed upon import. These results rule out the hypothesis that FtsZ2 proteins in *Arabidopsis*, and probably other plants, are components of the cytosolic PD ring.

Annu. Rev. Plant Physiol. Plant Mol. Biol. 2001. 52:335–61

Variations in the Biosynthesis of Seed-Storage Lipids

Toni Voelker

*Monsanto Corporation, Calgene Campus, 1920 Fifth Street, Davis, California 95691;
e-mail: toni.voelker@monsanto.com*

Anthony J Kinney

*Dupont Nutrition and Health, Experimental Station, P.O. Box 80402, Wilmington,
Delaware 19880-0402; e-mail: Anthony.Kinney@USA.dupont.com*

Key Words   fatty acid, metabolism, desaturation, elongation, triacylglyceride, wax

■ **Abstract**   In many plants lipids represent up to 80% of dry weight of storage tissues. In seeds, lipids accumulate as triacylglycerols (TAGs), which are formed by an extension of the membrane-lipid biosynthetic pathway common to all plant tissues. In contrast to the conserved fatty acid (FA) composition of membrane lipids, the observed divergence in seed oil acyl chains among different species is very high. The acyl groups of seed TAGs can vary in their chain length (from 8 to 24) as well as in their degree of unsaturation. In addition to methylene-interrupted double bonds, many seeds contain TAGs that have unusual functional groups in their FAs, such as hydroxyl, oxirane, or acetylene groups. All of the major steps in the biosynthetic pathway to TAG are now known and sequence information for genes encoding most of the enzymes involved is available. Here we present the current knowledge of the metabolic mechanisms involved in the divergence from the membrane-lipid biosynthetic pathway during storage lipid formation.

CONTENTS

INTRODUCTION

Lipids are an important form of carbon storage in many angiosperm seeds. In some storage organs, such as nuts, lipids may represent up to 80% of the total dry matter (29). The storage lipids of seeds usually consist of TAGs that accumulate during the maturation phase of the embryo and/or the endosperm.[1] During seed germination, the TAGs are catabolized and contribute to early seedling growth. The TAGs of most seeds contain the same acyl groups that are found in membrane lipids: These are predominantly palmitate (16:0), stearate (18:0), oleate (18:1), linoleate (18:2), and linolenate (18:3). Therefore, a seed programmed to synthesize a significant amount of storage lipid needs, at the very minimum, to have a scaled-up FA biosynthesis. In addition, it needs the ability to acylate the *sn*-3 position of 1,2 diacylglycerol in order to form TAG. The resulting TAG can then accumulate as an oil droplet in the cytoplasm or in specialized oil storage bodies. Thus, conceptually, only one new enzymatic step in addition to the membrane biosynthetic pathway is needed to transform a cell from making only membrane lipids to one that makes storage lipid.

In reality, many evolutionarily divergent angiosperm families deposit substantial amounts of "unusual" acyl chains in their seed-storage lipids and have numerous modifications to the standard membrane-lipid biosynthetic pathway. Seed oils from many species of Araceae, Lauraceae, Lythraceae, and Ulmaceae, for example, often contain saturated acyl chains ranging from C8 to C14. Brassicaceae preferentially deposit elongated chains with carbon lengths of 20–24. Some plants produce seed oils with double bonds at acyl chain positions not normally found in membrane lipids. Others produce oils with acyl chains containing functional groups other than methylene-interrupted double bonds. For example, castor oil is rich in hydroxylated FAs, whereas other plants have epoxidated or methylated acyl chains in their TAGs. The current list of FAs found in seed oils is well over 300 (3, 29, 56, 79, 95). Thus, in contrast to membrane lipids, the structure and physical properties of storage lipids are not highly conserved.

Vegetable oil is a large natural feed stock, with the global annual harvest reaching 50 million tons. Besides its caloric value of 9 cal/g, the utility of any oil is defined by its acyl composition. For example, the degree and position of unsaturation determines melting range and heat stability of the oil. Chain length determines the detergent property of a derived soap, and a certain active group might make a modified FA suitable as a special industrial feedstock. The existing natural diversity of seed TAGs indicates that there should be no theoretical barriers to producing exotic FAs in domesticated oilseed crops (which currently supply only half a dozen types of common FAs), but also provides a deep and potentially useful gene pool. Attractive targets for plant genetic engineering for altered TAG composition are the temperate oilseed crops, such as soybean, rapeseed, flax, and sunflower. In the past decade, this vision of modifying seed oils for commercial applications has driven the effort to identify key enzymes that have evolved in the species producing these unusual FAs. Through the metabolic engineering of the lipid biosynthetic pathways, traditional biochemical research has been supplemented by enzymatic redirection in vivo. Using genes encoding modified or exotic enzymes, oilseed plants harboring the common oil composition have been transformed genetically and the induced phenotype studied. This approach has allowed the identification and testing of key enzymes responsible for this divergence. It has also allowed us to define the minimum number of enzymatic alterations needed to create TAGs with an unusual composition and structure.

OVERVIEW OF TRIACYLGLYCEROL SYNTHESIS IN DEVELOPING OILSEEDS

The biosynthesis of plant glycerolipids has been reviewed extensively recently (52) [for a recent compilation of lipid biosynthesis genes in *Arabidopsis*, see (84)]. In this chapter we outline the common pathway only to provide a context for the discussion of its modifications (See Figures 1–3; see color inserts). Conceptually, the pathway leading to TAGs can be divided into six stages, described below.

Acyl Chain Elongation

In the stroma of plastids, saturated acyl chains are synthesized de novo by stepwise condensation of C2 units from malonyl-acyl carrier protein (ACP) to acyl chains, with stearoyl-ACP (18:0-ACP) as the predominant terminal product (Figure 1). For each elongation cycle resulting in the addition of two carbons to the growing acyl chain, four separate reactions are necessary. Each reaction is catalyzed by a separate enzyme activity encoded by an individual polypeptide. The first step in the elongation is the condensation of acetyl-CoA with malonyl-ACP to form 3-ketobutyl-ACP and CO_2. This is achieved by β-ketoacyl synthase III (KAS III) (114), followed by reduction to 3-hydroxylacyl-ACP, dehydration to an enoyl-ACP, and a second reduction to form the elongated 4:0-ACP. Subsequent rounds of condensation reactions of 4:0-ACP with malonyl-ACP through 14:0-ACP typically are catalyzed by an enzyme known as KAS I. The condensation of palmitoyl-ACP with malonyl-ACP is catalyzed by KAS II. The plastidial KAS I and II enzymes appear to be homo- or heterodimers of 46-kD and 50-kD polypeptides (64).

The current KAS nomenclature is confusing because the assignment of in vivo function (defined by enzymology) with respective gene products (defined by sequence classes) is only tentative. We therefore define a KAS terminology for the purposes of this review: Plastidial KAS subunits are encoded by two closely related *KASA* and *KASB* paralogues, both of which appear to have evolved from a bacterial *KAS II* gene (106). *KASB* encodes a polypeptide with an apparent M_r of 50 kD (64). A homodimer of this polypeptide appears to represent the plant KAS I enzyme. *KASA* encodes a polypeptide with an apparent M_r of 46 kD. There is circumstantial evidence that a heterodimer of KASA and KASB polypeptides represents the KAS II enzyme (64). In support of this classification is the observation in soybean that antisense inhibition of the *KASA* gene results in an increase in 16:0 acyl chains in the TAG, whereas antisense inhibition of KASB results in both an increase in 16:0 and a large reduction in flux through the entire FA biosynthetic pathway (AJ Kinney, unpublished results).

Desaturation, Termination and Release

In the common pathway, most of the 18:0-ACP undergoes desaturation at C9, which is catalyzed by Δ^9 desaturase, to form oleoyl-ACP (104, 105, 117). Typically, two different acyl-ACP thioesterases (TE), encoded by paralogous *FATA* and *FATB* genes, hydrolyze the acyl-ACPs to produce free FAs. FATA enzymes hydrolyze predominantly 18:1-ACP with minor activities toward 18:0-ACP and 16:0-ACP. FATB enzymes usually hydrolyze saturated C14-C18 ACPs, preferentially 16:0-ACP, but they will also hydrolyze 18:1-ACP. The interplay between the FA synthase, Δ^9 desaturase, and the two FAT thioesterases determines the ratio of plastidially produced acyl chains for TAG formation. The resulting free FAs leave the plastid by an unknown mechanism. Note also that stromal acyl transferases use some acyl chains of ACPs for biosynthesis of plastidial membrane lipids, a minor pathway in oilseeds (52).

TAG Formation

Upon arrival in the cytoplasm, the free FAs become esterified to coenzyme A (CoA) and now serve as substrates for the ER-based eukaryotic lipid formation [Kennedy pathway; see Frentzen (44) for a recent review] (Figure 2). Membrane-bound glycerol-3-phosphate acyltransferase (GPAT) initiates the process by transferring the acyl chain from CoA to the *sn*-1 position of glycerol-3-phosphate, forming lysophosphatidic acid. This enzyme appears to have a low selectivity for acyl chains (44). No gene has been identified for ER-localized GPAT in plants. Lysophosphatidic acid acyltransferase (LPAAT), catalyzes the transfer of acyl-chain from the CoA ester to *sn*-2, creating phosphatidic acid. In plants this enzyme prefers unsaturated acyl chains. There are two sequence-diverged gene subfamilies encoding LPAAT (44). Formation of TAG can be achieved in several ways. In one pathway, the phosphate is removed by phosphatidic acid phosphatase, forming diacylglycerol (DAG). The final enzyme, diacylglycerol acyltransferase (DAGAT), transfers an acyl group from acyl-CoA to *sn*-3 of DAG and forms TAG. Two unrelated genes have been identified as potentially encoding DAGAT enzymes in plants. One form is closely sequence-related to acyl CoA:cholesterol acyltransferase (128), whereas a second form does not resemble any other known genes (70). Evidence is also accumulating for an alternative mode of TAG formation in plants (112). This alternative pathway involves an enzyme normally involved in membrane biosynthesis, choline phosphotransferase (CPT). CPT esterifies *sn*-3 of DAG with choline, forming phosphatidylcholine (PC), a major membrane component. From there, it has been recently demonstrated that an enzyme called phospholipid:diacylglycerol acyltransferase, PDAT, can transfer the *sn*-2 acyl chain from PC to DAG, forming lyso-PC and TAG (Figure 2; see color insert) (30).

Polyunsaturation

While esterified to PC, 18:1 can be desaturated to 18:2 and 18:3 by two specialized microsomal membrane-associated desaturases, FAD2 (ω^6) and FAD3 (ω^3), respectively. From PC, acyl chains can be either esterified to CoA and become part of the cytoplasmic substrate pool for lipid formation, or choline of PC can be removed to form DAG (16).

Lipid Bodies

Oil is stored in the mature seed in the form of oil bodies (55). These are pools of TAG surrounded by a single monolayer membrane, most likely generated through budding of the outer ER membrane. The membrane contains proteins known as oleosins (58), which are thought to stabilize the oil body during desiccation of the seed.

OILS HIGH IN SATURATED FATTY ACIDS

Oilseed species with highly elevated levels of saturated FAs fall into two classes with respect to TAG structure. Coconut oil is the best known example of the fully saturated oils. More than 90% of its acyl chains are saturated, with chain lengths ranging from C8 to C16, predominantly laurate (12:0). Clearly, in this species the common pathway must be modified at the level of FA elongation to produce shorter chains. In addition, saturates reside at *sn*-2 of the TAGs, preferentially 12:0 (95, 124). Saturates are not normally found at this position in most oils because the normal LPAAT cannot use saturated acyl chains as substrates. This suggests that there is something unusual about LPAAT enzymes in species that have fully saturated oils. Other examples of these fully saturated oils can be found in many plant species, including members of the Lauraceae and Myristicaceae, which have, in their seed oils, predominantly laurate and myristate (14:0) acyl chains, respectively (56). The second class of saturated oilseed plants accumulate saturates up to approximately 60%, usually palmitate and stearate, both residing exclusively at *sn*-1 and *sn*-3 of the TAGs. Examples are cocoa butter (25% 16:0; 34% 18:0) and oil palm mesocarp (45% 16:0; 15% 18:0). The *sn*-2 position in these oils contains 18:1 (95).

Acyl-ACP Thioesterases

Despite intense research in several laboratories, satisfactory biochemical evidence for reduced-length acyl chain production remained elusive (51) until a 12:0-ACP hydrolytic activity was discovered in laurate-producing seeds of California bay trees (96). The protein with this activity was subsequently purified (32) and a cDNA encoding it was cloned. The encoded plastid-targeted enzyme conferred almost exclusive 12:0-ACP specificity in vitro. After expression in seeds of developing *Arabidopsis*, a large fraction of the seed oil was found to be laurate (121). This work demonstrated that a specialized thioesterase can redirect the common FA synthase of plants to medium chains, and the unusual FA is subsequently incorporated into TAG. Since then, evidence for medium-chain ACP hydrolytic activities have been found in extracts of other medium-chain producing seeds, such as *Cuphea*, coconut, and elm (31, 39). Many cDNAs encoding these medium-chain-specific thioesterases have been cloned from a variety of medium-chain producing angiosperms, and all belong to the *FATB* gene subfamily (Figure 1, blue box FATB).

For example, cDNAs encoding 8:0-ACP, 10:ACP, and 14:0-ACP hydrolyzing FATBs were isolated from *Cuphea* species with oils rich in the corresponding acyl chains [for more details on acyl-ACP thioesterases, see Voelker (119)]. The production of medium-chain (C8-C12) FAs in seeds such as *Cuphea* is thus catalyzed by novel FATB enzymes that have novel, shorter chain length specificities than the long-chain FATB enzymes found in all plants. The sequences of the medium-chain FATB enzymes invariably are found to be most similar to the long-chain FATB of the respective species (paralogues), which is direct evidence that they evolved independently several times from the common long-chain *FATB* after gene duplications (60, 119). This specialization also appeared to have involved an alteration of the respective promoters. The common *FATB* genes have general housekeeping function in all tissues with the highest expression in flowers (40, 41, 83), whereas the specialized medium-chain *FATB* genes are expressed exclusively in the developing embryo (35, 36, 76).

Although the greatest enzymatic divergence is observed in the FATB subfamily of thioesterases, there is one report of a specialized FATA thioesterase involved in the production of stearate (53). Stearate is the predominant FA (45–55% of total fatty acids) in the seed oil of mangosteen, *Garcinia mangostana*. When extracts from developing seeds were assayed for acyl-ACP thioesterase activities, no elevated 18:0-ACP hydrolysis could be detected. Exhaustive cloning of mangosteen seed *FAT* cDNAs yielded only one type of *FATB* clone, which encoded a classic FATB enzyme with highest activity toward 16:0-ACP. However, two different *FATA* transcripts were detected. One of these genes, *Garm FATA1*, encoded a thioesterase with unusually low activities with 16:0-ACP. When this cDNA was expressed in seeds of canola, stearate accumulation increased from 1% to 20% of the total fatty acids. These results raise the possibility of a specialized *FatA* having evolved in some high-stearate oilseeds (Figure 1, orange box).

β-Ketoacyl Synthases

The in vitro chain-length specificity of short-chain FATB enzymes and the induced phenotype of transgenic oilseeds in which they are expressed usually match rather closely. However, these transgenic phenotypes do not always correspond to the phenotypes of the species from which *FATB* genes were originally cloned. For example, *Cuphea hookeriana* accumulates predominantly C8:0, and lesser amounts of C10:0, but its seed-specific *FATB*, when expressed in *Escherichia coli*, is more active on 10:0-ACP than on 8:0-ACP in vitro [(36); see more cases discussed in (119)]. An even more extreme example of this divergence was observed with *Cuphea wrightii*, which accumulates 30% 10:0 and 54% 12:0. In seeds of transformed *Arabidopsis* expressing the *C. wrightii FATB* cDNAs, a broad range of saturates was observed (*Cw FATB1*: C12-C16; *Cw FATB2*: C10-C16), with the emphasis on mainly C14 and C16 chain lengths (76). These and other findings imply that although specialized FATB enzymes are necessary for medium-chain production, they may not represent all of the diverged enzymatic activities in the native plants.

In vitro evidence accumulated during studies of the developing seeds of medium-chain producers led to the conclusion that the FA synthase itself may also be modified to produce shorter chains (34, 102). Using KAS-specific antibodies, it was observed that a 46-kD (KASA) protein had a much weaker immunoblot signal than KASB (50 kD) in developing seeds of long-chain-producing members of this genus (106). In five of five medium-chain-producing *Cuphea* species, however, KASA accumulated to much greater levels than KASB during embryo development. More evidence was uncovered with a *C. viscosissima* mutant with a seed oil deficient in 10:0 FAs. Seed extracts of *C. viscossisima* elongate C8 to C10 in the presence of 10 μm cerulenin (a KASB inhibitor), but in the mutant extract cerulenin impaired this elongation reaction. The mutant also had a diminished 46-kD (KASA) immunoblot signal. In summary, these results suggested the involvement of a cerulenin-resistant condensing activity, possibly encoded by a KASA-type gene, in the production of medium-chain FAs in *Cuphea*.

To address this latter issue, Slabaugh et al used sequences conserved among KAS genes to isolate cDNAs from *C. wrightii* seeds that were most similar to the *KASA* (46-kD) sequences of other plants (106). The *Cw* KASA encoded enzyme activity could not be measured after expression in and purification from *E. coli*, but it was functionally tested in seeds of transgenic *Arabidopsis* (77). Overexpression of *Cw* KASA resulted only in a minor reduction of 16:0 in the seed oil but, when measured in the presence of the KAS I inhibitor cerulenin, increased 6:0-ACP and 8:0-ACP elongation of extracts in vitro. Lines transformed with *Cw KASA* cDNA were then crossed with lines expressing *Cw* FATB2 thioesterases. When compared with the TE-only parents, resulting F_1 seeds had greatly increased concentrations of 10:0 and 12:0. In contrast, 14:0 and 16:0 production was diminished. Thus *Cw* KASA apparently increases the interception efficiency of the medium-chain thioesterases somehow (Figure 1, blue box, KASA).

This finding is supported by the work of Dehesh et al (37), who isolated embryo-specific *KASA* cDNAs from 8:0- and 10:0-producing *Cuphea* species and functionally tested the encoded polypeptides in seeds of transgenic canola. In transgenic seed extracts, the medium-chain elongation reaction had increased resistance to cerulenin, and in double-constructs with C8/10-specific TEs, the medium-chain production was increased relative to TE-only transformants. Additional support for this hypothesis comes from experiments in which the *Cuphea* KASA was co-expressed with the C12/C14-specific California bay FATB1 thioesterase. Expression of this thioesterase in transgenic canola results in the accumulation of laurate and myristate levels in a ratio of 10:1 in seed oil FAs (120). Oils of transgenic canola expressing both *Cuphea* seed *KASA* and bay *FATB1* had increased amounts of 12:0, when compared with the *FATB1*-only plants and significantly less 14:0 (37).

KASA and *FATB* genes appear to have co-evolved in species that normally produce large quantities of medium-chain FAs. Assays with transgenic extracts from *Cuphea* mutants and from transgenic seeds expressing *KASA* genes lend support to the hypothesis that a KASA polypeptide probably confers a medium-chain-specific KAS activity to the common FAS. The transgenic data suggest that this modification results in elevated concentrations of medium-chain ACP intermediates, which in turn allows a more efficient interception of the FAS by the medium-chain FATB. Such a pathway-kinetic regulation of flux diversion is very effective when pathways are modeled by computer simulation (31). Since the activity of plant KASAs cannot be assayed in vitro, it is not known whether the resulting medium-chain production in plants such as *Cuphea* is the result of the increased expression in seeds of a medium-chain-specific KASA common to all plants, or of evolution and overexpression of a novel KASA polypeptide with specialized properties. Note that *Arabidopsis* appears to contain only one *KASA* gene (84), hence the *Cuphea* seed KASA enzymes are all likely to be derivatives of a common long-chain *KASA* gene that encodes the KAS II-conferring polypeptide.

Acyltransferases

When the California bay 12:0-ACP thioesterase *Uc* FATB1 was expressed in developing seeds of canola, up to 52 mol% of laurate accumulated in mature seeds lipids. TAG analysis revealed that laurate was deposited almost exclusively at *sn*-1 and *sn*-3 positions (75% laurate) and represented only 5% at *sn*-2 (120). This indicated that canola LPAAT strongly discriminated against laurate, but GPAT and DAGAT accommodated the novel substrate, a result expected from previous biochemical observations (44). In high saturate producers, however, TAG is often enriched in medium chains at the *sn*-2 position. For example, in coconut oil, which contains 50% laurate, *sn*-2 laurate represents 80% of the TAGs (95, 124). This is also true of *Cuphea wrightii*, whose oil contains 55% laurate (8). In *Cuphea lanceolata*, the *sn*-2 position of TAG is composed of 97% C10:0, whereas the *sn*-1 + *sn*-3 positions are composed of only 76% of this fatty acid (4).

Enzymatic evidence for an LPAAT enzyme specialized in the acylation of saturated substrates was first reported using lauroyl-CoA in feeding studies in extracts from laurate-producing developing palm endosperm (113). Oleoyl-lysophosphatidate LPAAT activity stayed constant during endosperm development, although a lauroyl-lysophosphatidate LPAAT activity was present when C12:0 FAs were being synthesized (73). This observation led to the suggestion of a specialized LPAAT gene, distinct from the housekeeping form. Finally, microsomes from developing *Cuphea lanceolata* embryos (90% 10:0 in oil) efficiently produced didecanoic diacylglycerol in vitro, providing further evidence of a possible medium-chain LPAAT in different plant families (4).

Davies et al (33) solubilized a LPAAT from membrane preparations of developing coconut endosperm. This enzyme displayed a marked preference for the transfer of medium-chain CoAs to 12:0-lysophosphatidic acid relative to unsaturated long-chain substrates. Using peptide sequences, a corresponding cDNA encoding a 299-amino acid integral membrane protein was cloned and expressed in *E. coli* and canola (65, 67). In both hosts, the coconut LPAAT conferred elevated medium-chain activity, with a preference for 12:0-CoA and 12:0-lysophosphatidic acid. The expression of the coconut LPAAT did not alter the TAG composition of normal canola oil (which contains no medium chains), but when crossed with thioesterase-engineered high-laurate canola, the resulting double-transformants produced TAGs with high levels of 12:0 at *sn*-2 (65). In seeds with 65% laurate, up to 80% of the *sn*-2 position was acylated with laurate, close to the positional distribution of this FA in coconut TAGs (95). Up to 15 % of TAGs were trilaurin.

Is there evidence for other specialized glycerolipid pathway enzymes in high saturate producers? To date there are no reports on substrate specificity of cloned microsomal GPAT and DAGAT (Figure 2), but there are observations from in vitro feeding studies and engineered plants. Analysis of a series of conventional and specialized oilseeds suggests that microsomal GPAT and DAGAT usually display broad acyl-CoA selectivities and even prefer saturated Co-A substrates (27, 44). This in vitro evidence was confirmed in vivo. Transgenic canola accumulated up to 80% saturates at *sn*-1 and *sn*-3 when FA production was engineered to medium-chain production (120, 125). These data support the view that the acyl-composition at *sn*-1 and *sn*-3 positions in TAGs depends on the acyl composition of the available substrates rather than acyl transferase specificity. The DAGAT activities in microsomes of safflower (a conventional oilseed) did utilize 10:0-CoA and dicaproyl-DAG but with no specific preference. In contrast, the microsomal DAGAT of *Cuphea procumbens* (a high 10:0 oilseed) preferred these substrates by a wide margin over oleoyl-containing substrates (126). Additionally, seed extracts from other natural medium-chain producers point to the existence of specialized GPAT and DAGAT activities (4, 7, 82, 122).

In summary, in high saturate oilseeds, a specialized and seed-specific LPAAT has apparently evolved to allow the synthesis of trisaturate TAG. Interestingly, orthologues to the coconut LPAAT have only been reported from seeds with specialized seed FA composition (*Limnanthes, Cuphea*). In conventional oilseed plants like *Arabidopsis*, with the complete genome basically sequenced, only members of a very distant LPAAT gene family have been detected [see phylogenetic tree in Frentzen (44)]. Circumstantial evidence indicates that specialized GPAT or DAGAT might also have developed. In contrast, while oilseeds with saturates restricted to the *sn*-1 and *sn*-3 of TAG, such as cocoa butter and mangosteen, might have an altered plastidial FA biosynthesis, they probably contain only conventional acyltransferases.

Other Mechanisms

Are there any modifications in FA biosynthesis besides the essential altered thioesterases and the synergistic KASA? There is no evidence that any of the three other enzymes of the FA synthase are significantly different in diverged oilseeds than in normal oilseeds. This observation supports the hypothesis that KAS determines the substrate specificity of elongation cycles. ACP (Figure 1, see color insert) isoforms are expressed specifically in developing seed tissue in *Cuphea lanceolata* (69), and recent evidence indicates that ACP isoforms might be somewhat optimized for a medium-chain FA synthase (103). Finally, the accumulated unusual TAGs need to be metabolized after germination. Laurate appears to be metabolized efficiently in germinating seeds of transgenic laurate canola, indicating biochemical flexibility (120). However, specialized lipases appear to be induced post germination in most species, with greater than 80% saturated FAs in their seeds (54). In summary, although the major players for the establishment of high saturates are defined, several more enzymes appear to be modified in high saturate producers to allow optimized saturate production and metabolism.

OILS WITH NOVEL MONOUNSATURATED FATTY ACIDS

Oleic acid (Δ^9 18:1) is a constituent of most common plant oils. Its relative abundance ranges from about 20% in soybean to over 80% in some mutant and transgenic varieties of canola, soybean, and sunflower (62). The insertion of the first double bond into FA chains is a plastid reaction catalyzed by a soluble desaturase enzyme, AAD1 (104, 105, 117). AAD1 normally inserts a double bond at the Δ^9 position of stearoyl-ACP to form oleoyl-ACP (Figure 1).

However, a number of naturally occurring oils contain monounsaturated FAs with double bonds in positions other than the ninth carbon from the carboxyl group (3, 95). Seeds of Umbelliferae species, for example, such as carrot and coriander,

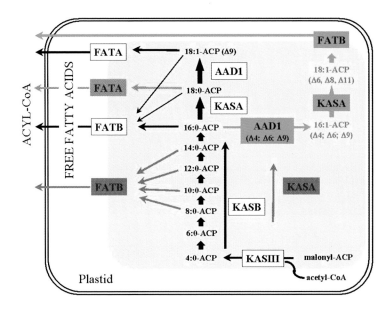

Figure 1 Deviations from the standard plastidal de novo fatty acid biosynthesis pathway. The enclosed rounded rectangle represents the stroma of a plastid surrounded by its double membrane. Yellow area symbolizes the acyl-ACP reactions. The FA synthase acyl chain elongation steps are shown. Enzymes are in boxes, see text for more detailed descriptions. Black: standard pathway. Blue: modifications present in very high saturate medium-chain producers. There are many variations where the elongation has become interrupted, leading to different compositions. Orange: high stearate mangosteen seeds. Green: alternate desaturation pathway. The variations are found in different plants, see text. The free FAs leave the plastids by an unknown mechanism and become esterified to CoA at the outer plastid membrane.

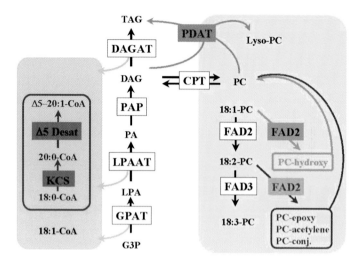

Figure 2 Variations in the ER-based desaturation pathway. All enzymes are localized in the ER. Light blue rounded rectangle represents CoA-pools and elongation reactions. Yellow represents the PC-based reactions. The glycerolipid pathway is shown in the center. Black: standard pathway. Enzymes are in rectangles. Blue: modification found in *Limnanthes*. Green and red: the alternative FAD2 enzymes found in several plants. Orange: PDAT, highly active in editing saturates or other unusual FAs from PC.

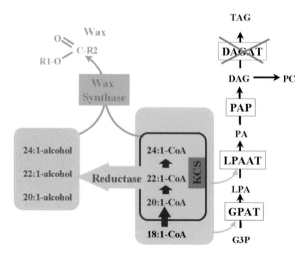

Figure 3 Jojoba wax biosynthesis. All reactions take place in the ER. To the right the conventional glycerolipid pathway is shown in black. Light blue rounded rectangle: acyl-CoA pools. Blue: KCS elongation (FAE1-like gene). Pink: fatty acid reductase (FAR). Green: wax formation, a general linear wax ester is shown. Since jojoba does not have TAGs in its seed oil, DAGAT appears to be inactivated.

contain oils rich in petroselenic acid (Δ^6 18:1). This unusual monounsaturate is the result of the activity of a plastidial Δ^4 desaturase that converts palmitoyl-ACP to Δ^4 hexadecanoyl-ACP. The hexadecanoyl-ACP is then elongated to petroselinoyl-ACP (26) (see Figure 1). Thus this soluble desaturase has both different substrate (chain length) specificity and different regiospecificity from the plastidal Δ^9 desaturase enzyme and yet, based on its primary amino acid sequence, is clearly a member of the same gene family (104).

This family of soluble acyl-ACP desaturases (*AAD1* gene family) includes other members that vary from the standard $\Delta^9$18:0-ACP in their substrate specificity, regiospecificity, or both. Examples include the Δ^6 16:0-ACP desaturase from *Thunbergia alata* (18, 21) and Δ^9 16:0-ACP desaturases from *Doxantha* spp. and from *Asclepias syriaca* (20), all of which have greater than 70% amino acid sequence similarity with Δ^9 18:0-ACP desaturases. Indeed, for members of this family, substitution of as few as two amino acids in a Δ^9 18:0-ACP desaturase can clearly result in changes in substrate specificity to a Δ^9 16:0-ACP desaturase. Substitution of as few as five amino acids can produce changes in both substrate and regiospecificities of an acyl-ACP desaturase, converting a Δ^6 16:0-ACP desaturase into a Δ^9 18:0-ACP desaturase (23) (Figure 1, green code).

It might be tempting to speculate, then, whether only a relatively minor evolutionary change in the primary structure of an *AAD1* gene resulted in the ability of, for example, coriander seeds to produce petroselenic acid instead of oleic acid. If this were so, it would be comparatively simple to convert a standard oilseed crop such as soybean to one that produces the industrially useful petroselenic acid simply by expressing the coriander divergent *AAD1* gene. However, Umbelliferae species producing this FA also have a variant *KASA* gene product, resulting in a condensing enzyme with specificity for Δ^4 hexadecanoyl-ACP. They also contain a variant *FATB* gene encoding a petroselinoyl-ACP thioesterase plus other variant polypeptides including acyl transferases and, as in high saturate plants, possibly even variant ACPs (22, 38).

These observations underline not only the complexity of the evolutionary process that has resulted in divergent vegetable oils but also the potential challenges of producing novel FAs in transgenic oilseed plants.

Not all unusual monounsaturated FAs are the result of variant soluble desaturases. For example, the oils of many *Limnanthes* species and a number of gymnosperm plants contain 20-carbon monounsaturated FAs with a double bond at the Δ^5 position, such as eicosa-5-enoic acid (Δ^5 20:1) (90, 115) (see Figure 2, blue code). These FAs are the result of a membrane-associated desaturase that inserts a double bond at the Δ^5 position of 20:0-CoA (24, 100). The gene encoding this enzyme is closely related to those encoding mammalian Δ^9 18:0-CoA desaturases and was the first confirmed member of this family in higher plants. This gene family appears widespread throughout the plant kingdom; in addition to finding Δ^5 fatty acids in ancient plants, a number of homologues of the *Limnanthes* Δ^5 desaturase gene have been identified in species as diverse as *Rosa* and *Arabidopsis* (46). The function of the gene products of these homologues has not yet been determined.

OILS WITH NOVEL POLYUNSATURATED FATS

Plants, in common with all eukaryotes, contain sphingolipids in their plasma membranes (81, 99). Although structurally analogous to phospholipids, sphingolipids contain only a single FA with an amide-linked long-chain amino alcohol (49). Plant sphingolipids contain a Δ^8 double bond, the result of the activity of a cytochrome b_5 fusion protein (108). This fusion protein is actually a Δ^6 desaturase that places a *trans* double bond six carbons from the closest oxygen-containing carbon (92, 108).

These sphingolipid desaturases have been identified in many plant species (46, 92, 108) and possibly represent the ancestral family of unique desaturases first identified in borage (*Borago officinalis*) seeds. Borage seeds, in common with a few other plants such as evening primrose (*Oenothera biennis*) and black currant (*Ribes nigrum*), contain oils rich in γ-linolenic acid (18:3 $\Delta^{6,9,12}$). The desaturase responsible for introducing the Δ^6 double bond in borage (and probably the other species) is a cytochrome b_5-fusion protein closely related to the plant sphingolipid desaturases (10, 101). Given the ubiquity of the sphingolipid desaturases among plants, the borage-type Δ^6 desaturases likely represent enzymes that have diverged in substrate specificity from the Δ^8/Δ^6 sphingolipid desaturase family. In contrast to the sphingolipid desaturases, which are effective on saturated acyl groups, the borage-type Δ^6 desaturase prefers an unsaturated acyl group derived from linoleic acid.

Curiously, the borage Δ^6 desaturase is very effective in producing γ-linolenic acid in transgenic soybean embryos (S Coughlan, unpublished results) but not in transgenic canola seeds (66) or *Arabidopsis* (101). It remains to be seen if this observation is of evolutionary significance. One interesting member of this cytochrome b_5-fusion superfamily is the recently identified bifunctional Δ^6 acetylenase/desaturase from the moss *Ceratodon purpureus* (107). Expression of this gene in *Saccharomyces cerevisiae* resulted in the formation of both a Δ^6 double bond and a Δ^6 triple bond in the yeast FAs. Thus the cytochrome b_5-fusion superfamily has members with divergence not only in substrate specificity but also in functional outcome of the reaction.

The greatest variation in novel functional groups in FAs described to date, however, is the result of divergence of another family of FA desaturases, the FAD2 family described below.

OILS WITH VARIATIONS ON THE METHYLENE-INTERRUPTED DOUBLE-BOND

Plant membrane phospholipids contain 18-carbon ω^6 and ω^3 polyunsaturated FAs, which are the result of the activity of membrane-associated FA desaturases. Oleoyl-CoA is first incorporated into membrane PC where it is desaturated to 18:2-PC by a membrane-associated, ω^6 desaturase encoded by *FAD2* (94)

(Figure 2, yellow box). Linoleoyl-PC can be further desaturated to 18:3-PC by a second membrane-associated desaturase, which inserts a double bond in the ω^3 position of 18:2-PC. The ω^3 desaturase is encoded by *FAD3* (2, 127).

Linoleic and linolenic acids are polyunsaturated FAs with two or three methylene-interrupted double bonds. A wide variety of plants have oils containing FAs with other types of functional groups or non-methylene-interrupted bonds, and many of these FAs are the result of the activity of diverged members of the FAD2 family. In contrast, no member of the FAD3-desaturase family identified to date does anything except place a double bond at the ω^3 position of linoleic acid.

The first of these diverged *FAD2* genes to be identified were the genes encoding ω^6 hydroxylases from *Ricinius communis* and *Lesquerella fendleri* (12, 78, 80) (Figure 2, blue in yellow box). FA hydroxylases catalyze the introduction of hydroxy groups into FAs. Thus expression of the *Ricinius* and *Lesquerella* diverged *FAD2* cDNAs in *Arabidopsis* seeds resulted in the production of hydroxylated FAs, up to 20% of the total FAs of the *Arabidopsis* seed oil (12, 14). There was also a concomitant increase in oleic acid, a factor that has almost always been observed when diverged *FAD2*s are expressed in heterologous plants (19, 24, 74). This increase in oleic acid, along with the observed accumulation of unusual FAs in the membrane lipids of transgenic plants, could be taken as an indication that the novel FA is not being properly metabolized during oil biosynthesis. Thus, as for the diverged soluble desaturases, additional diverged enzymes quite likely exist in species producing unusual FAs. To produce a relative abundance of novel FAs in transgenic plants similar to the corresponding native species, genes for these other diverged enzymes will probably need to be co-expressed along with the diverged *FAD2* genes.

One possible candidate family for divergence is the recently identified PDAT (phospholipid: diacylglycerol acyltransferase) family (30). This enzyme transfers acyl groups directly from membrane phospholipids into DAG to form TAG, and it has been demonstrated that PDATs from species that produce a novel FA do have increased specificity toward the particular FA produced by the plant (30). Other obvious candidates for divergence are the acyltransferases, which assemble acyl-CoAs into TAG (45).

The *Lesquerella* hydroxylase enzyme is actually bifunctional and has some ω^6 desaturase activity in addition to hydroxylase activity (12). Also, as for the amino acids controlling the substrate and regiospecificity of soluble acyl-ACP desaturases, only a few amino acids of a *FAD*-encoded polypeptide appear to control the functional outcome of the FAD2-type reaction, in this case desaturation versus hydroxylation (13). Taken together, these observations have led to the suggestion that small differences in active site geometry are responsible for the different functional outcomes of a FAD2-desaturases and FAD2-hydroxylases (104).

The similarities among FAD2-desaturases and FAD2 hydroxylases and their apparent similarity of reaction mechanism prompted the search for other *FAD2*-related genes in oilseed species that contained unusual FAs. This investigation led to the identification of FAD2-related epoxygenases from *Vernonia galemensis* (57, 63) and *Crepis palaestina* (75) and a FA acetylenase from *Crepis alpina* (75). These enzymes catalyze the formation of epoxy groups and triple bonds, respectively, into fatty acids and represent FAD2 members with divergent substrate specificity. Although oleoyl-PC is the substrate for desaturation and hydroxylation, the result of metabolic studies has shown that the substrate for this type of epoxidation and acetylation reaction is linoleoyl-PC (6, 48, 68) (Figure 2, red code).

Most recently, FAD2-related conjugase cDNAs from *Mormordica charantia*, *Impatiens balsamica*, and *Calendula officinalis* (24; E Cahoon, unpublished results) have been identified. Conjugated FAs are polyunsaturated FAs with non-methylene interrupted double bonds. *Momordica* is rich in α-eleostearic acid (18:3 $\Delta^{9\text{-cis, 11trans, 13trans}}$), *Impatiens* in α-parinaric acid (18:4 $\Delta^{9\text{cis,11trans, 13trans, 15cis}}$), and *Calendula* in calendic acid (18:3 $\Delta^{8\text{trans, 10trans, 12cis}}$). When the diverged FAD2s from each of these species were expressed in soybean embryos, the corresponding conjugated FA was observed in the embryo oil at a relative abundance of around 20% (19; E Cahoon, unpublished results). The *Calendula* conjugase is interesting because it represents the first example of divergence from an ω^6 regiospecificity for a FAD2-like gene product, in that the $\Delta^{8\text{trans/10trans}}$ conjugation is the result of action by the *Calendula* conjugase on the Δ^9 double bond of linoleoyl-PC. Furthermore, expression of this diverged FAD2 in tobacco and soybean results in the accumulation of calendic acid (to about 20% of total FAs) without the concomitant increase in oleic acid described above for other diverged FAD2s (E Cahoon, unpublished results). Calendic acid is likely to be metabolized normally by these transgenic plants.

In summary, the *FAD2*-gene family represents the widest variation from the path of oleic acid desaturation followed during membrane-lipid synthesis. There are now numerous examples of diverged FAD2 enzymes with variations in substrate specificity, regiospecificity, and most important, functional outcomes.

OILS WITH VERY LONG CHAIN FATTY ACIDS

The presence of Δ^5 20:1 FA in *Limnanthes* oil is indicative of another class of divergent enzymes. In addition to Δ^8 double bonds, plant membrane sphingolipids contain significant amounts of very long chain, unsaturated FAs (VLCFAs, 20–26 carbons). These unsaturated VLCFAs are also found in the storage oils of some plants, such as many of the members of the Cruciferae, and in epicuticular and storage wax esters. Most unsaturated VLCFAs are the result of the elongation of oleoyl-CoA by a membrane-bound elongase complex (52). A long-chain condensing enzyme (β-ketoacyl-CoA synthase) has been purified from jojoba (*Simmondsia chinensis*) seeds, which have oil rich in C20–24 monounsaturated acyl chains. The corresponding cDNA was cloned and the encoded enzyme characterized after expression in *E. coli* and canola. The recombinant enzyme caused the accumulation of very long chains in canola seeds (72). An *Arabidopsis* gene (*FAE1*) that is related to the jojoba condensing enzyme has also been cloned by insertional mutagenesis (59). *FAE1* complements *Arabidopsis* mutants that have reduced 20-carbon FAs and increased oleic acid and produces VCLFAs when expressed in tobacco (88). Based on these observations, a single condensing enzyme clearly controls the elongation of 18-, 20-, and 22-carbon acyl-CoAs in very long-chain FA-producing seeds (Figure 3, see color insert).

A *FAE1* homologue has also been cloned from *Limnanthes* and expressed in soybean seeds (24). The result is the formation of 20- and 22-carbon saturated fatty acids at the expense of palmitic acid (16:0). When co-expressed with the *Limnanthes* Δ^5 desaturase, 20:1 is formed at a relative abundance of around 20% (Figure 2, blue box). These results illustrate two points. First, the specificity of the elongation step of acyl-CoAs appears to be determined entirely by the FAE1 gene product. Second, this *FAE1* gene product from *Limnanthes* has substrate specificity for saturated FAs, unlike the monounsaturated specificity of *Arabidopsis* FAE1 and jojoba KCS1. The latter observation has been confirmed by metabolic studies that have shown a substrate specificity of the *Lim* FAE1 for C14-C18 saturated acyl-CoA substrates (100). *Limnanthes* seed extracts also had a separate 18:1-CoA elongation activity, indicating the presence of an additional, nondiverged *FAE1* gene (100).

The recently discovered *CUT1* gene from *Arabidopsis*, which encodes a VLCFA condensing enzyme involved in cuticular wax biosynthesis, displays a high degree of homology with the known *FAE1* (87). An *Arabidopsis KCS1* gene encoding a condensing enzyme involved in VLCFAs synthesis for wax biosynthesis has also been reported, again with good homology to *FAE1* (118). Because all angiosperm plants make epicuticular waxes, these discoveries may indicate that wax biosynthesis is a possible evolutionary origin of the condensing enzymes used for VLCFA biosynthesis in plant oils. Many plant oils contain at least trace amounts of saturated C20–24 VLCFAs (95), presumably resulting from saturated acyl-CoA elongation. Thus, the substrate specificity of different FAE1 homologues may be as broad as the *KASA* gene family of acyl-ACP condensing enzymes described above. This suggestion is also supported by the presence, in waxy coatings on plant leaves, of VLCFAs derived from the elongation of saturated acyl-CoAs such as palmitoyl-CoA and stearoyl-CoA (98).

As in saturated oils, VLCFA oils fall into two classes. Rapeseed oil contains 22:1 only at *sn*-1 and *sn*-3 because its LPAAT does not accept 22:1 (11). Hence, 22:1 is always less than 66% of total fatty acid content. However, other species, such as *Limnanthes* spp., have 92% VLCFAs in their seed oil and LPAATs specific for long-chain acyl groups have since been detected (73) and their cDNAs cloned (15). Expression of one of these cDNAs, from *Limnanthes*, led to the accumulation of 22:1 at the *sn*-2 of transgenic rapeseed TAG (71). These so-called Class B LPAATs are related to yeast and bacterial LPAATs and are distinct in their protein sequence from the Class A LPAATs involved in membrane-lipid biosynthesis (44).

LIQUID WAXES

Waxes, esters of long-chain alcohols and FAs, are abundant in plants as a component of hydrophobic barriers and for light reflection [reviewed in (98)]. Jojoba (*Simmondsia chinensis*), a desert shrub native to the Southwest of the United States, is the only angiosperm known to accumulate liquid waxes in its seeds as an energy store. Up to 60% of the seed dry weight comprises linear esters of monounsaturated C20, C22, and C24 FAs and alcohols. TAG is completely absent, even as an intermediate (93, 97).

Early biochemical evidence pointed to 18:1-CoA-based chain elongation as responsible for the very long acyl chains of jojoba wax. This was confirmed when a cDNA encoding a jojoba β-ketoacyl-CoA synthase was cloned and functionally expressed in canola, as discussed above (72). The additional enzyme activities thought to be necessary for jojoba wax synthesis were a fatty acyl reductase and a wax synthase (97) (Figure 3).

Metz et al (85) purified a 58-kD fatty acyl reductase (FAR) from jojoba seed microsomes and subsequently cloned its cDNA. Expression of this cDNA conferred FAR activity to *E. coli* and resulted in the accumulation of small amounts of fatty alcohols. In seeds of transgenic rape, small amounts of wax accumulated, predominantly with 22:1 alcohol groups, which indicated that jojoba FAR prefers very long-chain acyl-CoA substrates. In lines where the wax content of the transgenic rape was >1% of total seed lipids, free alcohols accumulated. Thus there appeared to be an insufficient capacity in rape to further metabolize the reduced fatty acids. Interestingly, the jojoba FAR gene is related to a gene family that includes *Arabidopsis* male-sterility-2, expressed in developing tapetum and essential for pollen formation (1).

Microsomes of jojoba seeds exhibit a very active wax synthase (fatty acyl CoA: fatty alcohol acyltransferase) activity, which accepts saturated and unsaturated alcohols and acyl-CoA substrates of many chain lengths. A wax synthase was partially purified from microsomes using chromatographic separation. Partial peptide sequencing of a 33-kD candidate allowed the cloning of a cDNA that encoded a very hydrophobic 352-amino acid protein. Expression in transgenic *Arabidopsis* seeds conferred high wax synthase activity. In mature transgenic *Arabidopsis* seeds expressing the jojoba KCS, FAR, and wax synthase cDNAs, large quantities of long-chain liquid wax accumulated, representing up to 70% of the *Arabidopsis* seed oil (70). These waxes contained 20:1, 22:1, and 24:1 alcohols. Thus, not only are a reductase and wax synthase sufficient for seed wax formation, but this new pathway can also efficiently divert carbon from TAG formation in vivo (Figure 3).

Interestingly, seven open reading frames with strong homology to the wax synthase were discovered, located adjacent to each other, on chromosome 5 of *Arabidopsis*. Transcripts of some of these ORFs were found up-regulated in flowers, others in developing seeds. They likely encode wax synthases involved in many of the ubiquitous pathways of wax formation in plants, such as epicuticular wax synthesis.

Early studies with germinating jojoba seeds demonstrated that they metabolize the storage waxes via β-oxidation. An oil body membrane-bound alkaline lipase was found associated with this catabolism (91). Thus it appears that during the evolutionary development of storage wax biosynthesis two enzymes were recruited, probably from existing pathways of wax formation. In addition, the evolution of a specialized lipase was required to initiate the catabolism of this novel storage compound. At some point during this process, the ancestral jojoba plant must have lost its TAG formation capability.

CHANNELING TO MEMBRANES AND TRIACYLGLYCERIDES

As discussed earlier, TAG production is an extension of the glycerolipid pathway essential for the biosynthesis of membrane lipids. Both processes occur simultaneously in the cells of the developing oil-storage tissues and share substrates (DAG, acyl-CoA) and location, the ER. This intimacy of the two pathways poses challenges to cells that accumulate TAGs with fatty acyl chains deleterious to membrane structure and function, such as saturated medium and long chains or oxygenated FAs (89). Indeed, the phospholipids of many seed tissues from plants producing highly saturated oils or unusual FAs have a conventional acyl composition. Very long and medium chains and oxygenated FAs appear only in traces, indicating an efficient "channeling" to TAG (4, 89, 109, 110, 123, 124).

This is not true of transgenic plants expressing genes from exotic oilseed species, however. For example, large quantities of medium-chain FAs are found during the oil-deposition phase in the phospholipids of transgenic canola embryos engineered for medium-chain production (124, 125). The lines with the highest laurate content in their oil (50%) had about 30% laurate in membrane PC plus substantial amounts in several other membrane lipid classes. Interestingly, laurate was much reduced, to about 7%, in the membrane lipids of mature seeds. This latter observation suggests there may be an active editing process in the membranes after the cessation of oil biosynthesis. Evidence from in vitro experiments supports the view that this pathway may be selectively activated in transgenic plants (124).

A similar editing mechanism may operate for other FAs. Mature *Arabidopsis* seeds expressing a *Ricinus* hydroxylase, for example, contained 17% hydroxylated FAs in their TAG but only about 1% in their seed phospholipid fraction (14). Because immature embryos were not analyzed in this experiment, exclusion as opposed to editing cannot be ruled out. However, because PC is the substrate for the hydroxylase (5), the hydroxylated FA must spend some time in this membrane lipid and thus simple exclusion from PC is unlikely. In contrast, the eleostearic acid produced by soybean embryos expressing the *Mormordica* conjugase appeared to be in equilibrium between TAG and phospholipids. In these tissues, conjugated fatty acids were equally distributed between PC and TAG (19). A similar distribution between membrane and storage lipids was also observed in mature soybean seeds from these lines (E Cahoon, unpublished results).

Thus, although an editing mechanism for removing unwanted FAs from membranes, appears to be present in most plants, it does not respond to all unusual FAs. Such a mechanism may have evolved to recognize and remove FA oxidation products from membranes. This may explain why shorter-chain and oxygenated FAs, common products of membrane-lipid oxidation (43, 50), might be more effectively removed from the membranes of transgenic plants than conjugated FAs. Moreover, conjugated fatty acids, or fatty acids with an unusual bond position, would probably be as damaging to membrane structure as medium chains or oxygenated fatty acids.

Transgenic plants, expressing divergent enzymes from other species, may or may not keep the resulting FA product out of their membranes by using an editing mechanism. However, native plants with divergent enzymes do not have unusual FAs in their membrane fractions in anywhere near the same abundance as in their TAG fraction, either in developing embryos or in mature seeds. What, then, allows the ER of these plants to make lipid classes with such divergent acyl compositions? In principle, this could be achieved by a spatial separation of TAG and membrane biosynthesis (ER differentiation), as proposed by Vogel & Browse (122). Alternatively, there may be some selectivity ("channeling") at the stage of DAG utilization by DAGAT and CPT (4, 122) (Figure 2). Or, as observed in transgenic plants, there may be a selective and efficient removal of unusual FAs from phospholipids by a more efficient editing mechanism (30, 110, 111).

Some evidence supports the DAG utilization hypothesis from lipid analysis of developing *Cuphea lanceolata* seeds, which produce medium-chain FAs. These seeds have 83% 10:0 FA in their TAG, but during oil deposition only 30% of the DAG is disaturated C10:0. When incubated with equimolar quantities of radioactive 10:0-CoA and 18:1-CoA, microsomes from developing *C. lanceolata* embryos incorporated both tracers into TAG at about equal rates during the course of the experiment. However, although high 18:1 incorporation into the DAG fraction was detected, only traces of radiolabeled 10:0 in DAGs were observed. Taken together, these results support the concept of selective and efficient utilization of disaturated DAGs by DAGAT (4).

In contrast, no evidence for a specialized CPT, able to reject medium-chain acyl-CoAs, was found in *C. lanceolata* (122). These investigators noted that the CPT activities of both conventional oil producers and *C. lanceolata* accepted medium-chain substrates quite well. Additionally, CPT assays, using microsomes from *C. lanceolata* with dicaproyl DAG as substrate, resulted in very high levels of lyso-PC among the reaction products (110). These results are suggestive of a selective removal of 10:0 from the *sn*-2 position of PC. This may be interpreted to be the action of a specialized microsomal lipase (110), but it could also be a result of PDAT or some other acyltransferase activity.

Not all medium-chain FAs are excluded from the PC of medium-chain producers either. For example, *Actinodaphne hookeri* seeds contain 95% laurate in their oil and about 7% laurate in their PC during seed development (109). Likewise, during seed development, palm endosperm contains 55% laurate and 15% myristate in its TAG and 1–2% 12:0 plus 2% myristate in its PC (123). Note that the TAG: PC ratio (mole %) for a given medium-chain FA is dependent on the chain length and PC exclusion or removal appears to be more stringent with shorter chain lengths. This observation may also apply to transgenics expressing diverged *FATB* genes. For example, transgenic canola accumulating C8:0, 10:0, and 12:0 in their seed oil excluded 8:0 most stringently from their phospholipids (125).

As mentioned above, PC is the substrate for many FA modifications by cytochrome P450-type enzymes (6) as well as the diverged FAD2s previously discussed. Thus, microsomes from the developing seeds of *Ricinus* catalyzed the transfer of oleate from ^{14}C oleoyl-CoA to PC (5). Likewise, labeled vernolic acid is transiently incorporated into the PC fraction of *Euphorbia lagascae* microsomes. There is even evidence that products of diverged soluble desaturases, such as petroselenic acid, cycle through PC before they enter TAG (18). These fatty acids are found in the PC fraction of mature seeds of *Ricinus*, *Euphorbia*, or coriander in considerably lower abundance than in the TAG fraction (25, 95). This observation strongly supports the idea of efficient editing of these FAs from membrane lipids, again by the action of specific lipases or by PDAT.

VLCFAs are also excluded from the phospholipids of plants that normally produce them. For example, 22:1 represents more than 60% of the TAG acyl fraction in *Crambe abysinnica* seed oil but only 3% of the phospholipids (47). In radioactive feeding studies, microsomes derived from high VLCFA seeds excluded VLCFA-CoA from phospholipids, but accepted 18:1-CoA (9, 113, 116). Interestingly, the heterologous expression, under the control of the 35S promoter, of *FAE1* in transgenic *Arabidopsis* resulted in up to 30% of C20 and C22 FAs in the phospholipids of the vegetative tissues. This caused alterations in plant morphology and organellar structures (86). Because *Arabidopsis* has a high proportion of 20:1 in its seed TAGs, the VLCFA exclusion mechanism is clearly not as efficient in non-seed tissues. Alternatively, the absence of a TAG sink or inefficient VLCFA catabolism in vegetative tissues simply leaves the cellular machinery no other choice (89). In contrast, the ectopic expression of a laurate-producing TE in canola did not result in laurate accumulation in leaves, probably due to efficient catabolism (42).

In summary, most natural producers of unusual FAs have developed efficient mechanisms to exclude them from membrane lipids. The study of ER lipid metabolism is very difficult owing to the membrane-bound nature of the enzymes and the hydrophobicity of many substrates and products. It is also complicated by the fact that many different processes might occur simultaneously in isolated microsomes, making the interpretation of data difficult. However, the current evidence supports the idea that, in natural producers of unusual FAs, there is some selectivity of DAGAT toward the novel FA, increasing the flux into DAG rather than phospholipids. This mechanism appears to be combined with an efficient removal of novel FAs from PC by PDAT and/or lipases. A similar removal mechanism also exists in transgenic plants expressing diverged enzymes, but appears to operate much less efficiently and does not recognize certain acyl moieties such as conjugated FAs. The invasion of laurate into many membrane lipid classes during the development of engineered canola embryos, and the direct modification of FAs esterified to the PC of ER membranes before incorporation into TAG, would argue against a spatial separation of TAG synthesis from the ER. However, we cannot exclude the possibility that some natural medium-chain or conjugated FA producers have developed such structures as well.

CONCLUDING REMARKS

A decade ago Browse & Somerville opened their review on Glycerolipid Synthesis: Biochemistry and Regulation in this series with the statement, "This is an exciting time to be working on lipid metabolism" (16). Indeed it was, and over the past ten years the rapid advances in biochemistry and molecular biology, along with extensive analysis of transgenic plants, have considerably deepened our understanding of plant lipid synthesis. During this time too, there has been much elucidation of the mechanisms by which the pathways of many oilseed plants diverge from the standard *Arabidopsis* pathway described by Browse & Somerville. Two fundamental questions remain, however: How are oilseeds that produce unusual fatty acids in their oil able to do so in such a large relative abundance and what is the evolutionary advantage for the plant of producing nonstandard fatty acids in seed oil?

A large, broad-based effort is currently under way to understand the first problem, primarily fueled by the desire of industry to produce commercial quantities of new and useful fatty acids in the oils of transgenic crops. No doubt a future review in this series will recount the success of this enterprise. It seems likely that there will be more that one mechanism involved, depending on the fatty acid type.

There are probably multiple answers to the second question also. One possibility is that unusual fatty acids confer minor evolutionary advantages by their potential as anti-feedants. Ricinoleic acid, after all, was known and feared by earlier generations for its effect on human digestive systems. Castor beans, however, offer a unique toxicity in the form of ricin that would surely have provided a greater selection pressure than anything ricinoleic acid had to offer. Perhaps shorter chain fatty acids allowed more rapid mobilization of resources and hence more competitive germination in a particular environment. Maybe storage waxes conferred a stability advantage over TAGs in high-temperature climates. Or in many cases, perhaps, there was no selective advantage or disadvantage for a plant to diverge its TAG biosynthetic pathway: It was just something that happened.

Whatever the reasons, one can only wonder at the many hundreds of different fatty acids found in natural plant oils that are mostly produced as a result of changes in a few amino acids of a handful of lipid biosynthetic genes.

ACKNOWLEDGMENTS

We are indebted to Stefanie Mertz for her excellent support during the manuscript preparation. We thank colleagues at Calgene Campus, the Dupont Experimental Station, and Vic Knauf of Tilligen (Seattle) for critically reading the manuscript.

Visit the Annual Reviews home page at www.AnnualReviews.org

LITERATURE CITED

1. Aarts MGM, Dirkse WG, Stiekema WJ, Pereira P. 1993. Transposon tagging of a male sterility gene in *Arabidopsis. Nature* 363:715–17

2. Arondel V, Lemieux B, Hwang I, Gibson S, Goodman HM, Somerville CR. 1992. Map-based cloning of a gene controlling ω^3 fatty acid desaturation in *Arabidopsis. Science* 258:1353–55

3. Badami RC, Patil KB. 1981. Structure and occurence of unusual fatty acids in minor seed oils. *Prog. Lipid Res.* 19:119–53

4. Bafor M, Jonsson L, Stobart AK, Stymne S. 1990. Regulation of triacylglycerol biosynthesis in embryos and microsomal preparations from the developing seeds of *Cuphea lanceolata. Biochem. J.* 272:31–38

5. Bafor M, Smith MA, Jonsson L, Stobart K, Stymne S. 1991. Ricinoleic acid biosynthesis and triacylglycerol assembly in microsomal preparations from developing castor-bean (*Ricinus communis*). *Biochem. J.* 280:507–14

6. Bafor M, Smith MA, Jonsson L, Stobart K, Stymne S. 1993. Biosynthesis of vernoleate (cis-12-epoxyoctadeca-cis-9-enoate) in microsomal preparations from developing endosperm of *Euphorbia lagascae. Arch. Biochem. Biophys.* 303:145–51

7. Bafor M, Stobart AK, Stymne S. 1990. Properties of the glycerol acylating enzymes in microsomal preparations from the developing seeds of safflower (*Carthamus tinctorius*) and turnip rape (*Brassica campestris*) and their ability to assemble cocoa-butter type fats. *J. Am. Oilseed Soc.* 67:217–25

8. Bafor M, Stymne S. 1992. Substrate specificities of glycerol acylating enzymes from developing embryos of two *Cuphea species. Phytochemistry* 31:2973–76

9. Battey JF, Ohlrogge JB. 1988. A comparison of the metabolic fate of fatty acids of different chain lengths in developing oilseeds. *Plant Physiol.* 90:835–40

10. Beremand PD, Nunberg A, Reddy AS, Thomas TL. 1996. Production of γ-linolenic acid by transgenic plants expressing cyanobacterial or plant Δ^6 desaturase genes. In *Physiology, Biochemistry and Molecular Biology of Plant Lipids*, ed. JP Williams, MU Khan, NW Lem, pp. 351–33. Dordrecht: Kluwer

11. Bernerth R, Frentzen M. 1990. Utilization of Erucoyl-CoA by acyltransferases from developing seeds of *Brassica napus* (L.) involved in triacylglycerol biosynthesis. *Plant Sci.* 67:21–28

12. Broun P, Boddupalli S, Somerville C. 1998. A bifunctional oleate 12-hydroxylase: desaturase from *Lesquerella fendleri. Plant J.* 13:201–10

13. Broun P, Shanklin J, Whittle E, Somerville C. 1998. Catalytic plasticity of fatty acid modification enzymes underlying chemical diversity of plant lipids. *Science* 282:1315–17

14. Broun P, Somerville C. 1997. Accumulation of ricinoleic, lesquerolic, and densipolic acids in seeds of transgenic *Arabidopsis* plants in microsomal preparations from developing endosperm of *Euphorbia lagascae. Arch. Biochem. Biophys.* 113:933–42

15. Brown A, Brough C, Kroon J, Slabas A. 1995. Identification of a cDNA that encodes a 1-acyl-*sn*- glycerol-3-phosphate acyltransferase from *Limnanthes douglasii. Plant Mol. Biol.* 29:267–78

16. Browse J, Somerville C. 1991. Glycerolipid synthesis: biochemistry and regulation. *Annu. Rev. Plant Physiol. Plant Mol. Biol.* 42:467–506

17. Deleted in proof

18. Cahoon EB, Becker CK, Shanklin J, Ohlrogge JB. 1994. cDNAs for isoforms of

the Δ^9-stearoyl-acyl carrier protein desaturase from *Thunbergia alata* endosperm. *Plant Physiol.* 106:807–8

19. Cahoon EB, Carlson TJ, Ripp KG, Schweiger BJ, Cook GA, et al. 1999. Biosynthetic origin of conjugated double bonds: production of fatty acid components of high-value drying oils in transgenic soybean embryos. *Proc. Natl. Acad. Sci. USA* 96:12935–40

20. Cahoon EB, Coughlan S, Shanklin J. 1997. Characterization of a structurally and functionally diverged ACP desaturase from milkweed seed. *Plant Mol. Biol.* 33:1105–10

21. Cahoon EB, Cranmer AM, Shanklin J, Ohlrogge JB. 1994. Δ^6 hexadecenoic acid is synthesized by the activity of a soluble Δ^6 palmitoyl-acyl carrier protein desaturase in *Thunbergia alata* endosperm. *J. Biol. Chem.* 269:27519–26

22. Cahoon EB, Dörmann P, Ohlrogge JB. 1994. Petroselinic acid biosynthesis and production in transgenic plants. *Prog. Lipid Res.* 33:155–63

23. Cahoon EB, Lindqvist Y, Schneider G, Shanklin J. 1997. Redesign of soluble fatty aid desaturases from plants for altered substrate specificity and double bond position. *Proc. Natl. Acad. Sci. USA* 94:4872–77

24. Cahoon EB, Marillia E-F, Stecca KL, Hall SE, Taylor DT, Kinney AJ. 2000. Production of fatty acid components of meadowfoam oil in somatic soybean embryos. *Plant Physiol.* 124:243–51

25. Cahoon EB, Ohlrogge JB. 1994. Apparent role of phosphatidylcholine in the metabolism of petroselinic acid in developing *Umbelliferae* endosperm. *Plant Physiol.* 104:845–55

26. Cahoon EB, Ohlrogge JB. 1994. Metabolic evidence for the involvement of a Δ^4 palmitoyl-ACP desaturase in petroselinic acid synthesis in coriander endosperm and transgenic tobacco cells. *Plant Physiol.* 104:827–37

27. Cao Y-Z, Huang AHC. 1987. Acyl coenzyme A preference of diacylglycerol acyltransferases from the maturing seeds of *Cuphea*, maize, rapeseed, and canola. *Plant Physiol.* 84:762–65

28. Deleted in proof

29. Crops UDN. http://www.ncaur.usda.gov/nc/nchome.htm.

30. Dahlqvist A, Ståhl U, Lenman M, Banas A, Lee M, et al. 2000. Phospholipid: diacylglycerol acyltransferase: an enzyme that catalyzes the acyl-CoA-independent formation of triacylglycerol in yeast and plants. *Proc. Natl. Acad. Sci. USA* 97:6487–92

31. Davies HM. 1993. Medium chain acyl-ACP hydrolysis activities of developing oilseeds. *Phytochemistry* 33:1353–56

32. Davies HM, Anderson L, Fan C, Hawkins DJ. 1991. Developmental induction, purification, and further characterization of 12:0-ACP thioesterase from immature cotyledons of *Umbellularia californica*. *Arch. Biochem. Biophys.* 290:37–45

33. Davies HM, Hawkins DJ, Nelsen JS. 1995. Lysophosphatidic acid acyltransferase from immature coconut endosperm having medium chain length substrate specificity. *Phytochemistry* 39:989–96

34. Deerberg S, von Twickel J, Förster H-H, Cole T, Fuhrmann J, Heise K-P. 1990. Synthesis of medium-chain fatty acids and their incorporation into triacylglycerols by cell-free fractions from *Cuphea embryos*. *Planta* 180:440–44

35. Dehesh K, Edwards P, Hayes T, Cranmer AM, Fillatti J. 1996. Two novel thioesterases are key determinants of the biomodal distribution of acyl chain length of *Cuphea palustris* seed oil. *Plant Physiol.* 110:203–10

36. Dehesh K, Jones A, Knutzon DS, Voelker TA. 1996. Production of high levels of 8:0 and 10:0 fatty acids in transgenic canola by over-expression of *ChFatB2*, a thioesterase cDNA from *Cuphea hookeriana*. *Plant J.* 9:167–72

37. Dehesh K, Edwards P, Fillati J, Slabaugh

M, Byrne J. 1998. KAS IV: a 3-ketoacyl-ACP synthase from *Cuphea* sp. is a medium chain specific condensing enzyme. *Plant J.* 15:383–90

38. Dörmann P, Frentzen M, Ohlrogge JB. 1994. Specificities of the ACP thioesterase and G3P acyltransferase for octadecenoyl-ACP isomers. *Plant Physiol.* 104:839–44

39. Dörmann P, Spener F, Ohlrogge JB. 1993. Characterization of two acyl-acyl carrier protein thioesterases from developing *Cuphea* seeds specific for medium-chain- and oleoyl-acyl carrier protein. *Planta* 189:425–32

40. Dörmann P, Voelker TA, Ohlrogge J. 2000. Accumulation of palmitate in *Arabidopsis* mediated by the acyl-acyl carrier protein thioesterase FATB1. *Plant Physiol.* 123:637–43

41. Dörmann P, Voelker TA, Ohlrogge JB. 1995. Cloning and expression in *Escherichia coli* of a novel thioesterase from *Arabidopsis thaliana* specific for long-chain acyl-acyl carrier proteins. *Arch. Biochem. Biophys.* 316:612–18

42. Eccleston V, Cranmer A, Voelker T, Ohlrogge J. 1996. Medium-chain fatty acid biosynthesis and utilization in *Brassica napus* plants expressing lauroyl-acyl carrier protein thioesterase. *Planta* 198:46–53

43. Frankel EN. 1982. Volatile lipid oxidation products. *Prog. Lipid Res.* 22:1–33

44. Frentzen M. 1998. Acyltransferases from basic science to modified seed oils. *Fett/Lipid.* 100:161–66

45. Frentzen M, Wolter FP. 1998. Molecular biology of acyltransferases involved in glycerolipid biosynthesis. In *Biosynthesis: Fundamental and Agricultural Applications*, ed. JL Harwood, pp. 247–72. Cambridge: Univ. Press

46. Girke T, Sperling P, Heinz E. 1998. Cloning of desaturases with new specificities. See Ref. 99a, pp. 103–9

47. Gurr MI, Blades J, Appleby R. 1972. Studies on seed-oil triglycerides: the composition of *Crambe abyssinica* triglycerides during seed maturation. *Eur. J. Biochem.* 29:362–68

48. Haigh WG, Morris LJ, James AT. 1968. Acetylenic acid biosynthesis in *Crepis rubra. Lipids* 3:307–12

49. Hakomori S. 1983. Chemistry and glycosphingolipids. In *Handbook of Lipid Research*, ed. JN Kanfer, S Hakomori, 3:1–165. New York: Plenum

50. Hamberg M, Hamberg G. 1996. Peroxygenase-catalyzed fatty acid epoxidation in cereal seeds. *Plant Physiol.* 110:807–15

51. Harwood JL. 1988. Fatty acid metabolism. *Annu. Rev. Plant Physiol. Plant Mol. Biol.* 39:101–38

52. Harwood JL. 1996. Recent advances in the biosynthesis of plant fatty acids. *Biochim. Biophys. Acta.* 130:7–56

53. Hawkins DJ, Kridl JC. 1998. Characterization of acyl-ACP thioesterases of mangosteen (*Garcinia mangostana*) seed and high levels of stearate production in transgenic canola. *Plant J.* 13:743–52

54. Hellyer SA, Chandler IC, Bosley JA. 1999. Can the fatty acid selectivity of plant lipases be predicted from the composition of the seed triglyceride? *Biochim. Biophys. Acta* 1440:215–24

55. Herman EM. 1995. Cell and molecular biology of seed oil bodies. In Seed *Development and Germination*, ed. J Kigel, G Galili, pp. 195–214. New York: Marcel Dekker

56. Hilditch TP, Williams PN. 1964. *The Chemical Constitution of Natural Fats.* London: Chapman & Hall

57. Hitz WD. 1998. *U. S. Patent No. 5846784*

58. Huang A. 1996. Oleosins and oil bodies in seeds and other organs. *Plant Physiol.* 110:1055–61

59. James DW, Lime E, Keller J, Plooy I, Ralston E, Dooner HK. 1995. Directed tagging of the *Arabidopsis FAE1* gene with the maize transposon activator. *Plant Cell* 7:309–19

60. Jones A, Davies HM, Voelker TA.

1995. Palmitoyl-acyl carrier protein (ACP) thioesterase and the evolutionary origin of plant acyl-ACP thioesterases. *Plant Cell* 7:359–71

61. Deleted in proof

62. Kinney AJ. 1994. Genetic modification of the storge lipids of plants. *Curr. Opin. Biotech.* 5:144–51

63. Kinney AJ, Hitz WD, Knowlton S, Cahoon EB. 1998. Re-engineering oilseed crops to produce industrially useful fatty acids. See Ref. 99a, pp. 623–28

64. Knauf V, Thompson G. 1995. *U.S. Patent No. 5475099*

65. Knutzon DS, Hayes TR, Wyrick A, Xiong H, Davies HM, Voelker TA. 1999. Lysophosphatidic acid acyltransferase from coconut endosperm mediates the insertion of laurate at the *sn*-2 position of triacylglycerols in lauric rapeseed oil and can increase total laurate levels. *Plant Physiol.* 120:739–46

66. Knutzon DS, Knauf VC. 1998. Manipulating seed oils for polyunsaturated fatty acid content. In *Plant Lipid Biosynthesis: Fundamental and Agricultural Applications*, ed. JL Harwood, pp. 287–304. Cambridge: Cambridge Univ. Press

67. Knutzon DS, Lardizabal KD, Nelsen JS, Bleibaum JL, Davies HM, Metz JG. 1995. Cloning of a coconut endosperm cDNA encoding a 1-acyl-*sn*-glycerol-3-phosphate acyltransferase that accepts medium-chain-length substrates. *Plant Physiol.* 109:999–1006

68. Kohn G, Hartman E, Stymne S, Beutelmannn J. 1994. Biosynthesis of acetylenic fatty acids in the moss *Ceratodon purpureus* (Hedw.) Brid. *J. Plant Physiol.* 144:265–71

69. Kopka J, Robers M, Schuch R, Spener F. 1993. Acyl carrier proteins from developing seeds of *Cuphea lanceolata Ait. Planta* 191:102–11

70. Lardizabal KD, Metz JG, Sakamoto T, Hutton WC, Pollard MR, Lassner MW. 2000. Purification of a jojoba embryo wax synthase, cloning of its cDNA, and production of high levels of wax in seeds of transgenic *Arabidopsis. Plant Physiol.* 122:645–55

71. Lassner M, Levering C, Davies H, Knutzon D. 1995. Lysophosphatidic acid acyltransferase from meadowfoam mediates insertion of erucic acid at the *sn*-2 position of triacylglycerol in transgenic rapeseed oil. *Plant Physiol.* 109:1389–94

72. Lassner MW, Lardizabal K, Metz JG. 1996. A jojoba β-ketoacyl-CoA synthase cDNA complements the canola fatty acid elongation mutation in transgenic plants. *Plant Cell* 8:281–92

73. Laurent P, Huang AHC. 1992. Organ- and development-specific acyl coenzyme A lysophosphatidate acyltransferases in palm and meadowfoam. *Plant Physiol.* 99:1711–15

74. Lee M. 2000. *Expression of desaturase-like genes to achieve novel fatty acid structures.* Presented at Fatty Acid Desaturases: Form, Function, and Future, 51st, Harden/EMBO Conf., Wye College, Kent, UK

75. Lee M, Lenman M, Banas A, Bafor M, Singh S, et al. 1998. Identification of non-heme diiron proteins that catalyze triple bond and epoxy group formation. *Science* 280:915–18

76. Leonard J, Slabaugh M, Knapp S. 1997. *Cuphea wrightii* thioesterases have unexpected broad specificities on saturated fatty acids. *Plant Mol. Biol.* 34:669–79

77. Leonard JM, Knapp SJ, Slabaugh MB. 1998. A *Cuphea* β-ketoacyl-ACP synthase shifts the synthesis of fatty acids towards shorter chains in *Arabidopsis* seeds expressing *Cuphea* FatB thioesterases. *Plant J.* 13:621–28

78. Lightner JE, Okuley JJ. 1994. *Int. Patent No. WO 94/11516*

79. Loo FJ van de, Fox BG, Somerville C. 1993. Unusual fatty acids. See Ref. 90a, pp. 91–126

80. Loo FN van de, Broun P, Turner S, Somerville CR. 1995. An oleate 12–hydroxylase from *Ricinus communis* L. is a

fatty acyl desaturase homolog. *Proc. Natl. Acad. Sci. USA* 92:6743–47

81. Lynch DV. 1993. Sphingolipids. See Ref. 90a, pp. 285–308

82. Manaf AM, Harwood JL. 2000. Purification and characterisation of acyl-CoA: glycerol 3-phosphate acyltransferase from oil palm (*Elaeis guineensis*) tissues. *Planta* 210:318–28

83. Martini N, Schell J, Töpfer R. 1995. Expression of acyl-ACP thioesterase in *Cuphea lanceolata* and in transgenic rapeseed. In *Plant Lipid Metabolism*, ed. J-C Kader, P Mazliak, pp. 495–98. Netherlands: Kluwer

84. Mekhedov S, Ilárduya OM de, Ohlrogge J. 2000. Toward a functional catalog of the plant genome. A survery of genes for lipid biosynthesis. *Plant Physiol.* 122:389–401

85. Metz JG, Pollard MR, Anderson L, Hayes TR, Lassner MW. 2000. Purification of a jojoba embryo fatty acyl-aoenzyme A reductase and expression of its cDNA in high erucic acid rapeseed. *Plant Physiol.* 122:635–44

86. Millar A, Wrischer M, Kunst L. 1998. Accumulation of very-long-chain fatty acids in membrane glycerolipids is associated with dramatic alterations in plant morphology. *Plant Cell* 11:1889–902

87. Millar AA, Clemens S, Zachgo S, Giblin EM, Taylor DC, Kunst L. 1999. *CUT1*, an *Arabidopsis* gene required for cuticular wax biosynthesis and pollen fertility, encodes a very-long-chain fatty acid condensing enzyme. *Plant Cell* 11:825–38

88. Millar AA, Kunst L. 1997. VLCFA biosynthesis in controlled through the expression and specificity of the condensing enzyme. *Plant J.* 12:121–31

89. Millar AA, Smith MA, Kunst L. 2000. All fatty acids are not equal: discrimination in plant membrane lipids. *Trends Plant Sci.* 5:95–101

90. Miller RW, Daxenbichler ME, Earle FR, Gentry HS. 1964. Search for new industrial oils VIII. The genus *Limnanthes*. *J. Am. Oilseed Soc.* 41:167–69

90a. Moore JTS, ed. 1993. *Lipid Metabolism in Plants*. Boca Raton: CRC Press

91. Moreau RA, Huang AHC. 1977. Gluconeogenesis from storage wax in the cotyledons of jojoba seedlings. *Plant Physiol.* 60:329–33

92. Napier J, Sayanova O, Sperling P, Heinz E. 1999. A growing family of cytochrome b_5-domain fusion proteins. *Trends Plant Sci.* 4:2–4

93. Ohlrogge JB, Pollard MR, Stumpf PK. 1977. Studies on biosynthesis of waxes by developing jojoba seed tissue. *Lipids* 13:203–10

94. Okuley J, Lightner J, Feldmann K, Yadav N, Lark E, Browse J. 1994. *Arabidopsis FAD2* gene encodes the enzyme that is essential for polyunsaturated lipid synthesis. *Plant Cell* 6:147–58

95. Padley FB, Gunstone FD, Harwood JL. 1994. Occurrence and characteristics of oil and fats. In *The Lipid Handbook*, ed. FD Gunstone, JL Harwood, FB Padley, pp. 49–170. London: Chapman & Hall

96. Pollard MR, Anderson L, Fan C, Hawkins DJ, Davies HM. 1991. A specific acyl-ACP thioesterase implicated in medium-chain fatty acid production in immature cotyledons of *Umbellularia californica*. *Arch. Biochem. Biophys.* 284:306–12

97. Pollard MR, McKeon T, Gupta LM, Stumpf PK. 1979. Studies on biosynthesis of waxes by developing jojoba seed. II. The demonstration of wax biosynthesis by cell-free homogenates. *Lipids* 14:651–62

98. Post-Beittenmiller D. 1996. Biochemistry and molecular biology of wax production in plants. *Annu. Rev. Plant Physiol. Mol. Biol.* 47:405–30

99. Rochester CP, Kjellbom P, Andersson B, Larsson C. 1987. Lipid composition of plasma membranes isolated from light-grown barley leaves: identification of

cerebroside as a major component. *Arch. Biochem. Biophys.* 255:385–91

99a. Sánchez J, Cerdá-Olmedo E, Martínez-Force E, eds. 1998. *Advances in Lipid Research*. Sevilla: Secr. Publ. Univ. Sevilla

100. Sandager L, Stymne S. 2000. Characterisation of enzymes determining fatty acid chain length in developing seeds of *Limnanthes douglasii*. *J. Plant Physiol.* 156:617–22

101. Sayanova O, Smith MA, Lapinskas P, Stobart AK, Dobson G, et al. 1997. Expression of a borage desaturase cDNA containing an N-terminal cytochrome b_5 domain results in the accumulation of high levels of Δ^6-desaturated fatty acids in transgenic tobacco. *Proc. Natl. Acad. Sci. USA* 94:4211–16

102. Schuch R, Brummel M, Spener F. 1993. *Medium-chain acyl-ACP thioesterase is not the exclusive tool for medium-chain fatty acid synthesis*. Presented at Int. Workshop Biotechnol. Asp. Plant Lipids, May 26–29, Carmona, Spain

103. Schütt BS, Brummel M, Schuch R, Spener F. 1998. The role of acyl carrier protein isoforms from *Cuphea lanceolata* seeds in the de-novo biosynthesis of medium-chain fatty acids. *Planta* 205:263–68

104. Shanklin J, Cahoon EB. 1998. Desaturation and related modifications of fatty acids. *Annu. Rev. Plant Physiol. Plant Mol. Biol.* 49:611–41

105. Shanklin J, Somerville C. 1991. Stearoyl-acyl-carrier-protein desaturase from higher plants is structurally unrelated to the animal and fungal homologues. *Proc. Natl. Acad. Sci. USA* 8:10–14

106. Slabaugh M, Leonard J, Knapp S. 1998. Condensing enzymes from *Cuphea wrightii* associated with medium chain fatty acid biosynthesis. *Plant J.* 13:611–20

107. Sperling P, Lee M, Girke T, Zähringer U, Stymne S, Heinz E. 2000. A bifunctional Δ^6-fatty acyl acetylenase/desaturase

from the moss *Ceratodon purpureus*: a new member of the cytochrome b_5 superfamily. *Eur. J. Biochem.* 267:3801–11

108. Sperling P, Zähringer U, Heinz E. 1998. A sphingolipid desaturase from higher plants. Identification of a new cytochrome b_5 fusion protein. *J. Biol. Chem.* 273:28590–96

109. Sreenivas A, Sastry PS. 1994. Synthesis of trilaurin by developing pisa seeds (*Actinodaphne hookeri*). *Arch. Biochem. Biophys.* 311:229–34

110. Ståhl U, Banas A, Stymne S. 1995. Plant microsomal phospholipid acyl hydrolases have selectivities for uncommon fatty acids. *Plant Physiol.* 107:953–62

111. Ståhl U, Ek B, Stymne S. 1998. Purification and characterization of a low-molecular-weight phospholipase A_2 from developing seeds of Elm. *Plant Physiol.* 117:197–205

112. Stobart K, Mancha M, Lenman M, Dahlqvist A, Stymne S. 1997. Triacylglycerols are synthesised and utilized by transacylation reactions in microsomal preparations of developing safflower (*Carthamus tinctorius* L.) seeds. *Planta* 203:58–66

113. Sun C, Cao Y-Z, Huang AHC. 1988. Acyl coenzyme A preference of the glycerol phosphate pathway in the microsomes from the maturing seeds of palm, maize, and rapeseed. *Plant Physiol.* 88:56–60

114. Tai H, Jaworski JG. 1993. 3-Ketoacyl-acyl carrier protein synthase III from spinach (*Spinacia oleracea*) is not similar to other condensing enzymes of fatty acid synthase. *Plant Physiol.* 103:1361–67

115. Takagi T, Itabshi Y. 1982. Cis-5 olefinic unusual fatty-acids in seed lipids of Gymnospermae and their distribution in triacylglycerols. *Lipids* 17:716–23

116. Taylor D, Weber N, Barton D, Underhill E, Hogge L, Weselake R, Pomeroy M. 1991. Triacylglycerol bioassembly in microspore-derived embryos of *Brassica*

napus L. cv Reston. *Plant Physiol.* 97:65–79

117. Thompson GA, Scherer DE, Aken SF-V, Kenny JW, Young HL, et al. 1991. Primary structures of the precursor and mature forms of stearoyl-acyl carrier protein desaturase from safflower embryos and requirement of ferredoxin for enzyme activity. *Proc. Natl. Acad. Sci. USA* 88:2578–82

118. Todd J, Post-Beittenmiller D, Jaworski JG. 1999. *KCS1* encodes a fatty acid elongase 3-ketoacyl-CoA synthase affecting wax biosynthesis in *Arabidopsis thaliana*. *Plant J.* 17:119–30

119. Voelker TA. 1996. Plant acyl-ACP thioesterases: chain-length determining enzymes in plant fatty acid biosynthesis. In *Genetic Engineering*, ed. JK Setlow, 18:111–33. New York: Plenum

120. Voelker TA, Hayes TR, Cranmer AM, Davies HM. 1996. Genetic engineering of a quantitative trait: metabolic and genetic parameters influencing the accumulation of laurate in rapeseed. *Plant J.* 9:229–41

121. Voelker TA, Worrell AC, Anderson L, Bleibaum J, Fan C, et al. 1992. Fatty acid biosynthesis redirected to medium chains in transgenic oilseed plants. *Science* 257:72–74

122. Vogel G, Browse J. 1996. Cholinephosphotransferase and diacylglycerol acyltransferase. *Plant Physiol.* 110:923–31

123. Wiberg E, Bafor M. 1995. Medium chain-length fatty acids in lipids of developing oil palm kernel endosperm. *Phytochemistry* 39:1325–27

124. Wiberg E, Banas A, Stymne S. 1997. Fatty acid distribution and lipid metabolism in developing seeds of laurate-producing rape (*Brassica napus* L.). *Planta* 203:341–48

125. Wiberg E, Edwards P, Byrne J, Stymne S, Dehesh K. 2000. The distribution of caprylate, caprate and laurate in lipids from developing and mature seeds of transgenic *Brassica napus* L. *Planta* 212:33–40

126. Wiberg E, Tillberg E, Stymne S. 1994. Substrates of diacylglycerol acyltransferase in microsomes from developing oil seeds. *Phytochemistry* 36:573–77

127. Yadav NS, Wierzbicki A, Aegerter M, Caster CS, Perez-Grau L, et al. 1993. Cloning of higher plant ω^3 fatty acid desaturases. *Plant Physiol.* 103:467–76

128. Zou J, Wei Y, Jako C, Kumar A, Selvaraj G, Taylor D. 1999. The *Arabidopsis thaliana tag1* mutant has a mutation in a diacylglycerol acyltransferase gene. *Plant J.* 19:645–53

Annu. Rev. Plant Physiol. Plant Mol. Biol. 2001. 52:363–406

CHLAMYDOMONAS AS A MODEL ORGANISM

Elizabeth H Harris

Developmental, Cell and Molecular Biology Group, Biology Department, Duke University, Durham, North Carolina 27708-1000; e-mail: chlamy@duke.edu

Key Words Volvocales, flagella, chloroplast, basal body, phototaxis

■ **Abstract** The unicellular green alga *Chlamydomonas* offers a simple life cycle, easy isolation of mutants, and a growing array of tools and techniques for molecular genetic studies. Among the principal areas of current investigation using this model system are flagellar structure and function, genetics of basal bodies (centrioles), chloroplast biogenesis, photosynthesis, light perception, cell-cell recognition, and cell cycle control. A genome project has begun with compilation of expressed sequence tag data and gene expression studies and will lead to a complete genome sequence. Resources available to the research community include wild-type and mutant strains, plasmid constructs for transformation studies, and a comprehensive on-line database.

CONTENTS

1040-2519/01/0601-0363$14.00

INTRODUCTION

At the Fifth International Chlamydomonas Conference in 1992, the venerable phycologist Ralph Lewin delivered a keynote address with the title, "The Cloaked One Emerges from Obscurity." Lewin's talk referred to the development of research on the unicellular green alga *Chlamydomonas* (Greek *chlamys*, a cloak; *monas*, solitary), beginning with nineteenth-century morphological descriptions and the first genetics studies in the early twentieth century. Pascher (1916, 1918, cited in 86) demonstrated the suitability of *Chlamydomonas* species for genetic analysis and pointed out the advantages of a haploid system in which all four products of meiosis could be recovered and analyzed. His investigations were not continued, but interest was soon renewed in this alga as a eukaryotic organism whose life cycle could be controlled in the laboratory. The work of Franz Moewus in the 1930s demonstrated that mutants could be isolated and characterized, but was clouded by irreproducibility of some of the reported results; it was only with the work of Lewin himself, Ruth Sager, and others in the 1940s and 1950s that a few *Chlamydomonas* species, in particular *C. reinhardtii* and *C. eugametos*, began to be developed as laboratory organisms (see 86 for review). The past 50 years have indeed seen the emergence of this organism from obscure beginnings into one of the premier model systems for diverse areas of cell and molecular biology.

Lewin's 1992 talk concluded with the arrival of his subject in the new age of molecular biology. Transformation of the chloroplast, nuclear, and mitochondrial genomes had been achieved, and the research presented at that meeting gave clear evidence that rapid progress lay ahead in developing new technologies for isolation and manipulation of genes. We are now embarking on a new era, as *Chlamydomonas* enters the age of genomics. Sequencing, gene expression studies, and molecular mapping projects are under way, and prospects are good for a complete genome sequence of *C. reinhardtii*. A review of the main features of this organism and its laboratory manipulation seems most appropriate at this time.

THE GENUS *CHLAMYDOMONAS*

Major Taxonomic Features

Historically, species of *Chlamydomonas* have been defined based solely on morphological criteria. The genus comprises unicellular chlorophyte algae with two anterior flagella, a basal chloroplast surrounding one or more pyrenoids, and a distinct cell wall (Figure 1). Species within the genus have been distinguished by

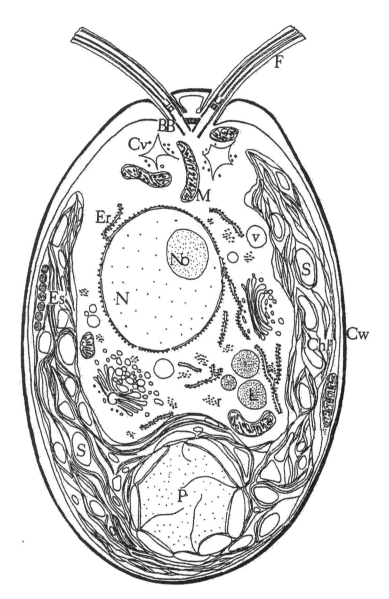

Figure 1 A semidiagrammatic representation of an interphase *Chlamydomonas* cell. Cell length, 10 μm; BB, basal bodies; Chl, chloroplast; Cv, contractile vacuole; Cw, cell wall; Er, endoplasmic reticulum; Es, eyespot; F, flagella; G, Golgi apparatus; L, lipid body; Mi, mitochondria; N, nucleus; No, nucleolus; P, pyrenoid; r, ribosomes; S, starch grain; v, vacuole. From (85), originally adapted from a figure by H Ettl, courtesy of John Harper.

differences in overall size and body shape, shape and position of the chloroplast and pyrenoids, flagellar length, number and position of contractile vacuoles, and more subtle structural features visible at the light microscope level. Ettl (1976, cited in 86) recognized 459 species, which he consigned to nine major morphological groups. Although many of these species are represented in culture collections, only a few have found significant roles as laboratory research organisms.

C. reinhardtii has emerged as the predominant laboratory species of *Chlamydomonas*, primarily owing to its ability to grow nonphotosynthetically with acetate as its sole carbon source, and is discussed at length below. Some research studies have utilized the interfertile species pair *C. eugametos* and *C. moewusii*. *C. eugametos*, of European origin, derives ultimately from Moewus and has been used particularly for investigation of sexuality, where it forms a useful contrast to *C. reinhardtii*. Gowans isolated a number of nutritional and resistance mutations in the *C. eugametos* background, but these are not under active investigation at present. *C. moewusii* was isolated in New York in 1948 by Provasoli and was used soon afterwards by Lewin for selection of flagellar mutants. One of the most active current topics of research with *C. eugametos* and *C. moewusii* is phospholipid-mediated signal transduction (see 119, 152 and references cited therein). Sequence of the nuclear genes encoding 18S ribosomal RNA, the nuclear ribosomal DNA spacer *ITS2*, and chloroplast ribosomal RNAs place *C. moewusii* and *C. eugametos* in a group more closely allied to *Haematococcus* and *Chlorogonium* than to the *C. reinhardtii* cluster (see 35). The predicted evolutionary distance between *C. reinhardtii* and *C. eugametos/C. moewusii* is consistent with the marked differences in chloroplast architecture and overall cell morphology and steps in the mating reaction, and with the inability of *C. eugametos* and *C. moewusii* to use acetate as their sole carbon source, presumably a very fundamental physiological difference. One suspects that the characters that place all these species within the same genus (two flagella, cell wall, presence of a pyrenoid) are not sufficient to define the genus *Chlamydomonas* as a phylogenetic entity. *Volvox carteri, Pandorina morum*, and some other colonial Volvocales used as research organisms appear to be closely allied with *C. reinhardtii* based on molecular criteria (21, 35, 131).

C. monoica is a homothallic *Chlamydomonas* species that has been used to investigate the processes of mating, chloroplast gene inheritance, and zygospore formation (228, 230). Some experimental work has also been done in various laboratories on *C. geitleri, C. segnis, C. chlamydogama*, and several other species (see 86).

Except as otherwise indicated, the remainder of this article focuses on *C. reinhardtii*.

Laboratory Strains of *C. reinhardtii*

The principal laboratory strains of *C. reinhardtii* are thought to derive from isolates made by GM Smith in 1945 from soil collected near Amherst, Massachusetts. Smith gave cultures to Sager, Lewin, Hartshorne, and perhaps others, and three main lineages deriving from Smith's collection have been separate since approximately 1950 (see Harris, Chapter 1 in 168). Although analyses of transposon insertion sites and chloroplast DNA restriction digests strongly suggest that all these strains do have a common origin, especially when compared with interfertile isolates from other localities (see 35 for citations), they are distinguished by inability of some of the strains to assimilate nitrate and by variability in light requirements for gametogenesis (202). AW Coleman (personal communication) has found significant differences among several of the Smith-derived strains in sequence of the ribosomal spacer *ITS2* and has advanced the hypothesis that Smith may have distributed more than one original isolate. The situation has been complicated further by later crosses among representatives of these three lineages and by poorly documented transfers of strains among laboratories.

It is only now, as sequencing of the entire genome begins, that nucleotide variations among descendants of the Smith strains are becoming significant. Sager's strain 21 gr (Chlamydomonas Genetics Center strain CC-1690) has been chosen as the primary target for sequencing efforts. Extensive EST (expressed sequence tag) data are also available from strain C9 (4), equivalent to 21 gr but separate from it since approximately 1955, and from CC-125, Smith's 137C strain as used by Levine and Ebersold, which differs from 21 gr and C9 in lacking nitrate reductase activity.

Strains S1 D2 and S1 C5 are isolates from soil collected in Plymouth, Minnesota (CH Gross et al, 1988, cited in 35). Although fully interfertile with 21 gr and 137C, these strains are distinguished from the Smith isolates by extensive nucleotide polymorphisms, especially in noncoding regions. The genomes appear to be colinear, however, without major chromosome rearrangements. A cross between 21 gr and S1 C5 has been used as the foundation of the molecular map (<http://www.biology.duke.edu/chlamy-genome/maps.html>), and EST data are also being obtained from this strain. Preliminary analyses indicate less than 1% sequence divergence between S1 D5 and the Smith strains in coding regions but as much as 7% in 3′ untranslated regions (CR Hauser, personal communication).

Isolates of *C. reinhardtii* have also been made from Quebec, Pennsylvania, North Carolina, and Florida, and may provide an additional source of diversity in future (see 35 for citations). A second Massachusetts isolate made by Smith in 1946, designated *C. smithii* mating type plus by Hoshaw & Ettl, should also be considered as part of the *C. reinhardtii* group based on interfertility (86). However, the strain identified by Hoshaw and Ettl as *C. smithii* mating type minus (CC-1372, from Santa Cruz, California) does not belong with the *C. reinhardtii* group based on its lack of full fertility and on DNA sequence criteria that suggest it is more closely related to *C. culleus* (35). All authentic *C. reinhardtii* isolates to date thus appear to derive from North America east of the Rocky Mountains.

Two additional isolates have been placed with *C. reinhardtii* (UG Schlösser 1984, cited by 35) based on their susceptibility to the *C. reinhardtii* vegetative cell lytic enzyme or autolysin, although they do not appear to be cross-fertile with the authentic *C. reinhardtii* strains (58). Originally identified as *C. incerta* (SAG

7.73, supposedly from Cuba), and *C. globosa* (SAG 81.72, supposedly from the Netherlands), these isolates appear to be identical based on restriction fragment analysis of chloroplast DNA (EH Harris et al 1991, cited by 35), the ribosomal *ITS* sequences (35), HindIII and PstI digests of total DNA probed with the beta-tubulin gene (59), and intron sequences from the *Ypt4* gene (59, 131).

CELL ARCHITECTURE AND FUNCTIONAL SYSTEMS

The Cell Wall

The wild-type *C. reinhardtii* cell (Figure 1) averages about 10 μm in diameter (with significant variation through the cell cycle) and is enclosed within a wall consisting primarily of hydroxyproline-rich glycoproteins that resemble plant extensins. Contrary to a few erroneous early reports that have unfortunately been perpetuated in some textbooks, the *C. reinhardtii* cell wall does not contain cellulose. The wild-type wall comprises seven principal layers (241). Genes for some wall components have been cloned and sequenced, and many mutants with defects in cell wall biogenesis have been isolated. Most of these mutants seem to make the precursor proteins of the wall in normal amounts but fail to assemble them into complete walls (232). Cell wall mutants have found widespread use as recipients for transformation with exogenous DNA, a process that is much more efficient with wall-less cells.

The Nucleus and the Nuclear Genome

The cell nucleus and nucleolus are prominent in cross-sections of *Chlamydomonas* cells. The nuclear membrane is continuous with the endoplasmic reticulum, and one to four Golgi bodies are situated nearby. Chromosome cytology is poor, with only eight discrete chromosomes being consistently visible by light microscopy in metaphase cells. Electron microscopy of synaptenemal complexes suggested 16 or more chromosomes, a number that is consistent with the 17 linkage groups now defined by genetic analysis. Attempts to separate chromosomes electrophoretically have not been fully successful (82). Vegetative cells are normally haploid, but stable diploids can be selected using auxotrophic markers. The nuclear genome size is estimated at approximately 1×10^8 base pairs (86, 194). It is GC-rich, approximately 62% overall in denaturation studies; sequence analysis gives a similar figure. This high GC content may produce difficulties in cloning genes. Amplification is improved by selection of primer sequences with 45% to 50% G-C content, and by including c7dGTP in the PCR reaction mixture (see 189 for methods).

Contractile Vacuoles and Osmotic Regulation

Two contractile vacuoles are located at the anterior end of the *C. reinhardtii* cell. Mutants requiring hyperosmotic media for survival (136) may provide a starting point for a study of genetic control of vacuole structure and function. Salt-sensitive mutants have also been isolated but are thought to affect ion transport across the plasma membrane and have not been implicated directly in vacuole function (179).

Mitochondria

Mitochondria are dispersed throughout the cytosol and are sometimes seen in electron micrographs as elongated or branching structures. The difficulty of purifying mitochondria free of chloroplast contamination has limited biochemical research on *Chlamydomonas* mitochondria, and methods for purification of active mitochondria have been developed only recently (14, 53). The 15.8-kb mitochondrial genome is linear and contains only a few genes: *cob*, *cox1*, five subunits of mitochondrial NADH dehydrogenase, the mitochondrial rRNAs (which are fragmented in the DNA sequence); three tRNAs, and an opening reading frame that resembles a reverse transcriptase (see GenBank Accession number U03843 for complete sequence and citations). Mutants that delete the *cob* gene are unable to grow on acetate in the dark but are viable when grown phototrophically. Point mutations in the *cob* gene can confer myxothiazol resistance. Nuclear mutants with respiratory deficiencies and a dark-dier phenotype have also been obtained (see 45 for citations).

The Chloroplast

A single cup-shaped chloroplast occupies the basal two thirds of the cell and partially surrounds the nucleus. Thylakoid membranes are arranged in well-defined appressed and non-appressed domains whose composition and functional organization have been extensively investigated in wild-type and mutant strains of *Chlamydomonas* (Olive & Wollman, in 196). A distinctive body within the chloroplast, the pyrenoid, is the site of CO_2 fixation and the dark reactions of photosynthesis. Starch bodies surround the pyrenoid and are also seen dispersed throughout the chloroplast under some conditions of growth. Presence or absence of a pyrenoid distinguishes *Chlamydomonas* from the genus *Chloromonas*, and within the genus *Chlamydomonas*, the number and arrangement of the pyrenoids is an important species character in traditional taxonomy.

Sequencing of the 195-kb chloroplast genome is nearly complete (DB Stern and colleagues, personal communication). The chloroplast genomes of all *Chlamydomonas* species examined have an inverted repeat structure reminiscent of that of most land plants, but gene order differs markedly from the plant model and cannot be accounted for by any simple scheme of rearrangements or inversions. The gene content of the chloroplast genome largely does resemble that of land plants, however, with only a few significant differences (19).

Chlamydomonas became known early on as an excellent model system in which to study both photosynthesis and biogenesis of the chloroplast. The *y1* mutant, originally isolated by Sager, loses chlorophyll and forms only a rudimentary proplastid when cultured on acetate-containing medium in the dark. On exposure to light, *y1* cells become green and form a complete chloroplast structure over the course of approximately 8 h. Although not precisely analogous to greening of an etiolated plant seedling in terms of how this process is regulated, *y1* re-greening has nevertheless proved to be a powerful and accessible system for studying synthesis and assembly of the photosynthetic machinery, and for investigation of the relative roles of nuclear and chloroplast genomes in this process (237 and references cited therein).

One avenue of research arising from these early studies has been investigation of the genetic control of chlorophyll synthesis (see 12 for review of chlorophyll biosynthesis in general). Besides *y1*, there are several additional, nonallelic, mutants that show a yellow-in-the-dark phenotype, including some temperature-sensitive alleles (see 23). *C. reinhardtii* has two pathways for conversion of protochlorophyllide to chlorophyllide. The *y* mutants are blocked in the light-independent pathway, homologous to the protochlorophyllide reductase seen in organisms ranging from purple bacteria through gymnosperms (23, 126). The core enzyme in *Chlamydomonas* consists of three subunits coded by the chloroplast genes *chlB*, *chlL*, and *chlN*. The nuclear loci *Y1* and *Y5* through *Y10* in *C. reinhardtii* all appear to be involved in expression of these chloroplast genes and/or assembly of their products (23). The *pc1* mutant is blocked in light-mediated protochlorophyllide conversion because of a deletion in the gene encoding NADPH:protochlorophyllide oxidoreductase (130), which is equivalent to the light-dependent enzyme found in angiosperms (126). Other mutants in the chlorophyll biosynthetic pathway in *Chlamydomonas* include strains in which formation of Mg protoporphyrin from protoporphyrin IX is blocked and mutants specifically deficient in chlorophyll *b*. A signal transduction pathway for light-induced expression of glutamate 1-semialdehyde aminotransferase, an early enzyme in synthesis of both chlorophyll and heme, has been analyzed by Im & Beale (101).

In the 1960s, Levine's laboratory at Harvard produced a series of papers demonstrating that the photosynthetic electron transfer chain was amenable to genetic dissection. Nonphotosynthetic mutants of *C. reinhardtii* were isolated, and identified by the prefix *ac*, for acetate-requiring. Many of these mutants were assigned to specific processes—water oxidation, photosynthetic electron transport, ATP synthesis, CO_2 fixation—but identification of lesions in specific proteins was not possible with technology available at that time. Investigation in the early years was limited to mutations in nuclear genes. A breakthrough was made in 1979, however, with development of methods to select nonphotosynthetic mutations by using 5-fluorodeoxyuridine to reduce the number of copies of the chloroplast genome prior to mutagenesis (HS Shepherd et al 1979, cited in 86). The list of photosynthetic genes cloned and marked by mutations is now impressive (41) (Table 1). Chloroplast transformation with exogenous DNA occurs by homologous replacement (see below), thereby potentially permitting analysis by site-directed mutagenesis of every chloroplast gene. More than 50 nuclear gene loci affecting chloroplast biogenesis and photosynthetic functions are marked by mutations, and nearly all the structural genes for chloroplast components known in land plants have also been identified in *Chlamydomonas* either by complete sequencing or as ESTs.

TABLE 1   Representative mutations affecting photosynthesis and the chloroplast in
Chlamydomonas reinhardtii

Component	References
Photosystem II reaction center and water-splitting complex	
Deletions of chloroplast-encoded *psbA* gene	See (86)
Site-directed mutations in *psbA* affecting photosynthesis	(87, 137, 220, 249)
Herbicide-resistance mutations in *psbA*	See (86)
Nuclear mutations that cause accumulation of excess D1 protein or make D1 unstable at high light intensity	(254)
Nuclear mutations that destabilize *psbB* mRNA	(225)
Mutation in chloroplast-encoded *psbC* gene	(195)
At least four nuclear mutations affecting translation of *psbC*	(195, 253)
Induced and site-directed mutations in chloroplast-encoded *psbD* gene	(107)
At least three nonallelic nuclear mutations affecting *psbD* translation	(18, 155)
Chloroplast *psbD* mutation producing unstable mRNA; three nuclear loci have been identified that suppress this mutation	(155)
psbE null mutant	(150)
Disruption of chloroplast-encoded *psbH* gene and site-directed mutations in this gene	(163, 219)
Disruption of chloroplast *psbI* gene; can grow photosynthetically but is light sensitive	See (219)
Disruption of chloroplast *psbK* gene	See (219)
Disruption of chloroplast *ycf8* gene; impairs PS II function under stress conditions	See (194)
Transposon insertion in *PsbO* gene	See (194)
Two allelic nuclear mutants deficient in OEE2 protein	(200)
State-transition mutations affecting LHCII phosphorylation	(118)
Cytochrome b$_6$/f complex	
Site-directed point and deletion mutations in chloroplast-encoded *petA* gene	(11, 31, 32, 36)
Five allelic nuclear mutations affecting *petA* mRNA stability and/or maturation	(41)
Point and deletion mutations in chloroplast-encoded *petB* gene	(41, 257)
A nuclear mutation affecting *petB* mRNA stability and/or maturation	(41)
Induced, null and site-directed mutations in the nuclear-encoded *PetC* gene	(41)
Numerous induced and site-directed mutations in chloroplast-encoded *petD* gene	(41, 92, 256)
Two nuclear mutations affecting *petD* mRNA stability and/or maturation	(41)
Several allelic mutations in nuclear-encoded*PetE* gene	(129)
Deletion of chloroplast-encoded *petG* gene	See (41)
A nuclear mutation affecting *petG* mRNA stability and/or maturation	(41)

(Continued)

TABLE 1   *(Continued)*

Component	References
Five nuclear gene loci involved in synthesis of chloroplast *c*-type cytochromes	(102, 246)
Chloroplast mutations in the *ccsA* (*ycf5*) gene, encoding a protein required for heme attachment of cytochrome *c*	(246, 247)
At least four nuclear mutations affecting heme attachment to cytochrome b_6	(120)
Disruptions of chloroplast *ycf7* (*petL*) gene; distabilization of the cytochrome b_6/f complex	(222)
Deletion of *petO* gene	(222)
	(83)
Photosystem I reaction center	
Deletion or disruption of chloroplast-encoded *psaA* gene	(36)
Site-directed point mutations in *psaA*	(55)
Disruption of *tscA*, a 430-nt RNA involved in *psaA trans*-splicing	(195)
At least 5 nuclear loci affecting *psaA* exon 2–3 splicing	(173, 195)
At least 2 nuclear loci affecting both *trans*-splicing steps	
At least 7 nuclear loci affecting exon 1–2 *trans*-splicing	
Frame-shift and site-directed mutations in chloroplast *psaB* gene	(63)
Mutation in a nuclear gene that blocks a post-transcriptional step in *psaB* expression	(195, 215)
Site-directed mutations in chloroplast *psaC* gene	(63)
Mutations in nuclear *PsaF* gene	(62, 93)
Disruptions of chloroplast *ycf3* and *ycf4* genes; produce PS I deficiency	(20, 41)
Site-directed mutations in *ycf3* and *ycf4*	(20)
Insertional mutations in nuclear *Crd1* gene; blocked in response to copper deficiency, fail to accumulate PS I and LHC I	(151)
Xanthophyll cycle and photoprotection	
At least three nonallelic nuclear mutants blocked in xanthophyll cycle	(161)
Several nonallelic nuclear mutants resistant to very high light intensities	(65)
Photophosphorylation	
Site-directed mutations in chloroplast *atpA* gene	(44)
Nuclear mutation affecting translation of chloroplast *atpA* gene	See (41)
Nuclear mutation that destabilizes *atpA* mRNA	
Nuclear mutation that destabilizes *atpB* mRNA	
Many point and deletion mutations in chloroplast *atpB* gene	See (86)
Site-drected mutations in *atpB*	e.g. (29, 30, 99)
Site-directed mutations in nuclear *AtpC* gene	(114, 199)
Induced mutations in chloroplast *atpE*, *atpF* and *atpI* genes	See (44)
Nuclear mutation affecting expression of the chloroplast-encoded *atpH* and *atpI* genes	
CO_2 uptake	
Mutation in nuclear *CAH3* gene encoding intracellular carbonic anhydrase	(71, 218)
Additional mutants that require high levels of CO_2 for growth	(110, 166)

TABLE 1 *(Continued)*

Component	References
Disruption of chloroplast *ycf10* gene; produces inefficient carbon uptake into chloroplast	(197)
nit1-tagged mutants affecting CO_2 uptake	(69)
Carbon fixation	
Many mutations in chloroplast *rbcL* gene	See (191)
Site-directed mutation in *rbcL* that alters its specificity for Rubisco activase	(125)
Nuclear mutation that inhibits *rbcL* expression; second-site suppressors of this mutation	(98)
Point mutation in structural gene for phosphoribulokinase	(7)
Chlorophyll biosynthesis	
Deletion mutation in gene encoding NADPH:protochlorophyllide oxidoreductase	(130)
Nuclear mutations in at least six loci affecting expression of the chloroplast-encoded *chlB*, *chlL*, and *chlN* genes and/or assembly of the protochlorophyllide reductase complex	(23)
Two allelic nuclear mutants in the nuclear gene encoding Mg chelatase	(E Chekunova, personal communication)
Chloroplast protein synthesis and protein translocation	
Many antibiotic resistance mutations in 16S and 23S ribosomal RNA genes	See (86)
Nuclear mutation that blocks processing of chloroplast rRNA	(96)
Additional nuclear mutations that result in deficiency in chloroplast ribosomes	See (86)
Nuclear mutations that suppress site-directed alterations in thylakoid signal sequences	(15)
Disruption of chloroplast-encoded *clpP* protease	See (194)
Nuclear mutation affecting LHC assembly, probably at the level of a chaperone protein	(H Naver, personal communication)

Among the greatest strengths of *Chlamydomonas* as a model organism in which to study chloroplast biogenesis has been its use to identify nuclear genes that regulate the expression of genes encoded in the chloroplast. Many of the mutants isolated in Levine's laboratory have turned out to be involved in processing of chloroplast mRNAs or other regulatory steps. For example, the *ac115* mutant, isolated by Gillham in 1960 and initially described as lacking several proteins of photosystem II (PS II), has finally revealed its true nature (190). The *Ac115* gene product, a small basic protein with a potential membrane-spanning domain at the carboxyl terminus, is required for translation of mRNA for the chloroplast-encoded *psbD* gene, encoding the D2 protein of the photosystem II reaction center.

The original *ac115* allele is a nonsense mutation near the 5′ end of this gene. The nuclear *NAC1* and *NAC2* loci, unlinked to *AC115*, are also involved in *psbD* translation, and a mutation that suppresses both *ac115* and *nac1* has been found (HY Wu & MR Kuchka, cited in 190). In *nac2* mutants, the *psbD* mRNA is unstable, leading to failure of assembly of the PS II reaction center. The *Nac2* gene product is a 140-kDa hydrophilic polypeptide containing nine tetratricopeptide repeats (18). Additional nuclear mutants have been isolated that suppress a site-directed mutation within the 5′ untranslated region of the *psbD* gene (155).

The chloroplast *psaA* gene presents an even more complex example of interactions between nuclear and chloroplast genes in *Chlamydomonas*. This gene is split into three separately transcribed exons in *C. reinhardtii*, and the mRNA is assembled by *trans*-splicing. At least 14 different nuclear genes affect the *trans*-splicing process, and a small chloroplast-encoded RNA molecule (*tscA*) is also required (81, 155, 173).

Synthesis and assembly of components of the cytochrome b_6/f complex have been investigated in several laboratories (e.g. 11, 32, 120, 257). As is also true for the reaction centers of photosystems I and II, this complex contains both chloroplast and nuclear gene products, and additional nuclear genes may be required for control of chloroplast gene expression. For example, one chloroplast locus and at least four nuclear loci are required for heme attachment to the cytochrome *c* apoprotein (246).

Wollman et al (cited in 32) have proposed a general model for stoichiometric accumulation of chloroplast-encoded proteins based on the concept of "control of epistasy of synthesis" or CES. Synthesis of some chloroplast-encoded subunits of the cytochrome b_6/f complex ("CES subunits") is strongly attenuated if other subunits of the complex ("dominant subunits") are absent. For example, mutants deficient in either cytochrome b_6 or subunit IV show a greatly reduced rate of translation of cytochrome *f*, encoded by the chloroplast *petA* gene (32). However, in mutants lacking cytochrome *f*, cytochrome b_6 and subunit IV are synthesized at normal rates and then degraded. Choquet et al (32) showed that the 5′ untranslated region of the *petA* mRNA regulates its own translation by interaction, either directly or through an intermediary protein, with the C-terminal domain of the unassembled cytochrome *f* protein.

Merchant and colleagues have studied regulation of the copper-containing protein plastocyanin (129), and the *c*-type cytochromes (144, 248). Copper deficiency in *Chlamydomonas* results in degradation of plastocyanin and induction of cytochrome c_6 and coproporphyrinogen oxidase, and copper-responsive sequences have been identified within the promoters of the *Cyc6* and *Cpx1* genes (185, 186). Mutants at the newly identified *CRD1* locus are chlorophyll deficient in the absence of copper and have defects in photosystem I (151). Restoration of copper rescues both phenotypes. The *Crd1* gene product is a 47-kDa hydrophilic protein with a carboxylate-bridged di-iron binding site, and it appears to be required for adaptation to either copper or oxygen deficiency.

These are only a few examples of the ways in which *Chlamydomonas* is currently being used for investigation of the chloroplast and photosynthesis. For a much more comprehensive treatment, the recent book edited by Rochaix, Goldschmidt-Clermont & Merchant (196) is highly recommended. Rochaix (194) and Davies & Grossman (38) have reviewed the use of *Chlamydomonas* for elucidation of photosynthetic processes. Niyogi (159) has reviewed photoprotection and photoinhibition, a process for which *Chlamydomonas* is proving to be a very useful model (9, 65, 90, 104, 139, 160, 161, 210). Xiong et al (250) have published a three-dimensional model for the photosystem II reaction center of *Chlamydomonas* in a paper that thoroughly reviews the literature on components of this complex. For an assessment of photosystem I function and its indispensability, see Redding et al (192). There is also a substantial literature on transcriptional and translational control of chloroplast gene expression in *Chlamydomonas* (44, 57, 73, 88, 116, 141, 252) and on processing of introns in chloroplast rRNA and *psbA* genes (95). Goldschmidt-Clermont (76) has reviewed coordinated expression of nuclear and chloroplast genes in plant cells, including *Chlamydomonas*, and Nickelsen & Kück (156) have reviewed the use of *C. reinhardtii* as a model system for study of chloroplast RNA metabolism. Chloroplast DNA replication has also been studied in several laboratories (28 and references cited therein).

Flagella

Two anterior flagella, 10 to 12 μm in length, protrude through specialized collar regions in the cell wall. The structure of the flagellar axoneme has been described thoroughly (147), and more than 250 component proteins have been resolved by two-dimensional electrophoresis. From the very beginning, *Chlamydomonas* has been among the very best organisms for research on flagellar function and assembly. Mutants with defects in motility were among the first to be isolated both in *C. moewusii* and *C. reinhardtii*. Many of these early mutants are extant and are finally revealing their precise defects.

Mutations have been identified that affect nearly all of the principal components of the flagellar axoneme. More than 75 genetic loci have been identified in *C. reinhardtii* that affect flagellar assembly and/or function, and more than 40 genes for flagellar components have been cloned and sequenced. Some of these mutants have parallels in mutations affecting animal cilia and sperm cells (33, 167–169). Complementation in the transient dikaryons formed after mating can be used to identify specific proteins of the radial spokes, central pair, and other complexes. Fusion of gametes of opposite mating type in *C. reinhardtii* produces a cell with two nuclei and four flagella. This quadriflagellate cell remains motile for about two hours before the flagella are resorbed and formation of the zygospore wall begins. During this motile period, flagellar assembly continues, and polypeptides contributed by both parental gametes are incorporated into all four flagella. Thus mating of two nonallelic paralyzed mutants usually results in restoration of full motility in this transient dikaryon, as each partner supplies a wild-type copy of the defective flagellar protein produced by the other gamete. The simple observation of restoration of motility makes a very nice laboratory exercise for students. Luck and colleagues (cited in 46, 86) used radioactive labeling and two-dimensional gel electrophoresis to identify the specific proteins that were restored by mating labeled mutant cells to unlabeled wild-type cells. The reviews by Dutcher (46) and Mitchell (147) of the genetics of flagellar assembly and structure are highly recommended as an introduction to this field of research for the non-specialist. Johnson (106) has reviewed flagellar beating motility and its structural correlates. Detailed reviews have also been published on dyneins (176), radial spokes (37), the central apparatus (213), kinesins (16), and intraflagellar transport (198).

In addition to mutants with primary defects in flagellar components, many second-site suppressor mutations have been found that restore partial or complete motility, and these mutations have permitted identification of additional structural components. Mutants with unusually long or short flagella are also known (5), and the regulation of flagellar length through the cell cycle in wild-type cells is being elucidated (224).

Gliding motility, by means of movement of the flagellar membrane, has long been known, and nongliding mutants have been isolated (RA Bloodgood in 43). This gliding motion can also be visualized by transport of adherent particles or polystyrene beads along the rigid, extended flagella of certain mutants with defects in the central pair microtubules (e.g. *pf18*; 17).

Flagellar assembly depends on yet another type of motility, intraflagellar transport (IFT), first identified in *Chlamydomonas* by Rosenbaum and colleagues (34, 117, 198). This process involves bi-directional movement of protein complexes ("rafts") along the flagella. Transport toward the flagellar tip is mediated by a kinesin, first identified as the site of the flagellar assembly mutation *fla10* (117). The return transport of rafts back toward the cell body is dependent on cytoplasmic dynein 1b and dynein light chain LC8 (34, 175). Mutants in which anterograde IFT is disrupted may have short or "stumpy" flagella and may accumulate flagellar proteins in the cell body, whereas mutants in which retrograde IFT is defective display a bulge in the flagellar membrane (34, 175). One of the components of IFT complex B shows homology to a mammalian protein implicated in a form of polycystic kidney disease, known from a mouse mutant in which renal cilia are abnormal. The IFT system is also implicated in retinitis pigmentosa, where retinal photoreceptor cells, whose outer sector is a modified cilium, are progressively lost (33, 34, 198).

Basal Bodies

The flagella arise from a pair of basal bodies located just beneath the apical end of the cell, surmounting the cell nucleus. The basal bodies are connected to one another by a distal striated fiber (Figure 2) and are attached at their proximal ends to four sets of microtubules that extend around the anterior portion of the cell. Proximal fibers connect the basal bodies to the nucleus, and a cruciate fibrous root is located directly beneath the basal bodies.

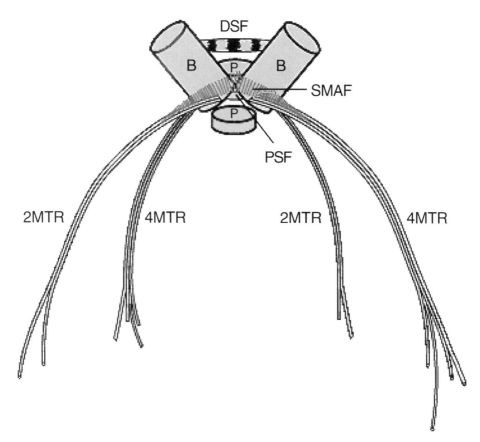

Figure 2   Flagellar root system of *Chlamydomonas*. B, basal bodies; P, pro-basal bodies; DSF, distal striated fiber; PSF, proximal striated fiber; SMAF, striated microtubule-associated fiber; 2MTR and 4MTR, 2- and 4-membered rootlet microtubules. Figure by Andrea Preble, courtesy of Susan Dutcher.

In cross-section, the basal bodies show a progression from a ring structure through a series of cartwheel configurations also seen in centrioles of animal cells, to the final 9 + 2 microtubule structure characteristic of eukaryotic flagella and cilia (Figure 3). *Chlamydomonas* has proved an especially favorable system in which to investigate the formation and function of basal bodies and flagella. Centrin, the 20-kDa contractile protein of the distal striated fiber and the nucleus-basal body connector, was discovered in *Chlamydomonas* (see 204), as was delta-tubulin, required for assembly of triplet microtubules in the basal body (49). Three additional centriole-associated proteins, BAp90, BAp95, and striated fiber assemblin, were also first identified in green algae (127).

Prior to mitosis, the basal bodies assume their alternative role as centrioles, components of the microtubule organizing center as in animal cells (138). The

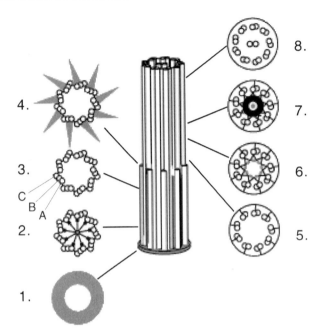

Figure 3 Cross-sectional views of a *Chlamydomonas* basal body, showing progression through triplet microtubule and stellate morphologies to the axonemal $9 + 2$ microtubule structure (from 178; courtesy of S Dutcher).

connections from the flagella to the basal bodies are lost early in mitosis, and the flagella are resorbed. The basal bodies (centrioles) duplicate in late G1 phase by forming a new partner next to each pre-existing one, and by prophase the cell has a pair of centrioles at each spindle pole, each pair consisting of an old and a new centriole. After cytokinesis, the basal bodies return to the cell anterior, and new flagella are formed. Recent studies indicate that centrioles are able to form de novo (49, 138).

When *Chlamydomonas* cells are treated with weak organic acids, mastoparan, calmodulin antagonists, detergent, or various other stimulants, the flagella are severed at the level of the transition region between the basal body and the flagellar axoneme (see Figure 3). The process is thought to be similar to katanin-mediated severing of cytoplasmic microtubules in mitotic *Xenopus* and starfish oocytes (see 132, 133, 182). Investigation of this phenomenon in *Chlamydomonas* has revealed a complex signal transduction pathway that is proving to be amenable to genetic analysis. Mutants at two genetic loci fail to sever their flagella in response to any stimulus and are thought to be defective in the calcium-activated severing process. The product of one of these loci is a 171-kDa protein with an N-terminal coiled-coil domain and three Ca^{+2}/calmodulin-binding domains (60). Mutants at a third locus are blocked in acid-stimulated deflagellation but respond to nonionic detergent plus Ca^{+2} and are proposed to affect protein-stimulated Ca^{+2} influx (61).

Deflagellation is followed by active transcription of the genes encoding tubulin and other flagellar components, and regeneration of the flagella over a 3-h period. This has proved an excellent system both for purification of axonemes and for study of the assembly process [see articles by SM King and PA Lefebvre in (43) for methods]. Deflagellation induces both transcription of genes for flagellar proteins and changes in mRNA half-life (79, 109, 172). In the presence of inhibitors of protein synthesis, assembly of half-length flagella still occurs, suggesting that there is a cytoplasmic pool of flagellar precursors (66). Pre-assembled complexes move from the cytoplasm to the flagellar compartment, where they are attached to microtubule-associated docking sites (162).

The Eyespot and Phototaxis

The eyespot, or stigma, appears bright orange at the light microscope level, owing to a high concentration of carotenoid pigments. Electron microscopy reveals it as a region of electron-dense granules located just inside the chloroplast membrane at the cell equator. The carotenoid-containing granules of the eyespot are thought to act as a quarter-wave plate to direct light to the true photoreceptor (KW Foster & RD Smyth, cited in 206), located in the overlying plasma membrane and now identified as a retinal-binding rhodopsin homologue (chlamyopsin; 42, 89). The complex functions as a directional antenna that enables swimming cells to orient themselves with respect to unidirectional light. Mutants lacking the eyespot structure show reduced efficiency of phototaxis but may still be able to perceive light through the photoreceptor. Mutants with defects in eyespot assembly have been grouped into six complementation groups, several of which map to a closely linked cluster of loci (123; DGW Roberts, MR Lamb & CL Dieckmann, submitted). Mutants deficient in the signal transduction pathway essential to the phototactic response have also been isolated (115, 170, 201). Methods for assaying phototaxis have been described by Moss et al (contained in 43).

The position of the eyespot gives the *Chlamydomonas* cell an inherent asymmetry, because it is associated with the distal end of one of the flagellar roots, specifically the four-membered rootlet emanating from newly formed basal body from the previous mitosis. This basal body is referred to as *cis* (relative to the eyespot), whereas the parent basal body is *trans*. The flagellar beat in normal forward swimming is a breast-stroke action that propels the cell in a helical path, with constant orientation of the eyespot relative to the helical axis. However, the *cis* and *trans* flagella respond differently to phototactic signals, thus effecting a turning response (205). The position of the eyespot is established during mitosis, when the old eyespot disappears and a new one is formed, invariably opposite the site of the cleavage plane.

Two distinct photoresponses have been observed in *Chlamydomonas*, the oriented movements of phototaxis in response to a constant unidirectional light and the photophobic or stop response to sudden light flashes. The same photoreceptor appears to mediate both responses (P Kröger & P Hegemann 1994, cited in 205). Analysis of mutants that show phototactic but not photophobic responses suggests that the photophobic response requires a calcium-dependent all-or-none electric current induced by photoreceptor-mediated depolarization of the flagellar membrane (140). Phototaxis also depends on calcium-induced changes in flagella beating, but at a lower molarity of calcium that shifts the balance in beating strength of the two flagella.

MITOTIC AND MEIOTIC LIFE CYCLES

Vegetative Cell Growth

Wild-type *C. reinhardtii* is easily grown in defined liquid or agar media at neutral pH, and has no requirements for supplementary vitamins or other co-factors (see 86). Strains in the Ebersold/Levine 137C background cannot assimilate nitrate and therefore require a reduced nitrogen source (usually NH_4Cl). Acetate can be used as a carbon source by wild-type strains, with the consequence that growth can occur in the dark, and mutants blocked in photosynthesis are viable if acetate is provided. Other intermediates in the citric acid cycle do not support growth in the dark, nor do various pentose or hexose sugars, ethanol, glycerol, or other organic compounds.

For wild-type strains, growth in light either with or without acetate is faster than dark growth and is therefore recommended. Optimal growth temperature is from 20° to 25°. At 25°, in minimal medium and with adequate light (200–400 μEinsteins/m^{2}sec photosynthetically active radiation), an average doubling time of 6 to 8 h should be achieved.

When grown on a 12:12, 14:10, or 16:8 light-dark cycle, cells remain in G1 throughout the light phase and divide during the dark phase, usually with two or sometimes three mitotic divisions taking place in rapid succession. Four daughter cells are retained within a common mother cell wall and released simultaneously on secretion of a specific lytic enzyme. Commitment to divide appears to be determined at a specific point in G1 phase, thought to be analogous to the START event in the yeast cell cycle (see 85 for review). Beyond this point, division will still occur even if light and nutrients are removed from the culture. The number of successive divisions that take place in a given cycle depends on the cell size reached during G1. A circadian oscillator may also be involved in determining timing of division (78).

The progress of mitosis in *C. reinhardtii* was described in 1968 by Johnson and Porter in a classic paper (cited in 86). Since that time, computer-assisted analysis of serial sections and immunofluorescence techniques have added to our understanding of the changes in cytoplasmic microtubules, actin, and the chloroplast during mitosis (51, 85).

Conditional mutants blocked at specific points in the cell division cycle at restrictive temperature were described more than 25 years ago by Howell and colleagues (reviewed in 85), but the state of knowledge of the cell cycle at that time did not permit full characterization of their defects. New conditional cell cycle mutants have been isolated by John and colleagues (203, 242), and the old mutants have been subjected to further study as well. The results now emerging indicate that *Chlamydomonas* has great potential as a system for genetic analysis of cell cycle control.

A nonconditional mutant defective in size control has been found to have a deletion in a gene encoding a homologue of the retinoblastoma family of tumor suppressors (3; J Umen, unpublished). This protein appears to function at two points in the cell cycle, in G1 and again in S phase. The result of its deletion in *Chlamydomonas* is impairment both in timing of commitment to divide and in control of the number of divisions that eventually occur.

Mutants of *C. moewusii* described as "twins" and "monsters" were reported by Lewin in 1952 (reviewed in 85). The twinning mutant is now thought to be defective in formation of the cleavage furrow. Cultures of monster mutants have a significant proportion of cells that are blocked in division but continue to grow. The *cyt1* mutant of *C. reinhardtii* resembles the monster mutants in its failure to complete cytokinesis in many cells of a culture, with the consequence that cells may be multinucleate, large, and multilobed (JR Warr, cited in 85). Ehler & Dutcher (51) found that *cyt1* cultures often produce cells with incomplete cleavage furrows. They also isolated an insertional allele of *cyt1* and a mutant at a second locus, *cyt2*, which makes additional, misplaced, cleavage furrows. The number of flagella on a given cell is correlated with the number of nuclei. Similar mutants (*oca1* and *oca2*, for occasional cytokinesis arrest) have been described by Hirono & Yoda (94).

Mutants of *C. reinhardtii* with abnormalities in the basal body cycle have proved to be particularly amenable to study. Several classes of mutants were first identified by their variable number of flagella. *Vfl1* cells have lost control of the timing and placement of basal body and flagellar formation and show abnormalities in the direction of the flagellar beat, as well as structural abnormalities in several of the doublet microtubules of the flagellar axoneme (223). New basal bodies can appear at any point during G1 phase, and the flagellar insertions can be anywhere on the cell surface. *Vfl2* mutants have alterations in the structural gene for centrin (221) and show random segregation of the basal bodies. Pedigree analysis of mitotic progeny from a *vfl2* mutant has been used to demonstrate de novo centriole assembly (138). *Vfl3* mutants are defective in placement of the probasal bodies and have been shown to have defects in striated fibers (HJ Hoops, RL Wright, JW Jarvik & GB Witman 1984, and RL Wright, Chojnacki & JW Jarvik, 1983, cited in 86). *Uni* mutants were so named because the majority of cells in a culture have only a single flagellum. The *uni1* and *uni2* mutants both show alterations in the transition zone (Figure 3, level 7) but are distinguishable at the ultrastructural level (49). The *uni3* mutant may have zero, one, or two flagella and exhibit aberrant cytokinesis. In this mutant, the C tubule is missing in the triplet microtubule of the basal body (Figure 3, level 3). The defect in *uni3* has been traced to delta-tubulin, a protein first identified when the *Uni3* gene was cloned from *Chlamydomonas* (49).

Bld ("bald") mutants lack flagella altogether. One such mutant, *bld2*, lacks functional basal bodies and has defects in cytokinesis consistent with loss of centrioles (52). The cleavage furrow loses its precise orientation with respect to the mitotic spindle. Another mutation affecting cytokinesis is *fla10*, originally isolated as a temperature-conditional flagellar assembly mutant, but subsequently shown to have a defect in a kinesin-homologous protein that functions in basal bodies both in flagellar assembly and in organization of the mitotic spindle (117, 231).

The Sexual Cycle

C. reinhardtii cells are normally haploid and are of one of two genetically fixed mating types, designated plus (mt^+) and minus (mt^-). The mating-type locus is a complex region of recombinational suppression on linkage group VI, comprising approximately 1 megabase and containing genes involved in cell recognition and fusion, zygospore maturation, and in the mating-type controlled inheritance of organelle genes, as well as some additional closely linked loci that have no apparent role in the sexual cycle (58, 59). Additional genes that map elsewhere in the genome but whose expression is sex-limited have also been identified (25, 77, 122, 226).

When deprived of nitrogen, cells of both mating types differentiate into sexually competent gametes (Figure 4). Some strains have an additional requirement for blue light to progress from a pregamete state to mating competence (13, 74, 165, 202). Plus and minus gametes pair initially along the lengths of their flagella in a reaction mediated by sex-specific agglutinin proteins. Flagellar pairing initiates a cAMP-mediated signal transduction cascade, which has been investigated extensively (181, 239). Pairing is followed by a morphological change ("activation") in the flagellar tips and by dissolution of the cell walls of the mating partners by a gamete-specific lytic enzyme. Flagellar agglutination, activation of the flagellar tips, and wall lysis can all be by-passed by supplying exogenous dibutryl cAMP and isobutyl methylxanthine (SM Pasquale & UW Goodenough, cited in 86; this observation has been exploited as a means of genetic analysis of mutants lacking flagella). Fusion of the mating partners begins at sex-specific structures at the anterior ends of the cells (238, 240), and continues laterally from anterior to posterior. The newly formed diploid zygote remains motile for several hours as a quadriflagellate cell.

In *C. moewusii, C. eugametos, C. monoica*, and some other *Chlamydomonas* species, flagellar contact is followed initially by fusion only at the extreme anterior ends of the cells, and the partner cells swim about for several hours as a "vis-à-vis" pair before full cell fusion occurs (229). This distinction in the mating process is probably a very fundamental character separating different ancestral lineages within the green algae. Sexual cycles have been described in relatively few *Chlamydomonas* species, so this has not been used as a character in traditional taxonomy. The overall process of recognition, signal transduction, and cell fusion in *C. eugametos* resembles that of *C. reinhardtii* in many ways, however, and a substantial body of literature exists on the sexual cycle in this species (see 229).

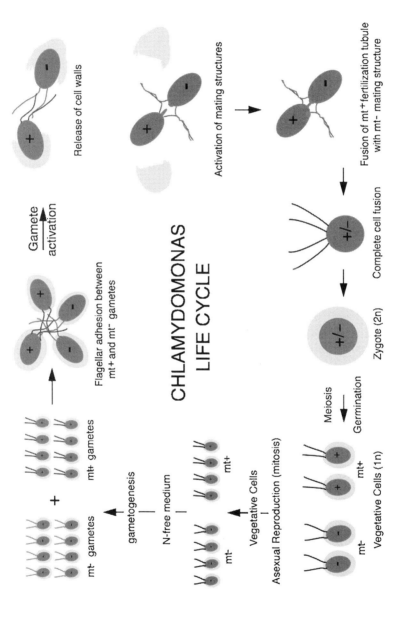

Figure 4 The sexual cycle of *Chlamydomonas reinhardtii.* Courtesy of William Snell.

Zygote-specific transcripts appear within minutes of gamete fusion (121 and references cited therein). Formation of a hard, impermeable zygospore wall begins, chloroplasts appear to disintegrate, with loss of chlorophyll, and lipid bodies accumulate over the ensuing 4 to 6 days. The zygospore wall in sexual species of *Chlamydomonas* affords protection against adverse environmental conditions. Like the vegetative cell wall, the zygospore wall of *C. reinhardtii* contains hydroxyproline-rich glycoproteins, some of which are marked by (SerPro)x repeats. Zygospores can remain viable in soil for many years. However, under laboratory conditions only a few days are required for zygospore maturation before germination can be induced by restoration of nitrogen in the presence of light. Meiosis occurs, with the subsequent release of the four haploid meiotic products. Under some conditions, a mitotic division follows meiosis prior to opening of the zygospore wall, with the resulting release of eight rather than four progeny cells; predilection for release of eight rather than four cells may be strain dependent (86).

A small percentage of mated pairs fail to initiate the zygospore maturation pathway and begin instead to divide mitotically as stable vegetative diploids (see 86). These can be deliberately selected using complementing auxotrophic markers, and can be recognized 3 or 4 days after mated cells have been plated on agar, as bright green hemispherical colonies visible using a dissected microscope, on a lawn of unmated gametes and immature zygospores.

Tetrad Analysis

Separation of all meiotic products from a single zygospore is the foundation of traditional *Chlamydomonas* genetics by tetrad analysis (see SK Dutcher in 43 and 86 for methods). Nuclear genes show 2:2 inheritance in crosses and are scored by their segregation in parental ditype, nonparental ditype, or tetratype tetrads. Chloroplast and mitochondrial genes show primarily uniparental inheritance, from the plus and minus mating types, respectively. Elucidating the mechanism by which uniparental inheritance is achieved was one of the earliest challenges in *Chlamydomonas* research. Although the mysteries are still not entirely solved, the tools of molecular biology are now being brought to bear on this problem (146, 158).

Mutations are readily induced in the nuclear genome of haploid *Chlamydomonas* cells by UV or chemical mutagenesis (86), or by insertional mutagenesis in which transformation with exogenous DNA results in disruption of nuclear genes (LW Tam & PA Lefebvre in 43). This technique is becoming increasingly common as a preliminary step in cloning genes for which a mutated phenotype is known or predictable and is discussed further below.

The spectrum of mutants available in *C. reinhardtii* includes nonphotosynthetic, nonmotile, and nonphototactic strains, auxotrophs, mutants resistant to antibiotics or herbicides, and other phenotypes (see 86, 128). As of this writing, nearly 200 nuclear gene loci have been identified by mapped mutations.

PHYSIOLOGICAL PROCESSES

Nutrient Update and Metabolic Stress

Most wild-type strains of *C. reinhardtii* can assimilate nitrogen as nitrate, nitrite, ammonium, or other small molecules such as urea, acetamide, etc. Strains in the 137C background carry two mutations blocking nitrate reductase activity. The *Nia1* gene (*NIT1* locus) is the structural gene for nitrate reductase (108); the *Nia2* gene (*NIT2*) encodes a regulatory protein in the nitrate assimilation pathway (207). The nitrate transport system has been characterized in some detail and several component genes have been cloned (153, 184, 255). Nitrite is transported by a separate system, regulated by blue light (187). The structural gene for nitrite reductase (*Nii1*) maps to a cluster that also includes nitrate assimilation genes and a light-regulated gene (183). Genes for some additional enzymes involved in nitrogen metabolism have also been cloned and are under investigation.

Arginine is the only amino acid for which auxotrophic mutations are readily isolated in *Chlamydomonas*. Mutations at six loci affect the arginine biosynthetic pathway (see 86). Only the argininosuccinate lyase gene has been completely sequenced (6), but ESTs have been found corresponding to ornithine transcarbamoylase (the step blocked by the *arg4* mutation) and argininosuccinate synthase (*arg8*). Efforts to obtain a broader spectrum of amino acid auxotrophs have not been successful, possibly owing to lack of active transport systems for these compounds. Some mutants resistant to amino acid analogs have been isolated, however. Auxotrophic mutants are also known for thiamine, nicotinamide, and para-aminobenzoic acid.

Carbon assimilation involves a complicated pathway with multiple forms of carbonic anhydrase (218), the genes for several of which have been cloned from *C. reinhardtii*. Expression of the periplasmic enzyme is regulated by acetate and pH (227). Carbonic anhydrase activity associated with the chloroplast (2, 71) is required for photosynthesis at ambient concentrations of CO_2. A novel 29.5-kDa alpha-type carbonic anhydrase associated with the thylakoid membrane has been cloned from *Chlamydomonas* by Karlsson et al (110). Mitochondrial carbonic anhydrase is induced at low CO_2 concentrations (54). Mutants blocked in carbonic anhydrase activity are dependent on high CO_2 levels for growth (69, 112, 214).

Limitation for CO_2 in the light or for acetate in the dark results in accumulation of large amounts of starch (amylopectin) by *Chlamydomonas* cells (22). Mutants deficient in amylose biosynthesis resemble waxy mutants of maize and other plants in accumulating an aberrant amylopectin. A mutant blocked in ADP-glucose pyrophosphorylase has also been isolated.

Sulfur deprivation induces expression of a high-affinity transport system (251) and a periplasmic arylsulfatase that has found utility as a reporter gene (164). Mutants at three loci show aberrant responses to sulfur deprivation; two of these loci have been shown to correspond to genes for regulatory proteins (39, 40).

Phosphorous starvation induces expression of several phosphatases (1, 8, 188) and of the *Psr1* gene, encoding a regulatory protein (245).

When grown under anaerobic conditions in the light, *Chlamydomonas* cells are capable of producing molecular hydrogen. Sulfur deprivation enhances hydrogen production by repressing photosynthetic oxygen evolution, and under laboratory conditions, cultures can be maintained that cycle between photosynthesis and hydrogen production as sulfur is alternately removed and resupplied (142). The wild-type hydrogenase enzyme is very sensitive to inhibition by oxygen, but efforts are under way to select mutants with a more oxygen-tolerant enzyme (T Flynn & M Ghirardi, in preparation). The process is potentially of enormous value as a source of renewable fuel.

Another potential commercial application of *Chlamydomonas* is in removal of heavy metal wastes from the environment. Tolerance for cadmium and other metals by *Chlamydomonas* cells can be altered by growth conditions, by mutation (177, 234), by treatment with phytochelatin inhibitors (24), or by genetic engineering (R Sayre, personal communication).

As our knowledge increases of genes involved in individual metabolic pathways, studies of the integration of these pathways is becoming feasible. Huppe & Turpin (100) provide a good summary of the relationships between carbon and nitrogen metabolism. Wykoff et al (244) have assessed effects of nutrient deprivation on photosynthesis. Rochaix (194) has discussed state transitions, chlororespiration and interactions between the chloroplast and mitochondria. The study of stress responses in *Chlamydomonas* is in fact emerging as an integrated discipline, encompassing nutrient limitation, excess light, heavy metal contamination, osmotic stress, and heat responses. Bell and colleagues have published a series of papers dealing with genetic fitness and response of *Chlamydomonas* cells to experimentally controlled environmental fluctuations (75, 111 and references cited therein).

Light-Mediated Responses

As mentioned in connection with the sexual cycle, blue light photoreceptors may be involved in regulation of gametogenesis in *Chlamydomonas* (74, 165). The blue-light-responsive *LRG5* locus encodes a protein rich in arginine, lysine, and alanine with a putative nuclear-localization signal at its C-terminal end. No significant sequence homology was found to proteins from other organisms, but DNA hybridization experiments suggest some conservation of related sequences in other Volvocales and in land plants. The blue-light signaling pathway in gametogenesis appears to involve consecutive action of a phosphatase and a kinase resembling protein kinase C (165). Disruption of the *LRG6* gene, encoding a protein with significant homology to the yeast membrane transport facilitator YJR124p, eliminates the requirement for blue light in gametogenesis (G Dame, G Glöckner & CF Beck, personal communication). Blue light has also been implicated in cell cycle regulation in *Chlamydomonas* (233), in chlorophyll biosynthesis (91), and in repair of UV-induced DNA damage (174). An early report that antibodies to plant phytochrome reacted with a *Chlamydomonas* protein was misleading; Bonenberger et al (1994, cited in 74) have shown that a monoclonal antibody to pea phytochrome reacts with a totally unrelated protein in *C. reinhardtii*, and there is no evidence to date for any phytochrome-mediated responses. The absence of red/far-red responses increases the utility of *Chlamydomonas* for the study of other light-regulated responses. A cryptochrome photoreceptor, *CPH1*, has recently been cloned from *C. reinhardtii* (NA Reisdorph & GD Small, in preparation). Although cryptochrome proteins have been implicated in molecular clock mechanisms in some organisms, the *CPH1* gene of *C. reinhardtii* does not seem to show circadian regulation. Promoter regions of light-responsive genes in *Chlamydomonas* do not have the conserved control elements seen in higher plants but do appear to have characteristic light-regulated *cis* sequences (80).

Circadian Rhythms

Like many other algae, *Chlamydomonas* does have a circadian clock system, however, and its potential for genetic analysis increases its utility as a model for this area of research. Circadian rhythms of phototactic aggregation were observed by Bruce and coworkers in the early 1970s, and mutants with altered rhythms were obtained (see 86). Mergenhagen isolated additional mutants and explored the nature of the timer, or zeitgeber, under various environmental conditions, including zero gravity. Circadian rhythms have also been found in abundance of mRNAs for a number of genes involved in nitrogen metabolism and in photosynthesis (68, 103), and in UV sensitivity (157). Circadian rhythm phases can be shifted by brief pulses of light given during the dark period. The action spectrum for this response shows peaks at 520 and 660 nm, but is not far-red reversible (T Kondo et al 1991, cited in 103). Mittag (1994, cited in 148) discovered a regulatory factor in the dinoflagellate *Gonyaulax polyedra* that binds to a *cis* element, a UG repeat in the 3′ untranslated region of the gene encoding the luciferin-binding protein in that alga. Further investigation revealed that *Chlamydomonas* has an analogous clock-controlled RNA-binding protein (148, 149) whose target sequence is also a UG repeat. This sequence appears in the 3′ untranslated region of many *Chlamydomonas* genes, including several involved in nitrogen metabolism and previously reported to exhibit temporal expression (H Waltenberger, C Schneid, J Grosch, A Bariess & M Mittag, submitted).

TECHNIQUES AND RESOURCES

The Molecular Tool Kit

Over the past 12 years transformation of the nuclear and chloroplast genomes with exogenous DNA has become routine (see 113 for review). The first successful transformations were accomplished using biolistic[TM] bombardment with tungsten or gold particles. Vortex-mixing with DNA-coated glass beads or silicon carbide whiskers is also effective, especially for nuclear gene transformation, as is electroporation (211). The glass bead method is especially recommended, as it requires no specialized equipment or expensive supplies. Highest frequencies are obtained with glass bead transformation and electroporation when cell walls are removed prior to transformation, and when steps are take to improve plating efficiency of cells after transformation (180). Wall-deficient mutant strains can be used, or the walls of wild-type cells can be removed prior to transformation with a preparation of the gamete lytic enzyme (113). With all methods, cotransformation with two different plasmids occurs at a high frequency (216). When selection is made for one of the introduced genes, most transformants are found to carry the unselected DNA as well. This observation suggests that the critical event in transformation is in sustaining a nonlethal "hit" by the particles, glass beads, fibers, etc, and that cells that survive such a hit are likely to assimilate whatever DNA was present at the moment of impact.

Chloroplast transformation usually occurs by homologous replacement and has been extensively used to study proteins of the photosynthetic complexes by site-directed mutagenesis (e.g. 63, 99, 124, 137, 193, 249, 257). Selectable markers for cotransformation include antibiotic resistance mutations in the chloroplast ribosomal RNA genes, the bacterial antibiotic resistance genes *aadA* (56, 57, 64) and *aphA-6* (10), *uidA* (GUS; 57), and *Renilla* luciferase (145). Transformation of the mitochondrial genome has also been reported (B Randolph-Anderson et al, 1993, cited in 45).

In contrast to the organelles, nuclear gene transformation generally occurs by nonhomologous insertion into the genome of one or (usually) more copies of the transforming DNA. Transformation with glass beads usually results in integration of fewer copies of the transforming DNA than does particle bombardment (79). Insertion usually results in deletion of 10 to 20 kb or more of DNA at the integration site (128). When this event disrupts a nonessential gene, the insertion can be used as a probe for hybridization to clone the gene (LW Tam & PA Lefebvre, in 43). More than 50 genes have already been cloned using this technique. Because the insertion nearly always disrupts the gene function, creating a null mutation, this method is not useful for cloning essential genes. However, insertion frequencies are sufficiently high that the method is a very efficient means of obtaining populations of mutant cells to screen for specific phenotypes, e.g. loss of motility or photosynthetic function (128).

Insertional mutagenesis has usually been accomplished by transformation of a mutant deficient in either nitrate reductase (*nit1*) or argininosuccinate lyase (*arg7*) with the corresponding wild-type gene. Transformants are selected by restoration of ability to grow on nitrate as sole N source (*NIT1*), or on minimal medium (*ARG7*), and can then be screened for other phenotypes resulting from nonhomologous insertion of the transforming DNA.

Transposon tagging of *Chlamydomonas* genes has also been used as a cloning strategy, although less extensively to date than *ARG7* or *NIT1* insertions. Transposable elements characterized in *C. reinhardtii* include a class I retrotransposon (*TOC*), three class II elements (*Gulliver*; *Pioneer*, and *TOC2*); and three elements, *Tcr1* through *Tcr3*, which are characterized by inverted terminal repeat sequences [for review, see (236)].

Other constructs that have been used for nuclear transformation include several selectable markers that can confer inhibitor resistance on wild-type cells. The *CRY1* and *ALS* markers are endogenous *Chlamydomonas* genes from mutant cells resistant to emetine and sulfmeturon methyl, respectively (JAE Nelson & PA Lefebvre, in 43; 70). Several bacterial antibiotic resistance genes have also been expressed successfully in *Chlamydomonas* (27, 212, 217).

The nuclear transforming constructs used to date generally include a native *C. reinhardtii* promoter and 3′ untranslated region, most commonly from the *RbcS2* gene encoding the small subunit of ribulose bisphosphate carboxylase. Improved expression of nuclear genes has been achieved by including the first intron of *RbcS2* (135). Further enhancement has been obtained with a construct that fuses the promoter of the *HSP70A* (heat shock protein) gene upstream of the promoter and first intron from *RbcS2* (208).

Failure to achieve satisfactory expression of some introduced genes has been attributed to posttranscriptional gene silencing, codon bias, and incomplete promoters, enhancers, or other regulatory sequences. Finally, these problems seem to be yielding to creativity, hard work, and persistence. Cerutti and colleagues (26) have investigated silencing of the bacterial *aadA* gene after transformation into *Chlamydomonas* in a construct where it is flanked by the *RbcS2* 5′ and 3′ noncoding regions. Expression of *aadA* was found to be unstable in approximately half the transformants recovered. Inactivation of the gene was epigenetic, i.e. no alterations were observed in the presence or sequence of the transforming DNA, and the changes were reversible in selected clones transferred to and from selective conditions (spectinomycin). Spectinomycin resistance always cosegregated with the integrated construct in crosses. Direct analysis of *aadA* expression showed that the gene was inactivated at the transcriptional level and that this inactivation was not correlated with cytosine methylation or with accessibility of the integrated construct to restriction enzymes (which would have suggested silencing by chromatin condensation). Insertional mutagenesis has been used to recover suppressors of this epigenetic silencing (243). Although methylation was not implicated in the *aadA* silencing, work with *Volvox* suggests that CpG methylation does have a role in expression of introduced genes in this alga, and by extension may be expected to have significance in *Chlamydomonas* as well (P Babinger, I Kobl, W Mages & R Schmitt, submitted).

C. reinhardtii nuclear genes show a pronounced codon bias, a consequence of the GC-rich genome. The search for foreign genes that can be used as selectable markers has led to bacterial genes whose codon usage is similar to that of *Chlamydomonas*. The *ble* gene from *Streptoalloteichus hindustanus*, conferring phleomycin resistance, and the *aphVIII* gene of *Streptomyces rimosus*, conferring resistance to aminoglycoside antibiotics, were chosen for this reason (212, 217). Expression of the green fluorescent protein gene was improved by resynthesizing it with a codon set more typical of native *C. reinhardtii* genes (67).

The molecular tool kit for *Chlamydomonas* includes several additional constructs useful for analyzing gene expression (also see 128, 134, 216). The arylsulfatase gene (*Ars1*), whose synthesis is induced when cells are starved for sulfur, can be used as a reporter for promoter function (164). The enzyme is assayed using a chromogenic sulfate substrate. Haring & Beck (84) have adapted insertional tagging to create a promoter trap system. Cells of a double mutant, *arg7 pf14*, are transformed with the *Arg7* gene and a promoter-less *Rsp3* gene (radial spoke protein 3, complementing the *pf14* mutation). Transformants are selected for ability to grow on minimal medium, and then screened for restoration of motility resulting from integration of the *Rsp3* gene downstream of an endogenous promoter. The gene whose promoter is now tagged with *Rsp3* can thus be cloned. Auchincloss et al (6) have reported development of a shuttle vector based on the cDNA for the *Arg7* gene that is able to complement both the *C. reinhardtii arg7* mutant and the *E. coli argH* mutant. Constructs have also been made to permit epitope tagging of cloned genes (e.g. 105).

Although targeted disruption of *Chlamydomonas* nuclear genes by transformation has succeeded only rarely owing to the rarity of homologous insertion (154), RNAi is showing promise as an alternative means of targeting and inactivating expression of specific genes (50, 209). For example, expression of chlamyopsin (the photoreceptor protein) has been studied in constructs driven by the *Hsp70A* and *RbcS2* promoters (M Fuhrmann, S Rank, E Govorunova & P Hegemann, in preparation). When the complete *Cop* gene encoding this protein, including introns, is expressed from these promoters, chlamyopsin levels are 5 to 10 times higher than in untransformed cells. Replacing the *Cop* gene with an inverted gene sequence capable of forming a double-stranded RNA structure reduced expression to as little as 10% of the wild-type level.

Fortunately, lack of directed homologous integration has not prevented rescue of mutants by transformation with cosmid or BAC clones derived from *C. reinhardtii* (71, 74, 189), and this technique is now becoming routine. In a variation of this technique suitable for genes with no selectable phenotype, Purton & Rochaix (180) prepared a cosmid library in a vector carrying the wild-type *Arg7* DNA. Arginine-independent transformants were selected and then screened for complementation of the original mutation. Rescue of mutant phenotypes by genes from other organisms may become feasible as better expression of heterologous genes is achieved.

A BAC library (http://www.biology.duke.edu/chlamy/ChlamyGen/libraries. html) with approximately 10- to 12-fold coverage of the *Chlamydomonas* genome is commercially available from Incyte Genomics and is being used to generate a molecular map (P Kathir, PA Lefebvre & CD Silflow, in preparation). Positional cloning using individual BAC clones together with this map has already been successful (CD Silflow & PA Lefebvre, personal communication) and will undoubtedly become more practical as the density of markers on the molecular map increases. As BAC clones are identified that hybridize to molecular markers, they can be used to assemble overlapping contigs that will eventually cover the entire genome.

The current molecular map contains 240 markers, with an average physical spacing of 400 to 500 kb. All molecular markers analyzed to date have been placed on 17 linkage groups, suggesting that this is indeed the definitive number of linkage groups for *C. reinhardtii*[1]. For nearly all of the linkage groups, the molecular and genetic maps can be anchored and oriented to each other by markers in common.

Sources of Strains and Information

The Chlamydomonas Genetics Center at Duke University provides cultures of wild-type and mutant strains of *C. reinhardtii, C. eugametos*, and *C. moewusii*. The web site is at http://www.biology.duke.edu/chlamy; mailing address c/o Elizabeth H. Harris, DCMB Box 91000, Duke University, Durham, NC 27708-1000. Wild-type strains of other genera are available from several major algal collections worldwide, including Culture Centre of Algae and Protozoa (CCAP; Freshwater Biology Association, The Ferry House, Ambleside, Cumbria, LA22 0LP, UK; http://wiua.nwi.ac.uk/ccap/ccaphome.html); Institute of Applied Microbiology, Tokyo (IAM; The University of Tokyo, 1-1-1 Yayoi, Bunkyou-ku, Tokyo 113, JAPAN); Sammlung von Algenkulturen (SAG; Pflanzen physiologisches Institut, Universität Göttingen, Nikolausberger Weg 18, D-3400 Göttingen, Germany (http://www.gwdg.de/~botanik/phykologia/epsag.html); University of Texas Algal Collection (UTEX; Department of Botany, Austin, TX 78713-7640, Section of Molecular Cell and Developmental Biology, University of Texas, Austin, TX 78713 (http://www.bio.utexas.edu/research/utex/); University of Toronto Culture Collection (UTCC; Department of Botany, University of Toronto, Toronto, Ontario M5S 3B2, Canada (http://www.botany.utoronto.ca/utcc/). ChlamyDB is a comprehensive database for information on *Chlamydomonas* and other algae in the Volvocales, including publications, sequence citations, gene descriptions, and genetic maps. This is available in a web presentation through the USDA-ARS Center for Bioinformatics and Comparative Genomics at Cornell University (http://arsgenome.cornell.edu/cgi-bin/WebAce/webace?db=chlamydb). Recommendations for nomenclature of Chlamydomonas genetic loci have been published by Dutcher (47) in the *Trends in Genetics Genetic Nomenclature*

---

[1] In early genetic mapping studies, 19 linkage groups were identified and numbered. Subsequent analysis (48) has shown that linkage groups XII and XIII in fact are colinear, as are groups XVII and XVIII. The UNI linkage group, or ULG, previously reported by Ramanis & Luck to be a circular linkage group having a specific association with the basal body (see 235), now appears to be a linear nuclear linkage group like the others and is now designated as group XIX (97).

Guide. The Chlamydomonas Genetics Center coordinates availability of names for loci and mutant alleles; contact Elizabeth Harris (chlamy@duke.edu) for assistance. The bionet.chlamydomonas newsgroup (http://www.bio.net:80/hypermail/CHLAMYDOMONAS/) provides a moderated forum for discussion of *Chlamydomonas* and other algae. The 10th International Conference on the Cell and Molecular Biology of Chlamydomonas will be held at the University of British Columbia (UBC) Conference Center in Vancouver, BC, Canada, June 11–16, 2002.

The Chlamydomonas Genetics Center is sponsored by National Science Foundation Grant 9970022. The initial phase of the Chlamydomonas Genome Project is sponsored by NSF Grant 9975765 under the direction of Arthur Grossman, Carnegie Institution of Washington, Stanford, CA.

Visit the Annual Reviews home page at www.AnnualReviews.org

LITERATURE CITED

1. Adam M, Loppes R. 1998. Use of the *ARG7* gene as an insertional mutagen to clone *PHON24*, a gene required for derepressible neutral phosphatase activity in *Chlamydomonas reinhardtii. Mol. Gen. Genet.* 258:123–32

2. Amoroso G, Weber C, Sueltemeyer D, Fock H. 1996. Intracellular carbonic anhydrase activities in *Dunaliella tertiolecta* (Butcher) and *Chlamydomonas reinhardtii* (Dangeard) in relation to inorganic carbon concentration during growth: Further evidence for the existence of two distinct carbonic anhydrases associated with the chloroplasts. *Planta* 199:177–84

3. Armbrust EV, Ibrahim A, Goodenough UW. 1995. A mating type-linked mutation that disrupts the uniparental inheritance of chloroplast DNA also disrupts cell-size control in *Chlamydomonas. Mol. Biol. Cell* 6:1807–18

4. Asamizu E, Nakamura Y, Sato S, Fukuzawa H, Tabata S. 1999. A large scale structural analysis of cDNAs in a unicellular green alga, *Chlamydomonas reinhardtii.* I. Generation of 3433 non-redundant expressed sequence tags. *DNA Res.* 6:369–73

5. Asleson CM, Lefebvre PA. 1998. Genetic analysis of flagellar length control in *Chlamydomonas reinhardtii:* a new long-flagella locus and extragenic suppressor mutations. *Genetics* 148:693–702

6. Auchincloss AH, Loroch AI, Rochaix JD. 1999. The argininosuccinate lyase gene of *Chlamydomonas reinhardtii:* cloning of the cDNA and its characterization as a selectable shuttle marker. *Mol. Gen. Genet.* 61:21–30

7. Avilan L, Gontero B, Lebreton S, Ricard J. 1997. Information transfer in multienzyme complexes. 2. The role of Arg64 of *Chlamydomonas reinhardtii* phosphoribulokinase in the information transfer between glyceraldehyde-3-phosphate dehydrogenase and phosphoribulokinase. *Eur. J. Biochem.* 250:296–302

8. Bachir F, Loppes R. 1997. Identification of a new derepressible phosphatase in *Chlamydomonas reinhardtii. FEMS Microbiol. Lett.* 149:195–200

9. Baroli I, Melis A. 1998. Photoinhibitory damage is modulated by the rate of photosynthesis and by the photosystem II light-harvesting chlorophyll antenna size. *Planta* 205:288–96

10. Bateman JM, Purton S. 2000. Tools for chloroplast transformation in *Chlamydomonas:* expression vectors and a new dominant selectable marker. *Mol. Gen. Genet.* 263:404–10

11. Baymann F, Zito F, Kuras R, Minai L, Nitschke W, Wollman FA. 1999. Functional characterization of *Chlamydomonas* mutants defective in cytochrome f maturation. *J. Biol. Chem.* 274:22957–67

12. Beale SI. 1999. Enzymes of chlorophyll biosynthesis. *Photosynth. Res.* 60:43–73

13. Beck CF, Haring MA. 1996. Gametic differentiation of *Chlamydomonas*. *Int. Rev. Cytol.* 168:259–302

14. Bennoun P, Atteia A, Pierre Y, Delosme M. 1995. Etiolated cells of *Chlamydomonas reinhardtii*: choice material for characterization of mitochondrial membrane polypeptides. *Proc. Natl. Acad. Sci. USA* 922:10202–6

15. Bernd KK, Kohorn BD. 1998. *Tip* loci: Six *Chlamydomonas* nuclear suppressors that permit the translocation of proteins with mutant thylakoid signal sequences. *Genetics* 149:1293–301

16. Bernstein M. 1995. Flagellar kinesins: new moves with an old beat. *Cell Motil. Cytoskel.* 32:125–28

17. Bloodgood RA, Salomonsky NL. 1998. Microsphere attachment induces glycoprotein redistribution and transmembrane signaling in the *Chlamydomonas* flagellum. *Protoplasma* 202:76–83

18. Boudreau E, Nickelsen J, Lemaire SD, Ossenbuhl F, Rochaix JD. 2000. The *Nac2* gene of *Chlamydomonas* encodes a chloroplast TPR-like protein involved in *psbD* mRNA stability. *EMBO J.* 19:3366–76

19. Boudreau E, Otis C, Turmel M. 1994. Conserved gene clusters in the highly rearranged chloroplast genomes of *Chlamydomonas moewusii* and *Chlamydomonas reinhardtii*. *Plant Mol. Biol.* 24:585–602

20. Boudreau E, Takahashi Y, Lemieux C, Turmel M, Rochaix JD. 1997. The chloroplast *ycf3* and *ycf4* open reading frames of *Chlamydomonas reinhardtii* are required for the accumulation of the photosystem I complex. *EMBO J.* 16:6095–104

21. Buchheim MA, Lemieux C, Otis C, Gutell RR, Chapman RL, Turmel M. 1996. Phylogeny of the Chlamydomonadales (Chlorophyceae): a comparison of ribosomal RNA gene sequences from the nucleus and the chloroplast. *Mol. Phylogenet. Evol.* 5:391–402

22. Buleon A, Gallant DJ, Bouchet B, Mouille C, D'Hulst C, Kossmann J. 1997. Starches from A to C—*Chlamydomonas reinhardtii* as a model microbial system to investigate the biosynthesis of the plant amylopectin crystal. *Plant Physiol.* 115:949–57

23. Cahoon AB, Timko MP. 2000. *yellow-in-the-dark* mutants of *Chlamydomonas* lack the CHLL subunit of light-independent protochlorophyllide reductase. *Plant Cell* 12:559–68

24. Cai XH, Traina SJ, Logan TJ, Gustafson T, Sayre RT. 1995. Applications of eukaryotic algae for the removal of heavy metals from water. *Mol. Mar. Biol. Biotechnol.* 4:338–44

25. Campbell AM, Rayala HJ, Goodenough UW. 1995. The *iso1* gene of *Chlamydomonas* is involved in sex determination. *Mol. Biol. Cell* 6:87–95

26. Cerutti H, Johnson AM, Gillham NW, Boynton JE. 1997. Epigenetic silencing of a foreign gene in nuclear transformants of *Chlamydomonas*. *Plant Cell* 9:925–45

27. Cerutti H, Johnson AM, Gillham NW, Boynton JE. 1997. A eubacterial gene conferring spectinomycin resistance on *Chlamydomonas reinhardtii*: integration into the nuclear genome and gene expression. *Genetics* 145:97–110

28. Chang CH, Wu M. 2000. The effects of transcription and RNA processing on the initiation of chloroplast DNA replication in *Chlamydomonas reinhardtii*. *Mol. Gen. Genet.* 263:320–27

29. Chen W, Hu CY, Crampton DJ, Frasch WD. 2000. Characterization of the metal binding environment of catalytic site 1 of chloroplast F1-ATPase from *Chlamydomonas*. *Biochemistry* 39:9393–400

30. Chen W, LoBrutto R, Frasch WD. 1999. EPR spectroscopy of VO^{2+}-ATP bound to

catalytic site 3 of chloroplast F_1–ATPase from *Chlamydomonas* reveals changes in metal ligation resulting from mutations to the phosphate-binding loop threonine (betaT168). *J. Biol. Chem.* 274:7089–99

31. Chi YI, Huang LS, Zhang ZL, Fernández-Velasco JG, Berry EA. 2000. X-ray structure of a truncated form of cytochrome *f* from *Chlamydomonas reinhardtii*. *Biochemistry* 39:7689–701

32. Choquet Y, Stern DB, Wostrikoff K, Kuras R, Girard-Bascou J, Wollman FA. 1998. Translation of cytochrome f is autoregulated through the 5' untranslated region of *petA* mRNA in *Chlamydomonas* chloroplasts. *Proc. Natl. Acad. Sci. USA* 95:4380–85

33. Cole DG. 1999. Kinesin-II, coming and going. *J. Cell Biol.* 147:463–66

34. Cole DG, Diener DR, Himelblau AL, Beech PL, Fuster JC, Rosenbaum JL. 1998. *Chlamydomonas* kinesin-II-dependent intraflagellar transport (IFT): in *Caenorhabditis elegans* sensory neurons. *J. Cell Biol.* 141:993–1008

35. Coleman AW, Mai JC. 1997. Ribosomal DNA *ITS-1* and *ITS-2* sequence comparisons as a tool for predicting genetic relatedness. *J. Mol. Evol.* 45:168–77

36. Cournac L, Redding K, Ravenel J, Rumeau D, Josse EM, et al. 2000. Electron flow between photosystem II and oxygen in chloroplasts of photosystem I-deficient algae is mediated by a quinol oxidase involved in chlororespiration. *J. Biol. Chem.* 275:17256–62

37. Curry AM, Rosenbaum JL. 1993. Flagellar radial spoke: a model molecular genetic system for studying organelle assembly. *Cell Motil. Cytoskel.* 24:224–32

38. Davies JP, Grossman AR. 1998. The use of *Chlamydomonas* (Chlorophyta: Volvocales) as a model algal system for genome studies and the elucidation of photosynthetic processes. *J. Phycol.* 34:907–17

39. Davies JP, Yildiz FH, Grossman AR. 1996. *Sac1*, a putative regulator that is critical for survival of *Chlamydomonas reinhardtii* during sulfur deprivation. *EMBO J.* 15:2152–59

40. Davies JP, Yildiz FH, Grossman AR. 1999. *Sac3*, an Snf1-like serine threonine kinase that positively and negatively regulates the responses of *Chlamydomonas* to sulfur limitation. *Plant Cell* 11:1179–90

41. de Vitry C, Vallon O. 1999. Mutants of *Chlamydomonas*: tools to study thylakoid membrane structure, function and biogenesis. *Biochimie* 81:631–43

42. Deininger W, Fuhrmann M, Hegemann P. 2000. Opsin evolution: out of wild green yonder? *Trends Genet.* 16:158–59

43. Dentler W, Witman G, eds. 1995. *Cilia and Flagella. Methods in Cell Biology.* San Diego: Academic. Vol. 47. 603 pp.

44. Drapier D, Suzuki H, Levy H, Rimbault B, Kindle KL, et al. 1998. The chloroplast *atpA* gene cluster in *Chlamydomonas reinhardtii*—functional analysis of a polycistronic transcription unit. *Plant Physiol.* 117:629–41

45. Duby F, Matagne RF. 1999. Alteration of dark respiration and reduction of phototrophic growth in a mitochondrial DNA deletion mutant of *Chlamydomonas* lacking *cob*, *nd4*, and the 3' end of *nd5*. *Plant Cell* 11:115–25

46. Dutcher SK. 1995. Flagellar assembly in two hundred and fifty easy-to-follow steps. *Trends Genet.* 11:398–404

47. Dutcher SK. 1995. *Chlamydomonas reinhardtii*. In *Trends in Genetics Genetic Nomenclature Guide*, ed. A Stewart, pp. 18–19. Cambridge: Elsevier. 43 pp.

48. Dutcher SK, Power J, Galloway RE, Porter ME. 1991. Reappraisal of the genetic map of *Chlamydomonas reinhardtii*. *J. Hered.* 82:295–301

49. Dutcher SK, Trabuco EC. 1998. The *UNI3* gene is required for assembly of basal bodies of *Chlamydomonas* and encodes delta-tubulin, a new member of the tubulin superfamily. *Mol. Biol. Cell* 9:1293–308

50. Ebnet E, Fischer M, Deininger W, Hegemann P. 1999. Volvoxrhodopsin, a light-regulated sensory photoreceptor of the spheroidal green alga *Volvox carteri*. *Plant Cell* 11:1473–84

51. Ehler LL, Dutcher SK. 1998. Pharmacological and genetic evidence for a role of rootlet and phycoplast microtubules in the positioning and assembly of cleavage furrows in *Chlamydomonas reinhardtii*. *Cell Motil. Cytoskel.* 40:193–207

52. Ehler LL, Holmes JA, Dutcher SK. 1995. Loss of spatial control of the mitotic spindle apparatus in a *Chlamydomonas reinhardtii* mutant strain lacking basal bodies. *Genetics* 141:945–60

53. Eriksson M, Gardestrom P, Samuelsson G. 1995. Isolation, purification, and characterization of mitochondria from *Chlamydomonas reinhardtii*. *Plant Physiol.* 107:479–83

54. Eriksson M, Villand P, Gardeström P, Samuelsson G. 1998. Induction and regulation of expression of a low-CO_2-induced mitochondrial carbonic anhydrase in *Chlamydomonas reinhardtii*. *Plant Physiol.* 116:637–41

55. Evans MCW, Purton S, Patel V, Wright D, Heathcote P, Rigby SEJ. 1999. Modification of electron transfer from the quinone electron carrier, A1, of Photosystem 1 in a site directed mutant D576>L within the Fe-Sx binding site of *PsaA* and in second site suppressors of the mutation in *Chlamydomonas reinhardtii*. *Photosynth. Res.* 61:33–42

56. Fargo DC, Boynton JE, Gillham NW. 1999. Mutations altering the predicted secondary structure of a chloroplast 5′ untranslated region affect its physical and biochemical properties as well as its ability to promote translation of reporter mRNAs both in the *Chlamydomonas reinhardtii* chloroplast and in *Escherichia coli*. *Mol. Cell. Biol.* 19:6980–90

57. Fargo DC, Zhang M, Gillham NW, Boynton JE. 1998. Shine-Dalgarno-like sequences are not required for translation of chloroplast mRNAs in *Chlamydomonas reinhardtii* chloroplasts or in *Escherichia coli*. *Mol. Gen. Genet.* 257:271–82

58. Ferris PJ, Goodenough UW. 1997. Mating type in *Chlamydomonas* is specified by *mid*, the minus-dominance gene. *Genetics* 146:859–69

59. Ferris PJ, Pavlovic C, Fabry S, Goodenough UW. 1997. Rapid evolution of sex-related genes in *Chlamydomonas*. *Proc. Natl. Acad. Sci. USA* 94:8634–39

60. Finst RJ, Kim PJ, Griffis ER, Quarmby LM. 2000. Fa1p is a 171 kDa protein essential for axonemal microtubule severing in *Chlamydomonas*. *J. Cell Sci.* 113:1963–71

61. Finst RJ, Kim PJ, Quarmby LM. 1998. Genetics of the deflagellation pathway in *Chlamydomonas*. *Genetics* 149:927–36

62. Fischer N, Boudreau E, Hippler M, Drepper F, Haehnel W, Rochaix J-D. 1999. A large fraction of *PsaF* is nonfunctional in photosystem I complexes lacking the *PsaJ* subunit. *Biochemistry* 38:5546–52

63. Fischer N, Sétif P, Rochaix JD. 1999. Site-directed mutagenesis of the *PsaC* subunit of photosystem I—FB is the cluster interacting with soluble ferredoxin. *J. Biol. Chem.* 274:23333–40

64. Fischer N, Stampacchia O, Redding K, Rochaix JD. 1996. Selectable marker recycling in the chloroplast. *Mol. Gen. Genet.* 251:373–80

65. Forster B, Osmond CB, Boynton JE, Gillham NW. 1999. Mutants of *Chlamydomonas reinhardtii* resistant to very high light. *J. Photochem. Photobiol.* 48:127–45

66. Fowkes ME, Mitchell DR. 1998. The role of preassembled cytoplasmic complexes in assembly of flagellar dynein subunits. *Mol. Biol. Cell* 9:2337–47

67. Fuhrmann M, Oertel W, Hegemann P. 1999. A synthetic gene coding for the green fluorescent protein (GFP) is a versatile reporter in *Chlamydomonas reinhardtii*. *Plant J.* 19:353–61

68. Fujiwara S, Ishida N, Tsuzuki M. 1996.

Circadian expression of the carbonic anhydrase gene, *Cah1*, in *Chlamydomonas reinhardtii*. *Plant Mol. Biol.* 32:745–49

69. Fukuzawa H, Ishizaki K, Miura K, Matsueda S, Ino-ue T, et al. 1998. Isolation and characterization of high-CO_2 requiring mutants from *Chlamydomonas reinhardtii* by gene tagging. *Can. J. Bot.* 76:1092–97

70. Funke RP, Kovar JL, Logsdon JM Jr, Corrette-Bennett JC, Straus DR, Weeks DP. 1999. Nucleus-encoded, plastid-targeted acetolactate synthase genes in two closely related chlorophytes, *Chlamydomonas reinhardtii* and *Volvox carteri*: phylogenetic origins and recent insertion of introns. *Mol. Gen. Genet.* 262:12–21

71. Funke RP, Kovar JL, Weeks DP. 1997. Intracellular carbonic anhydrase is essential to photosynthesis in *Chlamydomonas reinhardtii* at atmospheric levels of CO_2. Demonstration via genomic complementation of the high-CO_2-requiring mutant *ca-1*. *Plant Physiol.* 114:237–44

72. Gera JF, Baker EJ. 1998. Deadenylation-dependent and -independent decay pathways for alpha1-tubulin mRNA in *Chlamydomonas reinhardtii*. *Mol. Cell. Biol.* 18:1498–505

73. Gillham NW, Boynton JE, Hauser CR. 1994. Translational regulation of gene expression in chloroplasts and mitochondria. *Annu. Rev. Genet.* 28:71–93

74. Glöckner G, Beck CF. 1997. Cloning and characterization of *LRG5*, a gene involved in blue light signaling in *Chlamydomonas* gametogenesis. *Plant J.* 12:677–83

75. Goho S, Bell G. 2000. Mild environmental stress elicits mutations affecting fitness in *Chlamydomonas*. *Proc. R. Soc. London Ser. B* 267:123–29

76. Goldschmidt-Clermont M. 1998. Coordination of nuclear and chloroplast gene expression in plant cells. *Int. Rev. Cytol.* 177:115–80

77. Goodenough UW, Armbrust EV, Campbell AM, Ferris PJ. 1995. Molecular genetics of sexuality in *Chlamydomonas*. *Annu. Rev. Plant Physiol. Plant Mol. Biol.* 46:21–44

78. Goto K, Johnson CH. 1995. Is the cell division cycle gated by a circadian clock? The case of *Chlamydomonas reinhardtii*. *J. Cell Biol.* 129:1061–69

79. Gumpel NJ, Purton S. 1994. Playing tag with *Chlamydomonas*. *Trends Cell Biol.* 4:299–301

80. Hahn D, Kück U. 1999. Identification of DNA sequences controlling light- and chloroplast-dependent expression of the *lhcb1* gene from *Chlamydomonas reinhardtii*. *Curr. Genet.* 34:459–66

81. Hahn D, Nickelsen J, Hackert A, Kück U. 1998. A single nuclear locus is involved in both chloroplast RNA *trans*-splicing and 3′ end processing. *Plant J.* 15:575–81

82. Hails T, Jobling M, Day A. 1993. Large arrays of tandemly repeated DNA sequences in the green alga *Chlamydomonas reinhardtii*. *Chromosoma* 102:500–7

83. Hamel P, Olive J, Pierre Y, Wollman FA, de Vitry C. 2000. A new subunit of cytochrome b_6f complex undergoes reversible phosphorylation upon state transition. *J. Biol. Chem.* 275:17072–79

84. Haring MA, Beck CF. 1997. A promoter trap for *Chlamydomonas reinhardtii*: development of a gene cloning method using 5′ RACE-based probes. *Plant J.* 11:1341–48

85. Harper JDI. 1999. *Chlamydomonas* cell cycle mutants. *Int. Rev. Cytol.* 189:131–76

86. Harris EH. 1989. The *Chlamydomonas Sourcebook*. San Diego: Academic. 780 pp.

87. Hatano-Iwasaki A, Minagawa J, Inoue Y, Takahashi Y. 2000. Characterization of chloroplast *psbA* transformants of *Chlamydomonas reinhardtii* with impaired processing of a precursor of a photosystem II reaction center protein, D1. *Plant Mol. Biol.* 42:353–63

88. Hauser CR, Gillham NW, Boynton JE.

1996. Translational regulation of chloroplast genes—proteins binding to the 5′-untranslated regions of chloroplast mRNAs in *Chlamydomonas reinhardtii*. *J. Biol. Chem.* 271:1486–97

89. Hegemann P. 1997. Vision in microalgae. *Planta* 203:265–74

90. Heifetz PB, Lers A, Turpin DH, Gillham NW, Boynton JE, Osmond CB. 1997. *dr* and *spr/sr* mutations of *Chlamydomonas reinhardtii* affecting D1 protein function and synthesis define two independent steps leading to chronic photoinhibition and confer differential fitness. *Plant Cell Environ.* 20:1145–57

91. Herman CA, Im CS, Beale SI. 1999. Light-regulated expression of the *gsa* gene encoding the chrorophyll biosynthetic enzyme glutamate 1-semialdehyde aminotransferase in carotenoid-deficient *Chlamydomonas reinhardtii* cells. *Plant Mol. Biol.* 39:289–97

92. Higgs DC, Kuras R, Kindle KL, Wollman FA, Stern DB. 1998. Inversions in the *Chlamydomonas* chloroplast genome suppress a *petD* 5′ untranslated region deletion by creating functional chimeric mRNAs. *Plant J.* 14:663–71

93. Hippler M, Redding K, Rochaix JD. 1998. *Chlamydomonas* genetics, a tool for the study of bioenergetic pathways. *Biochim. Biophys. Acta Bio Energ.* 1367:1–62

94. Hirono M, Yoda A. 1997. Isolation and phenotypic characterization of *Chlamydomonas* mutants defective in cytokinesis. *Cell Struct. Funct.* 22:1–5

95. Holloway SP, Deshpande NN, Herrin DL. 1999. The catalytic group-I introns of the *psbA* gene of *Chlamydomonas reinhardtii*: core structures, ORFs and evolutionary implications. *Curr. Genet.* 36:69–78

96. Holloway SP, Herrin DL. 1998. Processing of a composite large subunit rRNA: Studies with *Chlamydomonas* mutants deficient in maturation of the 23S-like rRNA. *Plant Cell* 10:1197–206

97. Holmes JA, Johnson DE, Dutcher SK.

1993. Linkage group XIX of *Chlamydomonas reinhardtii* has a linear map. *Genetics* 133:865–74

98. Hong SJ, Spreitzer RJ. 1998. Nuclear-gene mutations suppress a defect in the expression of the chloroplast-encoded large subunit of ribulose-1,5-bisphosphate carboxylase/oxygenase. *Plant Physiol.* 116:1387–92

99. Hu DL, Fiedler HR, Golan T, Edelman M, Strotmann H, et al. 1997. Catalytic properties and sensitivity to tentoxin of *Chlamydomonas reinhardtii* ATP synthases changed in codon 83 of *atpB* by site-directed mutagenesis. *J. Biol. Chem.* 272:5457–63

100. Huppe HC, Turpin DH. 1994. Integration of carbon and nitrogen metabolism in plant and algal cells. *Annu. Rev. Plant Physiol. Plant Mol. Biol.* 45:577–607

101. Im CS, Beale SI. 2000. Identification of possible signal transduction components mediating light induction of the *Gsa* gene for an early chlorophyll biosynthetic step in *Chlamydomonas reinhardtii*. *Planta* 210:999–1005

102. Inoue K, Dreyfuss BW, Kindle KL, Stern DB, Merchant S, Sodeinde OA. 1997. *Ccs1*, a nuclear gene required for the post-translational assembly of chloroplast c-type cytochromes. *J. Biol. Chem.* 272:31747–54

103. Jacobshagen S, Kindle KL, Johnson CH. 1996. Transcription of *CABII* is regulated by the biological clock in *Chlamydomonas reinhardtii*. *Plant Mol. Biol.* 31:1173–84

104. Jahns P, Depka B, Trebst A. 2000. Xanthophyll cycle mutants from *Chlamydomonas reinhardtii* indicate a role for zeaxanthin in the D1 protein turnover. *Plant Physiol. Biochem.* 38:371–76

105. Jarvik JW, Adler SA, Telmer CA, Subramaniam V, Lopez AJ. 1996. CD-tagging: a new approach to gene and protein discovery and analysis. *BioTechniques* 20:896–904

106. Johnson KA. 1995. Keeping the beat: Form meets function in the *Chlamydomonas* flagellum. *BioEssays* 17:847–54

107. Johnston HG, Wang J, Ruffle SV, Sayre RT, Gustafson TL. 2000. Fluorescence decay kinetics of wild type and D2-H117N mutant photosystem II reaction centers isolated from *Chlamydomonas reinhardtii*. *J. Phys. Chem. B* 104:4777–81

108. Kalakoutskii KL, Fernandez E. 1995. *Chlamydomonas reinhardtii* nitrate reductase complex has 105 kDa subunits in the wild-type strain and a structural mutant. *Plant Sci.* 105:195–206

109. Kang Y, Mitchell DR. 1998. An intronic enhancer is required for deflagellation-induced transcriptional regulation of a *Chlamydomonas reinhardtii* dynein gene. *Mol. Biol. Cell* 9:3085–94

110. Karlsson J, Clarke AK, Chen ZY, Hugghins SY, Park YI, et al. 1998. A novel alpha-type carbonic anhydrase associated with the thylakoid membrane in *Chlamydomonas reinhardtii* is required for growth at ambient CO_2. *EMBO J.* 17:1208–16

111. Kassen R, Bell G. 2000. The ecology and genetics of fitness in *Chlamydomonas*. X. The relationship between genetic correlation and genetic distance. *Evolution* 54:425–32

112. Katzman GL, Carlson SJ, Marcus Y, Moroney JV. 1994. Carbonic anhydrase activity in isolated chloroplasts of wild-type and high-CO_2-dependent mutants of *Chlamydomonas reinhardtii* as studied by a new assay. *Plant Physiol.* 105:1197–202

113. Kindle KL. 1998. High-frequency nuclear transformation of *Chlamydomonas reinhardtii*. *Methods Enzymol.* 297:27–38

114. Kindle KL, Lawrence SD. 1998. Transit peptide mutations that impair in vitro and in vivo chloroplast protein import do not affect accumulation of the gamma-subunit of chloroplast ATPase. *Plant Physiol.* 116:1179–90

115. King SJ, Dutcher SK. 1997. Phosphoregulation of an inner dynein arm complex in *Chlamydomonas reinhardtii* is altered in phototactic mutant strains. *J. Cell Biol.* 136:177–91

116. Komine Y, Kwong L, Anguera MC, Schuster G, Stern DB. 2000. Polyadenylation of three classes of chloroplast RNA in *Chlamydomonas reinhardtii*. *RNA Publ. RNA Soc.* 6:598–607

117. Kozminski KG, Beech PL, Rosenbaum JL. 1995. The *Chlamydomonas* kinesin-like protein FLA10 is involved in motility associated with the flagellar membrane. *J. Cell Biol.* 131:1517–27

118. Kruse O, Nixon PJ, Schmid GH, Mullineaux CW. 1999. Isolation of state transition mutants of *Chlamydomonas reinhardtii* by fluorescence video imaging. *Photosynth. Res.* 61:43–51

119. Kuin H, Koerten H, Ghijsen WEJM, Munnik T, van den Ende H, Musgrave A. 2000. *Chlamydomonas* contains calcium stores that are mobilized when phospholipase C is activated. *Planta* 210:286–94

120. Kuras R, de Vitry C, Choquet Y, Girard-Bascou J, Culler D, et al. 1997. Molecular genetic identification of a pathway for heme binding to cytochrome b6. *J. Biol. Chem.* 272:32427–35

121. Kuriyama H, Takano H, Suzuki L, Uchida H, Kawano S, et al. 1999. Characterization of *Chlamydomonas reinhardtii* zygote-specific cDNAs that encode novel proteins containing ankyrin repeats and WW domains. *Plant Physiol.* 119:873–84

122. Kurvari V, Grishin NV, Snell WJ. 1998. A gamete-specific, sex-limited homeodomain protein in *Chlamydomonas*. *J. Cell Biol.* 143:1971–80

123. Lamb MR, Dutcher SK, Worley CK, Dieckmann CL. 1999. Eyespot-assembly mutants in *Chlamydomonas reinhardtii*. *Genetics* 153:721–29

124. Lardans A, Forster B, Prasil O, Falkowski

PG, Sobolev V, et al. 1998. Biophysical, biochemical, and physiological characterization of *Chlamydomonas reinhardtii* mutants with amino acid substitutions at the Ala251 residue in the D1 protein that result in varying levels of photosynthetic competence. *J. Biol. Chem.* 273:11082–91

125. Larson EM, O'Brien CM, Zhu GH, Spreitzer RJ, Portis ARJ. 1997. Specificity for activase is changed by a Pro-89 to Arg substitution in the large subunit of ribulose-1,5–bisphosphate carboxylase/oxygenase. *J. Biol. Chem.* 272:17033–37

126. Lebedev N, Timko MP. 1998. Protochlorophyllide photoreduction. *Photosynth. Res.* 58:5–23

127. Lechtreck KF, Melkonian M. 1998. SF-assemblin, striated fibers, and segmented coiled coil proteins. *Cell Motil. Cytoskel.* 41:289–96

128. Lefebvre PA, Silflow CD. 1999. *Chlamydomonas*: the cell and its genomes. *Genetics* 151:9–14

129. Li HH, Quinn J, Culler D, Girard-Bascou J, Merchant S. 1996. Molecular genetic analysis of plastocyanin biosynthesis in *Chlamydomonas reinhardtii*. *J. Biol. Chem.* 271:31283–89

130. Li JM, Timko MP. 1996. The pc-1 phenotype of *Chlamydomonas reinhardtii* results from a deletion mutation in the nuclear gene for NADPH: protochlorophyllide oxidoreductase. *Plant Mol. Biol.* 30:15–37

131. Liss M, Kirk DL, Beyser K, Fabry S. 1997. Intron sequences provide a tool for high-resolution phylogenetic analysis of volvocine algae. *Curr. Genet.* 31:214–27

132. Lohret TA, McNally FJ, Quarmby LM. 1998. A role for katanin-mediated axonemal severing during *Chlamydomonas* deflagellation. *Mol. Biol. Cell* 9:1195–207

133. Lohret TA, Zhao LF, Quarmby LM. 1999. Cloning of *Chlamydomonas* p60 katanin and localization to the site of outer doublet severing during deflagellation. *Cell Motil. Cytoskel.* 43:221–31

134. Lumbreras V, Purton S. 1998. Recent advances in *Chlamydomonas* transgenics. *Protist* 149:23–27

135. Lumbreras V, Stevens DR, Purton S. 1998. Efficient foreign gene expression in *Chlamydomonas reinhardtii* mediated by an endogenous intron. *Plant J.* 14:441–47

136. Luykx P, Hoppenrath M, Robinson DG. 1997. Osmoregulatory mutants that affect the function of the contractile vacuole in *Chlamydomonas reinhardtii*. *Protoplasma* 200:99–111

137. Mamedov F, Sayre RT, Styring S. 1998. Involvement of histidine 190 on the D1 protein in electron/proton transfer reactions on the donor side of photosystem II. *Biochemistry* 37:14245–56

138. Marshall WF, Rosenbaum JL. 2000. How centrioles work: lessons from green yeast. *Curr. Opin. Cell Biol.* 12:119–25

139. Martin RE, Thomas DJ, Tucker DE, Herbert SK. 1997. The effects of photooxidative stress on photosystem I measured in vivo in *Chlamydomonas*. *Plant Cell Environ.* 20:1451–61

140. Matsuda A, Yoshimura K, Sineshchekov OA, Hirono M, Kamiya R. 1998. Isolation and characterization of novel *Chlamydomonas* mutants that display phototaxis but not photophobic response. *Cell Motil. Cytoskel.* 41:353–62

141. Mayfield SP, Yohn CB, Cohen A, Danon A. 1995. Regulation of chloroplast gene expression. *Annu. Rev. Plant Physiol. Plant Mol. Biol.* 46:147–66

142. Melis A, Zhang LP, Forestier M, Ghirardi ML, Seibert M. 2000. Sustained photobiological hydrogen gas production upon reversible inactivation of oxygen evolution in the green alga *Chlamydomonas reinhardtii*. *Plant Physiol.* 122:127–35

143. Melkozernov AN, Su H, Lin S, Bingham S, Webber AN, Blankenship RE. 1997. Specific mutation near the primary donor

in photosystem I from *Chlamydomonas reinhardtii* alters the trapping time and spectroscopic properties of P700. *Biochemistry* 36:2898–907

144. Merchant S, Dreyfuss BW. 1998. Posttranslational assembly of photosynthetic metalloproteins. *Annu. Rev. Plant Physiol. Plant Mol. Biol.* 49:25–51

145. Minko I, Holloway SP, Nikaido S, Carter M, Odom OW, et al. 1999. Renilla luciferase as a vital reporter for chloroplast gene expression in *Chlamydomonas. Mol. Gen. Genet.* 262:421–25

146. Misumi O, Suzuki L, Nishimura Y, Sakai A, Kawano S, et al. 1999. Isolation and phenotypic characterization of *Chlamydomonas reinhardtii* mutants defective in chloroplast DNA segregation. *Protoplasma* 209:273–82

147. Mitchell DR. 2000. *Chlamydomonas* flagella. *J. Phycol.* 36:261–73

148. Mittag M. 1996. Conserved circadian elements in phylogenetically diverse algae. *Proc. Natl. Acad. Sci. USA* 93:14401–4

149. Mittag M, Waltenberger H. 1997. In vitro mutagenesis of binding site elements for the clock-controlled proteins CCTR and Chlamy 1. *Biol. Chem. Hoppe-Seyler* 378:1167–70

150. Morais F, Barber J, Nixon PJ. 1998. The chloroplast-encoded alpha subunit of cytochrome b-559 is required for assembly of the photosystem two complex in both the light and the dark in *Chlamydomonas reinhardtii. J. Biol. Chem.* 273:29315–20

151. Moseley J, Quinn J, Eriksson M, Merchant S. 2000. The *Crd1* gene encodes a putative di-iron enzyme required for photosystem I accumulation in copper deficiency and hypoxia in *Chlamydomonas reinhardtii. EMBO J.* 19:2139–51

152. Munnik T, Van Himbergen JAJ, Ter Riet B, Braun FJ, Irvine RF, et al. 1998. Detailed analysis of the turnover of polyphosphoinositides and phosphatidic acid upon activation of phospholipases C and D in *Chlamydomonas* cells treated with non-permeabilizing concentrations of mastoparan. *Planta* 207:133–45

153. Navarro MT, Guerra E, Fernandez E, Galvan A. 2000. Nitrite reductase mutants as an approach to understanding nitrate assimilation in *Chlamydomonas reinhardtii. Plant Physiol.* 122:283–89

154. Nelson JAE, Lefebvre PA. 1995. Targeted disruption of the *NIT8* gene in *Chlamydomonas reinhardtii. Mol. Cell. Biol.* 15:5762–69

155. Nickelsen J. 2000. Mutations at three different nuclear loci of *Chlamydomonas* suppress a defect in chloroplast psbD mRNA accumulation. *Curr. Genet.* 37:136–42

156. Nickelsen J, Kück U. 2000. The unicellular green alga *Chlamydomonas reinhardtii* as an experimental system to study chloroplast RNA metabolism. *Naturwissenschaften* 87:97–107

157. Nikaido SS, Johnson CH. 2000. Daily and circadian variation in survival from ultraviolet radiation in *Chlamydomonas reinhardtii. Photochem. Photobiol.* 71:758–65

158. Nishimura Y, Misumi O, Matsunaga S, Higashiyama T, Yokota A, Kuroiwa T. 1999. The active digestion of uniparental chloroplast DNA in a single zygote of *Chlamydomonas reinhardtii* is revealed by using the optical tweezer. *Proc. Natl. Acad. Sci. USA* 96:12577–82

159. Niyogi KK. 1999. Photoprotection revisited: genetic and molecular approaches. *Annu. Rev. Plant Physiol. Plant Mol. Biol.* 50:333–59

160. Niyogi KK, Bjorkman O, Grossman AR. 1997. The roles of specific xanthophylls in photoprotection. *Proc. Natl. Acad. Sci. USA* 94:14162–67

161. Niyogi KK, Bjorkman O, Grossman AR. 1997. *Chlamydomonas* xanthophyll cycle mutants identified by video imaging of chlorophyll fluorescence quenching. *Plant Cell* 9:1369–80

162. Norrander JM, Perrone CA, Amos LA,

Linck RW. 1996. Structural comparison of tektins and evidence for their determination of complex spacings in flagellar microtubules. *J. Mol. Biol.* 257:385–97

163. O'Connor HE, Ruffle SV, Cain AJ, Deak Z, Vass I, Nugent JHA, Purton S. 1998. The 9–kDa phosphoprotein of photosystem II. Generation and characterisation of *Chlamydomonas* mutants lacking PSII-H and a site-directed mutant lacking the phosphorylation site. *Biochim. Biophys. Acta Bio Energ.* 1364:63–72

164. Ohresser M, Matagne RF, Loppes R. 1997. Expression of the arylsulphatase reporter gene under the control of the *nit1* promoter in *Chlamydomonas reinhardtii*. *Curr. Genet.* 31:264–71

165. Pan JM, Haring MA, Beck CF. 1997. Characterization of blue light signal transduction chains that control development and maintenance of sexual competence in *Chlamydomonas reinhardtii*. *Plant Physiol.* 115:1241–49

166. Park YI, Karlsson J, Rojdestvenski I, Pronina N, Klimov V, Oquist G, Samuelsson G. 1999. Role of a novel photosystem II-associated carbonic anhydrase in photosynthetic carbon assimilation in *Chlamydomonas reinhardtii*. *FEBS Lett.* 444:102–5

167. Pazour GJ, Dickert BL, Vucica Y, Seeley ES, Rosenbaum JL, Witman GB, Cole DG. 2000. *Chlamydomonas* IFT88 and its mouse homologue, polycystic kidney disease gene Tg737, are required for assembly of cilia and flagella. *J. Cell Biol.* 151:709–18

168. Pazour GJ, Dickert BL, Witman GB. 1999. The DHC1b (DHC2) isoform of cytoplasmic dynein is required for flagellar assembly. *J. Cell Biol.* 144:473–81

169. Pazour GJ, Koutoulis A, Benashski SE, Dickert BL, Sheng H, et al. 1999. LC2, the *Chlamydomonas* homologue of the t complex-encoded protein Tctex2, is essential for outer dynein arm assembly. *Mol. Biol. Cell* 10:3507–20

170. Pazour GJ, Sineshchekov OA, Witman GB. 1995. Mutational analysis of the phototransduction pathway of *Chlamydomonas reinhardtii*. *J. Cell Biol.* 131:427–40

171. Pazour GJ, Wilkerson CG, Witman GB. 1998. A dynein light chain is essential for the retrograde particle movement of intraflagellar transport. *J. Cell Biol.* 141:979–92

172. Periz G, Keller LR. 1997. DNA elements regulating alpha1-tubulin gene induction during regeneration of eukaryotic flagella. *Mol. Cell. Biol.* 17:3858–66

173. Perron K, Goldschmidt-Clermont M, Rochaix JD. 1999. A factor related to pseudouridine synthases is required for chloroplast group II intron trans-splicing in *Chlamydomonas reinhardtii*. *EMBO J.* 18:6481–90

174. Petersen JL, Lang DW, Small GD. 1999. Cloning and characterization of a class II DNA photolyase from *Chlamydomonas*. *Plant Mol. Biol.* 40:1063–71

175. Piperno G, Siuda E, Henderson S, Segil M, Vaananen H, Sassaroli M. 1998. Distinct mutants of retrograde intraflagellar transport (IFT) share similar morphological and molecular defects. *J. Cell Biol.* 143:1591–601

176. Porter ME, Knott JA, Myster SH, Farlow SJ. 1996. The dynein gene family in *Chlamydomonas reinhardtii*. *Genetics* 144:569–85

177. Prasad MN, Drej K, Skawinska A, Strzalka K. 1998. Toxicity of cadmium and copper in *Chlamydomonas reinhardtii* wild-type (WT 2137) and cell wall deficient mutant strain (CW 15). *Bull. Environ. Contam. Toxicol.* 60:306–11

178. Preble AM, Giddings THJ, Dutcher SK. 2000. Extragenic bypass suppressors of mutations in the essential gene *BLD2* promote assembly of basal bodies with abnormal microtubules in *Chlamydomonas reinhardtii*. *Genetics* 157:163–81

179. Prieto R, Pardo JM, Niu XM, Bressan

RA, Hasegawa PM. 1996. Salt-sensitive mutants of *Chlamydomonas reinhardtii* isolated after insertional tagging. *Plant Physiol.* 112:99–104

180. Purton S, Rochaix J-D. 1995. Characterization of the *ARG7* gene of *Chlamydomonas reinhardtii* and its application to nuclear transformation. *Eur. J. Phycol.* 30:141–48

181. Quarmby LM. 1994. Signal transduction in the sexual life of *Chlamydomonas*. *Plant Mol. Biol.* 26:1271–87

182. Quarmby L. 2000. Cellular samurai: katanin and the severing of microtubules. *J. Cell Sci.* 113:2821–27

183. Quesada A, Gómez I, Fernández E. 1998. Clustering of the nitrite reductase gene and a light-regulated gene with nitrate assimilation loci in *Chlamydomonas reinhardtii*. *Planta* 206:259–65

184. Quesada A, Hidalgo J, Fernandez E. 1998. Three *Nrt2* genes are differentially regulated in *Chlamydomonas reinhardtii*. *Mol. Gen. Genet.* 258:373–77

185. Quinn JM, Barraco P, Eriksson M, Merchant S. 2000. Coordinate copper- and oxygen-responsive *Cyc6* and *Cpx1* expression in *Chlamydomonas* is mediated by the same element. *J. Biol. Chem.* 275:6080–89

186. Quinn JM, Nakamoto SS, Merchant S. 1999. Induction of coproporphyrinogen oxidase in *Chlamydomonas* chloroplasts occurs via transcriptional regulation of *Cpx1* mediated by copper response elements and increased translation from a copper-deficiency-specific form of the transcript. *J. Biol. Chem.* 274:14444–54

187. Quinones MA, Galvan A, Fernández E, Aparicio PJ. 1999. Blue-light requirement for the biosynthesis of an NO_2-transport system in the *Chlamydomonas reinhardtii* nitrate transport mutant S10. *Plant Cell Environ.* 22:1169–75

188. Quisel JD, Wykoff DD, Grossman AR. 1996. Biochemical characterization of the extracellular phosphatases pro-

duced by phosphorus-deprived *Chlamydomonas reinhardtii*. *Plant Physiol.* 111:839–48

189. Randolph-Anderson BBL, Sato R, Johnson AM, Harris EH, Hauser CR, et al. 1998. Isolation and characterization of a mutant protoporphyrinogen oxidase gene from *Chlamydomonas reinhardtii* conferring resistance to porphyric herbicides. *Plant Mol. Biol.* 38:839–59

190. Rattanachaikunsopon P, Rosch C, Kuchka MR. 1999. Cloning and characterization of the nuclear *AC115* gene of *Chlamydomonas reinhardtii*. *Plant Mol. Biol.* 39:1–10

191. Rawat M, Henk MC, Lavigne LL, Moroney JV. 1996. *Chlamydomonas reinhardtii* mutants without ribulose-1,5–bisphosphate carboxylase-oxygenase lack a detectable pyrenoid. *Planta* 198:263–70

192. Redding K, Cournac L, Vassiliev IR, Golbeck JH, Peltier G, Rochaix JD. 1999. Photosystem I is indispensable for photoautotrophic growth, CO_2 fixation, and H_2 photoproduction in *Chlamydomonas reinhardtii*. *J. Biol. Chem.* 274:10466–73

193. Redding K, MacMillan F, Leibl W, Brettel K, Hanley J, et al. 1998. A systematic survey of conserved histidines in the core subunits of Photosystem I by site-directed mutagenesis reveals the likely axial ligands of P700. *EMBO J.* 17:50–60

194. Rochaix J-D. 1995. *Chlamydomonas reinhardtii* as the photosynthetic yeast. *Annu. Rev. Genet.* 29:209–30

195. Rochaix J-D. 1996. Post-transcriptional regulation of chloroplast gene expression in *Chlamydomonas reinhardtii*. *Plant Mol. Biol.* 32:327–41

196. Rochaix J-D, Goldschmidt-Clermont M, Merchant S, eds. 1998. *The Molecular Biology of Chloroplasts and Mitochondria in Chlamydomonas*. Dordrecht: Kluwer. 733 pp.

197. Rolland N, Dorne AJ, Amoroso G, Sueltemeyer DF, Joyard J, Rochaix JD. 1997.

Disruption of the plastid *ycf10* open reading frame affects uptake of inorganic carbon in the chloroplast of *Chlamydomonas. EMBO J.* 16:6713–26

198. Rosenbaum JL, Cole DG, Diener DR. 1999. Intraflagellar transport: The eyes have it. *J. Cell Biol.* 144:385–88

199. Ross SA, Zhang MX, Selman BR. 1996. A role for the disulfide bond spacer region of the *Chlamydomonas reinhardtii* coupling factor 1 gamma-subunit in redox regulation of ATP synthase. *J. Bioenerg. Biomembr.* 28:49–57

200. Rova EM, McEwen B, Fredricksson PO, Styring S. 1996. Photoactivation and photoinhibition are competing in a mutant of *Chlamydomonas reinhardtii* lacking the 23–kDa extrinsic subunit of photosystem II. *J. Biol. Chem.* 271:28918–24

201. Rüffer U, Nultsch W. 1997. Flagellar photoresponses of *ptx1*, a nonphototactic mutant of *Chlamydomonas. Cell Motil. Cytoskel.* 37:111–19

202. Saito T, Inoue M, Yamada M, Matsuda Y. 1998. Control of gametic differentiation and activity by light in *Chlamydomonas reinhardtii. Plant Cell Physiol.* 39:8–15

203. Sakuanrungsirikul S, Hocart CH, Harper JDI, Parker CW, John PCL. 1996. Temperature conditional cAMP-requiring mutant strains of *Chlamydomonas reinhardtii* arrest in G1 and are rescued by added cAMP. *Protoplasma* 192:159–67

204. Salisbury JL. 1995. Centrin, centrosomes, and mitotic spindle poles. *Curr. Opin. Cell Biol.* 7:39–45

205. Schaller K, David R, Uhl R. 1997. How *Chlamydomonas* keeps track of the light once it has reached the right phototactic orientation. *Biophys. J.* 73:1562–72

206. Schaller K, Uhl R. 1997. A microspectrophotometric study of the shielding properties of eyespot and cell body in *Chlamydomonas. Biophys. J.* 73:1573–78

207. Schnell RA, Lefebvre PA. 1993. Isolation of the *Chlamydomonas* regulatory gene *NIT2* by transposon tagging. *Genetics* 134:737–47

208. Schroda M, Bloecker D, Beck CF. 2000. The *HSP70A* promoter as a tool for the improved expression of transgenes in *Chlamydomonas. Plant J.* 21:121–31

209. Schroda M, Vallon O, Wollman FA, Beck CF. 1999. A chloroplast-targeted heat shock protein 70 (HSP70) contributes to the photoprotection and repair of photosystem II during and after photoinhibition. *Plant Cell* 11:1165–78

210. Shapira M, Lers A, Heifetz PB, Irihimovitz V, Osmond CB, et al. 1997. Differential regulation of chloroplast gene expression in *Chlamydomonas reinhardtii* during photoacclimation: Light stress transiently suppresses synthesis of the Rubisco LSU protein while enhancing synthesis of the PS II D1 protein. *Plant Mol. Biol.* 33:1001–11

211. Shimogawara K, Fujiwara S, Grossman A, Usuda H. 1998. High-efficiency transformation of *Chlamydomonas reinhardtii* by electroporation. *Genetics* 148:1821–28

212. Sizova IA, Lapina TV, Frolova ON, Alexandrova NN, Akopiants KE, Danilenko VN. 1996. Stable nuclear transformation of *Chlamydomonas reinhardtii* with a *Streptomyces rimosus* gene as the selective marker. *Gene* 181:13–18

213. Smith EF, Lefebvre PA. 1997. The role of central apparatus components in flagellar motility and microtubule assembly. *Cell Motil. Cytoskel.* 38:1–8

214. Somanchi A, Handley ER, Moroney JW. 1998. *Chlamydomonas reinhardtii* cDNAs upregulated in low-CO_2 conditions: expression and analyses. *Can. J. Bot.* 76:1003–9

215. Stampacchia O, Girard-Bascou J, Zanasco JL, Zerges W, Bennoun P, Rochaix J-D. 1997. A nuclear-encoded function essential for translation of the chloroplast *psaB* mRNA in *Chlamydomonas. Plant Cell* 9:773–82

216. Stevens DR, Purton S. 1997. Genetic engineering of eukaryotic algae: progress and prospects. *J. Phycol.* 33:713–22

217. Stevens DR, Rochaix J-D, Purton S. 1996. The bacterial phleomycin resistance gene *ble* as a dominant selectable marker in *Chlamydomonas. Mol. Gen. Genet.* 251:23–30

218. Sueltemeyer D. 1998. Carbonic anhydrase in eukaryotic algae: characterization, regulation, and possible function during photosynthesis. *Can. J. Bot.* 76:962–72

219. Summer EJ, Schmid VHR, Bruns BU, Schmidt GW. 1997. Requirement for the H phosphoprotein in photosystem II of *Chlamydomonas reinhardtii. Plant Physiol.* 113:1359–68

220. Taguchi F, Takahashi Y, Satoh K. 1998. Viability of *Chlamydomonas* mutants with amino acid substitutions in the precursor D1 protein at the carboxyl-terminal processing site: an analysis by mixed-culture growth experiments. *Plant Cell Physiol.* 39:1324–29

221. Taillon BE, Jarvik JW. 1995. Central helix mutations in the centrosome-associated EF-hand protein centrin. *Protoplasma* 189:203–15

222. Takahashi Y, Rahire M, Breyton C, Popot J-L, Joliot P, Rochaix J-D. 1996. The chloroplast *ycf7 (petL)* open reading frame of *Chlamydomonas reinhardtii* encodes a small functionally important subunit of the cytochrome b_6f complex. *EMBO J.* 15:3498–506

223. Tam LW, Lefebvre PA. 1993. Cloning of flagellar genes in *Chlamydomonas reinhardtii* by DNA insertional mutagenesis. *Genetics* 135:375–84

224. Tuxhorn J, Daise T, Dentler WL. 1998. Regulation of flagellar length in *Chlamydomonas. Cell Motil. Cytoskel.* 40:133–46

225. Vaistij FE, Goldschmidt-Clermont M, Wostrikoff K, Rochaix JD. 2000. Stability determinants in the chloroplast *psbB/T/H* mRNAs of *Chlamydomonas reinhardtii. Plant J.* 21:469–82

226. Vallon O, Wollman F-A. 1995. Mutations affecting O-glycosylation in *Chlamydomonas reinhardtii* cause delayed cell wall degradation and sex-limited sterility. *Plant Physiol.* 108:703–12

227. Van K, Spalding MH. 1999. Periplasmic carbonic anhydrase structural gene (Cah1) mutant in *Chlamydomonas reinhardtii. Plant Physiol.* 120:757–64

228. VanWinkle-Swift K, Baron K, McNamara A, Minke P, Burrascano C, Maddock J. 1998. The *Chlamydomonas* zygospore: Mutant strains of *Chlamydomonas monoica* blocked in zygospore morphogenesis comprise 46 complementation groups. *Genetics* 148:131–37

229. van den Ende H. 1994. Vegetative and gametic development in the green alga *Chlamydomonas. Adv. Bot. Res.* 20:125–61

230. van den Ende H. 1995. Sexual development in the homothallic green alga *Chlamydomonas monoica* Strehlow. *Sex. Plant Reprod.* 8:139–42

231. Vashishtha M, Walther Z, Hall JL. 1996. The kinesin-homologous protein encoded by the *Chlamydomonas FLA10* gene is associated with basal bodies and centrioles. *J. Cell Sci.* 109:541–49

232. Voigt J, Hinklemann B, Harris EH. 1997. Production of cell wall polypeptides by different cell wall mutants of the unicellular green alga *Chlamydomonas reinhardtii. Microbiol Res.* 152:189–98

233. Voigt J, Münzner P. 1994. Blue light-induced lethality of a cell wall-deficient mutant of the unicellular green alga *Chlamydomonas reinhardtii. Plant Cell Physiol.* 35:99–106

234. Voigt J, Nagel K, Wrann D. 1998. A cadmium-tolerant *Chlamydomonas* mutant strain impaired in photosystem II activity. *J. Plant Physiol.* 153:566–73

235. Walther Z, Hall JL. 1995. The uni chromosome of *Chlamydomonas*: histone

genes and nucleosome structure. *Nucleic Acids Res.* 23:3756–63

236. Wang SC, Schnell RA, Lefebvre PA. 1998. Isolation and characterization of a new transposable element in *Chlamydomonas reinhardtii. Plant Mol. Biol.* 38:681–87

237. White RA, Wolfe GR, Komine Y, Hoober JK. 1996. Localization of light-harvesting complex apoproteins in the chloroplast and cytoplasm during greening of *Chlamydomonas reinhardtii* at 38°C. *Photosynth. Res.* 47:267–80

238. Wilson NF, Foglesong MJ, Snell WJ. 1997. The *Chlamydomonas* mating type plus fertilization tubule, a prototypic cell fusion organelle: isolation, characterization, and in vitro adhesion to mating type minus gametes. *J. Cell Biol.* 137:1537–53

239. Wilson NF, O'Connell JS, Lu M, Snell WJ. 1999. Flagellar adhesion between mt^+ and mt^- *Chlamydomonas* gametes regulates phosphorylation of the mt^+-specific homeodomain protein GSP1. *J. Biol. Chem.* 274:34383–88

240. Wilson NF, Snell WJ. 1998. Microvilli and cell-cell fusion during fertilization. *Trends Cell Biol.* 8:93–96

241. Woessner JP, Goodenough UW. 1994. Volvocine cell walls and their constituent glycoproteins: an evolutionary perspective. *Protoplasma* 181:245–58

242. Wu LP, Hepler PK, John PCL. 1997. The *met1* mutation in *Chlamydomonas reinhardtii* causes arrest at mitotic metaphase with persisting p34cdc2-like H1 histone kinase activity that can promote mitosis when injected into higher-plant cells. *Protoplasma* 199:135–50

243. Wu-Scharf D, Jeong B, Zhang C, Cerutti H. 2000. Transgene and transposon silencing in *Chlamydomonas reinhardtii* by a DEAH-box RNA helicase. *Science* 290:1159–63

244. Wykoff DD, Davies JP, Melis A, Grossman AR. 1998. The regulation of

photosynthetic electron transport during nutrient deprivation in *Chlamydomonas reinhardtii. Plant Physiol.* 117:129–39

245. Wykoff DD, Grossman AR, Weeks DP, Usuda H, Shimogawara K. 1999. Psr1, a nuclear localized protein that regulates phosphorus metabolism in *Chlamydomonas. Proc. Natl. Acad. Sci. USA* 96:15336–41

246. Xie ZY, Culler D, Dreyfuss BW, Kuras R, Wollman FA, et al. 1998. Genetic analysis of chloroplast c-type cytochrome assembly in *Chlamydomonas reinhardtii*: One chloroplast locus and at least four nuclear loci are required for heme attachment. *Genetics* 148:681–92

247. Xie ZY, Merchant S. 1996. The plastid-encoded *ccsA* gene is required for heme attachment to chloroplast c-type cytochromes. *J. Biol. Chem.* 271:4632–39

248. Xie ZY, Merchant S. 1998. A novel pathway for cytochrome *c* biogenesis in chloroplasts. *Biochim. Biophys. Acta Bio Energ.* 1365:309–18

249. Xiong J, Hutchison RS, Sayre RT, Govindjee. 1997. Modification of the photosystem II acceptor side function in a D1 mutant (arginine-269-glycine) of *Chlamydomonas reinhardtii. Biochim. Biophys. Acta Bio Energ.* 1322:60–76

250. Xiong J, Subramaniam S, Govindjee. 1998. A knowledge-based three dimensional model of the Photosystem II reaction center of *Chlamydomonas reinhardtii. Photosynth. Res.* 56:229–54

251. Yildiz FH, Davies JP, Grossman A. 1996. Sulfur availability and the *SAC1* gene control adenosine triphosphate sulfurylase gene expression in *Chlamydomonas reinhardtii. Plant Physiol.* 112:669–75

252. Yohn CB, Cohen A, Danon A, Mayfield SP. 1998. A poly(A) binding protein functions in the chloroplast as a message-specific translation factor. *Proc. Natl. Acad. Sci USA* 95:2238–43

253. Zerges W, Girard-Bascou J, Rochaix J-D.

1997. Translation of the chloroplast *psbC* mRNA is controlled by interactions between its 5′ leader and the nuclear loci *TBC1* and *TBC3* in *Chlamydomonas reinhardtii*. *Mol. Cell. Biol.* 17:3440–48

254. Zhang LP, Niyogi KK, Baroli I, Nemson JA, Grossman AR, Melis A. 1997. DNA insertional mutagenesis for the elucidation of a Photosystem II repair process in the green alga *Chlamydomonas reinhardtii*. *Photosynth. Res.* 53:173–84

255. Zhou JJ, Fernandez E, Galvan A, Miller AJ. 2000. A high affinity nitrate transport system from *Chlamydomonas* requires two gene products. *FEBS Lett.* 466:225–27

256. Zito F, Finazzi G, Delosme R, Nitschke W, Picot D, Wollman FA. 1999. The Q_o site of cytochrome b_6f complexes controls the activation of the LHCII kinase. *EMBO J.* 18:2961–69

257. Zito F, Kuras R, Choquet Y, Koessel H, Wollman F-A. 1997. Mutations of cytochrome b_6 in *Chlamydomonas reinhardtii* disclose the functional significance for a proline to leucine conversion by *petB* editing in maize and tobacco. *Plant Mol. Biol.* 33:79–86

Annu. Rev. Plant Physiol. Plant Mol. Biol. 2001. 52:407–36

ISOPRENE EMISSION FROM PLANTS

Thomas D Sharkey and Sansun Yeh

Department of Botany, University of Wisconsin, Madison, Wisconsin 53706;
e-mail: tsharkey@facstaff.wisc.edu, syeh2@students.wisc.edu

Key Words   deoxyxylulose 5-phosphate/methyl erythritol 4-phosphate, evolution, photosynthesis, thermoprotection, volatile organic carbon

■ **Abstract**   Very large amounts of isoprene are emitted from vegetation, especially from mosses, ferns, and trees. This hydrocarbon flux to the atmosphere, roughly equal to the flux of methane, has a large effect on the oxidizing potential of the atmosphere. Isoprene emission results from de novo synthesis by the deoxyxylulose phosphate/methyl erythritol 4-phosphate pathway in plastids. Dimethylallyl pyrophosphate made by this pathway is converted to isoprene by isoprene synthase. Isoprene synthase activity in plants has a high pH optimum and requirement for Mg^{2+} that is consistent with its location inside chloroplasts. Isoprene emission costs the plant significant amounts of carbon, ATP, and reducing power. Researchers hypothesize that plants benefit from isoprene emission because it helps photosynthesis recover from short high-temperature episodes. The evolution of isoprene emission may have been important in allowing plants to survive the rapid temperature changes that can occur in air because of the very low heat capacity of isoprene relative to water.

CONTENTS

1040-2519/01/0601-0407$14.00

INTRODUCTION

Isoprene (C_5H_8, 2-methyl 1,3-butadiene) is a natural product of many organisms (128). Sanadze & Kursunov discovered isoprene emission from plants in the 1950s (117). In a series of papers, he and his colleagues showed that a number of plants, especially trees, emit isoprene in a highly light- and temperature-dependent manner (112, 113, 116, 117). Rasmussen & Went discovered isoprene emission from plants independently of the work of Sanadze (106). It was not immediately accepted that plants made isoprene, and both Sanadze & Rasmussen eventually proved by mass spectrometry that the compound they saw was isoprene (102, 112).

Isoprene is well-known chemically as the root of the isoprenoid class of compounds. Researchers first made it by burning rubber and later by heating turpentine. The structural formula was identified in 1882 (152, also see citation in 111). Kekulé recognized that many components of turpentine oil had a C:H ratio of 5:8 and coined the term terpenoids for this class of compounds (85). Otto Wallach pointed out that the terpenes consist of a repeating, branched, five-carbon unit similar to isoprene, so terpenes are also known as isoprenoids. The generalization that terpenes could be seen as composed of isoprene units became known as the isoprene rule (85), which investigators used to work out structures of isoprenoids.

However, isoprenoids are not made from isoprene. The biological precursors to the isoprenoids are isopentenyl pyrophosphate (IPP) and its isomer dimethylallyl pyrophosphate (DMAPP), sometimes called the active isoprenes. Isoprene is a hemiterpene and is made from DMAPP (138). Monoterpenes (10 carbons) include many of the scents we associate with plants such as pine, lemon, and the smell of a freshly peeled orange. Adding IPP to DMAPP makes monoterpenes. Additional IPP molecules can be added to make sterols (C30, made from two C15 compounds) in the cytosol of plants and carotenoids (C40, made from two C20 compounds) in plant plastids. There are many other isoprenoids in plants (74, 159), but they are not discussed in this review.

Although the isoprenoids are very well known, much less is known about biological isoprene production because isoprene is not an intermediate in isoprenoid production and its concentration in the environment is low. These facts have led some authors to conclude, "Isoprene itself does not occur free in nature" (55, p. 10).

In fact, free isoprene is widespread in nature, and biogenic isoprene from plants is very important, both for plants and the atmosphere.

Recent estimates suggest that isoprene emission from plants is among the most important biosphere-atmosphere interactions. The total hydrocarbon flux from the biosphere to the atmosphere was estimated by Rasmussen & Went in 1965 (106) to be 432 Tg C yr^{-1}. The estimate for global isoprene emission is now about 500 Tg C yr^{-1}, making it the dominant hydrocarbon that moves from plants to the air, roughly equal to the flux of methane to the atmosphere (41, 162).

Atmospheric Chemistry

One of the more important reasons to understand isoprene emission from plants is its role in atmospheric chemistry (31, 151). Though isoprene is not a greenhouse gas, it can alter atmospheric chemistry, affecting the residence times of gases that do contribute to the greenhouse effect. Isoprene oxidation in the atmosphere can give rise to ozone and smog if nitrogen oxides are present in the atmosphere (18, 44). Some of the breakdown products include organic acids, CO, methacrolein, and methyl vinyl ketone (2, 158). When the nitrogen oxide levels are high, isoprene breakdown can lead to the formation of peroxyacetyl nitrate (PAN) and methyl peroxyacetyl nitrate (MPAN). Isoprene breakdown is the primary source of MPAN in the atmosphere (168). Isoprene breakdown in the atmosphere can be estimated from MPAN concentrations, which is useful because the concentration of isoprene in the atmosphere is normally very low (<10 ppb) (53, 105).

Another phenomenon associated with volatile isoprenoids from plants is the blue haze described by Went (164). Oxidation of monoterpenes causes them to stick together until they form a solid particle. These particles can act as cloud condensation nuclei. This is important because in some areas rainfall is limited by a lack of cloud condensation nuclei, which has given rise to the practice of cloud seeding in these areas. Raindrop size is also affected by the concentration of cloud condensation nuclei. These particles that are formed from monoterpenes also scatter light. When the particles are very small, blue light is scattered more than other colors, giving rise to the natural blue haze (164). By itself, isoprene does not cause particle formation, but it may contribute to their growth (64).

Despite early warnings from Rasmussen (103), Zimmerman (174), and then presidential candidate Reagan[1] (100), the role of isoprene emitted from plants (and other biogenic hydrocarbons) in atmospheric chemistry was ignored in early attempts to reduce ozone pollution. Early air quality regulations emphasized reduction of anthropogenic hydrocarbons, even if that meant some increase in nitrogen oxide emissions. This strategy was not effective (122). In 1987, Trainer et al (157) pointed out the importance of biogenic isoprene in clean environments. In 1988,

---

[1]"Approximately 80% of our air pollution stems from hydrocarbons released by vegetation, so let's not go overboard in setting and enforcing tough emission standards from man-made sources."

Chamedies et al (12) suggested that so much isoprene was coming from vegetation in the Atlanta, Georgia (USA) area that air pollution control strategies had to switch to reducing NO_x to be effective.

The 1988 paper by Chamedies et al made many people aware of isoprene emission from plants, but not much more information was available. Since then significant progress has been made. Estimates and reviews concerning the magnitude of plant isoprene emission are available (41, 99). This review is the first to cover this topic in this series, but reviews of plant isoprene emissions have been published elsewhere recently (31, 32, 48, 57, 67, 75, 94).

BIOCHEMISTRY OF ISOPRENE SYNTHESIS

Isoprene Emission Requires De Novo Synthesis

Isoprene emission is different from emissions of the related and better-known monoterpenes such as the pinenes and limonene. Emission of monoterpenes is, in most cases, from pools of hydrocarbon stored in resin ducts, glands, or trichomes. Monoterpene emission is therefore dependent in large measure on its volatility (66) and on damage of leaves and needles (72, 155, 156). However, isoprene emission requires de novo synthesis; this is demonstrated by the following two examples. First, researchers made estimates of the amount of isoprene stored in leaves by changing environmental conditions from those conditions that promote isoprene emission to those conditions that do not. Taking the extreme assumption that synthesis stopped instantaneously, the amount of isoprene emission that occurred after the switch is an upper limit of the amount of isoprene stored in the leaf (82). In addition, leaves can be flash frozen, and then researchers can extract and measure isoprene to determine the total pool (28, 76). Both measures indicate very little isoprene storage in leaves.

Second, investigators measured the rate at which ^{13}C appeared in isoprene when the $^{12}CO_2$ in air flowing past leaves was replaced with $^{13}CO_2$ (20) to assess the contribution of de novo synthesis. The stable isotope of carbon appeared in all five carbon atoms of the isoprene molecule with kinetics similar to the rate of 3-phosphoglycerate labeling. The results of Delwiche & Sharkey (20) differ from those of Sanadze and his colleagues (114, 115) who had found that only one or two carbon atoms were labeled. Sanadze et al used a closed labeling system in which the carbon dioxide concentration most likely fell to the compensation point, and so most of the isoprene was made from carbon derived from starch breakdown. The steady-state labeling system used by Delwiche & Sharkey kept the CO_2 concentration constant throughout the labeling period, so the isotopic composition reflects the normal relationship between photosynthesis and isoprene emission.

Dependence on de novo synthesis means that the temperature dependence of isoprene emission is not related to its volatility but rather to its metabolism. Isoprene emission increases with increasing leaf temperature. However, two distinct phases can be separated. The fastest phase has a time constant of 8.2 s and is followed by a phase with a time constant of 116 s (142). Thus, for small changes in rate, isoprene emission changes as quickly as leaf temperature; though for larger rate changes, enzyme activation and other metabolic adjustments are needed. This observation is consistent with emission from de novo synthesis rather than control of emission rate by volatility.

The light requirement for isoprene synthesis is also consistent with a dependence on de novo synthesis. Recent work has shown that some species, especially some Mediterranean oaks, also emit monoterpenes in a light-dependent manner (80, 145). These trees emit monoterpenes from recently synthesized carbon like the case with isoprene (77, 79). A few western United States conifer species will emit the closely related molecule 2-methyl-3-buten-2-ol in a light-dependent manner (3), but researchers have not yet determined whether this is by de novo synthesis. In a few cases trees will emit some monoterpenes as a result of de novo synthesis, though other monoterpenes are emitted from storage pools (77, 79). *Trans* β-ocimene in particular can be emitted from Mediterranean Pine in a light-dependent manner while other monoterpenes are released from wounded needles (81).

Isoprene Synthase

Isoprene emitted from plants is made from DMAPP by isoprene synthase (138). This enzyme has a relatively high pH optimum and a requirement for Mg^{2+} (118, 139), consistent with its location inside chloroplasts (90, 166, 167). The molecular weight of isoprene synthase has been reported at 95 in *Quercus robur* (118), 73 in *Salix discolor* (165), and a doublet of 58 and 62 in aspen (139) and kudzu (CA Downs & TD Sharkey, unpublished data). A contributing factor to the difficulty in working with this enzyme is that plants that make substantial amounts of isoprene tend to be difficult to work with biochemically. Repeated attempts to measure isoprene emission from *Arabidopsis* have failed. (Note added in proof: The gene for isoprene synthase was sequenced after this review was written. *Arabidopsis* does not have an isoprene synthase gene.)

Wildermuth & Fall found some isoprene synthase activity bound to thylakoid membranes, although other isoprene synthase activity was found to be soluble (166, 167). The membrane-bound form appeared to have the same kinetics as the soluble form. Whether the soluble form is converted to the bound form or vice versa and what effect this might have on the activity of isoprene synthase is not known. Wildermuth (165) showed that thylakoid-bound isoprene synthase activity could be stimulated threefold by the addition of GTP and palmitoyl CoA. There is potential for regulation by this mechanism, but studies to investigate this have not yet been carried out.

Investigators have suggested that DMAPP is converted to isoprene noncatalytically in animals (22). Acid will catalyze the conversion of DMAPP to isoprene, but this reaction is slow and it seems unlikely to explain isoprene emission from humans. Bacteria also make isoprene (60, 160). However, *Escherichia coli* makes more isoprene when fed tryptone media than when fed minimal media. Perhaps isoprene is a product of the breakdown of higher isoprenoids in *E. coli*. This could explain why there is no gene sequence in the fully sequenced *E. coli* genome that corresponds to isoprene synthase of *Populus* sp. (W Zimmer, D Gong, & TD Sharkey, unpublished). In *Bacillus subtilis*, isoprene emission occurs during distinct phases of culture growth (161).

The Methylerythritol Phosphate Pathway Is the Source of DMAPP

Two major metabolic pathways make DMAPP, the mevalonic acid (MVA) pathway and the recently discovered 2-deoxyxylulose 5-phosphate/2-methylerythritol 4-phosphate (MEP) pathway (108) (Figure 1). There are other ways that the five-carbon branched chain can be made, especially during leucine metabolism, but these are probably only minor sources of isoprenoids. The source of DMAPP within the chloroplast is the MEP pathway (109). The MEP pathway begins with pyruvate and glyceraldehyde 3-phosphate (109) and involves skeletal rearrangement to make the branched chain (1). Lichtenthaler and colleagues showed that this pathway is responsible for most, and probably all, isoprenoids made in plastids (70).

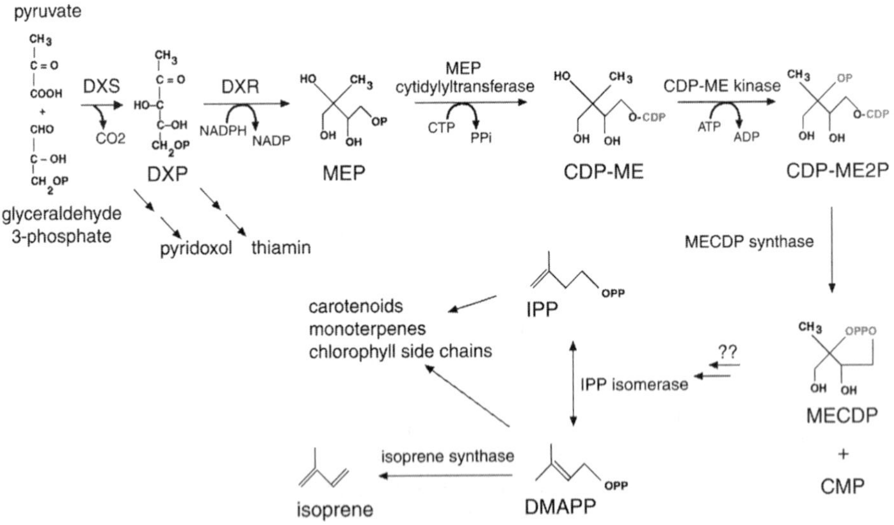

Figure 1 The MEP pathway is the source of DMAPP for isoprene synthesis. It is currently unknown whether this pathway makes IPP first, then DMAPP by isomerization, or if it makes DMAPP without first making IPP. CDP-ME, 4-(cytidine 5′-diphospho)-2-*C*-methyl-D-erythritol; CDP-ME2P, 2-phospho-4-(cytidine 5′-diphospho)-2-*C*-methyl-D-erythritol; DMAPP, dimethylallyl pyrophosphate; DXR, deoxyxylulose-5-phosphate reductoisomerase; DXS, deoxyxylulose-5-phosphate synthase; IPP, isopentenyl pyrophosphate; MECDP, 2-*C*-methyl-D-erythritol 2,4-cyclodiphosphate.

TABLE 1   Energetics of the MEP pathway in photosynthetic organisms. It is assumed that each carbon in the starting intermediates costs 3 ATPs plus 2 NADPH if at the redox level of a triose phosphate with CTP equivalent to ATP. This estimate differs from that of Niinemets et al (96) because of the additional steps now known in the MEP pathway

	ATP	NADPH
Glyceraldehyde 3-phosphate	9	6
Pyruvate	8	5
Deoxyxylulose reductoisomerase		1
MEP cytidylyltransferase	2	
4-(cytidine 5′-diphospho)-2-C-methyl-D-erythritol kinase	1	
Two hypothetical reduction steps	2	
Total	20	14

They specifically proved that this pathway is responsible for isoprene synthesis (120, 171). This pathway was recently reviewed in this series (69), and since that review three additional steps in the pathway have been reported. These steps include the addition of CTP to MEP (62), a phosphorylation (63), and cyclization (148). The MEP pathway can make IPP (88), which researchers presume can be isomerized to DMAPP. However, in *E. coli* the MEP pathway can make both IPP and DMAPP without the need for IPP isomerase (107). Investigators have yet to determine whether IPP isomerase is required for isoprene synthesis in higher plants.

The new knowledge of the biosynthetic pathway for isoprene allows the energy cost of isoprene emission (132) to be revised (Table 1). Using the MVA pathway, isoprene emission costs 9 carbon atoms, 24 ATP, and 14 NADPH. However, the MEP pathway is more efficient than the MVA pathway in photosynthetic organisms, and isoprene emission based on the MEP pathway costs only 6 carbon atoms, 20 ATP, and 14 NADPH (Table 1). Although the cost is less when calculated for the MEP pathway, it is still substantial, and any benefits ascribed to isoprene emission will have to be weighed against this cost in both carbon and energy.

Isotopic Fractionation

Isoprene synthesis discriminates against the heavier natural isotope of carbon, ^{13}C (133). This was originally interpreted in terms of the mevalonic acid pathway, which starts with acetyl CoA. However, the current finding that isoprene is made by the MEP pathway results in a need to reinterpret these data. Isoprene is isotopically lighter than the carbon it is presumably made from, but it is not clear where the discrimination occurs. One candidate for the cause of this discrimination is the deoxyxylulose synthase because it decarboxylates pyruvate in a reaction similar to the one that is responsible for discrimination in the formation of acetyl CoA (23).

Isoprene Degradation

Plants do not break down isoprene. When radioactive isoprene was passed over leaves of oak (an isoprene emitter) or *Phaseolus vulgaris* (a nonemitter), no radioactivity stayed in the plant (PJ Vanderveer & TD Sharkey, unpublished data). In humans and other animals, isoprene is probably converted to an epoxide. The diepoxide may be toxic; but isoprene is less likely to form the diepoxide than is 1,3 butadiene, and so isoprene is less toxic (7, 16, 17, 89).

Bacteria can metabolize isoprene (13), and some types of bacteria can use it as their sole carbon source (27). This metabolism involves addition of glutathione to the epoxide formed from isoprene, as well as additional steps that might lead to acetyl CoA through β-oxidation. Globally, this metabolism is likely to be small relative to emission from plants, but this metabolism could be important in soil ecology (27).

PHYSIOLOGY OF ISOPRENE EMISSION

Isoprene emission is a major metabolic pathway in some plants. Because the flux through isoprene metabolism is high relative to other processes such as carotenoid synthesis, it is likely that the regulation of the MEP pathway is geared to the requirements of isoprene synthesis. Isoprene synthesis physiology also includes sensitivity to a number of environmental parameters, most notably temperature and light.

Relative Rate of Isoprene Metabolism

Isoprene synthesis of major emitting plant species such as oak and aspen is typically 2% of photosynthesis at 30°C. In some cases, however, isoprene emission can account for substantially more of photosynthesis (130, 136). In nonphysiological conditions, leaves can easily be in negative carbon balance (net loss of carbon by isoprene emission) by having substantial isoprene emission at or below the CO_2 compensation point (82, 91).

Relative to the rate of isoprenoid synthesis in leaves, isoprene synthesis is by far the dominant product of the MEP pathway. Although isoprene emission is typically 2% of photosynthesis, carotenoid synthesis is 0.02 % of photosynthesis (119). Moreover, isoprene synthesis begins sometime after the leaf has reached full photosynthetic competence (92) and is no longer accumulating carotenoids (except in cases of changes in growth light levels).

Sanadze had postulated that isoprene synthesis competes with fatty acid synthesis for acetyl CoA. He found that feeding cerulenin, a fatty acid synthesis inhibitor, increased the rate of isoprene emission (113) (confirmed by F Loreto & TD Sharkey, unpublished data). However, the increase in isoprene emission was much greater than the normal rate of fatty acid synthesis [fatty acid synthesis may be about 0.03% of photosynthesis (119) or about 1% of the rate of isoprene emission]. In any case, researchers now know that isoprene is made by the MEP pathway and so does not directly compete with fatty acid synthesis for acetyl CoA. Why cerulenin increases isoprene emission remains unclear.

Relationship Between Isoprene Emission and Photosynthesis

Light   Isoprene emission is dependent on photosynthesis, especially the photosynthetic carbon reduction cycle (PCRC or Calvin cycle). The earliest reports of isoprene emission described its dependence on light (112, 116, 117), and the wavelength dependence was shown to be similar to that of photosynthesis (104). In most cases, isoprene emission saturates with the same light level as photosynthesis, but in some cases isoprene emission increases with increasing light intensity after photosynthesis is saturated (46, 68, 130, 131). The increase in the rate of isoprene emission can be caused by light activation of isoprene synthase, activation of the MEP pathway providing substrate, or some combination of these effects (29). For example, Fall & Wildermuth (29) reported that changes in pH and Mg that normally occur in thylakoids in response to light can cause an 11-fold stimulation in isoprene synthase activity, and a further 3-fold stimulation of activity was obtained by adding GTP and palmitoyl CoA.

Temperature   The temperature dependence of isoprene emission is very different from that of photosynthesis. Photosynthesis of C_3 plants in 350 ppm CO_2 normally exhibits a very broad temperature optimum with maximal rates at $30°C$ or below. The V_{max} of rubisco increases with approximately the same temperature dependence as the K_m for CO_2, and the overall rate is proportional to V_{max}/K_m at 350 ppm CO_2 (30). Isoprene emission, on the other hand, is very sensitive to temperature. The activation energy is between 60 and 90 kJ mol^{-1} (46, 135), which corresponds to a Q_{10} of 2 to 4 depending on the temperature range. The proportion of fixed carbon emitted as isoprene increases rapidly with temperature. Because photosynthesis is constant or declining and isoprene emission is increasing with temperature above $30°C$, at $30°C$ typically 2% of carbon fixed by photosynthesis is emitted as isoprene; but at $40°C$ 15% is emitted (136).

Carbon Dioxide   The responses of photosynthesis and isoprene emission to carbon dioxide are reverse to their temperature responses: Photosynthesis is highly sensitive but isoprene is relatively insensitive. In CO_2-free air, isoprene emission can be reduced 50% or more from its peak rate (82, 91). With 50 ppm CO_2, isoprene emission reaches a broad maximum and sometimes declines slightly at high (500 ppm) CO_2. The decline at high CO_2 is more pronounced in low oxygen atmospheres and at low temperature (82), consistent with an ATP dependence of isoprene emission. At high CO_2 and moderate to low temperature, feedback from carbon metabolism can limit ATP synthesis (137).

Isoprene emission in CO_2-free air can be 50% of maximal rates; but if oxygen is also removed, isoprene emission stops (82). The interpretation of this phenomenon is that isoprene emission requires an active PCRC. In CO_2-free air containing oxygen, photorespiration will keep the PCRC active as starch reserves are mobilized. However, without oxygen or CO_2, the PCRC is inhibited causing isoprene emission to cease (141), which also explains away the evidence for a link between photorespiration and isoprene emission (74) or carotenoid synthesis (54, 123). By feeding intermediates of photorespiration to CO_2-starved leaves, Jones & Rasmussen provided a carbon source that was essential for isoprene synthesis. The fact that these were intermediates of photorespiration did not indicate a link between photorespiration and isoprenoid metabolism, only that it requires an active photosynthetic carbon reduction cycle. Hewitt et al showed that photorespiration and isoprene emission are not linked (50).

Inhibitors   The requirement for an active PCRC probably explains why almost all inhibitors of photosynthesis inhibit isoprene emission (82). Among inhibitors that inhibit both processes are some that affect one or the other process a little more rapidly (82). One inhibitor in this class is methyl viologen, which catalyzes pseudocyclic electron transport. Methyl viologen initially reduces the availability of NADPH but increases availability of ATP. Methyl viologen fed to oak leaves caused isoprene emission to increase as photosynthesis started to decline, but the effect was for only a short time. As the PCRC stopped so did isoprene emission (82). The methyl viologen results are consistent with a big role for ATP availability in regulating the rate of isoprene emission; a conclusion strengthened by finding a correlation between whole leaf ATP content and isoprene emission rate (84). These results have been interpreted in terms of the requirement of the MVA pathway for ATP at the final steps. However, the presumed ATP cost of the MEP pathway is less than that of the MVA pathway (Table 1). Nevertheless, ATP status probably affects the rate of isoprene synthesis, perhaps through the 4-(cytidine 5′-diphospho)-2-C-methyl-D-erythritol kinase or through regulatory effects on isoprene synthase. Another compound that causes an initial increase in isoprene emission before it is inhibited is D,L glyceraldehyde (113).

There are two exceptions to the rule that photosynthesis (or at least the PCRC) and isoprene are always inhibited together. The first is an unpublished observation by S Gosh & TD Sharkey. They found that cytosolic protein synthesis inhibitors (e.g. cycloheximide) reduced photosynthesis without reducing isoprene emission. In those experiments it appeared that the inhibitor was stopping photosynthesis without stopping the PCRC. There is one way this could happen. If both starch and sucrose synthesis were stopped, carbon assimilation would have to slow to the rate at which amino acids could serve as the end products of photosynthesis. In other words, leaves fed these inhibitors would become limited by triose phosphate utilization (126). Loss of oxygen sensitivity confirmed this hypothesis (124). S Gosh & TD Sharkey (unpublished results) found that photosynthesis reduced by feeding cycloheximide became insensitive to changes in oxygen level, confirming that the leaves were limited by triose phosphate use. The interpretation of these experiments is that triose phosphate use limitation does not restrict the PCRC and so does not restrict isoprene emission. The second case of an inhibitor inhibiting

only one of the two processes is fosmidomycin, the inhibitor of 2-deoxyxylulose 5-phosphate reductoisomerase (61, 170). Zeidler et al (170) showed that isoprene emission was eliminated by low levels of fosmidomycin, and Sharkey et al (129) showed that photosynthesis was unaffected by fosmidomycin.

Wound Signals

Isoprene emission is a sensitive indicator of wound signals that can travel through plants (83). Wounding was inflicted by puncturing, smashing, cutting, and, burning leaves, the last of these being the most effective. The effect was greatest when a large interface between damaged and undamaged leaf surface was left. By wounding one leaf while monitoring isoprene emission from a different leaf, researchers could show the transmission of a signal. The time between wounding one leaf and a change in rate of isoprene emission of a different leaf was linearly related to the distance between the two leaves, allowing a calculation of travel rate of the signal. The signal traveled about 2 mm s^{-1}, which is likely to result from electrical signals traveling through the plant. The calcium chelator EGTA substantially delayed the wound signal effect on isoprene emission, indicating that the electrical signal may have caused calcium fluxes that ultimately affected isoprene emission.

Environmental Effects

Isoprene emission can be affected by nitrogen nutrition (47, 71). Trees with low nitrogen availability had lower rates of isoprene emission than did trees with higher nitrogen nutrition. This effect interacted with light. Trees grown in sun or shade but with low nitrogen availability had similar, low rates of isoprene emission; but trees with high nitrogen availability emitted substantially more isoprene when grown in the sun than when grown in the shade.

When plants were water-stressed, isoprene emission changed little, even when photosynthesis fell to zero (153). However, upon rewatering, isoprene emission increased several fold above the prestress rate and stayed high for several weeks (130). Apparently the reduced photosynthesis caused by water stress did not prevent increased rates of isoprene emission. On the other hand, defoliation may reduce isoprene emission by restricting whole plant carbon availability. Funk et al (35) defoliated trees to examine stress responses to whole tree carbon balance. They found that reducing the foliage carried by a tree reduced isoprene emission.

BENEFITS OF ISOPRENE EMISSION

What benefit, if any, do plants derive from isoprene emission? In other words, why do plants make isoprene? Explanations for other volatile emissions from plants are one place to look for answers (58). For example, acetone is probably lost as an unavoidable by-product of fatty acid metabolism (86); and methanol is emitted, possibly as a waste product of pectin methyl esterase (87, 95). However, neither of these explanations seems to apply to isoprene emission. Some of the reasons suggested for isoprene emission include a flowering hormone (150), an antioxidant (171), and a metabolite overflow to get rid of excess carbon (73a, 161). However, the hypothesis that has been studied most is the thermotolerance hypothesis.

The Thermotolerance Hypothesis

Sharkey & Singsaas (134) proposed that isoprene protects photosynthesis from damage caused by high leaf temperature. Holding leaves in darkness or in a nitrogen atmosphere to controll endogenous isoprene synthesis, they assessed damage to photosynthesis as the temperature at which chlorophyll fluorescence increased (121). Singsaas et al (141) showed that adding isoprene to an air stream (or nitrogen gas) that passed over these leaves could increase the temperature at which damage occurred from as low as 35°C to as high as 45°C. Another series of experiments determined the temperature at which photosynthesis, measured as CO_2 assimilation, fell to zero as leaves were heated (141). The zero temperature was related to the endogenous isoprene produced by the leaf. Leaf-to-leaf variation in isoprene emission provided a range of isoprene treatments. The zero-photosynthesis temperature increased with increasing endogenous isoprene emission. These experiments indicated that isoprene was having some effect on the temperature tolerance of photosynthesis, but none of the experiments were conclusive.

Given the tentative nature of the evidence, Logan & Monson's published statement that, "Thermotolerance of leaf discs from four isoprene-emitting species is not enhanced by exposure to exogenous isoprene," (73) was of substantial concern. They found that chlorophyll fluorescence of leaf discs held in darkness or light plus nitrogen did not increase until 45°C, regardless of whether isoprene was in the air stream. In their experiments the control leaf pieces did not exhibit photosynthetic damage below 45°C. Measurements of the temperature where CO_2 uptake fell to zero were not reported.

Two improvements have allowed definitive experiments. First, the thermotolerance hypothesis has been refined. Now, researchers hypothesize that isoprene protects against short high-temperature episodes (140, 142). Therefore, instead of heating leaves and determining where irreversible damage occurs (cook and look), investigators used a new protocol of measuring the recovery from a short high-temperature episode. The second improvement was the use of fosmidomycin, the inhibitor that eliminates isoprene production without affecting photosynthesis. With these improvements, much stronger evidence for the thermotolerance hypothesis has been obtained (129). Heating kudzu leaves to 46°C for two minutes caused photosynthesis to be eliminated. Twenty minutes after returning the leaf to 30°C, photosynthesis recovered by 90%. Photosynthesis of leaves fed fosmidomycin recovered only 60%. To show that the reduced recovery resulted from the loss of isoprene, researchers gave fosmidomycin-fed leaves physiological levels of isoprene in the air stream. With exogenous isoprene, recovery was similar to leaves in which isoprene emission had not been inhibited (129). This result shows that isoprene synthesis provides tolerance of short high-temperature episodes. Monoterpenes emitted in a light-dependent manner also provide this type of thermoprotection. Repeated cycles of high-temperature stress give reduced recovery in leaves without isoprene or monoterpene, although leaves with isoprene or monoterpene maintain high rates of photosynthesis, especially after repeated periods of high temperature (19, 80, 129).

What property of the isoprene molecule provides thermotolerance? Molecules similar to isoprene were tested to see what is important for thermotolerance. One rule was apparent in the results. All alkenes tested (1,3-butadiene, 1-butene, and *cis* 2-butene) provided thermotolerance though alkanes (2-methyl-butane, n-butane, and *iso*-butane) did not; they even increased the damage caused by heat (129).

Speculation concerning the mechanism by which isoprene protects against short high-temperature episodes depends upon characteristics of the high temperature damage. An attractive idea for which data exists is that thylakoid membranes become leaky at moderately high temperature (9, 97). Isoprene could reside in the thylakoid membrane for a (short) time and enhance hydrophobic interactions. It could even block the formation of water channels because of the large volume of the double bonds. Another possibility is that excursions to high temperature allow separation of the mono- and digalactosyldiacylglycerides of the thylakoid membrane, resulting in nonbilayer structures (37). Another alternative is that high temperature excursions could allow large membrane-bound protein complexes (e.g. photosystem II) to fragment. Isoprene could enhance hydrophobic interactions within either membranes or protein complexes. Because each excursion to high temperature could result in more nonbilayer structures or more disrupted protein complexes, repeated high temperature episodes would progressively reduce the photosynthetic capacity. As leaves can be subject to dozens of high-temperature episodes each day (140, 142), the increased recovery from each episode afforded by isoprene could become very important to the plant.

Antioxidant

A second hypothesis that investigators have considered is that isoprene serves as an antioxidant in leaves. This idea is normally put forward on the basis of the rapid reaction of isoprene with ozone and hydroxyl radicals. Although often discussed by researchers (147), this hypothesis has little evidence to support or reject it. Hewitt et al (49) found that isoprene-emitting plants were more sensitive to ozone damage because of hydroperoxides formed on the plants, which points out the weakness with the antioxidant hypothesis: Isoprene will propagate radicals not quench them. The result of isoprene interaction with hydroxyl radicals in the atmosphere is simply more radicals, and the same could be true inside of leaves.

On the other hand, F Loreto (unpublished data) has found that exogenous isoprene can protect leaves against a short, acute exposure to a high concentration of ozone (300 ppb). On the day following exposure, the leaves without isoprene developed large necrotic areas where cells had collapsed; leaves given isoprene with ozone showed little necrosis. One question that arises is whether the effect of isoprene is radical quenching or membrane strengthening. More work is required on the antioxidant hypothesis.

Getting Rid of Excess Energy or Carbon

Some people have speculated that isoprene emission may serve the plant as a safety valve, releasing excess carbon and energy (73a). However, the amount of energy that can be lost by this mechanism is small compared to the energy dissipation mechanisms associated with nonphotochemical quenching of chlorophyll fluorescence, zeaxanthin, (21) and possibly other thermal dissipation mechanisms (10). Similarly, Rubisco is deactivated when the leaf cannot use carbon as fast as the photosynthetic reactions can produce it (110, 125), which is a much more effective method of regulating carbon uptake during those rare times when there is excess carbon fixation capacity. Wagner et al (161) have proposed a more restricted version of this hypothesis to explain isoprene emission from *B. subtilis*. In this case, they proposed that a mismatch between DMAPP production and its use in higher isoprenoid synthesis or prenylation reactions can be remedied by isoprene emission. Metabolic pathways are commonly regulated to prevent carbon from accumulating in unusable intermediates. However, nothing is known about the regulation of the MEP pathway by which DMAPP for isoprene emission from bacteria is made (160), so it is possible that bacteria might need an overflow valve.

REGULATION OF ISOPRENE EMISSION

The regulation of isoprene emission is important for understanding physiological controls and for modeling isoprene emission in air quality models. Most work up to now has been directed toward improved air-quality modeling. For isoprene emission, two environmental controls are normally considered: light and temperature (26, 153, 154). Stomatal control need not be considered.

Isoprene Emission and Stomatal Closure

Isoprene emission is not controlled by stomatal closure (91), even though isoprene exits the leaf through the stomata (82), because isoprene synthesis is not affected by its concentration inside the leaf and its emission reflects synthesis (127). In other words, the leaf is analogous to a current generating circuit where the current output is constant regardless of the resistance downstream of the current generator. Fall & Monson showed that when stomata are closed by feeding abscisic acid to their leaves through the petiole, then the concentration of isoprene inside the leaf builds up to counteract the increased diffusion resistance until emission matches synthesis (28).

The Guenther Model for Predicting Isoprene Emission

Current models are primarily based on algorithms published by Guenther et al (42), although mechanistic models have also been proposed (43, 96, 173). The Guenther algorithms specify three parameters for predicting isoprene emission. First is a basal emission rate or capacity for emission, second is a light correction term, and third is a temperature correction term. The basal rate is the rate in arbitrary conditions agreed upon by people working in this field. The conditions chosen were 30°C and 1000 μmol m^{-2} s^{-1} photosynthetically active radiation. By choosing one set of conditions, researchers could compare measurements made by many different researchers at different times. The initial assumptions were that this rate reflected the capacity for isoprene emission and that it would not change over the normal growing season.

The correction for light was a rectangular hyperbola that was fit to data from a number of measured light responses. Generally, isoprene emission and photosynthesis exhibit similar light responses, but in some cases isoprene saturates at much higher light levels than does photosynthesis (68, 130).

The temperature correction incorporated an activation energy and a deactivation energy that described a high-temperature falloff. The activation energy is similar in many different situations. However, the falloff depends on how the measurements are made (140). When leaf temperature was raised to 35°C or more, isoprene emission at first increased then decreased. In some cases, the rate of emission at 40°C was initially 2–3 times greater than at 30°C; but over 30 min, the rate continually fell until it was less at 40°C than at 30°C (143). Because of this time dependence in the isoprene response to temperature, response curves measured over several hours show much less isoprene emission above 35°C than do curves measured over several minutes (140, 143). More isoprene is available when leaf temperature is rapidly fluctuating than when it is constant, even if the average temperature is the same. For predictive models, a simple activation energy correction algorithm may work well (143).

The basal rate was initially assumed constant for a given species over most of the growing season. Researchers soon recognized that leaves become photosynthetically competent before they begin to emit large amounts of isoprene (33, 39), especially when the temperature is low (47, 92). Similarly, the capacity for isoprene emission falls late in the season, giving a pronounced seasonality to both temperate and boreal forests (33, 34, 172). In predictive models this variation in the basal emission rate was taken into account by assuming a sine function for isoprene emission capacity over the growing season (40).

The basal rate is also dependent on light. Leaves that develop in the shade have lower basal emission rates than those that develop in the sun (131). As a result, leaves at the tops of trees emit more isoprene than leaves at the bottom because there is more sunlight at the top and leaves' capacity for emission is greater there (46, 136).

Even more basal rate variability has been reported recently (135, 146). By plotting basal rate measured on the same tree on six different occasions over three years of field work against several environmental variables, investigators have found that temperature measured over a few days could explain a great deal of variability in basal emission rate (135). Basal emission rates used in predictive models may need to be based on an algorithm that takes into account both seasonality and weather effects.

Physiological Regulation

The predictive modeling assumes either instantaneous changes in isoprene emission rates (the light and temperature correction factors) or very long-term (mostly seasonal) changes that are included in the basal emission rate. In the laboratory we see evidence for regulation over many different time frames. When leaf temperature is changed by changing the radiative heat load, isoprene emission initially increases as quickly as leaf temperature and then more slowly with a time constant of 116 s (142). The response to a change to 40°C is first an increase in emission rate that lasts for 5 to 15 min, followed by a decrease lasting for the next 15 min (143). Researchers have seen changes in isoprene emission capacity in response to temperature changes with a time constant of hours (DT Hanson & TD Sharkey, unpublished data), and the effect over a day or two of these changes has already been described (135).

The temperature response of isoprene emission was related to isoprene synthase activity (93). However, these measurements were made when the tools for measuring isoprene synthase were not as good as they are today. The results reported by Monson et al indicated that the drop-off temperature was likely caused by destruction of the isoprene synthase, but investigators now know that this is a regulatory phenomenon (143). The drop-off has also been ascribed to changes in electron transport activity of photosynthesis (96), but this model does not predict the variable temperature optima for isoprene emission rate that was reported by Singsaas et al (143).

The changes in basal emission rate have also been correlated with extractable isoprene synthase activity (59, 65, 165). In at least one case, the variation in extractable enzyme activity was not correlated with changes in protein amount as determined by Western blots (165). Much more work is still needed on measuring gene expression, message turnover, protein amount, and specific activity changes to see how the changes in isoprene emission are controlled.

In addition to changes in isoprene synthase activity, the activity of the MEP pathway must be regulated to accommodate the large changes in isoprene emission rates that occur. Preliminary results indicate that both deoxyxylulose synthase and deoxyxylulose reductoisomerase transcripts can be induced in kudzu leaves by switching to high temperature to induce isoprene emissions (findings based on RNA blots) (S Yeh & TD Sharkey, unpublished data). In *Arabidopsis*, which does not emit isoprene, high temperature did not induce changes in the abundance of transcripts encoding these enzymes. On the other hand, isopentenyl pyrophosphate isomerase transcript abundance did not change when kudzu leaves were induced to make isoprene. If the MEP pathway can make DMAPP without first making IPP, this isomerase is not needed.

One level of regulation that is not likely to be relevant is the competition between carotenoid synthesis and isoprene synthesis for the products of the MEP pathway. Because isoprene emission consumes so much more DMAPP than does carotenoid synthesis, changes in carotenoid synthesis will not affect isoprene emission capacity.

EVOLUTIONARY CONSIDERATIONS

Phylogenetics of Isoprene Emission

Isoprene emission is a common but not universal plant trait. Nearly all plant species emit very low levels of isoprene, but only about onethird of angiosperm species tested emit isoprene at substantial rates (45). The term substantial is intentionally vague in this case and reflects the fact that emission rate measurements are hard to compare among the various reports. A number of lists of emitters have been published, and most or all have been compiled into a database available at http://www.es.lancs.ac.uk/es/people/pg/pas/download.html or from the author. A more exhaustive list is maintained by R Rasmussen (unpublished data).

Several groups have hypothesized about the meaning of the phylogenetic relationships that characterize isoprene emission. In one case, Harley et al (48) concluded that high rates of isoprene emission are a derived character that evolved many times because, they believe, basal lineages of many plant groups often do not emit isoprene. On the other hand, Hanson et al (45) concluded that isoprene emission evolved once when mosses evolved and that the trait can be either suppressed, resulting in the very low levels of emission found in most plants, or not suppressed, resulting in the high levels found in those plants considered isoprene emitters. One difference in assumptions between these two reports is that Hanson et al assumed that loss of function was more parsimonious than gain of function, although Harley et al considered gain and loss of function equally probable.

Isoprene is also emitted from fungi, bacteria (27, 60, 160, 161), and animals (11, 98), especially humans (14, 36, 52, 149). A relationship between these emissions has not been clearly established. Because isoprene is made in plastids and is closely associated with photosynthesis, a connection between human isoprene emission and plant isoprene emission is unlikely, unless human emission is a product of bacteria resident in humans.

Costs Versus Benefits of Isoprene Emission

Isoprene emission is a substantial cost to the plant in terms of both carbon and energy loss. Given the cost, plants that do not emit would outcompete those that do emit, unless isoprene emission provides a benefit that exceeds the cost of emission. The thermotolerance hypothesis provides the explanation of what plants may gain from isoprene emission, and the effect can be large relative to the cost of emission. This hypothesis suggests plants that suffer short high-temperature episodes should emit isoprene. Trees often fit this description; the leaves at the tops of trees exposed to full sun can heat up substantially if the air is still (24). The heat of the leaves themselves would then cause convective air movement, cooling the leaf. Once the leaf was cooled, the air movement could stop and the cycle could be repeated. Thus, leaves at the tops of trees are potentially subject to numerous large swings in temperature. On the other hand, desert plants have very small leaves so that the boundary layer is small and the leaves cannot heat up much above air temperature. Generally, desert plants do not make isoprene. Crop plants that have been selected for high rates of photosynthesis will also have been selected for open stomata. When a leaf with open stomata begins to heat up, water will evaporate, keeping any leaf temperature change small relative to the case where stomata are more closed. Finally, when the humidity is high, heat loss by evaporation is reduced. Therefore, plants in tropical environments should, and do (56), emit relatively more isoprene than do most plants in temperate or cool climates.

Hanson et al (45) measured moss temperature and found that moss growing at some distance from the water surface experienced wide temperature changes, though moss growing close to water (within 2.5 cm) had much less temperature variation. They speculated that isoprene emission might have been an important step in the evolution of land plants. As plant progenitors started to stand up in the air, the low heat capacity of air allowed plant temperatures to vary much more than when the organisms were in water, which has a high heat capacity. Isoprene emission is common in mosses (45) but uncommon and possibly nonexistent in algae. Although investigators have reported some level of isoprene from algae and they have found isoprene in seawater (8), given the likely presence of bacteria in the algae, it is not clear whether marine algae or bacteria associated with the algae are responsible for the significant amounts of isoprene in the atmosphere above the oceans (169).

Liverworts may be the most primitive land plants, based on an analysis of three mitochondrial introns (101). The liverworts tested to date do not emit isoprene (45). Many mosses do emit isoprene, and so Hanson et al postulated that there was a major gain of function somewhere between the liverworts and mosses. There are some large-scale patterns concerning which lineages of plants emit and which do not. For example, cycads and ginkgo do not emit, but emission is common in conifers, ferns, and angiosperms. In addition to this large-scale pattern, there is a small-scale pattern in isoprene emission capacity. The best example is in the genus *Quercus*. All species endemic to North America emit isoprene, but a number of Eurasian species do not emit it (15, 48, 78). Other genera, such as *Picea*, also show a disjunct between North American species and Eurasian species as researchers have found for a number of flowering plant genera (163). Researchers believe this disjunct occurred 20 to 30 million years ago when a number of climatic changes caused the loss of land bridges that connected the Eurasian and American populations. Thus, we see both large-scale patterns that could have had their origins 200–300 million years ago and small-scale patterns that may have arisen 20–30 million (or fewer) years ago.

Paleoclimate

Climatic changes can be inferred from isotope and other geological records. In some cases, plant evolution can be interpreted in light of paleoclimatic changes. One of the best examples is the association of the evolution of the C_4 pathway of photosynthesis with lowered CO_2 and increased temperature that occurred between 10 and 30 million years ago (25). To make a similar analysis for isoprene, we must first consider the costs and benefits of isoprene emission. The cost is clearly the loss of carbon and energy needed for isoprene synthesis. The benefit can be assumed to be protection against short high-temperature episodes. Thus, when CO_2 is plentiful and the temperature is warm, the costs are less and the benefits more than when CO_2 levels and temperature are low.

The changes in CO_2, global temperature, and oxygen (which affects how costly the energy loss is because oxygen leads to photorespiration) were reconstructed from several models (4, 5, 6) (Figure 2). Two periods can be identified where the cost/benefit ratio for isoprene emission may have been high. When land plants first evolved, the CO_2 level and temperature were high while the oxygen level was less than the present day level of 20%. Under these conditions, isoprene emission may have been highly favored and, as argued by Hanson et al (45), possibly necessary

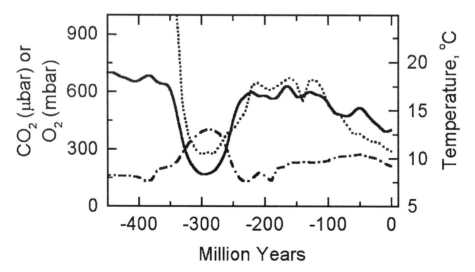

Figure 2 Possible levels of CO_2, O_2, and temperature over the time that land plants have existed. Derived from data of Berner (4, 5, 6). $CO_2 = \bullet\bullet\bullet\bullet\bullet\bullet\bullet$, $O_2 = -\bullet-\bullet$, temperature $= \rule{1cm}{0.4pt}$.

for the emergence of mosses. Because air has a very low heat capacity, as mosses started to grow up and away from the ground, they would be subject to large changes in temperature. Isoprene emission may have been required to cope with these large temperature changes.

During the Permian period, CO_2 levels were low, temperature was low, and oxygen levels were high. Therefore, the carbon and energy cost of isoprene was more important and the benefit (which occurs in high temperature) was less important. Perhaps during the Permian period, plant lineages that arose (e.g. cycads) (38) did not have the capability to emit isoprene because the cost benefit ratio was not favorable (Figure 3). By the time angiosperms evolved, the CO_2 level and temperature had gone back up and oxygen had gone back down. Many angiosperms have the capacity to make isoprene, and some researchers have argued that the first angiosperms had this ability (45); but this is not a universal view (48).

The CO_2 level fell and oxygen rose during the mid to late Miocene epoch of the Tertiary period ($\sim$5–20 million years ago), the time that C_4 plants are believed to have evolved. Perhaps a similar evolutionary pressure led to loss of isoprene emission capacity in some lineages of angiosperms (and other plant groups). Variation in loss of function during this period could lead to the evolution of certain groups within a genus that emit isoprene though other groups lack this trait, as seen in *Quercus*. In summary, the colonization of land by plants may have depended on the evolution of isoprene emission to cope with the low-heat capacity of air, but

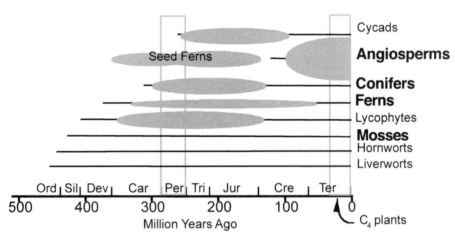

Figure 3 Relative abundances of major land plant groups (modified from Graham, 38).

then isoprene emission may have been lost in many land plants, especially during the Permian and Miocene (Figure 3).

FUTURE RESEARCH

From a physiological standpoint, the most important next step is to clone the isoprene synthase gene and study its regulation. This step will answer questions about metabolic regulation and provide tools for the further study of the regulation of isoprene emission capacity. The enzymes of the MEP pathway should also be studied in isoprene-emitting species. Because isoprene synthesis is perhaps 100 times faster than carotenoid synthesis, the regulation of the MEP pathway in isoprene-emitting species may be different from that in nonemitting species. How much regulation needs to be changed in order to change a nonemitting plant into an emitting plant and vice versa?

Studies are needed on the possible mechanisms by which isoprene can protect membranes against thermal stress. Whether thermotolerance is ultimately accepted as the driving force behind the evolution of isoprene synthesis in higher plants will depend on a clear understanding of its mechanism. These studies could lead to new discoveries concerning the effect of temperature on membranes.

Finally, additional work is needed to determine the complete MEP pathway. This could provide insight into why there are two independent pathways to make IPP. It would be interesting to know whether the lowered energy cost of the MEP pathway in photosynthetic organisms contributed to the evolution of this pathway.

ACKNOWLEDGMENTS

The National Science Foundation Integrative Plant Biology Program and the US Department of Agriculture National Research Initiative have supported this work. I thank Ray Fall, Deming Gong, Francesco Loreto, Eric Singsaas, Peter Vanderveer, and Mary Wildermuth for helpful reviews of the manuscript.

Visit the Annual Reviews home page at www.AnnualReviews.org

LITERATURE CITED

1. Arigoni D, Sagner S, Latzel C, Eisenreich W, Bacher A, Zenk MH. 1997. Terpenoid biosynthesis from 1-deoxy-D-xylulose in higher plants by intramolecular skeletal rearrangement. *Proc. Natl. Acad. Sci. USA* 94:10600–5
2. Atkinson R, Carter WPL. 1995. Kinetics and mechanisms of the gas-phase reactions of ozone with organic compounds under at-
mospheric conditions. *Chem. Rev.* 84:437–70
3. Baker B, Guenther A, Greenburg J, Goldstein A, Fall R. 1999. Canopy fluxes of 2-methyl-3-buten-2-ol over a ponderosa pine forest by relaxed eddy accumulation: Field data and model comparison. *J. Geophys. Res. Atmos.* 104:26107–14
4. Berner RA. 1991. A model for atmospheric

CO$_2$ over phanerozoic time. *Am. J. Sci.* 291:339–76

5. Berner RA. 1994. 3Geocarb II: a revised model of atmospheric CO$_2$ over phanerozoic time. *Am. J. Sci.* 294:56–91

6. Berner RA, Canfield DE. 1989. A new model for atmospheric oxygen over phanerozoic time. *Am. J. Sci.* 289:333–61

7. Bleasdale C, Small RD, Watson WP, Wilson J, Golding BT. 1996. Studies on the molecular toxicology of buta-1,3-diene and isoprene epoxides. *Toxicology* 113:290–93

8. Bonsang B, Polle C, Lambert G. 1992. Evidence for marine production of isoprene. *Geophys. Res. Lett.* 19:1129–32

9. Bukhov NG, Wiese C, Neimanis S, Heber U. 1999. Heat sensitivity of chloroplasts and leaves: leakage of protons from thylakoids and reversible activation of cyclic electron transport. *Photosynth. Res.* 59:81–93

10. Buschmann C. 1999. Thermal dissipation during photosynthetic induction and subsequent dark recovery as measured by photoacoustic signals. *Photosynthetica* 36:149–61

11. Cailleux A, Cogny M, Allain P. 1992. Blood isoprene concentrations in humans and in some animal species. *Biochem. Med. Metab. Biol.* 47:157–60

12. Chameides WL, Lindsay RW, Richardson J, Kiang CS. 1988. The role of biogenic hydrocarbons in urban photochemical smog: Atlanta as a case study. *Science* 241:1473–75

13. Cleveland CC, Yavitt JB. 1998. Microbial consumption of atmospheric isoprene in a temperate forest soil. *Appl. Environ. Microbiol.* 64:172–77

14. Conkle JP, Camp BJ, Welch BE. 1975. Trace composition of human respiratory gas. *Arch. Environ. Health* 30:290–95

15. Csiky O, Seufert G. 1999. Terpenoid emissions of Mediterranean oaks and their relation to taxonomy. *Ecol. Appl.* 9:1138–46

16. Dahl AR. 1996. Metabolism of isoprene in vivo. *Toxicology* 113:273–77

17. Dahl AR, Birnbaum LS, Bond JA, Gervasi PG, Henderson RF. 1987. The fate of isoprene inhaled by rats: comparison to butadiene. *Toxicol. Appl. Pharmacol.* 89:237–48

18. Daum PH, Kleinman LI, Nunnermacker LJ, Lee YN, Springston SR, et al. 2000. Analysis of O$_3$ formation during a stagnation episode in central Tennessee in summer 1995. *J. Geophys. Res. Atmos.* 105:9107–19

19. Delfine S, Csiky O, Seufert G, Loreto F. 2000. Fumigation with exogenous monoterpenes of a non-isoprenoid-emitting oak (*Quercus suber*): monoterpene acquisition, translocation, and effect on the photosynthetic properties at high temperatures. *New Phytol.* 146:27–36

20. Delwiche CF, Sharkey TD. 1993. Rapid appearance of ^{13}C in biogenic isoprene when ^{13}CO$_2$ is fed to intact leaves. *Plant Cell Environ.* 16:587–91

21. Demmig-Adams B, Adams WW III. 1992. Photoprotection and other responses of plants to high light stress. *Annu. Rev. Plant Physiol. Plant Mol. Biol.* 43:599–626

22. Deneris ES, Stein RA, Mead JF. 1985. Acid-catalyzed formation of isoprene from a mevalonate-derived product using a rat liver cytosolic fraction. *J. Biol. Chem.* 260:1382–85

23. DeNiro MJ, Epstein S. 1977. Mechanism of carbon isotope fractionation associated with lipid synthesis. *Science* 197:261–63

24. Ehleringer JR. 1991. Temperature and energy budgets. In *Plant Physiological Ecology*, ed. RW Pearcy, J Ehleringer, HA Mooney, PW Rundel, pp. 117–35. London: Chapman & Hall

25. Ehleringer JR, Cerling TE, Helliker BR. 1997. C$_4$ photosynthesis, atmospheric CO$_2$ and climate. *Oecologia* 112:285–99

26. Evans RC, Tingey DT, Gumpertz ML,

Burns WF. 1982. Estimates of isoprene and monoterpene emission rates in plants. *Bot. Gaz.* 143:304–10

27. Fall R, Copley SD. 2000. Bacterial sources and sinks of isoprene, a reactive atmospheric hydrocarbon. *Environ. Microbiol.* 2:123–30

28. Fall R, Monson RK. 1992. Isoprene emission rate and intercellular isoprene concentration as influenced by stomatal distribution and conductance. *Plant Physiol.* 100:987–92

29. Fall R, Wildermuth MC. 1998. Isoprene synthase: from biochemical mechanism to emission algorithm. *J. Geophys. Res.* 103:25599–609

30. Farquhar GD, Von Caemmerer S. 1982. Modelling of photosynthetic response to environmental conditions. In *Encyclopedia of Plant Physiology NS. Vol. 12B. Physiological Plant Ecology II Water Relations and Carbon Assimilation*, ed. OL Lange, PS Nobel, CB Osmond, H Ziegler, pp. 549–87. Berlin: Springer-Verlag

31. Fehsenfeld FC, Calvert J, Fall R, Goldan P, Guenther AB, et al. 1992. Emissions of volatile organic compounds from vegetation and the implications for atmospheric chemistry. *Global Biogeochem. Cycles* 6:389–430

32. Fuentes JD, Lerdau M, Atkinson R, Baldocchi D, Botteneheim JW, et al. 2000. Biogenic hydrocarbons in the atmospheric boundary layer: a review. *Bull. Am. Meteorol. Soc.* 81:1537–75

33. Fuentes JD, Wang D. 1999. On the seasonality of isoprene emission from a mixed temperate forest. *Ecol. Appl.* 9:1118–31

34. Fuentes JD, Wang D, Gu L. 1999. Seasonality variations in isoprene emissions from a boreal aspen forest. *J. Appl. Meteorol.* 38:855–69

35. Funk JL, Jones CG, Lerdau MT. 1999. Defoliation effects on isoprene emission from *Populus*. *Oecologia* 118:333–39

36. Gelmont D, Stein RA, Mead JF. 1981. Isoprene—the main hydrocarbon in human breath. *Biochem. Biophys. Res. Commun.* 99:1456–60

37. Gounaris K, Brain APR, Quinn PJ, Williams WP. 1984. Structural reorganization of chloroplast thylakoid membranes in response to heat stress. *Biochim. Biophys. Acta* 766:198–208

38. Graham LE. 1993. *Origin of Land Plants.* New York: Wiley

39. Grinspoon J, Bowman WD, Fall R. 1991. Delayed onset of isoprene emission in developing velvet bean (*Mucuna* sp.) leaves. *Plant Physiol.* 97:170–74

40. Guenther A. 1997. Seasonal and spatial variations in natural volatile organic compound emissions. *Ecol. Appl.* 7:34–45

41. Guenther A, Hewitt CN, Erickson D, Fall R, Geron C, et al. 1995. A global model of natural volatile organic compound emissions. *J. Geophys. Res.* 100:8873–92

42. Guenther AB, Monson RK, Fall R. 1991. Isoprene and monoterpene emission rate variability: observations with Eucalyptus and emission rate algorithm development. *J. Geophys. Res.* 96:10799–808

43. Guenther AB, Zimmerman PR, Harley PC. 1993. Isoprene and monoterpene emission rate variability: model evaluations and sensitivity analysis. *J. Geophys. Res.* 98:12609–17

44. Haagen-Smit AJ. 1952. Chemistry and physiology of Los Angeles smog. *Ind. Eng. Chem.* 44:1342–46

45. Hanson DT, Swanson S, Graham LE, Sharkey TD. 1999. Evolutionary significance of isoprene emission from mosses. *Am. J. Bot.* 86:634–39

46. Harley PC, Guenther AB, Zimmerman PR. 1996. Effects of light, temperature and canopy position on net photosynthesis and isoprene emission from sweetgum (*Liquidambar styraciflua*) leaves. *Tree Physiol.* 16:25–32

47. Harley PC, Litvak ME, Sharkey TD, Monson RK. 1994. Isoprene emission from velvet bean leaves. Interactions among nitrogen availability, growth photon flux

density, and leaf development. *Plant Physiol.* 105:279–85

48. Harley PC, Monson RK, Lerdau MT. 1999. Ecological and evolutionary aspects of isoprene emission from plants. *Oecologia* 118:109–23

49. Hewitt CN, Kok GL, Fall R. 1990. Hydroperoxides in plants exposed to ozone mediate air pollution damage to alkene emitters. *Nature* 344:56–58

50. Hewitt CN, Monson RK, Fall R. 1990. Isoprene emissions from the grass *Arundo donax* L. are not linked to photorespiration. *Plant Sci.* 66:139–44

51. Hill RE, Himmeldirk K, Kennedy IA, Pauloski RM, Sayer BG, et al. 1996. The biogenetic anatomy of vitamin B_6: a ^{13}C NMR investigation of the biosynthesis of pyridoxol in *Escherichia coli*. *J. Biol. Chem.* 271:30426–35

52. Hyspler R, Crhová S, Gasparic J, Zadák Z, Cízková M, Balasová V. 2000. Determination of isoprene in human expired breath using solid-phase microextraction and gas chromatography-mass spectrometry. *J. Chromatogr. B* 739:183–90

53. Jacob DJ, Wofsy SC. 1988. Photochemistry of biogenic emissions over the Amazon forest. *J. Geophys. Res.* 93:1477–86

54. Jones CA, Rasmussen RA. 1975. Production of isoprene by leaf tissue. *Plant Physiol.* 55:982–87

55. Kaufman PB, Cseke LJ, Warber S, Duke JA, Brielmann HL. 1999. *Natural Products from Plants*. Boca Raton, FL: CRC Press. 343 pp.

56. Keller M, Lerdau M. 1999. Isoprene emission from tropical forest canopy leaves. *Global Biogeochem. Cycles* 13:19–29

57. Kesselmeier J, Staudt M. 1999. Biogenic volatile organic compounds (VOC): an overview on emission, physiology and ecology. *J. Atmos. Chem.* 33:23–88

58. Kreuzwieser J, Schnitzler J-P, Steinbrecher R. 2000. Biosynthesis of organic compounds emitted by plants. *Plant Biol.* 1:149–59

59. Kuzma J, Fall R. 1993. Leaf isoprene emission rate is dependent on leaf development and the level of isoprene synthase. *Plant Physiol.* 101:435–40

60. Kuzma J, Nemecek-Marshall M, Pollock WH, Fall R. 1995. Bacteria produce the volatile hydrocarbon isoprene. *Curr. Microbiol.* 30:97–103

61. Kuzuyama T, Shimizu T, Takahashi S, Seto H. 1998. Fosmidomycin, a specific inhibitor of 1-deoxy-D-xylulose 5-phosphate reductoisomerase in the nonmevalonate pathway for terpenoid biosynthesis. *Tetrahedron Lett.* 39:7913–16

62. Kuzuyama T, Takagi M, Kaneda K, Dairi T, Seto H. 2000. Formation of 4-(cytidine 5′-diphospho)-2-*C*-methyl-D-erythritol from 2-*C*-methyl-D-erythritol 4-phosphate by 2-*C*-methyl-D-erythritol 4-phosphate cytidylyltransferase, a new enzyme in the nonmevalonate pathway. *Tetrahedron Lett.* 41:703–6

63. Kuzuyama T, Takagi M, Kaneda K, Watanabe H, Dairi T, Seto H. 2000. Studies on the nonmevalonate pathway: conversion of 4-(cytidine 5′-diphospho)-2-*C*-methyl-D-erythritol to its 2-phospho derivative by 4-(cytidine 5′-diphospho)-2-*C*-methyl-D-erythritol kinase. *Tetrahedron Lett.* 41:2925–28

64. Leaitch WR, Bottenheim JW, Biesenthal TA, Li SM, Liu PSK, et al. 1999. A case study of gas-to-particle conversion in an eastern Canadian forest. *J. Geophys. Res. Atmos.* 104:8095–111

65. Lehning A, Zimmer I, Steinbrecher R, Brüggemann N, Schnitzler JP. 1999. Isoprene synthase activity and its relation to isoprene emission in *Quercus robur* L-leaves. *Plant Cell Environ.* 22:495–504

66. Lerdau M. 1991. Plant function and biogenic terpene emissions. In *Trace Gas Emissions from Plants*, ed. TD Sharkey, EA Holland, HA Mooney, pp. 121–34. San Diego, CA: Academic

67. Lerdau M, Guenther A, Monson R. 1997. Plant production and emission of volatile

organic compounds. *BioScience* 47:373–83

68. Lerdau M, Keller M. 1997. Controls on isoprene emission from trees in a subtropical dry forest. *Plant Cell Environ.* 20:569–78

69. Lichtenthaler HK. 1999. The 1-deoxy-D-xylulose-5-phosphate pathway of isoprenoid biosynthesis in plants. *Annu. Rev. Plant Physiol. Plant Mol. Biol.* 50:47–65

70. Lichtenthaler HK, Schwender J, Disch A, Rohmer M. 1997. Biosynthesis of isoprenoids in higher plant chloroplasts proceeds via a mevalonate-independent pathway. *FEBS Lett.* 400:271–74

71. Litvak ME, Loreto F, Harley PC, Sharkey TD, Monson RK. 1996. The response of isoprene emission rate and photosynthetic rate to photon flux and nitrogen supply in aspen and white oak trees. *Plant Cell Environ.* 19:549–59

72. Litvak ME, Madronich S, Monson RK. 1998. The potential impact of herbivore-induced monoterpene emissions from coniferous forests on local tropospheric chemistry dynamics. *Ecol. Appl.* 9:1147–59

73. Logan BA, Monson RK. 1999. Thermotolerance of leaf discs from four isoprene-emitting species is not enhanced by exposure to exogenous isoprene. *Plant Physiol.* 120:821–25

73a. Logan BA, Monson RK, Potosnak MJ. 2000. Biochemistry and physiology of foliar isoprene production. *Trends Plant Sci.* 5:477–81

74. Loomis WD, Croteau R. 1980. Biochemistry of Terpenoids. In *The Biochemistry of Plants. Vol. 4. Lipids: Structure and Function*, ed. PK Stumpf, pp. 363–418. New York: Academic

75. Loreto F. 1997. Emission of isoprenoids by plants: their role in atmospheric chemistry, response to the environment, and biochemical pathways. *J. Environ. Pathol. Toxicol. Oncol.* 16:119–24

76. Loreto F, Ciccioli P, Brancaleoni E, Cecinato A. 1998. Measurement of isoprenoid content in leaves of Mediterranean *Quercus* spp. by a novel and sensitive method and estimation of the isoprenoid partition between liquid and gas phase inside the leaves. *Plant Sci.* 136:25–30

77. Loreto F, Ciccioli P, Brancaleoni E, Cecinato A, Frattoni M, Sharkey TD. 1996. Different sources of reduced carbon contribute to form three classes of terpenoid emitted by *Quercus ilex* L leaves. *Proc. Natl. Acad. Sci. USA* 93:9966–69

78. Loreto F, Ciccioli P, Brancaleoni E, Valentini R, De Lillis M., et al. 1998. A hypothesis on the evolution of isoprenoid emission by oaks based on the correlation between emission type and *Quercus* taxonomy. *Oecologia* 115:302–5

79. Loreto F, Ciccioli P, Cecinato A, Brancaleoni E, Frattoni M, et al. 1996. Evidence of the photosynthetic origin of monoterpenes emitted by *Quercus ilex* L. leaves by ^{13}C labeling. *Plant Physiol.* 110:1317–22

80. Loreto F, Förster A, Dürr M, Csiky O, Seufert G. 1998. On the monoterpene emission under heat stress and on the increased thermotolerance of leaves of *Quercus ilex* L. fumigated with selected monoterpenes. *Plant Cell Environ.* 21:101–7

81. Loreto F, Nascetti P, Graverini A, Mannozzi M. 2000. Emission and content of monoterpenes in intact and wounded needles of the Mediterranean pine, *Pinus pinea. Funct. Ecol.* 14:589–95

82. Loreto F, Sharkey TD. 1990. A gas-exchange study of photosynthesis and isoprene emission in *Quercus rubra* L. *Planta* 182:523–31

83. Loreto F, Sharkey TD. 1993. Isoprene emission by plants is affected by transmissible wound signals. *Plant Cell Environ.* 16:563–70

84. Loreto F, Sharkey TD. 1993. On the relationship between isoprene emission and photosynthetic metabolites under different environmental conditions. *Planta* 189:420–24

85. Loudon GM. 1988. *Organic Chemistry.* Menlo Park, CA: Benjamin Cummings. 1259 pp.

86. MacDonald RC, Fall R. 1993. Acetone emission from conifer buds. *Phytochemistry* 34:991–94

87. MacDonald RC, Fall R. 1993. Detection of substantial emissions of methanol from plants to the atmosphere. *Atmos. Environ.* A27:1709–13

88. McCaskill D, Croteau R. 1999. Isopentenyl diphosphate is the terminal product of the deoxyxylulose-5-phosphate pathway for terpenoid biosynthesis in plants. *Tetrahedron Lett.* 40:653–56

89. Melnick RL, Sills RC, Roycroft JH, Chou BJ, Ragan HA, Miller RA. 1996. Inhalation toxicity and carcinogenicity of isoprene in rats and mice: comparisons with 1,3-butadiene. *Toxicology* 113:247–52

90. Mgaloblishvili MP, Khetsuriana ND, Kalandaze AN, Sanadze GA. 1979. Localization of isoprene biosynthesis in poplar leaf chloroplasts. *Sov. Plant Physiol.* 26:837–42

91. Monson RK, Fall R. 1989. Isoprene emission from aspen leaves. The influence of environment and relation to photosynthesis and photorespiration. *Plant Physiol.* 90:267–74

92. Monson RK, Harley PC, Litvak ME, Wildermuth M, Guenther AB, et al. 1994. Environmental and developmental controls over the seasonal pattern of isoprene emission from aspen leaves. *Oecologia* 99:260–70

93. Monson RK, Jaeger CH, Adams WW III, Driggers EM, Silver GM, Fall R. 1992. Relationships among isoprene emission rate, photosynthesis, and isoprene synthase activity as influenced by temperature. *Plant Physiol.* 98:1175–80

94. Monson RK, Lerdau MT, Sharkey TD, Schimel DS, Fall R. 1995. Biological aspects of constructing volatile organic compound emission inventories. *Atmos. Environ.* 29:2989–3002

95. Nemecek-Marshall M, MacDonald RC, Franzen JJ, Wojciechowski CL, Fall R. 1995. Methanol emission from leaves. Enzymatic detection of gas-phase methanol and relation of methanol fluxes to stomatal conductance and leaf development. *Plant Physiol.* 108:1359–68

96. Niinemets Ü, Tenhunen JD, Harley PC, Steinbrecher R. 1999. A model of isoprene emission based on energetic requirements for isoprene synthesis and leaf photosynthetic properties for *Liquidambar* and *Quercus. Plant Cell Environ.* 22:1319–35

97. Pastenes C, Horton P. 1996. Effect of high temperature on photosynthesis in beans .1. Oxygen evolution and chlorophyll fluorescence. *Plant Physiol.* 112:1245–51

98. Peter H, Wiegand HJ, Bolt HM, Greim H, Walter G, et al. 1987. Pharmacokinetics of isoprene in mice and rats. *Toxicol. Lett.* 36:9–14

99. Pierce T, Waldruff P. 1991. A personal computer version of the biogenic emissions inventory system. *J. Air Waste Manag. Assoc.* 41:937–41

100. Pope C. 1980. The candidates and the issues. *Sierra* 65:15–17

101. Qiu Y-L, Cho Y, Cox JC, Palmer JD. 1998. The gain of three mitochondrial introns identifies liverworts as the earliest land plants. *Nature* 394:671–74

102. Rasmussen RA. 1970. Isoprene: identified as a forest-type emission to the atmosphere. *Environ. Sci. Technol.* 4:667–71

103. Rasmussen RA. 1972. What do the hydrocarbons from trees contribute to air pollution. *J. Air Pollut. Control Assoc.* 22:537–43

104. Rasmussen RA, Jones CA. 1973. Emission isoprene from leaf discs of *Hamamelis. Phytochemistry* 12:15–19

105. Rasmussen RA, Khalil MAK. 1988. Isoprene over the amazon basin. *J. Geophys. Res.* 93:1417–21

106. Rasmussen RA, Went FW. 1965. Volatile

organic material of plant origin in the atmosphere. *Proc. Natl. Acad. Sci. USA* 53:215–20

107. Rodríguez-Concepción M, Campos N, Lois LM, Maldonado C, Hoeffler JF, et al. 2000. Genetic evidence of branching in the isoprenoid pathway for the production of isopentenyl diphosphate and dimethylallyl diphosphate in *Escherichia coli. FEBS Lett.* 473:328–32

108. Rohmer M. 1993. The biosynthesis of triterpenoids of the hopane series in the Eubacteria: a mine of new enzyme reactions. *Pure Appl. Chem.* 65:1293–98

109. Rohmer M, Knani M, Simonin P, Sahm H. 1993. Isoprenoid biosynthesis in bacteria: A novel pathway for the early steps leading to isopentenyl diphosphate. *Biochem. J.* 295:517–24

110. Sage RF. 1990. A model describing the regulation of ribulose-1,5-bisphosphate carboxylase, electron transport, and triose phosphate use in response to light intensity and CO_2 in C_3 plants. *Plant Physiol.* 94:1728–34

111. Saltman WM. 1981. Isoprene. In *Kirk-Othmer Encyclopedia of Chemical Technology*, ed. RE Kirk, DF Othmer, M Grayson, DV Eckroth, pp. 818–37. New York: Wiley

112. Sanadze GA. 1969. Light-dependent excretion of molecular isoprene. *Prog. Photosyn. Res.* 2:701–6

113. Sanadze GA. 1991. Isoprene effect-light dependent emission of isoprene by green parts of plants. See Ref. 129a, pp. 135–52

114. Sanadze GA, Dzhaiani GI, Baazov DI, Khakhubiya GT, Ebralidze SS, Gvantseladze LG. 1976. Probability-statistical model of distribution of the carbon of $^{13}CO_2$ in the isoprene molecule during photosynthesis. *Sov. Plant Physiol.* 23:580–86

115. Sanadze GA, Dzhaiani GI, Tevzadze IM. 1972. Incorporation into the isoprene molecule of carbon from $^{13}CO_2$ assim-ilated during photosynthesis. *Sov. Plant Physiol.* 19:17–20

116. Sanadze GA, Kalandaze AN. 1966. Light and temperature curves of the evolution of C_5H_8. *Fiziol. Rast.* 13:458–61

117. Sanadze GA, Kursanov AL. 1966. On certain conditions of the evolution of the diene C_5H_8 from poplar leaves. *Sov. Plant Physiol.* 13:184–89

118. Schnitzler J-P, Arenz R, Steinbrecher R, Lehning A. 1996. Characterization of an isoprene synthase from leaves of *Quercus petraea* (Mattuschka) Liebl. *Bot. Acta* 109:216–21

119. Schulze-Siebert D, Heintze A, Schultz G. 1987. Substrate flow from photosynthetic carbon metabolism to chloroplast isoprenoid synthesis in spinach evidence for a plastidic phosphoglycerate mutase. *Z. Naturforsch.* 42 *Teil* C:570–80

120. Schwender J, Zeidler J, Gröner R, Müller C, Focke M, et al. 1997. Incorporation of 1-deoxy-D-xylulose into isoprene and phytol by higher plants and algae. *FEBS Lett.* 414:129–34

121. Seemann JR, Berry JA, Downton WJS. 1984. Photosynthetic response and adaptation to high temperature in desert plants: a comparison of gas exchange and fluorescence methods for studies of thermal tolerance. *Plant Physiol.* 75:364–68

122. Seinfeld JH, Atkinson R, Berglund RL, Chameides WL, Cotton WR, et al. 1991. *Rethinking the Ozone Problem in Urban and Regional Air Pollution.* Washington, DC: Natl. Acad. Press.

123. Shah SPJ, Rogers LJ. 1969. Compartmentation of terpenoid biosynthesis in green plants. *Biochem. J.* 114:395–405

124. Sharkey TD. 1985. O_2-insensitive photosynthesis in C_3 plants. Its occurrence and a possible explanation. *Plant Physiol.* 78:71–75

125. Sharkey TD. 1989. Evaluating the role of rubisco regulation in C_3 photosynthesis. *Philos. Trans. R. Soc. London Ser. B* 323:435–48

126. Sharkey TD. 1990. Feedback limitation of photosynthesis and the physiological role of ribulose bisphosphate carboxylase carbamylation. *Bot. Mag. Tokyo* 2:87–105

127. Sharkey TD. 1991. Stomatal control of trace gas emissions. See Ref. 129a, pp. 335–39

128. Sharkey TD. 1996. Isoprene synthesis by plants and animals. *Endeavor* 20:74–78

129. Sharkey TD, Chen X, Yeh S. 2001. Isoprene increases thermotolerance of fosmidomycin-fed leaves. *Plant Physiol.* In press

129a. Sharkey TD, Holland EA, Mooney HA, eds. 1991 *Trace Gas Emissions by Plants.* San Diego, CA: Academic

130. Sharkey TD, Loreto F. 1993. Water stress, temperature, and light effects on the capacity for isoprene emission and photosynthesis of kudzu leaves. *Oecologia* 95:328–33

131. Sharkey TD, Loreto F, Delwiche CF. 1991. High carbon dioxide and sun/shade effects on isoprene emission from oak and aspen tree leaves. *Plant Cell Environ.* 14:333–38

132. Sharkey TD, Loreto F, Delwiche CF. 1991. The biochemistry of isoprene emission from leaves during photosynthesis. See Ref. 129a, pp. 153–84

133. Sharkey TD, Loreto F, Delwiche CF, Treichel IW. 1991. Fractionation of carbon isotopes during biogenesis of atmospheric isoprene. *Plant Physiol.* 97:463–66

134. Sharkey TD, Singsaas EL. 1995. Why plants emit isoprene. *Nature* 374:769

135. Sharkey TD, Singsaas EL, Lerdau MT, Geron C. 1999. Weather effects on isoprene emission capacity and applications in emissions algorithms. *Ecol. Appl.* 9:1132–37

136. Sharkey TD, Singsaas EL, Vanderveer PJ, Geron CD. 1996. Field measurements of isoprene emission from trees in response to temperature and light. *Tree Physiol.* 16:649–54

137. Sharkey TD, Stitt M, Heineke D, Gerhardt R, Raschke K, Heldt HW. 1986. Limitation of photosynthesis by carbon metabolism. II O_2 insensitive CO_2 uptake results from limitation of triose phosphate utilization. *Plant Physiol.* 81:1123–29

138. Silver GM, Fall R. 1991. Enzymatic synthesis of isoprene from dimethylallyl diphosphate in aspen leaf extracts. *Plant Physiol.* 97:1588–91

139. Silver GM, Fall R. 1995. Characterization of aspen isoprene synthase, an enzyme responsible for leaf isoprene emission to the atmosphere. *J. Biol. Chem.* 270:13010–16

140. Singsaas EL, Laporte MM, Shi J-Z, Monson RK, Bowling DR, et al. 1999. Leaf temperature fluctuation affects isoprene emission from red oak (*Quercus rubra*) leaves. *Tree Physiol.* 19:917–24

141. Singsaas EL, Lerdau M, Winter K, Sharkey TD. 1997. Isoprene increases thermotolerance of isoprene-emitting species. *Plant Physiol.* 115:1413–20

142. Singsaas EL, Sharkey TD. 1998. The regulation of isoprene emission responses to rapid leaf temperature fluctuations. *Plant Cell Environ.* 21:1181–88

143. Singsaas EL, Sharkey TD. 2000. The effects of high temperature on isoprene synthesis in oak leaves. *Plant Cell Environ.* 23:751–57

144. Sprenger GA, Schörken U, Wiegert T, Grolle S, de Graaf AA, et al. 1997. Identification of a thiamin-dependent synthase in *Escherichia coli* required for the formation of the 1-deoxy-D-xylulose 5-phosphate precursor to isoprenoids, thiamin, and pyridoxol. *Proc. Natl. Acad. Sci. USA* 94:12857–62

145. Staudt M, Bertin N. 1998. Light and temperature dependence of the emission of cyclic and acyclic monoterpenes from holm oak (*Quercus ilex* L.) leaves. *Plant Cell Environ.* 21:385–95

146. Steinbrecher R, Hauff K, Rabong R,

Steinbrecher J. 1997. Isoprenoid emission of oak species typical for the Mediterranean area: source strength and controlling variables. *Atmos. Environ.* 31:79–88

147. Stokes NJ, Terry GM, Hewitt CN. 1998. The impact of ozone, isoprene and propene on antioxidant levels in two leaf classes of velvet bean (*Mucuna pruriens* L.). *J. Exp. Bot.* 49:115–23

148. Takagi M, Kuzuyama T, Kaneda K, Watanabe H, Dairi T, Seto H. 2000. Studies on the nonmevalonate pathway: formation of 2-*C*-methyl-D-erythritol 2,4-cyclodiphosphate from 2-phospho-4-(cytidine 5′-diphospho)-2-*C*-methyl-D-erythritol. *Tetrahedron Lett.* 41:3395–98

149. Taucher J, Hansel A, Jordan A, Fall R, Futrell JH, Lindinger W. 1997. Detection of isoprene in expired air from human subjects using proton- transfer-reaction mass spectrometry. *Rapid. Commun. Mass. Spectrom.* 11:1230–34

150. Terry GM, Stokes NJ, Hewitt CN, Mansfield TA. 1995. Exposure to isoprene promotes flowering in plants. *J. Exp. Bot.* 46:1629–31

151. Thompson AM. 1992. The oxidizing capacity of the Earth's atmosphere: probable past and future changes. *Science* 256:1157–65

152. Tilden WA. 1882. *Chem. News* 46:120

153. Tingey DT, Evans R, Gumpertz M. 1981. Effects of environmental conditions on isoprene emission from live oak. *Planta* 152:565–70

154. Tingey DT, Manning M, Grothaus LC, Burns WF. 1979. The influence of light and temperature on isoprene emission rates from live oak. *Physiol. Plant.* 47:112–18

155. Tingey DT, Manning M, Grothaus LC, Burns WF. 1980. Influence of light and temperature on monoterpene emission rates from slash pine. *Plant Physiol.* 65:797–801

156. Tingey DT, Turner DP, Weber JA. 1991. Factors controlling the emissions of

monoterpenes and other volatile organic compounds. See Ref. 129a, pp. 93–119

157. Trainer M, Williams EJ, Parrish DD, Buhr MP, Allwine EJ, et al. 1987. Models and observations of the impact of natural hydrocarbons on rural ozone. *Nature* 329:705–7

158. Tuazon EC, Atkinson R. 1990. A product study of the gas-phase reaction of isoprene with OH radical in the presence of NO_x. *Int. J. Chem. Kin.* 22:1221–36

159. Vickery ML, Vickery B. 1981. *Secondary Plant Metabolism.* Baltimore: University Park. 335 pp.

160. Wagner WP, Helmig D, Fall R. 2000. Isoprene biosynthesis in *Bacillus subtilis* via the methylerythritol phosphate pathway. *J. Nat. Prod.* 63:37–40

161. Wagner WP, Nemecek-Marshall M, Fall R. 1999. Three distinct phases of isoprene formation during growth and sporulation of *Bacillus subtilis. J. Bacteriol.* 181:4700–3

162. Wang KY, Shallcross DE. 2000. Modelling terrestrial biogenic isoprene fluxes and their potential impact on global chemical species using a coupled LSM-CTM model. *Atmos. Environ.* 34:2909–25

163. Wen J. 1999. Evolution of Eastern Asian and Eastern North American disjunct distributions in flowering plants. *Annu. Rev. Ecol. Syst.* 30:421–55

164. Went FW. 1960. Blue hazes in the atmosphere. *Nature* 187:641–43

165. Wildermuth MC. 1997. *Subcellular location and biophysical regulation of foliar isoprene production (chloroplasts).* PhD thesis. Univ. Colo. Boulder. 307 pp.

166. Wildermuth MC, Fall R. 1996. Light-dependent isoprene emission - characterization of a thylakoid-bound isoprene synthase in *Salix discolor* chloroplasts. *Plant Physiol.* 112:171–82

167. Wildermuth MC, Fall R. 1998. Biochemical characterization of stromal and thylakoid-bound isoforms of isoprene

synthase in willow leaves. *Plant Physiol.* 116:1111–23

168. Williams J, Roberts JM, Fehsenfeld FC, Bertman SB, Buhr MP, et al. 1997. Regional ozone from biogenic hydrocarbons deduced from measurements of PAN, PPN, and MPAN. *Geophys. Res. Lett.* 24:1099–102

169. Yokuchi Y, Li HJ, Machida T. 1999. Isoprene in the marine boundary layer (Southeast Asian Sea, Eastern Indian Ocean, and Southern Ocean): Comparison with dimethyl sulfide and bromoform. *J. Geophys. Res. Atmos.* 104:8067–76

170. Zeidler J, Schwender J, Müller C, Wiesner J, Weidemeyer C, et al. 1998. Inhibition of the non-mevalonate 1-deoxy-D-xylulose-5-phosphate pathway of plant isoprenoid biosynthesis by fosmidomycin. *Z. Naturforsch. Teil C* 53:980–86

171. Zeidler JG, Lichtenthaler HK, May HU, Lichtenthaler FW. 1997. Is isoprene emitted by plants synthesized via the novel isopentenyl pyrophosphate pathway? *Z. Naturforsch. Teil C* 52:15–23

172. Zhang XS, Mu YJ, Song WZ, Zhuang YH. 2000. Seasonal variations of isoprene emissions from deciduous trees. *Atmos. Environ.* 34:3027–32

173. Zimmer W, Brüggemann N, Emeis S, Giersch C, Lehning A, et al. 2000. Process-based modelling of isoprene emission by oak leaves. *Plant Cell Environ.* 23:585–95

174. Zimmerman PR. 1979. Determination of emission rates of hydrocarbons from indigenous species of vegetation in the Tampa/St. Petersburg Florida area. *EPA* 904/977:1–104

NOTE ADDED IN PROOF

The DNA sequence for the gene encoding isoprene synthase has now been determined independently by W Zimmer and D Gong and TD Sharkey. The gene is similar to limonene synthases of many species. There is no similar gene in any of the bacterial genomes or the human genome, consistent with the idea that plant isoprene emission is unrelated to that of bacteria and humans.

Annu. Rev. Plant Physiol. Plant Mol. Biol. 2001. 52:437–67

BIOSYNTHESIS OF ASCORBIC ACID IN PLANTS: A Renaissance

Nicholas Smirnoff

School of Biological Sciences, University of Exeter, Hatherly Laboratories, Prince of Wales Road, Exeter, EX4 4PS, United Kingdom; e-mail: N.Smirnoff@exeter.ac.uk

Patricia L Conklin[1]

Boyce Thompson Institute for Plant Research at Cornell University, Tower Road, Ithaca, NY 14853; e-mail: plc3@cornell.edu

Frank A Loewus

Institute of Biological Chemistry, Washington State University, P.O. Box 646340, Pullman, WA 99164-6340; e-mail: loewus@mail.wsu.edu

Key Words *Arabidopsis thaliana*, erythroascorbic acid, fungi, L-galactose, genetics, mannose, oxalate

■ **Abstract** The structure of the familiar antioxidant L-ascorbic acid (vitamin C) was described in 1933 yet remarkably, its biosynthesis in plants remained elusive until only recently. It became clear from radioisotopic labeling studies in the 1950s that plant ascorbic acid biosynthesis does not proceed in toto via a route similar to that in mammals. The description in 1996 of an *Arabidopsis thaliana* mutant deficient in ascorbic acid prompted renewed research effort in this area, and subsequently in 1998 a new pathway was discovered that is backed by strong biochemical and molecular genetic evidence. This pathway proceeds through the intermediates GDP-D-mannose, L-galactose, and L-galactono-1,4-lactone. Much research has focused on the properties of the terminal enzyme responsible for conversion of the aldonolactone to ascorbate, and on related enzymes in both mammals and fungi. Two of the plant biosynthetic genes have been studied at the molecular level and additional ascorbate-deficient *A. thaliana* mutants may hold the key to other proteins involved in plant ascorbate metabolism. An analysis of the biosynthesis of ascorbate and its analogues in algae and fungi as well as the study of alternative proposed pathways should broaden our understanding of ascorbate metabolism in plants. With a biosynthetic pathway in hand, research on areas such as the control of ascorbate biosynthesis and the physiological roles of ascorbate should progress rapidly.

---

[1]Current address: SUNY-Cortland, 223 Bowers Hall, Cortland, NY 13045.

CONTENTS

INTRODUCTION

Understanding ascorbic acid (AA) biosynthesis is of interest for two major reasons. First, it is a key component of the plant antioxidant system and it has a number of other proposed physiological roles. Second, plants provide the major source of dietary vitamin C for humans. Functions of AA in plants include its role as an antioxidant (114, 146–149, 152). Its efficiency as an antioxidant may rest on the relative stability of the monodehydroascorbate radical (152). It is a cofactor for violaxanthin de-epoxidase (148) and dioxygenase type enzymes involved in the synthesis of hydroxyproline (2), ethylene, gibberellic acid, anthocyanins, and a number of other secondary metabolites (27, 151, 152). AA and cell wall–localized ascorbate oxidase are suggested to be involved in cell division and growth (48, 147). As the functions of AA and the reactions concerned with regenerating it from its two oxidized forms, monodehydroascorbate and dehydroascorbate, have been extensively reviewed (114, 147, 152), these aspects are not considered here.

Despite its multitude of functions, knowledge of AA biosynthesis has remained very incomplete until recently. In the mid-1990s, our understanding of AA biosynthesis in plants underwent a renaissance when Conklin & Last (17, 21) isolated ozone-hypersensitive mutants of Arabidopsis thaliana that were AA-deficient. Their observations led to re-evaluation of AA biosynthesis in plants (19) and shortly thereafter, to discovery of a functional pathway of AA biosynthesis (18, 166). The purpose of this review is to assess recent advances in the understanding of the pathway and control of AA biosynthesis in plants and to attempt to anticipate future developments.

HISTORICAL PERSPECTIVE

Isolation of vitamin C from plant and mammalian sources, crystallization of the physiologically active compound, and evidence to show that vitamin C and the crystalline compound were in reality the same substance were accomplished in 1932 (159, 162, 165). Scarcely a year later, the structure of vitamin C, now assigned the trivial term *ascorbic acid*, was established as L-*threo*-hex-2-enono-1,4-lactone (46) and its synthesis was achieved (4, 132). Industrial production of AA, which quickly followed [reviewed in (24)], provided access to an unlimited supply of this vitamin and opened new avenues for exploration of its physiological, biochemical, and biomedical properties.

Early studies on rats stimulated by Chloretone to increase their urinary excretion of AA and then injected interperitoneally with [1-^{14}C]Glc or [6-^{14}C]Glc (Glc = D-glucose) resulted in excretion of labeled AA with a major portion of the [^{14}C]AA in C6 or C1, respectively, i.e. an "inversion" of the carbon skeleton (13, 50, 51). This observation of carbon chain "inversion" during AA biosynthesis in the rat was further supported by a study involving interperitoneal injection of [2-^{14}C]Glc in a normal rat, excision of the liver, and isolation of both AA and glycogen-derived Glc from this tissue. The greatest fraction of ^{14}C in AA was in C5 whereas it remained in C2 in glycogen-derived Glc (91), results supporting a biosynthetic pathway from Glc to AA with preservation of the carbon chain of Glc and "inverse numbering" of that carbon chain due to reduction at C1 and oxidation at C6. Further studies led to the following scheme of AA biosynthesis in the rat (12):

$$D\text{-Glc} \dashrightarrow D\text{-Glucuronic acid} \rightarrow L\text{-Gulonic acid}$$
$$\rightarrow L\text{-Gulono-1,4-lactone} \rightarrow AA$$

In 1954, Isherwood et al (55) proposed a scheme analogous to that from the rat study for AA biosynthesis in plants. They based their scheme on the finding that cress seedlings (*Lepidium sativum* L.) readily oxidized L-galactono-1,4-lactone (GalL) to AA and they invoked a D-galacto/L-galacto transition as the basic difference between the animal and plant pathways:

$$D\text{-Galactose} \dashrightarrow D\text{-Galacturonate} \rightarrow L\text{-Galactonate} \rightarrow L\text{-GalL} \rightarrow AA$$

Although it was assumed that the initial step involved oxidation of D-galactose, this premise was not tested and these investigators did not undertake radiotracer studies. Subsequently, Loewus et al (85) did undertake such studies and found that conversion proceeded directly, i.e. without inversion of the carbon chain of D-Glc. Details of these experiments and related studies have been reviewed previously (80–82, 94).

A critical reassessment of AA function and metabolism reset experimental efforts to resolve the matter of AA biosynthesis in plants (19, 146). This involved at least three separate considerations. First, reappraisal of a proposed pathway (97, 139) involving the osones, D-glucosone and L-sorbosone, which had been invoked to explain labeling data supporting noninversion of the hexose precursor (19, 122); second, isolation of a semidominant ozone-sensitive *A. thaliana* mutant *soz1* (renamed *vtc1*) that accumulates only 30% of the AA concentration of wild-type plants (19, 21); and finally, discovery of a rational scheme for AA biosynthesis in plants that accommodates all experimental observations previously garnered from enzymatic and radiotracer studies and linkage of this scheme to genetic evidence (18, 166).

BIOSYNTHESIS OF ASCORBIC ACID IN PLANTS

The studies noted above provided a clear demonstration that AA biosynthesis in plants is different from that in mammals but there was no clue as to the identity of the intermediates. ^{14}C-labeling results show that the carbon skeleton of Glc remains intact and its C6 hydroxymethyl moiety is conserved. Loss of ^{3}H labeling at C5 shows that there is an epimerization that accounts for conversion to the L configuration (77). Therefore, to produce AA from Glc (or from other aldoses) without inversion of the carbon chain, three steps are required. These are oxidation at C1 followed by formation of the 1,4-lactone, oxidation at C2 or C3 to form the *ene*diol group, and epimerization at C5 to change from the D configuration to the L configuration (81, 82). A biosynthetic pathway in plants, encompassing all the above criteria, in which AA is produced from Glc via GalL [already defined] with no "inversion" of the initial hexose carbon skeleton has been proposed (166). This Smirnoff-Wheeler pathway emerged from studies employing genetic and biochemical approaches. For practical reasons, these approaches are addressed in separate sections.

Figure 1   Biosynthesis of ascorbic acid in plants via D-mannose and L-galactose (Smirnoff-Wheeler pathway). The diagram shows the proposed intracellular compartmentation of the pathway and its relationship with cell wall polysaccharide synthesis, protein glycosylation, and mannitol synthesis. Alternative pathway to L-galactono-1,4-lactone, whose significance remains to be determined, is shown in italics. Mutants identified in *A. thaliana* are *vtc1* (19, 22) and *cyt1* (GDP-mannose pyrophosphorylase) (109, W Lukowitz & C Somerville, personal communication) and *mur1* (11, 133). Key to enzymes (numbers in italics on the diagram indicate that the plant gene has been cloned): 1. glucose 6-phosphate isomerase; 2. phosphomannose isomerase; 3. phosphomannose mutase; 4. GDP-mannose pyrophosphorylase; 5. GDP-mannose-3,5-epimerase; 6. activity present but enzyme(s) uncharacterized; 7. L-galactose dehydrogenase; 8. mitochondrial L-galactono-1,4-lactone dehydrogenase; 9. GDP-glucose-2-epimerase. Other abbreviations: imm, inner mitochondrial membrane; omm, outer mitochondrial membrane.

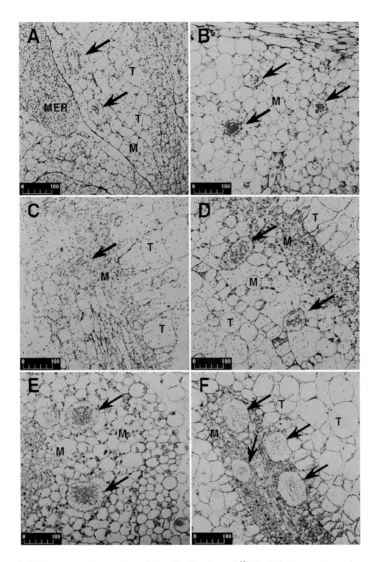

Figure 2 Microautoradiographs of the distribution of ^{14}C in *Pistia stratiotes* tissue pulse-chase labeled with selected ^{14}C-tagged compounds. Images were collected with a confocal microscope in two channels with the silver grains from ^{14}C decay appearing as magenta dots on the blue transmitted image of the tissue section. Arrows indicate developing calcium oxalate (CaOx) crystal idioblasts. M = mesophyll cell, T = trichome. Bar units in μm. (*A*) [^{14}C]OxA. (*B*) L-[1-^{14}C]AA. (*C*) L-[6-^{14}C]AA. (*D*) D-[1-^{14}C]Erythorbic acid. (*E*) L-[1-^{14}C]Galactose. (*F*) Calcium [1-^{14}C]glycolate. Reprinted from Phytochemistry, Vol. 53, SE Keates, NM Tarlyn, FA Loewus, VR Franceschi, "L-Ascorbic acid and L-galactose are sources for oxalic acid and calcium oxalate in *Pistia stratoites*". pp. 433-440, 2000, with permission from Elsevier.

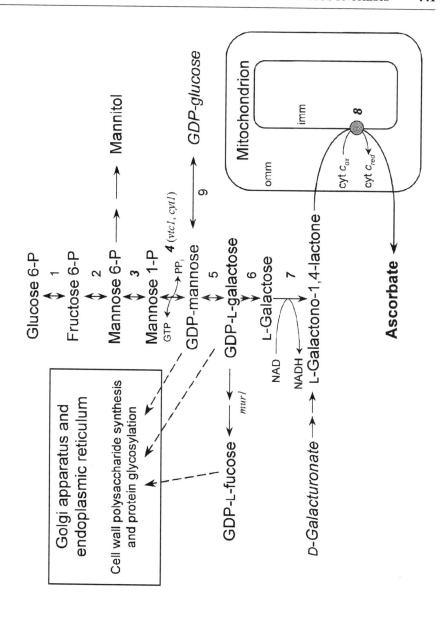

The Smirnoff-Wheeler Pathway of
Ascorbate Biosynthesis in Plants

In this pathway GalL is formed by oxidation of L-Gal and L-Gal is derived from GDP-D-mannose (GDP-D-Man) via GDP-L-Gal (Figure 1). The initial observation resulting in the proposal of this pathway was that exogenous L-Gal resulted in a large increase in the total AA pool of plant tissues similar to that caused by GalL. A novel enzyme, NAD-specific L-galactose dehydrogenase, was detected that oxidizes L-Gal at C1 to form GalL. GalL was then oxidized to AA by the previously described mitochondrial GalL dehydrogenase (100). The existence of free L-Gal has never been reported in plants but it is a minor component of cell wall polysaccharides (135). It is considered to originate from GDP-D-Man by a double epimerization at C3 and C5 (6, 7, 33). The enzyme responsible, GDP-D-Man-3,5-epimerase, has not, to date, been purified or cloned. The presence of epimerase activity was confirmed in both pea and *A. thaliana* cell-free extracts (166). In addition to GDP-L-Gal, the reaction products from GDP-D-Man also include L-Gal-1-P (8; GL Wheeler & N Smirnoff, unpublished data) and L-Gal (166). Because very little D-Man or D-Man-1-P are formed, this suggests that there are specific enzymes that sequentially form L-Gal-1-P and L-Gal from GDP-L-Gal. GDP-D-Man is formed from GTP and D-Man-1-P by GDP-D-Man pyrophosphorylase. The proposed pathway suggests that D-Man should be readily incorporated into AA. This is confirmed by the observation that at least 10% of exogenously supplied D-[U-^{14}C]Man is converted to AA in vivo after a short labeling period (19, 166). AA is therefore a previously unrecognized major product of D-Man metabolism. Interestingly, very early studies on AA synthesis in pea seedlings (131) showed that exogenous Man elevated the AA pool. GDP-D-Man and GDP-L-Gal are also substrates for polysaccharide and glycoprotein synthesis but the formation of L-Gal-1-P and all the subsequent reactions appear to be dedicated to AA biosynthesis.

An illustration of the AA biosynthesis pathway has been provided by the synthesis of calcium oxalate crystals in the floating aquatic plant *Pistia stratiotes* (161). Oxalate is synthesized from AA in a number of species (35–37, 49, 62, 81–83, 115, 141, 164, 169). Calcium oxalate crystals are deposited in specialized cells (crystal idioblasts). In *P. stratiotes*, this is stimulated by calcium (62). *P. stratiotes* leaves (Figure 2, see color insert) labeled with [^{14}C]oxalate, L-[1-^{14}C]AA or D-[1-^{14}C]erythorbic acid (the C5 diastereomer of AA) show clear labeling of calcium oxalate crystals in their idioblasts (Figure 2A, B, D). ^{14}C from L-[6-^{14}C]AA is not incorporated (Figure 2C) into oxalate since only C1 and 2 of AA are used in oxalate synthesis (82). L-[1-^{14}C]Gal labels the oxalate crystals, showing that it is converted to AA and then cleaved at C2/C3 to form oxalate (Figure 2E). Glycolate, another postulated oxalate precursor (82), does not label oxalate crystals in *P. stratiotes* (Figure 2F). In further studies, idioblast protoplasts were isolated and found to incorporate label from D-[1-^{14}C]Man, L-[1-^{14}C]Gal, L-[1-^{14}C]AA and [^{14}C]oxalic acid into oxalate crystals (71). This shows that all the enzymes required for AA and subsequent oxalate synthesis are present in the idioblasts.

Ascorbate Biosynthetic Enzymes

Phosphomannose Isomerase (EC 5.3.1.8, PMI)   PMI converts D-Fru-6-P (Figure 1, reaction 2) to D-Man-6-P and so is the first step in directing hexose phosphates into D-Man metabolism. Despite its possible importance in controling flux to Man, very little is known about PMI. Earlier reports have suggested that many plants lack PMI or have very low activities (47). Exogenous D-Man is readily phosphorylated to D-Man-6-P and is also toxic (43, 98, 125, 156). Its toxicity may in part result from a very low flux from D-Man-6-P to D-Fru-6-P and Glc phosphates causing phosphate sequestration and thus ATP deficiency. This supports the possibility of a low flux through PMI. However, some species or tissues require PMI activity, for example those that accumulate mannitol as a major product of photosynthesis and germinating seeds that have mannan storage reserves. Consequently, germinating seeds in these species possess appreciable levels of PMI activity (74). Additionally, a large number of species (including umbelliferous plants such as celery) synthesize the polyol mannitol for use as a translocated carbohydrate and osmoticum (127). These plants have PMI activity to form D-Man-6-P, which is then reduced to mannitol-1-P by mannitol-6-P reductase (137). Evidence of PMI activity is provided by radiolabeled D-Man incorporation into derivatives of D-Fru-6-P in cultured cells of spinach, rose, and maize (9). However D-[^{14}C]Man was not metabolized via glycolytic intermediates in maize roots (135). Even though all plants synthesize D-Man, the contradictory results suggest that PMI activity is very low in most plants. However, unless there is an alternative route to GDP-D-Man, all plants must contain PMI. An alternative route via a GDP-Glc-2-epimerase has been suggested in pine and *Lilium testaceum* (25, 30, 168). The conclusions were based on radiolabeling patterns of polysaccharide mannosyl residues and enzyme activity was not detected directly. Evidence for this activity was not found in pea and *A. thaliana* extracts (GL Wheeler & N Smirnoff, unpublished results). Further evidence that GDP-Glc is not a major source of GDP-Man is provided by the decreased Man content of cell wall polysaccharides in the GDP-Man pyrophosphorylase-deficient *vtc1* mutant (19; GL Wheeler & N Smirnoff, unpublished results) and in antisense potatoes with reduced GDP-D-Man (63). This suggests that a substantial part of the Man pool is produced via PMI. It is clear that further information is needed, and PMI is yet to be purified or cloned from plants so very little is known about its properties. Bacterial, yeast, and mammalian PMIs have been cloned (16, 129, 153). In *Pseudomonas aeruginosa* and *Acetobacter xylinum*, PMI and GDP-D-Man pyrophosphorylase activities reside in a bifunctional enzyme (39, 144), while in other eukayotes such as *Escherichia coli* these activities are encoded by separate genes (19).

Bacterial and *Candida albicans* PMIs contain zinc (124, 128), and the crystal structure of *C. albicans* PMI has been determined (15). Sugar beet has been transformed with *E. coli* PMI and the resulting plants are more tolerant to mannose, presumably because they are able to metabolize it (58–60). Inclusion of PMI in *Agrobacterium* vectors has been suggested as selectable marker for plant transformation (58–60).

Phosphomannose Mutase (EC 5.4.2.8, PMM)   PMM converts D-Man-6-P to D-Man-1-P (Figure 1, reaction 3). In vivo formation of Man-6-P followed by Man-1-P from exogenous Man can be detected by NMR (98). The properties of plant PMM have not been studied in great detail. Like the enzyme from other organisms, it requires a low concentration of a sugar bisphosphate such as Man- or Glc-1,6-bisphosphate, for activation (118). Maize leaves are reported to contain two enzymes with PMM activity; one which is specific to mannose whereas the other, designated as a phosphoglucomutase, has equal activity with Glc-1-P and Man-1-P (126). Mammalian, yeast, and bacterial PMMs have been cloned (29, 31, 42) and an *A. thaliana*-expressed sequence tag in *E. coli* has PMM activity (S Gatzek & N Smirnoff, unpublished data).

GDP-D-Mannose Pyrophosphorylase (EC 2.7.7.13, D-Mannose-1-Phosphate Guanylyltransferase)   The enzyme (Figure 1, reaction 4) has been partially characterized from a number of plant sources (33). The gene encoding GDP-D-Man pyrophosphorylase from *A. thaliana* (*VTC1*) has significant sequence homology with the mammalian, yeast, and bacterial genes (19). The demonstration that the ascorbate-deficient *vtc1 A. thaliana* mutant has reduced GDP-D-Man pyrophosphorylase activity, described below, has provided strong support for the proposed pathway.

GDP-D-Mannose-3,5-Epimerase   This enzyme catalyzes the equilibration of GDP-D-Man and GDP-L-Gal (Figure 1, reaction 5) (33). Very little is known about this epimerase and it has only been studied in *Chlorella pyrenoidosa* in any detail (6, 11, 44). ^{3}H from ^{3}H$_2$O is incorporated into C3 and C5 during the reaction and the proposed reaction involves oxidation of the C4 alcohol to a ketone, water elimination, re-addition of water from the opposite face of the double bond, and reduction of the C4 carbonyl, also from the opposite face. The electron carrier is probably a tightly bound pyridine nucleotide (7, 33).

Conversion of GDP-L-GAL to L-Gal   Incubation of GDP-D-Man with cell-free extracts results in formation of GDP-L-Gal, L-Gal-1-P, and L-Gal (6, 166). It therefore appears that GDP-L-Gal is initially broken down to L-Gal-1-P. L-Gal-1-P is subsequently hydrolyzed to L-Gal. These enzymes (Figure 1, reaction 6) may be of some importance as they catalyze the first committed steps of AA synthesis.

L-Galactose Dehydrogenase (L-GalDH)   L-GalDH oxidizes L-Gal at C1, forming GalL (Figure 1, reaction 7) (152, 166). It has been purified from pea seedlings and information about the N-terminal sequence was used to clone an *A. thaliana* gene by RT-PCR. This gene produces a protein with L-GalDH activity when expressed in *E. coli* (S Gatzek & N Smirnoff, unpublished results). The pea and recombinant *A. thaliana* enzymes have a strong preference for NAD over NADP and have K_m values between 0.08 and 0.3 mM for L-Gal. L-GalDH recognizes L-gulose, L-sorbosone and, in the case of the recombinant *A. thaliana* enzyme, L-fucose (= 6-deoxy-L-Gal). However, no other commonly occurring aldoses (D-Ara, D-Gal, D-Man, and D-Glc) (D-Ara = D-arabinose) are oxidized. A number of other C1 aldose dehydrogenases have been described from bacteria (102), mammals (142), and fungi (23, 67). They all differ from the plant enzyme in having wider substrate specificity and sugar substrate affinities up to 10 times lower. D-Arabinose dehydrogenase (AraDH) is involved in erythroascorbate synthesis by fungi (67, 68). The sequence of *A. thaliana* L-GalDH has little similarity to any other eukaryotic genes but has about 34% identity and 45% similarity to the predicted amino acid sequence of *Pseudomonas* L-fucose dehydrogenase (S Gatzek & N Smirnoff, unpublished results).

L-Galactono-1,4-Lactone Dehydrogenase (GalLDH)   Intact mitochondria oxidize GalL to AA, and GalLDH activity was initially characterized in mitochondria from germinating pea seedlings (100, 101). More recent studies have confirmed the mitochondrial location of GalLDH (8, 106, 145) and shown that it is associated with the inner membrane (8, 145). Isolated GalLDH has been assayed with cytochrome (cyt) *c* and phenazine methosulfate/dichlorophenolindophenol as electron acceptors. No other electron acceptors are active. Recently, studies on the effect of inhibitors on GalL oxidation by isolated mitochondria have shown that cyt *c* is the physiological electron acceptor for GalL oxidation and therefore it is likely that GalLDH activity is located on the outer side of the inner membrane (8). The sequence of sweet potato GalLDH predicts 3 putative transmembrane domains and an FAD binding site on the outer side of the membrane (8, 54). It is therefore likely that, similarly to other low-molecular-weight solutes, GalL can cross the outer membrane without the need for a carrier, whereas ascorbate can similarly leave without a carrier. GalLDH has been cloned from cauliflower (121) and sweet potato (54). The first 83–91 amino acid residues are cleaved from the mature protein and are typical of mitochondrial targeting sequences, which is consistent with its mitochondrial localization.

Purified GalLDH from several sources is specific for GalL as substrate (54, 106, 121). However, the conversion of L-gulono-1,4-lactone (GulL) to ascorbate in whole tissue has been demonstrated in cress (55), strawberry, and bean (5), and also by partially purified GalLDH from potato (116). Three possibilities exist to explain this discrepancy. First, GalLDH could exist as different isoforms, some of which can utilize GulL. The existence of a microsomal protein accounting for 20% of GalLDH activity in potato that is immunologically distinct from the mitochondrial enzyme (8) supports this view. Second, GulL could be oxidized by a separate specific enzyme, and third, GulL could be epimerized at C3 to produce GalL (5). The physiological relevance of this is discussed later with reference to alternative ascorbate biosynthesis pathways.

Sweet potato GalLDH apparently has a noncovalently bound flavin and has an absorption spectrum similar to that of riboflavin (54, 117). Activity inhibition by acriflavine was at least partially reversed by addition of FAD or FMN (117). However, Østergaard et al (121) found no evidence that the cauliflower GalLDH is a flavoprotein. Clearly, this issue needs to be resolved by further research.

In addition to the GalLDH enzyme detailed above, there is some evidence that higher plants may also contain an additional, related enzyme(s). Separation of cauliflower extracts by cation-exchange chromatography revealed the presence of two distinct peaks of GalLDH activity. The larger of these two peaks was further purified and found to contain the GalDH enzyme detailed above. The activity in the second peak was not further described (121). Additional evidence suggestive of a second related plant enzyme comes from partial purification of white potato tuber GalLDH from mitochondrial extracts. In this preparation, two distinct K_ms were observed using GalL as a substrate (116). These authors also state that they have additional evidence for the existence of two GalLDH isoenzymes, although these data have remained unpublished (116). More research is needed to clarify this issue. Because exogenous GulL is converted to AA it is possible that, in contrast to the currently purified and cloned enzymes, these additional enzymes are also able to oxidize GulL. This is discussed further in the section on alternative AA biosynthesis pathways.

The alkaloid lycorine inhibits ascorbate synthesis in plants and has been used in some studies as a tool to study the function of ascorbate (1). It has been suggested that this alkaloid's mode of action is to inhibit GalLDH (3). Lycorine inhibits partially purified GalLDH from *Vicia faba* and *Zea mays* mitochondria (3) and the purified sweet potato enzyme (54) but is completely without effect on the cauliflower enzyme (121) and GalL oxidation by lily pollen (76). It remains to be resolved whether these differences are related to different enzyme properties, methods of extraction, or lycorine preparations, so care is needed in interpreting results based on the use of lycorine.

BIOSYNTHESIS OF ASCORBIC ACID IN ALGAE AND FUNGI

Of the green algae (Chlorophyta) that have been investigated, *Chlorella pyenoidosa* and its heterotrophic relative *Prototheca moriformis* (JA Running, RP Burlingame, DK Severson, KL Nielsen, BL Walsh, M Anderson, L Song, BB Logan & A Berry, personal communication) synthesize AA via the Smirnoff-Wheeler pathway. The evidence includes lack of label inversion (134) and efficient conversion of L-[^{14}C]Gal and D-[^{14}C]Man to AA (41). Mutants of *C. pyenoidosa* (138) and *P. moriformis* (JA Running, RP Burlingame, DK Severson, KL Nielsen, BL Walsh,

M Anderson, L Song, BB Logan & A Berry, personal communication) that synthesize significantly more AA than wild type have been isolated. A limited number of studies on other photosynthetic protists including *Euglena gracilis* (Euglenophyta) (143), *Ochromonas danica* (Chrysophyta) (45), and *Cyclotella cryptica* (Bacillariophyta) (40) suggest that they do not synthesize AA via the Smirnoff-Wheeler pathway. In all cases, radiolabeling studies indicate that the hexose precursor is inverted, which is not predicted by the Smirnoff-Wheeler pathway. However, unlike the inversion pathway of mammals, L-GalL rather than L-GulL is the preferred precursor of AA (40, 45, 143). These protists might therefore employ a pathway resembling the D-galacto/L-galactono-pathway that was originally proposed for higher plants (55). The proposed pathways in these algae and protists are summarized in Figure 3.

It is worth mentioning here that ascomycete fungi such as the yeasts *Candida* and *Saccharomyces* (28, 41, 61, 67, 82, 104, 105, 108, 119, 120, 155, 160) and the fungus *Sclerotinia sclerotiorum* (96) lack AA but instead contain an analogue

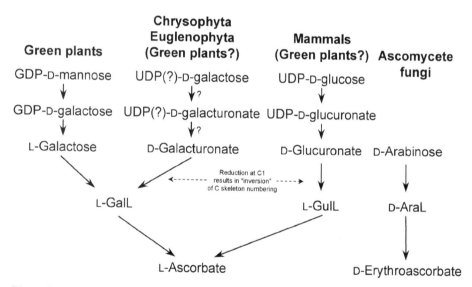

Figure 3   Comparison of ascorbic acid and erythroascorbic acid biosynthetic pathways in various organisms. The biosynthetic pathway of ascorbic acid varies between different groups of organisms. In green plants (including chlorophytic algae) the aldonolactone precursor of ascorbic acid is produced from an aldose while in mammals, and the very few protists that have been studied (Chrysophytes and Euglenophytes), it is produced from a uronic acid. There is some evidence, discussed in the text, that green plants can also produce a small amount of ascorbic acid through one or both of the uronic acid pathways. Ascomycete fungi, including yeast, produce D-erythroascorbate, a C_5 analogue of ascorbic acid, via an aldose pathway similar to green plants. Comparisons between the amino acid sequences of the aldonolactone dehydrogenases (green plants)/oxidases (rat) that produce ascorbate or erythroascorbate (yeast) show 26 to 31% identity.

of AA, often D-erythroascorbic acid (D-*glycero*-pent-2-enono-1,4-lactone, EAA). EAA is synthesized from D-Ara (Figure 3):

D-Arabinose → D-Arabinono-1,5-lactone → D-Arabinono-1,4-lactone → EAA

Enzymes catalyzing the first and last steps have been isolated from *Candida albicans* (52, 53, 67, 68). The intermediate step, rearrangement of the 1,5-lactone to a more stable 1,4-lactone, is probably nonenzymic. An NADP-specific dehydrogenase catalyzes the first oxidative step. With purified NADP-specific D-AraDH from either *C. albicans* or *S. cerevisiae*, D-Ara and L-Fuc exhibit highest and nearly equal rates followed by L-Xyl and L-Gal. The *S. cerevisiae* dehydrogenase is a heterodimeric protein of the aldo-keto reductase family (67, 68). The last step is catalyzed D-arabinono-1,4-lactone oxidase (52, 53, 73a; AraLO; Table 1) whose properties are discussed in the section on comparative analysis of aldonolactone oxidases and dehydrogenases. 5-*O*-(D-Galactosyl)-EAA has been identified in *Sclerotinia sclerotiorum* (61). The biosynthetic pathway of EAA in ascomycetes is compared with AA biosynthesis pathways in Figure 3.

TABLE 1 Comparative analysis of enzyme responsible for the final step in the biosynthesis of either ascorbic acid or an analogue (erythroascorbic acid) across three kingdoms

Properties	GalLDH (plant)[a]	GulLO (animal)[b]	AraLO (fungi)[c,d]
E.C. No.	1.3.2.3	1.1.3.8	1.1.3.24
Product	L-Ascorbic acid	L-Ascorbic acid	D-Erythroascorbic acid
Compartment	Mitochondria	Microsomes	Mitochondria
Native molecular mass (KD)	56	51	56–60
Relative substrate specificity:			
L-GalL	100	87	87[e]
L-GulL	0–20	100	24[e]
D-AraL	—	—	100[e]
D-Xylonolactone	0	—	84.6[e]
K_m (preferred substrate)	0.12–3.3 mM	0.066 mM (rat) 0.15 mM (goat)	44.1 mM (*C. albicans*)
Prosthetic group	Noncovalent flavin (proposed)	Covalent flavin	Covalent flavin
Electron acceptor	Cyt *c*	O_2	O_2
Essential sulfhydryl groups	Yes	Yes	Yes
Divalent cation requirement	No	No	No

[a]Compiled from cauliflower (100, 121), spinach (106), sweet potato (54, 117), and white potato (116) enzymes.

[b]Compiled from rat, goat, and chicken enzymes (69, 113).

[c]Compiled from *Saccharomyces cerevisiae* (53, 112) and *Candida albicans* (52) enzymes.

[d]Previously known as GalLDH (see text for details).

[e]*C. albicans* enzyme (52).

A COMPARATIVE ANALYSIS OF ALDONOLACTONE OXIDASES AND DEHYDROGENASES OF PLANTS, FUNGI, AND MAMMALS

Plant GalLDH has counterparts in both animals and fungi. As discussed below, mammals with the capacity to synthesize AA catalyze the oxidation of GulL to AA with GulLO (Figure 3) while in both *Candida albicans* and *Saccharomyces cerevisiae*, EAA is synthesized from D-arabinono-1,4-lactone (AraL) by AraLO (Figure 3). Based on a number of experimental observations, it has been previously proposed that the *S. cerevisiae* enzyme previously identified as "GalLDH" be called ArabLO to better represent its physiologically relevant activity (52, 155). Therefore, in this discussion, data compiled for the fungal "GalLDH" is included under the umbrella of fungal AraLO. Basic properties of these different enzymes (GalLDH, GulLO, and AraLO) are compiled in Table 1.

Common features shared by these proteins should be noted. As most flavo-proteins contain noncovalently bound flavin (130), it is unusual that the flavins in both GulLO and AraLO are covalently bound to the protein (52, 64, 69, 112). In the case of GulLO and AraLO, the flavin is attached via an 8α-[N(1)-histidyl] linkage (64, 69, 112).

The gene and/or cDNAs encoding GalLDH, GulLO, and AraLO have been isolated and described from several organisms including cauliflower, sweet potato (GalLDH, 54, 121), rat (GulLO, 70), and *Saccharomyces cerevisiae* (53). In addition, complete nucleotide coding sequences of the *A. thaliana* and *Nicotiana tabacum* GalLDH genes (Accession No. AB042279.1, AB024527.1), and the *Candida albicans* AraLO gene (Accession No. AF031228) have been submitted directly to GenBank and associated databases. The predicted amino acid sequences of these related proteins share substantial amounts of identity. The mature cauliflower GalLDH amino acid sequence shares 28% overall identity with the rat GulLO and 26% identity with the *Candida albicans* AraLO (using the J Hein method with PAM250 residue weight table). Upon closer inspection, the N-terminal halves of these proteins share the most similarity, suggestive of a commonality of function in these portions of the proteins (121). The over-all amino acid sequence comparison suggests that the rat and fungal enzymes are more closely related to each other (31% identity) than either is to the plant enzyme.

Several additional lines of evidence also suggest that the AraLO and GulLO enzymes are more closely related to each other than to GalLDH. Both AraLO and GulLO use oxygen as an electron acceptor and contain a covalently bound flavin while in contrast, the plant GalLDH may contain a noncovalently bound flavin. AraLO and GulLO use molecular oxygen as the electron acceptor while GalLDH uses cyt *c* (8) and, as mentioned above, may contain a noncovalently bound flavin. Finally, the specificity of GalLDH for its physiologically relevant substrate (GalL) is much stricter than the substrate specificity of either GulLO or AraLO (see Table 1) (106, 117, 121). Although the fungal and animal enzymes appear to be more closely related, both GalLDH and AraLO are mitochondrially localized proteins whereas GulLO has been localized to the microsomal fraction.

Enzymes related to those listed in Table 1 have been described in both fungi and bacteria. Nearly 20 years ago a *S. cerevisiae* mitochondrial enzyme was purified that had several properties that were quite different from the fungal AraLO described above (10). This tetrameric enzyme does not utilize GulL as a substrate, a property shared with plant GalLDH. Yet in contrast, it can utilize AraL as a substrate in addition to GalL. Like AraLO, it has a bound flavin coenzyme and utilizes molecular oxygen as an electron acceptor. There has also been a report of a bacterial enzyme with L-gulono-1,4-lactone dehydrogenase activity isolated from a strain of *Gluconobacter oxydans* (158). This flavoprotein was identified as a L-gulono-1,4-lactone dehydrogenase as it does not utilize oxygen as an electron acceptor but rather uses dyes such as phenazine methosulfate. This enzyme cannot utilize GalL as a substrate and utilizes D-xylose slightly more efficiently than GulL. Therefore, it was concluded that the most likely physiologically relevant function of this D-xylose dehydrogenase enzyme is catabolism of the carbon source D-xylose to D-xylosone (158). Further molecular and biochemical analyses of related enzymes such as this bacterial D-xylose dehydrogenase may shed new information on conserved protein domains required for conversion of 1,4-lactones to AA.

Transgenic plants and animals have been generated that express mammalian GulLO, with varied results. Tobacco and lettuce that produce GulLO from a rat cDNA were reported to synthesize increased levels of AA relative to nontransgenic controls (57). It is not known if this rat GulLO is utilizing endogenous plant GalL and/or possible endogenous GulL as its substrate. GulLO activity is missing in humans, other primates, guinea pigs, bats, certain species of birds, and teleost fishes (12, 14). At the molecular level, the human and guinea pig genomes contain only highly mutated, nonfunctional pseudogenes related to GulLO (110, 111). Attempts to produce AA-synthesizing salmon and medaka fishes using the rat GulLO cDNA as a transgene have met with little success (72, 163). Surprisingly, there are no published reports on the generation of primate cell lines that synthesize rat GulLO.

GENETIC APPROACHES TO ASCORBIC ACID BIOSYNTHESIS IN PLANTS

Ascorbate-Deficient *A. thaliana* Mutants

Ascorbate-deficient *A. thaliana* mutants have proven to be a powerful tool in furthering the understanding of ascorbate biosynthesis in plants. These mutants provide an opportunity to both rigorously test proposed ascorbate biosynthetic pathways and, without any preconceived mechanistic hypotheses, isolate genes involved in ascorbate metabolism.

The initial isolation of AA-deficient mutants arose from a more general desire to understand mechanisms used by plants for protection against reactive oxygen species (ROS). The isolation and characterization of *A. thaliana* mutants altered in their response to enhanced ROS (from O_3) led to several new research initiatives including a focused study of ascorbic acid in plants. Screening a total of 100,000 ethyl methanesulfonate (EMS)-mutagenized M_2 seed with either 250 or 400 ppb O_3/8h identified 42 *soz* (<u>s</u>ensitive to <u>oz</u>one) mutants that show enhanced visible injury (tissue collapse and/or necrotic lesions) 24 h after the end of fumigation. Several of the mutants could be grouped into three classes: (*a*) 13 mutants are deficient in superoxide dismutase (D Kliebenstein & RL Last, unpublished), (*b*) four fail to respond to O_3 with additional accumulation of antioxidant proteins (D Kliebenstein & RL Last, unpublished), and (*c*) two are AA-deficient (19–22).

Identification of the *VTC1* Gene

Published results from biochemical and genetic analysis of the O_3-sensitive, AA-deficient mutant *soz1*, now known as *vtc1-1* (for <u>vi</u>tamin <u>c</u>-<u>1</u>), are consistent with the hypothesis that the O_3 sensitivity is conferred by a monogenic trait that causes reduced accumulation of AA (22). This mutant consistently accumulates ~25–30% of levels of wild-type AA. In contrast, total glutathione content is identical to that of wild-type. *vtc1-1* is clearly defective in ROS detoxification as treatment with O_3 causes visible tissue damage and increased lipid peroxide accumulation as measured by malondialdehyde accumulation (22). In addition to O_3 sensitivity, the *vtc1-1* mutant also has altered sensitivity to other conditions that generate ROS including H_2O_2, UV-B, SO_2 (22), and combined high light and salt stress (148). A range of AA-deficient *vtc* mutants (21) also have lower zeaxanthin-dependent nonphotochemical quenching, presumably as a result of limited violaxanthin de-epoxidase (VDE) activity (148). This supports the proposal from in vitro evidence that VDE uses AA as a cofactor (107). An AA-deficiency could result from increased turnover or decreased biosynthesis. Alteration in the activity of an enzyme that oxidizes AA or regenerates reduced AA could cause increased turnover. However, the activities of AA oxidase, monodehydroascorbate reductase, dehydroascorbate reductase, ascorbate peroxidase, and glutathione reductase were measured in crude extracts and not found to be aberrant in *vtc1-1* (20). Ascorbate turnover analysis in dark-adapted leaves also suggests that turnover is not elevated in *vtc1-1* relative to wild-type (20).

Although *vtc1-1* does not appear to be defective in ascorbate turnover, this mutant is defective in the conversion of both D-Glc and D-Man to ascorbic acid. (19, 20). These results strongly support the hypotheses that *vtc1-1* is defective in ascorbate biosynthesis and that D-Man is an intermediate in this biosynthetic pathway. Indeed, it was the finding that this mutant is defective in AA biosynthesis that appeared to galvanize the recent renaissance in plant ascorbate biosynthesis research.

Several lines of evidence have led to the conclusion that *VTC1* encodes a GDP-D-Man pyrophosphorylase, an enzyme in the Smirnoff-Wheeler pathway for ascorbate biosynthesis in plants (19). First, the *VTC1* gene maps genetically to a region encoding a putative GDP-D-Man pyrophosphorylase. This genetic locale locates *VTC1* to the 92-kb region of the genome contained on BAC (bacterial artificial chromosome) T5I7. This sequenced BAC carries a predicted gene annotated by The Institute for Genomic Research (TIGR) to encode a putative GDP-D-Man pyrophosphorylase: (http://www.tigr.org/tigr-scripts/bac_scripts/bac_display.spl?bac_name=T5I7).

Second, the GDP-D-Man pyrophosphorylase activity is lower in extracts from *vtc1-1* than wild-type. Finally, there is compelling molecular and genetic evidence that the GDP-D-Man pyrophosphorylase gene on BAC T5I7 is the *VTC1* locus. *vtc1-1* and a second allele *vtc1-2* (see below) both harbor a mis-sense mutation that alters a highly conserved proline at predicted amino acid residue 22 in this gene to a serine (P22S). In addition, a wild-type copy of the GDP-D-Man pyrophosphorylase gene genetically complements the *vtc1-1* mutation in transgenic plants, elevating the AA in the transgenic *vtc1-1* lines to levels similar to wild-type and cosegregating with the selectable marker. Together, these results confirm that the *VTC1* locus encodes a GDP-D-Man pyrophosphorylase structural gene and strongly support the assertion that GDP-D-Man has a major role in AA biosynthesis.

Given the many varied roles of AA both as an antioxidant and a cofactor, one presumes that mutant plants totally devoid of AA would be inviable. Indeed, the embryo-lethal *A. thaliana* mutant *cyt1-2* (109) contains a mutation that creates a premature stop codon in the GDP-D-Man pyrophosphorylase gene on BAC T5I7 (C Somerville & W Lukowitz, personal communication). Failure of *cyt1-2* to complement *vtc1-1* and restore wild-type levels of AA suggests that *VTC1* and *CYT1* are the same locus (PL Conklin, unpublished results). In addition, several *cyt1* alleles with severe cell wall defects have been identified among collections of embryonic lethals (D Meinke, S Gillmor, W Lukowitz & C Somerville, personal communication; 154). The identification of these mutants as embryo-lethals suggests that a mutant with no AA may be inviable. However, as mutations at the *VTC1/CYT1* locus are predicted to be pleiotropic, it is difficult to say whether cell wall defects, protein glycosylation alterations, and/or AA deficiency cause the lethality.

Identification of Additional *VTC* Loci

The AA-deficient mutant *vtc1* provides powerful genetic and molecular evidence for the role of GDP-D-Man in AA biosynthesis and is a very useful tool for probing the roles of AA in plants. Additional AA-deficient mutants are therefore predicted to also yield useful information. As O_3 screening resulted in the isolation of only two *vtc* mutants (*vtc1-1*, *vtc2-1*, a frequency of only 0.001%), a rapid, semiquantitative assay for AA, depending on its ability to reduce nitroblue tetrazolium (NBT), was developed for use in identifying additional *VTC* loci (21). In a F_2 population segregating for AA deficiency, the lack of visible formazan (NBT-) was shown to cosegregate with the deficiency (21).

Using the above described assay, ~10,000 M_2 *A. thaliana* plants (ecotype Col-0) from an EMS-mutagenized population were screened for an AA deficiency (21;

PL Conklin & S Broadley, unpublished data). Six mutant lines were recovered that exhibit heritable AA deficiencies (0.06% frequency). This direct screening method was therefore 60-times more effective than O_3-sensitivity for the identification of AA-deficient mutants. All mutants rescoring negative in the NBT test in the M_3 generation are AA-deficient, highlighting the value of this method in identification of AA mutants. The AA deficiencies in these mutants are single monogenic traits. Allelism tests revealed that these mutants describe four *VTC* loci, including a second mutant allele of *VTC1* (*vtc1-2*), two additional *VTC2* mutants, (*vtc2-2, vtc2-3*), two mutant alleles of a new locus, *VTC3* (*vtc3-1, vtc3-2*), and one mutant allele of another new locus, *VTC4* (*vtc4-1*) (21; PL Conklin & S Broadley, unpublished data).

The AA-deficiencies in the *vtc* mutants were found to vary with age and tissue type (21). At 2 weeks of age, all the *vtc* mutants contain ~30 to ~50% of the AA present in the wild type (wt). In leaves from 5-week-old plants, almost all the mutants maintain AA at ~40% of wt. However, two of the *vtc2* alleles have very low AA levels (~10% of wt) in these leaves. It was hypothesized that perhaps either these two mutants contain specific mutations negatively affecting the biosynthetic activity such that it becomes rate-limiting in older tissue, or *VTC2* encodes a regulatory function, which has a developmental component (21). The AA levels in wt *A. thaliana* are increased in reproductive tissue (green developing siliques, inflorescence) relative to vegetative tissue. For example, siliques were found to contain approximately 9 μmole g^{-1} fresh weight total AA whereas the rosette leaves contained ~4 μmole g^{-1} fresh weight. Interestingly, the mutant alleles maintained this developmental increase in AA, albeit at a lower absolute level, suggesting that the mutations do not affect this regulatory component of AA biosynthesis/turnover (21).

Oddly, the *vtc* mutants have differing sensitivities to O_3, even within an allelic series (21). When exposed to 400 ppb O_3/8 hr, the *vtc1-1* and *vtc1-2* mutants have the same severe O_3-sensitive phenotype: total collapse and death of both cotyledons and fully expanded leaves. This is not surprising given that these two independently isolated mutant alleles harbor the same point mutation (19). The mutant *vtc2-1* (originally isolated by the O_3-sensitivity screen) is virtually as sensitive as the *vtc1* mutants. Curiously, the mutant *vtc2-2* contains levels of AA similar to *vtc2-1* yet is not visibly injured by this high dose of O_3. The mutants *vtc2-3*, *vtc3-1*, and *vtc4-1* all appear to be only somewhat O_3-sensitive as O_3 exposure of each of these mutants leads to partial collapse of at least one leaf. Given that these AA-deficient mutants have widely different O_3-sensitive phenotypes despite similar deficiencies in AA, there appears to be some additional factor(s) distinguishing one from another. It is suggested that intermediates are accumulating in the O_3-insensitive *vtc* mutants that have some antioxidant capacity (21). In addition, this differing sensitivity also suggests that the NBT-based direct screen is less biased for different classes of AA-deficiencies than the O_3 sensitivity-based screening method.

Finally, there is preliminary evidence that the mutants *vtc2-1*, *vtc3-1*, and *vtc4-1* are defective in AA biosynthesis. None of these mutants appears to turn over AA more rapidly than wt. In addition, neither mutant appears to convert D-[U-^{14}C]Man to [^{14}C]AA as efficiently as wild-type (SR Norris, GL Wheeler, & N Smirnoff, unpublished results).

The candidate gene approach that was utilized successfully for the cloning of *VTC1* is not viable for the cloning of the *VTC2-VTC4* genes. All the *VTC* genes have been mapped to sequenced and annotated regions of the *A. thaliana* genome (VTC1 and VTC3, chromosome 2; VTC2, chromosome 4; VTC4, chromosome 3) (21). None of these regions contains genes annotated to encode enzymes in the Smirnoff-Wheeler biosynthetic pathway. However, as gene(s) encoding the enzyme(s) that catalyze the synthesis of L-Gal from GDP-L-Gal have not yet been cloned from any source, these genes would not appear in the annotation database. In addition, the activities of several proposed AA biosynthetic enzymes (PMM, GDP-D-Man epimerase, L-GalDH, and GalLDH) were measured in *vtc2-1*, *vtc3-1*, and *vtc4-1* and were not significantly different than those in wild-type (N Smirnoff, G Wheeler, PL Conklin & SR Norris, unpublished data). Therefore, it is hypothesized that *VTC2–VTC4* are involved in conversion of GDP-L-Gal to L-Gal and/or in the synthesis of some necessary cofactor or regulatory protein. Alternatively, these genes could encode enzymes involved in alternative AA biosynthetic pathways such as those outlined in Figure 3. *VTC3* and *VTC4* are currently being cloned by the technique of positional cloning. *VTC2* has recently been cloned using this approach and has similarity to three other proteins in the database that have unknown function(s) (SR Norris & RL Last, personal communication). Experiments are currently under way to determine the function of the VTC2 protein.

ALTERNATIVE PATHWAYS IN PLANTS TO ASCORBIC ACID

Evidence in support of the Smirnoff-Wheeler pathway (166) continues to mount (8, 19, 21, 26, 62, 63, 123, 145) and it is tempting to regard this process as an exclusive biosynthetic path to AA in plants. Although this pathway appears to function as the major physiological route, other AA-producing pathways also may occur in plants. These include processes involving D-glucurono-1-4-lactone (GlcUL), D-galacturonate (GalUA), methyl D-galacturonate (MeGalUA), and L-gulono-1,4-lactone (GulL), putative intermediates first considered by Isherwood et al (55) and more recently, in the case of GulL, in transformed plants (57) (Figure 3).

An enzymic path of conversion of GlcUL and GalUA to AA in plants has yet to be established (see later in this section). Free D-glucuronate (GlcUA) is apparently not involved (78). Only GlcUL (or MeGalUA/GalUA) served as substrate for uronoyl-linked AA biosynthesis in strawberry. Plants contain two biosynthetic routes to UDP-GlcUA, one involving oxygenative cleavage of *myo*-inositol (MI) and the other oxidation of UDP-D-Glc by UDP-D-Glc dehydrogenase (EC 1.1.1.22) (95). Both contribute UDP-GlcUA and its metabolic products (UDP-GalUA, UDP-D-Xyl, UDP-L-Ara, and UDP-D-apiose) as substrates for cell wall polysaccharide formation (79, 95, 103). Neither pathway appears to be directly involved in AA

biosynthesis. Free GlcUA is rapidly converted to α-GlcUA-1-P by a highly specific GlcUA-kinase (EC 2.7.1.43) (75) and this product is converted to UDP-GlcUA by GlcUA-1-P uridylyltransferase (EC 1.7.7.44) (136). Presumably, a similar process converts GalUA to UDP-GalUA. In the case of MI, the product is free GlcUA, which follows the same path of conversion to UDP-GlcUA taken by exogenously supplied GlcUA. Feingold (33) has noted that GalUA-kinase (EC 2.7.1.44) provides a salvage mechanism for GalUA whereas GlcUA-kinase provides a more functional role as part of the MI oxidation pathway (95).

Anecdotally, discovery of MI's role in cell wall polysaccharide biosynthesis emerged from experiments in which [3]H- or ^{14}C-labeled MI was supplied to ripening strawberries and parsley leaves (90, 92). No ^{14}C appeared in AA but upwards of 90% of the incorporated radiolabel was incorporated into uronosyl and pentosyl residues of pectic polysaccharides. The aim of that study was to seek a putative role for endogenously generated GlcUA as precursor of AA on the premise that a MI oxygenase resembling the activities found in kidney or yeast also occurs in plants. MI oxygenase catalyzes oxidative cleavage of the cyclitol ring of MI at C1-C6 to form GlcUA. Labeling studies clearly establish the presence of a MI oxygenase (EC 1.13.99.1) in plants but scant information is yet available regarding its plant-related properties (93, 95).

Of the various sugar acid derivatives tested by Isherwood et al (55), GlcUL, GulL, MeGalUA, and GalL increased the AA content in germinating cress seedlings (*Lepidum sativum* L.). They did not test free GalUA. Their results with MeGalUA and GalL led them to propose an inversion scheme for AA biosynthesis analogous to one describing the animal pathway. Isolation and partial purification of GalLDH from plant mitochondria provided additional evidence for their scheme (100). When presented with radioisotopic data favoring a noninversion pathway (84–86), Isherwood & Mapson suggested that such results would also be expected if the labeled product was D-araboascorbic acid (D-erythorbic acid) (56). To re-examine this matter, labeled AA was recovered from a [6-^{14}C]Glc-labeled ripening strawberry and divided into two portions, one was diluted with unlabeled AA, the other with D-erythorbic acid. After three recrystallizations, only the portion diluted with AA retained its ^{14}C, 71% in C6 and 14% in C1, a redistribution pattern indicative of triose/hexose cycling (73) and noninversion (89). As we now know, the Smirnoff-Wheeler pathway fulfills both requirements.

Administration of [1-^{14}C]glucurono-1,4-lactone (GlcUL), [6-^{14}C]GlcUL, or D-[1-^{14}C]GalUA to detached strawberry fruits resulted in formation of radiolabeled AA with complete inversion of the position, i.e. [6-^{14}C]AA from [1-^{14}C]GlcUL or D-[1-^{14}C]GalUA, and [1-^{14}C]AA from [6-^{14}C]GlcUL (34, 77). There was no evidence of triose/pentose/hexose cycling (73) such as that encountered when specifically labeled Glc is used to demonstrate noninversion of the carbon chain during AA biosynthesis (77, 85). Apparently, these uronic acids enter metabolic processing beyond the triose/pentose/hexose phosphate cycling steps.

Since exogenously supplied GlcUL, GalUA, and MeGalUA follow an inversion pathway through GulL and/or GalL to AA, two enzymic steps are prescribed: first, a reductive step to produce the corresponding aldonic acid (lactone) and then a terminal oxidative step to AA. Plants, as represented by the ripening strawberry, reduce D-GlcUL to L-gulonic acid (87). Conditions used to recover and characterize gulonic acid and its 1,4-lactone precluded assignment as to whether the acid or its lactone or both accumulate in the berry. As noted above, [1-^{14}C]- and [6-^{14}C]GluL were converted to [6-^{14}C]- and [1-^{14}C]GulL, respectively (with inversion of the carbon chain) and without redistribution of ^{14}C. It was assumed that GulL accumulates under physiological conditions. Oxidation of GulL within the berry produced radiolabeled AA with the same inverted carbon chain as its aldonolactone precursor (34, 86). In contrast to this, sucrose-derived Glc from [1-^{14}C]GlcUL-labeled berries had a typical triose/pentose/hexose-type redistribution of ^{14}C (73), a clear indication of the fact that [1-^{14}C]GlcUL was converted to AA independently of the processes that recycle [1-^{14}C]GlcUL into the hexose phosphate pool.

The Smirnoff-Wheeler pathway, along with numerous supporting studies, singles out GalLDH as the functional activity for the terminal step in AA biosynthesis in plants. This may also be the terminal step when radiolabeled GalUA (or MeGalUA) is supplied to plant tissue (88). Whether this enzyme is also involved in conversion of GlcUL to AA in plants remains equivocal. Davey and colleagues (26) have identified GulL in *A. thaliana* extracts and are in the process of characterizing an NADPH-dependent activity that catalyzes reduction of GlcUL. Purification of such an activity and comparison of its properties with those of GalLDH could provide new information regarding the existence of one or more terminal dehydrogenases/oxidases for AA biosynthesis in plants (5).

Brief mention might be made of the so-called "osone" pathway to AA (97, 139, 140), a tentative scheme consistent with radiolabeling studies (77) but now superceded by discovery of the Smirnoff-Wheeler pathway. Pallanca & Smirnoff (122) revisited the osone pathway and found several lines of evidence to suggest that D-glucosone and L-sorbosone are unlikely physiological intermediates of AA synthesis but that both can act as pseudosubstrates.

In summary, the possibility exists that one or more of these alternative uronate pathways contribute to AA synthesis. It now remains to provide evidence that they occur in vivo and to identify the enzymes involved. Reduction of GalL formation from L-Gal by antisense suppression of L-GalDH might reveal if GulL or alternative sources of GalL are available. Also, further information is needed on the nature of the enzyme that oxidizes exogenous GulL: Does the substrate specificity of L-GalLDH (see Table 1) vary between species, and is there a separate L-GulL dehydrogenase or oxidase?

CONTROL OF ASCORBATE SYNTHESIS

Different plant species and tissues have characteristically different AA concentrations, and in leaves there is strong evidence that the AA pool size is light dependent. Leaves normally contain 2–5 μmol g^{-1} fresh weight although a few species, including some high mountain plants and temperate evergreen species, can contain up to 10 times more (38, 157, 167). Certain fruits are also very rich in AA compared to leaves (27). Higher AA concentrations have been reported in meristematic and reproductive tissues but it is not clear if this reflects a high proportion of cytoplasm in these cells. Very little is known about the control of ascorbate synthesis or of the expression and regulatory properties of the enzymes involved. However, with the current availability of gene probes and antibodies to some of the component enzymes, this situation should change rapidly. Radiolabeling studies have shown a slow but appreciable ascorbate turnover in pea seedlings (123) and *A. thaliana* leaves (20). The pool size therefore results from a balance between synthesis and breakdown. In pea seedlings, incorporation of ^{14}C-Glc into AA is inhibited when the pool is elevated by prior AA feeding, providing evidence for control of AA synthesis by feedback or repression at an unidentified point(s) (123). Conversion of D-Fru-6-P to D-Man-6-P might be limited by PMI activity (see earlier section on ascorbate biosynthetic enzymes) while synthesis of GDP-L-Fuc and use of GDP-D-Man and GDP-L-Gal as precursors for glycoproteins and cell wall polysaccharides will potentially compete with AA synthesis. As would be predicted, both antisense suppression of GDP-Man pyrophosphorylase (63) and lowered activity in *vtc1* (GL Wheeler et al, unpublished results) decrease AA content and the proportion of Man in the cell wall. The factors that determine formation of L-Gal from GDP-L-Gal are likely to be key in determining flux to AA. The limited data available from *vtc1* (19) and antisense suppression of GDP-Man pyrophosphorylase in potato (63) suggest that this enzyme exerts significant control since a reduction in activity of 40–50% results in 30–44% of wild-type AA content. Interestingly, the last two steps, L-GalDH and GALDH, have extremely high capacity compared to earlier steps since exogenous L-Gal and GalL increase the AA pool very rapidly (26, 166). This might explain why L-Gal and GalL are barely detectable in tissue extracts and are certainly far below the K_m of either enzyme (121; GL Wheeler & N Smirnoff, unpublished data).

In leaves of a number of species, there is a strong relationship between light and AA content. Acclimation to high light increases the AA pool whereas transfer to low light or darkness causes a decrease (32, 148, 150). In either case, the adjustment is relatively slow, taking several days to complete. In vivo GalLDH activity, determined by the rate of AA accumulation after feeding GalL, is faster in high light–acclimated leaves. Furthermore, in leaves acclimated to a particular light intensity, the in vivo GalLDH activity is greater at higher light intensity (148). GALDH capacity is therefore light dependent and its activity is influenced by the current light regime. It is surprising that the last step of the pathway behaves in this way but it suggests that there are some intriguing interactions between light, mitochondrial metabolism, and ascorbate synthesis. AA decreases in darkened detached leaves of a number of species (20, 148, 150) indicating an altered balance between synthesis and turnover. Feeding with Glc or sucrose in the dark partially reverses this, perhaps by providing hexose substrate (150).

Intracellular compartmentation could affect AA synthesis by altering the extent of feedback inhibition or repression (123). AA occurs in all subcellular compartments but at different concentrations (48, 123). Chloroplasts in particular can contain 20–50 mM AA while enormous concentrations of up to 0.3 M have been estimated in some high mountain species (148, 157). Various AA transporters have been detected but so far little is known about their role in determining intracellular AA distribution (48).

AA turnover has been measured by following metabolism of radiolabeled AA (20, 123). Quantitative estimates suggest that 2.5 (in *A. thaliana* leaves) to 13% (in germinating pea seedlings) of the pool turns over per hour (20, 123). Elevating the AA pool of pea seedlings by AA feeding increases the rate of turnover (123), which suggests that turnover could contribute to controlling AA pool size. AA turnover could result from a number of processes. Accumulation of dehydroascorbate as a result of AA oxidation could lead to its delactonization to 2,3-diketogulonate. The low AA content of the quiescent center of maize root meristems has been attributed to very high AA oxidase activity (65). There is recent evidence that whereas AA oxidase activity in the quiescent center is regulated by auxin, high auxin appears to elevate AA oxidase activity. In turn, AA oxidase oxidatively decarboxylates auxin, suggestive of a feedback control mechanism to regulate AA oxidase, and therefore AA content, in the quiescent center (66). The other fate of AA is cleavage of the carbon skeleton to produce oxalate, L-*threo*nate, L-tartrate, and other products (71, 81, 82).

A relationship between AA pool size and boron (B) supply has been suggested. Depriving squash (*Cucurbita pepo*) roots of B results in a rapid drop in their AA content. Inhibition of root growth can be partially restored by AA feeding (99). The results suggest that B supply affects AA synthesis or turnover and that at least part of the symptoms of B deficiency could be related to AA deficiency.

CONCLUDING REMARKS

In recent years interest in the metabolism and function of AA has increased and a biosynthesis pathway has been proposed that is fully supported by biochemical and molecular genetic evidence from AA-deficient *vtc* mutants. This now opens the way for understanding how AA biosyntheis is controlled and for probing its physiological roles. Key areas to be addressed include the following.

1. Characterization and molecular cloning of GDP-Man-3,5-epimerase and the enzymes that form L-Gal from GDP-L-Gal.

2. Understanding the control of AA synthesis, particularly its interaction with cell wall biosynthesis, mitochondrial metabolism, and light.

3. Metabolic engineering of AA synthesis to explore its roles in growth, photosynthesis, and tolerance to oxidative stress.

4. Assess the physiological significance of suggested alternative AA biosynthesis "inversion" type pathways via uronic acids.

5. Fully characterize the "inversion" type AA biosynthetic pathways in protists.

6. Reassess the role of AA in oxalate biosynthesis in a wider range of plant species and identify the enzymes and genes involved.

Clearly, much progress has been made in the last few years in understanding the synthesis of AA in plants. Even more apparent is that fact that many questions regarding this pathway have yet to be answered. It is hoped that the next decade of research on plant AA biosynthesis will be as fruitful as the last.

ACKNOWLEDGMENTS

Research in NS's laboratory is supported by the Biotechnology and Biological Sciences Research Council (UK) and Bio-Technical Resources (Wisconsin, USA). PLC's research is funded by the Plant Responses to the Environment Program of the USDA National Research Initiative Competitive Grants Program.

Visit the Annual Reviews home page at www.AnnualReviews.org

LITERATURE CITED

1. Arrigoni O. 1994. Ascorbate system in plant development. *J. Bioenerg. Biomemb.* 26:407–19
2. Arrigoni O, Arrigoni-Liso R, Calabrese G. 1977. Ascorbic acid requirement for biosynthesis of hydroxyproline-containing proteins in plants. *FEBS Lett.* 82:135–38
3. Arrigoni O, De Gara L, Paciolla C, Evidente A, de Pinto MC, Liso R. 1997. Lycorine: a powerful inhibitor of L-galactono-γ-lactone dehydrogenase activity. *J. Plant Physiol.* 150:362–64
4. Ault RG, Baird DK, Carrington HC, Haworth WN, Herbert R, et al. 1933. Synthesis of d- and l-ascorbic acid and of analogous substances. *J. Chem. Soc.* 1419–23
5. Baig MM, Kelly S, Loewus F. 1970. L-Ascorbic acid biosynthesis in higher plants from L-gulono-1,4-lactone and L-galactono-1,4-lactone. *Plant Physiol.* 46:277–80
6. Barber GA. 1971. The synthesis of L-glucose (sic: L-galactose) by plant enzyme systems. *Arch. Biochem. Biophys.* 147:619–23
7. Barber GA. 1979. Observations on the mechanism of the reversible epimerization

of GDP-mannose to GDP-L-galactose by an enzyme from *Chlorella pyrenoidosa.* *J. Biol. Chem.* 245:7600–3
8. Bartoli CG, Pastori GM, Foyer CH. 2000. Ascorbate biosynthesis in mitochondria is linked to the electron transport chain between complexes III and IV. *Plant Physiol.* 123:335–43
9. Baydoun EA-H, Fry SC. 1988. [2–^{3}H] Mannose incorporation in cultured plant cells: investigation of L-galactose residues of the primary wall. *J. Plant Physiol.* 132:484–90
10. Bleeg HS, Christensen F. 1982. Biosynthesis of ascorbate in yeast. *Eur. J. Biochem.* 127:391–96
11. Bonin CP, Potter I, Vanzin GF, Reiter WD. 1997. The *MUR1* gene of *Arabidopsis thaliana* encodes an isoform of GDP-D-mannose-4,6-dehydratase, catalyzing the first step in the *de novo* synthesis of GDP-L-fucose. *Proc. Natl. Acad. Sci. USA* 94:2085–90
12. Burns JJ. 1967. Ascorbic acid. In *Metabolic Pathways*, ed. DM Greenberg, 1:394–411. New York: Academic. 3rd ed.
13. Burns JJ, Mosbach EH. 1956. Further observations in the biosynthesis of L-ascorbic

acid from D-glucose in the rat. *J. Biol. Chem.* 221:107–11

14. Chatterjee IB. 1973. Evolution and biosynthesis of ascorbic acid. *Science* 21:1271–72

15. Cleasby A, Wonacott A, Skarzynski T, Hubbard RE, Davies GJ, et al. 1996. The X-ray crystal structure of phosphomannose isomerase from *Candida albicans* at 1.7 angstrom resolution. *Nat. Struct. Biol.* 3:470–79

16. Collins LV, Hackett J. 1991. Sequence of the phosphomannose isomerase-encoding gene of *Salmonella typhimurium. Gene* 103:135–36

17. Conklin PL, Last RL. 1995. Isolation of ozone-hypersensitive mutants in *Arabidopsis thaliana. Plant Physiol.* (Suppl.) 108:35. Abstr. 102

18. Conklin PL, Last RL. 1995. Differential accumulation of antioxidant mRNAs in *Arabidopsis thaliana* exposed to ozone. *Plant Physiol.* 109:203–12

19. Conklin PL, Norris SR, Wheeler GL, Williams EH, Smirnoff N. 1999. Genetic evidence for the role of GDP-mannose in plant ascorbic acid (vitamin C) biosynthesis. *Proc. Natl. Acad. Sci. USA* 96:4198–93

20. Conklin PL, Pallanca JE, Last RL, Smirnoff N. 1997. L-Ascorbic acid metabolism in the ascorbate-deficient Arabidopsis mutant *vtc1. Plant Physiol.* 115:1277–85

21. Conklin PL, Saracco SA, Norris SR, Last RL. 2000. Identification of ascorbic acid-deficient *Arabidopsis thaliana* mutants. *Genetics* 154:847–56

22. Conklin PL, Williams EH, Last RL. 1996. Environmental stress sensitivity of an ascorbic acid-deficient Arabidopsis mutant. *Proc. Natl. Acad. Sci. USA* 93:9970–74

23. Conter PF, Guimarães MF, Veiga LA. 1984. Induction and repression of L-fucose dehydrogenase of *Pullularia pullulans. Can. J. Microbiol.* 30:753–57

24. Crawford TC, Crawford SA. 1980. Syn-

thesis of L-ascorbic acid. *Adv. Carbohydr. Chem. Biochem.* 37:79–155

25. Dalessandro G, Piro G, Northcote DH. 1986. Glucomannan-synthase activity in differentiating cells of *Pinus sylvestris* L. *Planta* 169:564–74

26. Davey MW, Gilot C, Persiau G, Østergaard J, Han Y, et al. 1999. Ascorbate biosynthesis in Arabidopsis cell suspension culture. *Plant Physiol.* 121:535–43

27. Davey MW, van Montagu M, Inzé D, Sanmartin M, Kanellis A, et al. 2000. Plant L-ascorbic acid: chemistry, function, metabolism, bioavailability and effects of processing. *J. Sci. Food Agric.* 80:825–60

28. Dumbrava V, Pall ML. 1987. Control of nucleotide and erythroascorbic acid pools by cyclic AMP in *Neurospora crassa. Biochim. Biophys. Acta* 926:331–38

29. Dwivedi K, Post AF, Bullerjahn GS. 1996. Cloning and functional analysis of the *pmmA* gene encoding phosphomannomutase from the photosynthetic prokaryote *Prochlorothrix hollandica. Biochim. Biophys. Acta* 1291:252

30. Elbein AD. 1969. Biosynthesis of a cell wall glucomannan in mung bean seedlings. *J. Biol. Chem.* 244:1608–16

31. Elling L, Ritter JE, Verseck S. 1996. Expression, purification and characterization of recombinant phosphomannomutase and GDP-α-D-mannose pyrophosphorylase from *Salmonella enterica*, group B, for the synthesis of GDP-α-D-mannose from D-mannose. *Glycobiology* 6:591–97

32. Eskling M, Åkerlund HE. 1998. Changes in the quantities of violaxanthin de-epoxidase, xanthophylls and ascorbate in spinach upon shift from low to high light. *Photosynth. Res.* 57:41–50

33. Feingold DS. 1982. Aldo (and keto) hexoses and uronic acids. In *Encyclopedia of Plant Physiology. Plant Carbohydrates I: Intracellular Carbohydrates*, ed. FA Loewus, W Tanner, 13A:3–76. New York: Springer

34. Finkle BJ, Kelly S, Loewus FA. 1960.

Metabolism of D-[1-^{14}C]- and D-[6-^{14}C] glucuronolactone by the ripening strawberry. *Biochim. Biophys. Acta* 38:332–39

35. Franceschi VR. 1987. Oxalic acid metabolism and calcium oxalate formation in *Lemna minor* L. *Plant Cell Environ.* 10: 397–406

36. Franceschi VR, Horner HT Jr. 1979. Use of *Psychotria punctata* callus in study of calcium oxalate crystal idioblast formation. *Z. Pflanzenphysiol.* 92:61–75

37. Franceschi VR, Loewus FA. 1995. Oxalate biosynthesis and function in plants and fungi. In *Calcium Oxalate in Biological Systems*, ed. SR Khan, pp. 113–30. Boca Raton, FL:CRC

38. Grace SC, Logan BA. 1996. Acclimation of foliar antioxidant systems to growth irradiance in three broadleaved evergreen species. *Plant Physiol.* 112:1631–40

39. Griffin AM, Poelwijk EA, Morris VJ, Gasson MJ. 1997. Cloning of the aceF gene encoding the phosphomannose isomerase and GDP-mannose pyrophosphorylase activities involved in acetan biosynthesis in *Acetobacter xylinum*. *FEMS Microbiol. Lett.* 154:389–96

40. Grün M, Loewus FA. 1984. L-Ascorbic acid biosynthesis in the euryhaline diatom *Cyclotella criptica*. *Planta* 160:6–11

41. Hancock RD, Galpin JR, Viola R. 2000. Biosynthesis of L-ascorbic acid (vitamin C) by *Sacchararomyces cerevisiae*. *FEMS Microbiol. Lett.* 186:245–50

42. Hansen SH, Frank SR, Casanova JE. 1997. Cloning and characterization of human phosphomannomutase, a mammalian homologue of yeast SEC53. *Glycobiology* 7:829–34

43. Harris GC, Gibbs PM, Ludwig G, Un A, Sprengnether M, Kolodny N. 1986. Mannose metabolism in corn and its impact on leaf metabolites, photosynthetic gas exchange, and chlorophyll fluorescence. *Plant Physiol.* 82:1081–89

44. Hebda PA, Behrman EJ, Barber GA. 1979. The guanosine 5′-diphosphate D-mannose:

guanosine 5′-diphosphate L-galactose epimerase of *Chlorella pyrenoidosa*. *Arch. Biochem. Biophys.* 194:496–502

45. Helsper JP, Kagan L, Hilby CL, Maynard TM, Loewus FA. 1982. L-Ascorbic acid biosynthesis in *Ochromonas danica*. *Plant Physiol.* 69:465–68

46. Herbert RW, Hirst EL, Percival EGV, Reynolds RJW, Smith F. 1933. The constitution of ascorbic acid. *J. Chem. Soc.* 1270–90

47. Herold A, Lewis DH. 1977. Mannose and green plants: occurrence, physiology and metabolism, and use as a tool to study the role of orthophosphate. *New Phytol.* 79:1–40

48. Horemans N, Foyer CH, Asard H. 2000. Transport and action of ascorbate at the plant plasma membrane. *Trends Plant Sci.* 5:263–67

49. Horner HT, Kausch AP, Wagner BL. 2000. Ascorbic acid serves as precursor for oxalate synthesis in calcium oxalate idioblasts of *Yucca torreyi* in liquid root culture. *Intl. J. Plant Sci.* 161:861–68

50. Horowitz HH, Doerschuk AP, King CG. 1952. The origin of L-ascorbic acid in the albino rat. *J. Biol. Chem.* 199:193–98

51. Horowitz HH, King CG. 1953. The conversion of glucose-6-C^{14} to ascorbic acid by the albino rat. *J. Biol. Chem.* 200:125–28

52. Huh W-K, Kim S-T, Yang K-S, Seok Y-J, Hah YC, Kang S-O. 1994. Characterization of D-arabinono-1,4-lactone oxidase from *Candida albicans* ATCC 10231. *Eur. J. Biochem.* 225:1073–79

53. Huh W-K, Lee B-H, Kim S-T, Kim Y-R, et al. 1998. D-Erythroascorbic acid is an important antioxidant molecule in *Saccharomyes cerevisiae*. *Mol. Microbiol.* 30:895–903

54. Imai T, Karita S, Shiratori G, Hattori M, Nunome T, et al. 1998. L-Galactono-γ-lactone dehydrogenase from sweet potato: purification and cDNA sequence analysis. *Plant Cell Physiol.* 39:1350–58

55. Isherwood FA, Chen YT, Mapson LW.

1954. Synthesis of L-ascorbic acid in plants and animals. *Biochem. J.* 56:1–15

56. Isherwood FA, Mapson LW. 1961. Biosynthesis of L-ascorbic acid in animals and plants. *Ann. NY Acad. Sci.* 92:6–20

57. Jain AK, Nessler CL. 2000. Metabolic engineering of an alternative pathway for ascorbic acid biosynthesis in plants. *Mol. Breed.* 6:73–78

58. Joersbo M, Donaldson I, Kreiberg J, Petersen SG, Brunstedt J, Okkels FT. 1998. Analysis of mannose selection used for transformation of sugar beet. *Mol. Breed.* 4:111–17

59. Joersbo M, Mikkelsen JD, Brunstedt J. 2000. Relationship between promoter strength and transformation frequencies using mannose selection for the production of transgenic sugar beet. *Mol. Breed.* 6:207–13

60. Joersbo M, Petersen SG, Okkels FT. 1999. Parameters interacting with mannose selection employed for the production of transgenic sugar beet. *Physiol. Plant.* 105:109–15

61. Keates SE, Loewus FA, Helms GL, Zink DL. 1998. 5–*O*-(α-D-galactopyranosyl)-D-*glycero*-pent-2–enono-1,4–lactone: characterization in the oxalate-producing fungus, *Sclerotinia sclerotiorum*. *Phytochemistry* 49:2397–401

62. Keates SE, Tarlyn NM, Loewus FA, Franceschi VR. 2000. L-Ascorbic acid and L-galactose are sources for oxalic acid and calcium oxalate in *Pistia stratiotes*. *Phytochemistry* 53:433–40

63. Keller R, Springer F, Renz A, Kossmann J. 1999. Antisense inhibition of the GDP-mannose pyrophosphorylase reduces the ascorbate content in transgenic plants leading to developmental changes during senescence. *Plant J.* 19:131–41

64. Kenney WC, Edmondson DE, Singer TP, Nakagawa H, Asano A, Sato R. 1976. Identification of covalently bound flavin of L-gulono-γ-lactone oxidase. *Bioch. Biophy. Res. Commun.* 71:1194–200

65. Kerk NM, Feldman LJ. 1995. A biochemical model for the initiation and maintenance of the quiescent center: implications for organization of root meristems. *Development* 121:2825–33

66. Kerk NM, Jiang K, Feldman LJ. 2000. Auxin metabolism in the root apical meristem. *Plant Physiol.* 122:925–32

67. Kim H-S, Huh W-K, Kim J-Y, Hwang S-W, Kang S-O. 1996. D-Arabinose dehydrogenase and biosynthesis of D-erythroascorbic acid in *Candida albicans*. *Biochim. Biophys. Acta* 1297:1–8

68. Kim S-T, Huh W-K, Lee B-H, Kang S-O. 1998. D-Arabinose dehydrogenase and its gene from *Saccharomyces cerevisiae*. *Biochim. Biophys. Acta* 1429:29–39

69. Kiuchi K, Nishikimi M, Yagi K. 1982. Purification and characterization of L-gulonolactone oxidase from chicken kidney microsomes. *Biochemistry* 21:5076–82

70. Koshizaka T, Nishikimi M, Ozawa T, Yagi K. 1988. Isolation and sequence analysis of a complementary DNA encoding rat liver L-gulono-γ-lactone oxidase, a key enzyme for L-ascorbic acid biosynthesis. *J. Biol. Chem.* 263:1619–21

71. Kostman TA, Tarlyn NM, Loewus FA, Franceschi VR. 2001. Biosynthesis of L-ascorbic acid and conversion of carbons 1 and 2 of L-ascorbic acid to oxalic acid occurs within individual calcium oxalate crystal idioblasts. *Plant Physiol.* 125:634–40

72. Krasnov A, Reinisalo M, Pitkänen TI, Nishikimi M, Mölsä H. 1998. Expression of rat gene for L-gulono-γ-lactone oxidase, the key enzyme of L-ascorbic acid biosynthesis, in guinea pig cells and in teleost rainbow trout (*Oncorhynchus mykiss*). *Biochim. Biophys. Acta* 1381:241–48

73. Krook J, Vreugdenhil D, Dijkema C, van der Plas LHW. 2000. Uptake of ^{13}C-glucose by cell suspensions of carrot (*Daucus carota*) measured by in vivo NMR: cycling of triose-, pentose- and

hexose-phosphates. *Physiol. Plant.* 108: 125–33

73a. Lee B-H, Huh W-K, Kim S-T, Kang S-O. 1999. Bacterial production of D-erythroascorbic acid and L-ascorbic acid through functional expression of *Saccharomyces cerevisiae* D-arabinono-1,4-lactone oxidase in *Escherichia coli. Appl. Environ. Microbiol.* 65:4685–87

74. Lee BT, Matheson NK. 1984. Phospho-mannoisomerase and phosphoglucoiso-merase in seeds of *Cassia coluteoides* and some other legumes that synthesise galactomannan. *Phytochemistry* 23:983–87

75. Leibowitz MD, Dickinson DB, Loewus FA, Loewus MW. 1977. Partial purifica-tion and study of pollen glucuronokinase. *Arch. Biochem. Biophys.* 179:559–64

76. Leung CT, Loewus FA. 1985. Concern-ing the presence and formation of ascor-bic acid in yeasts. *Plant Sci.* 38:65–69

77. Loewus FA. 1963. Tracer studies on ascorbic acid formation in plants. *Phyto-chemistry* 2:109–28

78. Loewus F. 1965. Inositol metabolism and cell wall formation in plants. *FASEB Fed. Proc.* 24:855–62

79. Loewus F, ed. 1973. *Biogenesis of Plant Cell Wall Polysaccharides*. New York: Academic. 370 pp.

80. Loewus FA. 1980. L-Ascorbic acid: metabolism, biosynthesis, function. In *The Biochemistry of Plants*, ed. J Priess, 3:77–99. New York: Academic

81. Loewus FA. 1988. Ascorbic acid and its metabolic products. In *The Biochemistry of Plants*, ed. J Preiss, 14:85–107. Boca Raton, FL: Academic

82. Loewus FA. 1999. Biosynthesis and meta-bolism of ascorbic acid in plants and of analogs of ascorbic acid in fungi. *Phyto-chemistry* 52:193–210

83. Loewus FA, Helsper JPFG. 1982. Metabolism of L-ascorbic acid in plants. In *Ascorbic acid: Chemistry, Metabolism, and Uses*, ed. PA Seib, BM Tolbert, *Adv.*

Chem. Ser. 200, pp, 249–61. Washington DC: Am. Chem. Soc.

84. Loewus FA, Jang R. 1957. Further studies on the formation of ascorbic acid in plants. *Biochim. Biophys. Acta* 23:205–6

85. Loewus FA, Jang R, Seegmiller CG. 1956. The conversion of ^{14}C-labeled sugars to L-ascorbic acid in ripening strawberries. *J. Biol. Chem.* 222:649–64

86. Loewus FA, Jang R, Seegmiller CG. 1958. The coversion of ^{14}C-labeled sugars to L-ascorbic acid in ripening strawberries. IV. A comparative study of D-galacturonic acid and L-ascorbic acid formation. *J. Biol. Chem.* 232:533–41

87. Loewus FA, Kelly S. 1959. The conversion of D-glucuronolactone to L-gulonic acid by the detached ripening strawberry. *Biochem. Biophys. Res. Commun.* 1:143–46

88. Loewus FA, Kelly S. 1961. The meta-bolism of D-galacturonic acid and its methyl ester in the detached ripening straw-berry. *Arch. Biochem. Biophys.* 95:483–93

89. Loewus FA, Kelly S. 1961. Identity of L-ascorbic acid formed from D-glucose by the strawberry (*Fragaria*). *Nature* 191:1059–61

90. Loewus FA, Kelly S. 1963. Inositol metabolism in plants. I. Labeling patterns in cell wall polysaccharides from detached plants given *myo*-inositol-2-t or -2-[14]C. *Arch. Biochem. Biophys.* 102:96–105

91. Loewus FA, Kelly S, Hiatt HH. 1960. Ascorbic acid synthesis from D-glucose-2-C[14] in the liver of the intact rat. *J. Biol. Chem.* 235:837–39

92. Loewus FA, Kelly S, Neufeld EF. 1962. Metabolism of *myo*-inositol in plants: con-version to pectin, hemicellulose, D-xylose, and sugar acids. *Proc. Natl. Acad. Sci. USA* 48:421–25

93. Loewus FA, Loewus MW. 1983. *myo*-Inositol: its biosynthesis and metabolism. *Annu. Rev. Plant Physiol.* 34:137–61

94. Loewus FA, Loewus MW. 1987. Biosyn-thesis and metabolism of ascorbic acid in

plants. *CRC Crit. Rev. Plant Sci.* 5:101–19

95. Loewus FA, Murthy PPN. 2000. *myo*-Inositol metabolism in plants. *Plant Sci.* 150:1–19

96. Loewus FA, Saito K, Suto RK, Maring E. 1995. Conversion of D-arabinose to D-erythroascorbic acid and oxalic acid in *Sclerotinia sclerotiorum*. *Biochem. Biophys. Res. Commun.* 212:196–203

97. Loewus MW, Bedgar DL, Saito K, Loewus FA. 1990. Conversion of L-sorbosone to L-ascorbic acid by a NADP+-dependent dehydrogenase in bean and spinach leaf. *Plant Physiol.* 94:1492–95

98. Loughman BC, Ratcliffe RG, Southon TE. 1989. Observations on the cytoplastic and vacuolar orthophosphate pools in leaf tissues using *in vivo* ³¹P-NMR spectroscopy. *FEBS Lett.* 242:279–84

99. Lukaszewski KM, Blevins DG. 1996. Root growth inhibition in boron-deficient or aluminum-stressed squash may be a result of impaired ascorbate metabolism. *Plant Physiol.* 112:1135–40

100. Mapson LW, Breslow E. 1958. Biological synthesis of ascorbic acid: L-Galactono-γ-lactone dehydrogenase. *Biochem. J.* 68:395–406

101. Mapson LW, Isherwood FA, Chen YT. 1954. Biological synthesis of L-ascorbic acid: the conversion of L-galactono-γ-lactone into L-ascorbic acid by plant mitochondria. *Biochem. J.* 56:21–28

102. Maier E, Kurtz G. 1982. D-Galactose dehydrogenase from *Pseudomonas fluorescens*. *Meth.Enzymol.* 89:176–81

103. Morré DJ, Boss WF, Loewus FA, eds. 1990. *Inositol Metabolism in Plants*. New York:Wiley-Liss. 393 pp.

104. Murakawa T, Sano S, Yamashita H, Takahashi T. 1977. Biosynthesis of D-erythroascorbic acid by *Candida*. *Agric. Biol. Chem.* 41:1799–800

105. Murakawa T, Takahashi T. 1977. Biosynthesis of a new ascorbic acid analog by D-gluconolactone dehydrogenase of *Penicillium cyano-fulvum*. *Agric. Biol. Chem.* 41:2103–4

106. Mutsada M, Ishikawa T, Takeda T, Shigeoka S. 1995. Subcellular localization and properties of L-galactono-γ-lactone dehydrogenase in spinach leaves. *Biosci. Biotech. Biochem.* 59:1983–84

107. Neubauer C, Yamamoto HY. 1994. Membrane barriers and Mehler-peroxidase limit the ascorbate available for violaxanthin de-epoxidase activity in intact chloroplasts. *Photosynth. Res.* 39:137–47

108. Nick JA, Leung CT, Loewus FA. 1986. Isolation and identification of erythroascorbic acid in *Saccharomyces cerevisiae* and *Lipomyces starkeyi*. *Plant Sci.* 46:181–87

109. Nickle TC, Meinke DW. 1998. A cytokinesis-deficient mutant of Arabidopsis (cyt1) characterized by embryonic lethality, incomplete cell walls and excessive callose accumulation. *Plant J.* 15:321–32

110. Nishikimi M, Kawai T, Yagi K. 1992. Guinea pigs possess a highly mutated gene for L-gulono-γ-lactone oxidase, the key enzyme for L-ascorbic acid biosynthesis missing in this species. *J. Biol. Chem.* 267:21967–72

111. Nishikimi M, Koshizaka T, Ozawa T, Yagi K. 1988. Occurrence in humans and guinea pigs of the gene related to their missing enzyme L-gulono-γ-lactone oxidase. *Arch. Biochem. Biophys.* 267:842–46

112. Nishikimi M, Noguchi E, Yagi K. 1978. Occurrence in yeast of L-galactonolactone oxidase which is similar to a key enzyme for ascorbic acid biosynthesis in animals. *Arch. Biochem. Biophys.* 191:479–86

113. Nishikimi M, Tolbert BM, Udenfriend S. 1976. Purification and characterization of L-gulono-γ-lactone oxidase from rat and goat liver. *Arch. Biochem. Biosphys.* 175:427–35

114. Noctor G, Foyer CH. 1998. Ascorbate and glutathione: keeping active oxygen under control. *Annu. Rev. Plant Physiol. Plant Mol. Biol.* 49:249–79

115. Nuss RF, Loewus FA. 1978. Further studies on oxalic acid biosynthesis in oxalate-accumulating plants. *Plant Physiol.* 56:590–92

116. Ôba K, Fukui M, Imai Y, Iriyama S, Nogami K. 1994. L-Galactono-γ-lactone dehydrogenase: partial characterization, induction of activity and role in the synthesis of ascorbic acid in wounded white potato tuber tissue. *Plant Cell Physiol.* 35:473–78

117. Ôba K, Ishikawa S, Nishikawa M, Mizuno H, Yamamoto T. 1995. Purification and properties of L-galactono-γ-lactone dehydrogenase, a key enzyme for ascorbic acid biosynthesis, from sweet potato roots. *J. Biochem.* 117:120–24

118. Oesterhelt C, Schnarrenberger C, Gross W. 1997. The reaction mechanism of phosphomannomutase in plants. *FEBS Lett.* 401:35–37

119. Okamura M. 1994. Distribution of ascorbic acid analogs and associated glycosides in mushrooms. *J. Nutr. Sci. Vitaminol.* 40:81–94

120. Okamura M. 1998. Separative determination of ascorbic acid analogs contained in mushrooms by high-performance liquid chromatography. *J. Nutr. Sci. Vitaminol.* 44:25–35

121. Østergaard J, Persiau G, Davey MW, Gauw G, van Montagu M. 1997. Isolation of a cDNA coding for L-galactono-γ-lactone dehydrogenase, an enzyme involved in the biosynthesis of ascorbic acid in plants. *J. Biol. Chem.* 272:30009–16

122. Pallanca JE, Smirnoff N. 1999. Ascorbic acid metabolism in pea seedlings. A comparison of D-glucosone, L-sorbosone, and L-galactono-1,4-lactone as ascorbate precursors. *Plant Physiol.* 120:453–61

123. Pallanca JE, Smirnoff N. 2000. The control of ascorbic acid synthesis and turnover in pea seedlings. *J. Exp. Bot.* 51:669–74

124. Papoutsopoulou SV, Kyriakidis DA. 1997. Phosphomannose isomerase of Xanthomonas campestris: a zinc-activated enzyme. *Mol. Cell. Biol.* 177:183–91

125. Pego JV, Weisbeck PJ, Smeekens SCM. 1999. Mannose inhibits *Arabidopsis* germination via a hexokinase-mediated step. *Plant Physiol.* 119:1017–23

126. Popova TN, Matasova LV, Lapot'ko AA. 1998. Purification, separation and characterization of phosphoglucomutase and phosphomannomutase from maize leaves. *Biochem. Mol. Biol. Int.* 46:461–70

127. Popp M, Smirnoff N. 1995. Polyol accumulation and metabolism during water deficit. In *Environment and Plant Metabolism: Flexibility and Acclimation*, ed. N Smirnoff, pp. 199–215. Oxford: Bios Sci.

128. Proudfoot AEI, Goffin L, Payton MA, Wells TNC, Bernard AR. 1996. *In vivo* and *in vitro* folding of a recombinant metalloenzyme, phosphomannose isomerase. *Biochem. J.* 318:437–42

129. Proudfoot AEI, Turcatti G, Wells TNC, Payton MA, Smith DJ. 1994. Purification, cDNA cloning and heterologous expression of human phosphomannose isomerase. *Eur. J. Biochem.* 219:415–23

130. Raibekas AA, Fukui K, Massey V. 2000. Design and properties of human D-amino acid oxidase with covalently attached flavin. *Proc. Natl. Acad. Sci. USA* 97:3089–93

131. Ray SN. 1934. On the nature of the precursor of the vitamin C in the vegetable kingdom. I. Vitamin C in the growing pea seedling. *Biochem. J.* 28:996–1003

132. Reichstein T, Grüssner A, Oppenauer R. 1933. Synthesis of D- and L-ascorbic acids (vitamin C). *Helv. Chim. Acta* 16:1019–33

133. Reiter WD, Chapple CCS, Somerville

CR. 1993. Altered growth and cell walls in a fucose-deficient mutant of Arabidopsis. *Science* 261:1032–35

134. Renstrøm B, Grün M, Loewus FA. 1982/1983. Biosynthesis of L-ascorbic acid in *Chlorella pyrenoidosa. Plant Sci. Lett.* 28:299–305

135. Roberts RM. 1971. The metabolism of D-mannose-^{14}C to polysaccharide in corn roots. Specific labelling of L-galactose, D-mannose, and L-fucose. *Arch. Biochem. Biophys.* 145:685–92

136. Roberts RM, Cetorelli JJ. 1973. UDP-D-glucuronic acid pyrophosphorylase and the formation of UDP-D-glucuronic acid in plants. In *Biogenesis of Plant Cell Wall Polysaccharides*, ed. F Loewus, pp. 49–68. New York: Academic

137. Rumpho MF, Edwards GE, Loescher WH. 1983. A pathway for photosynthetic carbon flow to manitol in celery leaves. Activity and localization of key enzymes. *Plant Physiol.* 73:869–73

138. Running JA, Huss RJ, Olson PT. 1994. Heterotrophic production of ascorbic acid by microalgae. *J. Appl. Phycol.* 6:99–104

139. Saito K. 1996. Formation of L-ascorbic acid and oxalic acid from D-glucosone in *Lemna minor. Phytochemistry* 41:145–49

140. Saito K, Nick JA, Loewus FA. 1990. D-glucosone and L-sorbosone, putative intermediates of L-ascorbic acid biosynthesis in detached bean and spinach leaves. *Plant Physiol.* 94:1496–500

141. Saito K, Ohmoto J, Kuriha N. 1997. Incorporation of ^{18}O into oxalic, L-*threo*nic and L-tartaric acids during cleavage of L-ascorbic acid and 5–keto-D-gluconic acids in plants. *Phytochemistry* 44:805–9

142. Schachter H, Sarney J, McGuire EJ, Roseman S. 1969. Isolation of diphosphopyridine nucleotide-dependent L-fucose dehydrogenase from pork liver. *J. Biol. Chem.* 244:4785–92

143. Shigeoka S, Nakano Y, Kitaoka S. 1979. The biosynthetic pathway of L-ascorbic acid in *Euglena gracilis Z. J. Nutr. Sci. Vitaminol.* 25:299–307

144. Shinabarger D, Barry A, May TB, Rothmel R, Fialho A, Chakrabarty AM. 1991. Purification and characterization of phosphomannose isomerase-guanosine diphospho-D-mannosepyrophosphorylase— a bifunctional enzyme in the alginate biosynthetic-pathway of *Pseudomonas aeruginosa. J. Biol. Chem.* 266:2080–88

145. Siendones E, González-Reyes JA, Santos-Ocaña Navas P, Córdoba F. 1999. Biosynthesis of ascorbic acid in kidney bean; L-galactono-γ-lactone dehydrogenase is an intrinsic protein located at the mitochondrial inner membrane. *Plant Physiol.* 120:907–12

146. Smirnoff N. 1996. The function and metabolism of ascorbic acid in plants. *Ann. Bot.* 78:661–69

147. Smirnoff N. 2000. Ascorbic acid: metabolism and functions of a multifacetted molecule. *Curr. Opinion Plant Biol.* 3:229–35

148. Smirnoff N. 2000. Ascorbate biosynthesis and function in photoprotection. *Phil. Trans. R. Soc. Biol. Sci.* 355:1455–64

149. Smirnoff N. 2000. L-Ascorbic acid biosynthesis. In *Vitamins and Hormones*, ed. T Begley. 61:241–66. San Diego: Academic

150. Smirnoff N, Pallanca JE. 1996. Ascorbate metabolism in relation to oxidative stress. *Biochem. Soc. Trans.* 24:472–78

151. Smirnoff N, Wheeler GL. 1999. Ascorbic acid metabolism in plants. In *Plant Carbohydrate Biochemistry*, ed. JA Bryant, MM Burrell, NJ Kruger, pp 215–29. Oxford: BIOS Sci. Publ.

152. Smirnoff N, Wheeler GL. 2000. Ascorbic acid in plants: biosynthesis and function. *CRC Crit. Rev. Plant Sci.* 19:267–90; *CRC Crit. Rev. Biochem. Mol. Biol.* 35:291–314

153. Smith DJ, Proudfoot AEI, Detiani M, Wells TNC, Payton MA. 1995. Cloning and heterologous expression of the

Candida albicans gene PMI-1 encoding phosphomannose isomerase. *Yeast* 11:301–10

154. Somerville CR, Turner S, Schieble W-R, Lukowitz W, Nichols T, et al. 1998. Genetic dissection of cell wall composition in Arabidopsis. *Plant Physiol. Annu. Meet. Session* 27:S-500001

155. Spickett CM, Smirnoff N, Pitt AR. 2000. The biosynthesis of erythroascorbate in *Saccharomyces cerevisiae* and its role as an antioxidant. *Free Radic. Biol. Med.* 28:183–92

156. Stein JC, Hansen G. 1999. Mannose induces an endonuclease responsible for DNA laddering in plants. *Plant Physiol.* 121:71–79

157. Streb P, Feierabend J, Bligny R. 1997. Resistance to photoinhibition of photosystem II and catalase and antioxidative protection in high mountain plants. *Plant Cell Environ.* 20:1030–40

158. Sugisawa T, Ojima S, Matzinger PK, Hoshino T. 1995. Isolation and characterization of a new vitamin C producing enzyme (L-gulono-lactone dehydrogenase). *Biosci. Biotech. Biochem.* 59:190–96

159. Svirbely JL, Szent-Gyorgyi A. 1932. Hexuronic acid as the antiscorbutic factor. *Nature* 129:576, 610

160. Takahashi T, Murakawa S, Barada M. 1976. Ascorbic acid analogs as indirect products of *Serratia marcescens*. *Agric. Biol. Chem.* 40:1255–56

161. Tarlyn NM, Kostman TA, Nakata PA,

Keates SE, Franceschi VR. 1998. Axenic culture of *Pistia stratiotes* for use in plant biochemical studies. *Aquat. Bot.* 60:161–68

162. Tillmans J, Hirsch P. 1932. Vitamin C. *Biochem. Z.* 250:312–20

163. Toyohara H, Nakata T, Touhata K, Hashimoto H, Kinoshita M, et al. 1996. Transgenic expression of L-gulono-γ-lactone oxidase in Medaka (*Oryzias Iatipes*), a teleost fish that lacks this enzyme necessary for L-ascorbic acid biosynthesis. *Biochem. Biophys. Res Commun.* 223:650–53

164. Wagner GJ. 1981. Vacuolar deposition of ascorbate-derived oxalic acid in barley. *Plant Physiol.* 67:591–93

165. Waugh WA, King CG. 1932. The isolation and identification of vitamin C. *J. Biol. Chem.* 97:325–31

166. Wheeler GL, Jones MA, Smirnoff N. 1998. The biosynthetic pathway of vitamin C in higher plants. *Nature* 393:365–69

167. Wildi B, Lutz C. 1996. Antioxidant composition of selected high alpine plant species from different altitudes. *Plant Cell Environ.* 19:138–46

168. Wozniewski T, Blaschek W, Franz G. 1991. In vitro biosynthesis of a reserve glucomannan from *Lilium testaceum*. *Phytochemistry* 30:3579–83

169. Yang J, Loewus FA. 1975. Metabolic conversion of L-ascorbic acid to oxalic acid in oxalate-accumulating plants. *Plant Physiol.* 56:283–85

Annu. Rev. Plant Physiol. Plant Mol. Biol. 2001. 52:469–97

TONOPLAST TRANSPORTERS: Organization and Function

Masayoshi Maeshima

Laboratory of Biochemistry, Graduate School of Bioagricultural Sciences, Nagoya University, Nagoya 464-8601, Japan; e-mail: maeshima@agr.nagoya-u.ac.jp

Key Words aquaporin, H^+-ATPase, H^+-pyrophosphatase, ion transporters, tonoplast, vacuole

■ **Abstract** Regulation of the contents and volume of vacuoles in plant cells depends on the coordinated activities of transporters and channels located in the tonoplast (vacuolar membrane). The three major components of the tonoplast are two proton pumps, the vacuolar H^+-ATPase (V-ATPase) and H^+-pyrophosphatase (V-PPase), and aquaporins. The tertiary structure of the V-ATPase complex and properties of its subunits have been characterized by biochemical and genetic techniques. These studies and a comparison with the F-type ATPase have enabled estimation of the dynamics of V-ATPase activity during catalysis. V-PPase, a simple proton pump, has been identified and cloned from various plant species and other organisms, such as algae and phototrophic bacteria, and functional motifs of the enzyme have been determined. Aquaporin, serving as the water channel, is the most abundant protein in the tonoplast in most plants. A common molecular architecture of aquaporins in mammals and plants has been determined by two-dimensional crystallographic analysis. Furthermore, recent molecular biological studies have revealed several other types of tonoplast transporters, such as the Ca^{2+}-ATPase, Ca^{2+}/H^+ antiporter and Na^+/H^+ antiporter. Many other transporters and channels in the tonoplast remain to be identified; their activities have already been detected. This review presents an overview of the field and discusses recent findings on the tonoplast protein components that have been identified and their physiological consequences.

CONTENTS

OVERVIEW

The plant cell vacuole has attracted attention recently because of its multifaceted roles, including recycling of cell components, regulation of turgor pressure, detoxification of xenobiotics, and accumulation of many useful substances. Furthermore, the space-filling function of the vacuole is essential for cell growth, because cell enlargement is accompanied by expansion of the vacuole rather than of the cytoplasm. The vacuole occupies as much as 90% of most mature cells. A large number of proteins in the tonoplast support the function of multifaceted vacuoles, including active pumps, carriers, ion channels, receptors, and structural proteins. To date, membrane proteins identified in the tonoplast are limited to several different types. The tonoplast proteins can be separated into 60–80 bands by one-dimensional SDS-polyacrylamide gel electrophoresis (PAGE), but of these, only a dozen major proteins can be distinguished on the gel as already known components, such as the subunits of proton pumps.

Several major proteins of the tonoplast have been extensively investigated and information on their molecular properties has accumulated over the past decade. The three most abundant proteins of the tonoplast are vacuolar H^+-ATPase (V-ATPase), H^+-pyrophosphatase (V-PPase), and water channels (aquaporins). The V-ATPase, composed of several subunits, is the largest complex in the tonoplast. The V-PPase, an alternative proton pump, is also a major component of the tonoplast in most plant tissues. Activities of Ca^{2+}-ATPase, Ca^{2+}/H^+ antiporter, Na^+/H^+ antiporter, and the ATP-binding cassette (ABC) transporters have been identified in tonoplast membrane vesicles or vacuoles, but their polypeptides have not been isolated owing to their low abundance. These transporters have plural isoforms, which are located not only in the tonoplast but also in other organelles such as the plasma membrane and the endoplasmic reticulum (ER). The final localization of their isoforms in cell organelles remains a matter of debate in most cases.

In the case of ion channels in the tonoplast, electrochemical patch clamp analyses have provided fundamental information on the functional properties of single channel molecules, such as ion selectivity, ion conductivity, and regulatory elements. However, it remains difficult to determine the biochemical properties because of the existence of various different types and isoforms, and the extremely low amounts of channel proteins. Since the rate of ion transport with a channel is much higher than that with a transporter, a small number of channel protein complexes is enough for rapid transmembrane ion translocation, which yields a measurable ion current. In contrast to ion channels, tonoplast intrinsic proteins (TIP) known as water channels are the most abundant tonoplast proteins in most plant tissues. In addition to these components, cDNAs for several other transporters have been cloned, and their localization in the tonoplast has been demonstrated. Also, biochemical and electrochemical analyses have revealed that the tonoplast has the functions of several additional transport systems. Recent reviews emphasize the importance of tonoplast transport systems in Ca^{2+} signaling (121), ion homeostasis (18), and turgor pressure regulation (142).

The tonoplast is a functionally, highly organized membrane, with proton pumps and several H^+/X antiporters, which use a pH gradient generated by proton pumps, cooperatively working in the same membrane. Thus, there is a proton circuit on the tonoplast. Various ion channels also utilize the membrane potential generated by proton pumps, and aquaporin function also is influenced by these other primary and secondary active transporters. The cooperative work of these different transport systems regulates the vacuole lumenal pH, amount of stored substances, and volume of the vacuole. To understand the functional organization of the tonoplast transport systems, the individual components must be examined. This review focuses on recent progress in studies on fundamental molecular and biochemical properties of aquaporins and transporters, which have been identified in the tonoplast.

VACUOLAR H^+-ATPase

Enzymatic Characteristics

V-ATPase is a universal enzyme distributed in the membrane of various acidic organelles in eukaryotic cells and in the plasma membrane of insect and certain bacterial cells. Several fine reviews are available on the V-ATPase in various organisms: plants (115, 134), yeast (36, 131), *Neurospora crassa* (93), and mammals (37). The K_m value of V-ATPase for Mg-ATP is about 0.1 to 0.2 mM. Chloride ion stimulates ATP hydrolysis and H^+ transport of the V-ATPase, with a K_m of 1 to 2 mM (150). Bafilomycin A_1, concanamycin C, and nitrate have been used as specific inhibitors of the V-ATPase. Patch clamp experiments have shown that the H^+/ATP coupling ratio ranges from 1.75 to 3.28, depending on the cytoplasmic and vacuolar lumenal pH in red beet vacuoles (23). In lemon fruit, the coupling ratio is reported to vary with the state of the enzyme; a normal and an altered state with a low coupling ratio that generate a steep transmembrane pH gradient (102, 103).

Interestingly, a recent paper reported on ATP synthesis by the yeast V-ATPase using an electrochemical proton gradient generated by a V-PPase heterologously expressed in yeast (53). This report does not dispute that the V-ATPase normally functions as a proton pump, since the V_{max} value for ATP synthesis was extremely low (3–5 nmol/mg/min).

By applying the patch clamp technique to the vacuole in haploid giant yeast cells under well-controlled conditions, Yabe et al (155) demonstrated that the K_m value of V-ATPase for the ATP-induced H^+ current was 159 μM, and the H^+/ATP ratio estimated from the reversible potential of the voltage-current curve was 3.5 $\pm$ 0.3. This value was determined with a ΔpH of 2.0 units across the tonoplast where pH was 5.5, corresponding to the lumenal vacuole pH, and a bath solution pH of 7.5, corresponding to cytoplasmic pH. The pH dependence of the H^+/ATP ratio remains to be examined by the same experimental system. This elegant work has paved the way for analysis of the physicochemical properties of the mutated V-ATPase and other plant transporters that are heterologously expressed in yeast.

Subunits and Higher-Order Structure of the V-ATPase

The tertiary structure of the V-ATPase complex is similar to that of F-type ATPases as visualized by electron microscopy (29, 42, 102, 114, 115). The number of subunits (up to 10 subunits) in plant V-ATPases varies according to the plant species (30, 58, 68, 98, 111, 115, 149). V-ATPase is the largest complex in the tonoplast, with a total molecular size of about 750 kDa. The V-ATPase complex is composed of two functional sectors, a peripheral sector (V_1), which contains the catalytic sites involved in ATP hydrolysis, and a transmembrane sector (V_O), which functions as a channel for protons. The catalytic portion (10–12 nm in diameter) of V_1 consists of three copies of A- and B-subunits. The other subunits (C–H) in V_1 form a central stalk (6–7 nm in height) linking the V_1 and V_O sectors. The V_O sector contains the a- and c-subunits, six copies of the c-subunit being present in the complex. The molecular size of the c-subunit (16 kDa) of V-ATPase is about twice that of the c-subunit of F-ATPase. The subunits of the *Arabidopsis thaliana* V-ATPase that have been cloned are shown in Table 1. The F (13–14 kDa), H (51–54 kDa), a (100 kDa), and d (about 45 kDa) subunits have not yet been cloned from plants. They have been detected as protein bands in SDS-PAGE, and some were found in the EST databases of *A. thaliana* and rice.

Judging from the similarities in the primary sequences of subunits and in the tertiary structure of V-ATPase to F-ATPases, it is likely that ATP hydrolysis in the V-ATPase occurs via a similar mechanism to that in F-type ATPase (14, 132). The accepted mechanism of ATP synthesis in the F-ATPase is the so-called binding change mechanism coupled with a rotational mechanism (14). As protons move through the F_O channel of the F-ATPase, energy is released that results in rotation (counter clockwise rotation) of the single-copy γ-subunit. This rotation causes

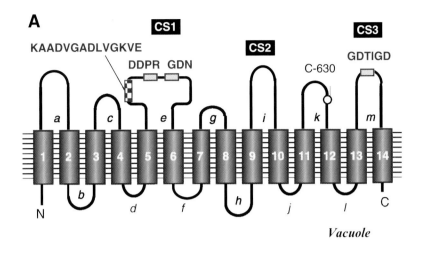

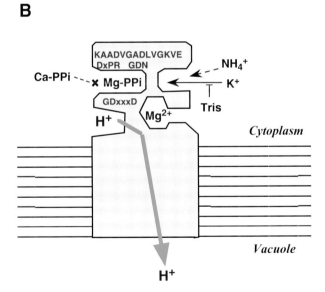

Figure 2 A structural model of V-PPase. (*A*) The 14 putative transmembrane helices are depicted as cylinders and conserved motifs are shown in boxes. The NEM-binding cysteine residue (Cys630 of *Vigna* V-PPase, Cys634 of Arabidopsis enzyme) (161) is shown as a circle. The hydrophilic loops are numbered from *a* to *m*. The conserved segments in the cytosolic loops are indicated as CS1, CS2, and CS3. (*B*) Schematic presentation of the functional motifs in the V-PPase, such as the substrate-binding site, binding pockets for K^+, Mg^{2+}, and the H^+ transport path. See text for details.

TABLE 1   Protein components identified in the tonoplast

Component plant	Amino acids	Accession number	Name	References
V-PPase				
Arabidopsis	770	M81892	AVP3 (AVP1)	122
Mung bean	766	AB009077	VVP2	105
Red beet	766	L32791	BVP1*	69
Tobacco	764	X77915	TVP5*	77
Barley	761	D13472	PP10	138
Rice	771	D45383	OVP1*	119
Chara	793	AB018529	CPP1	107
Acetabularia	721	D88820	AcVP	60
Rhodospirillum	660	AF044912	PP4	5
V-ATPase				
Arabidopsis				
A subunit	623	U65638		90
B subunit	492	J04185	pAt57	92
C subunit	375	AF208261	DET3	123
D subunit	261	AJ225059	vATPD	72
E subunit	230	X92117		26
G subunit	110	AJ005901	VAG1	
G subunit	106	AJ005902	VAG2	
c subunit	164	L44581	AVA-P1	111
c subunit	165	L44582	AVA-P2	111
c subunit	166	AF153677	AVA-P4	79
α-TIP				
Common bean	265	—	α-TIP(Pv)	65
Arabidopsis	258	M84343	α-TIP(At)	57
γ-TIP				
Arabidopsis	251	M84344	γ-TIP(At)	57
Radish	253	D84669	VIP1	52
Rape	253	AF118381	Bng-TIP2	38
δ-TIP				
Arabidopsis	251	U39485	δ-TIP(At)	21
Radish	248	AB010416	VIP3	52
Cotton	248	U62778	δ-TIP(Gh)	32
Ca^{2+}/H^+ antiporter				
Arabidopsis	459	U57411	CAX1	56
Arabidopsis	399	U57412	CAX2	56
Radish	444	AB012932	VCAX1	144
Ca^{2+}-ATPase				
Wild cabbage	1025	X99972	BCA1	91
Tomato	1048	M96324	LCA	153

(Continued)

TABLE 1   (*Continued*)

Component plant	Amino acids	Accession number	Name	References
Na$^+$/H$^+$ antiporter				
Arabidopsis	538	AF106324	AtNHX1	39
Zn transporter				
Arabidopsis	398	AF072858	ZAT	146
Ca^{2+}-binding protein				
Tobacco	316	AF113545	Anx3	127
Radish	248	AB035900	RVCaB	158

Asterisks indicate the presence of plural isoforms.

conformational changes in the three nucleotide-binding sites of the F_1 sector. It has been shown recently that the complex of 12 copies of the c-subunit in F_O rotates with the γ-subunit during ATP hydrolysis (120). The V-ATPase may also have a rotational mechanism; namely, ATP hydrolysis in V_1 drives the rotation of the γ-subunit. The rotation of the γ-subunit of the *Thermus thermophilus* V-ATPase during ATP hydrolysis has been demonstrated recently (S Ohkuma, personal communication), but the question remains as to which subunit of V_1 corresponds to the γ-subunit of F_1. At present, the D-subunit is the most likely candidate for the γ-subunit homolog of V-ATPase, because its sequence is similar to that of the γ-subunit, in addition to having two long α-helices (72). The subunit of V-ATPase that binds for bafilomycin A, a specific inhibitor of V-ATPase, has not been identified. The a-subunit of the bovine enzyme has a binding site for this reagent (160), although oat V-ATPase lacking the a-subunit is reported to be bafilomycin-sensitive (81).

Figure 1 shows a structural model of a plant V-ATPase. The topology of subunits C, E, F, G, H, and d in the complex is still unclear. The a-subunit (100 kDa) of the yeast V-ATPase has been demonstrated to expose its N-terminal region to the cytosol, and there are nine transmembrane domains at the C-terminal part (76). In these transmembrane α helices, several charged residues participate in proton translocation. Thus, it has been proposed that the interface between the a- and c-subunits provides a pathway for proton transport across the membrane in the yeast V-ATPase (36), in a manner similar to that of the F-ATPase (132). The a-subunit is not associated with the fully assembled V-ATPase in some cases (81, 98), but has been detected in the other purified V-ATPases (68, 110). This apparent contradiction may be due to its biochemical properties and function; the a-subunit functions as a stator in a relatively weak association with the hexamer of the c-subunit. One possibility is that calnexin, an integral protein on the ER membrane associated with V-ATPase (80), sustains the interaction between the a- and c-subunits.

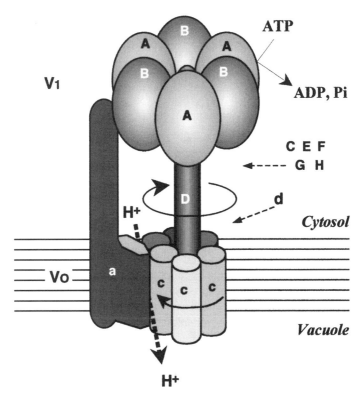

Figure 1 Hypothetical model for the tertiary structure of plant V-ATPase. The V_1 catalytic domain consists of subunits A and B in an A_3B_3 arrangement. The V_O membrane sector is composed of a- and c-subunits in the ac_6 complex. The detailed spatial positions of the other subunits (C, E, F, G, H, and d) are not clear. The model is based on recent reports (see text) and the structure of F-ATPase (132).

Subunit Isoforms and Tissue Specificity

The plant V-ATPase is found mainly in the vacuolar membrane. It can also be associated with membranes of the ER, Golgi bodies, coated vesicles, and provacuoles (50, 80, 97). This multiple localization of the V-ATPase in plant cells raises the question as to what subunit(s) defines the target organelle. In addition to V-ATPases in yeast and mammals (36, 37, 131), the plant V-ATPase has also been reported to have subunit isoforms. Two cDNAs encoding the c-subunit were identified in ice plant (*Mesembryanthemum crystallinum*) (83) and cotton (*Gossypium hirsutum*) (48), and three cDNAs were identified in *A. thaliana* (79, 112). Also, two isoforms were found for the A- (43, 83), B- (10, 83), and G-subunits (accession Nos. AJ005901 and AJ00502) of several plant species. In addition to these reports, the presence of two isoforms of D- and E-subunits has also been demonstrated in mung bean and pea at the protein level (68). Organelle-specific isoforms have not been reported to date, although several subunit isoforms have been found to be expressed in a tissue-specific manner (48, 68, 112) and in a salt-stress specific manner (83, 84, 115). Recent reports on the genetic manipulation of the V-ATPase subunit genes indicate that V-ATPase is essential for morphogenesis of *N. crassa* (A-subunit) (13) and photomorphogenesis of *A. thaliana* (C-subunit) (123) and carrot (A-subunit) (43).

VACUOLAR TYPE H$^+$-PYROPHOSPHATASE

Molecular Properties of V-PPase

An alternative vacuolar proton pump is the V-PPase, for which inorganic pyrophosphate (PPi) is used in place of ATP as an energy donor. The V-PPase is essential for maintaining the acidity of the large central vacuole (86). In the early 1980s (117), PPi-dependent H$^+$ transport activity was defined as being located in the tonoplast. The H$^+$/PPi stoichiometry has been determined to be 1, and the steady-state pH gradient generated across the tonoplast against the neutral cytoplasmic pH has been shown to be approximately 3 pH units (24). Using the patch-clamp technique, we recently detected PPi-dependent current (10–20 pA) at zero membrane potential in vacuoles isolated from giant cells of *Saccharomyces cerevisiae* heterologously expressing the mung bean V-PPase (Y Nakanishi, I Yabe, M Maeshima, unpublished data). Unlike the complex F-ATPases involved in ATP synthesis (14), V-PPase is representative of simple energy-transducing enzymes. This proton pump consists of a single polypeptide, and its substrate, inorganic pyrophosphate (PPi), is one of the simplest high-energy compounds (6, 86, 117, 161). Recent investigations suggest the presence of a new-type of H$^+$-PPase, which may not be localized in the tonoplast in *A. thaliana* (28, 106). Thus, the vacuolar H$^+$-PPase is designated as V-PPase and distinguished from this new type of H$^+$-PPase and other soluble PPases.

V-PPases have been cloned from various organisms; land plants [see references in (86)], marine alga (*Acetabularia acetabulum*) (60), green alga (*Chara corallina*) (107), photosynthetic bacteria (*Rhodospirillum rubrum*) (5), protozoa (*Trypanosoma cruzi*) (accession No. AF159881) (126), and archaebacteria (*Pyrobaculum aerophilum*) (AF182812) (27). However, the V-PPase does not exist in plasma and endomembranes of mammalian or yeast cells. The plant V-PPases consist of 761 to 771 amino acid residues (Table 1). The calculated molecular mass ranges from 80 to 81 kDa, and the apparent size on SDS-polyacrylamide gel is from 70 to 73 kDa (89, 117). Amino acid sequences are highly conserved among V-PPases of land plants, with 86% to 91% identity. *Chara* V-PPase is 71% identical to those in land plants (107), whereas *Acetabularia* V-PPase is only 47% identical to the V-PPases in land plants (60). This sequence similarity suggests that

Chara is evolutionarily closer to land plants. The V-PPase may be a key enzyme for understanding the origin and evolution of central vacuoles in plant cells.

Functional Motifs in V-PPases

From a comparison of all H^+-PPases of various organisms, some highly conserved sequences have been found (6, 86, 117), especially the three conserved regions of CS1, CS2, and CS3 (Figure 2A; see color insert). The CS1 segment contains a common motif DVGADLVGKVE that is essential for the catalytic site. Immuno-chemical analysis confirmed that this sequence is exposed to the cytosol (137). By expressing mutated forms of the mung bean CS1 region in yeast, it was shown that the acidic residues in this motif are critical for PPi hydrolysis and proton transport (108). In addition to the catalytic site, the binding sites for Mg^{2+}, K^+, and reagents, such as N,N'-dicyclohexylcarbodiimide (DCCD), 7-chloro-4-nitrobenzo-2-oxa-1,3-diazole (NBDCl), and N-ethylmaleimide (NEM), have also been identified [see references in (86, 161)].

V-PPases contain several motifs that are also conserved in P-type ATPases such as the Ca^{2+}-ATPase. For example, a common motif GDGxND in P-ATPases is conserved in the CS3 domain of V-PPases as the consensus sequence <u>GDTIGD</u> (722–727 in mung bean V-PPase) (Figure 2A). It has been proposed that this motif is located directly above the stalk portion, which connects a cytoplasmic domain to the transmembrane α helices of the P-ATPase, and this motif is involved in hydrolysis of a phosphoanhydride bond of ATP (3). A large cytoplasmic domain of the P-ATPase contains the other conserved DPPR and TGDN motifs, which are also conserved in the V-PPase (DDPR[271] and VGDN[285] in mung bean V-PPase) (Figure 2A). It has been proposed that DPPR and TGDN motifs in the P-type ATPases are involved in hydrolysis of a phosphoanhydride bond and that the adenosine moiety of ATP interacts with other motifs such as a KGAP motif in the P-ATPases (82, 141, 152). These interesting motifs are lined in tandem in the large cytoplasmic loop (Figure 2A, CS1). The GDTIGD motif, by contrast, is far from this loop and is in the cytoplasmic loop near the N terminus. These three motifs (DDPR, VGDN and GDTIGD) may form the catalytic core domain of the V-PPase (Figure 2B). At least, all the aspartic acid residues in these motifs have been demonstrated to be essential for the enzymatic function of mung bean V-PPase (108). Although there is no overall sequence identity between the primary sequences of V-PPase and P-type ATPases, the presence of these essential motifs suggests a weak relationship between these transporters. At present, V-PPase cannot be classified as belonging to the P-type ATPase family, because there is no experimental evidence for formation of the intermediate-phosphorylation state in the V-PPase. Furthermore, the V-PPase does not possess the common DKTGTLT motif containing the aspartate residue that is transiently phosphorylated by ATP in the reaction cycle.

Site-directed mutagenesis and analysis using specific chemical modifiers and inhibitors have provided information on the structure-function relationship of V-PPases. Combined with these studies, the crystallographic, high-resolution structure of the V-PPase may enable us to understand the coupling mechanism of PPi hydrolysis and H^+ translocation at the molecular level, as has been done for F-ATPase and Ca^{2+}-ATPase (1, 141). At present, the author's group is trying to obtain two-dimensional and three-dimensional crystals of V-PPase for electron-micrography and X-ray crystallography, respectively.

METAL ION TRANSPORTERS

Vacuolar Ca^{2+}-ATPase

The vacuole serves as a primary pool of free calcium ions in plant cells and the vacuole is a major source of Ca^{2+} for intracellular calcium signaling. The Ca^{2+}-ATPase and Ca^{2+}/H^+ antiporter perform active Ca^{2+} transport into the vacuole (122). The Ca^{2+}-ATPase is one of the best-characterized ion-transport ATPases in all organisms. The crystal structure of the Ca^{2+}-ATPase of muscle sarcoplasmic reticulum (SERCA) has been reported recently (141). A transmembrane domain containing a Ca^{2+}-binding site and three cytoplasmic domains (A, N and P) of the Ca^{2+}-ATPase were recognized in the molecular architecture. A phosphorylation site is located in domain P, and the adenosine moiety of ATP is bound to domain N. Plant Ca^{2+}-ATPases have been divided into two groups: type IIA and IIB. Type IIA Ca^{2+}-ATPases have a structure similar to mammalian SERCA. Type IIB Ca^{2+}-ATPases are similar to the mammalian calmodulin-stimulated Ca^{2+}-ATPases (PMCA) in the plasma membrane (135).

In *A. thaliana*, cDNAs for four isoforms of the type IIA Ca^{2+}-ATPase (AtECA) and six isoforms of type IIB Ca^{2+}-ATPase (AtACA) have been cloned [see references in (41, 135)]. These isoforms consist of 998–1069 amino acid residues and the calculated molecular masses are 108–116 kDa. AtACA1 has been demonstrated to be located in the chloroplast inner envelope (59), AtACA2 in the ER membrane (46), and AtECA1 in the ER and Golgi apparatus membranes (82). Although no isoforms of *Arabidopsis* Ca^{2+}-ATPases have been reported to be localized in the tonoplast, a type IIA Ca^{2+}-ATPase from tomato (LCA) and a type IIB Ca^{2+}-ATPase from *Brassica* (BCA1) have been shown to be localized in the tonoplast (Table 1) (33, 91). High Ca^{2+}-ATPase activity has been reported for tonoplast vesicles purified from several plant species (135), but the enzyme content in the tonoplast is insufficient for detection as a protein band on SDS-polyacrylamide gels. Further studies are needed to determine which Ca^{2+}-ATPase isoforms are localized on the *Arabidopsis* tonoplast, and to elucidate the mechanism of intracellular calcium homeostasis.

Vacuolar Ca^{2+}/H^+ Antiporter

The activity of a Ca^{2+}/H^+ antiporter in the tonoplast has been detected in various plant species (9, 16, 124). The Ca^{2+}/H^+ antiporter together with the Ca^{2+}-ATPase plays a key role in vacuolar Ca^{2+} accumulation. The antiporter is driven by a transmembrane pH gradient generated by the V-ATPase and V-PPase. The first Ca^{2+}/H^+ antiporter was cloned from *S. cerevisiae* (VCX1) (20), an event quickly followed by cloning of Ca^{2+}/H^+ antiporters from *A. thaliana* (CAX1 and CAX2) (56) and *V. radiata* (VCAX1) (144) (Table 1). Plant Ca^{2+}/H^+ antiporters consist of a single polypeptide of 399–444 amino acid residues. The antiporter has 11 putative transmembrane domains and a highly acidic motif between the sixth and seventh transmembrane domains, but the structure-function relationships remain to be resolved.

The tonoplast localization of plant Ca^{2+}/H^+ antiporters has been demonstrated by three different approaches: functional complementation in a yeast mutant lacking a vacuolar Ca^{2+}/H^+ antiporter (56, 145), immunological detection in organelles fractionated from plant tissue (144), and localization of a mung bean VCAX1-green fluorescent protein (GFP) fusion protein by fluorescence microscopy (145). Ca^{2+}/H^+ antiporter activity has been detected not only in the tonoplast but also in the plasma membrane (148) and chloroplast thylakoid membranes (31). Localization of the antiporter in the Golgi apparatus has also been suggested in mung bean (145). An antibody specific to VCAX1 reacted with a protein in tonoplast and Golgi membranes but not in plasma membranes or chloroplasts (143, 145). Thus, the cloned Ca^{2+}/H^+ antiporter was thought to be specific to the tonoplast and Golgi membranes. The tonoplast Ca^{2+}/H^+ antiporter has also been immuno-chemically quantified in mung bean (143). The content was highest in the epicotyl (1.1 μg/mg of the tonoplast protein) and almost absent in the leaf and root of mung bean seedlings. The amount of antiporter protein is very low compared with the vacuolar proton pumps and TIPs, making it difficult to recognize the antiporter protein in SDS-polyacrylamide gels.

The reported K_m values for Ca^{2+} in Ca^{2+} transport via the tonoplast Ca^{2+}/H^+ antiporter are relatively high (10–40 μM) compared with those of the tonoplast Ca^{2+}-ATPase (9, 56, 124, 144), whereas the V_{max} value of the antiporter was markedly higher than that of Ca^{2+}-ATPase. From these enzymatic properties, a major function for the Ca^{2+}/H^+ antiporter is thought to be to lower the concentration of cytosolic Ca^{2+} to 1–2 μM after external and/or internal stimuli increase the concentration of cytosolic Ca^{2+}. The Ca^{2+}-ATPase may then act to lower the concentration of Ca^{2+} still further. There are many questions to be answered about the Ca^{2+}/H^+ antiporter, e.g. with respect to the transport mechanism for Ca^{2+} and H^+, tertiary structure, structural similarity to the Na^+/H^+ antiporter, functional cooperation with the Ca^{2+}-ATPase, intracellular distribution, and tissue-specific expression. A recent report suggested that an isoform of the *Arabidopsis* Ca^{2+}/H^+ antiporter (CAX2) with a broad substrate range (Mn^{2+} and Cd^{2+}) might confer tolerance of plants to heavy metal ions (55).

Vacuolar Na^+/H^+ Antiporter

The Na^+/H^+ antiporter can export Na^+ from the cytosol both to the extracellular space and to the vacuole driven by proton gradients across the plasma membrane and tonoplast (11). The Na^+/H^+ group of antiporters has long attracted attention in relation to salt tolerance in plants (11, 12). An *Arabidopsis* Na^+/H^+ antiporter (AtNHX1) was cloned as a homologue to the yeast antiporter, NHX1 (2, 39). The antiporter protein consists of 538 amino acid residues, has several putative transmembrane domains, and an amiloride binding site, which is a specific inhibitor of Na^+/H^+ antiporters (39). The localization of AtNHX1 on the vacuolar membrane has been determined by immunological methods, functional complementation analysis in yeast (39), and overexpression of *AtNHX1* in *A. thaliana* (2). Interestingly, transgenic plants overexpressing *AtNHX1* grew in the presence of 200 mM NaCl. This observation supports a role for the vacuolar Na^+/H^+ antiporter in salt tolerance. Further studies may help us understand the response of plants to salt stress and elucidate a functional relationship between the Na^+/H^+ antiporter and vacuolar proton pumps under stress conditions.

Zinc Transporter

Zinc is an essential plant micronutrient and functions as an essential cofactor for many enzymes: alcohol dehydrogenase, carbonic anhydrase, carboxypeptidase, DNA polymerase, RNA polymerase, and transcription factors with zinc fingers. However, excess zinc has toxic effects on plants. Interestingly, Zn transport across the tonoplast in the Zn-tolerant plant, *Silene vulgaris*, was 2.5 times higher than in Zn-sensitive plants of the same species (147). Thus, the plant vacuole may play a role in sequestering and detoxifying Zn (44). A candidate for the tonoplast Zn transporter (ZAT) has been identified in *A. thaliana* (146). The ZAT protein of 398 amino acid residues has six putative transmembrane domains. The primary sequence is similar to the ZnT (Zn transporter) family of mammalian Zn transporters (over 35% identity), especially the endosome/lysosomal-type Zn transporter ZnT-2 (41%). A common motif HxHSHG, which is in the cytoplasmic loop between the fourth and fifth transmembrane domains, has been thought to be responsible for the binding of Zn^{2+}. Although the tonoplast location of ZAT has not been demonstrated, *Arabidopsis* transgenic lines overexpressing ZAT exhibited enhanced accumulation of Zn in the root and showed a marked increase in resistance to high concentrations of Zn^{2+} in growth media (up to 0.25 mM) (146).

AQUAPORIN

Structural Characteristics of Aquaporin

Aquaporins facilitate water transport across biomembranes in an osmotic pressure-dependent manner. With the discovery of aquaporins, studies have progressed on intracellular and whole-plant water transport at the molecular level (8, 18, 63, 71, 99, 142). Aquaporins belong to a ubiquitous family of membrane intrinsic proteins (MIP). MIP family proteins have a common, basic structure consisting of six membrane-spanning α helices and two Asn-Pro-Ala (NPA) motifs linked to a short

α helix of several hydrophobic residues (51, 104, 118). The transmembrane and half-membrane-spanning α helices of MIPs form a single relatively hydrophobic transmembranous channel for water transport (Figure 3). The two NPA motifs are adjacent to each other in the central part of aquaporin and form the narrowest part of the pore. In the case of human red cell aquaporin, the narrowest part of the pore is about 0.3 nm, which is slightly larger than the diameter of a water molecule (0.28 nm) (104). Recently, it has been proposed that the NPA motif functions as a water-selective filter and the aspartate residue in the motif interacts with a water molecule (104).

Plant cells have two types of aquaporins, located either in the plasma membrane (PIP, or plasma membrane intrinsic protein) or the tonoplast (TIP, or tonoplast intrinsic protein), respectively (18, 99). The TIP endomembrane-type aquaporins are peculiar to plants. TIPs (23–26 kDa) are smaller than PIPs (30 kDa) and the N-terminal hydrophilic portions are shorter in TIPs than in PIPs. The identity of amino acid sequences between TIPs and PIPs in radish is less than 40%, but 64 residues are identical among the two groups (Figure 3A). Interestingly, all the conserved residues among plant and mammalian aquaporins are located in the transmembrane domains (M1 to M6, HB and HE). Some of these conserved residues, such as glycine and alanine, have been proposed to be involved in transmembrane helix-helix association (51, 104). A few sequences specific to TIPs or PIPs may contribute to membrane trafficking, assembly, and regulation of aquaporin function (17, 63, 133).

Aquaporins exist as a homotetramer of subunits of 23–30 kDa. Water molecules cross the central pore of each monomer (51, 129). The three-dimensional structure of mammalian aquaporins has been determined from two-dimensional crystallography (51, 118, 104). A plant aquaporin (α-TIP) has also been demonstrated to exist as a 6 nm square tetramer by electron cryocrystallography (22). The TIP protein tends to form dimers and tetramers even in the presence of SDS (85), and equilibration between the monomer, dimer, and tetramer in SDS solution depends on the protein concentration (K Inoue & M Maeshima, unpublished data). These observations point to a strong association between subunits even in the presence of SDS.

TIP Isoforms in Plants

Structural diversity is a characteristic of aquaporins in plants (17, 99). In *A. thaliana*, there are 23 isoforms of aquaporin (63, 151). Among them, the α-, β-, γ- (three isoforms), δ- (two isoforms), and ε-TIPs have been identified as members of the tonoplast aquaporin group. α-TIPs have been detected in the membrane of protein-storage vacuoles, and γ- and δ-TIPs are localized to the membrane of central vacuoles. β-TIP is classified as a member of the α-TIP subgroup. In general, the existence of different isoforms has three different physiological meanings: coordinate expressions of several isoforms in the same cell can produce a large amount of protein, different isoforms may be spatially and temporally expressed, and different isoforms may possess different functional properties. As described later,

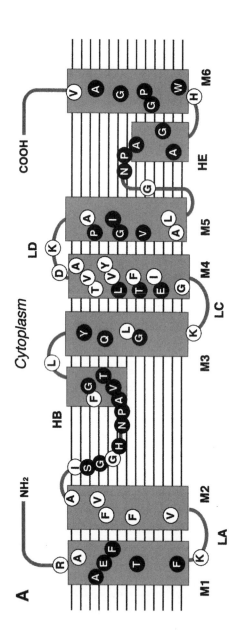

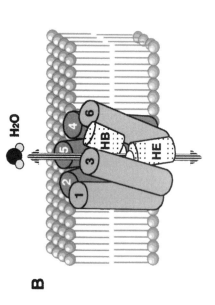

TIPs and PIPs are abundant in the tonoplast and plasma membrane, respectively. Production of a large quantity of aquaporins may occur due to the coordinate expression of different isoforms. In fact, several aquaporin isoforms are simultaneously transcribed and translated in the same tissues such as the phloem and xylem parenchyma in radish (S Suga & M Maeshima, unpublished data).

Certain TIP isoforms are induced and accumulated in specific cells under specific conditions (63). In radish taproots, γ-TIP protein occupies over 60% of the total amount of TIP protein (52). Radish γ-TIP protein accumulated in all organs except for mature seeds, while the δ-TIP was not expressed in leaves and seedling roots (133). Spinach δ-TIP was abundant in mature vacuolated cells in all vegetative tissues (66). It also has been shown, by immunocytochemical techniques, that δ-TIP is expressed in the cells of petunia flower petals and potato tubers in which neither α-TIP nor γ-TIP was detected (61). The specificity of TIP isoforms has been defined with respect not only to the type of cell but also to the type of vacuole in the same cell (8, 45, 61, 62, 87, 96, 136). However, the detailed relationship between the TIP isoforms and microheterogeneity of vacuoles remains to be defined, as do the tonoplast components specific for each type of vacuole. The regulation of aquaporin gene expression and water channel activity under normal and stress conditions have been described in recent reviews (38, 64, 142). The functional differences between the PIP and TIP groups and between the isoforms in each group have been studied in terms of water permeability and sensitivity to sulfhydryl reagents (17, 63, 100).

Abundance of TIPs

PIPs, and especially TIPs, are the major proteins in their respective membranes in land plants (99). The TIP proteins account for about 40% of the radish tonoplast on the basis of the protein amount, and γ-TIP (γ-VM23) is the major isoform (52). A high water permeability for the tonoplast, facilitated by TIPs, may be important in protecting the call against plasmolysis. An abundance of TIPs enables vacuoles to transport water quickly and in large quantities to the cytosol, even with a small osmotic gradient across the tonoplast. PIPs are also abundant in the plasma membrane of spinach leaves (64) and of radish taproot, in which PIPs accounted for 10% of the amount of plasma membrane proteins (S Imagawa & M Maeshima, unpublished data). The protein content of each isoform is reported to

---

Figure 3   A structural model of plant aquaporin. (*A*) The amino acid residues conserved among six isoforms of PIP and two isoforms of TIP in radish are shown in open circles (133). Conserved residues among plant and mammalian aquaporins are highlighted in closed circles. Six putative transmembrane α helices (M1 to M6) and two short α helices (HB and HE) are shown as rectangles. Hydrophilic loops between the transmembrane domains are designated LA, LC, and LD. (*B*) Schematic arrangement of six transmembrane helices (1 to 6) and two short helices (HB and HE).

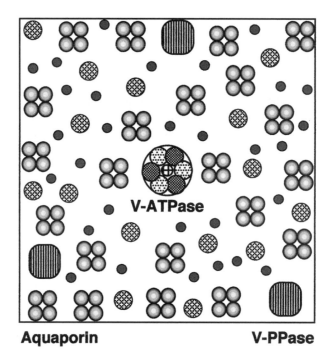

Figure 4 Relative densities of V-ATPase, V-PPase, and TIP. The number of complexes is expressed relative to that of V-ATPase. The values were calculated from the contents of V-ATPase (15%), V-PPase (10%), and TIP (40%) on the assumption that V-ATPase, V-PPase, and TIP form a 750-kDa complex, a dimer, and a tetramer in the tonoplast, respectively (see text for details).

differ markedly with cell type, as reported for spinach TIPs (66), *M. crystallinum* PIPs (70), *M. pudica* γ-TIP (34), and soybean nodule γ-TIP (128), but it is difficult to determine accurately the amount of aquaporins in individual cells. The osmotic water permeability of the tonoplast is reported to be markedly higher than that for plasma membrane (100). This may be due to a high abundance and a high specific activity of TIPs compared with that of PIPs.

Total tonoplast membrane protein has been estimated to be composed of 15% V-ATPase, 10% V-PPase and 40% TIP protein on the basis of protein amount for the tonoplast of mung bean hypocotyls (52, 89, 98). As illustrated in Figure 4, all of the different tonoplast proteins may be surrounded by aquaporin tetramers in the lipid bilayer. The effect of the abundance of TIPs on the fluidity of the tonoplast and on the activity and stability of other tonoplast transporters remains to be examined. Note that the TIP content is relatively low in the tonoplast of tobacco cultured cells (97) and is extremely low in the tonoplast of *Kalanchoë blossfeldiana* (a CAM plant), *Conocephalum conicum* (moss), and *C. corallina* (green alga) (88). At least in CAM plants, it can be speculated that the absence of TIP proteins could be of benefit to the water-storing function of parenchyma tissues in succulent plants.

Function of TIPs

Using the *Xenopus*-oocyte expression system (101), water transport activity has been demonstrated for several plant aquaporins (18, 52, 63, 78, 99). A high abundance of γ-TIP in the motor cell of *Mimosa pudica* is a good example of aquaporin-mediated water transport in plants. The motor cell is responsible for the sudden drooping of a leaf, which results from a dramatic reduction of the volume of the central vacuole triggered by mechanical touch. In addition to vacuolar proton pumps, γ-TIP protein is extremely abundant in tonoplast of the central vacuole of motor cells compared with tannin-storage vacuoles in the same motor cell and with central vacuoles in nonreactive cells of mimosa (34).

With respect to the physiological regulation of aquaporin function, external pH and Ca^{2+} concentration have been demonstrated to regulate water channel activity of mammalian aquaporins expressed in oocytes (109, 159). In plants, phosphorylation of PIPs has been shown to occur in response to an increased Ca^{2+} concentration and apoplastic turgor pressure (64). Functional regulation of water channel activity by phosphorylation of aquaporins including α-TIP has been reviewed recently (18, 63, 142).

There are other functions of aquaporins worth noting. Recently, tobacco TIP (Nt-TIPa) (40) and nodulin 26 (25) have been reported to be able to translocate not only water but also glycerol and urea. Some plants accumulate glycerol in certain tissues during adaptation to low temperatures in late autumn and TIPs and PIPs may take part in the transport of glycerol into vacuoles. Furthermore, the aquaporin in erythrocytes and lungs (AQP1) has been demonstrated to transport both water and CO_2, but not HCO_3^- (113, 156). Whether the CO_2 molecule is transported across the plasma membrane by simple diffusion or by a PIP-mediated system is the focus of active research in plants. To answer this question, the CO_2 permeability through different types of aquaporins should be determined using either oocytes or reconstituted proteoliposomes with the purified aquaporin.

Ca^{2+}-BINDING PROTEINS ASSOCIATED WITH TONOPLAST

Two different Ca^{2+}-binding proteins are reported to be associated with the tonoplast. Proteins of the annexin family show Ca^{2+}-dependent binding to acidic phospholipids in the tonoplast membrane. A 42-kDa annexin in tobacco, VCaB42, has been reported to be located on the cytosolic surface of the vacuole and to function in vesicle fusion during vacuole biogenesis (127). A new type of Ca^{2+}-binding protein, RVCaB, was found associated with the radish vacuole. RVCaB has been demonstrated to be weakly associated to the lumenal surface of the vacuole (158) and has a high capacity but low affinity for Ca^{2+}. It has been proposed that RVCaB functions as a Ca^{2+}-buffer and/or Ca^{2+}-sequestering protein in the vacuole.

UNIDENTIFIED TRANSPORTERS AND CHANNELS

The tonoplast possesses diverse transport activities for various metabolites, inorganic ions and xenobiotics. Plant vacuoles can accumulate and store sucrose, glucose, fructose, sorbitol, and fructans. There must be active and facilitated transporters in the tonoplast to mediate their storage and retrieval. In recent years, various sucrose transporters (73, 75) and monosaccharide transporters (15) have been identified. Detailed studies have revealed the phylogenetic relationships of large gene families of sugar transporters, as well as their specific gene expression in plants. Many groups have been searching for tonoplast sugar transporters, but none has yet been found in the tonoplast. The vacuole is the most attractive sugar-storage organelle in the plant cell. The molecular characterization of tonoplast sugar transporters should advance our understanding of vacuole function and may promote the genetic engineering of fruits and vegetables with altered carbohydrate storage.

The plant vacuole also can contain a variety of inorganic ions, such as Cl^-, nitrate, phosphate, sulfate, K^+, Mg^{2+}, and micronutrients/heavy metals, in addition to Ca^{2+} and Na^+. Functional analyses have revealed that many kinds of transporters and ion channels for these substances exist in the tonoplast (18, 35, 94, 121). Considerable information on the cDNAs for these transporters and channels in plants has accumulated, but the actual transport proteins in the tonoplast are still poorly characterized. Chloride is one of the most tonoplast-permeable ions. A tonoplast Cl^- channel, whose current is carried by Cl^- or malate in *Vicia faba* guard cells, has been characterized in detail, and several cDNAs for plant Cl^- channels have been cloned [references in (7)]. A recent report suggested that AtCLC-d, a member of the *Arabidopsis* Cl^- channel family, is localized in the Golgi apparatus (49, 125). However, no tonoplast-localized Cl^- channels have been reported. Phosphate is also essential for plant growth, and cDNA clones encoding phosphate transporters have been isolated and characterized from several plants. A vacuolar phosphate transporter has not yet been identified (130).

Many other transport systems for organic acids, amino acids, secondary metabolites such as flower pigments and phenol compounds, and xenobiotics have been investigated in the tonoplast of various plants (74, 94, 110, 154). There has been considerable recent progress in understanding ABC (ATP-binding cassette) transporters in plants. The ABC transporter superfamily in *A. thaliana* includes about 50 members, and is thought to be involved in membrane transport of an enormous number of secondary metabolites and xenobiotics across the tonoplast and plasma membrane (94, 95, 116, 140). Further studies at the molecular and cell biological levels may shed more light on the multifunctions and microheterogeneity of the tonoplast of the plant vacuole and its role in cell differentiation and function.

LIPIDS IN THE TONOPLAST

Tonoplast lipids are likely to be important in regulating enzyme activity, vesicle trafficking during tonoplast biogenesis, protein targeting to the tonoplast, signal transduction via membrane lipids, and physicochemical properties of the tonoplast. In most cases, the tonoplast has the smallest density (about $1.10–1.12$ g/cm^3 in sucrose gradients) among several organelle membranes. This property reflects a high ratio of membrane lipid to protein. Lipid composition has been investigated in detail for the tonoplast and plasma membrane of mung bean hypocotyls and compared (157). The tonoplast is composed of phospholipids (51% on molar ratio), free sterols (18%), ceramide monohexoside (16.6%), and digalactosyldiglyceride (3.4%). The major phospholipids are phosphatidylcholine and phosphatidylethanolamine. It has also been reported that relatively high contents of ceramide monohexoside and free sterols are found in the tonoplast of other plant species (47, 139). In mammalian cells, these lipids are specifically localized in the plasma membrane. Therefore, the tonoplast has a characteristically high content of ceramide monohexoside (cerebroside) compared with other organelles except for the chloroplast thylakoid, which contains large amounts of glycolipids. The interaction between glycolipids and the V-ATPase has also been investigated with respect to the chilling sensitivity of plants (67). The fluidity of the tonoplast is higher than that of the plasma membrane, although the degree of unsaturation of tonoplast phospholipids is lower than that of the plasma membrane (157). This is mainly caused by a low molar ratio of sterol to phospholipid in the tonoplast (0.54) (0.89, plasma membrane) (157). Detailed information concerning the tonoplast lipids is essential for understanding physiological function of tonoplast. Future investigations may clarify effects of membrane lipids on the permeability of water and ions across the lipid bilayer and the catalytic properties of tonoplast transporters.

PERSPECTIVES

The plant vacuole contains essential substances important both for the plant cell itself and various compounds that may be of practical benefit to society. Our knowledge of the tonoplast has increased dramatically over the past decade, although much of our understanding has focused on the several classes of transporters described here. More information is needed concerning the individual proteins, protein-ligand interactions, the functional correlation between the transport systems, and tonoplast biogenesis.

Publication of the complete genome sequence of *A. thaliana* and its organization, as well as the rice genome sequence will provide invaluable new information, but this knowledge will only be one key to opening new fields in the plant sciences. We are still far from the goal of understanding living plant cells. The information required to determine the location and function of membrane proteins based on primary sequence information is limited. A number of researchers are concentrating on determining the mechanisms and pathways of intracellular trafficking for membrane proteins, while other groups have initiated a proteome analysis of the tonoplast and plasma membrane. In the near future, we should be able to estimate the location of unknown proteins from their primary sequences.

Accurate tertiary structures of membrane proteins cannot be deduced from amino acid sequences. Crystallographic analysis of membrane transporters and channels is critical for understanding many aspects of these transporters including the transport pathway of various solutes, transport mechanisms, energy transduction for the V-ATPase and V-PPase, and the response mechanisms to biochemical signals such as vacuolar lumenal pH and membrane voltage. Recent advances in structural biology offer tools for future two-dimensional crystallization of tonoplast transporters and channels. The three-dimensional structure of other membrane proteins such as aquaporins (22, 51, 118) and the plasma membrane H^+-ATPase (4), has been revealed from the analysis of two-dimensional crystals at a high resolution (4–8 Å). The V-PPase is one of the most attractive future targets for this type of study since it is peculiar to plants.

Reverse genetic techniques are now being applied to determine the physiological role of each transporter and channel in plants. At present, antisense suppression, cosuppression by overexpression of the target gene, targeted gene disruption, and PCR approaches for the screening of T-DNA insertion libraries are available. Double-stranded RNA-mediated interference with the expression of a specific gene has also been successfully applied to *A. thaliana* (19). This new method may be a potent and efficient way to obtain loss-of-function or reduction-of-function mutants. Also, it is expected to be useful for genetic manipulation to obtain transgenic plants, especially fruits, vegetables and cereal crops, with gain-of-function or induction-of-function through modification of the tonoplast transporters.

ACKNOWLEDGMENTS

I am grateful to the many colleagues in our laboratories who have contributed to the work described here. I thank Dr. Lincoln Taiz and Dr. Judy Noguchi for critical reading of the manuscript. I am grateful to Dr. I Yabe and Dr. S Ohkuma for sharing data before publication. Because of space limitations, I have often cited reviews rather than the primary literature. This work is supported in part by Grants-in-Aid for Scientific Research (nos 12037206, 11660084, 10219203) from the Ministry of Education, Science, Sports and Culture of Japan, and by the Daiko Foundation.

Visit the Annual Reviews home page at www.AnnualReviews.org

LITERATURE CITED

1. Abrahams JP, Leslie AGW, Lutter R, Walker JE. 1994. Structure at 2.8 Å resolution of F_1-ATPase from bovine heart mitochondria. *Nature* 370:621–28
2. Apse MP, Aharon GS, Snedden WA, Blumwald E. 1999. Salt tolerance conferred by overexpression of a vacuolar Na^+/H^+ antiport in Arabidopsis. *Science* 285:1256–58
3. Aravind L, Galperin MY, Koonin EV. 1998. The HD domain defines a new superfamily of metal-dependent phosphohydrolases. *Trends Biochem. Sci.* 23:127–29
4. Auer M, Scarborough GA, Kühlbrandt W. 1984. Three-dimensional map of the plasma membrane H^+-ATPase in the open conformation. *Nature* 392:840–43
5. Baltscheffsky M, Nadanaciva S, Schultz A. 1998. A pyrophosphate synthase gene: molecular cloning and sequencing of the cDNA encoding the inorganic pyrophosphate synthase from *Rhodospirillum rubrum*. *Biochim. Biophys. Acta* 1364:301–6
6. Baltscheffsky M, Schultz A, Baltscheffsky H. 1999. H^+-PPases: a tightly membrane-bound family. *FEBS Lett.* 457:527–33
7. Barbier-Brygoo H, Vinauger M, Colcombet J, Ephritikhine G, Frachisse JM, Maurel C. 2000. Anion channels in higher plants: functional characterization, molecular structure and physiological role. *Biochim. Biophys. Acta* 1465:199–218
8. Barkla BJ, Vera-Estrella R, Pantoja O, Kirch HH, Bohnert HJ. 1999. Aquaporin localization: how valid are the TIP and PIP label? *Trends Plant Sci.* 4:86–88
9. Blackford S, Rea PA, Sanders D. 1990. Voltage sensitivity of H^+/Ca^{2+} antiport in higher plant tonoplast suggests a role in vacuolar calcium accumulation. *J. Biol. Chem.* 265:9617–20
10. Berkelman T, Houtchens KA, DuPont FM. 1994. Two cDNA clones encoding iso-

forms of the B subunit of the vacuolar ATPase from barley roots. *Plant Physiol.* 104:287–88
11. Blumwald E, Aharon GS, Apse MP. 2000. Sodium transport in plant cells. *Biochim. Biophys. Acta* 1465:140–51
12. Blumwald E, Poole RJ. 1987. Salt tolerance in suspension cultures of sugar beet: induction of Na^+/H^+ antiport activity at the tonoplast by growth in salt. *Plant Physiol.* 83:884–87
13. Bowman EJ, Kedle R, Bowman BJ. 2000. Disruption of *vma-1*, the gene encoding the catalytic subunit of the vacuolar H^+-ATPase, causes severe morphological changes in *Neurospora crassa*. *J. Biol. Chem.* 275:167–76
14. Boyer PD. 1997. The ATP synthase: a splendid molecular machine. *Annu. Rev. Biochem.* 66:717–49
15. Büttner M, Sauer N. 2000. Monosaccharide transporters in plants: structure, function and physiology. *Biochim. Biophys. Acta* 1465:263–74
16. Chanson A. 1991. A Ca^{2+}/H^+ antiport system driven by the tonoplast pyrophosphate-dependent proton transport of maize root membranes. *Plant Physiol.* 84:1431–36
17. Chaumont F, Barrieu F, Jung R, Chrispeels MJ. 2000. Plasma membrane intrinsic proteins from maize cluster in two sequence subgroups with differential aquaporin activity. *Plant Physiol.* 122:1025–34
18. Chrispeels MJ, Crawford NM, Schroeder JI. 1999. Proteins for transport of water and mineral nutrients across the membranes of plant cells. *Plant Cell* 11:661–75
19. Chuang CF, Meyerowitz EM. 2000. Specific and heritable genetic interference by double-stranded RNA in *Arabidopsis thaliana*. *Proc. Natl. Acad. Sci. USA* 97:4985–90

20. Cunningham W, Fink GR. 1996. Calcineurin inhibits VCX1-dependent H^+/Ca^{2+} exchanger and induces Ca^{2+}-ATPases in *Saccharomyces cerevisiae. Mol. Cell. Biol.* 16:2226–37

21. Daniels MJ, Chaumont F, Mirkov TE, Chrispeels MJ. 1996. Characterization of a new vacuolar membrane aquaporin sensitive to mercury at a unique site. *Plant Cell* 8:587–99

22. Daniels MJ, Chrispeels MJ, Yeager M. 1999. Projection structure of a plant vacuole membrane aquaporin by electron cryo-crystallography. *J. Mol. Biol.* 294:1337–49

23. Davies JM, Hunt I, Sanders D. 1994. Vacuolar H^+-pumping ATPase variable transport coupling ratio controlled by pH. *Proc. Natl. Acad. Sci. USA* 91:8547–51

24. Davies JM, Poole RJ, Sanders D. 1993. The computed free energy change of hydrolysis of inorganic pyrophosphate and ATP: apparent significance for inorganic-pyrophosphate-driven reactions of intermediary metabolism. *Biochim. Biophys. Acta* 1141:29–36

25. Dean RM, Rivers RL, Zeidel ML, Roberts DM. 1999. Purification and functional reconstitution of soybean nodulin 26. An aquaporin with water and glycerol transport properties. *Biochemistry* 38:347–53

26. Dietz KJ, Hollenbach B, Arnold J. 1996. Nucleotide sequences of subunit E of the vacuolar proton-ATPase of *Spinacia oleracea* (Acc. No. X96785) and *Arabidopsis thaliana* (Acc. No. X92117) (PGR 96-037). *Plant Physiol.* 111:652

27. Drozdowicz YM, Lu YP, Patel V, Fitz-Gibbon S, Miller JH, et al. 1999. A thermostable vacuolar-type membrane pyrophosphatase from the archaeon *Pyrobaculum aerophilum*: implications for the origins of pyrophosphate-energized pumps. *FEBS Lett.* 460:505–12

28. Drozdowicz YM, Kissinger JC, Rea PA. 2000. AVP2, a sequence-divergent, K^+-insensitive H^+-translocating inorganic pyrophosphatase from Arabidopsis. *Plant Physiol.* 123:353–62

29. Dschida WJ, Bowman BJ. 1992. Structure of the vacuolar ATPase from *Neurospora crassa* as determined by electron microscopy. *J. Biol. Chem.* 267:18783–89

30. DuPont FM, Morrissey PJ. 1992. Subunit composition and Ca-ATPase activity of the vacuolar ATPase from barley roots. *Arch. Biochem. Biophys.* 294:341–46

31. Ettinger WG, Clear AM, Fanning KJ, Peck ML. 1999. Identification of a Ca^{2+}/H^+ antiporter in the plant chloroplast thylakoid membrane. *Plant Physiol.* 119:1379–86

32. Ferguson DL, Turley RB, Kloth RH. 1997. Identification of a δ-TIP cDNA clone and determination of related A and D genome subfamilies in *Gossypium* species. *Plant Mol. Biol.* 34:111–18

33. Ferrol N, Bennet AB. 1996. A single gene may encode differentially localized Ca^{2+}-ATPase in tomato. *Plant Cell* 8:1159–69

34. Fleurat-Lessard P, Frangne N, Maeshima M, Ratajczak R, Bonnemain JL, et al. 1997. Increased expression of vacuolar aquaporin and H^+-ATPase related to motor cell function in *Mimosa pudica* L. *Plant Physiol.* 114:827–34

35. Forde BG. 2000. Nitrate transporters in plants: structure, function and regulation. *Biochim. Biophys. Acta* 1465:219–35

36. Forgac M. 1999. Structure and properties of the vacuolar H^+-ATPases. *J. Biol. Chem.* 274:12951–54

37. Futai M, Oka T, Sun-Wada G, Moriyama Y, Kanazawa, et al. 1999. Luminal acidification of diverse organelles by V-ATPase in animal cells. *J. Exp. Biol.* 203:107–16

38. Gao YP, Young L, Bonham-Smith P, Gusta L. 1999. Characterization and expression of plasma and tonoplast membrane aquaporins in primed seed of *Brassica napus* during germination under stress conditions. *Plant Mol. Biol.* 40:635–44

39. Gaxiola RA, Rao R, Sherman A, Grisafi P, Alper SL, et al. 1999. The *Arabidopsis thaliana* proton transporters, AtNhx1

and Avp1, can function in cation detoxification in yeast. *Proc. Natl. Acad. Sci. USA* 96:1480–85

40. Gerbeau P, Güclü J, Ripoche P, Maurel C. 1999. Aquaporin Nt-TIPa can account for the high permeability of tobacco cell vacuolar membrane to small neutral solutes. *Plant J.* 18:577–87

41. Geisler M, Axelsen KB Harper JF, Palmgren MG. 2000. Molecular aspects of higher plant P-type Ca^{2+}-ATPases. *Biochim. Biophys. Acta* 1465:52–78

42. Getz HP, Klein M. 1995. The vacuolar ATPase of red beet storage tissue: electron microscopic demonstration of the "head-and-stalk" structure. *Bot. Acta* 108:14–23

43. Gogarten JP, Fichmann J, Braun Y, Morgan L, Styles P, Taiz SL, Delapp K, Taiz L. 1992. The use of antisense mRNA to inhibit the tonoplast proton ATPase in carrot. *Plant Cell* 4:851–64

44. Guerinot ML. 2000. The ZIP family of metal transporters. *Biochim. Biophys. Acta* 1465:190–98

45. Hara-Nishimura I, Maeshima M. 2000. Vacuolar processing enzymes and aquaporins. *Annu. Plant Rev.* 5:20–42

46. Harper JF, Hong B, Hwang I, Guo HQ, Stoddard R, et al. 1998. A novel calmodulin-regulated Ca^{2+}-ATPase (ACA2) from Arabidopsis with an N-terminal autoinhibitory domain. *J. Biol. Chem.* 52:1091–106

47. Haschke HP, Kaiser G, Martinoia E, Hammer U, Teucher T, et al. 1990. Lipid profiles of leaf tonoplasts from plants with different CO_2-fixation mechanisms. *Bot. Acta* 103:32–38

48. Hasenfratz M, Tsou CL, Wilkins TA. 1995. Expression of two related vacuolar H^+-ATPase 16-kilodalton proteolipid genes is differentially regulated in a tissue-specific manner. *Plant Physiol.* 108:1395–404

49. Hechenberger M, Schwappach B, Fischer WN, Frommer WB, Jentsch TJ, et al. 1996. A family of putative chloride channels from *Arabidopsis* and functional comple-

mentation of a yeast strain with a *CLC* gene disruption. *J. Biol. Chem.* 271:33632–38

50. Herman EM, Li X, Su RT, Larsen P, Hsu HT, et al. 1994. Vacuolar-type H^+-ATPases are associated with the endoplasmic reticulum and provacuoles of root tip cells. *Plant Physiol.* 106:1313–24

51. Heymann JB, Engel A. 2000. Structural clues in the sequences of the aquaporins. *J. Mol. Biol.* 295:1039–53

52. Higuchi H, Suga S, Tsuchiya T, Hisada H, Morishima S, et al. 1998. Molecular cloning, water channel activity and tissue specific expression of two isoforms of radish vacuolar aquaporin. *Plant Cell Physiol.* 39:905–13

53. Hirata T, Nakamura N, Omote H, Wada Y, Futai M. 2000. Regulation and reversibility of vacuolar H^+-ATPase. *J. Biol. Chem.* 275:386–89

54. Hirschi KD. 1999. Expression of *Arabidopsis CAX1* in tobacco: altered calcium homeostasis and increased stress sensitivity. *Plant Cell* 11:2113–22

55. Hirschi KD, Korenkov V, Wilganowski NL, Wagner GJ. 2000. Expression of *Arabidopsis* CAX2 in tobacco. Altered metal accumulation and increased manganese tolerance. *Plant Physiol.* 124:125–34

56. Hirschi KD, Zhen RG, Cunningham KW, Rea PA, Fink GR. 1996. CAX1, an H^+/Ca^{2+} antiporter from *Arabidopsis*. *Proc. Natl. Acad. Sci. USA* 93:8782–86

57. Höfte H, Hubbard L, Reizer J, Ludevid D, Herman EM, et al. 1992. Vegetative and seed-specific forms of tonoplast intrinsic protein in the vacuolar membrane of *Arabidopsis thaliana*. *Plant Physiol.* 99:561–70

58. Hosaka M, Kanayama Y, Shiratake K, Yamaki S. 1994. Tonoplast H^+-ATPase of mature pear fruit. *Phytochemistry* 36:565–67

59. Huang L, Berkelman T, Franklin AE, Hoffman NE. 1993. Characterization of a gene encoding a Ca^{2+}-ATPase-like protein in

the plastid envelope. *Proc. Natl. Acad. Sci. USA* 90:10066–70

60. Ikeda M, Tanabe E, Rahman MH, Kadowaki H, Moritani C, et al. 1999. A vacuolar inorganic H^+-pyrophosphatase in *Acetabularia acetabulum*: partial purification, characterization and molecular cloning. *J. Exp. Bot.* 50:139–40

61. Jauh G-Y, Fischer AM, Grimes HD, Ryan CA Jr, Rogers JC. 1998. δ-Tonoplast intrinsic protein defines unique plant vacuole functions. *Proc. Natl. Acad. Sci. USA* 95:12995–99

62. Jauh GY, Phillips TE, Rogers JC. 1999. Tonoplast intrinsic protein isoforms as markers for vacuolar functions. *Plant Cell* 11:1867–82

63. Johansson I, Karlsson M, Johanson U, Larsson C, Kjellbom P. 2000. The role of aquaporins in cellular and whole plant water balance. *Biochim. Biophys. Acta* 1465:324–42

64. Johansson I, Larsson C, Ek B, Kjellbom P. 1996. The major integral proteins of spinach leaf plasma membranes are putative aquaporins and are phosphorylated in response to Ca^{2+} and apoplastic water potential. *Plant Cell* 8:1181–91

65. Johnson KD, Höfte H, Chrispeels MJ. 1990. An intrinsic tonoplast protein of protein storage vacuoles in seeds is structurally related to a bacterial solute transporter (GlpR). *Plant Cell* 2:525–32

66. Karlsson M, Johansson I, Bush M, McCann MC, Maurel C, et al. 2000. An abundant TIP expressed in mature highly vacuolated cells. *Plant J.* 21:83–90

67. Kasamo K, Yamaguchi M, Nakamura Y. 2000. Mechanism of the chilling-induced decrease in proton pumping across the tonoplast of rice cells. *Plant Cell Physiol.* 41:840–49

68. Kawamura Y, Arakawa K, Maeshima M, Yoshida S. 2000. Tissue specificity of E subunit isoforms of plant vacuolar H^+-ATPase and existence of isotype enzymes. *J. Biol. Chem.* 275:6515–22

69. Kim Y, Kim EJ, Rea PA. 1994. Isolation and characterization of cDNAs encoding the vacuolar H^+-pyrophosphatase of Beta vulgaris. *Plant Physiol.* 106:375–82

70. Kirch HH, Vera-Estrella R, Golldack D, Quigley F, Michalowski CB, et al. 2000. Expression of water channel proteins in *Mesembryanthemum crystallinum*. *Plant Physiol.* 123:111–24

71. Kjellbom P, Larsson C, Johansson I, Karlsson M, Johanson U. 1999. Aquaporins and water homeostasis in plants. *Trends Plant Sci.* 4:308–14

72. Kluge C, Golldack D, Dietz K-J. 1999. Subunit D of the vacuolar H^+-ATPase of *Arabidopsis thaliana*. *Biochim. Biophys. Acta* 1419:105–10

73. Kuhn C, Barker L, Burkle L, Frommer WB. 1999. Update on sucrose transport in higher plants. *J. Exp. Bot.* 50:935–53

74. Leigh RA. 1997. Solute compartmentation of vacuoles. *Adv. Bot. Res.* 25:171–94

75. Lemoine R. 2000. Sucrose transporters in plants: update on function and structure. *Biochim. Biophys. Acta* 1465:246–62

76. Leng XH, Nishi T, Forgac M. 1999. Transmembrane topography of the 100-kDa a subunit (Vph1p) of the yeast vacuolar proton-translocating ATPase. *J. Biol. Chem.* 274:14655–61

77. Lerchl J, König S, Zrenner R, Sonnewald U. 1995. Molecular cloning, characterization and expression analysis of isoforms encoding tonoplast-bound proton-translocating inorganic pyrophosphatase in tobacco. *Plant Mol. Biol.* 29:833–40

78. Li L, Li S, Tao Y, Kitagawa Y. 2000. Molecular cloning of a novel water channel from rice: its product expression in *Xenopus* oocytes and involvement in chilling tolerance. *Plant Sci.* 154:43–51

79. Li X, Perera IY, Lin S, Sze H. 1999. Cloning and characterization of a genomic clone (AF153677) encoding a 16 kDa subunit c of vacuolar H^+-ATPase (Ava-p4) from *Arabidopsis thaliana* (PGR99-106). *Plant Physiol.* 120:1205

80. Li X, Su RTC, Hsu H, Sze H. 1998. The molecular chaperone calnexin associates with the vacuolar H$^+$-ATPase from oat seedlings. *Plant Cell* 10:119–30
81. Li X, Sze H. 1999. A 100 kD polypeptide associates with the V$_O$ membrane sector but not with the active oat vacuolar H$^+$-ATPase, suggesting a role in assembly. *Plant J.* 17:19–30
82. Liang F, Cunningham KW, Harper JF, Sze H. 1997. ECA1 complements yeast mutants defective in Ca^{2+} pumps and encodes an endoplasmic reticulum-type Ca^{2+}-ATPase in *Arabidopsis thaliana*. *Proc. Natl. Acad. Sci. USA* 94:8579–84
83. Löw R, Rockel B, Kirsch M, Ratajczak R, Lüttge R, et al. 1996. Early salt stress effects on the differential expression of vacuolar H$^+$-ATPase genes in roots and leaves of *Mesembryanthemum crystallinum*. *Plant Physiol.* 110:259–65
84. Lüttge U, Ratajczak R. 1997. The physiology, biochemistry and molecular biology of the plant vacuolar ATPase. *Adv. Bot. Res.* 25:253–96
85. Maeshima M. 1992. Characterization of the major integral protein of vacuolar membrane. *Plant Physiol.* 98:1248–54
86. Maeshima M. 2000. Vacuolar H$^+$-pyrophosphatase. *Biochim. Biophys. Acta* 1465:37–51
87. Maeshima M, Hara-Nishimura I, Takeuchi Y, Nishimura M. 1994. Accumulation of vacuolar H$^+$-pyrophosphatase and H$^+$-ATPase during reformation of the central vacuole in germinating pumpkin seeds. *Plant Physiol.* 106:61–69
88. Maeshima M, Mimura T, Sato T. 1994. Distribution of vacuolar H$^+$-pyrophosphatase and the membrane integral protein in a variety of green plants. *Plant Cell Physiol.* 35:323–28
89. Maeshima M, Yoshida S. 1989. Purification and properties of vacuolar membrane proton-translocating inorganic pyrophosphatase from mung bean. *J. Biol. Chem.* 264:20068–73
90. Magnotta S, Gogarten JP. 1997. Characterization and isolation of a vacuolar type H$^+$-ATPase subunit A cDNA from *Arabidopsis thaliana* (Acc. No. U65638) (PGR97-177). *Plant Physiol.* 115:1730
91. Malmström S, Askerlund P, Palmgren MG. 1997. A calmodulin-stimulated Ca^{2+}-ATPase from plant vacuolar membranes with a putative regulatory domain at its N-terminus. *FEBS Lett.* 400:324–28
92. Manolson MF, Ouellette BF, Filion M, Poole RJ. 1988. cDNA sequence and homologies of the '57-kDa' nucleotide-binding subunit of the vacuolar ATPase from Arabidopsis. *J. Biol. Chem.* 263:17987–94
93. Margolles-Clark E, Tenney K, Bowman EJ, Bowman BJ. The structure of the vacuolar ATPase in *Neurospora crassa*. *J. Bioenerg. Biomemb.* 31:29–37
94. Martinoia M, Massonneau A, Frangne N. 2000. Transport processes of solutes across the vacuolar membrane of higher plants. *Plant Cell Physiol.* 41:1175–86
95. Martinoia M, Ratajczak R. 1997. Transport of organic molecules across the tonoplast. *Adv. Bot. Res.* 25:365–400
96. Marty F. 1999. Plant vacuoles. *Plant Cell* 11:587–99
97. Matsuoka K, Higuchi T, Maeshima M, Nakamura K. 1997. A vacuolar type H$^+$-ATPase in a nonvacuolar organelle is required for the sorting of soluble vacuolar protein precursors in tobacco cells. *Plant Cell* 9:533–46
98. Matsuura-Endo C, Maeshima M, Yoshida S. 1990. Subunit composition of vacuolar membrane H$^+$-ATPase from mung bean. *Eur. J. Biochem.* 187:745–51
99. Maurel C. 1997. Aquaporins and water permeability of plant membranes. *Annu. Rev. Plant Physiol. Plant Mol. Biol.* 48:399–429
100. Maurel C, Tacnet F, Güclü J, Guern J, Ripoche P. 1997. Purified vesicles of tobacco cell vacuolar and plasma membranes exhibit dramatically different

water permeability and water channel activity. *Proc. Natl. Acad. Sci. USA* 94: 7103–8

101. Miller AJ, Zhou JJ. 2000. *Xenopus* oocyte as an expression system for plant transporters. *Biochim. Biophys. Acta* 1465:343–58

102. Müller ML, Irkens-Kiesecker U, Kramer D, Taiz L. 1997. Purification and reconstitution of the vacuolar H$^+$-ATPases from lemon fruits and epicotyls. *J. Biol. Chem.* 272:12762–70

103. Müller ML, Jensen M, Taiz L. 1999. The vacuolar H$^+$-ATPase of lemon fruits is regulated by variable H$^+$/ATP coupling and slip. *J. Biol. Chem.* 274:10706–16

104. Murata K, Mitsuoka K, Hirai T, Walz T, Agre P, et al. 2000. Structural determinants of water permeation through aquaporin-1. *Nature* 407:599–605

105. Nakanishi Y, Maeshima M. 1998. Molecular cloning of vacuolar H$^+$-pyrophosphatase and its developmental expression in growing hypocotyl of mung bean. *Plant Physiol.* 116:589–97

106. Nakanishi Y, Maeshima M. 2000. Isolation of a cDNA for a H$^+$-pyrophosphatase-like protein from *Arabidopsis thaliana* (Acc. No. AB034696) and its functional expression in yeast (PGR00-026). *Plant Physiol.* 122:619

107. Nakanishi Y, Matsuda N, Aizawa K, Kashiyama T, Yamamoto K, et al. 1999. Molecular cloning of the cDNA for vacuolar H$^+$-pyrophosphatase from *Chara corallina. Biochim. Biophys. Acta* 1418:245–50

108. Nakanishi Y, Saijo T, Wada Y, Maeshima M. 2001. Mutagenic analysis of functional residues in putative substrate-binding site and acidic domains of vacuolar H$^+$-pyrophosphatase. *J. Biol. Chem.* 276. In press

109. Németh-Cahalan KL, Hall JE. 2000. pH and calcium regulate the water permeability of aquaporin 0. *J. Biol. Chem.* 275:6777–82

110. Ortiz-Lopez A, Chang HC, Bush DR. 2000. Amino acid transporters in plants. *Biochim. Biophys. Acta* 1465:275–80

111. Parry RV, Turner JC, Rea PA. 1989. High purity preparations of higher plant vacuolar H$^+$-ATPase reveals additional subunits. *J. Biol. Chem.* 264:20025–32

112. Perera IY, Li X, Sze H. 1995. Several genes encode nearly identical 16 kDa proteolipids of the vacuolar H$^+$-ATPase from *Arabidopsis thaliana. Plant Mol. Biol.* 29:227–44

113. Prasad GV, Coury LA, Finn F, Zeidel ML. 1998. Reconstituted aquaporin 1 water channels transport CO$_2$ across membranes. *J. Biol. Chem.* 273:33123–26

114. Radermacher M, Ruiz T, Harvey W, Wieczorek H, Grueber G. 1999. Molecular architecture of *Manduca sexta* midgut V$_1$ ATPase visualized by electron microscopy. *FEBS Lett.* 453:383–86

115. Ratajczak R. 2000. Structure, function and regulation of the plant vacuolar H$^+$-translocating ATPase. *Biochim. Biophys. Acta* 1465:17–36

116. Rea PA, Li ZS, Lu YP, Drozdowicz YM, Martinoia E. 1998. From vacuolar GS-X pumps to multispecific ABC transporters. *Annu. Rev. Plant Physiol. Plant Mol. Biol.* 49:727–60

117. Rea PA, Poole RJ. 1993. Vacuolar H$^+$-translocating pyrophosphatase. *Annu. Rev. Plant Physiol. Plant Mol. Biol.* 44:157–80

118. Ren G, Cheng A, Reddy V, Melnyk P, Mitra A. 2000. Three-dimensional fold of the human AQP1 water channel determined at 4 Å resolution by electron crystallography of two-dimensional crystals embedded in ice. *J. Mol. Biol.* 301:369–87

119. Sakakibara Y, Kobayashi H, Kasamo K. 1996. Isolation and characterization of cDNAs encoding vacuolar H$^+$-pyrophosphates isoforms from rice (*Oryza sativa* L.). *Plant Mol. Biol.* 31:1029–38

120. Sambongi Y, Iko Y, Tanabe M, Omote H,

Iwamoto-Kihara A, et al. 1999. Mechanical rotation of the c subunit oligomer in ATP synthase (F_OF_1): direct observation. *Science* 26:1722–24

121. Sanders D, Brownlee C, Harper JF. 1999. Communicating with calcium. *Plant Cell* 11:691–706

122. Sarafian V, Kim Y, Poole RJ, Rea PA. 1992. Molecular cloning and sequence of cDNA encoding the pyrophosphate-energized vacuolar membrane proton pump of *Arabidopsis thaliana*. *Proc. Natl. Acad. Sci. USA* 89:1775–79

123. Schumacher K, Vafeados D, McCarthy M, Sze H, Wilkins TA, et al. 1999. The Arabidopsis det3 mutant reveals a central role for the vacuolar H^+-ATPase in plant growth and development. *Genes Dev.* 13:3259–70

124. Schumaker KS, Sze H. 1986. Calcium transport into the vacuole of oat roots: characterization of H^+/Ca^{2+} exchange activity. *J. Biol. Chem.* 261:12172–78

125. Schwappach B, Stobrawa S, Hechenberger M, Steinmeyer K, Jentsch TJ. 1998. Golgi localization and functionally important domains in the NH_2 and COOH terminus of the yeast CLC putative chloride channel Gef1p. *J. Biol. Chem.* 273:15110–18

126. Scott DA, de Souza W, Benchimol M, Zhong L, Lu HG, et al. 1998. Presence of a plant-like proton-pumping pyrophosphatase in acidocalcisomes of *Trypanosoma cruzi*. *J. Biol. Chem.* 273: 22151–58

127. Seals DF, Randall SK. 1997. A vacuole-associated annexin protein, VCaB42, correlates with the expression of tobacco cells. *Plant Physiol.* 115:753–61

128. Serraj R, Frangne N, Maeshima M, Fleurate-Lessard P, Drevon JJ. 1998. A γ-TIP cross-reacting protein is abundant in the cortex of soybean N_2-fixing nodules. *Planta* 206:681–84

129. Shi LB, Skach WR, Verkman AS. 1994. Functional independence of monomeric CHIP28 water channels revealed by expression of wild-type mutant heterodimers. *J. Biol. Chem.* 269:10417–22

130. Smith FW, Rae AL, Hawkesford MJ. 2000. Molecular mechanisms of phosphate and sulphate transport in plants. *Biochim. Biophys. Acta* 1465:236–45

131. Steven TH, Forgac M. 1997. Structure, function, and regulation of the vacuolar H^+-ATPase. *Annu. Rev. Cell Dev. Biol.* 13:779–808

132. Stock D, Leslie AGW, Walker JE. 1999. Molecular architecture of the rotary motor in ATP synthase. *Science* 286:1700–5

133. Suga S, Imagawa S, Maeshima M. 2000. Specificity of the accumulation of mRNAs and proteins of the plasma membrane and tonoplast aquaporins in radish organs. *Planta* 212:294–304

134. Sze H, Li X, Palmgren MG. 1999. Energization of plant cell membranes by H^+-pumping ATPases: regulation and biosynthesis. *Plant Cell* 11:677–89

135. Sze H, Liang F, Hwang I, Curran AC, Harper JF. 2000. Diversity and regulation of plant Ca^{2+} pumps: insights from expression in yeast. *Annu. Rev. Plant Physiol. Plant Mol. Biol.* 51:433–62

136. Swanson SJ, Bethke PC, Jones RL. 1998. Barley aleurone cells contain two types of vacuoles: characterization of lytic organelles by use of fluorescent probes. *Plant Cell* 10:685–98

137. Takasu A, Nakanishi Y, Yamauchi T, Maeshima M. 1997. Analysis of the substrate binding site and carboxyl terminal region of vacuolar H^+-pyrophosphatase of mung bean with peptide antibodies. *J. Biochem.* 122:883–89

138. Tanaka Y, Chiba K, Maeda M, Maeshima M. 1993. Molecular cloning of cDNA for vacuolar membrane proton-translocating inorganic pyrophosphatase in *Hordeum vulgare*. *Biochem. Biophys. Res. Commun.* 190:1110–14

139. Tavernier E, Quoc DL, Quoc KL. 1993. Lipid composition of the vacuolar

membrane of *Acer pseudoplatanus* cultured cells. *Biochim. Biophys. Acta* 167: 242–47

140. Theodoulou FL. 2000. Plant ABC transporters. *Biochim. Biophys. Acta* 1465:79–103

141. Toyoshima C, Nakasako M, Nomura H, Ogawa H. 2000. Crystal structure of the calcium pump of sarcoplasmic reticulum at 2.6 Å resolution. *Nature* 405:647–55

142. Tyerman SD, Hohnert HJ, Maurel C, Steudle E, Smith JAC. 1999. Plant aquaporins: their molecular biology, biophysics and significance for plant water relations. *J. Exp. Bot.* 50:1055–71

143. Ueoka-Nakanishi H, Maeshima M. 2000. Quantification of Ca^{2+}/H^+ antiporter VCAX1p in vacuolar membranes and its absence in roots of mung bean. *Plant Cell Physiol.* 41:1067–71

144. Ueoka-Nakanishi H, Nakanishi T, Tanaka Y, Maeshima M. 1999. Properties and molecular cloning of Ca^{2+}/H^+ antiporter in the vacuolar membrane of mung bean. *Eur. J. Biochem.* 262:417–25

145. Ueoka-Nakanishi H, Tsuchiya T, Sasaki M, Nakanishi Y, Cunningham KW, et al. 2000. Functional expression of mung bean Ca^{2+}/H^+ antiporter in yeast and its intracellular localization in the hypocotyl and tobacco cells. *Eur. J. Biochem.* 267:3090–98

146. van der Zaal BJ, Neuteboom LW, Pinas JE, Chardonnens AN, Schat H, et al. 1999. Overexpression of a novel Arabidopsis gene related to putative zinc-transporter genes from animals can lead to enhanced zinc resistance and accumulation. *Plant Physiol.* 119:1047–56

147. Verkleij JAC, Koevoets PLM, Blake-Kalff MMA, Chardonnens AN. 1998. Evidence for an important role of the tonoplast in the mechanism of naturally selected zinc tolerance in *Silene vulgaris*. *J. Plant Physiol.* 153:188–91

148. Vicente JAF, Vale MGP. 1995. Activities of Ca^{2+} pump and low affinity Ca^{2+}/H^+ antiporter in plasma membrane vesicles of corn roots. *J. Exp. Bot.* 46:1551–59

149. Ward JM, Sze H. 1992. Subunit composition and organization of the vacuolar H^+-ATPase from oat roots. *Plant Physiol.* 99:170–79

150. Ward JM, Sze H. 1992. Proton transport activity of the purified vacuolar H^+-ATPase from oats. Direct stimulation by Cl^-. *Plant Physiol.* 99:925–31

151. Weig A, Deswarte C, Chrispeels MJ. 1997. The major intrinsic protein family of Arabidopsis has 23 members that form three distinct groups with functional aquaporins in each group. *Plant Physiol.* 114:1347–57

152. Williams LE, Pittman JK, Hall JL. 2000. Emerging mechanisms for heavy metal transport in plants. *Biochim. Biophys. Acta* 1465:104–26

153. Wimmers LE, Ewing NN, Bennett AB. 1992. Higher plant Ca^{2+}-ATPase: primary structure and regulation of mRNA abundance by salt. *Proc. Natl. Acad. Sci. USA* 89:9205–9

154. Wink M. 1997. Compartmentation of secondary metabolites and xenobiotics in plant vacuoles. *Adv. Bot. Res.* 25:141–69

155. Yabe I, Horiuchi K, Nakahara K, Hiyama T, Yamanaka T, et al. 1999. Patch clamp studies on V-type ATPase of vacuolar membrane of haploid *Saccharomyces cerevisiae*. Preparation and utilization of a giant cell containing a giant vacuole. *J. Biol. Chem.* 274:34903–10

156. Yang B, Fukuda N, van Hoek A, Matthay MA, Ma T, et al. 2000. Carbon dioxide permeability of aquaporin-1 measured in erythrocytes and lung of aquaporin-1 null mice and in reconstituted proteoliposomes. *J. Biol. Chem.* 275:2686–92

157. Yoshida S, Uemura M. 1986. Lipid composition of plasma membranes and tonoplasts isolated from etiolated seedlings of mung bean (*Vigna radiata* L.). *Plant Physiol.* 82:807–12

158. Yuasa K, Maeshima M. 2000. Purification, properties and molecular cloning of a novel Ca^{2+}-binding protein in radish vacuoles. *Plant Physiol.* 124:1069–78

159. Zeuthen T, Klaerke DA. 1999. Transport of water and glycerol in aquaporin 3 is gated by H^+. *J. Biol. Chem.* 274:21631–36

160. Zhang J, Feng Y, Forgac M. 1994. Pro-ton conduction and bafilomycin binding by the V_O domain of the coated vesicle V-ATPase. *J. Biol. Chem.* 269:23518–23

161. Zhen RG, Kim EJ, Rea PA. 1997. The molecular and biochemical basis of pyrophosphate-energized proton translocation at the vacuolar membrane. *Adv. Bot. Res.* 25:297–337

Annu. Rev. Plant Physiol. Plant Mol. Biol. 2001. 52:499–526

PROBING PLANT METABOLISM WITH NMR

R George Ratcliffe

Department of Plant Sciences, University of Oxford, South Parks Road, Oxford, OX1 3RB, United Kingdom; e-mail: george.ratcliffe@plants.ox.ac.uk

Yair Shachar-Hill

Department of Chemistry and Biochemistry, New Mexico State University, Las Cruces, New Mexico 88003; e-mail: yairhill@nmsu.edu

Key Words compartmentation, flux analysis, metabolic phenotype, metabolite profiling, stable isotope labeling

■ **Abstract** Analytical methods for probing plant metabolism are taking on new significance in the era of functional genomics and metabolic engineering. Among the available methods, nuclear magnetic resonance (NMR) spectroscopy is a technique that can provide insights into the integration and regulation of plant metabolism through a combination of in vivo and in vitro measurements. Thus NMR can be used to identify, quantify, and localize metabolites, to define the intracellular environment, and to explore pathways and their operation. We review these applications and their significance from a metabolic perspective. Topics of current interest include applications of NMR to metabolic flux analysis, metabolite profiling, and metabolite imaging. These and other areas are discussed in relation to NMR investigations of intermediary carbon and nitrogen metabolism. We conclude that metabolic NMR has a continuing role to play in the development of a quantitative understanding of plant metabolism and in the characterization of metabolic phenotypes.

CONTENTS

1040-2519/01/0601-0499$14.00 **499**

INTRODUCTION

The current renaissance in the investigation of plant metabolism is being driven by two factors. First, the continuing advances in molecular genetics are creating unprecedented opportunities for dissecting the operation of metabolic pathways. For example, the increasingly facile transformation of plants is providing a powerful tool for exploring the contribution of specific enzymes to the control of metabolic flux, as well as generating increasing demand for the characterization of metabolic phenotypes. Second, progress in the development of new tools for the quantitative analysis and modeling of pathways is permitting increasingly sophisticated investigations of the integration of metabolism. Taken together these two factors have invigorated the field and raised the profile of plant metabolism in plant biology (22).

Despite this renaissance, the fundamental metabolic questions that need to be answered remain much the same. These questions revolve around the identity and quantity of the metabolites that are present, the identification of the pathways that link them, and the factors that allow the resulting metabolic fluxes to be controlled. Moreover, the underlying pattern of gene expression is expected to lead to answers that are generally both spatially and time dependent. Thus while the revolution in molecular genetics has provided new tools for addressing these questions, and new contexts in which they need to be answered, the ultimate goals of contemporary metabolic analysis are really little different from the targets first identified by the pioneers of metabolic research when they embarked on the study of fermentation in yeast (28).

Analytical tools are the key to answering metabolic questions. Accordingly, this review describes the contribution of a versatile technique, nuclear magnetic resonance (NMR) spectroscopy, to the investigation of plant metabolism. The evolution of this particular application of NMR can be traced back to the ground-breaking ^{13}C NMR studies of Schaefer & Stejskal on carbohydrate and lipid metabolism (140, 141). The subsequent development of the technique and its applications have been charted at regular intervals in the review literature (81, 111, 117, 120, 144, 146), and although not as widely exploited as its proponents might wish, NMR is now an established technique in the armory of the plant biochemist.

This review focuses on the metabolic applications of NMR in higher plants, with the emphasis on the pathways of primary metabolism. We therefore largely ignore secondary metabolites, despite the fact that NMR has long been used for the elucidation of their synthesis in plants and other organisms (13, 151). We also ignore a number of nonmetabolic areas in which NMR contributes to our understanding of plant biology. These areas include the investigation of water and water movement in plants, which are frequently studied by low resolution ^{1}H NMR (157) and NMR imaging (26, 85, 111); the many contributions of NMR spectroscopy to macromolecular structure determination; the investigation of plant ultrastructure and root architecture by NMR imaging (26, 85, 111); and the rapidly developing application of solid-state NMR methods to the characterization of plant cell walls (44, 55, 67).

IDENTIFYING AND QUANTIFYING METABOLITES

Primary metabolites are composed of hydrogen, carbon, nitrogen, oxygen, phosphorus, and sulfur. All of these elements have magnetic isotopes detectable by NMR, and with the exception of sulfur, the resulting signals can be used to identify metabolites in plant tissues and their extracts. The signals are observed by placing the sample in the magnet of an NMR spectrometer, and the resulting spectrum often contains sufficient information to identify and quantify the metabolites that are present. Moreover, since the measurement is nondestructive, it is possible to record a series of in vivo spectra from the same sample, and then to interpret the time course in terms of the metabolic response of the plant material to any change in its physiological state.

Full details of the practical aspects of recording and interpreting plant tissue NMR spectra are readily available elsewhere (111, 113, 129, 146). Suffice it to say that interpretable spectra can be recorded from a wide variety of material, including cell suspensions, excised tissues, and intact seedlings, and that it is possible to impose a range of physiological conditions on such samples within the confines of the NMR magnet. The sensitivity of the experiment is extremely variable, since it is strongly dependent on the nature of the sample, the isotope that is detected, the magnetic field strength of the spectrometer, and the way in which the NMR signals are recorded. As a very rough guide, a reasonable spectrum can often be obtained in 30 minutes from the metabolites present at millimolar concentrations in a 1 g sample, but this estimate could easily change by an order of magnitude according to the nature of the experiment. For example, ^{13}C-labeled fermentation products have been detected within a minute in a maize root tip sample weighing only 0.1 g (148). In contrast, it may take 12 h or more to define the unlabeled ^{13}C NMR signals from metabolites present at millimolar concentrations in extracts prepared from several grams of tissue. These considerations indicate that the practicality of an in vivo NMR experiment is often best judged empirically.

The magnetic properties of the detectable isotopes are very different, and this results in significant differences in the utility of the corresponding NMR spectra. Nevertheless, characteristic signals can be detected from many metabolites (34), and in some cases, in vivo NMR analysis has even led to the detection of new or unexpected compounds (35, 52, 134, 135). The salient features of the most useful NMR approaches are summarized in the following paragraphs. Note that the description is restricted to the specific role of NMR spectroscopy in identifying and quantifying metabolites, and that subsequent sections of the review consider the ways in which the same techniques can be used for other purposes.

Metabolite Detection Strategies

The hydrogen atom has three magnetic isotopes—^1H, ^2H, and ^3H—but only ^1H is relevant here. The high sensitivity of ^1H NMR, which stems from the favorable magnetic properties of the ^1H isotope and its 99.985% natural abundance, is a considerable advantage, but the usefulness of the technique is somewhat reduced by the overlapping of the signals from the detectable metabolites. This problem can be alleviated by the use of two-dimensional NMR experiments, for example COSY and TOCSY, and these methods also provide valuable information for metabolite identification by correlating different signals from the same molecule. The practicality of investigating plant metabolism with in vivo ^1H NMR was first demonstrated in root tissues (36). Recent applications include an analysis of the ligands in barley root exudates (37), the identification of a range of metabolites in the red alga *Gracilariopsis lemaneiformis* (21), and detailed analysis of the composition of tomato fruits (79, 97).

As well as using ^1H NMR to detect the signals from hydrogen atoms, it is also possible to use ^1H NMR methods to detect the presence of neighboring ^{13}C and ^{15}N atoms. This strategy is known as indirect detection, and it is important partly because it allows the ^{13}C and ^{15}N atoms to be detected with greatly increased sensitivity and partly because it provides further information on the identity of the metabolites. In practice, this is achieved using a further selection of two-dimensional methods (HSQC, HMQC, and HMBC), and these are easier to implement on extracts than in vivo. This approach has been used to analyze anaerobic metabolism in maize root tips (148), the composition of barley root exudates (37), and nitrogenous metabolites extracted from ^{15}N-labeled *Nicotiana plumbaginifolia* cell suspension cultures (93). Indirect detection is also important because it provides a straightforward method for measuring the absolute enrichment of specific carbon and nitrogen atoms with ^{13}C and ^{15}N respectively (e.g. 31).

For carbon the relevant magnetic isotope is ^{13}C. This has a natural abundance of only 1.11%, contributing to a considerably lower sensitivity for ^{13}C NMR than ^1H NMR. Accordingly, the application of ^{13}C NMR in unlabeled systems is largely confined to the detection of the most abundant metabolites, such as the organic solutes that accumulate in response to salt stress (6, 132) or certain secondary metabolites (83). As noted above, indirect detection increases the sensitivity of the experiment, and an example of this approach can be found in an analysis of the solutes in sugar beet suspension cells (99). Moreover, the sensitivity of ^{13}C NMR can be greatly increased by labeling the system with exogenously supplied substrates that are either intrinsically permeant or readily transported. The former, with representative examples of their recent application, include acetate (14, 89), carbon dioxide (14), formate (103), and methanol (52), whereas the latter include amino acids (96, 103, 136) and carbohydrates (31, 33, 100). Again it is often advantageous to use indirect detection methods, although these are not yet widely used.

The nitrogen atom has two magnetic isotopes—^{14}N and ^{15}N—and both can be useful for the detection of metabolites in vivo and in extracts. The practicality of detecting the naturally abundant (99.63%) ^{14}N isotope was first demonstrated in root tissues (18) and subsequently in vivo ^{14}N NMR has mainly been used for the analysis of ammonium and nitrate (48, 63, 74, 75). The low natural abundance of the ^{15}N isotope (0.037%) rules out the detection of unlabeled metabolites, but after labeling with [^{15}N]ammonium or [^{15}N]nitrate it is possible to use in vivo ^{15}N NMR to detect amino acids (62, 63, 131), as well as certain secondary products, such as nicotine, agropine, and conjugated polyamines (39). Indirect detection of ^{15}N-labeled metabolites is potentially advantageous, but its use is largely restricted to tissue extracts because indirect detection of amino-N groups is only possible over a limited range of acidic pH values with the HMQC technique (62, 93, 148).

Phosphorylated metabolites can be identified and quantified in plant material by ^{31}P NMR, and again the practicality of this approach was first demonstrated in root tissues (126). Signals are usually observed from a relatively small number of abundant metabolites—typically phosphomonoesters, inorganic phosphate (Pi), nucleoside triphosphates, and nucleoside diphosphosugars. The metabolic importance of these compounds continues to stimulate many in vivo ^{31}P NMR applications, and the usefulness of such studies can be greatly enhanced by complementary analyses of tissue extracts (7). The phosphorylation of exogenously supplied compounds, such as mannose and galactose (82), choline (19, 91), glycerol (10), and homoserine (9), is also readily observed by in vivo ^{31}P NMR.

It may be useful to conclude this section with a caveat relating to the detection of in vivo NMR signals. It turns out that there are several factors that may make an NMR signal undetectable, even though the ion or metabolite is present at a concentration higher than the detection threshold. First, the signal may be obscured by overlap with larger signals; second, the metabolite may be immobile due to precipitation or tight binding to macromolecules; and third, the signals from a chemically active metabolite may be intrinsically too broad to detect under high-resolution conditions. Although these features of the NMR technique are entirely familiar to NMR practitioners, they can be disconcerting to plant biochemists and they emphasize the need for close collaboration between the two groups.

Metabolite Profiling

Although as yet little used for this purpose, the wealth of metabolic information contained in the NMR spectra of plant tissue extracts suggests that there could be a role for NMR analysis in metabolite profiling. There are at least two reasons for believing that this proposition should be explored further. First, because NMR is a nondestructive technique, it is easy to combine the NMR analysis with a complementary technique, such as GC-MS. The scope of this strategy for analyzing complex mixtures of plant origin has been clearly demonstrated (34, 36, 37) and further investigation is warranted. Second, the NMR analysis of complex mixtures can be combined with an in-line separation technique, such as liquid chromatography, to create analytical tools that have already been used extensively for metabolic analysis in the field of biomedical research (70, 77).

In contrast to these applications, which demonstrate that numerous specific metabolites can be identified in complex mixtures, other investigators have addressed the question of whether computer-aided comparisons of the ^{1}H NMR spectra of partially fractionated extracts can yield statistically meaningful metabolic fingerprints of the extracted tissue (79, 97). Using this approach, it was possible to show that there were minimal compositional differences between certain transgenic and nontransgenic tomato varieties, but only after accounting for the substantial effects of external factors. Thus up to 30% of the compounds from the fruit of a single line were found to vary significantly between batches grown under nominally the same conditions at different times, and there were also significant variations within a batch (97). This very careful study highlights the formidable challenges that are likely to be encountered in metabolite profiling endeavors as a result of the plasticity of plant metabolism.

DEFINING THE INTRACELLULAR ENVIRONMENT

As well as identifying and quantifying metabolites, it is also important to explore the nature of the intracellular environment in which the interconnecting pathways are operating. This environment is defined by several factors, including ionic composition, energy status, redox state, viscosity, and subdivision through compartmentation. Moreover, changes in the extracellular environment can lead to alterations in one or more of these intracellular parameters. NMR methods, some of which are identical to those already discussed, can be used to probe the intracellular environment, and these applications are discussed in the following paragraphs.

The energetic status of a plant tissue can be assessed quantitatively using ^{31}P NMR (118, 130), and this approach is used routinely to check the physiological state of a sample during in vivo NMR experiments (111). Free ADP levels are generally too low to be detectable by NMR in vivo, so a detectable ADP signal is generally taken to indicate that the respiratory state of the tissue has been compromised. Furthermore, detailed NMR analysis of maize root tip extracts indicates that much of the ADP may be bound to proteins, reducing the chance of detecting it in vivo and complicating the interpretation of the NMR spectra recorded from tissue extracts (59, 60). In passing it may also be noted that NMR imaging has also been used to detect the oxygen diffusion barrier in nitrogen fixing nodules (27, 84).

NMR provides several opportunities for probing the ionic composition of plant tissues (110, 111). Ions that can be observed directly, with the relevant NMR nucleus in parentheses, include potassium (^{39}K), sodium (^{23}Na), chloride

(^{35}Cl and ^{37}Cl) and aluminum (^{27}Al), as well as nitrate (^{14}N and ^{15}N), ammonium (^{14}N and ^{15}N), and phosphate (^{31}P). In other cases, it is possible to use the NMR signal from a suitable ligand to act as a probe for the indirect detection of an ion that binds to it. Thus phosphate can be used as a ^{31}P NMR probe for Mn^{2+} (106), and the ^{133}Cs NMR signals from tissues that have been incubated with cesium salts are sensitive to the intracellular anionic composition (101).

The use of a similar indirect approach to measure intracellular pH is of much greater metabolic significance, and for this purpose NMR-detectable weak acids with pK_a values that are comparable to the pH of the cytoplasm or the vacuole are the most suitable ligands. Inorganic phosphate (^{31}P) and various organic acids (^{1}H, ^{13}C) are the most commonly used endogenous ligands, and the intracellular pH is determined by comparing the position of the in vivo NMR signal with the values obtained from an in vitro calibration procedure (127). NMR is frequently used for pH measurements in plant tissues, and a recent paper on pH changes during the development of cherry tomato fruits provides a representative example (133).

Compartmentation

Although the signals detected by in vivo NMR spectroscopy are averaged over the whole sample, they may still contain interpretable information on the spatial location of the detected metabolites (17). This is possible because differences in the intracellular environment can alter the properties of the NMR signals, leading in favorable cases to information on the compartmentation of the system. Thus, depending on the circumstances, it may be possible to obtain separate signals from subcellular pools, most commonly those originating in the cytoplasm and the vacuole, or to distinguish between signals from inside and outside the cells. The differences in the intracellular environment that give rise to these effects may be intrinsic to the system, with their origin in the spatial variation of the pH, viscosity, ionic composition, or protein content. Alternatively, they may be introduced through the use of paramagnetic ions, in the form of so-called shift reagents or susceptibility reagents. It is also possible to impose externally applied magnetic field gradients in the technique known as NMR imaging, and this powerful method for increasing the spatial information content of the NMR signal is considered in a later section.

Imaging aside, the most commonly encountered manifestation of compartmental analysis involves exploiting the pH difference between the cytoplasm and the vacuole to distinguish the cytoplasmic and vacuolar pools of various ions and metabolites (76, 113). For example, the second pK_a of Pi (6.8) lies between the pH of the cytoplasm (7.4–7.6) and the pH of the vacuole (typically 5–5.5, but often somewhat lower). Since the position of the Pi signal in the ^{31}P NMR spectrum depends on the degree of dissociation of the ion, it follows that separate signals can be detected from the cytoplasmic and vacuolar fractions. Thus the pH dependence of the signal and the pH difference between the two compartments allows both the subcellular distribution of Pi and the corresponding subcellular pH values to be determined from the same experiment (126). The pH dependence of the NMR signals from a number of other metabolites with suitable pK_a values can also be exploited. These include organic acids (25, 54, 154) and ammonium (75). Moreover, the separate cytoplasmic and vacuolar signals of these metabolites can themselves be used to probe the subcellular compartmentation of particular ions that interact with the observed metabolites. Thus organic acids can be used as pH probes (53) in the same way as phosphate, and both types of ligand can be used to probe the subcellular distribution of paramagnetic cations such as Mn^{2+} (53, 107) and Gd^{3+} (108).

Recently, it has been shown that it is possible to extend these investigations of subcellular compartmentation to amino acids (9, 12). Under normal circumstances, the pK_a values of amino acids are too remote from the cytoplasmic and vacuolar pH values to affect the NMR signals. However, by pretreating certain tissues with an ammonium solution at high pH, it is possible to induce an alkalinization of the cytoplasm that is sufficient to generate separate ^{13}C NMR signals from the cytoplasmic and vacuolar amino acid pools. Although the method has been successfully applied to sycamore cells (9) and the leaves of the Kerguelen cabbage (12), there are some doubts about its generality (47). The method depends on being able to increase the pH of the cytoplasm before the inevitable accumulation of the ammonium in the more acidic vacuole leads to a substantial increase in the vacuolar pH. This suggests that the method is likely to be strongly influenced by such factors as the accessibility of the cells to ammonium, the cytoplasmic to vacuolar volume ratio, and the buffering capacity of the two compartments. However, pH measurements in ammonium-treated maize root tips show that it may be difficult to satisfy these criteria in dense heterogeneous tissues (47). Despite these reservations, this new method can generate new insights into the distribution of amino acids in favorable cases.

There are also a number of instances in which subcellular information can be obtained from plant tissues on the basis of intrinsic factors other than pH. The first example is the chloride ion, where interactions with cytosolic proteins render the cytoplasmic pool invisible and allow the vacuolar pool to be monitored in vivo directly (150). Second, separate signals from cytoplasmic and vacuolar cesium are readily observed when plant tissues are incubated with cesium salts because the ^{133}Cs NMR signals are highly sensitive to the anionic composition and protein content of each compartment (101). Thus ^{133}Cs NMR provides opportunities for probing cation transport and the compartmentation of anions. Third, bound manganese in chloroplasts gives rise to an internal magnetic susceptibility effect that separates the ^1H NMR signals from chloroplast and nonchloroplast water in the leaves of several species, and this permits measurements of water exchange across the chloroplast membrane (90).

Bulk magnetic susceptibility effects have also been exploited in another recent development in the application of NMR to compartmental analysis (145, 149). It has been shown that adding nonpermeant and nontoxic complexes of paramagnetic ions to the suspending medium provides a versatile method for distinguishing all intracellular and extracellular signals from samples with cylindrical symmetry. The method has been applied to roots, shoots, and giant algal cells, and it is likely to find particular application in the measurement of fluxes across the plasma membrane (145).

EXPLORING PATHWAYS AND THEIR OPERATION

The primary motivation for using NMR methods to investigate plant metabolism stems from the current incomplete understanding of the way in which individual pathways operate within metabolic networks. Thus any method that can probe the operation of pathways in vivo is potentially valuable, and as this section and the one that follows will make clear, NMR makes a significant contribution to this endeavor. There are, of course, many other ways of investigating metabolic pathways and so NMR is but one of many complementary approaches. At the same time, an NMR analysis can often provide a very direct and convenient window on metabolism, and this is particularly true in the burgeoning field of stable isotope labeling (120).

Ultimately, the ability to explore the operation of metabolic pathways with NMR is simply an extension of its use as a nondestructive technique for identifying metabolites in tissues and extracts. Thus much can be achieved by using in vivo NMR methods to measure the changes in detectable metabolites as a function of time in labeled and unlabeled tissues. The resulting in vivo time courses have an inherent statistical advantage over time courses that have been constructed from a series of replicate measurements because all the spectra are recorded from the same sample. Moreover, in vivo time courses facilitate the correlation of simultaneous metabolic events, because the metabolic information is recorded throughout the experiment rather than at arbitrary time points, and they also make it easier to characterize oscillatory phenomena (159). These benefits can only be obtained by paying particular attention to the physiology of the tissue in the magnet (7, 111, 113, 129), and in some cases it may be advantageous to forgo them in favor of the greater sensitivity and resolution of an extract analysis. For example, there is no particular advantage in using in vivo NMR methods for the analysis of steady-state isotopic labeling experiments, and the analysis of a tissue extract is usually much more informative (138).

NMR methods are particularly suitable for the analysis of labeling experiments (80). The information that can be obtained includes both the relative and absolute fractional enrichments of particular atoms, as well as the identity and relative abundance of the isotopomers in the extract. Isotopomers are sets of labeled molecules that contain different distributions of labeled atoms, for example a mixture of [1,2-^{13}C]- and [1,3-^{13}C]glucose. NMR has a particular advantage over GC-MS, which is the other principal method for analyzing stable isotope labeling, because it provides direct information on the positional distribution of the labeled atoms within a molecule. This arises because structurally inequivalent carbon atoms within the same metabolite are usually magnetically inequivalent as well, and therefore give separate ^{13}C NMR signals. Furthermore, the presence of neighboring magnetically inequivalent carbon atoms causes a characteristic splitting of the NMR signals. As a result, the signals from [1,2-^{13}C]- and [1,3-^{13}C]glucose in the mixture of the two isotopomers above are readily identified. Some of the first metabolic applications of isotopomeric analysis were in plant metabolism (140, 141) and these early papers demonstrated the value of the approach in identifying and quantifying the pathways responsible for the redistribution of the label.

The in vivo and in vitro approaches to pathway analysis sketched out above become even more informative when combined with the controlled manipulation of the system. Transgenic technology offers unprecedented opportunities for probing metabolic pathways (20), and NMR has a role to play in defining the metabolic phenotypes of transgenic organisms (69). The first NMR investigations of transgenic plants are beginning to appear (38, 158) and this is likely to be an increasingly important feature of the field. At the same time, traditional approaches to perturbing metabolism, including the use of inhibitors (104, 163) and manipulating the intracellular pH (24, 45), continue to provide opportunities for testing metabolic hypotheses in vivo. It is against this background that we review the areas of plant metabolism in which NMR is making a significant contribution.

Photosynthetic Carbon Metabolism

NMR investigations of the pathways of photosynthetic carbon metabolism usually depend on the analysis of tissue extracts because of the apparently insurmountable difficulties in applying in vivo NMR methods to illuminated leaves (111). Following an early application of ^{13}C NMR to the analysis of photorespiration in ^{13}C-labeled C3 and C4 plants (140), the interest in using NMR methods was largely confined to the empirical analysis of site-specific natural isotope fractionation (SNIF) in the end-products of photosynthetic carbon metabolism (88). SNIF involves measuring the fractional enrichment or depletion of particular carbon and hydrogen atoms, and this can often be done conveniently by ^{13}C and ^{2}H NMR. Thus in one application, a ^{2}H SNIF-NMR analysis showed that it was possible to distinguish between C3 and C4 plants on the basis of the deuterium distribution in glucose samples derived from hydrolyzed starch (164). However, the emphasis was on establishing an empirical correlation, rather than on probing the metabolic implications of the results, and this aspect was not examined in detail.

More recently, two studies have shown that it is possible to extract mechanistic information from the nonrandom distribution of deuterium in the glucose extracted from sucrose (143) and leaf starch (142). First, in an important study on carbon transport, it was shown that the bulk of the carbon that is exported from chloroplasts at night is in the form of hexoses rather than triose phosphate (143). This conclusion was based on a ^{2}H NMR analysis of the glucose moiety of the sucrose obtained from leaves labeled with [2]H-enriched water, and this analysis showed that the bulk of the sucrose must have been synthesized directly from glucose. In a subsequent study, it was found that the glucose isolated from leaf starch was depleted in deuterium at carbon 2 in comparison with the glucose extracted from leaf sucrose or endosperm starch. This was explained in terms of a kinetic isotope effect that manifested itself because of the disequilibrium of the chloroplast phosphoglucose isomerase (142). It remains to be seen whether the novel approach used in these studies can be extended to the analysis of other pathways that include solvent exchange steps.

Nonphotosynthetic Carbon Metabolism

Several substrates can be used to introduce ^{13}C-labels into the pathways of primary metabolism in heterotrophic plant tissues. The use of $[^{13}C]$bicarbonate, which provides a convenient method for investigating the synthesis of malate and citrate (25, 54), is one possibility, but it is the use of $[^{13}C]$glucose that is currently attracting most attention. An important early study highlighted the reversible interconversion of hexose and triose phosphates in the cytosol of wheat endosperm (65). This paper also provided strong evidence against the import of triose phosphates into the amyloplast for the synthesis of starch, and thus played a significant part in focusing attention on the uptake of hexose phosphates. Cycling between hexose and triose phosphates has since been studied in a number of other systems, including potato tubers (160) and potato cell suspensions (71), and in a recent study in transgenic tobacco cells it was shown that elevated levels of fructose-2,6-bisphosphate (Fru-2,6-P_2) increased the rate of cycling (38). In the latter study the analysis of the cycling rate provided compelling evidence that pyrophosphate: fructose-6-phosphate 1-phosphotransferase (PFP) is not necessarily fully activated in vivo in heterotrophic tissue and that its activity can be modulated by changes in the level of Fru-2,6-P_2 within the normal physiological range (38).

The usefulness of $[^{13}C]$glucose labeling extends far beyond the exploration of the first few steps in the glycolytic pathway. In an important paper (31), it was shown that glycolysis, the oxidative pentose phosphate cycle, sucrose turnover, polysaccharide synthesis, and entry into the TCA cycle could all be detected in maize root tips by using suitable isotopomers of $[^{13}C]$glucose and analyzing the specific enrichment of the carbons in a range of carbohydrates and amino acids. Most of the 20 metabolic fluxes that were quantified in this study were determined from the NMR data, providing an impressive demonstration of the potential of ^{13}C NMR in the analysis of the pathways of intermediary metabolism. The pathways that are operating can be determined by identifying the labeling of particular intermediates and end-products. For example, the relative contribution of malic enzyme and pyruvate kinase to the synthesis of pyruvate has been assessed in maize root tips by measuring the incorporation of label from $[1-^{13}C]$glucose into alanine (31, 33). In this case synthesis via pyruvate kinase leads to labeling of carbon 3, whereas synthesis via malic enzyme leads to labeling at all three alanine carbons. Thus the labeling of carbon 2 provides clear evidence that the malic enzyme pathway is active (125), and a quantitative analysis of the alanine isotopomers allows an assessment of the contribution of the pathway to respiration (31, 33). The oxidative pentose phosphate pathway is another pathway that is accessible via [^{13}C]glucose labeling (31), and the suitability of using this approach for analyzing the subcellular compartmentation of the pathway is under investigation (72, 73, 138).

Valuable information about the operation of certain metabolic pathways can also be obtained by a careful ^{31}P NMR analysis of the levels of phosphorylated metabolites (105). Thus NMR analysis of the glycolytic intermediates, ATP, NAD$^+$, NADP$^+$, and NADPH, in perchloric acid extracts, provided strong evidence for an activation of glycolysis and the oxidative pentose phosphate pathway as part of the initial response of tobacco cells to the fungal elicitor cryptogein (105). As in many other NMR studies, perturbing the system, in this case by applying the fungal elicitor, shed light on the metabolic response of the cell suspension. Other commonly used perturbations include sucrose starvation (11, 30), oxygen deprivation (33), and salt stress (136).

Fermentation Pathways

Oxygen deprivation causes serious disruption of the normal aerobic pathways of plant metabolism (32). This disruption has been studied extensively by NMR and comprehensive reviews of the field have been published elsewhere (114, 130). In outline, the NMR studies of the anoxic response have focused on the contribution of particular pathways to energy production and pH control in the absence of oxygen, and on the origin and significance of the pH changes that occur in hypoxic and anoxic tissues.

Initially, in vivo NMR methods were used to show that (*a*) the switch from lactate to ethanol production observed under anoxia in maize root tips was caused by a fall in the cytoplasmic pH (124); and (*b*) cytoplasmic acidosis, caused by inadequate pH regulation, could be used as an indicator of flooding intolerance (121, 123). Subsequently, the analysis was extended to allow an assessment of the contribution of malate and amino acid metabolism to intracellular pH regulation under anoxia, and it was concluded that (*a*) the initial acidification of the cytoplasm could be attributed to lactate and alanine synthesis; (*b*) this initial fall in pH was limited by the activation of pyruvate decarboxylase and malic enzyme; and (*c*) the proton-consuming synthesis of GABA was quantitatively insignificant during the initial stabilization of the pH (125). More recent NMR investigations of the metabolic response to oxygen deprivation include in vivo demonstrations of the pH-sensitivity of pyruvate decarboxylase (45) and glutamate decarboxylase (GDC) (24) and an analysis of the metabolic factors that confer improved pH regulation on root tips that have been acclimated to a low oxygen environment (161–163). While there is continuing debate about the extent to which the picture that emerges from these studies is generally applicable (112, 115, 139), it is clear that it constitutes a major contribution to our understanding of plant anaerobiosis.

One-Carbon Metabolism

In yeast it has been possible to make significant progress in the analysis of one-carbon metabolism by using ^{13}C NMR to measure metabolic fluxes in genetically modified cells (5). Encouragingly, ^{13}C NMR has recently been adopted in the study of one-carbon metabolism in plants, and the metabolism of serine and glycine via glycine decarboxylase (GDC) and serine hydroxymethyltransferase (SHMT) has been explored in both photosynthetic (103, 104) and nonphotosynthetic (96) cells. These experiments employ ^{13}C-labeled substrates, and their interpretation depends on the subsequent quantitative analysis of the [2-^{13}C]-, [3-^{13}C]-, and [2,3-^{13}C]serine isotopomers. This approach has generated new insights into serine and glycine metabolism, and recent evidence suggests that the mitochondrial 5,10-methylene-tetrahydrofolate (CH$_2$-THF) pool does not equilibrate with the cytosolic and plastidic pools (96, 104). Methanol also enters metabolism via the THF pool and this has been investigated using [^{13}C]methanol and ^{13}C NMR (52). NMR applications to other parts of one-carbon metabolism include analyses of the uptake of phosphocholine and phosphoethanolamine (7), and the testing of several assumptions and predictions of a model of choline metabolism in transgenic tobacco (91). The use of genetic engineering and flux analysis is likely to be the key to understanding the regulation of one-carbon metabolism in plants (57), and the examples given here suggest that NMR analysis will play a significant role in achieving this objective.

Nitrogen Metabolism

Good evidence for the assimilation of ammonium via the glutamine synthetase/glutamate synthase (GS/GOGAT) cycle has been obtained by in vivo ^{15}N NMR in many systems, including cell suspensions (4, 131), embryogenic cultures (62, 63), root tissues (3, 40), and the peat moss *Sphagnum fallax* (64). The label is usually introduced in the form of [^{15}N]ammonium or [^{15}N]nitrate, and the identification of the pathway is based on an analysis of the subsequent incorporation of the label into amino acids in the presence and absence of inhibitors of GS and GOGAT. Particular interest attaches to the potential role of glutamate dehydrogenase (GDH) in the assimilation process, but with the exception of some observations on *Chlorella fusca* (2, 23), all the NMR analyses are consistent with a negligible role for GDH in the synthesis of glutamate. In contrast, the combined use of in vivo ^{15}N NMR and GC-MS has provided good evidence for the involvement of GDH in the oxidative deamination of glutamate in sucrose-starved carrot cells (46, 131). This conclusion has been queried (98), but a recent ^{13}C NMR investigation of isolated mitochondria has provided further support for the catabolic role of GDH (8). NMR evidence has also been presented for the involvement of the GS/GOGAT cycle in the recycling of the ammonium released by the deamination of phenylalanine during phenylpropanoid metabolism (116, 152).

Glutamate and glutamine are the precursors of many other metabolites, and in vivo ^{15}N NMR has been used to investigate several other pathways by following the subsequent metabolism of the ^{15}N-label. One example is the conversion of glutamate to GABA by glutamate decarboxylase (GDC), which was shown to be stimulated by processes that acidify the cytoplasm in both carrot cells (24) and root cultures of *Datura stramonium* (40). This result was consistent with the pH-dependent kinetic properties of GDC, and it suggests a role for GABA in pH regulation (24, 29) since GDC catalyzes a proton-consuming reaction. Elsewhere the operation of the ornithine cycle has been inferred on the basis of the substantial labeling of arginine in some tissues (1, 62, 63), while in other studies, it has been possible to investigate pathways of secondary metabolism (41–43). In one study, in vivo ^{15}N NMR observations of the conjugated polyamine pool in a *D. stramonium* root culture led to the hypothesis that the phytohormone-induced dedifferentiation of the culture required the presence of free polyamines. The hypothesis was supported by results obtained with metabolic inhibitors (42).

Phosphorylation

In vivo ^{31}P NMR allows the ready detection of phosphorylated metabolites present at tissue concentrations of the order of 1 μmol g^{-1} fr wt and this permits the investigation of a range of phosphorylation reactions. In one approach, plant tissues are supplied with a precursor that is readily phosphorylated, and NMR is used to monitor the accumulation, compartmentation, and subsequent metabolism of the product. Early applications examined the metabolism of galactose (82) and choline (19), and more recently, there have been detailed investigations of the phosphorylation of glycerol (10) and homoserine (9). For example, supplying glycerol to sucrose-starved sycamore cells led to the rapid accumulation of glycerol-3-phosphate in the cytoplasm (10). This led to an arrest of gluconeogenesis and the oxidative pentose phosphate pathway, and although glycerol prevented the development of autophagy, most probably by providing carbon skeletons for respiration, it was unable to support biosynthesis. Glycerol also caused the accumulation of a cytoplasmic pool of *O*-phosphohomoserine in cells supplied with sucrose, and this was interpreted in terms of an inhibitory effect of glycerol-3-phosphate on the pathways utilizing *O*-phosphohomoserine (10).

Several other approaches have been used in recent investigations of phosphorylation reactions. First, a bacterial polyphosphate kinase was expressed in the chloroplasts of potato plants with the intention of creating a novel Pi reserve for photosynthesis. The subsequent NMR analysis provided an unequivocal demonstration of the existence of a polyphosphate pool in the transgenic plants and a quantitative measure of its structural organization (158). Second, nucleotide metabolism has been investigated in isolated potato mitochondria by combining ^{31}P NMR measurements of phosphotransferase activity with oxygen electrode measurements of the respiratory state. This novel approach highlighted the interaction between adenylate kinase and ATP synthase in the regeneration of ATP from AMP and nucleoside diphosphates (122). Finally, the steady-state fluxes between a number of bioenergetically important phosphorylated metabolites have been measured by ^{31}P NMR (137) and this is discussed in the section on analyzing metabolic flux.

Mycorrhizal Metabolism

The challenge of observing fungal and plant metabolic processes separately in intimately connected symbionts is considerable (153). However, the identification of NMR signals from metabolites unique to either the host or the fungus in spectra recorded from the intact system provides a method for probing mycorrhizal metabolism (102). Thus the uptake and transfer of phosphorus by the fungal partner, which is the source of the principal nutritional benefit to the plant, can be analyzed by ^{31}P NMR. However, from a mycocentric perspective, the crucial transfer of fixed carbon from the plant to the fungus can be analyzed by ^{13}C NMR.

The uptake and metabolism of Pi by ecto- and endomycorrhizal fungi in the free-living and symbiotic states, as well as the structure and metabolism of polyphosphates, continues to be the subject of investigations by ^{31}P NMR (50, 102, 109). The chelation of aluminum (87) by polyphosphates and the effects of aluminum on phosphate uptake and metabolism (49) have also been assessed. ^{31}P NMR has also been used to analyze phosphate and phosphonate levels in the roots and shoots of *Allium cepa* treated with a fungicide (155).

Valuable information on the pathways of carbon metabolism that operate at different stages of the fungal life cycle has been obtained by ^{13}C NMR. These studies have provided evidence as to which forms of carbon are taken up by the fungus (100, 102), as well as identifying fungal storage compounds (16, 86, 147), and they have also led to the delineation of the principal pathways of fungal carbon metabolism (14, 86, 100). Interestingly, experiments on an endomycorrhizal symbiosis have revealed that hexose acquired by the fungus inside the root is converted to lipid before being exported to the extraradical mycelium, where some of it is converted back into carbohydrate for anabolic purposes (100). Taken together, these studies have significantly advanced our knowledge of carbon metabolism in ecto- and endomycorrhizas (15, 56).

ANALYZING METABOLIC FLUX

As described in the preceding section, NMR methods can be used to investigate numerous metabolic pathways either in vivo or via the analysis of tissue extracts. Although the qualitative observation of flow through a pathway can be informative, an important trend in recent years has been to use NMR techniques to obtain quantitative measurements of metabolic flux. Currently, there is particular interest in calculating such fluxes from the measurements of fractional enrichment obtained in labeling experiments. Comparisons can then be made between the fluxes obtained from different systems, or from the same system in different physiological states, and this can lead to insights into the integration and regulation of metabolism. Ultimately, the goal of such an approach is a predictive model of the metabolic network, in which the observed fluxes can be reconciled with the kinetics properties of the enzymes. The increasing emphasis on quantitative NMR analyses of metabolic pathways is a significant development in the plant NMR field, and several features of the NMR analysis of metabolic flux are discussed here.

One approach to flux measurement is to construct a time course on the basis of a series of in vivo or in vitro NMR spectra. The accumulation of phosphorylated metabolites, for example glycerol-3-phosphate (10), or labeled endproducts, for example a methyl glucoside (52), in cells supplied with suitable precursors are typical situations in which metabolic time courses can be obtained, and net fluxes to such compounds, if not data on turnover and lifetime, are often reported. However, as discussed elsewhere (138), a more flexible approach to the measurement of metabolic flux is to introduce suitable labels into the metabolic network and then to analyze the distribution of the label after the system has reached an isotopic steady state. This approach exploits the underlying relationship between the observed labeling of a metabolite and the multiple pathways that might lead to labeling in a complex metabolic network. One immediate advantage of the steady state approach is that it is only necessary to record a limited number of NMR spectra, each with a high information content, while another advantage is that NMR is ideal for discerning the fractional enrichment at specific carbon atoms in particular metabolites. These fractional enrichments provide primary data from which metabolic fluxes can be deduced, provided it is possible to construct an appropriate flux model that matches the underlying metabolic network.

A specific example that illustrates the approach is the redistribution of ^{13}C-label from carbon 1 to carbon 6 in hexose phosphates. This redistribution is caused by cycling between the hexose phosphate and triose phosphate pools, and its extent is determined by the other processes that contribute to the labeling of the hexose phosphate pool. This scrambling of the label has been investigated in several systems (38, 65, 71, 160) and a detailed theoretical analysis has been presented (138). Qualitatively, if the gluconeogenic flux is small relative to the flux into the hexose phosphate pool via hexokinase, then little label will reach carbon 6, whereas if the reverse is the case, and cycling is rapid, then equilibration will be complete and carbons 1 and 6 will have the same fractional enrichment. In fact, the observed situation is usually intermediate, with ratios of the fractional enrichment at carbon 6 to carbon 1 in the range 15–30% (38). This shows that the degree of cycling is significant, and a quantitative analysis of the fractional enrichments gives a quantitative measure of the ratio of the two fluxes of label into the hexose phosphate pool (138). The principal assumptions in such an analysis are that the pool sizes are constant, that the labeling has reached steady state, and that no complicating pathways are operating to alter the redistribution of the label. Note also that the analysis of the fractional enrichments generates a flux ratio, rather than absolute fluxes through the contributing pathways, and that no metabolite pool sizes or kinetic parameters for the enzymes that generate the fluxes are required or predicted.

In principle, the analysis of fractional enrichments can be used to investigate other competing pathways (33), and given the necessary data, multiple fluxes can be obtained from much more extensive metabolic networks (31). However, there have been few investigations of plant metabolism on this scale, and even when the necessary labeling data have been obtained for smaller-scale flux analyses, few attempts have been made to extract the metabolic fluxes. For example, in a study of carbon metabolism in a mycorrhizal fungus, prolonged exposure to a range of ^{13}C-labeled precursors allowed the measurement of the fractional enrichment at every carbon atom in trehalose (14). However, the analysis was restricted to identifying the pathways of carbon flow from the labeling pattern, even though the converging pathways involved should permit a steady-state flux analysis. The emphasis in this and many other studies is on pathway delineation, and exploring the possibility of reaching an isotopic steady state with the aim of quantifying relative metabolic fluxes is usually a low priority. The development of an appropriate flux model for converting fractional enrichments into the underlying metabolic fluxes is often not trivial, and this may have a deterrent effect on the application of the approach to plant metabolism. Indeed, the theoretical development of modeling approaches in general appears to be outstripping their adoption by the plant science community (51).

There is another way in which NMR can be used to measure metabolic fluxes from a steady-state analysis. This approach can shed light on unidirectional fluxes that occur over a time scale of seconds between certain phosphorylated metabolites. In this type of experiment the labels are magnetic and the fluxes are revealed through the use of ^{31}P NMR. In the simplest version of this technique, individual fluxes are measured between pairs of phosphorylated metabolites, notably ATP and Pi (128). The same approach has also been used to investigate the flux between UDPglucose and glucose 1-phosphate in maize root tips (119). An alternative version of the same experiment (EXSY) allows the simultaneous detection of all the observable fluxes (137). In practice, the experiment is lengthy and somewhat demanding, but it allows the observation of a number of important metabolic steps. The power of the method has clearly been demonstrated (137), and it awaits application in appropriate situations.

Quantifying fluxes is not an end in itself and it is comparisons between fluxes that leads to metabolic insights. Thus flux ratios or differences between fluxes within a metabolic network are likely to be useful, and comparing the same fluxes in closely related systems can also be informative. A good example can be found in the study of the contribution of malic enzyme to the synthesis of pyruvate in maize root tips where it was shown that the activity of malic enzyme increased by more than a factor of six early in hypoxia (33). Another approach is to use genetic manipulation to alter the metabolic landscape, as in an investigation of the effect of Fru-2,6-P_2 on the activity of PFP and hexose phosphate to triose phosphate cycling (38). Information obtained by manipulating metabolic fluxes is likely to be crucial in the construction of the metabolic models needed for an accurate and detailed description of metabolic networks.

IMAGING METABOLITES

As indicated above, NMR imaging provides a method for extracting spatial information from NMR signals. The method is most easily applied to the ^{1}H NMR water signal, since this is the strongest signal that can be detected in vivo, and the images reflect the state and distribution of the water in the imaged tissue (26, 85, 111). The images can be interpreted in terms of tissue anatomy and water movement, and the technique has now reached the point where it is capable of generating physiologically important information. The current power of NMR imaging can be judged from a recent paper on water flow in castor bean seedlings (66). Water flow through the xylem and phloem was quantified in intact seedlings using a flow-sensitive NMR imaging method, and it was shown that conventional measurements of the flow through the phloem, based on exudation rates, greatly overestimated the actual flow rate. It was also shown that there is an internal circulation between the phloem and the xylem, and that this phenomenon maintains water flow through the xylem in the absence of transpiration. Overall this paper provides a powerful demonstration of the contribution to be made by NMR imaging in studies of water flow (66).

Although the metabolites in a tissue are invariably present at concentrations that are orders of magnitude lower than the tissue water, there are have been several reports in which imaging methods were used to generate maps of the more abundant primary and secondary metabolites (61, 68, 92, 94, 95, 156, 165). The aim of this approach is to develop methods for mapping the tissue distribution of carbohydrates and amino acids, and from a metabolic perspective it is the spatial resolution of such maps that will eventually determine their value. However, it is still too early to define the likely limits of metabolic imaging and there have been few comparative studies of the different techniques (156).

In broad terms, there has to be a compromise between the spatial and temporal resolution of the experiment, and the current status of the field can be judged from some representative results (94, 159, 165). Thus sucrose, glucose, glutamine/glutamate, lysine, and arginine have been simultaneously mapped in the hypocotyls of castor bean seedlings using the technique known as correlation peak imaging (94, 165). The sensitivity of this experiment was judged to be sufficient to allow the detection of a metabolite present at 10 mM with a spatial resolution of 0.375 by 0.375 by 4 mm (a voxel volume of 0.56 μl) in 4 h 33 min (94). Sucrose has also been mapped on its own in the castor bean hypocotyl using the technique known as chemical shift imaging, and in this case a spatial resolution of 0.094 by 0.094 by 2 mm (a voxel volume of 0.018 μl) was achieved in 1 h 10 min (159). Although this approach to in vivo histochemistry is still limited by the available sensitivity, chemical shift imaging has generated some physiologically important information about the translocation of sucrose in the phloem (159). In particular, it was shown that sucrose equilibration occurred between vascular bundles, indicating radial translocation through the parenchyma.

Arguably the most exciting recent technical development in metabolic imaging is the localization of ^{13}C labeling (58). This can be achieved by indirect ^{1}H detection of the ^{13}C-labeled metabolites and it is a technically demanding area still in development. In the only study so far, ^{13}C-labeled glucose and fructose were taken up by the cotyledons of castor bean seedlings, and the subsequent synthesis of labeled sucrose and its translocation to the hypocotyl were observed with a time resolution of the order of 1 h. The spatial resolution achieved in this study was markedly less than in the chemical shift–imaging study (159), but the ability to measure newly synthesized sucrose by monitoring the incorporation of a ^{13}C label is a potential advantage. It remains to be seen whether this will become the basis of a worthwhile metabolic tool, but the current pace of development in the imaging field gives grounds for optimism.

CONCLUDING REMARKS

Modern metabolic research is increasingly aimed at defining metabolic phenotypes. This is not merely an exercise in identifying and quantifying metabolites, otherwise known as metabolite profiling, or even of mapping their distribution, since defining a metabolic phenotype also involves gaining an understanding of the integration and regulation of the underlying metabolic transformations. This in turn depends on delineating pathways, defining the intracellular environment, and quantifying metabolic fluxes. As discussed, NMR has a part to play in defining metabolic phenotypes, and its value is further increased when it is used in conjunction with the other techniques of metabolic analysis. Against this background it is arguable that NMR is likely to become increasingly important in two areas. First, there is considerable potential for using NMR methods in the characterization of transgenics, and indeed for using transgenic material to make NMR experiments more informative. Second, it is clear that the combination of steady-state isotope labeling and NMR detection of the resulting fractional enrichments can provide valuable information for metabolic flux analysis. Thus one may reasonably expect that NMR will continue to make worthwhile contributions to our understanding of plant metabolism.

ACKNOWLEDGMENTS

This review was prepared while the authors' research was supported by funding from BBSRC and Aventis CropScience UK (RGR), and USDA-NRICGP and NIST (YSH).

Visit the Annual Reviews home page at www.AnnualReviews.org

LITERATURE CITED

1. Aarnes H, Eriksen AB, Southon TE. 1995. Metabolism of nitrate and ammonium in seedlings of Norway spruce (*Picea abies*) measured by in vivo ^{14}N and ^{15}N NMR spectroscopy. *Physiol. Plant.* 94:384–90

2. Altenburger R, Callies R, Grimme LH, Leibfritz D, Mayer A. 1995. The mode of action of glufosinate in algae: the role of uptake and nitrogen assimilation pathways. *Pestic. Sci.* 45:305–10

3. Amâncio S, Santos H. 1992. Nitrate and ammonium assimilation by roots of maize (*Zea mays* L.) seedlings as investigated by in vivo ^{15}N NMR. *J. Exp. Bot.* 43:633–39

4. Amâncio S, Clarkson DT, Diogo E, Lewis M, Santos H. 1997. Assimilation of nitrate and ammonium by sulphur deficient *Zea mays* cells. *Plant Physiol. Biochem.* 35:41–48

5. Appling DR, Kastanos E, Pasternack LB, Woldman YY. 1997. Use of ^{13}C nuclear magnetic resonance to evaluate metabolic flux through folate one-carbon pools in *Saccharomyces cervisiae*. *Methods Enzymol.* 281:218–31

6. Aubert S, Assard N, Boutin J-P, Frenot Y, Dorne A-J. 1999. Carbon metabolism in the subantarctic Kerguelen cabbage *Pringlea antiscorbutica* R. Br.: environmental controls over carbohydrates and proline contents and relation to phenology. *Plant Cell Environ.* 22:243–54

7. Aubert S, Bligny R, Douce R. 1996. NMR studies of metabolism in cell suspensions and tissue cultures. See Ref. 146, pp. 109–54

8. Aubert S, Bligny R, Douce R, Gout E, Ratcliffe RG, et al. 2001. Contribution of glutamate dehydrogenase to mitochondrial glutamate metabolism studied by ^{13}C and ^{31}P nuclear magnetic resonance. *J. Exp. Bot.* 52:37–45

9. Aubert S, Curien G, Bligny R, Gout E, Douce R. 1998. Transport, compart-

mentation and metabolism of homoserine in higher plant cells. Carbon-13 and phosphorus-31 nuclear magnetic resonance studies. *Plant Physiol.* 116:547–57

10. Aubert S, Gout E, Bligny R, Douce R. 1994. Multiple effects of glycerol on plant cell metabolism. Phosphorus-31 nuclear magnetic resonance studies. *J. Biol. Chem.* 269:21420–27

11. Aubert S, Gout E, Bligny R, Marty-Mazars D, Barrieu F, et al. 1996. Ultrastructural and biochemical characterization of autophagy in higher plant cells subjected to carbon deprivation: control by the supply of mitochondria with respiratory substrates. *J. Cell Biol.* 133:1251–63

12. Aubert S, Hennion F, Bouchereau A, Gout E, Bligny R, et al. 1999. Subcellular compartmentation of proline in the leaves of the subantarctic Kerguelen cabbage *Pringlea antiscorbutica* R. Br. In vivo ^{13}C NMR study. *Plant Cell Environ.* 22:255–59

13. Bacher A, Rieder C, Eichinger D, Arigoni D, Fuchs G, et al. 1998. Elucidation of novel biosynthetic pathways and metabolite flux patterns by retrobiosynthetic NMR analysis. *FEMS Microbiol. Rev.* 22:567–98

14. Bago B, Pfeffer PE, Douds DD, Brouillette J, Bécard G, et al. 1999. Carbon metabolism in spores of the arbuscular mycorrhizal fungus *Glomus intraradices* as revealed by nuclear magnetic resonance spectroscopy. *Plant Physiol.* 121:263–71

15. Bago B, Pfeffer PE, Shachar-Hill Y. 2000. Carbon metabolism and transport in arbuscular mycorrhizas. *Plant Physiol.* 124:949–57

16. Bécard G, Doner LW, Rolin DB, Douds DD, Pfeffer PE. 1991. Identification and quantification of trehalose in vesicular arbuscular mycorrhizal fungi by in vivo ^{13}C NMR and HPLC analyses. *New Phytol.* 118:547–52

17. Belton PS, Ratcliffe RG. 1985. NMR and compartmentation in biological tissues. *Prog. Nucl. Magn. Reson. Spectrosc.* 17:241–79

18. Belton PS, Lee RB, Ratcliffe RG. 1985. A ^{14}N nuclear magnetic resonance study of inorganic nitrogen metabolism in barley, maize and pea roots. *J. Exp. Bot.* 36:190–210

19. Bligny R, Foray M-F, Roby C, Douce R. 1989. Transport and phosphorylation of choline in higher plant cells. Phosphorus-31 nuclear magnetic resonance studies. *J. Biol. Chem.* 264:4888–95

20. Bouchez D, Höfte H. 1998. Functional genomics in plants. *Plant Physiol.* 118:725–32

21. Broberg A, Kenne L, Pedersén M. 1998. In situ identification of major metabolites in the red alga *Gracilariopsis lemaneiformis* using high resolution magic angle spinning magnetic resonance spectroscopy. *Planta* 206:300–7

22. Browse J, Coruzzi G. 2000. Physiology and metabolism. Two old grannies catch fire in the new millennium. *Curr. Opin. Plant Biol.* 3:179–81

23. Callies R, Altenburger R, Abarzua S, Mayer A, Grimme LH, et al. 1992. In situ nuclear magnetic resonance of ^{15}N pulse labels monitors different routes for nitrogen assimilation. *Plant Physiol.* 100:1584–86

24. Carroll AD, Fox GG, Laurie S, Phillips R, Ratcliffe RG, et al. 1994. Ammonium assimilation and the role of γ-aminobutyric acid in pH homeostasis in carrot cell suspensions. *Plant Physiol.* 106:513–20

25. Chang K, Roberts JKM. 1992. Quantitation of rates of transport, metabolic fluxes, and cytoplasmic levels of inorganic carbon in maize root tips during K^+ uptake. *Plant Physiol.* 99:291–97

26. Chudek JA, Hunter G. 1997. Magnetic resonance imaging of plants. *Prog. Nucl. Magn. Reson. Spectrosc.* 31:43–62

27. Chudek JA, Hunter G, Sprent JI, Wurz G. 1997. An application of NMR microimaging to investigate nitrogen fixing root nodules. *Magn. Reson. Imaging* 15:361–68

28. Cornish-Bowden A. 1999. The origins of enzymology. *Biochemist* 19:36–38

29. Crawford LA, Bown AW, Breitkreuz KE, Guinel FC. 1994. The synthesis of γ-aminobutyric acid in response to treatments reducing cytosolic pH. *Plant Physiol.* 104:865–71

30. Dieuaide-Noubhani M, Canioni P, Raymond P. 1997. Sugar starvation induced changes of carbon metabolism in excised maize root tips. *Plant Physiol.* 115:1505–13

31. Dieuaide-Noubhani M, Raffard G, Canioni P, Pradet A, Raymond P. 1995. Quantification of compartmented metabolic fluxes in maize root tips using isotope distribution from [13]C- or ^{14}C-labeled glucose. *J. Biol. Chem.* 270:13147–59

32. Drew M. 1997. Oxygen deficiency and root metabolism: injury and acclimation under hypoxia and anoxia. *Annu. Rev. Plant Physiol. Plant Mol. Biol.* 48:223–50

33. Edwards S, Nguyen B-T, Do B, Roberts JKM. 1998. Contribution of malic enzyme, pyruvate kinase, phospho*enol*pyruvate carboxylase, and the Krebs cycle to respiration and biosynthesis and to intracellular pH regulation during hypoxia in maize root tips observed by nuclear magnetic resonance and gas chromatography-mass spectrometry. *Plant Physiol.* 116:1073–81

34. Fan TW-M. 1996. Metabolite profiling by one- and two-dimensional NMR analysis of complex mixtures. *Prog. Nucl. Magn. Reson. Spectrosc.* 28:161–219

35. Fan TW-M. 1996. Recent advances in profiling plant metabolites by multi-nuclear and multi-dimensional NMR. See Ref. 146, pp. 181–254

36. Fan TW-M, Higashi RM, Lane AN, Jardetzky O. 1986. Combined use of ^{1}H NMR and GC-MS for metabolite monitoring and in vivo ^{1}H NMR assignments. *Biochim. Biophys. Acta* 882:154–67

37. Fan TW-M, Lane AN, Pedler J, Crowley D, Higashi RM. 1997. Comprehensive analysis of organic ligands in whole root exudates using nuclear magnetic resonance and gas chromatography-mass spectrometry. *Anal. Biochem.* 251:57–68

38. Fernie AR, Roscher A, Ratcliffe RG, Kruger NJ. 2001. Fructose 2,6-bisphosphate activates pyrophosphate: fructose-6-phosphate 1-phosphotransferase and increases triose phosphate to hexose phosphate cycling in heterotrophic cells. *Planta* 212:250–63

39. Ford YY, Fox GG, Ratcliffe RG, Robins RJ. 1994. In vivo ^{15}N NMR studies of secondary metabolism in transformed root cultures of *Datura stramonium* and *Nicotiana tabacum*. *Phytochemistry* 36:333–39

40. Ford YY, Ratcliffe RG, Robins RJ. 1996. Phytohormone-induced GABA production in transformed root cultures of *Datura stramonium*: an in vivo ^{15}N NMR study. *J. Exp. Bot.* 47:811–18

41. Ford YY, Ratcliffe RG, Robins RJ. 1996. In vivo NMR analysis of tropane alkaloid metabolism in transformed root and dedifferentiated cultures of *Datura stramonium*. *Phytochemistry* 43:115–20

42. Ford YY, Ratcliffe RG, Robins RJ. 1998. In vivo nuclear magnetic resonance analysis of polyamine and alkaloid metabolism in transformed root cultures of *Datura stramonium* L.: evidence for the involvement of putrescine in phytohormone-induced dedifferentiation. *Planta* 205:205–13

43. Ford YY, Ratcliffe RG, Robins RJ. 2000. An in vivo ^{15}N NMR study of agropine synthesis in transformed root cultures of *Nicotiana tabacum*. *Physiol. Plant.* 109:123–28

44. Foster TJ, Ablett S, McCann MC, Gidley MJ. 1996. Mobility-resolved ^{13}C NMR spectroscopy of primary plant cell walls. *Biopolymers* 39:51–66

45. Fox GG, McCallan NR, Ratcliffe RG 1995. Manipulating cytoplasmic pH under anoxia: a critical test of the role of pH in the switch from aerobic to anaerobic metabolism. *Planta* 195:324–30

46. Fox GG, Ratcliffe RG, Robinson SA, Stewart GR. 1995. Evidence for deamination by glutamate dehydrogenase in higher plants: commentary. *Can. J. Bot.* 73:1112–15

47. Gerendás J, Ratcliffe RG. 2000. Intracellular pH regulation in maize root tips exposed to ammonium at high external pH. *J. Exp. Bot.* 51:207–19

48. Gerendás J, Ratcliffe RG, Sattelmacher B. 1995. The influence of nitrogen and potassium supply on the ammonium content of maize (*Zea mays* L.) leaves including a comparison of measurements made in vivo and in vitro. *Plant Soil* 173:11–20

49. Gerlitz TGM. 1996. Effects of aluminium on polyphosphate mobilization of the ectomycorrhizal fungus *Suillus bovinus*. *Plant Soil* 178:133–40

50. Gerlitz TGM, Gerlitz A. 1997. Phosphate uptake and polyphosphate metabolism of mycorrhizal and nonmycorrhizal roots of pine and of *Suillus bovinus* at varying external pH measured by in vivo P-31 NMR. *Mycorrhiza* 7:101–6

51. Giersch C. 2000. Mathematical modelling of metabolism. *Curr. Opin. Plant Biol.* 3:249–53

52. Gout E, Aubert S, Bligny R, Rébeillé F, Nonomura AR, et al. 2000. Metabolism of methanol in plant cells. Carbon-13 nuclear magnetic resonance studies. *Plant Physiol.* 123:287–96

53. Gout E, Bligny B, Douce R. 1992. Regulation of intracellular pH values in higher plant cells. Carbon-13 and phosphorus-31 nuclear magnetic resonance studies. *J. Biol. Chem.* 267:13903–9

54. Gout E, Bligny R, Pascal N, Douce R. 1993. [13]C nuclear magnetic resonance studies of malate and citrate synthesis and compartmentation in higher plant cells. *J. Biol. Chem.* 268:3986–92

55. Ha M-A, Apperley DC, Jarvis MC. 1997. Molecular rigidity in dry and hydrated

onion cell walls. *Plant Physiol.* 115:593–98

56. Hampp R, Schaeffer C, Wallenda T, Stulten C, Johann R, et al. 1995. Changes in carbon partitioning or allocation due to ectomycorrhiza formation: biochemical evidence. *Can. J. Bot.* 73 (Suppl.):S548–56

57. Hanson AD, Gage DA, Shachar-Hill Y. 2000. Plant one-carbon metabolism and its engineering. *Trends Plant Sci.* 5:206–13

58. Heidenreich M, Köckenberger W, Kimmich R, Chandrakumar N, Bowtell R. 1998. Investigation of carbohydrate metabolism and transport in castor bean seedlings by cyclic *J* cross polarization imaging and spectroscopy. *J. Magn. Reson.* 132:109–24

59. Hooks MA, Clark MA, Nieman RH, Roberts JKM. 1989. Compartmentation of nucleotides in corn root tips studied by ^{31}P NMR and HPLC. *Plant Physiol.* 89:963–69

60. Hooks MA, Shearer GC, Roberts JKM. 1994. Nucleotide availability in maize (*Zea mays* L.) root tips. *Plant Physiol.* 104:581–89

61. Ishida N, Koizumi M, Kano H. 1996. Location of sugars in barley seeds during germination by NMR microscopy. *Plant Cell Environ.* 19:1415–22

62. Joy RW, McIntyre DD, Vogel HJ, Thorpe TA. 1996. Stage-specific nitrogen metabolism in developing carrot somatic embryos. *Physiol. Plant.* 97:149–59

63. Joy RW, Vogel HJ, Thorpe TA. 1997. Inorganic nitrogen metabolism in embryogenic white spruce cultures: a nitrogen 14/15 NMR study. *J. Plant Physiol.* 151:306–15

64. Kahl S, Gerendás J, Heeschen V, Ratcliffe RG, Rudolph H. 1997. Ammonium assimilation in bryophytes. L-glutamine synthetase from *Sphagnum fallax*. *Physiol. Plant.* 101:86–92

65. Keeling PL, Wood JR, Tyson RH, Bridges IG. 1988. Starch biosynthesis in developing wheat grain. Evidence against the direct involvement of triose phosphates in the

metabolic pathway. *Plant Physiol.* 87:311–19

66. Köckenberger W, Pope JM, Xia Y, Jeffrey KR, Komor E, et al. 1997. A non-invasive measurement of phloem and xylem water flow in castor bean seedlings by nuclear magnetic resonance microimaging. *Planta* 201:53–63

67. Koh TH, Melton LD, Newman RH. 1997. Solid state ^{13}C NMR characterization of cell walls of ripening strawberries. *Can. J. Bot.* 75:1957–64

68. Koizumi M, Ishida N, Kano H. 1995. Location of sucrose and oils in a maize seed by NMR microscopy. *Biosci. Biotech. Biochem.* 59:2321–23

69. Koretsky AP. 1994. Nuclear magnetic resonance detection of the consequences of transgene expresion. *News Physiol. Sci.* 9:197–202

70. Korhammer SA, Bernreuther A. 1996. Hyphenation of high-performance liquid chromatography (HPLC) and other chromatographic techniques (SFC, GPC, GC, CE) with nuclear magnetic resonance (NMR): a review. *Fresenius J. Anal. Chem.* 354:131–35

71. Kosegarten H, Kalinowski H-O, Mengel K. 1995. Long-term ^{13}C labelling of starch and sucrose during the course of amyloplast development in intact suspension-cultured storage cells of potato (*Solanum tuberosum*). *J. Plant Physiol.* 146:405–10

72. Krook J, Vreugdenhil D, Dijkema C, van der Plas LHW. 1998. Sucrose and starch metabolism in carrot (*Daucus carota* L.) cell suspensions analysed by ^{13}C-labelling: indications for a cytosol and a plastid-localised oxidative pentose phosphate pathway. *J. Exp. Bot.* 49:1917–24

73. Krook J, Vreugdenhil D, Dijkema C, van der Plas LHW. 2000. Uptake of ^{13}C-glucose by cell suspensions of carrot (*Daucus carota*) measured by in vivo NMR: cycling of triose-, pentose- and hexose-phosphates. *Physiol. Plant.* 108:125–33

74. Lee RB, Purves JB, Ratcliffe RG, Saker

LR. 1992. Nitrogen assimilation and the control of ammonium and nitrate absorption by maize roots. *J. Exp. Bot.* 43:1385–96

75. Lee RB, Ratcliffe RG. 1991. Observations on the subcellular distribution of the ammonium ion in maize root tissues using in vivo ^{14}N NMR spectroscopy. *Planta* 183:359–67

76. Lee RB, Ratcliffe RG. 1993. Nuclear magnetic resonance studies of the location and function of plant nutrients in vivo. *Plant Soil* 155/156:45–55

77. Lindon JC, Nicholson JK. 1997. Recent advances in high-resolution NMR spectroscopic methods in bioanalytical chemistry. *TRAC-Trends Anal. Chem.* 16:190–200

78. Linskens HF, Jackson JF, eds. 1986. *Modern Methods of Plant Analysis. New Ser.*, Vol. 2. *Nuclear Magnetic Resonance.* Berlin: Springer Verlag

79. Lommen A, Weseman JM, Smith GO, Noteborn HPJM. 1998. On the detection of environmental effects on complex matrices combining off-line liquid chromatography and ^{1}H NMR. *Biodegradation* 9:513–25

80. London RE. 1988. [13]C labeling in studies of metabolic regulation. *Prog. Nucl. Magn. Reson. Spec.* 20:337–83

81. Loughman BC, Ratcliffe RG. 1984. Nuclear magnetic resonance and the study of plants. In *Advances in Plant Nutrition*, ed. PB Tinker, A Läuchli, 1:241–83. New York: Praeger

82. Loughman BC, Ratcliffe RG, Schwabe JR. 1989. Galactose metabolism in *Zea mays* root tissues observed by ^{31}P NMR spectroscopy. *Plant Sci.* 59:11–23

83. Lutterbach R, Stöckigt J. 1996. Dynamics of the biosynthesis of methylursubin in plant cells employing in vivo ^{13}C NMR without labelling. *Phytochemistry* 40:801–6

84. MacFall JS, Pfeffer PE, Rolin DB, MacFall JR, Johnson GA. 1992. Observation of the oxygen diffusion barrier in soybean (*Glycine max*) nodules with magnetic resonance microscopy. *Plant Physiol.* 100:1691–97

85. MacFall JS, Van As H. 1996. Magnetic resonance imaging of plants. See Ref. 146, pp. 33–76

86. Martin F, Boiffin V, Pfeffer PE. 1998. Carbohydrate and amino acid metabolism in the *Eucalyptus globulus-Pisolithus tinctorius* ectomycorrhiza during glucose utilization. *Plant Physiol.* 118:627–35

87. Martin F, Rubini P, Côté R, Kottke I. 1994. Aluminium polyphosphate complexes in the mycorrhizal basidiomycete *Laccaria bicolor*: a [27]Al nuclear magnetic resonance study. *Planta* 194:241–46

88. Martin GJ, Martin ML, Zhang B-L. 1992. Site-specific natural isotope fractionation of hydrogen in plant products studied by nuclear magnetic resonance. *Plant Cell Environ.* 15:1037–50

89. Marty D, Mesnard F, Gillet-Manceau F, Fliniaux M-A, Monti J-P. 1997. Changes in primary metabolism in connection with alkaloid biosynthesis in solonaceous cell suspensions: a ^{13}C NMR study. *Plant Sci.* 122:11–21

90. McCain DC. 2000. NMR study of chloroplast water in *Acer platanoides*: water exchange at membrane-bound sites and across the chloroplast envelope membrane. *Plant Biol.* 2:204–7

91. McNeil SD, Rhodes D, Russell BL, Nuccio ML, Shachar-Hill Y, et al. 2000. Metabolic modeling identifies key constraints on an engineered glycine betaine synthesis pathway in tobacco. *Plant Physiol.* 124:153–62

92. Meininger M, Stowasser R, Jakob PM, Schneider H, Koppler D, et al. 1997. Nuclear magnetic resonance microscopy of *Ancistrocladus heyneanus*. *Protoplasma* 198:210–17

93. Mesnard F, Azaroual N, Marty D, Fliniaux M-A, Robins RJ, et al. 2000. Use of ^{15}N reverse gradient two-dimensional nuclear magnetic resonance spectroscopy to follow metabolic activity in *Nicotiana*

plumbaginifolia cell suspension cultures. *Planta* 210:446–53

94. Metzler A, Izquierdo M, Ziegler A, Köckenberger W, Komor E, et al. 1995. Plant histochemistry by correlation peak imaging. *Proc. Natl. Acad. Sci. USA* 92:11912–15

95. Metzler A, Köckenberger W, von Kienlin M, Komor E, Haase A. 1994. Quantitative measurement of sucrose distribution in *Ricinus communis* seedlings by chemical shift microscopy. *J. Magn. Reson.* 105:249–52

96. Mouillon J-M, Aubert S, Bourguignon J, Gout E, Douce R, et al. 1999. Glycine and serine catabolism in non-photosynthetic higher plant cells: their role in C1 metabolism. *Plant J.* 20:197–205

97. Noteborn HPJM, Lommen A, van der Jagt RC, Weseman JM. 2000. Chemical fingerprinting for the evaluation of unintended secondary metabolic changes in transgenic food crops. *J. Biotech.* 77:103–14

98. Oaks A. 1994. Primary nitrogen assimilation in higher plants and its regulation. *Can. J. Bot.* 72:739–50

99. Omarzad O, Pichon R, Kervarec N, Hagège D. 1998. NMR natural abundance estimation of ^{13}C metabolic solutes in normal and habituated sugarbeet cell lines. *Protoplasma* 202:145–52

100. Pfeffer PE, Douds DD, Bécard G, Shachar-Hill Y. 1999. Carbon uptake and the metabolism and transport of lipids in an arbuscular mycorrhiza. *Plant Physiol.* 120:587–98

101. Pfeffer PE, Rolin DB, Brauer D, Tu S-I, Kumosinski TF. 1990. In vivo [133]Cs NMR: a probe for studying subcellular compartmentation and ion uptake in maize root tissue. *Biochim. Biophys. Acta* 1054:169–75

102. Pfeffer PE, Shachar-Hill Y. 1996. Plant/microbe symbioses. See Ref. 146, pp. 77–107

103. Prabhu V, Chatson KB, Abrams GD, King J. 1996. [13]C nuclear magnetic resonance detection of interactions of serine hydroxymethyltransferase with C1-tetrahydrofolate synthase and glycine decarboxylase complex activities in Arabidopsis. *Plant Physiol.* 112:207–16

104. Prabhu V, Chatson KB, Lui H, Abrams GD, King J. 1998. Effects of sulfanilamide and methotrexate on ^{13}C fluxes through the glycine decarboxylase/serine hydroxymethyltransferase enzyme system in Arabidopsis. *Plant Physiol.* 116:137–44

105. Pugin A, Frachisse J-M, Tavernier E, Bligny R, Gout E, et al. 1997. Early events induced by the elicitor cryptogein in tobacco cells: involvement of a plasma membrane NADPH oxidase and activation of glycolysis and the pentose phosphate pathway. *Plant Cell* 9:2077–91

106. Quiquampoix H, Bačić G, Loughman BC, Ratcliffe RG. 1993. Quantitative aspects of the ^{31}P NMR detection of manganese in plant tissues. *J. Exp. Bot.* 44:1809–18

107. Quiquampoix H, Loughman BC, Ratcliffe RG. 1993. A ^{31}P NMR study of the uptake and compartmentation of manganese by maize roots. *J. Exp. Bot.* 44:1819–27

108. Quiquampoix H, Ratcliffe RG, Ratković S, Vučinić Z. 1990. A ^{1}H and ^{31}P NMR investigation of gadolinium uptake in maize roots. *J. Inorg. Biochem.* 38:265–75

109. Rasmussen N, Lloyd DC, Ratcliffe RG, Hansen PE, Jakobsen I. 2000. ^{31}P NMR for the study of P metabolism and translocation in arbuscular mycorrhizal fungi. *Plant Soil.* 226:245–53

110. Ratcliffe RG. 1986. NMR and the inorganic composition of plants. *J. Inorg. Biochem.* 28:347–54

111. Ratcliffe RG. 1994. In vivo NMR studies of higher plants and algae. *Adv. Bot. Res.* 20:43–123

112. Ratcliffe RG. 1995. Metabolic aspects of the anoxic response in plant tissue. In *Environment and Plant Metabolism:*

Flexibility and Acclimation, ed. N Smirnoff, pp. 111–27. Oxford: BIOS Sci.

113. Ratcliffe RG. 1996. In vivo NMR spectroscopy: biochemical and physiological applications to plants. See Ref. 146, pp. 1–32

114. Ratcliffe RG. 1997. In vivo NMR studies of the metabolic response of plant tissues to anoxia. *Ann. Bot.* 79(Suppl. A):39–48

115. Ratcliffe RG. 1999. Intracellular pH regulation in plants under anoxia. In *Regulation of Tissue pH in Plants and Animals: A Reappraisal of Current Techniques*, ed. S Egginton, EW Taylor, JA Raven, pp. 193–213. Cambridge: Cambridge Univ. Press

116. Razal RA, Ellis S, Singh S, Lewis NG, Towers GHN. 1996. Nitrogen recycling in phenylpropanoid metabolism. *Phytochemistry* 41:31–35

117. Roberts JKM. 1984. Study of plant metabolism in vivo using NMR spectroscopy. *Annu. Rev. Plant Physiol.* 35:375–86

118. Roberts JKM. 1986. Determination of the energy status of plant cells by ^{31}P nuclear magnetic resonance spectroscopy. See Ref. 78, pp. 43–59

119. Roberts JKM. 1990. Observation of uridine triphosphate:glucose-1-phosphate uridyltransferase activity in maize root tips by saturation transfer ^{31}P NMR. Estimation of cytoplasmic PPi. *Biochim. Biophys. Acta* 1051:29–36

120. Roberts JKM. 2000. NMR adventures in the metabolic labyrinth within plants. *Trends Plant Sci.* 5:30–34

121. Roberts JKM, Andrade FH, Anderson IC. 1985. Further evidence that cytoplasmic acidosis is a determinant of flooding intolerance in plants. *Plant Physiol.* 77:492–94

122. Roberts JKM, Aubert S, Gout E, Bligny R, Douce R. 1997. Cooperation and competition between adenylate kinase, nucleoside diphosphokinase, electron transport, and ATP synthase in plant mitochondria studied by ^{31}P nuclear mag-

netic resonance. *Plant Physiol.* 113:191–99

123. Roberts JKM, Callis J, Jardetzky O, Walbot V, Freeling M. 1984. Cytoplasmic acidosis as a determinant of flooding intolerance in plants. *Proc. Natl. Acad. Sci. USA* 81:6029–33

124. Roberts JKM, Callis J, Wemmer D, Walbot V, Jardetzky O. 1984. Mechanism of cytoplasmic pH regulation in hypoxic maize root tips and its role in survival under hypoxia. *Proc. Natl. Acad. Sci. USA* 81:3379–83

125. Roberts JKM, Hooks MA, Miaullis AP, Edwards S, Webster C. 1992. Contribution of malate and amino acid metabolism to cytoplasmic pH regulation in hypoxic maize root tips studied using nuclear magnetic resonance spectroscopy. *Plant Physiol.* 98:480–87

126. Roberts JKM, Ray PM, Wade-Jardetzky N, Jardetzky O. 1980. Estimation of cytoplasmic and vacuolar pH in higher plant cells by ^{31}P NMR. *Nature* 283:870–72

127. Roberts JKM, Wade-Jardetzky N, Jardetzky O. 1981. Intracellular pH measurements by ^{31}P nuclear magnetic resonance. Influence of factors other than pH on ^{31}P chemical shifts. *Biochemistry* 20:5389–94

128. Roberts JKM, Wemmer D, Jardetzky O. 1985. Measurement of mitochondrial ATPase activity in maize root tips by saturation transfer ^{31}P nuclear magnetic resonance. *Plant Physiol.* 74:632–39

129. Roberts JKM, Xia J-H. 1995. High-resolution NMR methods for study of higher plants. In *Methods in Plant Cell Biology*, ed. DW Galbraith, HJ Bohnert, DP Bourque, 49A:245–58. New York: Academic

130. Roberts JKM, Xia J-H. 1996. NMR contributions to understanding of plant responses to low oxygen stress. See Ref. 146, pp. 155–80

131. Robinson SA, Slade AP, Fox GG, Phillips R, Ratcliffe RG, et al. 1991. The role of

glutamate dehydrogenase in plant nitrogen metabolism. *Plant Physiol.* 95:509–16

132. Rodríguez HG, Roberts JKM, Jordan WR, Drew MC. 1997. Growth, water relations, and accumulation of organic and inorganic solutes in roots of maize seedlings during salt stress. *Plant Physiol.* 113:881–93

133. Rolin DB, Baldet P, Just D, Chevalier C, Biran M, et al. 2000. NMR study of low subcellular pH during the development of cherry tomato fruit. *Aust. J. Plant Physiol.* 27:61–69

134. Rolin DB, Boswell RT, Sloger C, Tu S-I, Pfeffer PE. 1989. In vivo ^{31}P NMR spectroscopic studies of soybean *Bradyrhizobium* symbiosis. 1. Optimization of parameters. *Plant Physiol.* 89:1238–46

135. Rolin DB, Pfeffer PE, Osman SF, Szwergold BS, Kappler F, et al. 1992. Structural studies of a choline phosphate substituted β-(1,3);(1,6) macrocyclic glucan from *Bradyrhizobium japonicum* USDA 110. *Biochim. Biophys. Acta* 1116:215–25

136. Roosens NH, Willem R, Li Y, Verbruggen I, Biesemans M, et al. 1999. Proline metabolism in the wild-type and in a salt tolerant mutant of *Nicotiana plumbaginifolia* studied by ^{13}C nuclear magnetic resonance. *Plant Physiol.* 121:1281–90

137. Roscher A, Emsley L, Raymond P, Roby C. 1998. Unidirectional steady state rates of central metabolism enzymes measured simultaneously in a living plant tissue. *J. Biol. Chem.* 273:25053–61

138. Roscher A, Kruger NJ, Ratcliffe RG. 2000. Strategies for metabolic flux analysis in plants using isotope labelling. *J. Biotech.* 77:81–102

139. Sakano K, Kiyota S, Yazaki Y. 1997. Acidification and alkalinization of culture medium by *Catharanthus roseus* cells— Is anoxic production of lactate a cause of cytoplasmic acidification? *Plant Cell Physiol.* 38:1053–59

140. Schaefer J, Kier LD, Stejskal EO. 1980. Characterization of photorespiration in intact leaves using ^{13}carbon dioxide labeling. *Plant Physiol.* 65:254–59

141. Schaefer J, Stejskal EO, Beard CF. 1975. Carbon-13 nuclear magnetic resonance analysis of metabolism in soybeans labeled by $^{13}CO_2$. *Plant Physiol.* 55:1048–53

142. Schleucher J, Vanderveer P, Markley JL, Sharkey TD. 1999. Intramolecular deuterium distributions reveal disequilibrium of chloroplast phosphoglucose isomerase. *Plant Cell Environ.* 22:525–33

143. Schleucher J, Vanderveer PJ, Sharkey TD. 1998. Export of carbon from chloroplasts at night. *Plant Physiol.* 118:1439–45

144. Schneider B. 1997. In vivo nuclear magnetic resonance spectroscopy of low molecular weight compounds in plant cells. *Planta* 203:1–8

145. Shachar-Hill Y, Befroy DE, Pfeffer PE, Ratcliffe RG. 1997. Using bulk magnetic susceptibility to resolve internal and external signals in the NMR spectra of plant tissues. *J. Magn. Reson.* 127:17–25

146. Shachar-Hill Y, Pfeffer PE, eds. 1996. *Nuclear Magnetic Resonance in Plant Biology*. Rockville, MD: Am. Soc. Plant Physiol.

147. Shachar-Hill Y, Pfeffer PE, Douds D, Osman SF, Doner LW, et al. 1995. Partitioning of intermediary carbon metabolism in vesicular-arbuscular mycorrhizal leek. *Plant Physiol.* 108:7–15

148. Shachar-Hill Y, Pfeffer PE, Germann MW. 1996. Following plant metabolism in vivo and in extracts with heteronuclear two-dimensional nuclear magnetic resonance spectroscopy. *Anal. Biochem.* 243:110–18

149. Shachar-Hill Y, Pfeffer PE, Ratcliffe RG. 1996. Measuring nitrate in plant cells by in vivo NMR using Gd^{3+} as a shift reagent. *J. Magn. Reson. Ser. B* 111:9–14

150. Shachar-Hill Y, Shulman RG. 1992. Co^{2+} as a shift reagent for ^{35}Cl NMR of

chloride with vesicles and cells. *Biochemistry* 31:6272–78

151. Simpson TJ. 1986. ^{13}C NMR in metabolic studies. See Ref. 78, pp. 1–42

152. Singh S, Lewis NG, Towers GHN. 1998. Nitrogen recycling during phenylpropanoid metabolism in sweet potato tubers. *J. Plant Physiol.* 153:316–23

153. Smith SE, Read DJ. 1997. *Mycorrhizal Symbiosis.* London: Academic

154. Stidham MA, Moreland DE, Siedow JN. 1983. ^{13}C nuclear magnetic resonance studies of Crassulacean acid metabolism in intact leaves of *Kalanchoë tubiflora. Plant Physiol.* 73:517–20

155. Sukarno N, Smith FA, Scott ES, Jones GP, Smith SE. 1998. The effect of fungicides on vesicular-arbuscular mycorrhizal symbiosis. III. The influence of VA mycorrhiza on phytotoxic effects following application of fosetyl-Al and phosphonate. *New Phytol.* 139:321–30

156. Tse TY, Spanswick RM, Jelinski LW. 1996. Quantitative evaluation of NMR and MRI methods to measure sucrose concentrations in plants. *Protoplasma* 194:54–62

157. Van As H. 1992. NMR in horticulture: in situ plant water balance studies with NMR. *Acta Hortic.* 304:103–12

158. Van Voorthuysen T, Regierer B, Springer F, Dijkema C, Vreugdenhil D, et al. 2000. Introduction of polyphosphate as a novel phosphate pool in the chloroplast of transgenic potato plants modifies carbohydrate partitioning. *J. Biotech.* 77:65–80

159. Verscht J, Kalusche B, Köhler J, Köckenberger W, Metzler A, et al. 1998. The kinetics of sucrose concentration in

the phloem of individual vascular bundles of the *Ricinus communis* seedling measured by nuclear magnetic resonance microimaging. *Planta* 205:132–39

160. Viola R, Davies HV, Chudeck AR. 1991. Pathways of starch and sucrose biosynthesis in developing tubers of potato (*Solanum tuberosum* L.) and seeds of faba bean (*Vicia faba* L.). Elucidation by ^{13}C nuclear magnetic resonance. *Planta* 183:202–8

161. Xia J-H, Roberts JKM. 1994. Improved cytoplasmic pH regulation, increased lactate efflux, and reduced cytoplasmic lactate levels are biochemical traits expressed in root tips of whole maize seedlings acclimated to a low oxygen environment. *Plant Physiol.* 105:651–57

162. Xia J-H, Roberts JKM. 1996. Regulation of H$^+$ extrusion and cytoplasmic pH in maize root tips acclimated to a low oxygen environment. *Plant Physiol.* 111:227–33

163. Xia J-H, Saglio P, Roberts JKM. 1995. Nucleotide levels do not critically determine survival of maize root tips acclimated to a low oxygen environment. *Plant Physiol.* 108:589–95

164. Zhang B-L, Quemerais B, Martin ML, Martin GJ, Williams JM. 1994. Determination of the natural deuterium distribution in glucose from plants having different photosynthetic pathways. *Phytochem. Anal.* 5:105–10

165. Ziegler A, Metzler A, Köckenberger W, Izquierdo M, Komor E, et al. 1996. Correlation peak imaging. *J. Magn. Reson. Ser. B* 112:141–50

Annu. Rev. Plant Physiol. Plant Mol. Biol. 2001. 52:527–60

FUNCTION AND MECHANISM OF ORGANIC ANION EXUDATION FROM PLANT ROOTS

PR Ryan, E Delhaize

CSIRO Plant Industry, GPO Box 1600, Canberra, ACT 2601, Australia;
e-mail: p.ryan@pi.csiro.au; e.delhaize@pi.csiro.au

DL Jones

School of Agricultural and Forest Sciences, University of Wales, Bangor, Gwynedd, LL57 2UW, United Kingdom; e-mail: d.jones@bangor.ac.uk

Key Words rhizosphere, aluminum, phosphorus, anion channel, nutrition, organic acids, efflux

■ **Abstract** The rhizosphere is the zone of soil immediately surrounding plant roots that is modified by root activity. In this critical zone, plants perceive and respond to their environment. As a consequence of normal growth and development, a large range of organic and inorganic substances are exchanged between the root and soil, which inevitably leads to changes in the biochemical and physical properties of the rhizosphere. Plants also modify their rhizosphere in response to certain environmental signals and stresses. Organic anions are commonly detected in this region, and their exudation from plant roots has now been associated with nutrient deficiencies and inorganic ion stresses. This review summarizes recent developments in the understanding of the function, mechanism, and regulation of organic anion exudation from roots. The benefits that plants derive from the presence of organic anions in the rhizosphere are described and the potential for biotechnology to increase organic anion exudation is highlighted.

CONTENTS

1040-2519/01/0601-0527$14.00

INTRODUCTION

Organic acids are carbon compounds that possess at least one carboxyl group. Although this definition describes a large and structurally diverse group of compounds ranging from fatty acids and amino acids to secondary metabolites, this review focuses on the low-molecular-weight, non-amino organic-acid anions such as citrate, malate, oxalate, fumarate, and malonate. Some of these (e.g. citrate, malate, fumarate) are present in all living cells as intermediates of the tricarboxylic acid (TCA) cycle, the main respiratory pathway involved in the oxidation of pyruvate (Figure 1; see color insert). They are also directly or indirectly involved with many other metabolic processes including the assimilation of carbon and nitrogen, the regulation of cytosolic pH and osmotic potential, the balancing of charges during excess cation uptake, and the supply of energy to symbiotic bacteria.

Due to the central role played by many organic acids in cellular metabolism, their synthesis and concentrations tend to be strictly regulated. Compartmentation within the cell is shared between several organelles, of which the vacuole and mitochondria are most important. Organic acid concentrations in the cytosol are relatively stable whereas those in the vacuole can vary by one or two orders of magnitude in response to nutrient availability and metabolic activity (49). Apart from exceptional cases, such as species that undergo crassulacean acid metabolism (CAM), the total internal organic acid concentration is usually in the 5–50 mM range, depending on the tissue type, the nutrient status of the plant, and the proportion of the cell volume occupied by a vacuole (72). At the near-neutral pH of the cytosol, most of these acids exist as fully dissociated anions. For instance, at pH 7 approximately 80% of citric acid occurs as the citrate^{3-} anion and 99% of malic acid will be in the malate^{2-} form. In this review, we refer to organic anion exudation because these compounds are almost certainly released as anions (dissociated from protons) and not as acids. The large electrical potential difference (ΔE_{io}) across the plasma membrane of most plant cells (inside negative) ensures that the electrochemical gradient ($\Delta \mu_{io}$) for the organic anions greatly favors their passive movement out of the cell. Therefore, provided a pathway is available across the membrane, organic anions can move out of the cells without the direct expenditure of energy.

FUNCTION OF ORGANIC ANIONS EXUDED BY ROOTS

Three environmental stimuli associated with enhanced exudation of organic anions from roots are nutrient deficiency (particularly phosphorus), exposure to toxic cations (particularly Al^{3+}), and anoxia (9, 106a, 111, 120). Exuded organic anions benefit plants under these conditions by increasing the availability of nutrients for uptake by roots, by reducing the concentration of toxic cations in the rhizosphere, or by reducing the accumulation of potentially toxic metabolites in the cytoplasm. The first two processes rely largely on the capacity of organic anions to bind cations such as Al^{3+}, Fe^{3+}, and Ca^{2+} in the rhizosphere. The number of carboxyl groups and their arrangement relative to other carboxyl and hydroxyl moieties determine the stability of the ligand:metal complexes (9, 12, 65, 166). Generally, the tricarboxylates (citrate^{3-}) chelate these cations more strongly than dicarboxylates (malate^{2-}, oxalate^{2-}, malonate^{2-}), whereas monocarboxylates (acetate$^-$) are weaker still (Table 1). When deprived of oxygen, plants undergo anaerobic respiration, which produces ethanol or lactic acid as end-products (140). Lactic acid is potentially toxic to cellular metabolism, and some plants release it to the rhizosphere

TABLE 1 Formation constants between some commonly exuded organic anions (L) with various cations (M). Except for protons, the values are for a ratio L:M of 1:1 derived in zero ionic strength media at 25°C

Metals	Citrate^{3-}	Oxalate^{2-}	Malate^{2-}	Malonate^{2-}	Fumarate^{2-}	Acetate$^-$
H$^+$ (M:L)						
1:1	6.40	4.27	5.10	5.70	4.49	4.76
2:1	4.76	1.25	3.46	2.85	3.05	
3:1	3.13					
Al^{3+}	9.6[f]	6.1[c]	5.4[g]	5.7[h]	—	1.51[c]
	12.3[h]	6.53[h]	6.0[h]			
Fe^{3+}	11.5[a,e]	7.74[d]	7.1[a,e]	7.52[b]	—⊥	3.38[a,e]
Ca^{2+}	4.68	3.0[e]	2.66	2.35	2.0	1.18
Cu^{2+}	5.9[a,e]	6.23	3.42[a,e]	5.7	2.51	2.22
Zn^{2+}	4.98[a,e]	4.87	2.93[a,e]	3.84	—	1.57
Mn^{2+}	4.15[a]	3.95	2.24[a]	3.28	0.99[a]	1.4

Symbols: [a]0.1 or 0.16 M, [b]0.5 M, [c]1.0 M, [d]3.0 M ionic strength; [e]18°C or 20°C; [f]From (9); [g]From (12); [h]From (65) at 31°C. From Reference 111a or as shown.

to avoid excessive accumulation in the cytoplasm. This process is not considered further in this review and readers are referred to other sources (139, 179, 180).

Acquisition of Phosphorus

Phosphorus (P) availability is one of the major constraints to plant growth. Plants can suffer from P deficiency even though the total P content of the soil appears more than adequate. The reason for this apparent discrepancy is that the concentration of soluble P is often very low ($<5\,\mu$M) compared to the total amount of P bound to soil minerals and charged sites or fixed into organic forms that are inaccessible to plants (23, 138, 150). Therefore, the availability of P to plants is limited, to a large extent, by the rate of the reactions that replenish the pool of soluble P (Figure 2). Plants have evolved different strategies to cope with restricted P supplies that either increase P-use efficiency or help to extract more P from the soil (137, 151). These strategies include changes to cellular metabolism and root development; initiation

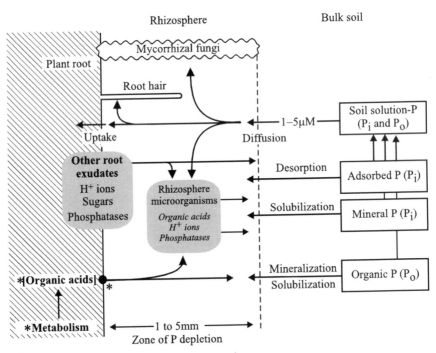

Figure 2 Processes influencing the availability of P in the soil solution for uptake by roots and mycorrhiza. Organic anions increase the concentration of P in the soil solution by solubilizing minerals and desorbing P from mineral surfaces. Root exudates can also affect the activity of microorganisms in the rhizosphere, which may also influence these processes. Possible regulatory points for organic anion exudation are labeled with an asterisk. (Adapted from Reference 138a with permission).

of mycorrhizal associations; acidification of the rhizosphere which can promote the release of nutrients from soil minerals; and the exudation of phosphatases and organic anions. The benefits derived from having organic anions in the rhizosphere are twofold: they compete with phosphate groups for binding sites in the soil, and they form stronger complexes with Al^{3+}, Fe^{3+} and Ca^{2+} than phosphate does. In particular, P can be liberated from Ca-P minerals as the organic anions complex with Ca (74) or block the sorption of P to other charged sites (103). Ligand exchange can also occur in which the P bound to Fe or Al oxyhydroxides is replaced by the organic anions (97). Organic anions can also stimulate microbial activity in the rhizosphere, which is likely to influence the availability of other minerals and nutrients as well (7, 41, 66, 141, 181).

Many dicotyledonous species release organic anions from their roots when P deficient (Table 2) and this can continue throughout much of the plant's life. The amount of carbon released can exceed 20% of the total plant dry weight in *Lupinus albus* (32, 42, 70). Most of this carbon is fixed in the leaves and transported to the roots via the phloem, but up to 30% is also derived from nonphotosynthetic carbon fixation in the roots (70). Citrate and malate exudation from *L. albus* and *Brassica napus* is associated with changes in cellular metabolism and with increases in internal organic anion concentrations (69, 117). Exudation is usually localized to specific regions of the root system. In P-stressed *B. napus*, organic anion efflux is restricted largely to the root apices (61). Other species modify their root anatomy in response to P deficiency, and exudation is restricted to these new root structures. An important example is the formation of proteoid roots, otherwise known as cluster roots (31, 44). These structures are clusters of short lateral rootlets covered with a dense mat of hairs that develop in many members of the Proteaceae, as well as the economically more important species *L. albus* (43, 44, 82, 176). These specialized roots enhance the ability of plants to access poorly soluble pools of P in the soil that are unavailable to most species (15, 60). In addition to exuding large amounts of citrate and malate, they increase the surface area available for nutrient absorption, acidify the rhizosphere, and release phosphatases (31).

Acquisition of Other Nutrients and Heavy Metals

Organic anions can potentially change the concentrations of micronutrients (Fe^{3+}, Mn^{2+}, Cu^{2+}, and Zn^{2+}) in the soil solution and possibly increase their availability to plants (31, 32, 74). In contrast to P deficiency, few reports associate Fe^{3+} deficiency with enhanced organic anion efflux (Table 2). Although Fe^{3+} deficiency can induce the development of cluster roots in some species (44, 177), whether they release organic anions is not known. However, citrate can complex Fe^{3+} adsorbed to the surface of soil minerals such as goethite and ferrihydrite, suggesting that even the low rates of exudation occurring under nutrient-sufficient conditions may be adequate to improve Fe^{3+} availability (50, 56, 76). The organic anion composition under different vegetation types growing on the same soil can be very different (53, 158, 163); hence organic anions might aid the establishment

TABLE 2 Enhanced organic anion exudation from the roots of selected species in response to environmental stimuli

Species	Major organic anions released	Stimulus	Efflux 1 (nmol/gFW/h)	Efflux 2 (units shown)	Comments	References
Wheat	Malate	+Al	4000[c]	2.0 nmol/apex/h	Root apices	143
Maize	Citrate	+Al	55[b]	0.25 nmol/apex/h	Root apices	127
Tobacco	Citrate	+Al	240[d]	0.18 nmol/apex/h	Root apices	28
Cassia tora	Citrate	+Al	280[a]		Wr	107
Triticale	Citrate, malate	+Al	7, 9[a]		Wr	106[a]
Rye	Citrate, malate	+Al	70, 35[a]		Wr	100
Buckwheat	Oxalate	+Al	70[a]		Wr	186
Soybean	Citrate	+Al	55		Wr	182
Taro	Oxalate	+Al	46		Wr	108
Sunflower	Citrate	+Al		150, 25 nmol/plant/h		148
Oats	Citrate	+Al	6[a]		Wr	185
Radish	Citrate	+Al	23[a]		Wr	185
Brassica napus	Citrate, malate	+Al	4, 4[a]		Wr	185
	Citrate	+Al	38[a]		Wr	104
Paraserianthes falcataria	Citrate	+Al		1.4 nmol/plant/h		123
Wheat	Malate	+Er	1000	0.5 nmol/apex/h	Root apices	uo
Arabidopsis thaliana	Citrate	+Cu	122[a]		Wr	116
Brassica napus	Malate, citrate	−P	200, 70[c]	0.43, 0.14 nmol/cm root/h		61
Rice	Citrate	−P	337		Rhizosphere	84
Lupinus albus	Citrate, malate	−P	570, 510 1160, 130 2380		Cluster roots " "	70 118 82
Alfalfa	Citrate	−P	3.5[a]			101
Chickpea	Malonate, tartarate citrate, fumarate	−Fe		2.0, 0.4, 0.4, 0.4 nmol/plant/h		122
Maize	Malate, citrate	ND	430, 90[a]		Wr	75

Assumptions used in calculating efflux to common units: (a) DW = 7% FW; (b) root apex = 6 mm × 1 mm dia; (c) root apex = 2 mm × 0.5 mm dia; (d) root apex = 6 mm × 0.4 mm dia. Symbols: −P, phosphorus deficient; −Fe, iron deficient; Wr, whole roots; ND, nutrient deficient; uo, unpublished observations by T Kataoka, A Stekelenburg, A Delhaize & PR Ryan.

of plants in a particular environment. For instance, plants that establish on calcareous soils (calcicole) tend to exude larger quantities of organic anions in these conditions than plants that grow mainly on lower pH, silicate soils (calcifuge) (163, 164). Ström and coworkers (163, 164) have speculated that calcicole plants release more organic anions to enhance the uptake of P and micronutrients, which limit plant growth on calcareous soils. Organic anions can also chelate heavy metals (134, 173), and some reports show that artificially raising soil organic anion concentrations can increase the accumulation in leaves of heavy metals like Cr^{3+}, Cd^{2+}, or U^- (22, 63, 160).

Organic Anion Exudation and Al^{3+} Tolerance

Aluminum (Al^{3+}) toxicity limits plant productivity on acid soils and micromolar concentrations in the soil solution can rapidly inhibit the root growth of many species (89, 167). Species vary enormously in their sensitivity to Al^{3+} stress. Many economically important species (wheat, maize, soybean) display a large intraspecific variation in Al^{3+} tolerance that can be exploited by plant breeders to enhance the tolerance of commercial lines. Over the past decade, physiologists have made tangible progress toward unraveling the mechanisms of tolerance in plants. A pattern has emerged in many Al^{3+}-tolerant genotypes: These plants exclude Al^{3+} from their tissues by releasing organic anions from their roots (29, 89, 106a). Exposure to Al^{3+} triggers the release of the organic anions, which protect the roots by chelating the Al^{3+} ions in the rhizosphere to form nontoxic complexes. A growing list of plant species shows this general response (Table 2). In wheat, buckwheat, and tobacco, the activation of organic anion efflux (malate, oxalate, and citrate, respectively) is rapid and occurs without any discernible delay after exposure to Al^{3+} (Table 2). The rapid kinetics of this response suggests that all the necessary metabolic "machinery" is constitutively expressed in the root and that organic anion efflux is simply triggered by the stimulus. In other species such as maize, *Cassia tora*, triticale, and rye, a lag is observed between the addition of Al^{3+} and the start of citrate release. Exudation begins slowly but increases gradually over the following 6 to 24 h. The delay suggests intermediate steps occur between the reception of the stimulus and anion efflux (106a). Since cellular signal-transduction pathways function over seconds or minutes, a delay of hours more likely reflects de novo protein synthesis.

The system that has been characterized in greatest detail is the Al^{3+}-activated efflux of malate from wheat. This example also provides the most convincing evidence that organic anion efflux is involved in the mechanism of Al^{3+} tolerance (3, 10, 21, 30, 88, 128, 143, 144, 146, 184). Delhaize and coworkers (26, 30) examined a pair of near-isogenic wheat lines that differ in Al^{3+} tolerance at a single dominant locus, and showed that in progeny derived from a cross between these lines, tolerance to Al^{3+} treatment cosegregated with a greater capacity for the Al^{3+}-activated efflux of malate. This loss of malate anions from the root cells is largely balanced by an equivalent efflux of K^+ (143).

Other metal ions can also activate organic anion efflux from roots. Several elements in the lanthanide series activate malate efflux from wheat roots in a very similar manner to Al^{3+} (T Kataoka, A Stekelenburg, E Delhaize & PR Ryan, unpublished observations). Copper (Cu^{2+}) tolerance in *Arabidopsis thaliana* is associated with a rapidly activated release of citrate (116) and greater tolerance to lead (Pb^{2+}) in selected varieties of rice is correlated with the stimulation of oxalate efflux (181a).

ORGANIC ANIONS IN THE RHIZOSPHERE

After passage from the cell to the soil solution (pH > 4.5), organic anions still carry from one to three negative charges. Understanding the function of these anions in the rhizosphere requires information on their local concentration as well as the main reactions that they participate in. Root exudation largely determines organic anion concentrations in the rhizosphere but this is also influenced by soil solid phase reactions (sorption and desorption), losses from leaching, degradation by soil microorganisms, and complexation and precipitation reactions (72, 73, 103). Organic anions in the soil solution can be estimated mathematically with models that simulate root exudation (84, 85) or they can be measured directly (163, 171).

Modeling Organic Anion Concentrations in Soils

The movement of organic anions in the soil can be calculated using well-established models (8, 169). These models rely on Fick's diffusion laws to predict the radial diffusion of organic anions away from the root as well as the back diffusion of liberated nutrients (76, 84, 85). Using this approach, Jones et al (76) modeled malate exudation from the roots of P-deficient *B. napus* and from wheat roots exposed to Al^{3+}. The model estimates an organic anion concentration at the root surface of 1 to 50 μM and predicts the concentration will increase almost linearly with the rate of exudation. Current models are limited by the assumption that intimate contact is made between the root surface and the soil, and that the reactions involving organic anions occur immediately after release into the soil (8, 76, 84, 85). In fact, water-filled gaps occur between soil particles and root cells (25) and therefore, most models underestimate the concentration of organic anions at the root surface. When this underestimate is taken into account, the predicted organic anion concentration in the water film at the root surface increases to 0.3 mM under P stress or 1 mM under Al^{3+} stress (76).

Modeling the interactions of organic anions with metal ions in soils is hindered by a poor understanding of the basic chemistry of organometallic complexes (8, 169). Many of the complexes in the soil solid phase need to be identified and the relative diffusion coefficients of the free anions and the metal-organic anion complexes need to be quantified. Despite these limitations, some simulations find a close agreement with experimental data (84, 85). Current models also indicate that the efficiency of organic anions in mobilizing soil P is highly dependent upon the rate of biodegradation. This process is controlled by the activity of the soil microbial community (84, 85), which is also poorly understood.

Measuring Organic Anion Concentrations in the Soil Solution

Many investigators have attempted to measure the concentration of organic anions in the root environment and, in particular, the soil solution (1, 11, 22, 158, 164, 171, 172). These measurements will represent the quasi steady-state levels between inputs [root, microbial, and atmospheric inputs (72, 83)] and outputs from the system [biodegradation, sorption and leaching (13, 36, 72, 77)]. Although many methods have been developed to measure root exudates (120), destructive soil sampling and extraction of the soil solution by centrifugal drainage is a commonly used method because of its ease and rapidity (171). This procedure generally extracts solution from a large volume of soil ($\sim$10 to 100 g) and, therefore, the results will underestimate concentrations in the rhizosphere. New techniques have also been developed for measuring submicromolar concentrations of organic anions in soil solution (11, 20, 158, 172). The concentration of organic anions measured in the soil solution usually range from 100 nM to more than 580 μM in the rhizosphere of cluster roots (1, 31, 32, 51, 54, 72, 95, 158). Millimolar concentrations of organic anion are likely required in the soil solution to effectively increase soluble P concentrations (120). Typically, organic acids constitute 5% to 10% of the total organic carbon in soil solution (95, 132, 158). The monocarboxylic anions (acetate, formate), which often dominate the soil pools (11, 20, 22, 35, 158, 172), are probably products of anaerobic metabolism by microorganisms with only minor inputs from the atmosphere and roots (34, 72).

Degradation of Organic Anions in the Soil

Microbial activity and biomass increase rapidly around plant roots (14, 115, 178). The consumption of organic anions by microorganisms is probably an important process reducing their effectiveness in dissolving minerals or detoxifying metals (84, 85). Microbial activity is stimulated by the release of soluble sugars from roots (37) but organic anion exudates can support microbial growth as well (36, 77). Bacterial and fungal cultures can also exude significant quantities of organic anions (41, 66, 141, 181) but it is likely that, in the soil, efflux is closely balanced by uptake. Persistence of organic anions in the soil is variable, with estimated half-lives ranging from 0.5 to 6 h depending upon temperature and soil type (77). Laboratory studies indicate that organic anions complexed with metals are more resistant to microbial uptake and mineralization (13, 16), but attempts to verify this effect in soil have failed (17).

REGULATION OF ORGANIC ANION EXUDATION

The next two sections examine how environmental stimuli cause the release of organic anions from plant roots, and how this process is regulated. The topic can be examined at many levels, but one point is clear: A single mechanism for organic anion release is unlikely to explain the range of responses described above and in Table 2. This review discusses four areas that have been implicated in the regulation of exudation: (*a*) root development, (*b*) plant-cell metabolism, (*c*) internal organic anion concentrations, and (*d*) organic anion transport. The first three topics are examined here, whereas organic anion transport is examined separately in a following section.

Root Development and Organic Anion Exudation

Phosphorus Deficiency and Cluster Root Development   Proteoid or cluster root formation is closely linked to P deficiency in a number of plant species (31, 176). As P availability is restricted, the development of new clusters increases; when P nutrition is improved, the development of new clusters declines (82) but small numbers even develop on plants well-supplied with P (71, 82). The synchronous development of clusters on lupin roots (175) suggests that a systemic signal regulates their development. It now appears likely that part of this signal is comprised of plant hormones because exogenous application of synthetic auxins can stimulate cluster root formation in P-sufficient plants (52). In *L. albus*, citrate efflux begins just as the rootlets reach their final length (about 3 to 4 days after the emergence) and continues for only 2 to 3 days (175). Therefore, citrate efflux and cluster development are coordinated under normal circumstances because efflux consistently begins as the rootlets stop growing (174). Perhaps the factors controlling the determinacy of rootlet growth also affect the transporters that facilitate organic anion release. Alternatively, the products of a heightened carbon metabolism might be released because they place an unacceptable load on the cells when they are no longer consumed by continued growth. However, in the clusters formed in response to the application of synthetic auxins, the changes in cellular metabolism normally associated with their development in P-deficient plants (see below) are absent and organic anion efflux is unlikely to occur from these clusters (52). Therefore, in *L. albus*, cluster development and organic anion efflux appear to be regulated differently, even though they are linked.

Other Environmental Signals   No obvious changes in root morphology have been reported in plants that release organic anions when exposed to Al^{3+}. This finding is not surprising in view of the rapidity with which Al^{3+} stimulates exudation. For those species that have been examined closely (wheat, maize, buckwheat, tobacco) exudation occurs from the same general region at the root apex (28, 127, 143, 186). Functionally, this is a useful strategy because the root apex is the region of the root most susceptible to Al^{3+} stress (145, 159). Interestingly, for species such as *B. napus*, which release organic anions during P deficiency, but do not grossly alter their root morphology, exudation is also localized near the root apices (61). These results suggest that the capacity to release organic anions in response to Al^{3+} treatment, or to P deficiency, is restricted to cells at a particular stage of development.

Linking Metabolism with Organic Anion Exudation

Two general lines of evidence support the proposal that cell metabolism regulates organic anion efflux from root cells by increasing organic acid synthesis. First, similar changes in metabolism are associated with organic anion efflux in several different species (see below), and second, transgenic plants overexpressing enzymes for organic acid synthesis are reported to show enhanced organic anion efflux (24, 91). This section considers whether changes in metabolism drive organic acid efflux or whether their association is related, but not regulatory. A later section discusses the potential for genetic modifications to manipulate organic anion efflux from plant roots.

Metabolism and Phosphorus Deficiency   Phosphorus plays an essential role in the energy cycle of all cells, and the finding that P deficiency causes substantial changes in metabolism is not unexpected. Reduced P uptake from the soil will alter the internal concentrations of inorganic P, ATP, and ADP; affect respiratory metabolism; and influence the reactions that depend on these intermediates (5, 69, 118, 147, 168). Remarkably, the flexibility of plant metabolism can partially compensate for these disruptions so that enzymes in the glycolytic pathway that are sensitive to inorganic P or nucleotide levels can be bypassed by alternate pathways (168). Phosphorus deficiency is most notably associated with changes in the activities of enzymes involved in carbon metabolism (33, 62, 69, 118, 175) but other changes include disrupted nitrogen metabolism (70), reduced RNA synthesis (71), increased amino acid and NADH concentrations (70, 78), and enhanced alcohol dehydrogenase activity (117). Some of these changes may be general responses to stress, but others may initiate metabolic adjustments that ultimately enable plants to cope with P deficiency. Therefore, it is tempting to link these changes with the synthesis and exudation of organic anions (117). For instance, organic anion release from the cluster roots of *L. albus* and other species has been associated with enhanced activities of PEPC, malate dehydrogenase, and citrate synthase (31, 69, 70, 175). These enzymes play an important role in the synthesis of citrate and malate, and changes in their activities could have a marked effect on carbon supply and organic acid metabolism. PEPC, in particular, can contribute in many different ways from bypassing pyruvate kinase in glycolysis (Figure 1) to fixing inorganic carbon into organic acids in the root tissue (69, 70, 168). Neumann & Römheld (119) also found a 25% decrease in aconitase activity, which prompted the idea that citrate exudation may depend on the coordination of synthetic and catabolic reactions (Figure 1). A similar conclusion was proposed by Takita et al (165) from their studies of carrot and alfalfa cell lines that exhibit enhanced citrate release. Neumann and coworkers (117) conclude that the release of organic anions from P-deficient *L. albus* is primarily a means of preventing cytoplasmic acidiosis, which could result from the excessive accumulation of these compounds in root cells. This idea is reminiscent of "overflow metabolism" in microorganisms in which partially oxidized metabolites are excreted following a phase of rapid metabolic activity. It is also similar to the exudation of lactate from maize roots during anaerobic respiration (139, 179, 180).

While there are ongoing attempts to make sense of these biochemical perturbations and to link them to organic acid efflux, overspeculation can be risky. In vitro measurements of enzyme activity may not reflect in situ activity because substrate concentrations and other cellular conditions can affect endogenous enzyme function. It is also important to remember that P-deficient plants are stressed plants and every metabolic perturbation that they display will not necessarily be directed toward increasing P availability in the rhizosphere. Indeed, not all P-deficient plants release organic acids even though they display many of the symptoms described above. For instance, P-deficient wheat and tomato plants have increased total organic acid concentrations in roots and shoots, as well as enhanced PEPC activity, but little or no exudation of organic anions (119). Conversely, organic anions are released, albeit in smaller amounts, from the cluster roots of hydroponically grown lupin plants that show no symptoms of P stress, indicating that efflux need not always be tied to P deficiency (82). In the unusual case of pigeon pea, the exudation of organic acids is actually enhanced by an excess supply of P (124). Watt & Evans (175) argue against a regulatory role for enzyme activity in organic anion exudation because, for instance, in *L. albus*, the maximum (in vitro) activities of PEPC, and other enzymes involved in organic acid synthesis do not always correlate with periods of greatest efflux (82, 175). Instead, they suggested that the transport of organic anions is an important regulatory step. In summary, although many of the metabolic changes initiated by P stress will help meet the demands for carbon during periods of exudation, the increased synthesis of organic acids in the root tissue may not be sufficient, in itself, to drive organic anion efflux.

Metabolism and Metal-Ion Stress   Most of the evidence from those species that release organic anions in response to Al^{3+} treatment argues against a regulatory role for enzymes involved in organic acid synthesis. Malate release from wheat continues for several hours without significant changes to the activities of PEPC or malate dehydrogenase measured in vitro. Furthermore, these enzyme activities are similar in closely related genotypes of wheat even though malate efflux occurs from only one of the lines (143). In rye, five- to tenfold increases in malate and citrate efflux occur in the absence of any changes in PEPC, malate dehydrogenase, and isocitrate dehydrogenase activities, and with only a 25% increase in citrate synthase activity (100). However a few reports do associate an increase in organic acid efflux with changes in metabolism. For instance, increases in citrate synthase expression and activity are associated with Al^{3+}-dependent citrate efflux in the tropical tree species *Paraserianthes falcataria* L. (122a, 123). A carrot cell line, selected for its ability to grow on poorly soluble $AlPO_4$, displays 30% to 40% more citrate synthase activity and 30% to 60% less NADP-isocitrate dehydrodrogenase activity. Since these changes were associated with a threefold increase in citrate efflux, the authors concluded that altered metabolism may play a key role in the ability of these cells to release citrate at higher rates (165).

Is Organic Anion Exudation Dependent on Internal Concentrations?

Increases in organic anion concentrations have been reported in the roots of P-deficient and Al^{3+}-treated plants (61, 70, 118, 127, 148). There is an implicit assumption in many studies that greater internal concentrations of organic anion lead to enhanced efflux. In fact, the dependence of organic anion efflux on internal concentration has not been rigorously tested. In many species where organic anion release is activated by Al^{3+} (wheat, maize, and buckwheat) no correlations are apparent between internal concentrations and efflux. For instance, in wheat and maize the differences in organic anion release from Al^{3+}-tolerant and Al^{3+}-sensitive genotypes is unrelated to their internal concentrations (30, 127). Similarly, organic anion efflux is localized to the root apices of wheat and buckwheat even though the internal concentrations are equal or higher in the older root tissues (143, 186).

A number of studies with P-deficient plants have reported higher organic anion concentrations in root tissues exuding organic anions. Some of these reports show general associations between organic anion efflux and internal concentrations (61, 119) whereas others claim striking correlations (79). However, in most cases this correlation does not hold through time. For instance, in *L. albus*, citrate concentrations in the cluster roots begin to increase one or two days before the period of citrate efflux and remain high well after efflux has stopped (118). Furthermore, the diurnal fluctuations of citrate efflux from cluster roots reported by Watt & Evans (175) are not accompanied by similar changes in the internal citrate concentrations (174). Other studies have not found a correlation between exudation and concentration in P-deficient plants (82, 118, 175).

Collectively, these results suggest that although the magnitude of efflux and the organic anion concentrations in the root tissue can be correlated, internal concentrations are unlikely to directly regulate efflux. This conclusion also makes sense when the compartmentation of the organic anions is accounted for and the thermodynamics of the ion gradients ions are considered. Large increases in internal organic anion concentration are mostly confined to the vacuole, whereas the cytosolic concentrations remain relatively stable. Therefore, increases in total tissue organic acid concentrations are unlikely to have a significant effect on electrochemical gradient (driving force) of the organic anions across the plasma membrane ($\Delta\mu_{io}$). Equally important is the major contribution of the membrane potential (ΔE_{io}) to $\Delta\mu_{io}$, which strongly favors efflux of anions in plant cells. Even large increases in the organic anion concentrations in the cytosol will cause relatively minor changes to $\Delta\mu_{io}$. For example, a fivefold increase in the cytosolic malate concentration will increase the $\Delta\mu_{io}$ for $malate^{2-}$ anions by less than 25% (assuming the initial malate level in the cytoplasm is tenfold higher than the apoplasm and ΔE_{io} is -120 mV). Moreover, the capacity of the TCA cycle and other enzymes to synthesize organic acids may well exceed the demands of efflux and maintain stable internal concentrations. This appears to be the situation for the Al^{3+}-activated efflux of malate from wheat roots where the internal concentration of malate in excised root apices remains unchanged after 6 h of Al^{3+} treatment even though the total amount of malate released during this period is threefold more than the amount initially present in the tissue (143).

MECHANISMS AND REGULATION
OF ORGANIC ANION TRANSPORT

Although malate, citrate, and other anions can accumulate to high concentrations in the vacuole, exudation of these molecules ultimately involves their transport from the cytosol to the outside medium. Most organic acids are almost fully dissociated in the cytosol and, since cell membranes are virtually impermeable to ions, exudation is restricted to three possible pathways: (*a*) *trans*-membrane diffusion of the undissociated (protonated) organic acids that are relatively soluble in lipids, (*b*) exocytosis, and (*c*) transport of organic anions via membrane-bound proteins.

Because the concentrations of the undissociated organic acids are very low in the cytosol, diffusion of this species across the membrane cannot explain the rates of organic anions released from roots. For instance, if the total malate concentration in the cytosol is 1.0 mM, the concentration of the malic acid (protonated) species would be about 3.0 nM. The permeability of malic acid through membranes would therefore need to be more than 100-fold greater than water to account for the observed fluxes across the plasma membrane. [It remains possible that the undissociated organic acid species cross the membrane via channel proteins that are permeable to small neutral molecules (48, 121)]. Little is known about the release of ions via exocytosis (the process in which membrane-bound vesicles fuse with the plasma membrane and exude their contents into the apoplasm), but there is growing interest in its role in solute transport (110). Some estimates of vesicular volumes and their rates of production suggest it might provide a significant pathway for ion exudation (93). Of the pathways mentioned above, membrane-bound transporters are likely to be most important in organic anion release. As explained in the Introduction, the transport step involved in organic anion exudation is a passive process that can be facilitated by transporters such as ion channels. Anion channels contribute to many important cellular functions that include mineral nutrition, turgor adjustment, signal transduction, and the stability of membrane potential (8a, 154, 170). Convincing evidence now indicates that anion channels are also involved in the release of organic anions from plant and animal cells (86) and, in some systems, these channels may also regulate efflux.

Anion Channels and Aluminum Tolerance in Wheat

The first indications that anion channels were involved with the release of organic anions emerged from inhibitor studies. The anion channel antagonists niflumic acid, 5-nitro-2-(3-phenyl-propylamino)benzoic acid (NPPB), and others are inhibitory to the Al^{3+}-activated efflux of malate from wheat roots (143). These results provided the impetus to investigate the role of anion channels in Al^{3+} tolerance using the patch-clamp technique. In the first of two studies, Ryan et al (146) examined the effect of Al^{3+} on the ion currents of protoplasts isolated from the root apices of an Al^{3+}-tolerant wheat genotype. In almost half of the cells tested, addition of $AlCl_3$ to the bathing solution (equivalent to apoplasm) triggered a large inward current in the whole-cell configuration, which corresponded to Cl⁻ efflux, the only permeable anion in the pipette solution. The current remained active for as long as Al^{3+} was in the external solution and was sensitive to niflumic acid. Single-channel recordings revealed an inwardly rectifying channel with a conductance of between 27 and 66 pS. The striking similarities between this Al^{3+}-activated anion channel (ALAAC) and malate efflux from intact wheat roots (30, 143) strongly suggest that this channel mediates malate efflux. Two important findings in a second study confirm this conclusion (184). The first demonstrates that ALAAC is permeable to malate^{2-} anions as well as to Cl⁻ (Figure 3) with a ratio (P_{mal}/P_{Cl}^{-}) of 2.6. The second finding is the conspicuous disparities in channel activity observed

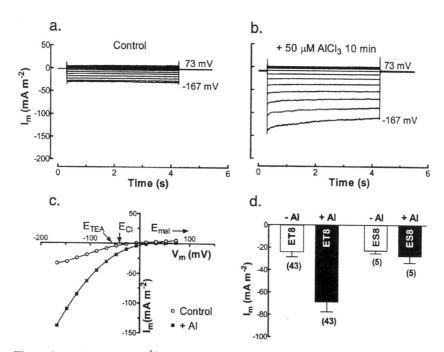

Figure 3 Activation, by Al^{3+}, of an inward current carried by malate anions (efflux) in protoplasts prepared from the apices of wheat roots. Parts (*a*) and (*b*) show superimposed current traces measured across the plasma membrane in response to a range of voltage-pulses as shown. Currents are shown before (*a*) and after (*b*) addition of 50 μM $AlCl_3$ to the bath solution. Part (*c*) shows the current-voltage curves of the data shown in (*a*) (*open circle*) and (*b*) (*closed circle*). Bath solution (mM): 10 tetraethylammonium chloride, 0.2 $CaCl_2$, pH 4.0. Pipette solution (mM): 40 malate, 1 $CaCl_2$, 2 $MgSO_4$, 2 Na_2ATP, 10 EGTA, 10 HEPES, pH 7.2 with 110 tetraethylammonium hydroxide. Part (*d*) compares the maximum inward current densities before and after addition of 50 μM $AlCl_3$ in protoplasts prepared from the near-isogenic wheat genotypes ET8 (Al^{3+}-tolerant) and ES8 (Al^{3+} sensitive). Currents were measured at -180 mV and the number of replicates are shown in brackets. (This material is copyrighted by the American Society of Plant Physiologists and was adapted, with permission, from Reference 184).

between a pair of near-isogenic wheat lines that differ in Al^{3+} tolerance at a single genetic locus. These differences include: (a) a greater frequency of responses to Al^{3+} observed in cells of the tolerant line compared with the sensitive line; (b) a larger current density in the tolerant line after addition of Al^{3+} (Figure 3d); and (c) a shorter delay between the addition of Al^{3+} and the activation of inward current for the tolerant line (184). These results are important because they represent the first physiological differences measured at the single-cell level between these near-isogenic lines of wheat. They also indicate that the transport protein itself regulates organic anion efflux.

These findings improve our understanding of the mechanism of Al^{3+} tolerance in wheat but two central questions remain: (a) How does Al^{3+} activate the anion channel? and (b) What are the differences between the Al^{3+}-tolerant and Al^{3+}-sensitive lines that allow sustained malate efflux from the tolerant but not from the sensitive line? It is not known whether Al^{3+} activates malate efflux directly by interacting with the channel protein or whether intermediate steps are involved. Consequently, the Al^{3+}-tolerance gene(s) in wheat could encode the anion channel itself or a protein that directly, or indirectly, modulates channel activity (Figure 4; see color insert). Such modulators could include kinases, phosphatases, or other proteins that alter the cytosolic concentrations of soluble effectors (38, 59, 126, 152, 155). Two results provide some evidence that activation of the anion channel might involve intermediate steps. First, a delay of 5 to 30 minutes is often detected between the addition of Al^{3+} and the activation of the inward current (146, 184). While this delay could be an artifact of protoplast preparation (because it does not occur in intact wheat tissue; 143), it could also indicate that intermediate steps are involved in the activation. The reason for this is that the efficiency of any soluble protein or secondary messenger involved in channel activation would be reduced by the whole-cell patch configuration because the cytoplasm in the protoplast is diluted by the pipette solution. It is also possible that the delay reflects the time required for Al^{3+} to cross the membrane to activate the channel from inside the cell: but this does not explain why some responses are rapid. A second result that suggests soluble intermediates are required for the sustained activation of ALAAC is the finding that inclusion of cAMP in the pipette solution maintains the outward K^+ current during Al^{3+} treatment (184). This finding is relevant because K^+ efflux appears to balance most of the loss of organic anions from the root cells (143) and this is discussed later in more detail (Figure 4).

Anion Channels and Aluminum Tolerance in Maize

Aluminum tolerance in maize is associated with the efflux of citrate and malate from root apices (127). Piñeros & Kochian (129) used the patch-clamp technique to investigate the effect of Al^{3+} on the ion currents in protoplasts prepared from the root apices of an Al^{3+}-tolerant genotype of maize. In the whole-cell configuration, addition of extracellular $AlCl_3$ activated an inward current in about 40% of cells examined which corresponded to Cl^- efflux, the only permeable anion. Single-channel recordings revealed Al^{3+}-dependent channel activity with a single-channel Cl^- conductance of 18–27 pS. Although permeability to citrate anions was not demonstrated in that study, the other similarities between this anion channel and the activation of citrate release from intact roots by Al^{3+} suggest that it is the likely pathway for citrate efflux. Another important result from this study was the finding that the anion current could be activated by Al^{3+} in outside-out patches. In this configuration, a patch of cell membrane, representing only a fraction of the protoplast surface area, is bathed by artificial solution on both sides, so the involvement of soluble cytosolic intermediates is extremely unlikely. Therefore, in maize, Al^{3+} interacts either directly with the channel protein itself, or with an adjacent membrane-bound receptor that then activates the anion channel (Figure 4).

A novel anion channel has also been observed in root protoplasts prepared from maize seedlings pretreated with Al^{3+} (M Kollmeier & WJ Horst, unpublished observations). These workers observe differences in this response between Al^{3+}-tolerant and Al^{3+}-sensitive cultivars, and, importantly, claim that the anion channel is permeable to malate and citrate anions as well as to Cl^-.

What Types of Proteins are These Anion Channels?

Anion channels are probably ubiquitous in plant, animal, and microbial cells but, in most cases, the proteins and genes have not been identified. All anion channel proteins are not the same, as demonstrated by the wide variety of protein families with members that exhibit anion channel activity (86). Examples from animal cells include the CLC family of chloride channels (162); the ATP binding cassette (ABC) protein family, which includes the cystic fibrosis transmembrane regulator (CFTR) (2); and aquaporins (183). The only anion channel genes that have been cloned from plants show some homology to the voltage-dependent CLC protein family (58, 105). However, no functional similarity has been demonstrated between these plant CLC genes and any of the channels characterized in plant cells (but see 46).

Apart from one unpublished report from maize (M Kollmeier & WJ Horst, unpublished observations), no other study has demonstrated citrate permeability in a plant plasma membrane channel. However, several plant and animal channels show some permeability to malate ions (86). In plant cells these channels are found on the tonoplast of CAM and non-CAM species (18, 19, 67, 125) and on the plasma membrane of guard cells (153), hypocotyl cells (39), and xylem parenchyma (90). The permeability of these channels to malate^{2-} relative to Cl^- (P_{mal}/P_{Cl}) ranges from 0.03 to 3.5 (18, 39). As mentioned above, none of the genes encoding these channels has been cloned.

What, then, can be said about the channel proteins involved in the Al^{3+} tolerance of wheat and maize? Both are likely to be ligand-gated anion channels because they require Al^{3+} or perhaps cytosolic intermediates to activate them. The ALAAC also shares a number of features with the "slow" anion channel from guard cells, and this may help to reveal additional information about ALAAC in the future. For instance, both these channels are inhibited by niflumic acid, NPPB, and diphenylamine-2-carboxylic acid (DPC) but not by 4,4-diisothiocyano-2,2-stilbene disulfonate (DIDS); aspects of their kinetics are similar; and both have been ascribed roles that require the sustained release of solutes from cells (143, 146, 154, 156, 184). The slow anion channel from guard cells also shows some intriguing pharmacological similarities with the CFTR Cl^- channel (99, 152, 156), leading some to suggest that the "slow" anion channel is either homologous to CFTR or tightly controlled by an ABC protein (99). Indeed, these similarities now raise the possibility that ALAAC is itself an ABC protein or is regulated by one (184). Interestingly, another ABC protein (Pdr12) is believed to facilitate the release of monocarboxylic acids from cells of *Saccharomyces cerevisiae* (131).

Organic Anion Efflux in Other Systems

Little information is available on the mechanisms of organic anion efflux in other systems. Specific transporters are likely to be involved, because root exudates do not reflect the composition of the internal organic anion pools. The use of inhibitors in a few studies supports this conclusion and provides some clues as to the mechanism involved. For instance, the finding that anthracene-9-carboxylic acid partially inhibits the citrate efflux from cluster roots of *L. albus* (118) suggests anion channels might be involved. Similarly, the Al^{3+}-activated efflux of oxalate from buckwheat is inhibited by phenylglyoxal, which implicates a role for anion channels in that system as well (186). However, inhibitor studies should be supported by additional physiological data because most of these compounds have uncertain specificities. In one relevant example, Garrill et al (45) showed that the anion channel antagonists niflumic acid and NPPB inhibited a K^+ channel in wheat-root protoplasts more potently than a Cl^- channel present in the same cells.

Balancing the Charges

Efflux of organic anions cannot occur alone because the membrane potential would collapse to the equilibrium potential of the permeant anion and rapidly stall the transporter. In practice, the change in membrane potential would activate other transporters to stabilize the membrane potential (154, 170). Therefore the release of each anion is balanced by the release of a cation or replaced by the uptake of another anion. Only a few studies have examined the counter-ions associated with organic anion release from plant roots. Local acidification of the rhizosphere is associated with organic anion efflux in a number of species that are deficient in P (32, 61) or Fe^{3+} (122). Proton efflux via the H^+-ATPase is likely to balance at least part of the anion release in these cases. By contrast, citrate release from the roots of Cu-tolerant ecotypes of *A. thaliana* is associated with short-term K^+ leakage (116), which can account for just over half of the citrate released from these roots. Potassium is also a counter-ion for the Al^{3+}-activated efflux of malate from wheat roots (143). On a molar basis, the K^+ released from excised root apices was approximately double the amount of malate, supporting the idea that malate is released as the divalent anion from wheat. Surprisingly, Ryan et al (146) found that the outward K^+ current in these root cells was almost completely inhibited by Al^{3+}, which posed the question: How does K^+ efflux occur from Al^{3+}-treated roots? The answer appears to reside, at least in part, in the requirement for cytosolic

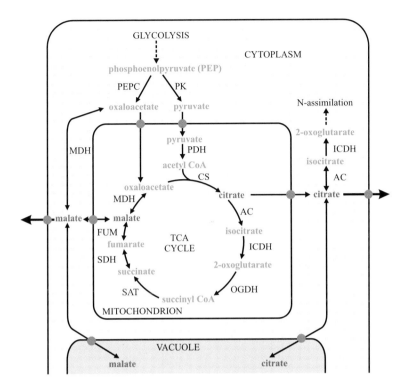

Figure 1 Enzymes of the tricarboxylic acid (TCA) cycle and other reactions involved in organic acid metabolism. Mitochondrial and cytoplasmic isoforms of the enzymes are shown. Green circles denote transporters. PEPC: phospho*enol*pyruvate carboxylase; PK: pyruvate kinase; PDH: pyruvate dehydrogenase; CS: citrate synthase; AC: aconitase; ICDH: isocitrate dehydrogenase; OGDH: 2-oxoglutarate dehydrogenase; SAT: succinate thiokinase; SDH: succinate dehydrogenase; FUM: fumurase; MDH: malate dehydrogenase.

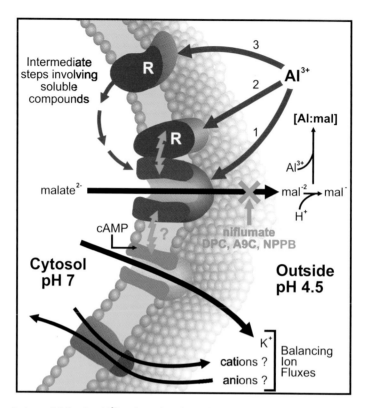

Figure 4 A model for the Al^{3+}-activated malate efflux from wheat roots. Possible mechanisms (*red arrows*) include: 1. Al^{3+} interacts directly with the anion channel protein; 2. Al^{3+} interacts with a membrane-bound receptor protein (R) which then activates the anion channel (*blue arrow*); 3. Al^{3+}-activates the anion channel indirectly perhaps via a receptor protein (R) and intermediate steps involving soluble intermediates. A proportion of the malate anions will be protonated as they move from the cytosol to the more acidic environment outside and before they chelate Al^{3+} cations. Malate^{2-} efflux is balanced by K^+ efflux and perhaps other ion fluxes. cAMP maintains the activity of the outward K^+ channel during Al^{3+} treatment. Regulation of the malate-permeable anion channel and the K^+ channel may be coordinated (*blue arrow with question mark*).

compounds to maintain channel activity during Al^{3+} treatment. Zhang et al (184) found that when cAMP was included in the pipette solution, the inhibition of the outward K^+ current by Al^{3+} was reduced. Furthermore, the outward K^+ current is sensitive to glibenclamide and DPC (W-H Zhang, unpublished observations), which signals another similarity with the "slow" anion channel in guard cells and with ABC proteins in general (99). As discussed above, a recent model for guard cell function invokes a CFTR-like protein that facilitates anion efflux and is directly coordinated with K^+ release (99). The pharmacological evidence suggests that a similar model may be operating in wheat roots to facilitate the Al^{3+}-activated efflux of malate and K^+ (Figure 4).

In all these examples the efflux of organic anions is balanced by cation efflux. With time, this loss of solute from the cell will reduce the internal osmolality, and therefore additional changes in transport activity or cell metabolism are expected to occur for exudation to be sustained.

GENETIC MANIPULATIONS TO ENHANCE ORGANIC ANION EXUDATION

The fact that plants can benefit from organic anion exudation in a number of ways has roused interest in the potential of genetic engineering to increase organic anion exudation in crop and pasture species. This could reduce the application of costly P-fertilizer and provide a larger range of Al^{3+}-tolerant genotypes for the management of acid soils. To release organic anions, a plant must possess the biosynthetic pathway for the organic acid in question, as well as a transport system to allow organic anion efflux.

All plants are capable of synthesizing the organic acids involved in the TCA cycle. Of these, citrate and malate are implicated in both Al^{3+} tolerance and enhanced P-nutrition. Genes encoding enzymes of the TCA cycle as well as other enzymes involved in organic acid metabolism have been cloned from many organisms (including plants) and these offer the potential for manipulating the biosynthetic pathways of malate and citrate (Figure 1). Pathways for the synthesis of malonic and oxalic acids [two other organic anions implicated in P-nutrition and Al^{3+} tolerance (Table 2)] are less well characterized, and genes encoding the enzymes involved have not been cloned. Large changes in organic acid production can be achieved in yeast and bacteria by inactivating or overexpressing specific genes whose products are involved in organic acid biosynthesis. These studies with microorganisms may be helpful in determining which enzymes could be successfully manipulated to alter organic acid biosynthesis and exudation in plants.

Manipulating Organic Acid Biosynthesis in Microorganisms

A collection of *S. cerevisiae* strains with mutations in all of the genes of the TCA cycle is now available for use in assessing the effect that inactivation of a particular gene has on organic acid synthesis and accumulation (136). For example, a strain of *S. cerevisiae* mutated in the gene encoding the mitochondrial NAD-dependent isocitrate dehydrogenase (NAD-ICDH) accumulates five- to sevenfold more citrate and isocitrate than the wild-type yeast (40). As expected, these mutants have low NAD-ICDH activity and require substrates that can be oxidized by alternate pathways such as fermentation (40). The simplest explanation for the greater organic anion concentrations is that the conversion of isocitrate to 2-oxoglutarate is blocked, which results in accumulation of organic acids "upstream" of this block (Figure 1). Similarly, when the NAD-ICDH gene in *Bacillus subtilis* is inactivated, large amounts of citrate and isocitrate are accumulated and exuded (114). However, these changes come at a cost in that the bacterium grows poorly and has a reduced ability to sporulate. Mutations in other genes lead to changes that are counterintuitive. When the gene encoding the mitochondrial form of citrate synthase in *S. cerevisiae* is inactivated (Figure 1), internal concentrations of citrate and malate are increased (87). Other TCA cycle genes that have been disrupted in *S. cerevisiae*, and which cause changes to organic acid production, include fumurase, 2-oxoglutarate dehydrogenase, and succinate dehydrogenase (4).

In an alternative approach to gene inactivation, overexpression of a gene encoding a cytoplasmic form of malate dehydrogenase (*MDH2*) increased the efflux of both malate and citrate in yeast (130). However, this increased efflux occurred only when the yeast was deprived of nitrogen and in the presence of a nonfermentable sugar. Another example is the expression of a bovine lactate dehydrogenase in the yeast *Kluyveromyces lactis* to increase lactic acid biosynthesis and exudation (133). A further increase in lactic acid production was achieved when the endogenous pyruvate carboxylase gene was also deleted, illustrating that in some cases, multiple modifications may be required to achieve the desired phenotype. Strains of *Aspergillus niger* are used to produce citrate commercially, and some effort has been directed toward increasing citrate production by genetic manipulation of biosynthetic pathways. Recently, Ruijter et al (142) overexpressed the mitochondrial citrate synthase in *A. niger* and showed that, although citrate synthase activity was increased by up to 11-fold over wild type, no increases in either internal concentrations or efflux of citrate were observed. The authors concluded that citrate synthase activity did not limit the amount of citrate produced and that citrate pools could not be increased by simply overexpressing enzymes in the biosynthetic or related pathways. Another striking example of this comes from the *nuo* mutant of *A. niger*. A mutation in the gene encoding the NADH-binding subunit of the NADH:ubiquinone oxidoreductase complex increases citrate biosynthesis and causes a 30-fold increase in the internal citrate under certain conditions (135). Despite these changes, citrate efflux from the mutant is tenfold lower than the wild type, and the authors conclude that the transport of citrate, and not its synthesis, is the rate-limiting step for exudation. These examples serve to illustrate that metabolic engineering in microorganisms can produce large changes in organic acid biosynthesis. However, in many of these cases, the transgenic organisms either grow poorly or require specific culture conditions for enhanced synthesis and exudation to occur.

Manipulating Organic Acid Biosynthesis in Plants

Notwithstanding clear examples of altered organic acid production in microorganisms through genetic manipulations, the few examples reported for plants are either modest by comparison or subject to controversy. Although inactivating genes encoding enzymes of the TCA cycle are potentially detrimental to plant growth, antisense techniques have enabled enzyme activities to be significantly reduced without severe phenotypes (98). There is also scope for changing the activity of the cytoplasmic isoforms of these enzymes as well as expressing genes from other organisms. For instance, Kruse et al (94) used antisense techniques to reduce the expression of cytoplasmic NADP-ICDH by over 90% in potato. Although there was no visible phenotype in these plants, citrate concentrations in leaves were increased about twofold above wild-type plants. The ICDH activity in tubers was reduced by about 50% but the effect on citrate accumulation and exudation were not assessed. de la Fuente et al (24) expressed a citrate synthase gene from *Pseudomonas aeruginosa* in tobacco and targeted the protein to the cytoplasm. They reported tenfold increases in citrate concentrations in the root and fourfold greater citrate efflux compared to control plants. The increase in citrate efflux was reported to enhance both the Al^{3+} tolerance of the transgenic tobacco (24) as well as their ability to acquire phosphate from poorly soluble forms present in alkaline soils (102). By contrast, Delhaize et al (28) found that these same transgenic tobacco lines, and different lines engineered to produce 100-fold more *P. aeruginosa* citrate synthase protein, had no effect on either internal citrate concentrations or efflux of citrate from the roots. These conflicting findings are difficult to reconcile and question the utility of the *P. aeruginosa* gene to increase citrate exudation in plants. Perhaps active expression of this gene in plants is sensitive to environmental conditions, or the reports of enhanced Al^{3+} tolerance (24) and P-acquisition (102) might be due to other factors. Recent evidence suggests that overexpression of a plant mitochondrial citrate synthase in plant cells can lead to a modest increase in citrate efflux. Koyama et al (92) overexpressed an *A. thaliana* gene encoding a mitochondrial citrate synthase in carrot cells, and observed a threefold increase in citrate efflux and enhancement in their ability to acquire phosphate from $AlPO_4$. More recently, the same group expressed the carrot mitochondrial citrate synthase in intact *A. thaliana* plants and found a 60% increase in citrate efflux (91). These transgenic plants also showed a 30% increase in root growth at 1 μM Al^{3+} and an enhanced ability to use poorly soluble forms of P. An unpublished report claims significantly improved Al^{3+} tolerance in alfalfa plants transformed with its own nodule-enhanced MDH gene. Greater MDH activity in these transgenic plants is reportedly associated with increased internal organic acid concentrations and enhanced efflux of malate, succinate and acetate (D Samac, M Tesfaye, S Temple, D Allan, C Vance, unpublished observations).

   As part of a study to establish the role of lactate dehydrogenase in the control of cytosolic pH under anoxic conditions, Rivoal & Hanson (140) expressed a barley gene encoding lactate dehydrogenase in tomato roots. The in vitro enzyme activity in the transgenic roots increased by up to 50-fold, but no increases in internal lactate concentration or efflux were detected under aerobic or anaerobic conditions. The authors conclude that lactate dehydrogenase activity is negatively regulated by a decrease in pH during anoxia and that the absolute amount of lactate dehydrogenase protein does not regulate lactate accumulation or efflux. Instead, the authors suggest that a transporter in the plasma membrane, which facilitates lactate efflux, exerts the major control over lactate fermentation in plants.

Several studies have tried to improve the efficiency of photosynthesis in C3 plants by increasing the expression of PEPC. Some of these have managed to increase enzyme activity and malate concentrations by two- to fourfold in the leaves of tobacco (64) and potato (47, 57), but no information on the exudation of organic anions from the roots was provided. Increasing the amount of enzyme by genetic engineering may have little effect on organic acid synthesis if the enzyme is already present in excess, or if its activity is regulated by the concentration of reaction products or by phosphorylation [e.g. PEPC (157)]. For instance, Landschütze et al (98) found that reducing the mitochondrial form of potato CS to less than 10% of wild type by antisense techniques resulted in no observable phenotypes except during flowering, when ovule development was affected. The authors concluded that CS was normally present at levels in excess of normal requirements and that ovule development was a situation where the activity of CS in the transgenic lines could become limiting owing to the high energy demands of this tissue. To overcome endogenous controls of enzyme activity, it may be necessary to express genes from different organisms, from different tissues, or to redirect the enzymes to cellular compartments where they are not normally expressed. Furthermore, many enzymes have multiple forms present in different organelles (112) and the successful alteration of organic acid synthesis may depend on the overexpression of a specific isoenzyme.

Manipulating Organic Anion Transport

Increasing organic acid synthesis and accumulation as a way of increasing organic anion efflux from roots will be fruitless if it is not coupled with a transport mechanism to facilitate efflux. The evidence from some plants also indicates that the rate-limiting step for organic anion efflux is the transport across the plasma membrane, and not the biosynthesis. A current challenge in manipulating the organic anion efflux from roots is to clone an appropriate transporter from any organism. Genes encoding transporters involved in organic anion uptake have been cloned from bacteria and yeast (6, 55, 113, 149), as have genes encoding transporters that move citrate across the inner membranes of mitochondria (80). However, these transporters function differently from proteins involved in anion exudation and they are unlikely to share significant sequence similarities.

Malate transporters, including malate-permeable channels, have been detected on the tonoplast (see above), and some of these may be similar to those occurring in the plasma membrane. Promising reports have appeared regarding the purification of these proteins as a prelude to the cloning of the corresponding genes. Steiger et al (161) reported that a protein purified from the tonoplast of the CAM plant *Kalanchoë daigremontiana* elicited high malate transport activity when reconstituted into liposomes. Elsewhere, Lahjouji et al (96) used photoaffinity labeling with a malate analogue to identify a tonoplast protein, which they concluded was likely to be involved in malate transport. Despite these promising results, the genes that encode these proteins have not yet been cloned.

The use of yeast complementation has proven to be a powerful and effective method for cloning plant genes encoding a range of transporters. However, to date, no yeast mutants are available that are suitable for cloning channels permeable to dicarboxylic and tricarboxylic anions. Another approach is to express plant genes, or overexpress yeast genes, in wild-type yeast and then screen for some function that is related to enhanced efflux of organic anions. For example, screening of yeast for Al^{3+} tolerance should, in principle, allow the isolation of plant genes that increase malate or citrate efflux from yeast. This approach has identified a number of plant and yeast genes that enhance Al^{3+} tolerance in yeast but none of these encodes organic anion transporters (27, 109). Clearly, there are ways of conferring Al^{3+} tolerance to yeast that do not rely on organic anion efflux. Another possible functional approach for cloning an organic acid transporter is to express plant genes in a heterologous system and assay directly for activity of the transporter. For example, the first voltage-gated chloride channel gene from animals was cloned by expressing mRNA in oocytes and measuring chloride-dependent currents across the oocyte membrane (68).

SUMMARY

The exudation of organic and inorganic compounds from roots is an important way by which plants can respond to their immediate environment. By modifying the biochemical and physical properties of the rhizosphere plants increase nutrient availability and buffer the effects of hostile surroundings. Although the fate of exuded organic anions in the rhizosphere, and the nature of the reactions they are involved with in soils, remain poorly understood, they clearly contribute significantly to plant growth. Organic anion efflux is often associated with changes in root-cell metabolism, which can increase organic acid synthesis and accumulation in root tissues. In some species, these changes in synthesis and internal concentrations may be necessary to increase organic anion exudation but it is unlikely that they are sufficient, in themselves, to regulate exudation. Instead, much of the evidence from plants and microorganisms indicates that it is the transport of organic anions, rather than their synthesis, that is limiting. Therefore, the proteins that transport organic anions across the plasma membrane are likely to regulate exudation. Physiological studies have recently revealed a role for ion channels in the exudation of organic anions from some species. The current challenge is to clone the genes that encode these channels or other proteins that facilitate organic anion exudation. Attempts to modify organic anion exudation from roots, by changing the activity of biosynthetic enzymes with gene manipulation, has met with mixed success. Progress will rely on researchers establishing which of the many possible strategies will be the most efficient for developing plants with a greater capacity for organic anion exudation.

ACKNOWLEDGMENTS

We are grateful to Tony Ashton, Peter Hocking, Peter Randall, Stephen Tyerman & Michelle Watt for comments on the manuscript; to Rebecca Schmidt for proof reading; and to many authors who supplied copies of their manuscripts prior to publication.

Visit the Annual Reviews home page at www.AnnualReviews.org

LITERATURE CITED

1. Adams JF, Wood CW, Mitchell RI. 1999. Loblolly pine plant community structure and soil solution aluminum, organic acids, calcium, magnesium, and pH. *Commun. Soil Sci. Plant Anal.* 30:1939–50
2. Anderson MP, Gregory RJ, Thompson S, Souza DW, Paul S, et al. 1991. Demonstration that CFTR is a chloride channel by alteration of its anion selectivity. *Science* 253:202–5
2a. Ando T, Fujita K, Mae T, Matsumoto H, Mori S, Sekiya J, eds. 1997. *Proc. Int. Plant Nutr. Colloq., 18th.* Dordrecht: Kluwer. 981 pp.
3. Andrade LRMD, Ikeda M, Ishizuka J, de Andrade LRM. 1997. Stimulation of organic acid excretion by roots of aluminum-tolerant and aluminum-sensitive wheat varieties under aluminum stress. *Rev. Bras. Fisiol. Veg.* 9:27–34
4. Arikawa Y, Kuroyanagi T, Shimosaka M, Muratsubaki H, Enomoto K, et al. 1999. Effect of gene disruptions of the TCA cycle on the production of succinic acid in *Saccharomyces cerevisiae. J. Biosci. Bioeng.* 87:28–36
5. Ashihara H, Li X-N, Ukaji T. 1988. Effect of inorganic phosphate on the biosynthesis of purine and pyrimidine nucleotides in

suspension-cultured cells of *Catharanthus roseus. Anal. Bot.* 61:225–32
6. Bandell M, Lhotte ME, Marty-Teysset C, Veyrat A, Prévost H, et al. 1998. Mechanism of the citrate transporters in carbohydrate and citrate cometabolism in *Lactococcus* and *Leuconostoc species. Appl. Environ. Microbiol.* 64:1594–600
7. Banfield JF, Barker WW, Welch SA, Taunton A. 1999. Biological impact on mineral dissolution: application of the lichen model to understand mineral weathering in the rhizosphere. *Proc. Natl. Acad. Sci. USA* 96:3404–11
8. Barber SA. 1995. *Soil Nutrient Bioavailability: A Mechanistic Approach,* New York: Wiley. 414 pp.
8a. Barbier-Brygoo H, Vinauger M, Colcombet J, Ephritikhine G, Frachisse J-M, et al. 2000. Anion channels in higher plants: functional characterization, molecular structure and physiological role. *Biochim. Biophys. Acta* 1465:199–218
9. Bar-Yosef B. 1991. Root excretions and their environmental effects. Influence on availability of phosphorus. In *Plant Roots. The Hidden Half,* ed. Y Waisel, A Eshel, U Kafkafi, pp. 529–57. New York: Marcel Dekker. 948 pp.

10. Basu U, Godbold D, Taylor GJ. 1994. Aluminum resistance in *Triticum aestivum* associated with enhanced exudation of malate. *J. Plant Physiol.* 144:747–53

11. Baziramakenga R, Simard RR, Leroux GD. 1995. Determination of organic acids in soil extracts by ion chromatography. *Soil Biol. Biochem.* 27:349–56

12. Bolan NS, Naidu R, Mahimairaja S, Baskaran S. 1994. Influence of low molecular-weight organic acids on solubilization of phosphates. *Biol. Fertil. Soils* 18:311–19

13. Boudot JP. 1992. Relative efficiency of complexed aluminum, noncrystalline Al hydroxide, allophane and imogolite in retarding the biodegradation of citric acid. *Geoderma* 52:29–39

14. Bowers JH, Nameth ST, Riedel RM, Rowe RC. 1996. Infection and colonization of potato roots by *Verticillium dahliae* as affected by *Pratylenchus penetrans* and *P. crenatus*. *Phytopathology* 86:614–21

15. Braum SM, Helmke PA. 1995. White lupin utilizes soil phosphorus that is unavailable to soybean. *Plant Soil* 176:95–100

16. Brynhildsen L, Allard B. 1994. Influence of metal complexation in the metabolism of citrate by *Klebsiella-oxytoca*. *Biometals* 7:163–69

17. Brynhildsen L, Rosswall T. 1997. Effects of metals on the microbial mineralization of organic acids. *Water Air Soil Pollut.* 94:45–57

18. Cerana R, Giromini L, Colombo R. 1995. Malate-regulated channels permeable to anions in vacuoles of *Arabidopsis thaliana*. *Aust. J. Plant Physiol.* 22:115–21

19. Cheffings CM, Pantoja O, Ashcroft FM, Smith JAC. 1997. Malate transport and vacuolar ion channels in CAM plants. *J. Exp. Bot.* 48:623–31

20. Chen ZL, Tang C, Yu JC. 1999. Simultaneous determination of inorganic anions and organic acids in environmental samples by capillary zone electrophoresis with indirect UV detection. *J. High Resolut. Chromatogr.* 22:379–85

21. Christiansen-Weniger C, Groneman AF, Van Veen JA. 1992. Associative N_2 fixation and root exudation of organic acids from wheat cultivars of different aluminium tolerance. *Plant Soil* 139:167–74

22. Cieslinski G, Van Rees KCJ, Szmigielska AM, Krishnamurti GSR, Huang PM. 1998. Low-molecular-weight organic acids in rhizosphere soils of durum wheat and their effect on cadmium bioaccumulation. *Plant Soil* 203:109–17

23. Dalal RC. 1977. Soil organic phosphorus. *Adv. Agron.* 29:85–117

24. de la Fuente JM, Ramírez-Rodríguez V, Cabrera-Ponce JL, Herrera-Estrella L. 1997. Aluminum tolerance in transgenic plants by alteration of citrate synthesis. *Science* 276:1566–68

25. de Willegen P, van Noordwick M. 1987. *Roots: Plant Production and Nutrient Use Efficiency*. Wageningen: Insit. Bodemvruchtbaarheid. 282 pp.

26. Delhaize E, Craig S, Beaton CD, Bennet RJ, Jagadish VC, et al. 1993. Aluminum tolerance in wheat (*Triticum aestivum* L.) I. Uptake and distribution of aluminum in root apices. *Plant Physiol.* 103:685–93

27. Delhaize E, Hebb DM, Richards KD, Lin J-M, Ryan PR, et al. 1999. Cloning and expression of a wheat (*Triticum aestivum* L.) phosphatidylserine synthase cDNA: Overexpression in plants alters the composition of phospholipids. *J. Biol. Chem.* 274:7082–88

28. Delhaize E, Hebb DM, Ryan PR. 2001. Expression of a *Pseudomonas aeruginosa* citrate synthase gene in tobacco is not associated with either citrate overproduction or efflux. In press

29. Delhaize E, Ryan PR. 1995. Aluminum toxicity and tolerance in plants. *Plant Physiol.* 107:315–21

30. Delhaize E, Ryan PR, Randall PJ. 1993. Aluminum tolerance in wheat (*Triticum*

aestivum L.) II. Aluminum-stimulated excretion of malic acid from root apices. *Plant Physiol.* 103:695–702

31. Dinkelaker B, Hengeler C, Marschner H. 1995. Distribution and function of proteoid roots and other root clusters. *Bot. Acta* 108:183–200

32. Dinkelaker B, Römheld V, Marschner H. 1989. Citric acid excretion and precipitation of calcium citrate in the rhizosphere of white lupin (*Lupinus albus* L.). *Plant Cell Environ.* 12:285–92

33. Duff SMG, Moorhead GBG, Lefebvre DD, Plaxton WC. 1989. Phosphate starvation inducible "bypass" of adenylate and phosphate dependent glycolytic enzymes in *Brassica nigra* suspension cells. *Plant Physiol.* 90:1275–78

34. Dutton MV, Evans CS. 1996. Oxalate production by fungi—its role in pathogenicity and ecology in the soil environment. *Can. J. Microbiol.* 42:881–95

35. Elkhatib EA. 1990. Simultaneous determination of low-molecular-weight organic acids in soil solution by ion chromatography. *Z. Pflanzenernähr. Bodenkd.* 153: 201–5

36. Evans A. 1998. Biodegradation of ^{14}C-labelled low molecular organic acids using three biometer methods. *J. Geochem. Explor.* 65:17–25

37. Farrar JF, Jones DL. 2000. Control of carbon partitioning. *New Phytol.* 147:43–53

38. Frachisse J-M, Colcombet J, Guern J, Barbier-Brygoo H. 2000. Characterization of a nitrate-permeable channel able to mediate sustained anion efflux in hypocotyl cells from *Arabidopsis thaliana*. *Plant J.* 21:361–71

39. Frachisse J-M, Thomine S, Colcombet J, Guern J, Barbier-Brygoo H. 1999. Sulfate is both a substrate and an activator of the voltage-dependent anion channel of Arabidopsis hypocotyl cells. *Plant Physiol.* 121:253–61

40. Gadde DM, McCammon MT. 1997. Mutations in the *IDH2* gene encoding the catalytic subunit of the yeast NAD^+-dependent isocitrate dehydrogenase can be suppressed by mutations in the *CIT1* gene encoding citrate synthase and other genes of oxidative metabolism. *Arch. Biochem. Biophys.* 344:139–49

41. Gallmetzer M, Muller B, Burgstaller W. 1998. Net efflux of citrate in *Penicillium simplicissimum* is mediated by a transport protein. *Arch. Microbiol.* 169:353–59

42. Gardner WK, Barber DA, Parbery DG. 1983. The acquisition of phosphorus by *Lupinus albus* L. III. The probable mechanism by which phosphorus movement in the soil/root interface is enhanced. *Plant Soil* 70:107–24

43. Gardner WK, Parbery DG, Barber DA. 1981. Proteoid root morphology and function in *Lupinus albus*. *Plant Soil* 60:143–47

44. Gardner WK, Parbery DG, Barber DA. 1982. The acquisition of phosphorus by *Lupinus albus* L. II. The effect of varying phosphorus supply and soil type on some characteristics of the soil-root interface. *Plant Soil* 68:33–41

45. Garrill A, Tyerman SD, Findlay GP, Ryan PR. 1996. Effects of NPPB and niflumic acid on outward K^+ and Cl^- currents across the plasma membrane of wheat root protoplasts. *Aust. J. Plant Physiol.* 23:527–34

46. Geelen D, Lurin C, Bouchez D, Frachisse J-M, Lelièvre F, et al. 2000. Disruption of putative anion channel gene *AtCLC-a* in *Arabidopsis* suggests a role in the regulation of nitrate content. *Plant J.* 21:259–67

47. Gehlen J, Panstruga R, Smets H, Merkelbach S, Kleines M, et al. 1996. Effects of altered phospho*enol*pyruvate carboxylase activities on transgenic C3 plant *Solanum tuberosum*. *Plant Mol. Biol.* 32:831–48

48. Gerbeu P, Guclu J, Ripoche P, Maurel C. 1999. Aquaporin Nt-TIPa can account for the high permeability of tobacco cell vacuolar membrane to small neutral solutes. *Plant J.* 18:577–87

49. Gerhardt R, Stitt M, Heldt HW. 1987. Subcellular metabolite levels in spinach leaves. *Plant Physiol.* 83:399–407

50. Gerke J. 1993. Solubilization of Fe(III) from humic-Fe complexes, humic Fe oxide mixtures and from poorly ordered Fe-oxide by organic acids: consequences for P-adsorption. *Z. Pflanzenernähr. Bodenkd.* 156:253–57

51. Gerke J, Romer W, Jungk A. 1994. The excretion of citric and malic by proteoid roots of *Lupinus albus* L.; effects on soil solution concentrations of phosphate, iron, and aluminum in the proteoid rhizosphere in samples of an oxisol and a luvisol. *Z. Pflanzenernähr. Bodenkd.* 157:289–94

52. Gilbert GA, Knight JD, Vance CP, Allan DL. 2000. Proteoid root development of phosphorus deficient lupin is mimicked by auxin and phosphonate. *Ann. Bot.* 85:921–28

53. Graff JE, Hermann RK, Zaerr JB. 1999. Ionic balance and organic acids in western red cedar, western hemlock, and Douglas fir seedlings grown in low and high N soils. *Can. J. For. Res.* 29:669–78

54. Grierson PF. 1992. Organic acids in the rhizosphere of *Banksia integrifolia* L.f. *Plant Soil* 144:259–65

55. Grobler J, Bauer F, Subden RE, van Vuuren HJJ. 1995. The *mae1* gene of *Schizosaccharomyces pombe* encodes a permease for malate and other C_4 dicarboxylic acids. *Yeast* 11:1485–91

56. Guerinot ML, Yi Y. 1994. Iron: nutritious, noxious, and not readily available. *Plant Physiol.* 104:815–20

57. Häusler RE, Kleines M, Uhrig H, Hirsch H-J, Smets H. 1999. Overexpression of phosphoenolpyruvate carboxylase from *Corynebacterium glutamicum* lowers the CO2 compensation point (Γ^*) and enhances dark and light respiration in transgenic potato. *J. Exp. Bot.* 50:1231–42

58. Hechenberger M, Schwappach B, Fischer WN, Frommer WB, Jentsch TJ, et al. 1996. A family of putative chloride channels from *Arabidopsis* and functional complementation of a yeast strain with a *CLC* gene disruption. *J. Biol. Chem.* 271:33632–8

59. Hedrich R, Busch H, Raschke K. 1990. Ca^{2+} and nucleotide dependent regulation of voltage-dependent anion channels in the plasma membrane of guard cells. *EMBO J.* 9:3889–92

60. Hocking PJ, Keerthisinghe G, Smith FW, Randall PJ. 1997. Comparison of the ability of different crop species to access poorly-available soil phosphorus. See Ref. 2a, pp. 305–8

61. Hoffland E, Findenegg GR, Nelemans JA. 1989. Solubilization of rock phosphate by rape. II. Local root exudation of organic acids as a response to P-starvation. *Plant Soil* 113:161–65

62. Hoffland E, Van Den Boogaard R, Nelemans J, Findenegg G. 1992. Biosynthesis and root exudation of citric and malic acids in phosphate-starved rape plants. *New Phytol.* 122:675–80

63. Huang JWW, Blaylock MJ, Kapulnik Y, Ensley BD. 1998. Phytoremediation of uranium contaminated soils: role of organic acids in triggering uranium hyperaccumulation in plants. *Environ. Sci. Technol.* 32:2004–8

64. Hudspeth RL, Grula JW, Dai Z, Edwards GE, Ku MSB. 1992. Expression of maize phospho*enol*pyruvate carboxylase in transgenic tobacco. *Plant Physiol.* 98:458–64

65. Hue NV, Craddock GR, Adams F. 1986. Effect of organic acids on aluminum toxicity in subsoils. *Soil Sci. Am. J.* 50:28–34

66. Illmer P, Barbato A, Schinner F. 1995. Solubilization of hardly-soluble $AlPO_4$ with P-solubilizing microorganisms. *Soil Biol. Biochem.* 27:265–70

67. Iwasaki I, Arata H, Kijima H, Nishimura M. 1992. Two types of channels involved in the malate ion transport across the tonoplast of a c crassulacean acid metabolism plant. *Plant Physiol.* 98:1494–97

68. Jentsch TJ, Steinmeyer K, Schwarz G. 1990. Primary structure of a *Torpedo marmorata* chloride channel isolated by expression cloning in *Xenopus* oocytes. *Nature* 348:510–14

69. Johnson JF, Allan DL, Vance CP. 1994. Phosphorus stress-induced proteoid roots show altered metabolism in *Lupinus albus*. *Plant Physiol.* 104:657–65

70. Johnson JF, Allan DL, Vance CP, Weiblen G. 1996. Root carbon dioxide fixation by phosphorus-deficient *Lupinus albus*. *Plant Physiol.* 112:19–30

71. Johnson JF, Vance CP, Allen DL. 1996. Phosphorus deficiency in *Lupinus albus*. Altered lateral root development and enhanced expression of phospho*enol*pyruvate carboxylase. *Plant Physiol.* 112:31–41

72. Jones DL. 1998. Organic acids in the rhizosphere—a critical review. *Plant Soil* 205:25–44

73. Jones DL, Brassington DS. 1998. Sorption of organic acids in acid soils and its implications in the rhizosphere. *Eur. J. Soil Sci.* 49:447–55

74. Jones DL, Darrah PR. 1994. Role of root derived organic acids in the mobilization of nutrients from the rhizosphere. *Plant Soil* 166:247–57

75. Jones DL, Darrah PR. 1995. Influx and efflux of organic acids across the soil-root interface of *Zea mays* L. and its implications in rhizosphere C flow. *Plant Soil* 173:103–9

76. Jones DL, Darrah PR, Kochian LV. 1996. Critical-evaluation of organic-acid mediated iron dissolution in the rhizosphere and its potential role in root iron uptake. *Plant Soil* 180:57–66

77. Jones DL, Prabowo AM, Kochian LV. 1996. Kinetics of malate transport and decomposition in acid soils and isolated bacterial-populations—the effect of microorganisms on root exudation of malate under Al stress. *Plant Soil* 182:239–47

78. Juszczuk IM, Rychter AM. 1997. Changes in pyridine nucleotide levels in leaves and roots of bean plants (*Phaseolus vulgaris* L.) during phosphate deficiency. *J. Plant Physiol.* 151:399–404

79. Kamh M, Horst WJ, Amer F, Mostafa H, Maier P. 1999. Mobilization of soil and fertilizer phosphate by cover crops. *Plant Soil* 211:19–27

80. Kaplan RS, Mayor JA, Gremse DA, Wood DO. 1995. High level expression and characterization of the mitochondrial citrate transport protein from the yeast *Saccharomyces cerevisiae*. *J. Biol. Chem.* 270:4108–14

81. Deleted in proof

82. Keerthisinghe G, Hocking PJ, Ryan PR, Delhaize E. 1998. Effect of phosphorus supply on the formation and function of proteoid roots of white lupin (*Lupinus albus* L.). *Plant Cell Environ.* 21:467–78

83. Khare P, Kumar N, Kumari KM, Srivastava SS. 1999. Atmospheric formic and acetic acids: an overview. *Rev. Geophys.* 37:227–48

84. Kirk GJD, Santos EE, Findenegg GR. 1999. Phosphate solubilization by organic anion excretion from rice (*Oryza sativa* L.) growing in aerobic soil. *Plant Soil* 211:11–18

85. Kirk GJD, Santos EE, Santos MB. 1999. Phosphate solubilization by organic anion excretion from rice growing in aerobic soil: rates of excretion and decomposition, effects on rhizosphere pH and effects on phosphate solubility and uptake. *New Phytol.* 142:185–200

86. Kirk K, Strange K. 1998. Functional properties and physiological roles of organic solute channels. *Annu. Rev. Physiol.* 60:719–39

87. Kispal G, Rosenkrantz M, Guarente L, Srere PA. 1988. Metabolic changes in *Saccharomyces cerevisiae* strains lacking citrate synthases. *J. Biol. Chem.* 263:11145–49

88. Kitagawa T, Morishita T, Tachibana Y,

Namai H, Ohta Y. 1986. Differential aluminum resistance of wheat varieties and organic acid secretion. *Jpn. J. Soil Sci. Plant Nutr.* 57:352–58

89. Kochian LV. 1995. Cellular mechanisms of aluminum toxicity and resistance in plants. *Annu. Rev. Plant Physiol. Plant Mol. Biol.* 46:237–60

90. Köhler B, Raschke K. 2000. The delivery of salts to the xylem. Three types of anion conductance in the plasmalemma of the xylem parenchyma of roots of barley. *Plant Physiol.* 122:243–54

91. Koyama H, Kawamura A, Kihara T, Hara T, Takita E, et al. 2000. Overexpression of mitochondrial citrate synthase in *Arabidopsis thaliana* improved growth on a phosphorus limited soil. *Plant Cell Physiol.* 41:1030–37

92. Koyama H, Takita E, Kawamura A, Hara T, Shibata D. 1999. Overexpression of mitochondrial citrate synthase gene improves the growth of carrot cells in Al-phosphate medium. *Plant Cell Physiol.* 40:482–88

93. Kronestedt-Robards E, Robards AW. 1991. Exocytosis in gland cells. In *Endocytosis, Exocytosis and Vesicle Traffic in Plants*, ed. CR Hawes, JOD Coleman, DE Evans, pp. 199–232. Cambridge: Cambridge Univ. Press. 252 pp.

94. Kruse A, Fieuw S, Heineke D, Müller-Röber B. 1998. Antisense inhibition of cytosolic NADP-dependent isocitrate dehydrogenase in transgenic potato plants. *Planta* 205:82–91

95. Krzyszowska AJ, Blaylock MJ, Vance GF, David MB. 1996. Ion-chromatographic analysis of low molecular weight organic acids in spodsol forest solutions. *Soil Sci. Soc. Am. J.* 60:1565–71

96. Lahjouji K, Carrasco A, Bouyssou H, Cazaux L, Marigo G, et al. 1996. Identification with a photoaffinity reagent of a tonoplast protein involved in vacuolar malate transport of *Catharanthus roseus*. *Plant J.* 9:799–808

97. Lan M, Comerford NB, Fox TR. 1995. Organic anions effect on phosphorus release from spodic horizons. *Soil Sci. Soc. Am. J.* 59:1745–49

98. Landschütze V, Willmitzer L, Müller-Röber B. 1995. Inhibition of flower formation by antisense repression of mitochondrial citrate synthase in transgenic potato plants leads to a specific disintegration of the ovary tissues of flowers. *EMBO J.* 14:660–66

99. Leonhardt N, Vavasseur A, Forestier C. 1999. ATP binding cassette modulators control abscisic acid-regulated slow anion channels in guard cells. *Plant Cell* 11:1141–51

100. Li XF, Ma JF, Matsumoto H. 2000. Pattern of Al-induced secretion of organic acids differs between rye and wheat. *Plant Physiol.* 123:1537–43

101. Lipton DS, Blanchar RW, Blevins DG. 1987. Citrate, malate, and succinate concentration in exudates from P-sufficient and P-stressed *Medicago sativa* L. seedlings. *Plant Physiol.* 85:315–17

102. López-Bucio J, Martínez de la Vega O, Guevara-García A, Herrera-Estrella L. 2000. Enhanced phosphorus uptake in transgenic tobacco plants that overproduce citrate. *Nat. Biotechnol.* 18:450–53

103. Lunstrom US, Van Breemen N, Jongmans AG. 1995. Evidence for microbial decomposition of organic acids during podzolization. *Eur. J. Soil Sci.* 46:489–96

104. Luo HM, Watanabe T, Shinano T, Tadano T. 1999. Comparison of aluminum tolerance and phosphate absorption between rape (*Brassica napus* L) and tomato (*Lycopersicum esculentum* Mill.) in relation to organic acid exudation. *Soil Sci. Plant Nutr.* 45:897–907

105. Lurin C, Geelen D, Barbier-Brygoo H, Guern J, Maurel C. 1996. Cloning and functional expression of a plant voltage-dependent chloride channel. *Plant Cell* 8:701–11

106. Ma JF. 2000. Role of organic acids

in detoxification of aluminum in higher plants. *Plant Cell Physiol.* 41:383–90

106a. Ma JF, Taketa S, Yang ZM. 2000. Al tolerance genes on the short arm of chromosome 3R are linked with organic acid release in Triticale. *Plant Physiol.* 122:1–8

107. Ma JF, Zheng SJ, Matsumoto H. 1997. Specific secretion of citric acid induced by Al stress in *Cassia tora* L. *Plant Cell Physiol* 38:1019–25

108. Ma Z, Miyasaka SC. 1998. Oxalate exudation by taro in response to Al. *Plant Physiol.* 118:861–65

109. MacDiarmid CW, Gardner RC. 1998. Overexpression of the *Saccharomyces cerevisiae* magnesium transport system confers resistance to aluminum ion. *J. Biol. Chem.* 273:1727–32

110. MacRobbie EAC. 1999. Vesicle trafficking: a role in *trans*-tonoplast ion movements? *J. Exp. Bot.* 50:925–34

111. Marschner H. 1995. *Mineral Nutrition of Higher Plants*. London: Academic. 889 pp.

111a. Martell AE, Smith RM. 1977. *Critical Stability Constants*. New York: Plenum. Vol 3. 495 pp.

112. Martinoia E, Rentsch D. 1994. Malate compartmentation-responses to a complex metabolism. *Annu. Rev. Plant Physiol. Plant Mol. Biol.* 45:447–67

113. Marty-Teysset C, Lolkema JS, Schmitt P, Divies C, Konings WN. 1995. Membrane potential-generating transport of citrate and malate catalyzed by CitP of *Leuconostoc mesenteroides. J. Biol. Chem.* 270:25370–76

114. Matsuno K, Blais T, Serio AW, Conway T, Henkin TM, et al. 1999. Metabolic imbalance and sporulation in an isocitrate dehydrogenase mutant of *Bacillus subtilis. J. Bacteriol.* 181:3382–91

115. Mawdsley JL, Burns RG. 1994. Root colonization by a *Flavobacterium* species and the influence of percolating water. *Soil Biol. Biochem.* 26:861–70

116. Murphy AS, Eisinger WR, Shaff JE,

Kochian LV, Taiz L. 1999. Early copper-induced leakage of K^+ from Arabidopsis seedlings is mediated by ion channels and coupled to citrate efflux. *Plant Physiol.* 121:1375–82

117. Neumann G, Massonneau A, Langlade N, Dinkelaker B, Hengeler C, et al. 2000. Physiological aspects of cluster root function and development in phosphorus-deficient white lupin (*Lupinus albus* L.). *Ann. Bot.* 85:909–19

118. Neumann G, Massonneau A, Martinoia E, Römheld V. 1999. Physiological adaptations to phosphorus deficiency during proteoid root development in white lupin. *Planta* 208:373–82

119. Neumann G, Römheld V. 1999. Root excretion of carboxylic acids and protons in phosphorus-deficient plants. *Plant Soil* 211:121–30

120. Neumann G, Römheld V. 2000. The release of root exudates as affected by the plant's physiological status. In *The Rhizosphere: Biochemistry and Organic Substances in the Soil-Plant Interface*, ed. R Pinton, Z Varanini, Z Nannipieri, pp. 41–93. New York/Basel. Marcel Dekker. 424 pp

121. Niemietz CM, Tyerman SD. 2000. Channel-mediated permeation of ammonia gas through the peribacteriod membrane of soybean nodules. *FEBS Lett.* 465:110–14

122. Ohwaki Y, Sugahara K. 1997. Active extrusion of protons and exudation of carboxylic acids in response to iron deficiency by roots of chickpea (*Cicer arietinium* L). *Plant Soil* 189:49–55

122a. Osawa H. 1999. *Al tolerance regulated by citrate metabolism in leguminous trees.* PhD thesis. Univ. Tokyo, Tokyo. 96 pp.

123. Osawa H, Kojima K, Sasaki S. 1997. Excretion of citrate as an aluminium-tolerance mechanism in tropical leguminous trees. See Ref. 2a, pp. 455–56

124. Otani T, Ae N. 1997. The exudation of

organic acids by pigeon pea roots for solubilising iron- and aluminum-bound phosphorus. See Ref. 2a, pp. 325–26

125. Pantoja O, Gelli A, Blumwald E. 1992. Characterization of vacuolar malate and K^+ channels under physiological conditions. *Plant Physiol.* 100:1137–41

126. Pei Z-M, Schroeder JI, Schwarz M. 1998. Background ion channel activities in *Arabidopsis* guard cells and review of ion channel regulation by protein phosphorylation events. *J. Exp. Bot.* 49:319–28

127. Pellet DM, Grunes DL, Kochian LV. 1995. Organic acid exudation as an aluminum-tolerance mechanism in maize (*Zea mays* L.). *Planta* 196:788–95

128. Pellet DM, Papernik LA, Jones DL, Darrah PR, Grunes DL, et al. 1997. Involvement of multiple aluminium exclusion mechanisms in aluminium tolerance in wheat. *Plant Soil* 192:63–68

129. Piñeros MA, Kochian LV. 2001. A patch clamp study on the physiology of aluminium toxicity and aluminium tolerance in *Zea mays*: identification and characterisation of Al^{3+}-induced anion channels. *Plant Physiol.* 125:292–305

130. Pines O, Shemesh S, Battat E, Goldberg I. 1997. Overexpression of cytosolic malate dehydrogenase (MDH2) causes overproduction of specific organic acids in *Saccharomyces cerevisiae. Appl. Microbiol. Biotechnol.* 48:248–55

131. Piper P, Mahe Y, Thompson S, Pandjaitan R, Holyoak C, et al. 1998. The Pdr12 ABC transporter is required for the development of weak acid resistance in yeast. *EMBO J.* 17:4257–65

132. Pohlman AA, McColl JG. 1986. Kinetics of metal dissolution from forest soils by soluble organic acids. *J. Environ. Qual.* 15:86–92

133. Porro D, Bianchi MM, Brambilla L, Menghini R, Bolzani D, et al. 1999. Replacement of a metabolic pathway for large-scale production of lactic acid from

engineered yeasts. *Appl. Environ. Microbiol.* 65:4211–15

134. Poulsen IF, Hansen HCB. 2000. Soil sorption of nickel in the presence of citrate or arginine. *Water Air Soil Pollut.* 120:249–59

135. Prömper C, Schneider R, Weiss H. 1993. The role of the proton-pumping and alternative respiratory chain NADH: ubiquinone oxidoreductases in overflow catabolism of *Aspergillus niger. Eur. J. Biochem.* 216:223–30

136. Przybyla-Zawislak B, Gadde DM, Ducharme K, McCammon MT. 1999. Genetic and biochemical interactions involving tricarboxylic acid cycle (TCA) function using a collection of mutants defective in all TCA cycle genes. *Genetics* 152:153–66

137. Raghothama KG. 1999. Phosphate acquisition. *Annu. Rev. Plant Physiol. Plant Mol. Biol.* 50:665–93

138. Randall PJ, Hayes JE, Hocking PJ, Richardson AE. 2001. Root exudates in phosphorus acquisition by plants. In *Plant Nutrient Acquisition: New Perspectives*, ed. N Ae, J Arihara, K Okada, A Srinivasan. Tokyo: Springer-Verlag. In press

138a. Richardson AE. 1994. Soil microorganisms and phosphorus availability. In *Soil Biota Management in Sustainable Farming Systems*, ed. CE Pankhurst, BM Doube, VVSR Gupta, PR Grace, pp. 50–62. CSIRO, Australia. 262 pp.

139. Rivoal J, Hanson AD. 1993. Evidence for a large and sustained glycolytic flux to lactate in anoxic roots of some members of the halophystic genus Limonium. *Plant Physiol.* 101:553–60

140. Rivoal J, Hanson AD. 1994. Metabolic control of anaerobic glycolysis: Overexpression of lactate dehydrogenase in transgenic tomato roots supports the Davies-Roberts hypothesis and points to a critical role for lactate secretion. *Plant Physiol.* 106:1179–85

141. Rózycki H. 1985. Production of organic acids by bacteria isolated from soil, rhizosphere and mycorrhizosphere of pine (*Pinus sylvestris* L.). *Acta Microbiol. Polon.* 34:301–8

142. Ruijter G, Panneman H, Xu D-B, Visser J. 2000. Properties of *Aspergillus niger* citrate synthase and effects of *citA* overexpression on citric acid production. *FEMS Lett.* 184:35–40

143. Ryan PR, Delhaize E, Randall PJ. 1995. Characterisation of Al-stimulated efflux of malate from the apices of Al-tolerant wheat roots. *Planta* 196:103–10

144. Ryan PR, Delhaize E, Randall PJ. 1995. Malate efflux from root apices and tolerance to aluminium are highly correlated in wheat. *Aust. J. Plant Physiol.* 22:531–36

145. Ryan PR, DiTomaso JM, Kochian LV. 1993. Aluminium toxicity in roots: an investigation of spatial sensitivity and the role of the root cap. *J. Exp. Bot.* 44:437–46

146. Ryan PR, Skerrett M, Findlay GP, Delhaize E, Tyerman SD. 1997. Aluminum activates an anion channel in the apical cells of wheat roots. *Proc. Natl. Acad. Sci. USA* 94:6547–52

147. Rychter AM, Chauveau M, Bomsel J-L, Lance C. 1992. The effect of phosphate deficiency on mitochondrial activity and adenylate levels in bean roots. *Physiol. Plant.* 84:80–86

148. Saber NE, Abdel-Moneim AM, Barakat SY. 1999. Role of organic acids in sunflower tolerance to heavy metals. *Biol. Plant.* 42:65–73

149. Saier MH. 2000. A functional-phylogenetic classification system for transmembrane solute transporters. *Microbiol. Mol. Biol. Rev.* 64:354–411

150. Sample EC, Soper RJ, Racz GJ. 1980. Reactions of phosphate fertilizers in soils. In *The Role of Phosphorus in Agriculture*, ed. EC Khasawneh, CE Sample, EJ Kamprath, pp. 263–310. Madison, WI: Am. Soc. Agron. 910 pp.

151. Schachtman DP, Reid RJ, Ayling SM. 1998. Phosphorus uptake by plants: from soil to cell. *Plant Physiol.* 116:447–53

152. Schmidt C, Schelle I, Liao Y-J, Schroeder JI. 1995. Strong regulation of slow anion channels and abscisic acid signalling in guard cells by phosphorylation and dephosphorylation events. *Proc. Natl. Acad. Sci. USA* 92:9535–39

153. Schmidt C, Schroeder JI. 1994. Anion selectivity of slow anion channels in the plasma membrane of guard cells. *Plant Physiol.* 106:383–91

154. Schroeder JI. 1995. Anion channels as central mechanisms for signal transduction in guard cells and putative functions in roots for plant-soil interactions. *Plant Mol. Biol.* 28:353–61

155. Schroeder JI, Hagiwara S. 1989. Cytosolic calcium regulates ion channels in the plasma membrane of *Vicia faba* guard cells. *Nature* 338:427–30

156. Schroeder JI, Schmidt C, Sheaffer J. 1993. Identification of high-affinity slow anion channel blockers and evidence for stomatal regulation by slow anion channels in guard cells. *Plant Cell* 5:1831–41

157. Schuller KA, Werner D. 1993. Phosphorylation of soybean (*Glycine max* L.) nodule phospho*enol*pyruvate carboxylase in vitro decreases sensitivity to inhibition by L-malate. *Plant Physiol.* 101:1267–73

158. Shen Y, Ström L, Jonsson JA, Tyler G. 1996. Low-molecular organic-acids in the rhizosphere soil solution of beech forest (*Fagus sylvatica*.) cambisols determined by ion chromatography using supported liquid membrane enrichment technique. *Soil Biol. Biochem.* 28:1163–9

159. Sivaguru M, Horst WJ. 1998. The distal part of the transition zone is the most aluminum-sensitive apical root zone of *Zea mays* L. *Plant Physiol.* 116:155–63

160. Srivastava S, Prakash S, Srivastava MM. 1999. Studies on the mobilization of chromium with reference to its

plant availability—Role of organic acids. *Biometals* 12:201–7

161. Steiger S, Pfeifer T, Ratajczak R, Martinoia E, Lüttge U. 1997. The vacuolar malate transporter of *Kalanchoë daigremontiana*: a 32-kDa polypeptide? *J. Plant Physiol.* 151:137–41

162. Steinmeyer K, Ortland C, Jentsch TJ. 1991. Primary structure and functional expression of a developmentally regulated skeletal muscle chloride channel. *Nature* 354:301–4

163. Ström L. 1997. Root exudation of organic acids: importance to nutrient availability and the califuge and calcicole behavior of plants. *Oikos* 80:459–66

164. Ström L, Olsson T, Tyler G. 1994. Differences between califuge and acidifuge plants in root exudation of low-molecular organic acids. *Plant Soil* 167:239–45

165. Takita E, Koyama H, Hara T. 1999. Organic acid metabolism in aluminum-phosphate utilizing cells of carrot (*Daucus carota* L.). *Plant Cell Physiol.* 40:489–95

166. Tam S-C, McColl JG. 1990. Aluminum-calcium-binding affinities of some organic ligands in acidic conditions. *J. Environ. Qual.* 19:514–20

167. Taylor GJ. 1988. The physiology of aluminum phytotoxicity. In *Metal Ions in Biological Systems*, ed. H Sigel, A Sigel, 24:123–63. New York: Marcel Dekker

168. Theodorou ME, Plaxton WC. 1993. Metabolic adaptations of plant respiration to nutritional phosphate deprivation. *Plant Physiol.* 101:339–44

169. Tinker PB, Nye P. 2000. *Solute Movement in the Rhizosphere.* Oxford: Oxford Univ. Press. 464 pp.

170. Tyerman SD. 1992. Anion channels in plants. *Annu. Rev. Plant Physiol. Plant Mol. Biol.* 43:351–73

171. Van Hees PAW, Andersson AMT, Lundström US. 1996. Separation of organic low-molecular-weight aluminum complexes in soil solution by liquid-chromatography. *Chemosphere* 33:1951–66

172. Van Hees PAW, Dahlen J, Lundström US, Boren H, Allard B. 1999. Determination of low molecular weight organic acids in soil solution by HPLC. *Talanta* 48:173–9

173. Wasay SA, Barrington SF, Tokunaga S. 1998. Remediation of soils polluted by heavy metals using salts of organic acids and chelating agents. *Environ. Technol.* 19:369–79

174. Watt M. 1999. *Proteoid roots: development and physiology in* Lupinus albus *L.* PhD thesis. Aust. Natl. Univ., Canberra. 195 pp.

175. Watt M, Evans JR. 1999. Linking development and determinacy with organic acid efflux from proteoid roots of white lupin grown with low phosphorus and ambient or elevated atmospheric CO_2 concentration. *Plant Physiol.* 120:705–16

176. Watt M, Evans JR. 1999. Proteoid roots. Physiology and development. *Plant Physiol.* 121:317–23

177. White PF, Robson AD. 1989. Rhizosphere acidification and Fe^{3+} reduction in lupins and peas: Iron deficiency in lupins is not due to a poor ability to reduce Fe^{3+}. *Plant Soil* 119:163–75

178. Wiehe W, Hechtbuchholz C, Hoflich G. 1994. Electron-microscopic investigations on root colonization of *Lupinus albus* and *Pisum sativum* with two associative plant-growth promoting rhizobacteria, *Pseudomonas fluorescens* and *Rhizobium leguminosarum* bv *trifolii*. *Symbiosis* 17:15–31

179. Xia JH, Roberts JKM. 1994. Improved cytoplasmic pH regulation, increased lactate efflux, and reduced cytoplasmic lactate levels are biochemical traits expressed in root tips of whole maize seedlings acclimated to a low-oxygen environment. *Plant Physiol.* 105:651–57

180. Xia JH, Saglio PH. 1992. Lactic acid

efflux as a mechanism of hypoxic acclimation of maize root tips to anoxia. *Plant Physiol.* 100:40–46

181. Xu DB, Madrid CP, Rohr M, Kubicek CP. 1989. The influence of type and concentration of the carbon source on production of citric acid by *Aspergillus niger. App. Microbiol. Biotech.* 30:553–58

181a. Yang Y-Y, Jung J-Y, Song W-Y, Suh H-S, Lee Y. 2000. Identification of rice varieties with high tolerance or sensitivity to lead and characterization of the mechanism of tolerance. *Plant Physiol.* 124:1019–26

182. Yang ZM, Sivaguru M, Horst WJ, Matsumoto H. 2000. Aluminium tolerance is achieved by exudation of citric acid from roots of soybean (*Glycine max*). *Physiol. Plant.* 110:72–77

183. Yasui M, Hazama A, Kwon T-H, Nielsen S, Guggio WB, et al. 1999. Rapid gating and anion permeability of an intracellular aquaporin. *Nature* 402:184–87

184. Zhang W-H, Ryan PR, Tyerman SD. 2001. Malate-permeable channels and cation channels activated by aluminum in the apical cells of wheat roots. *Plant Physiol.* 125:1459–72

185. Zheng SJ, Ma JF, Matsumoto H. 1998. Continuous secretion of organic acids is related to aluminium resistance during relatively long-term exposure to aluminium stress. *Physiol. Plant.* 103:209–14

186. Zheng SJ, Ma JF, Matsumoto H. 1998. High aluminum resistance in buckwheat. 1. Al-induced specific secretion of oxalic acid from root tips. *Plant Physiol.* 117:745–51

Annu. Rev. Plant Physiol. Plant Mol. Biol. 2001. 52:561–91

PLANT MITOCHONDRIA AND OXIDATIVE STRESS: Electron Transport, NADPH Turnover, and Metabolism of Reactive Oxygen Species

Ian M Møller

*Department of Plant Physiology, Lund University, Box 117, S-221 00 Lund, Sweden;
Address for correspondence: Plant Biology and Biogeochemistry Department, Risø
National Laboratory, Building 301, P.O. Box 49, DK-4000 Roskilde, Denmark;
e-mail: ian.max.moller@risoe.dk*

Key Words glutathione, hydrogen peroxide, NAD(P)H dehydrogenases,
superoxide, superoxide dismutase

■ **Abstract** The production of reactive oxygen species (ROS), such as O_2^- and
H_2O_2, is an unavoidable consequence of aerobic metabolism. In plant cells the mitochondrial electron transport chain (ETC) is a major site of ROS production. In addition
to complexes I–IV, the plant mitochondrial ETC contains a non-proton-pumping alternative oxidase as well as two rotenone-insensitive, non-proton-pumping NAD(P)H
dehydrogenases on each side of the inner membrane: NDex on the outer surface and
NDin on the inner surface. Because of their dependence on Ca^{2+}, the two NDex may
be active only when the plant cell is stressed. Complex I is the main enzyme oxidizing NADH under normal conditions and is also a major site of ROS production,
together with complex III. The alternative oxidase and possibly NDin(NADH) function to limit mitochondrial ROS production by keeping the ETC relatively oxidized.
Several enzymes are found in the matrix that, together with small antioxidants such as
glutathione, help remove ROS. The antioxidants are kept in a reduced state by matrix
NADPH produced by NADP-isocitrate dehydrogenase and non-proton-pumping transhydrogenase activities. When these defenses are overwhelmed, as occurs during both
biotic and abiotic stress, the mitochondria are damaged by oxidative stress.

CONTENTS

1040-2519/01/0601-0561$14.00

INTRODUCTION

Oxidative stress occurs when there is a serious imbalance in any cell compartment between production of reactive oxygen species $(ROS)^1$ and antioxidant defense, leading to damage (36). Oxidative stress is a central factor in abiotic and biotic stress phenomena

The production of ROS, e.g. O_2^-, H_2O_2, $^1O_2$, is an unavoidable consequence of aerobic metabolism. In plants ROS are produced in mitochondria (16), chloroplasts (28), and nitrogen-fixing nodules (6) as unwanted byproducts. ROS production also occurs in the course of major metabolic pathways, especially those in the peroxisomes, and ROS are used as a weapon against invading pathogens in the oxidative burst. Because ROS can cause damage to proteins, lipids, and DNA, ROS production and removal must be strictly controlled. All cell compartments should therefore have mechanisms for preventing and repairing damage caused by ROS.

In the present review ROS metabolism in plant mitochondria is presented for the first time. Some relevant plant-specific features of the mitochondrial electron transport chain (ETC) are described and the main site(s) of ROS production in the ETC are identified. The matrix turnover of NADPH is reviewed in relation to the role of NADPH-specific enzymes in ROS detoxification. Finally, information to

---

[1]Abbreviations: [0]AOX, alternative oxidase; CCO, cytochrome c oxidase; DPIs, diphenyleneiodonium; ETC, electron transport chain; GDC, glycine decarboxylase complex; GSH and GSSG, reduced and oxidized form of glutathione, respectively; IMM, inner mitochondrial membrane; NDex(NADH), external rotenone-insensitive NADH dehydrogenase; NDex(NADPH), external rotenone-insensitive NADPH dehydrogenase; NDin(NADH), internal rotenone-insensitive NADH dehydrogenase; NDin(NADPH) internal rotenone-insensitive NADPH dehydrogenase; ROS, reactive oxygen species; SMP, submitochondrial particles; SOD, superoxide dismutase; TH, transhydrogenase; Trx(SH)$_2$ and Trx(S-S), reduced and oxidized form of thioredoxin, respectively.

date on ROS production and detoxification in plant mitochondria is reviewed in detail and compared with the situation in mammalian mitochondria.

Components of the ETC in plant mitochondria have been reviewed previously in this series by Møller & Lin (79), Douce & Neuburger (25), and Vanlerberghe & McIntosh (140), and elsewhere (62, 76, 82, 83, 87, 129, 133, 141). Other reviews have covered various aspects of ROS turnover and oxidative stress in plants (e.g. 28, 29, 92, 125). The recent book by Halliwell & Gutteridge (36) is an outstanding reference for all aspects of ROS turnover, with an emphasis on biomedicine.

THE NAD(P)H DEHYDROGENASES IN THE ELECTRON TRANSPORT CHAIN OF PLANT MITOCHONDRIA

The ETC of plant mitochondria contains complexes I–IV with electron transport properties similar to those of other mitochondria (111, 128, 129, 141). In addition, the plant ETC contains five enzymes not present in mammalian mitochondria: an alternative oxidase (AOX; 140) and four NAD(P)H dehydrogenases (Figure 1) (76, 82). The properties of these NAD(P)H dehydrogenases, which are very likely to be flavoproteins and thus potential sites of ROS synthesis, are described and compared with those of complex I, the H^+-pumping NADH dehydrogenase.

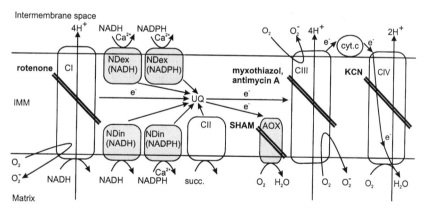

Figure 1 The electron transport chain in the inner membrane of plant mitochondria. Plant-specific enzymes are shown in grey. Also indicated are H^+-pumping of complexes I, III, and IV (per $2e^-$), inhibitors of complexes I, III, and IV, as well as ROS production at the two main sites, complexes I and III. Since $UQ^\bullet$ is bound to two sites in complex III, one close to the inner surface of the IMM, the other close to the outer surface (91), ROS might be formed on either side of the membrane. Abbreviations: CI-CIV, respiratory complexes; CI, complex I, NADH dehydrogenase; CII, succinate dehydrogenase; CIII, ubiquinol-cytochrome bc1 reductase; CIV, cytochrome c oxidase; cyt., cytochrome; succ., succinate; SHAM, salicylhydroxamic acid.

External NAD(P)H Dehydrogenases in Other Organisms

The presence of NAD(P)H dehydrogenases on the outer surface of the inner mitochondrial membrane (NDex) makes it possible for the mitochondrion to oxidize cytosolic NAD(P)H. This ability depends upon the presence in the outer membrane of pores, i.e. voltage-dependent anion channels, that permit passage to all molecules of <5 kDa, at least in isolated mitochondria. The permeability of these pores may be regulated in vivo (138).

Mammalian mitochondria are thought to lack a distinct NDex; however, heart mitochondria have been reported to oxidize external NADH via a rotenone-sensitive route (110). Whether this activity is due to an NDex is still uncertain (Figure 2). Generally, cytosolic NADH can be oxidized by mammalian

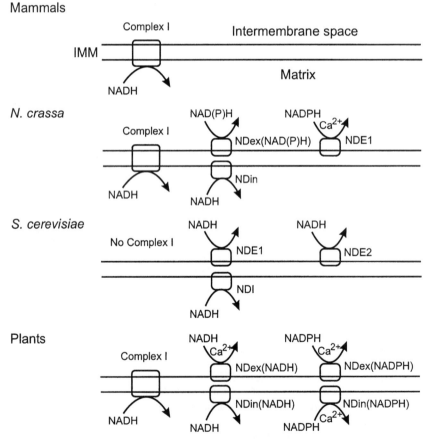

Figure 2   NAD(P)H dehydrogenases in the respiratory chain of mitochondria from mammals, *Neurospora crassa*, *Saccharomyces cerevisiae*, and plants.

mitochondria either by a glycerol 3-phosphate dehydrogenase, a flavoprotein passing electrons directly from the substrate to ubiquinone via the flavin in a Ca^{2+}-dependent manner (37), or indirectly by means of a malate-oxaloacetate shuttle (58).

Mitochondria from *Saccharomyces cerevisiae* have two external NADH dehydrogenases, NDE1 and NDE2 (61, 131). The ability of these mitochondria to oxidize NADH is lost in a double mutant, indicating that there are no more than two NDex (61). *S. cerevisiae* mitochondria do not appear to be able to oxidize cytosolic NADPH (131).

Neurospora crassa mitochondria oxidize both NADH and NADPH in a partially Ca^{2+}-dependent manner (85). A gene encoding a 64-kDa mitochondrial NADPH dehydrogenase (NDI1) has been cloned, sequenced, and characterized. The deduced amino acid sequence shows a high degree of similarity with that of NDE1 and NDE2, but the *N. crassa* enzyme has an insert with an EF-hand motif, indicating that it is Ca^{2+}-dependent (71). In a mutant where this gene is inactivated, the mitochondria specifically lose their ability to oxidize NADPH in a Ca^{2+}-dependent manner at neutral pH. This enzyme is therefore the first mitochondrial NADPH dehydrogenase to be positively identified (70). In addition, *N. crassa* mitochondria contain another enzyme able to oxidize both NADH and NADPH (Figure 2).

NDex in Plant Mitochondria

Two NDex with Distinct Substrate Specificities   With the possible exception of red beetroots (117; but see also 3, 31), all plant mitochondria investigated to date are able to oxidize external NADH and, where tested, NADPH (76, 79). Several lines of evidence indicate that NADH and NADPH are oxidized by two distinct enzymes in plant mitochondria:

1. Mitochondrial NADH oxidation can be induced without inducing NADPH oxidation in red beetroots (3, 31, 72).

2. The relative activities of NADH and NADPH oxidation vary in mitochondria from different tissues and cell cultures of sugar beet, which cannot be explained by the presence of a single enzyme (156).

3. NADPH oxidation is much more sensitive to inhibition by diphenyleneiodonium (DPI) than is NADH oxidation (122). It has been suggested that DPI preferentially inhibits flavoenzymes that function by one-electron transfer (94). If this is correct, then the two NDex would be expected to have different reaction mechanisms. Given that NDex(NADH) can be released from the inner membrane without the use of detergent (24, 30), and that the released enzyme can donate electrons directly to a quinone (30), NDex(NADH) most likely passes electrons directly to UQ. Thus, the interaction between NDex(NADH) and UQ may differ from that between NDex(NADPH) and UQ.

Molecular Properties of NDex   Numerous attempts have been made to purify NDex(NADH), as reviewed previously (76). In some investigations (e.g. 60), platanetin was used as a diagnostic inhibitor to identify NDex activity. However, platanetin was later shown to inhibit all five NAD(P)H dehydrogenases in plant mitochondria, with KI value of 4–15 μM for the four rotenone-insensitive enzymes (123), and therefore cannot be used to distinguish the various dehydrogenases. For red beetroot mitochondria, a 58-kDa protein is hypothesized to be the NDex(NADH) that is induced by washing red beetroot slices (72), a conclusion consistent with an earlier report (60).

Rasmusson et al (116) have identified a nuclear gene in potato encoding a 65-kDa protein (NDB) homologous to bacterial and yeast non-proton-pumping NADH dehydrogenases and with import characteristics indicating that it is an NDex. It has an apparent size of 60 kDa on SDS-PAGE, very similar to the size proposed previously for beetroot NDex(NADH) (see above). The amino acid sequence of NDB contains two motifs for nucleotide binding, presumably one for NAD(P)H and one for a flavin. In addition, there is an insert unique among the homologues and containing an EF-hand motif, suggesting Ca^{2+}-dependence. Since the enzyme appears to have a charged amino acid in a position unfavorable for NADPH binding, a preliminary identification of the enzyme is NDex(NADH) (116). However, until the enzyme has been isolated (e.g. following overexpression in *Escherichia coli*) and the properties examined, this protein cannot be identified with certainty. This uncertainty is reinforced by the recent finding that a Ca^{2+}-dependent NDex(NADPH) in *N. crassa* contains an insert with an EF-hand motif (70, 71; see above).

The Activities of NDex are Regulated by Cytosolic Factors   The total concentration of NAD (0.6–0.7 mM) in the cytosol of cells of spinach and barley leaves is higher than that of NADP (0.2–0.3 mM), as determined by extraction and enzymatic determination (38, 151). However, whereas NADP is mostly reduced, giving cytosolic NADPH concentrations of 0.15–0.2 mM, NAD is highly oxidized so that NADH is almost undetectable. By measuring metabolite levels and assuming equilibrium of reactions catalyzed by key cytosolic enzymes, the concentration of free NADH in the plant cytosol is estimated at around 1 μM, similar to that in rat liver cells (38 and references therein). Based on the kinetics of the two NDex in spinach leaf mitochondria, it was concluded that "in a leaf cell NADPH oxidation is oxidized by mitochondria at a much higher rate than NADH" (55). However, these calculations were all based on data obtained at relatively high concentrations of free Ca^{2+} so that under physiological conditions, NADPH oxidation may not be much higher than NADH oxidation.

The external oxidation of both NADH and NADPH is dependent on Ca^{2+} (3, 77, 80), for which various mechanisms have been proposed (see 76 and references therein). The identification of genes encoding NAD(P)H dehydrogenases with Ca^{2+}-binding motifs (71, 116) has rendered some of this speculation obsolete. The $K_m(Ca^{2+})$ for NDex(NADH) is around 0.3 μM (86), and it may well be higher for NDex(NADPH) (88). Taken together with the substrate concentrations available, both enzymes will therefore be inactive in an unstressed plant cell where the cytosolic concentration of free Ca^{2+} is 0.1–0.2 μM (e.g. 50). However, when the plant cell is stressed, two phenomena will contribute to an activation of NDex: (*a*) the increase in the cytosolic concentration of free Ca^{2+} to 1–2 μM (e.g. 50, 103); (*b*) the synthesis of polyamines (132), which lower the $K_m(Ca^{2+})$ at least for NDex(NADH) (156). Since a high reduction level of the ETC leads to ROS production, activation of NDex may help prevent or minimize ROS production under stress conditions by keeping the cytosolic NAD(P) pool relatively oxidized.

Complex I in Plant Mitochondria

The following specific assays on inside-out SMP with oxygen as electron acceptor can be used to demonstrate that plant mitochondria contain three different NAD(P)H dehydrogenases on the inner surface of the IMM:

Deamino-NADH oxidation with O_2 as electron acceptor is specific for complex I because only complex I can oxidize deamino-NADH. This activity is completely rotenone-sensitive.

NADH oxidation in the presence of rotenone to inhibit complex I, and EGTA to inhibit NDin(NADPH) (or DPI to inhibit both) will measure only NDin(NADH).

NADPH oxidation in the presence of Ca^{2+} to activate the NDin(NADPH) and rotenone to inhibit complex I will measure only NDin(NADPH).

Note that short-chain quinones should not be used as electron acceptors in these assays as there is a risk that the specificity for NAD(P)H and their analogues changes (84).

Under the above conditions the following activities (in nmol O_2 min^{-1} mg protein^{-1}) can be observed in potato tuber (69) and pea leaf (1) SMP: Complex I, 400–600; NDin(NADH), 350–450; NDin(NADPH), 70 and 250, respectively.

All known mitochondria, except those of fermentative yeast, contain the proton-pumping NADH dehydrogenase (EC 1.6.5.3), also known as complex I. This extremely complex enzyme contains as many as 43 different subunits with 1 FMN and 6 Fe-S centers in mammalian mitochondria. The complex has been purified in intact or partly intact form from plant mitochondria, and so far there has been no indication that it has properties substantially different from those of mammalian complex I (reviewed in 111). The reconstituted complex has been reported to be partially (112) or completely (40) rotenone sensitive. In situ, the enzyme is completely inhibited by rotenone (Ki 1 μM), as shown by the 100% rotenone inhibition of deamino-NADH oxidation (to O_2) by inside-out SMP from potato tubers (69, 112, 114) and pea leaves (1). Plant complex I activity is completely inhibited by DPI (1, 69), as is its mammalian counterpart, where the inhibition is probably caused by covalent modification at or near the active site for NADH (63).

In potato tuber mitochondria, complex I has a K_m(NADH) of around 3 μM, whereas its K_m(NADPH) is more than two orders of magnitude higher (114). Considering the low matrix concentration of NADP (see below), complex I is unlikely to contribute significantly to the oxidation of matrix NADPH. In contrast, complex I is probably the main NADH-oxidizing enzyme under state 3 conditions (ADP present) where the steady-state concentration of NADH is low (2, 89). Complex I may also have an important function in interconverting matrix NADH and NADPH through a transhydrogenase activity (see below).

Internal Rotenone-Insensitive NAD(P)H Dehydrogenases

NDin in Other Organisms   Mammalian mitochondria do not contain any NDin, whereas fungal mitochondria contain at least one (Figure 2). In *S. cerevisiae*, NDI is a 53-kDa flavoprotein responsible for the reoxidation of matrix NADH produced in the Krebs cycle. It does not oxidize NADPH, and it is not dependent on bivalent cations; the standard assay for this enzyme contains 1 mM EDTA (22, 66).

When complex I-deficient Chinese hamster cells were transfected with the gene for this yeast dehydrogenase (NDI1), the ability of the cells to grow in the absence of glucose was restored. Thus the non-proton-pumping dehydrogenase has properties sufficiently similar to complex I to replace it functionally, at least under some conditions (127).

NDin(NADH) in Plant Mitochondria   Although the presence of NDin was discovered almost 20 years ago (81) relatively little is known about its properties. It is specific for NADH, has a K_m(NADH) about tenfold higher than that of complex I, is not Ca^{2+}-dependent, and has a Ki(DPI) over two orders of magnitude higher than NDin(NADPH) (1, 69, 81, 114, 115). Owing to the lack of a specific inhibitor, the activity of NDin(NADH) can be quantified only as residual NADH oxidation activity after complex I has been inhibited; access to a specific inhibitor would greatly facilitate the study of this enzyme. 7-Iodo-acridone-4-carboxylic acid is a potent inhibitor of NDI from yeast (95), but in plant mitochondria it is not a specific inhibitor for NDin(NADH) (123). Flavone, a specific inhibitor of NDI in yeast, inhibits all five respiratory chain NAD(P)H dehydrogenases in potato tuber mitochondria (ÅS Svensson & AG Rasmusson, personal communication).

The NDI1 homologue, NDA, identified in potato by Rasmusson et al (116), has import characteristics indicating that it resides inside the inner membrane. The deduced amino acid sequence contains two nucleotide binding sites, presumably for NAD(P)H and a flavin, while there is no indication of a Ca^{2+}-binding site. NDA may be identical to NDin(NADH), in which case we can expect to gain much more information about NDin(NADH) in the coming years.

NDin(NADH) is responsible for the reoxidation of matrix NADH under conditions where its concentration is increased, such as when electron flow through complex I is limited in state 4 (no ADP, only ATP present) (2, 81, 89, 98).

Rotenone-insensitive malate oxidation by red beetroot mitochondria increased two- to threefold during aging of tissue slices. Since the concentration of NAD^+ in the mitochondria was unchanged, an increased NDin(NADH) activity was probably responsible. No induction was seen when cycloheximide was present in the aging solution, indicating that NDin(NADH) is encoded by a nuclear gene (18). This is consistent with the absence of NDA homologues in the mitochondrial genome in Arabidopsis (116, 137).

NDin(NADPH) in Plant Mitochondria   This enzyme has a relatively high affinity for NADPH (K_m 25 μM) (69, 114), it is Ca^{2+}-specific (K_m 3 μM) (115), and very sensitive to DPI inhibition (Ki 0.2 μM) (1). NDin(NADPH) is the main respiratory chain dehydrogenase oxidizing NADPH. It appears to contribute to the oxidation of NAD(P)-linked substrates by intact potato tuber and pea leaf mito chondria, as estimated by measuring DPI-inhibition in the presence of rotenone to inhibit complex I (1). However, there are two problems with such estimations: (*a*) Although the concentration of DPI in the medium (5 μM) was chosen so as to inhibit NDin(NADPH) completely (Ki 0.2 μM) without affecting NDin(NADH) (Ki 63 μM), the effective concentration of DPI in the matrix is not known. DPI is very hydrophobic and carries a delocalized positive charge, allowing the molecule to diffuse across membranes (91). Because actively respiring mitochondria have a transmembrane potential with the inside negative, the concentration of DPI may be much higher in the matrix than in the medium and the inhibition seen may be due to partial inhibition of NDin(NADH). Such an accumulation has been observed for an acridinium derivative (59). (*b*) Even if the estimates of the contribution by NDin(NADPH) to respiration are correct, it is not clear to what extent the enzyme contributes under conditions where complex I is active. NDin(NADPH) is probably competing with NADPH-dependent ROS-detoxifying enzymes for matrix NADPH (see below).

Complex I Mutants

In several studies mitochondrial deletion mutants for complex I have been investigated and a number of respiratory parameters measured in mitochondria from the mutants and wild-type plants (reviewed in 141). Mitochondria from the mitochondrial NCS2 mutant of maize oxidized malate at reduced rates, probably owing to reduced complex I activity, whereas the rates of oxidation with succinate and NADH were unchanged (64). In a later study, western blots of wild-type and NCS2 mitochondria were probed with antibodies raised against three putative NAD(P)H dehydrogenases—the external 32-kDa enzyme from maize (51), the internal 43-kDa enzyme from red beetroot (73), and the external 58-kDa enzyme from red beetroot (60). No change in the amount of any of these proteins could be detected (48), but it is difficult to draw any conclusions from these results until the identification of the various NAD(P)H dehydrogenases is complete. Mitochondria from the leaves of both the mitochondrial mutants CMS I and II of tobacco have strongly reduced (and rotenone-insensitive) glycine oxidation, indicating an impaired complex I. Succinate oxidation was the same as in wild-type mitochondria, indicating that complexes II–IV were unaffected by the mutations. In both mutants external NADH oxidation was strongly increased, which was suggested to be a compensatory mechanism. At the same time there was a clear increase in the amount and capacity of the AOX (35).

Treatment with chloramphenicol can be used to inhibit mitochondrial protein synthesis in cell cultures, tissue slices or intact tissues. A four-day treatment of tobacco cells caused a 50–70% decrease in the activity of all four respiratory complexes (154). This is not unexpected since all four complexes contain subunits encoded in the mitochondrial genome (65), and it indicates that the turnover of the complexes is slow, with a half-life of several days. The general loss of respiratory activity makes the results difficult to interpret. However, both NDex(NADH) activity and AOX capacity appeared to be several-fold higher in mitochondria from chloramphenicol-treated wheat leaves than in mitochondria from control leaves (153). Chloramphenicol treatment of red beetroot slices during washing gave an increased rate of rotenone-insensitive malate oxidation, indicating that NDin(NADH) [or possibly NDin(NADPH)] was induced (18).

In conclusion, the above studies indicate that NDex(NADH), AOX, and probably NDin(NADH) increase in response to a (marked) decrease in complex I activity, whether caused by a mitochondrial mutation or by disruption of mitochondrial protein synthesis.

NAD(P)H TURNOVER IN THE PLANT MITOCHONDRIAL MATRIX

Total, Bound, and Free NAD(P)

Plant mitochondria from several species take up NAD^+ by a carrier mechanism dependent on the eletrochemical proton gradient. Under nonenergized conditions, such as when isolated mitochondria are stored on ice, NAD^+ is slowly lost from the mitochondrial matrix, presumably by a reversal of the uptake mechanism (25 and references therein). The total concentration of NAD (NAD^+ and NADH) in isolated plant mitochondria is 1–10 nmol mg^{-1} protein or 1–10 mM, assuming a matrix volume of 1 $\mu l\, mg^{-1}$ protein (2, 25). The matrix NAD is only partly reduced (10–20%) in barley leaf protoplasts in vivo, as determined by rapid fractionation followed by enzymatic determination. In vitro, extraction and HPLC analysis of isolated mitochondria indicates that the reduction level of NAD can be as high as 60–70% when malate is oxidized in state 4 at pH 6.5 (2).

The NADP concentration in the matrix of plant mitochondria is much lower— 0.2 to 0.7 mM—than that of NAD (2, 11, 121). In mitochondria extracted from potato slices and analyzed immediately, NADP was more reduced than NAD (11).

In contrast, NADPH formation could not be detected in vitro in potato tuber mitochondria, even under anaerobiosis where the NAD pool was completely reduced (2). More work is clearly needed in this area.

The origin of matrix NADP is not known with certainty. $NADP^+$ in the medium is reported to stimulate the oxidation of potentially NADP-linked substrates by potato tuber mitochondria, possibly owing to $NADP^+$ uptake (113). However, the commercial $NADP^+$ used in this investigation contained small amounts of NAD, and when the experiments were repeated with NAD^+-free $NADP^+$, no stimulation could be detected (SC Agius, AG Rasmusson & IM Møller, unpublished). If $NADP^+$ uptake (12a) is not a universal phenomenon associated with plant mitochondria, then mitochondrial NADP is probably synthesized in the matrix by an NAD^+ kinase. An NAD^+ kinase has been reported to be found in the outer membrane of corn coleoptile mitochondria (23), where it would not be able to synthesize $NADP^+$ for the matrix, but this point requires further study.

However, the above measurements refer to the *total* extractable concentration and not to the concentration of free pyridine nucleotides, the relevant parameter when discussing enzymatic rates and equilibria. Using time-resolved fluorescence analysis, it has been estimated that virtually all of the NADH in the matrix of rat liver mitochondria is bound to proteins (148), presumably dehydrogenases. A crude calculation will illustrate how this is possible: In the matrix of pea leaf mitochondria, the glycine-oxidizing glycine decarboxylase complex (GDC) comprises 0.13 g ml^{-1} but has only one NADH binding site per approximately 650 kDa (96). Based on these values, the concentration of NADH binding sites on GDC can be estimated to be approximately 0.2 mM. There are several other "housekeeping" dehydrogenases, the concentration of which is considerable. Thus, depending on the binding constants of the various enzymes, a large proportion of the NAD can be bound, and calculations of rates and equilibria based on total concentrations may be misleading.

Transhydrogenase Activities Produce NADPH in the Matrix

Mammalian mitochondria contain a transmembrane transhydrogenase (TH; EC 1.6.1.2) in the inner membrane that catalyzes the following reaction:

$$NADH + NADP^+ + nH^+(\text{out}) \longrightarrow NAD^+ + NADPH + nH^+(\text{in}).$$

It is driven to the right by the proton-motive force across the inner membrane. Because the active sites are on the matrix side, this enzyme keeps matrix NADP much more reduced than matrix NAD. The enzyme is also found in many bacteria and fungi, although not in *S. cerevisiae*. TH activity has been suggested to have a number of functions: removal of ROS, biosynthesis, ATP synthesis, redox buffering, and fine-tuning of the Krebs cycle (42, 124).

It has been reported that plant mitochondria contain an H^+-TH similar to that in mammalian mitochondria (14), but this has never been independently confirmed. Recently, two TH activities were identified in inside-out SMP from potato tubers and pea leaves (13). The major activity, at least when assayed with NADPH and the NAD$^+$ analogue 3-acetylpyridine adenine dinucleotide, was catalyzed by complex I, as indicated by its sensitivity to DPI and its elution as a high-molecular-mass complex from a gel-filtration column loaded with solubilized SMP. The other, DPI-insensitive activity eluted at 220 kDa and was specific for the 4B-proton on NADH (13) rather than for the 4A-proton, the latter characteristic for the mammalian H$^+$-TH (42). The enzyme responsible for the second TH activity could be related to the soluble TH (EC 1.6.1.1) found in certain aerobic bacteria (32). Consistent with this possibility, there is preliminary evidence (NV Bykova, AG Rasmusson & IM Møller, unpublished results) indicating that most of the enzyme is present in the matrix fraction and that only a small amount is loosely attached to the IMM. The presence in plants of a mammalian type H$^+$-TH, although it cannot be excluded, is not necessary to explain the activities observed in plant mitochondria.

Evidence for the participation of the TH activities in the metabolism of plant mitochondria is still only indirect. GDC is strictly NAD$^+$-specific, yet rotenone-insensitive glycine oxidation by pea leaf mitochondria is substantially inhibited by low concentrations of DPI, indicating that NDin(NADPH) also contributes to this oxidation. Thus, NADH produced by glycine decarboxylase may be converted by a transhydrogenase into NADPH, which is reoxidized by NDin(NADPH) (12a).

Other Matrix Enzymes Can Produce NADPH

The matrix of plant mitochondria contains a number of enzymes that can catalyze NADP$^+$ reduction, probably mainly NADP-isocitrate dehydrogenase (EC 1.1.1.42), but also malic enzyme (EC 1.1.1.39), Δ^1-pyrroline-5-carboxylate dehydrogenase (EC 1.5.1.12), glutamate dehydrogenase (EC 1.4.1.3), and methylenetetrahydrofolate dehydrogenase (EC 1.5.1.5) (82, 113 and references therein). The catalytic rate of mitochondrial malic enzyme with NADP+ is 20–50% of the rate of NAD+ (see 82). Thus, substantial rates of NADPH synthesis may be sustained in the matrix of plant mitochondria under various physiological conditions. The main sinks for this NADPH may well be NDin(NADPH) and ROS metabolism (see below), although other processes such as folate turnover (90) and fatty acid biosynthesis (145) may also be important.

TURNOVER OF REACTIVE OXYGEN SPECIES IN PLANT MITOCHONDRIA

When oxygen interacts with the complex IV and AOX, two terminal oxidases in plant mitochondria, four electrons are transferred and water is the product (87, 128, 129). However, oxygen can also interact with the reduced form of other electron transport components, e.g. flavins and ubiquinone, and the result is ROS formation. ROS can react with proteins, lipids, and DNA causing decreased enzyme activities, increased membrane permeability and mutations, respectively

TABLE 1   Strategies for the defense against oxidative stress in (plant) mitochondria

Not all of the listed mechanisms and enzymes have been firmly established as present in plant mitochondria. See the text for a critical evaluation.

First line of defense	Avoidance of ROS production
	ETC is kept adequately oxidized by
	(a) Maintaining a balance between substrate availability
	and ATP requirement
	(b) Activation of AOX
	(c) Activation of uncoupler protein
	(d) Activation of rotenone-insensitive NAD(P)H dehydrogenases
Second line of defense	Detoxification of ROS[a]
	Superoxide—converted to H_2O_2 by MnSOD
	Hydrogen peroxide—detoxified by
	(a) Catalase
	(b) The ascorbate/glutathione cycle
	(c) The glutathione peroxidase system
	(d) The thioredoxin system
Third line of defense	Repair of ROS-mediated damage
	Fatty acid hydroperoxides, by glutathione peroxidase
	Proteins, e.g. by reduction of disulfide bridges
	DNA, e.g. by excission repair

[a]See Figure 4.

(36). For example, as a result of ROS production, both the amount of the lipid cardiolipin and CCO activity in isolated bovine heart SMP decreased by 40% in 60 min. CCO activity was restored with cardiolipin but not with peroxidized cardiolipin (99).

Thus, the production of ROS must be avoided or minimized and, if produced, ROS should be detoxified efficiently. Finally, any damage should be repaired (Table 1). As we shall see, plant mitochondria have mechanisms for minimizing ROS production, such as that involving the AOX, as well as several different systems for removing ROS once formed.

Mitochondria are Major Sites of ROS Production

An estimated 1% of the total O_2 consumption of a plant tissue goes to ROS production (105). In mammalian cells the mitochondria are a major, if not the major, source of ROS (36). The same has been suggested for nonphotosynthesizing plant cells (104). The relative importance of mitochondria and chloroplasts in ROS production in the light is not known.

The steady-state cellular concentrations of O_2^- and H_2O_2 in mammalian cells are 10^{-12}–10^{-11} M and 10^{-9}–10^{-7} M, respectively (16); thus, the ROS concentration is kept very low. To my knowledge, the only estimate published for plant tissues is 5 μM H_2O_2 in soybean embryonic axes under normal conditions, increasing to 50 μM when catalase is inhibited with aminotriazole (105). These values are orders of magnitude higher than the estimates for mammalian cells and need to be confirmed.

Mitochondrial ROS production is usually measured in two ways: (*a*) O_2^- is measured by oxidation of epinephrine to form adrenochrome (16). O_2^- has a short half-life and does not cross membranes, at least not in its charged unprotonated form. Because it can also be degraded by MnSOD in the matrix, it is difficult to detect in intact mitochondria. It is therefore usually assayed using inside-out SMP where the active sites of complexes I, II, and IV face the medium and in which MnSOD is absent. (*b*) H_2O_2 is measured using a peroxidase (e.g. from horseradish) and an oxidizable substrate (e.g. scopoletin). This assay is usually performed on intact mitochondria because H_2O_2 can easily cross the membranes and be detected in the medium. Any O_2^- formed inside the inner membrane must first be converted to H_2O_2 either by the action of MnSOD or by spontaneous dismutation.

In mammalian mitochondria, 1–5% of the oxygen consumed in vitro goes to ROS production, depending on the species, organ, respiratory substrate, and respiratory state. ROS production is higher in state 4, where the ETC components are reduced, than in state 3 (e.g. 39). The major sites of ROS production are complex I (16, 136) and the ubisemiquinone in complex III (135). The latter activity is completely inhibited by the complex IV inhibitor KCN, which interrupts the Q cycle and prevents the formation of ubisemiquinone (Figure 3) (135). Addition of KCN can thus be used to distinguish between complex I and III contributions to ROS formation. Note that MnSOD is KCN-insensitive (36), so ROS production can be inhibited at complex III without affecting SOD activity (but KCN will inhibit the peroxidase used to detect H_2O_2!).

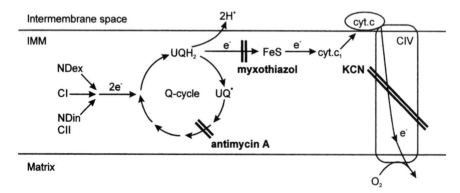

Figure 3   A simplified scheme showing the sites of interaction of antimycin A and myxothiazol in complex III and KCN in complex IV. The presence of KCN or myxothiazol prevents ubisemiquinone (UQ•) formation and therefore ROS production by complex III. In contrast, antimycin A inhibition permits ubisemiquinone formation and therefore does not interfere with ROS production. CI, CII, CIV, respiratory complexes (modified from 91, 135).

The situation in plant mitochondria is less clear for several reasons: (*a*) Very few studies have been performed; (*b*) the reported rates of ROS synthesis vary by a factor of almost 100 (see Table 2); (*c*) most of the studies have failed to consider the possible contribution by the non-proton-pumping NAD(P)H dehydrogenases; (*d*) when characterizing biochemical events on the inner surface of the IMM, inside-out SMP should be used, a point that is often not considered. Inside-out SMP can be isolated by sonicating mitochondria in a high-salt medium (33, 49, 78).

Despite these problems, the following general conclusions can be drawn from the data summarized in Table 2:

Plant mitochondria produce both O_2^- and H_2O_2 at rates equal to or greater than mammalian mitochondria both on an absolute basis and as a percentage of the rate of electron transport (typically 100–500 nmol O_2 consumed min^{-1} mg^{-1}).

The rate of ROS production is much lower in state 3 or under uncoupled conditions, whether caused by the addition of a chemical uncoupler (10, 106, 120) or by activation of the uncoupling protein using linolenic acid (15, 54), than in state 4. High rates of ROS production are observed when both terminal oxidases are inhibited (108, 119). These findings are consistent with the rate of ROS production being dependent on the reduction level of the ETC.

ROS production decreases when the AOX is activated, such as by addition of pyruvate (10, 106 see also below).

Substantial rates of O_2^- formation can be detected in intact mitochondria from several species during substrate oxidation (Table 2) (106, 108). In these experiments, the O_2^- detected during succinate and malate/pyruvate oxidation may have crossed the inner membrane, e.g. in the protonated form (HO_2).

In some cases, ROS production is completely inhibited by KCN, indicating that complex III may have been the only source of ROS before KCN addition (see above; 8, 105, 108). In other cases, there is high ROS production in the presence of KCN, indicating that complex I and/or the other dehydrogenases are major sites of ROS production (108, 119).

The production of O_2^- by intact mitochondria oxidizing NADH was completely inhibited by KCN (105, 108), indicating that NDex(NADH) did not produce ROS under these conditions.

The contribution of the two NDin to ROS production has not been considered. However, it is possible that the very DPI-sensitive NDin(NADPH) is also a site of ROS production: DPI has been suggested to inhibit primarily one-electron transfer flavoproteins (94), and this reaction mechanism would make the flavoprotein particularly prone to produce ROS since O_2^- is formed by the transfer of one electron to molecular oxygen (36).

Note that complex I will still produce ROS in the presence of rotenone because rotenone blocks electron transfer downstream of the FMN-containing active site

TABLE 2   ROS production by isolated plant mitochondria and submitochondrial particles

Species and tissue	Succinate		Other substrates		Reference
			Rate, nmol min^{-1} (mg protein)$^{-1}$		
			Hydrogen peroxide formation[a]		
Intact mitochondria					
Mung bean hypocotyl	Control	1.17	NADH	1.75	120
	+ Uncoupler	0.02			
	+ Uncoupler + A/A	0.74			
Potato tuber	Rot./ATP/Ca^{2+}	0.70			54
	+ Linolenic acid[d]	0.28			
Pea stem	Control	1.47	Malate/glu.	0.19	10
	+ Pyruvate	0.89	+ pyruvate	0.09	
	Control	1.36			
	+ Rot[b].	1.34			
	+ Rot. + A/A[d]	0.54			
	Control	1.37			
	+ ADP	0.32			
	ADP + Atractylate				
	+ Oligomycin	1.31			
	Control	1.05			
	+ Uncoupler	0			
Submitochondrial particles					
Arum maculatum spadix			NADH	30	44
Mung bean hypocotyls			NADH + A/A[d]	20	120
			Superoxide formation[a]		
Intact mitochondria					
Green bell pepper	Control	24	NADH	62	108
	+ A/A[d]	11	NADH + A/A	57	
	+ A/A[d] + disulf.	67			
	+ ADP	15	NADH + ADP	47	
	+ KCN	0	NADH + KCN[c]	0	
	Control	14			106
	+ADP	6			
	+Uncoupler	4			
	+A/A[d]	21			
	Control	27			
	+ Disulf.	33			
	+ Pyr	7			
	+ Pyr + disulf.	38			
Arum maculatum spadix	+ A/A[d]	0.7	NADH +A/A[d]	2.0	119
Potato tuber	+ Glu. (state 3)	13			8
	+ A/A[d]	15			
	+ KCN[c]	0.9			
Soybean embryonic axis	+ Glu.	0.95	NADH	1.3	105
			+ KCN[c]	0.2	
2 h germination			NADH	1.0	104
30 h germination			NADH	3.5	

TABLE 2   (*Continued*)

Species and tissue	Rate, nmol min^{-1} (mg protein)$^{-1}$				
	Succinate		Other substrates		Reference
Submitochondrial particles					
Potato tuber	A/A^d + SHAM	1.1	NADH + KCN	1.6	119
	A/A^d + SHAM	0	NADH +KCN + SHAM		
	+ KCN		+ A/A^d	1.5	
Arum maculatum spadix			NADH	8.3	44
	A/A^d	3.1	NADH + A/A^d	9.5	119
Mung bean hypocotyl	+ KCN^c	<2	NADH + KCN^c		119
			+ A/A^d	5.5	
	+ SHAM	<2	NADH + SHAM		
			+ A/A^d	10.3	
			NADH + KCN^c +		
			SHAM + A/A^d	4.9	
Pea leaf	Control	42	NADH	50	46
	+ A/A^d	52	+ Rot.^{b}	56	

^{a}Hydrogen peroxide was detected, e.g., by horseradish peroxidase-mediated oxidation of scopoletin. Superoxide was detected by the (often SOD-sensitive) oxidation of epinephrine to adrenochrome (36). Only in some of the studies were purified mitochondria used and the sideness and quality of SMP were often not reported.

^{b}Rotenone addition to mitochondria oxidizing succinate prevents reduction of complex I by reverse electron transport so that only the complex III contribution is measured (e.g., 10).

^{c}Cyanide addition prevents ubisemiquinone formation in complex III (Figure 3), and only ROS production by complex I [plus the rotenone-insensitive NAD(P)H dehydrogenases] is measured.

^{d}In the presence of antimycin A, both complexes I and III contribute maximally (135) in the absence of an active alternative oxidase.

Abbreviations: A/A, antimycin A; disulf., disulfiram; glu., glutamate; pyr, pyruvate; rot., rotenone.

(97). Here DPI would be a more suitable inhibitor because it inhibits at or near the flavin (63).

In summary, actively respiring plant mitochondria produce ROS at quite high rates, a more reduced ETC gives more ROS, and the main sites of production are the respiratory complexes I and III (Figure 1). Much more research is needed in this area.

The Alternative Oxidase Helps Minimize Mitochondrial ROS Production

Since molecular oxygen interacts with reduced electron transport components, one way to minimize ROS production is to prevent overreduction of the ETC. Avoidance can be viewed as the first line of defense against the potential detrimental effects of ROS (Table 1). The AOX has long been thought to act as an "overflow mechanism" taking over when the cytochrome chain is saturated with electrons (57, 97). More recently it has been shown that in the presence of pyruvate, the AOX will actually compete with an unsaturated cytochrome chain for electrons (41). In either case, the AOX becomes engaged at a particular UQ reduction level, thus preventing further UQ reduction (41). In this way, the reduction level of the UQ pool and therefore of the whole ETC is stabilized (75). Likewise, AOX is induced when the activities of complexes I–IV decrease as a result of chloramphenicol treatment of cells and tissues (see above).

Purvis & Shewfelt (107) first suggested that the AOX helps minimize ROS production by the ETC. Wagner (146) reported that H_2O_2 induces AOX synthesis in *Petunia* cell cultures. Recently, Maxwell et al (67) showed that cells in which the AOX had been overexpressed contained half as much ROS as control cells. In contrast, cells in which the expression of AOX had been reduced by antisensing contained five times more ROS than control cells.

Activation of the uncoupling protein, which was recently discovered to be present in plant mitochondria (56, 142), by fatty acids decreases ROS production by plant mitochondria (Table 2) (15, 64). This indicates that mild uncoupling may also be a mechanism for limiting ROS production (53).

NDin(NADH) may also help minimize ROS production by acting as an overflow under conditions where complex I activity is inadequate. This would be consistent with the induction of NDin(NADH) in washed beetroot slices when complex I activity is decreased by chloramphenicol treatment (see above).

ROS Detoxification by Superoxide Dismutase and (Possibly) Catalase

Once formed, the ROS must be detoxified as efficiently as possible to minimize damage; thus, detoxification constitutes the second line of defense against the detrimental effects of ROS (Table 1, Figure 4).

O_2^- is converted into O_2 and H_2O_2 by SOD (EC 1.15.1.1), and H_2O_2 is broken down into O_2 and water by catalase (EC 1.11.1.6). Both plant and animal mitochondria contain MnSOD in the matrix (36, 125). Mammalian cells overexpressing mitochondrial MnSOD show increased resistance to the O_2^--generating reagent paraquat (149). When plant mitochondrial MnSOD was expressed in the mitochondria of an MnSOD-deficient yeast strain, the cells regained their resistance to oxidative stress (125, 155). Likewise, overexpression of mitochondrial Mn-SOD from *Nicotiana plumbagnifolia* in *Nicotiana tabacum* mitochondria protected the latter from oxidative damage (9).

Catalase has been reported to be present in the matrix of rat heart mitochondria (109), but whether it is present in plant mitochondria is still an open question. In maize, CAT3 coisolates with mitochondria on a sucrose gradient (126). The N-terminal domain of the amino acid sequence deduced from the *cat3* cDNA (118) shows no clear resemblance to a mitochondrial targeting sequence according to the criteria identified by von Heijne et al (144). In fact, there may be no need for catalase in the mitochondrial matrix. First, several other matrix enzymes can remove H_2O_2 (see below); second, H_2O_2 is very mobile, and it may suffice that it is detoxified elsewhere in the cell, e.g. in the peroxisomes; third, H_2O_2 may be used

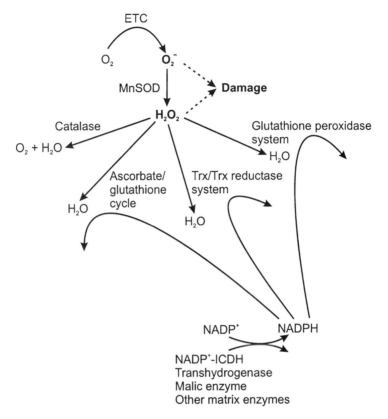

Figure 4   Summary of the enzyme systems possibly involved in ROS detoxification in plant mitochondria. Abbreviations: Trx, thioredoxin; ICDH, isocitrate dehydrogenase.

as an indicator of oxidative stress—a signal molecule—to activate nuclear genes involved in the stress response (101), as is likely for the AOX (146).

In maize leaves under oxidative stress induced by photoactivation of an exogenous fungal toxin, the amounts of both SOD3, the mitochondrial form of MnSOD in maize, and CAT3 mRNA increase markedly; however, whereas the amount of CAT3 protein also increases, that of SOD3 remains constant. The latter observation may mean that the rate of SOD turnover increases under oxidative stress (152).

The Role of Glutathione and Ascorbate in ROS Detoxification in Plant Mitochondria

The Ascorbate/Glutathione Cycle   The ascorbate/glutathione cycle is the main ROS-removing system in the chloroplast (e.g. 28). It uses four enzymes, ascorbate peroxidase (EC 1.11.1.11), dehydroascorbate reductase (EC 1.8.5.1), monodehydroascorbate reductase (EC 1.6.5.4), and glutathione reductase (EC 1.6.4.2), as well as two low-molecular-mass molecules, ascorbate and glutathione, to remove H_2O_2. The entire ascorbate/glutathione cycle has been reported to be found in pea leaf mitochondria (45), but this remains to be confirmed. Since glutathione reductase also acts together with glutathione peroxidase (see below), the well-established presence of glutathione reductase in the matrix of plant mitochondria (19, 26, 113) is not necessarily indicative of the function of the ascorbate/-glutathione cycle in the matrix. The main H_2O_2-removing enzyme in mammalian mitochondria is glutathione peroxidase (see below), and the ascorbate/glutathione cycle appears not to be present (36).

The levels of glutathione and ascorbate are about 6 and 24 nmol (mg protein)$^{-1}$ in pea leaf mitochondria or about 6 and 24 mM in the matrix (assuming 1 μl mg^{-1} protein) (45). This is over ten times the matrix concentration of NADP and somewhat above that of NAD (see above). The plant cell can synthesize ascorbate via several routes, but the main route includes a mitochondrial enzyme in the last step (20, 150). Here the flavoprotein L-galactono-γ-lactone dehydrogenase, an intrinsic protein in the inner membrane with the active site facing the intermembrane space, converts L-galactono-γ-lactone into ascorbate and donates electrons to the ETC between complexes III and IV (5, 93, 130).

Although the last step in ascorbate synthesis is carried out by the mitochondrion, the de novo synthesized ascorbate is not immediately available to the putative ascorbate/glutathione cycle in the mitochondrial matrix. An ascorbate transporter presumably exists to take the ascorbate across the inner membrane, but none has been identified to date. Mitochondria apparently lack the enzymes for GSH synthesis and, therefore, must import GSH from the cytosol (36, 92). In mammalian mitochondria glutathione synthesis takes place in the cytosol, and GSH is taken up across the inner membrane via a special transporter (68). Nothing is known about the uptake characteristics of glutathione across the inner membrane of plant mitochondria.

Glutathione Peroxidases   Glutathione peroxidases (EC 1.11.1.9) comprise another family of enzymes using GSH to reduce H_2O_2, lipid hydroperoxides, and other hydroperoxides (27, 36). Glutathione peroxidase has been found in mammalian mitochondria, where it is the main enzyme for removing H_2O_2 (36, 43). Although several homologues have been identified in plants and one enzyme purified and characterized, no information is available for plant mitochondria (17, 27). One member of the glutathione peroxidase superfamily is the phospholipid-hydroperoxide glutathione peroxidase (EC 1.11.1.12), which can act directly on lipid hydroperoxide without the need for release of the hydroperoxy fatty acid. Thus, glutathione peroxidases can also contribute to repair—the third line of defense against ROS damage (Table 1).

In the mitochondrial matrix, the regeneration of reduced glutathione from oxidized glutathione, whether produced in the ascorbate/glutathione cycle or by glutathione peroxidase, is catalyzed by the NADPH-specific glutathione reductase

(19, 26, 113). It may well be the main NADPH-consuming enzyme under metabolic conditions where ROS production and glutathione oxidation is high. In rat forebrain mitochondria the NADPH used in the regeneration of reduced glutathione comes from NADP-ICDH, malic enzyme, and transhydrogenase (143), which may also be true of plant mitochondria (see above). GSSH is suggested to inhibit NADPH-consuming enzymes other than those involved in ROS-detoxification in order to conserve NADPH (21). If this were true in plant mitochondria, NDin(NADPH) would be predicted to be inhibited by GSSH.

The Thioredoxin and Thioredoxin Reductase System Can Also Detoxify ROS

Thioredoxin is a small protein (12–14 kDa) with two cysteines in its active site that can form a disulfide in the oxidized form [Trx-(S-S)]. Together with the enzyme thioredoxin reductase (EC 1.6.4.5), which uses NADPH to convert Trx-(S-S) into reduced thioredoxin [Trx-(SH)$_2$], thioredoxin is involved in the regulation of enzyme activities as well as in scavenging hydroperoxides and H$_2$O$_2$ (36, 47, 74). Thioredoxin has long been known to regulate the activities of a number of Calvin cycle enzymes in the chloroplast stroma (12).

In plant mitochondria, two thioredoxins (52) and recently also an NADPH-thioredoxin reductase (4) have been identified. Nothing is yet known about the function of this enzyme system in plant mitochondria, but by analogy with yeast (100) and mammalian (47) mitochondria, it is possibly involved in protection against oxidative stress. It may also funtion in the reductive activation of citrate synthase (134) and the AOX (139), thereby activating the first line of defense against ROS (see above) while favoring flow through the Krebs cycle and the respiratory chain over fermentative processes (134).

PLANT MITOCHONDRIA AND OXIDATIVE STRESS: Perspectives

Mitochondria are a major site of ROS production in the plant cell, and they contain a number of enzymes designed to detoxify ROS (Figure 4); however, the picture is still very fragmentary. We need to know more about ROS production and the role(s) of NDin, NDex, the AOX, and the uncoupling protein in its regulation. Although there are several potential mechanisms for ROS detoxification in plant mitochondria (Figure 4), only MuSOD is firmly established. In several of the ROS-detoxification pathways, NADPH is involved in regenerating the low-molecular-mass antioxidant, but very little is known about NADPH turnover in plant mitochondria.

A possible sequence of events occurring in plant mitochondria during stress has been proposed (Figure 5) (146, 147): A constraint on the ETC, such as that

Figure 5 Possible sequence of events involving plant mitochondria in response to stress. Based on Wagner (146) and Wagner & Krab (147).

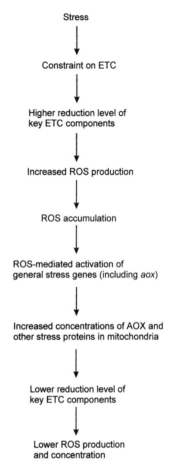

caused by loss of CCO in chilling-stressed maize mitochondria (102), leads to enhanced ROS production. H_2O_2 released from the mitochondria signals for increasing the synthesis of enzymes that lower ROS production such as the AOX and perhaps the uncoupling protein (Table 2). The AOX is induced by many stresses, including H_2O_2, and both enzymes are induced by cold stress (56, 140, 146). It is therefore likely that the uncoupling protein is also part of the general response to oxidative stress and that it is induced by a variety of stresses. In fact, the reverse prediction is also possible: An ETC component induced by H_2O_2 treatment of the cell is likely to have a role in maintaining a low ROS level either by limiting production or by helping detoxify ROS in the mitochondrion. This would be a simple method to identify more components involved in ROS turnover in plant mitochondria.

ACKNOWLEDGMENTS

I am grateful to Drs. Allan G. Rasmusson and Thomas H. Roberts for stimulating discussions, for critical reading of the manuscript and, to the latter, for help in preparing the figures. Cited work from the author's laboratory has been supported by grants from the Swedish Natural Science Research Council and the Swedish Institute.

Visit the Annual Reviews home page at www.AnnualReviews.org

LITERATURE CITED

1. Agius SC, Bykova NV, Igamberdiev AU, Møller IM. 1998. The internal rotenone-insensitive NADPH dehydrogenase contributes to malate oxidation by potato tuber and pea leaf mitochondria. *Physiol. Plant.* 104:329–36

2. Agius SC, Rasmusson AG, Åkerlund HE, Møller IM. 1998. Dynamic changes in the redox level of NAD in potato tuber mitochondria oxidising malate. In *Plant Mitochondria: From Gene to Function,* ed. IM Møller, P Gardeström, K Glimelius, E Glaser, pp. 343–46. Leiden: Backhuys

3. Arron GP, Edwards GE. 1979. Oxidation of reduced nicotinamide adenine dinucleotide phosphate by plant mitochondria. *Can. J. Biochem.* 57:1292–99

4. Banze M, Follmann H. 2000. Organelle-specific NADPH thioredoxin reductase in plant mitochondria. *J. Plant Physiol.* 156:126–29

5. Bartoli CG, Pastori GM, Foyer CH. 2000. Ascorbate biosynthesis in mitochondria is linked to the electron transport chain between complexes III and IV. *Plant Physiol.* 123:335–43

6. Becana M, Dalton DA, Moran JF, Iturbe-Ormaetxe I, Matamoros MA, Rubio MC. 2000. Reactive oxygen species and antioxidants in legume nodules. *Physiol. Plant.* 109:372–81

7. Boveris A, Chance B. 1973. The mitochondrial generation of hydrogen peroxide. *Biochem. J.* 134:707–16

8. Boveris A, Sánchez RA, Beconi MT. 1978. Antimycin- and cyanide-resistant respiration and superoxide anion production in fresh and aged potato tuber mitochondria. *FEBS Lett.* 92:333–38

9. Bowler C, Slooten L, Vandenbranden S, De Rycke R, Botterman J, et al. 1991. Manganese superoxide dismutase can reduce cellular damage mediated by oxygen radicals in transgenic plants. *EMBO J.* 10:1723–32

10. Braidot E, Petrussa E, Vianello A, Macrì F. 1999. Hydrogen peroxide generation by higher plant mitochondria oxidizing complex I or complex II substrates. *FEBS Lett.* 451:347–50

11. Brinkman FG, van der Plas LHW, Verleur JD. 1973. Pyridine nucleotide levels in potato tuber tissue and its mitochondrial fraction after wounding. *Z. Pflanzenphysiol.* 68:364–72

12. Buchanan BB. 1980. Role of light in the regulation of chloroplast enzymes. *Annu. Rev. Plant Physiol.* 31:341–74

12a. Bykova NB, Møller IM. 2001. Involvement of matrix NADP turnover in the oxidation of NAD^+-linked substrates by pea leaf mitochondria. *Physiol. Plant.* In press

13. Bykova NV, Rasmusson AG, Igamberdiev AU, Gardeström P, Møller IM. 1999. Two separate transhydrogenase activities are present in plant mitochondria. *Biochem. Biophys. Res. Commun.* 265:106–11

14. Carlenor E, Persson B, Glaser E, Andersson B, Rydström J. 1988. On the presence of a nicotinamide nucleotide transhydrogense in mitochondria from potato tuber. *Plant Physiol.* 88:303–8

15. Casolo V, Braidot E, Chiandussi E, Macrí F, Vianello A. 2000. The role of mild uncoupling and non-coupled respiration in the regulation of hydrogen peroxide generation by plant mitochondria. *FEBS Lett.* 474:53–57

16. Chance B, Sies H, Boveris A. 1979. Hydroperoxide metabolism in mammalian organs. *Physiol. Rev.* 59:527–605

17. Churin Y, Schilling S, Börner T. 1999. A gene family encoding glutathione peroxidase homologues in *Hordeum vulgare* (barley). *FEBS Lett.* 459:33–38

18. Cook-Johnson RJ, Zhang Q, Wiskich JT, Soole KL. 2000. The nuclear origin of the non-phosphorylating NADH dehydrogenase of plant mitochondria. *FEBS Lett.* 454:37–41

19. Creissen G, Reynolds H, Xue Y, Mullineaux P. 1995. Simultaneous targeting of pea glutathione reductase and of a bacterial fusion protein to chloroplasts and mitochondria in transgenic plants. *Plant J.* 8:167–75

20. Davey MW, Gilot C, Persiau G, Østergaard J, Han Y et al. 1999. Ascorbate biosynthesis in Arabidopsis cell suspension cultures. *Plant Physiol.* 121:535–43

21. Del Corso A, Cappiello M, Mura U. 1994. Thiol dependent oxidation of enzymes: The last chance against oxidative stress. *Int. J. Biochem.* 26:745–50

22. de Vries S, Grivell LA. 1988. Purification and characterization of a rotenone-insensitive NADH:Q6 oxidoreductase from mitochondria of *Saccharomyces cerevisiae. Eur. J. Biochem.* 176:377–84

23. Dieter P, Marmé D. 1984. A Ca^{2+}, calmodulin-dependent NAD kinase from corn is located in the outer mitochondrial membrane. *J. Biol. Chem.* 259:184–89

24. Douce R, Mannella CA, Bonner WD Jr.

1973. The external NADH dehydrogenase of intact plant mitochondria. *Biochim. Biophys. Acta* 292:105–16

25. Douce R, Neuburger M. 1989. The uniqueness of plant mitochondria. *Annu. Rev. Plant Physiol.* 40:371–404

26. Edwards EA, Rawsthorne S, Mullineaux PM. 1990. Subcellular distribution of multiple forms of glutathione reductase in leaves of pea (*Pisum sativum* L.). *Planta* 180:278–84

27. Eshdat Y, Holland D, Faltin Z, Ben-Hayyim G. 1997. Plant glutathione peroxidases. *Physiol. Plant.* 100:234–40

28. Foyer CH, Lelandais M, Kunert KJ. 1994. Photooxidative stress in plants. *Physiol. Plant.* 92:696–717

29. Foyer CH, Lopez-Delgado H, Dat JF, Scott IM. 1997. Hydrogen peroxide- and glutathione-associated mechanisms of acclimatory stress tolerance and signalling. *Physiol. Plant.* 100:241–54

30. Fredlund KM. 1996. *NAD(P)H dehydrogenases in plant mitochondria.* PhD thesis. Lund Univ., Sweden

31. Fredlund KM, Rasmusson AG, Møller IM. 1991. The effects of aging on the oxidation of external NAD(P)H in purified red beetroot (*Beta vulgaris* L.) mitochondria. *Plant Physiol.* 97:99–103

32. French CE, Boonstra B, Bufton KAJ, Bruce NC. 1997. Cloning, sequence, and properties of the soluble pyridine nucleotide transhydrogenase of *Pseudomonas fluorescens. J. Bacteriol.* 179:2761–65

33. Gardeström P, Petit PX, Møller IM 1994. Purification and characterization of plant mitochondria and submitochondrial particles. *Methods Enzymol.* 228:424–31

34. Deleted in proof

35. Gutierres S, Sabar M, Lelandais C, Chetrit P, Diolez P, et al. 1997. Lack of mitochondrial and nuclear-encoded subunits of complex I and alteration of the respiratory chain in *Nicotiana sylvestris* mitochondrial deletion mutants. *Proc. Natl. Acad. Sci. USA* 94:3436–41

36. Halliwell B, Gutteridge JMC. 1999. *Free Radicals in Biology and Medicine*, Oxford: Oxford Univ. Press. 3rd ed.

37. Hansford RG. 1991. Dehydrogenase activation by Ca^{2+} in cells and tissues. *J. Bioenerg. Biomembr.* 23:823–54

38. Heineke D, Riens B, Grosse H, Hoferichter P, Peter U, et al. 1991. Redox transfer across the inner chloroplast envelope membrane. *Plant Physiol.* 95:1131–37

39. Herrero A, Barja G. 1997. ADP-regulation of mitochondrial free radical production is different with complex I- or complex II-linked substrates: implications for the exercise paradox and brain hypermetabolism. *J. Bioenerg. Biomembr.* 29:241–49

40. Herz U, Schröder W, Liddell A, Leaver CJ, Brennicke A, Grohmann L. 1994. Purification of the NADH:ubiquinone oxidoreductase (complex I) of the respiratory chain from the inner mitochondrial membrane of *Solanum tuberosum. J. Biol. Chem.* 269:2263–69

41. Hoefnagel MHN, Millar AH, Wiskich JT, Day DA. 1995. Cytochrome and alternative respiratory pathways compete for electrons in the presence of pyruvate in soybean mitochondria. *Arch. Biochem. Biophys.* 318:394–400

42. Hoek JB, Rydström J. 1988. Physiological roles of nicotinamide nucleotide transhydrogenase. *Biochem. J.* 254:1–10

43. Huang J, Philbert MA. 1995. Distribution of glutathione and glutathione-related enzyme systems in mitochondria and cytosol of cultured cerebellar astrocytes and granule cells. *Brain Res.* 680:16–22

44. Huq S, Palmer JM. 1978. Superoxide and hydrogen peroxide production in cyanide resistant *Arum maculatum* mitochondria. *Plant Sci. Lett.* 11:351–58

45. Jimenez A, Hernández JA, del Rio LA, Sevilla F. 1997. Evidence for the presence of the ascorbate-glutathione cycle in mitochondria and peroxisomes of pea leaves. *Plant Physiol.* 114:275–84

46. Jimenez A, Hernández JA, Pastori G, del Rio LA, Sevilla F. 1998. Role of the ascorbate-glutathione cycle of mitochondria and peroxisomes in the senescence of pea leaves. *Plant Physiol.* 118:1327–335

47. Kang SW, Chae HZ, Seo MS, Kim K, Baines IC, Rhee SG. 1998. Mammalian peroxiredoxin isoforms can reduce hydrogen peroxide generated in response to growth factors and tumor necrosis factor-α. *J. Biol. Chem.* 273:6297–302

48. Karpova OV, Newton KJ. 1999. A partially assembled complex I in NAD4-deficient mitochondria of maize. *Plant J.* 17:511–21

49. Kay CJ, Ericson I, Gardeström P, Palmer JM, Møller IM. 1985. Generation and purification of submitochondrial particles of different polarities from plant mitochondria. *FEBS Lett.* 193:169–74

50. Knight H, Trewavas AJ, Knight MR. 1996. Cold calcium signaling in Arabidopsis involves two cellular pools and a change in calcium signature after acclimation. *Plant Cell* 8:489–503

51. Knudten AF, Thelen JJ, Luethy MH, Elthon TE. 1994. Purification, characterization, and submitochondrial localization of the 32-kilodalton NADH dehydrogenase from maize. *Plant Physiol.* 106:1115–22

52. Konrad A, Banze M, Follmann H. 1996. Mitochondria of plant leaves contain two thioredoxins. Completion of the thioredoxin profile of higher plants. *J. Plant Physiol.* 149:317–21

53. Korshunov SS, Korkina OV, Ruuge EK, Skulachev VP, Starkov AA. 1998. Fatty acids as natural uncouplers preventing generation of O_2^--and H_2O_2 by mitochondria in the resting state. *FEBS Lett.* 435:215–18

54. Kowaltowski AJ, Costa ADT, Vercesi AE. 1998. Activation of the potato uncoupling mitochondrial protein inhibits reactive oxygen species generation by the respiratory chain. *FEBS Lett.* 425:213–16

55. Krömer S, Heldt HW. 1991. Respiration of pea leaf mitochondria and redox transfer

between the mitochondrial and extramito-chondrial compartment. *Biochim. Biophys. Acta* 1057:42–50

56. Laloi M, Klein M, Riesmeier JW, Müller-Röber B, Fleury C, et al. 1997. A plant cold-induced uncoupling protein. *Nature* 389:135–36

57. Lambers H. 1982. Cyanide-resistant res-piration: a non-phosphorylating elec-tron transport pathway acting as an energy over-flow. *Physiol. Plant.* 55:478–85

58. Lehninger AL, Nelson DL, Cox MM. 1993. *Principles of Biochemistry.* New York:Worth Publ. 2nd Ed.

59. Li Y, Stansbury KH, Zhu H, Trush MA. 1999. Biochemical characterization of lucigenin (bis-N-methylacridinium) as a chemiluminescent probe for detecting in-tramitochondrial superoxide anion radical production. *Biochem. Biophys. Res. Com-mun.* 262:80–87

60. Luethy MH, Thelen JJ, Knudten AF, Elthon TE. 1995. Purification, character-ization and submitochondrial localization of a 58-kilodalton NAD(P)H dehydroge-nase. *Plant Physiol.* 107:443–50

61. Luttik MAH, Overkamp KM, Kötter P, de Vries S, van Dijken JP, Pronk JT. 1998. The *Saccharomyces cerevisiae* NDE1 and NDE2 genes encode separate mitochon-drial NADH dehydrogenases catalyzing the oxidation of cytosolic NADH. *J. Biol. Chem.* 273:24529–34

62. Mackenzie S, McIntosh L. 1999. Higher plant mitochondria. *Plant Cell* 11:571–85

63. Majander A, Finel M, Wikström M. 1994. Dephenyleneiodonium inhibits reduction of iron-sulfur clusters in the mitochondrial NADH-ubiquinone oxidoreductase (Com-plex I). *J. Biol. Chem.* 269:21037–42

64. Marienfeld JR, Newton KJ. 1994. The maize NCS2 abnormal growth mutant has a chimeric *nad4–nad7* mitochondrial gene and is associated with reduced complex I function. *Genetics* 138:855–63

65. Marienfeld JR, Unseld M, Brennicke A. 1999. The mitochondrial genome of Ara-bidopsis is composed of both native and immigrant information. *Trends Plant Sci.* 4:495–502

66. Marres CAM, de Vries S, Grivell L. 1991. Isolation and inactivation of the nuclear gene encoding the rotenone-insensitive int-ernal NADH:ubiquinone oxidoreductase of mitochondria from *Saccharomyces cere-visiae. Eur. J. Biochem.* 195:857–62

67. Maxwell DP, Wang Y, McIntosh L. 1999. The alternative oxidase lowers mitochon-drial reactive oxygen production in plant cells. *Proc. Natl. Acad. Sci. USA* 96:8271–76

68. Meister A. 1995. Mitochondrial changes associated with glutathione deficiency. *Biochim. Biophys. Acta* 1271:35–42

69. Melo AMP, Roberts TH, Møller IM. 1996. Evidence for the presence of two rotenone-insensitive NAD(P)H dehydro-genases on the inner surface of the in-ner membrane of potato tuber mito-chondria. *Biochim. Biophys. Acta* 1276: 133–39

70. Melo AMP, Duarte M, Møller IM, Prokisch H, Dolan P, et al. 2001. NDE1 is the ex-ternal calcium-dependent NADPH dehy-drogenase in *Neurospora crassa* mitochon-dria. *J. Biol. Chem.* In press

71. Melo AMP, Duarte M, Videira A. 1999. Primary structure and characterisation of a 64 kDa NADH dehydrogenase from the inner membrane of *Neurospora crassa* mitochondria. *Biochim. Biophys. Acta* 1412:282–87

72. Menz RI, Day DA. 1996a. Identifi-cation and characterization of an in-ducible NAD(P)H dehydrogenase from red beetroot mitochondria. *Plant Physiol.* 112:607–13

73. Menz RI, Day DA. 1996b. Purifica-tion and characterization of a 43-kDa rotenone-insensitive NADH dehydroge-nase from plant mitochondria. *J. Biol. Chem.* 271:23117–20

74. Meyer Y, Vervoucz L, Vignols F. 1999. Plant thioredoxins and glutaredoxins:

identity and putative roles. *Trends Plant Sci.* 4:388–94

75. Millenaar FF, Benschop JJ, Wagner AM, Lambers H. 1998. The role of the alternative oxidase in stabilizing the in vivo reduction state of the ubiquinone pool and the activation state of the alternative oxidase. *Plant Physiol.* 118:599–607

76. Møller IM. 1997. The oxidation of cytosolic NAD(P)H by external NAD(P)H dehydrogenases in the respiratory chain of plant mitochondria. *Physiol. Plant.* 100:85–90

77. Møller IM, Johnston SP, Palmer JM. 1981. A specific role for Ca^{2+} in the oxidation of exogenous NADH by Jerusalemartichoke (*Helianthus tuberosus*) mitochondria. *Biochem. J.* 194:487–95

78. Møller IM, Lidén AC, Ericson I, Gardeström P. 1987. Isolation of submitochondrial particles with different polarities. *Methods Enzymol.* 148:442–53

79. Møller IM, Lin W. 1986. Membrane-bound NAD(P)H dehydrogenases in higher plant cells. *Annu. Rev. Plant Physiol.* 37:309–34

80. Møller IM, Palmer JM. 1981. The inhibition of exogenous NAD(P)H oxidation in plant mitochondria by chelators and mersalyl as a function of pH. *Physiol. Plant.* 55:413–20

81. Møller IM, Palmer JM. 1982. Direct evidence for the presence of a rotenoneresistant NADH dehydrogenase on the inner surface of the inner membrane of plant mitochondria. *Physiol. Plant.* 54:267–74

82. Møller IM, Rasmusson AG. 1998. The role of NADP in the mitochondrial matrix. *Trends Plant Sci.* 3:21–27

83. Møller IM, Rasmusson AG, Fredlund KM. 1993. NAD(P)H-ubiquinone oxidoreductases in plant mitochondria. *J. Bioenerg. Biomembr.* 25:377–84

84. Møller IM, Roberts TH, Rasmusson AG. 1996. Ubiquinone-1 induces external deamino-NAD(P)H oxidation in potato tuber mitochondria. *Plant Physiol.* 112:75–78

85. Møller IM, Schwitzguébel J-P, Palmer JM.

1982. Binding and screening by cations and the effect on exogenous NAD(P)H oxidation in *Neurospora crassa* mitochondria. *Eur. J. Biochem.* 123:81–88

86. Moore AL, Åkerman KEO. 1982. Ca^{2+} stimulation of the external NADH dehydrogenase in Jerusalem artichoke (*Helianthus tuberosus*) mitochondria. *Biochem. Biophys. Res. Commun.* 109:513–17

87. Moore AL, Siedow JN 1991. The regulation and nature of the cyanide-resistant alternative oxidase of plant mitochondria. *Biochim. Biophys. Acta* 1059:121–40

88. Nash D, Wiskich DT. 1983. Properties of substantially chlorophyll-free pea leaf mitochondria prepared by sucrose density gradient separation. *Plant Physiol.* 71:627–34

89. Neuburger M, Day DA, Douce R 1984. The regulation of malate oxidation in plant mitochondria by the redox state of endogenous pyridine nucleotides. *Physiol. Vég.* 22:571–80

90. Neuburger M, Rebeillé F, Jourdain A, Nakamura S, Douce R. 1996. Mitochondria are a major site for folate and thymidylate synthesis in plants. *J. Biol. Chem.* 271:9466–72

91. Nicholls DG, Ferguson SJ. 1992. *Bioenergetics 2.* London: Academic

92. Noctor G., Foyer CH. 1998. Ascorbate and glutathione. Keeping active oxygen under control. *Annu. Rev. Plant Physiol. Plant. Mol. Biol.* 49:249–79

93. Oba K, Ishikawa S, Nishikawa M, Mizuno H, Yamamoto T. 1995. Purification and propterties of L-galactono-γ-lactone dehydrogenase, a key enzyme for ascorbic acid biosynthesis, from sweet potato roots. *J. Biochem.* 117:120–24

94. O'Donnell VB, Smith GCM, Jones OTG. 1994. Involvement of phenyl radicals in iodonium compound inhibition of flavoenzymes. *Mol. Pharmacol.* 46:778–85

95. Oettmeier W, Masson K, Soll M, Reil E. 1994. Acridones and quinolones as

inhibitors of ubiquinone functions in the mitochondrial respiratory chain. *Biochem. Soc. Trans.* 22:213–16

96. Oliver DJ, Neuburger M, Bourgignon J, Douce R. 1990. Glycine metabolism by plant mitochondria. *Physiol. Plant.* 80:487–91

97. Palmer JM. 1976. The organization and regulation of electron transport in plant mitochondria. *Annu. Rev. Plant Physiol.* 27:133–57

98. Palmer JM, Schwitzguébel J-P, Møller IM. 1982. Regulation of malate oxidation in plant mitochondria. Response to rotenone and exogenenous NAD$^+$. *Biochem. J.* 208:703–11

99. Paradies G, Petrosillo G, Pistolese M, Ruggiero FM. 2000. The effect of reactive oxygen species generated from the mitochondrial electron transport chain on the cytochrome c oxidase activity and on the cardiolipin content in bovine heart submitochondrial particles. *FEBS Lett.* 466:323–26

100. Pedrajas JR, Kosmidou E, Miranda-Vizuete A, Gustafsson J-Å, Wright APH, Spyrou G. 1999. Identification and functional characterization of a novel mitochondrial thioredoxin system in *Saccharomyces cerevisiae*. *J. Biol. Chem.* 274:6366–73

101. Prasad TK, Anderson MD, Martin BA, Stewart CR. 1994. Evidence for chilling-induced oxidative stress in maize seedlings and a regulatory role for hydrogen peroxide. *Plant Cell* 6:65–74

102. Prasad TK, Anderson MD, Stewart CR. 1994. Acclimation, hydrogen peroxide, and abscisic acid protect mitochondria against irreversible chilling injury in maize seedlings. *Plant Physiol.* 105:619–27

103. Price AH, Taylor A, Ripley SJ, Griffiths A, Trewavas AJ, Knight MR. 1994. Oxidative signals in tobacco increase cytosolic calcium. *Plant Cell* 6:1301–10

104. Puntarulo S, Galleano M, Sanchez RA, Boveris A. 1991. Superoxide anion and hydrogen peroxide metabolism in soybean embryonic axes during germination. *Biochim. Biophys. Acta* 1074:277–83

105. Puntarulo S, Sanchez RA, Boveris A. 1988. Hydrogen peroxide metabolism in soybean embryonic axes at the onset of germination. *Plant Physiol.* 86:626–30

106. Purvis AC. 1997. Role of the alternative oxidase in limiting superoxide production by plant mitochondria. *Physiol. Plant.* 100:165–70

107. Purvis AC, Shewfelt RL. 1993. Does the alternative pathway ameliorate chilling injury in sensitive plant tissues? *Physiol. Plant.* 88:712–18

108. Purvis AC, Shewfelt RL, Gegogeine JW. 1995. Superoxide production by mitochondria isolated from green bell pepper fruit. *Physiol. Plant.* 94:743–49

109. Radi R, Turrens JF, Chang LY, Bush KM, Crapo JD, Freeman BA. 1991. Detection of catalase in rat heart mitochondria. *J. Biol. Chem.* 266:22028–34

110. Rasmussen UF, Rasmussen HN. 1985. The NADH oxidase system (external) of muscle mitochondria and its role in the oxidation of cytoplasmic NADH. *Biochem. J.* 229:631–41

111. Rasmusson AG, Heiser V, Zabaleta E, Brennicke A, Grohmann L. 1998. Physiological, biochemical and molecular aspects of mitochondrial complex I in plants. *Biochim. Biophys. Acta* 1364:101–11

112. Rasmusson AG, Mendel-Hartvig J, Møller IM, Wiskich JT. 1994. Isolation of the rotenone-sensitive NADH-ubiquinone reductase (Complex I) from red beet mitochondria. *Physiol. Plant.* 90:607–15

113. Rasmusson AG, Møller IM. 1990. NADP-Utilizing enzymes in the matrix of plant mitochondria. *Plant Physiol.* 94:1012–18

114. Rasmusson AG, Møller IM. 1991a. NAD(P)H dehydrogenases on the inner surface of the inner mitochondrial

membrane studied using inside-out sub-mitochondrial particles. *Physiol. Plant.* 83:357–65

115. Rasmusson AG, Møller IM. 1991b. Effect of calcium ions and inhibitors on internal NAD(P)H dehydrogenases in plant mito-chondria. *Eur. J. Biochem.* 202:617–23

116. Rasmusson AG, Svensson ÅS, Knoop V, Grohmann L, Brennicke A. 1999. Homo-logues of yeast and bacterial rotenone-insensitive NADH dehydrogenases in higher eukaryotes: two enzymes are present in potato mitochondria. *Plant J.* 20:79–87

117. Rayner JR, Wiskich JT. 1983. Develop-ment of NADH oxidation by red beet mi-tochondria on slicing and aging of the tis-sues. *Aust. J. Plant Physiol.* 10:55–63

118. Redinbaugh MG, Wadsworth GJ, Scan-dalios JG. 1988. Characterization of cata-lase transcripts and their differential ex-pression in maize. *Biochim. Biophys. Acta* 951:104–16

119. Rich PR, Bonner WD Jr. 1978. The sites of superoxidide anion generation in higher plant mitochondria. *Arch. Biochem. Biophys.* 188:206–13

120. Rich PR, Boveris A, Bonner WD, Moore AL. 1976. Hydrogen peroxide genera-tion by the alternate oxidase of higher plants. *Biochem. Biophys. Res. Commun.* 71:695–703

121. Roberts JKM, Aubert S, Gout E, Bligny R, Douce R. 1997. Cooperation and competition between adenylate ki-nase, nucleoside diphosphokinase, elec-tron transport, and ATP synthase in plant mitochondria studied by ^{31}P-nuclear magnetic resonance. *Plant Physiol.* 113:191–99

122. Roberts TH, Fredlund KM, Møller IM. 1995. Direct evidence for the presence of two external NAD(P)H dehydrogenases coupled to the electron transport chain in plant mitochondria. *FEBS Lett.* 373:307–9

123. Roberts TH, Rasmusson AG, Møller I.M.

1996. Platanetin and 7-iodo-acridone-4-carboxylic acid are not specific inhibitors of respiratory NAD(P)H dehydrogenases in potato tuber mitochondria. *Physiol. Plant.* 96:263–67

124. Sazanov LA, Jackson JB. 1994. Proton-translocating transhydrogenase and NAD- and NADP-linked isocitrate dehy-drogenases operate in a substrate cycle which contributes to fine regulation of the tricarboxylic acid cycle activity in mitochondria. *FEBS Lett.* 344:109–16

125. Scandalios JC. 1993. Oxygen stress and superoxide dismutases. *Plant Physiol.* 101:7–12

126. Scandalios JG, Tong W-F, Roupakias DG. 1980. *Cat3*, a third gene locus coding for a tissue-specific catalase in maize: ge-netics, intracellular location, and some biochemical properties. *Mol. Gen. Genet.* 179:33–41

127. Seo BB, Kitajima-Ihara T, Chan EKL, Scheffler IE, Matsuno-Yagi A, Yagi T. 1998. Molecular remedy of complex I detects: roteone-insensitive internal NADH-quinone oxidoreductase of *Sac-charomyces cerevisiae* mitochondria re-stores the NADH oxidase activity of com-plex I-deficient mammalian cells. *Proc. Natl. Acad. Sci. USA* 95:9167–71

128. Siedow JN. 1995. In *The Molecular Biol-ogy of Plant Mitochondria*, ed. CS Lev-ings III, IK Vasil, pp. 281–312, Dordre-cht: Kluwer

129. Siedow JN, Umbach A. 1995. Plant mito-chondrial electron transfer and molecular biology. *Plant Cell* 7:821–31

130. Siendones E, González-Reyes JA, Santos-Ocana C, Navas P, Córdoba F. 1999. Biosynthesis of ascorbic acid in kidney bean. L-Galactono-γ-lactone dehydroge-nase is an intrinsic protein located at the mitochondrial inner membrane. *Plant Physiol.* 120:907–12

131. Small WC, McAlister-Henn L. 1998. Identification of a cytosolically directed

NADH dehydrogenase in mitochondria of *Saccharomyces cerevisiae. J. Bacteriol.* 180:4051–55

132. Smith TA. 1985. Polyamines. *Annu. Rev. Plant Physiol.* 36:117–43

133. Soole KL, Menz RI. 1995. Functional molecular aspects of the NADH dehydrogenases of plant mitochondria. *J. Bioenerg. Biomembr.* 27:397–406

134. Stevens FJ, Li AD, Lateef SS, Anderson LE. 1997. Identification of potential interdomain disulfides in three higher plant mitochondrial citrate synthases: Paradoxical differences in redox-sensitivity as compared to the animal enzyme. *Photosynth. Res.* 54:185–97

135. Turrens JF, Alexandre A, Lehninger AL. 1985. Ubisemiquinone is the electron donor for superoxide formation by complex III of heart mitochondria. *Arch. Biochem. Biophys.* 237:408–14

136. Turrens JF, Boveris A. 1980. Generation of superoxide anion by the NADH dehydrogenase of bovine heart mitochondria. *Biochem. J.* 191:421–27

137. Unseld M, Marienfeld JR, Brandt P, Brennicke A. 1997. The mitochondrial genome of *Arabidopsis thaliana* contains 57 genes in 366,924 nucleotides. *Nat. Genet.* 15:57–61

138. Vander Heiden MG, Chandel NS, Li XX, Schumacker PT, Colombini M, Thompson CB. 2000. Outer membrane permeability can regulate coupled respiration and cell survival. *Proc. Natl. Acad. Sci. USA* 97:4666–71

139. Vanlerberghe GC, Day DA, Wiskich JT, Vanlerberghe AE, McIntosh L. 1995. Alternative oxidase activity in tobacco leaf mitochondria. Dependence on tricarboxylic acid cycle-mediated redox regulation and pyruvate activation. *Plant Physiol.* 109:353–61

140. Vanlerberghe GC, McIntosh L. 1997. Alternative oxidase: from gene to function. *Annu. Rev. Plant Physiol. Plant Mol. Biol.* 48:703–34

141. Vedel F, Lalanne É, Sabar M, Chétrit P, De Paepe R. 1999. The mitochondrial respiratory chain and ATP synthase complexes: composition, structure and mutational studies. *Plant Physiol. Biochem.* 37:629–43

142. Vercesi AE, Martins IS, Silva MAP, Leite HMF. 1995. PUMPing plants. *Nature* 375:24

143. Vogel R, Wiesinger H, Hamprecht B, Dringen R. 1999. The regeneration of reduced glutathione in rat forebrain mitochondria identifies metabolic pathways providing the NADPH required. *Neurosci. Lett.* 275:97–100

144. von Heijne G, Steppuhn J, Herrmann RG. 1989. Domain-structure of mitochondrial and chloroplast targeting peptides. *Eur. J. Biochem.* 180:535–45

145. Wada H, Shintani D, Ohlrogge J. 1997. Why do mitochondria synthesize fatty acids? Evidence for involvement in lipoic acid production. *Proc. Natl. Acad. Sci. USA* 94:1591–96

146. Wagner AM. 1995. A role for active oxygen species as second messengers in the induction of alternative oxidase gene expression in *Petunia hybrida* cells. *FEBS Lett.* 368:339–42

147. Wagner AM, Krab K. 1995. The alternative respiration pathway in plants. Role and regulation. *Physiol. Plant.* 95:318–25

148. Wakita M, Nishimura G, Tamura M. 1995. Some characteristics of the fluorescence lifetime of reduced pyridine nucleotides in isolated mitochondria, isolated hepatocytes, and perfused rat liver in situ. *J. Biochem.* 118:1151–60

149. Wenk J, Brenneisen P, Wlaschek M, Poswig A, Briviba K, et al. 1999. Stable overexpression of manganese superoxide dismutase in mitochondria identifies hydrogen peroxide as a major oxidant in the AP-1-mediated induction of matrix-degrading metalloprotease-1. *J. Biol. Chem.* 174:25869–76

150. Wheeler GL, Jones MA, Smirnoff N. 1998. The biosynthetic pathway of vitamin C in higher plants. *Nature* 393:365–69

151. Wigge B, Krömer S, Gardeström P. 1993. The redox levels and subcellular distribution of pyridine nucleotides in illuminated barley leaf protoplasts studied by rapid fractionation. *Physiol. Plant.* 88:10–18

152. Williamson JD, Scandalios JG. 1992. Differential response of maize catalases and superoxide dismutases to the photoactivated fungal toxin cercosporin. *Plant J.* 2:351–58

153. Zhang Q, Mischis L, Wiskich JT. 1996. Respiratory responses of pea and wheat seedlings to chloramphenicol treatment. *Aust. J. Plant Physiol.* 23:683–92

154. Zhang Q, Wiskich JT, Soole KL. 1999. Respiratory activities in chloramphenicol-treated tobacco cells. *Physiol. Plant.* 105:224–32

155. Zhu D, Scandalios JG. 1992. Expression of the maize *MnSod* (*Sod3*) gene in MnSOD-deficient yeast rescues the mutant yeast under oxidative stress. *Genetics* 131:803–9

156. Zottini M, Mandolino G, Zannoni D. 1993. Oxidation of external NAD(P)H by mitochondria from taproots and tissue cultures of sugar beet (*Beta vulgaris*). *Plant Physiol.* 102:579–85

Annu. Rev. Plant Physiol. Plant Mol. Biol. 2001. 52:593–626

PHOTOSYSTEM I: Function and Physiology

Parag R Chitnis

Department of Biochemistry, Biophysics, and Molecular Biology, Iowa State University, Ames, Iowa 50011; e-mail: chitnis@iastate.edu

Key Words chloroplasts, cyanobacteria, electron transfer, photosynthesis, thylakoids

■ **Abstract** Photosystem I is the light-driven plastocyanin-ferredoxin oxidoreductase in the thylakoid membranes of cyanobacteria and chloroplasts. In recent years, sophisticated spectroscopy, molecular genetics, and biochemistry have been used to understand the light conversion and electron transport functions of photosystem I. The light-harvesting complexes and internal antenna of photosystem I absorb photons and transfer the excitation energy to P700, the primary electron donor. The subsequent charge separation and electron transport leads to the reduction of ferredoxin. The photosystem I proteins are responsible for the precise arrangement of cofactors and determine redox properties of the electron transfer centers. With the availability of genomic information and the structure of photosystem I, one can now probe the functions of photosystem I proteins and cofactors. The strong reductant produced by photosystem I has a central role in chloroplast metabolism, and thus photosystem I has a critical role in the metabolic networks and physiological responses in plants.

CONTENTS

1040–2519/01/0601–0593$14.00

INTRODUCTION

Photosytem I (PSI) functions as the light-driven plastocyanin-ferredoxin oxidoreductase in the thylakoid membranes of cyanobacteria and chloroplasts. PSI contains 11–14 different proteins and several types of organic and inorganic cofactors.
The overall function of PSI involves harvesting photons and using their energy
for electron transfer through a series of redox centers. When pigments in the
antenna absorb light, the photon energy is transferred through antenna pigment
molecules to the P700 reaction center, which is made up of a pair of chlorophyll
molecules. In the reaction center, the excitation energy is trapped and used for energizing an electron, which is transferred to an acceptor chlorophyll a molecule (A_0),
resulting in charge separation. Subsequently, $P700^+$, a weak oxidant, accepts an
electron from the reduced plastocyanin. Electrons from the reduced A_0 are transferred through a chain of redox centers that includes phylloquinones (A_1) and three
[4Fe-4S] clusters, F_X, F_A, and F_B. The terminal electron donor, F_B, reduces ferredoxin. The reduced ferredoxin is a strong reductant and provides electrons in a
variety of chloroplast reactions, including NADPH production, nitrate assimilation, and fatty acid desaturation. The reduced ferredoxin is also involved in the
redox regulation of chloroplast metabolism through the thioredoxin system.

In the past decade, molecular genetic approaches in cyanobacteria, algae, and
plants have generated subunit-deficient and site-directed mutants in PSI. Similarly,
the structure of PSI has been determined with X-ray diffraction crystallography
(26, 66, 67). Thus, the research on PSI is entering a new era. This article attempts
to capture the excitement in the PSI research and focuses on some major issues
that have emerged in the recent years. Many scholarly reviews contain detailed
discussions and list original references to the earlier work on PSI structure and
function (11, 17, 25, 26, 30, 77).

PROTEIN SUBUNITS OF PSI

Architecture of PSI Proteins

A cyanobacterial PSI monomer consists of 11–12 protein subunits, whereas the
plant and algal PSI complexes contain 3 additional proteins. Of these, only PsaA,
PsaB, and PsaC bind the cofactors of the electron transfer system. PsaA
and PsaB form the core complex around which other subunits are organized. The
PsaC, PsaD, PsaH, and PsaE proteins form the stromal peripheral domain that
contains the terminal electron donors and the ferredoxin-docking site. PsaN of

plant and algal PSI is a lumenal peripheral protein. PsaN and the large lumenal domain of PsaF form the plastocyanin docking site of plant and algal PSI. The remaining proteins of PSI are integral membrane proteins with 1–3 transmembrane helices (Table 1). The crystal structure of cyanobacterial PSI contains an additional protein that was not reported in the earlier biochemical studies (26). This protein contains one transmembrane helix and does not have substantial extramembrane segments. It is not known if this additional protein is present in other cyanobacteria or in eukaryotes.

The PsaA and PsaB proteins of the PSI core are homologous in their primary sequences and transmembrane topography. They contain 11 transmembrane helices each with their N termini in the stroma. Two domains in these proteins can be defined based on evolutionary and functional considerations. The C-terminal domains of PsaA and PsaB contain five transmembrane helices each and contain residues whose side chains provide coordinating groups for the redox centers. Interactions among the helices in the C-terminal domains of PsaA and PsaB are primarily responsible for forming the heterodimer. The tilted ten transmembrane helices, along with four parallel helices of the C-terminal domain, make a cage for coordination and protection of the electron transfer chain. The overall architecture of this domain resembles that of the reaction centers of photosynthetic bacteria. The N-terminal domain contains the remaining six transmembrane helices, which resemble the transmembrane topology of the CP43 and CP47 proteins of PSII. These helices, along with the transmembrane segments of other PSI proteins, coordinate the chlorophyll molecules of the internal antenna of PSI.

Functions of PSI Proteins

Resolution-reconstitution biochemistry and molecular genetics in cyanobacteria, *Chlamydomonas reinhardtii*, and *Arabidopsis thaliana* have been instrumental in identifying the functions of PSI proteins (Table 1). The protein subunits of PSI play many roles in the function and organization of the PSI complex. First, they bind organic and inorganic cofactors and orient them optimally for light-harvesting and electron transfer. PsaA and PsaB proteins bind most chlorophyll, all carotenoids, both phylloquinone molecules, and the F_X Fe-S cluster. The PsaC protein binds the remaining two [4Fe-4S] clusters. Many small hydrophobic proteins bind 1–3 chlorophyll a molecules. The proteins influence cofactor properties by providing metal ligands, H-bonds, pi interactions, or hydrophobic pockets (26).

Another major function of PSI proteins is to provide binding surfaces for the proteins that associate with PSI. Specific basic residues in PsaD and PsaE are involved in the binding of ferredoxin (3, 83). PsaH may also contribute to the interactions between PSI and ferredoxin (98). The N-terminal lumenal domain of PsaF in the algal and plant PSI provide electrostatic interactions for the binding of plastocyanin (53). A similar role is played by PsaN (37). These docking functions are discussed later. The PsaK protein is involved in interaction with the light-harvesting complexes (LHC) (57, 58). The PsaK protein can be cross-linked

TABLE 1 Polypeptide subunits of PSI

Subunits	Predicted mass[a]	Cofactors	Structural features	Cyanobacterial mutants[b]	Plant or algal mutants[b]
PsaA and PsaB	83.0 and 82.4	85 chlorophyll a, 22 β carotenes, 2 phylloquinones, 1 [4Fe-4S] cluster (F_X)	11 transmembrane α-helices each	No PSI in *Synechocystis* mutants	No PSI in the *C. reinhardtii* mutants
PsaC	8.9	2[4Fe-4S] clusters (F_A, F_B)	Peripheral on stromal side	*Synechocystis* and *Anabaena* mutants contain PSI core, but lack terminal electron donors and the PsaD and PsaE proteins	*C. reinhardtii* mutants lack assembled PSI complexes
PsaD	15.6	None	Peripheral on stromal side	Ferredoxin or flavodoxin reduction decreased or absent in *Synechocystis* mutants	Not reported
PsaE	8.0	None	Peripheral on stromal side	Ferredoxin or flavodoxin reduction decreased in *Synechocystis* mutants	Transposon-tagged mutant of Arabidopsis shows decreased PsaD and PsaC and increased light-sensitivity (129)
PsaF	15.7		Two transmembrane α-helices	No effect on photosynthesis in *Synechocystis*, *Synechococcus* 7002, or *Synechococcus elongatus* mutants	Both *C. reinhardtii* mutants and Arabidopsis cosuppression plants have different kinetics of plastocyanin-mediated P700 reduction
PsaI	4.3		One transmembrane α-helix	PsaL assembly and trimer formation altered in the *Synechocystis* and *Synechococcus* mutants	

	Mass	Chlorophyll	Structure		
PsaJ	4.4	3 Chlorophyll a	One transmembrane α-helix	PsaF assembly and organization affected in the mutants	PsaF assembly and function (P700 rereduction kinetics) affected in the C. reinhardtii mutants (24)
PsaK/K2	8.5/13.7	2 Chlorophyll a	Two transmembrane α-helices	No effect on PSI activity when PsaK 1 (97) or PsaK2 or both genes inactivated in Synechocystis	Interaction with LHC I affected in the Arabidopsis plants with no PsaK (58)
PsaL	16.6	3 Chlorophyll a	Two transmembrane α-helices	No PSI trimers in Synechocystis or Synechococcus mutants	Interaction with LHC I?
PsaM	3.4	1 Chlorophyll a	One transmembrane α-helix	Less trimer formation in the PsaM-less mutants of Synechocystis	Not detected
PsaU	3.0	1 Chlorophyll a	One transmembrane α-helix	Detected in the crystal structure	Not detected
PsaN	9	None	Peripheral on the lumenal side	Not detected	The interaction between plastocyanin and PSI is inefficient in transgenic Arabidopsis plants lacking PsaN(37)
PsaG	11	Chlorophyll?	2 transmembrane helices	Not detected	Not yet reported
PsaH	10	None	Peripheral on the stromal side	Not detected	Electron transfer efficiency and stability of PSI is affected upon cosuppression of psaH in Arabidopsis (98)

[a]Mass predicted from Synechocystis genes. PsaH, PsaG, and PsaN masses predicted from the Arabidopsis genes.
[b]For original references not included in the table, see (77).

chemically to the LHCI apoproteins (57). The PsaK-less Arabidopsis plants have less capacity to utilize light energy and perform state 1–state 2 transition (58). The PsaK-less transgenic plants contain reduced levels of Lhca2 and Lhca3 proteins, which are the apoproteins of LHCI-680. Thus, PsaK may mediate the association of LHCI-680 with the core antenna of PSI. In Arabidopsis plants with reduced PsaF levels, LHCI-730 is unable to transfer energy to the P700 reaction center (38). Therefore, PsaF is involved in transferring excitation energy from LHCI-730. Cyanobacteria also contain the PsaK and PsaF proteins, but they do not contain membrane-bound LHCI. The functions of cyanobacterial PsaK and PsaF proteins remain elusive. The cyanobacterial mutants that lack PsaK or PsaF have a normal phenotype (36, 96, 142). In the PsaH-less *Arabidopsis plant*, LHCII cannot transfer energy to the PSI, and state transitions are impaired (74a). Therefore, PsaH is involved in interaction with LHCII.

Some PSI proteins assist other PSI proteins to assemble properly and mediate supramolecular organization of PSI. Cyanobacterial PSI complexes can exist as monomers or trimers. The PsaL protein in cyanobacterial PSI is required for the trimerization of PSI (18, 109). However, the PSI complexes of plants and algae are not known to form trimers. The PsaL protein in these organisms may be involved in association with LHCI complexes or in interaction with other integral factors. PsaI, PsaJ, and PsaM are small hydrophobic proteins of PSI and contain one transmembrane helix each. These proteins may be involved in the stabilization of other transmembrane helices (17).

The PSI proteins also play a significant, passive role in the protection of redox centers in PSI. For example, the PSI in the cyanobacterial PsaD-less mutants contain damaged terminal redox centers (15). When both PsaD and PsaE are absent, the PSI complexes are inactivated and degraded more rapidly than in the wild type. Similarly, the lack of PsaF and PsaE make the A_1 centers accessible to the solvent (143). The electron transfer chain of PSI is located at the center of the complex and is wrapped by proteins on the membrane and aqueous phases, thereby protecting the highly reactive, low-potential redox centers.

PSI COFACTORS

PSI contains several organic and inorganic cofactors (Table 2). Chlorophyll *a* is the most abundant cofactor in PSI. The roles of these molecules in light absorption, charge separation, electron transfer, and biogenesis are described later. Chemical analysis of the pigments in the PSI complexes has revealed the presence of chlorophyll *a'* in the complexes (135). The high-resolution structure of PSI shows that one member of the P700 special pair is a chlorophyll *a'* molecule, indicating the functional importance of this modification. The mechanism of epimerization and the significance of the presence of a chlorophyll heterodimer in P700 are not known.

Carotenoids are essential photoprotective and light-harvesting pigments in the photosynthetic complexes. Cyanobacterial PSI complexes contain 22 molecules

TABLE 2   Cofactors in PSI

Cofactor	Number/complex	Function
Chlorophyll a	95	Light harvesting, excitation transfer, and electron transfer
Chlorophyll a'	1	A constituent of the P700 chlorophyll pair
β carotenes	22	Light harvesting and photoprotection
Phylloquinones	2	Intermediate electron transfer centers
Iron-sulfur clusters	3	Electron transfer centers
Ca^{2+}	1	Stabilization of PSI trimers?
Lipids	4	Function not known

of β-carotene molecules, 17 of which are in all-*trans* configuration (26). The PSI complex of cyanobacteria and chloroplasts contains two phylloquinone molecules, which function in the electron transfer as the redox center A_1. The biosynthetic pathway for phylloquinones has been inferred from the menaquinone biosynthetic pathway, and cyanobacterial homologues of the *menA*, *menB*, *menD*, and *menE* genes have been inactivated to generate mutant strains that lack phylloquinone (61, 62). The phylloquinone-less PSI complexes contain plastoquinone in the A_1 site (62, 150) but can sustain high rates of electron transfer from cytochrome c_6 to flavodoxin (62).

A PSI complex contains 12 iron atoms that constitute 3 [4Fe-4S] clusters (F_X, F_A, and F_B). Four lipid molecules can be assigned unambiguously in the high-resolution structure of PSI. Three of these molecules are phosphatidylglycerol and one is monogalactosyldiacylglycerol. These molecules are embedded in the PSI complex, with the acyl chains anchored among transmembrane helices. The phosphodiester group of one of the phospholipids coordinates an antenna chlorophyll molecule. The functions of the other lipid cofactors of PSI are not known. The high-resolution structure also reveals the presence of a divalent cation, which is tentatively identified as a calcium ion. Calcium regulates trimerization of PSI in some cyanobacteria. The PsaL protein in *Synechocystis* sp. PCC 6803 binds calcium, which in turn may regulate the formation of PSI trimers (VP Chitnis, J Kruip, & PR Chitnis, unpublished results).

PATHWAYS FOR ENERGY AND ELECTRON TRANSFER

Light is absorbed by the chlorophyll molecules of the LHCI and the core antenna. When the photons are absorbed by one of the antenna chlorophyll molecules, the excitation energy is delocalized over the antenna chlorophyll molecules and funneled to the P700 reaction center chlorophyll dimer through distinct groups of antenna chlorophyll molecules (11). Figure 1 describes a proposed pathway

LHC I - 680

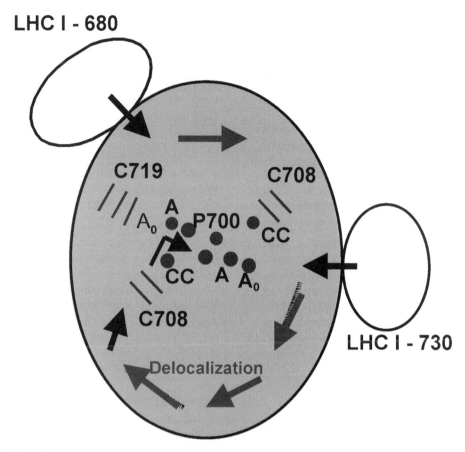

Figure 1   A model for the excitation energy transfer in PS I. The positions of LHC I–730 and LHC I–680 are based on their interactions with PsaF and PsaK, respectively, in plant PSI complexes. The chlorophyll dimers and trimers that are observed in the cyanobacterial PSI are proposed to be the C708 and C719 red chlorophylls, respectively. CC refers to the connecting chlorophylls believed to mediate photon transfer from the red chlorophylls to the chlorophylls of the electron transfer chain. The broken arrows represent the excitation delocalization among antenna chlorophyll *a* molecules.

for excitation energy transfer. The absorption spectrum of the PSI complexes is broad, representing different groups of antenna chlorophyll molecules that can be defined from their spectroscopic characteristics (Figure 1). In the 4 Å structure of PSI (110), antenna chlorophylls occupy a hollow elliptical cylinder that narrows slightly toward the lumenal side. Each antenna chlorophyll molecule has at least one neighboring chlorophyll molecule within a center-to-center distance of 7–16 Å (70). The bulk internal antenna exhibits nearly C_2 symmetry, with pigments grouped into four clusters. Whether any correspondences exist between these clusters and the spectral pools that are identified by deconvolution of the PSI absorption spectrum or by ultrafast spectroscopy is still unknown.

The components of electron transfer pathway in PSI (Figure 2) were identified from spectroscopic analyses of PSI complexes from plants and cyanobacteria (11). The P700, A_0, A_1, F_X, F_A, and F_B centers have distinct spectroscopic signatures in their reduced and oxidized states. These redox centers are arranged in a chain that spans the PSI complex from the lumenal to the stromal side. The edge-to-edge distance between two neighboring redox centers is kept around 10 Å to ensure efficiency of electron transfer.

The structure of PSI based on X-ray crystallography has revealed several unexpected features, which were not previously detected by spectroscopy (70). First, similar to the bacterial reaction centers, there are accessory chlorophyll molecules (termed A) between P700 and A_0. In the structure of PSI, there are four chlorophyll molecules arranged in twofold symmetrical positions between the P700 chlorophyll pair and the F_X Fe-S cluster (70, 110). A pair of chlorophyll a molecules is positioned 16 Å from P700. By an analogy to the positions of bacteriopheophytins in the photoreaction center of the purple bacteria, investigators assume that at least one of them is equivalent to the spectroscopically characterized primary acceptor A_0. Another pair of chlorophyll a monomers is located approximately halfway between P700 and the A_0 equivalent chlorophyll molecules. They are assigned as accessory chlorophylls, which may participate in exciton transfer or electron transfer, or both.

Second, the mode in which the chlorophyll molecules of the bulk antenna may communicate with the reaction center chlorophyll molecules was revealed by the structure. Each monomeric PSI unit shows an approximate C_2 axis that passes between three pairs of rotationally equivalent chlorophyll a pigments. An additional symmetry-related pair of chlorophyll molecules is located near the core antenna/reaction center boundary, and it appears to be positioned to relay excitation from the relatively distant bulk antenna to the reaction center. However, these connecting chlorophyll molecules are proximate to the electron transfer chain pigments, rather than to the presumed special pair. This suggests that the antenna to the P700 trapping mechanism may follow an indirect pathway through the connecting, accessory, and A_0 chlorophyll molecules. Thus, the A_0 and A may have an unprecedented dual function in both excitation transfer to P700 and electron transfer from P700.

Last, a PSI complex contains two symmetrical electron transfer paths between P700 and F_X. There are two sets of chlorophyll and phylloquinone molecules that are present at approximately symmetrical locations. The bacterial reaction centers contain a similar arrangement of redox centers. Therefore, the arrangement of the electron transfer pathways is conserved in the Fe-S–type reaction centers (e.g. PSI) and quinone-type of reaction centers (e.g. PSII and bacterial reaction center). In the quinone-type reaction centers, only one of the two branches is active (45). This makes functional sense as the two terminal quinones in these centers are not functionally equivalent. In contrast, the electrons in PSI proceed from the quinones to the F_X Fe-S cluster. Therefore, there is no significant functional advantage in using either one or two branches of electron transfer between P700 and F_X.

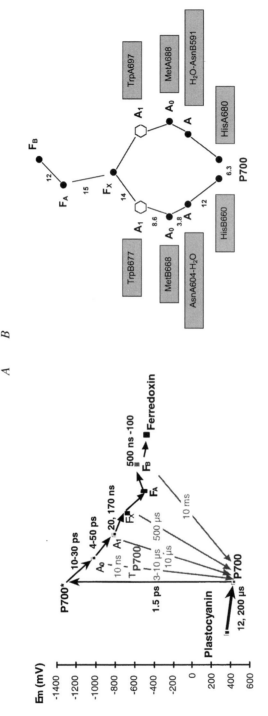

Figure 2 Electron transfer pathway in PSI. (*A*) Electron carriers are arranged according to the sequence of electron flow on the scale of midpoint redox potentials (Em). Typical lifetimes for the forward- and back-reactions are indicated. (*B*) The arrangement of electron transfer centers in the PSI structure and distances (in Å) among different centers are shown. The cofactors are identified as P700, the primary donor; A_0, the chlorophyll a molecules that could serve as the primary acceptor; A, the accessory chlorophylls; A_1, two phylloquinones; and F_X, F_A, and F_B, the three iron-sulfur clusters [Based on (110)]. The residues that provide Mg-ligands to chlorophyll and π interactions to phylloquinones are shown (numbers according to S. *elongatus* proteins).

Are both branches of electron transfer active in a PSI complex? There is some contradictory evidence regarding the ability of these pathways to function in electron transfer. In determining how many and which of these two branches are active, many efforts have concentrated on examining the redox changes in A_1. An EPR signal due to an A_1^- semiquinone radical can be photoaccumulated under reducing conditions that reduce Fe-S clusters. Analysis of this signal indicates that it has originated from one phylloquinone molecule (6). Three alternative scenarios can produce this result: (*a*) Only one phylloquinone could function as A_1, (*b*) two phylloquinones may have indistinguishable properties, or (*c*) only one phylloquinone can be detected with EPR in photoaccumulation experiments. Subunit-deficient mutants of *Synechococcus* 7002 have been used to address this question (143). The PsaE- and PsaF-less PSI particles that had been prepared with Triton-X100 show an altered photoaccumulated A_1 signal. PsaE and PsaF are located on the outside surface of PSI trimers where the phylloquinone bound to PsaA is located (143). Therefore, the EPR-visible A_1 signal is produced by the phylloquinone in the PsaA branch. However, these results do not provide unequivocal proof that the other branch is not active. A more direct approach is to create site-specific mutants in the phylloquinone-binding sites of both PsaA and PsaB and then to study their effects on A_1. Site-directed mutants have been obtained in *Synechocystis* and *C. reinhardtii*. Many mutations in *psaA* as well as in *psaB* influence photosynthetic phenotypes and spectroscopic characteristics of A_1 (PR Chitnis & JH Golbeck, unpublished results; AN Webber, personal communication; K Redding, personal communication). Therefore, both quinones may be actively engaged in electron transfer. Alternatively, only one quinone is active in the wild-type PSI complexes, but mutations allow electron transport through the branch that is inactive in the wild-type PSI complexes.

Recently, evidence has been accumulating in support of a scenario in which both branches of PSI are engaged actively in electron transfer. Photoaccumulated Fourier transform infrared (FTIR) difference spectra with $P700^+$ and $P700^+A_1^-$ have been obtained using *Synechocystis* PSI complexes (G Hastings, personal communication). Interpretation of the $A_1^- -A_1$ difference spectrum is consistent with the reduction of both quinones in PSI. In algal cells, an absorption decrease at 377 nm reflects the oxidation of A_1^-, which occurs with a two-phase kinetics of about equal amplitude with halftimes of $\sim$18 and $\sim$160 ns (63). The existence of two phases could be a result of the heterogeneity in the PSI complexes in vivo. Alternatively, these results indicate that both branches of PSI are active, but they are not identical in their electron transport rates. To distinguish between these two possibilities, site-directed mutants were generated in the A_1 pockets of the PsaA and PsaB proteins of *C. reinhardtii*. The PsaA mutations increase the halftime of the slow phase, whereas the PsaB mutations decrease the fast phase (35). A double mutant slows down both phases. These results indicate that both branches of electron transfer are active in PSI, but they are not identical. The differences in the two branches could result from different environments in the phylloquinone-binding sites of PsaA and PsaB. The amino acids lining the A_1 site are conserved highly in the two proteins, with the exception of a tryptophenyl residue that is present only in the PsaB-side A_1 pocket. Another variation is the dissimilar orientation of the carotenoids that are present near the phylloquinones on both sides. In addition, different lipid molecules are present near phylloquinones. Long-range effects of the amino acid sidechains can also influence the properties of the binding sites.

EXCITATION ENERGY TRANSFER

The core complexes of PSI contain 90 chlorophyll a molecules for harvesting photons. Seventy-nine of these chlorophylls are coordinated by the PsaA-PsaB heterodimer, which also binds to the redox centers. This hard-wired antenna is unique to PSI and other Fe-S–type reaction centers. In PSII and purple bacterial reaction centers, different proteins bind reaction center and antenna pigments. In addition to the internal antenna, the PSI complex of plants and algae can also associate with the membrane-bound light-harvesting complexes (LHC) that contain both chlorophyll a and b molecules.

Light-harvesting Complexes

LHCI complexes contain four chlorophyll a/b binding proteins, Lhca1, Lhca2, Lhca3, and Lhca4, with molecular masses of 21–24 kDa [for excellent reviews on LHC, see (32, 33, 55, 85, 100, 116)]. LHCI complexes contain 80–120 chlorophyll a and chlorophyll b molecules per PSI reaction center, with a chlorophyll $a : b$ ratio of ~3.5. Two types of LHCI complexes have been isolated from higher plants. LHCI-680 and LHCI-730 have characteristic composition and spectral properties (116). Lhca2 and Lhca3 form homodimers that make subpopulations of LHCI-680. In contrast, LHCI-730 is composed of heterodimers of Lhca1 and Lhca4 (32). The overall architecture of LHCI may be similar to the major light-harvesting complex of PSII, the structure of which is known at 3.4 Å (71).

LHCI-730 is responsible for most of the characteristic low-temperature fluorescence emission at 735–740 nm, when measured in leaves or in membranes (68). This is a remarkable property; LHCI-730 has chlorophyll molecules with significantly lower energy levels than the absorption maximum of the PSI reaction center. Ultrafast pump-probe experiments have revealed that a 200–400 fs depolarization lifetime exists for native bulk LHCI (88). This lifetime may indicate fast hopping of excitons among chlorophyll molecules. Two energy transfer processes with 30 ps and 200 ps lifetimes exist in isolated LHCI-730 complexes. The 30–50 ps phase is caused by the intersubunit energy distribution from Lhca1 to Lhca4 within a heterodimer (89).

Internal Antenna of PSI

The excited state dynamics of different PSI complexes can be considered in distinct steps that involve spectrally and structurally separate groups of pigments

(Figure 1). The number and peak wavelengths of the spectral pools vary with species and/or preparation. The core antenna in *Synechocystis* contains most pigments absorbing below 700 nm and one chlorophyll species absorbing at 708 nm (C708) (107). These red chlorophylls bind to the PsaA-PsaB core (122). In contrast, the PSI complexes of *Synechococcus elongatus* contain two spectral pools of red chlorophylls (C-708 and C-719) (12). Simulations of temperature-dependent antenna chlorophyll fluorescence decays suggest that the bulk of the chlorophyll spectral forms are randomly distributed about the reaction center. In contrast, the red chlorophyll molecules are adjacent to the reaction center and geometrically serve to focus excitation toward the center (59, 79, 122). Structure-based modeling in PSI of *S. elongatus* indicates that the red antenna pigments, C720, are preferentially located at the periphery of the PSI core complex, whereas the A708 must connect the A719 to the reaction center. The crystal structure of PSI shows three dimers and a trimer of chlorophyll *a* molecules. These coupled chlorophyll molecules might function as red chlorophyll molecules. The chlorophyll dimers that are close to the connecting chlorophyll molecules may be the C708 chlorophyll *a* molecules. In contrast, the trimer and a dimer are close to the outer edge of the complex; and thus, one of them may represent the C719 species of chlorophylls in PSI.

Ultrafast spectroscopic studies on core complexes from cyanobacterial, green algal, and plant species suggest that subpicosecond spectral equilibration occurs among spectral pools for the bulk of the antenna pigments (40). Slower downhill transfers (3.7–7.5 ps) then occur from the bulk to red pigments. This is followed by trapping of the excitation energy at the reaction center with a 19–24 ps lifetime (23, 40, 41). At room temperature, an analysis of the wavelength dependence of P700 oxidation indicates that all absorbed light, even of wavelengths of up to 750 nm, has the same probability of resulting in a stable P700 photooxidation (99).

ELECTRON TRANSFER PATHWAY IN PSI

P700: The Reaction Center of PSI

The electron transfer process in PSI begins with the charge separation at the primary electron donor P700, which exhibits a characteristic bleaching at $\sim$430 nm and $\sim$700 nm after photochemical oxidation (hence, P700). Like other reaction centers of photosynthetic complexes, P700 provides an efficient sink for the excitonic light energy and converts it to redox equivalents with a near-unity quantum yield. P700 is a chlorophyll dimer with tetrapyrrole rings oriented perpendicular to the thylakoid membranes (105). The high-resolution structure of PSI also shows that two chlorophyll molecules in the P700 dimer are chemically different (26). One is chlorophyll *a* whereas the other is chlorophyll *a'*, the $C13^2$-epimer of chlorophyll *a*.

Many structural factors can make the P700 chlorophyll pair special compared to other chlorophyll molecules. First, they are centrally located in the PSI reaction center, oriented parallel to each other, and perpendicular to the lipid plane (9, 70). Second, the distance between the chlorophyll molecules is relatively short, thus the excitonic coupling (70). Last, the unique protein environment influences the spectral and redox properties of the P700 chlorophyll pair. The Mg^{2+} of P700 chlorophyll molecules is coordinated by specific histidyl residues (75). In addition, some residues of the PsaA protein interact with the P700 chlorophyll molecules through H-bonds (26). Site-directed mutagenesis has demonstrated the function of the histidyl residue (656 in PsaB of *C. reinhardtii*) that interacts closely with one of the P700 chlorophylls (102, 137). Mutation of His-656 to Asn or Ser increases the oxidation midpoint potential of $P700/P700^+$ by 40 mV (69, 137). Thus, axial ligands have significant influence on the redox properties of the reaction center.

Because of the unique functional properties of P700, the electronic structure of $P700^+$ and the localization of the triplet state have been extensively investigated. Analysis of P700 by vibrational spectroscopy has led to the suggestion that the unpaired electron in a P700 radical is delocalized over both halves of the dimer, with a 1:1 to 2:1 ratio (10). In contrast, ENDOR and ESEEM experiments show that spin distribution on P700 is asymmetrically distributed, ranging from 3:1 to 10:1 (64, 103) and even to complete localization on a single chlorophyll *a* (75). Site-directed mutations in the axial ligands of the dimer have shown that the electronic spin of $P700^+$ and the triplet state are localized mainly on the PsaB-side chlorophyll *a* molecule (69). Structural basis for asymmetry may lie in the differences in the chlorophyll identity (*a* and *a'*) and protein interactions (H-bonds only on PsaA side). The functional consequences of the asymmetry in P700 are not understood clearly.

The early electron transfer events in PSI are difficult to delineate, because selective excitation of P700 reaction center pigments is not possible and selective monitoring of P700 or A_0 is difficult. Under the assumption that the antenna excitation transfer and trapping kinetics are independent of the P700 oxidation state, the open (P700)-closed ($P700^+$) difference profile can depict the reaction center kinetics (40–42, 65, 106). For PSI complexes from cyanobacteria, green algae, and higher plants, the open-closed difference profiles can be interpreted as an equilibration process(es) with a 3.7–7.5 ps lifetime, followed by a 19–24 ps process that is associated with the trapping of excitation energy in P700 (40). The antenna chlorophyll molecules absorb the photons and the excitation energy is transferred to the P700 chlorophyll dimer, where it is trapped primarily because of the low energy status and excitonic coupling of the chlorophyll molecules. The excited P700 ($P700^*$) donates an electron to the primary acceptor, undergoing charge separation (P700 $A_0 \rightarrow P700^+ A_0^-$). Overall, one can conclude that the excited P700 donates an electron to A_0 with a time constant of about 1–2 ps, when the excitation resides on P700 (41, 54, 72, 138). In ultrafast experiments, the major antenna decay component has a lifetime of $\sim$30 ps, which is much longer than the charge separation time (1–2 ps). To explain this delay between exciton transfer to P700 and charge separation, various models with limitations that range from nearly diffusion-limited to essentially trap-limited scenarios have been proposed. Recent fluorescence induction experiments combined with picosecond time-resolved fluorescence measurements show that the excitation energy is not completely thermally equilibrated over the core PSI complex of *S. elongatus* before being trapped (12). Therefore, the excited-state decay kinetics in PSI may be neither purely trap-limited nor purely transfer (to the trap)-limited; instead, they seem to be somewhat balanced.

Early Acceptors in Electron Transfer

Upon the transfer of an electron from the excited P700, the primary acceptor A_0 is reduced to an anion form. At physiological temperature, the accumulated A_0^- can be seen in light as bleaching at 692, 412, and 438 nm (133). A_1, an intermediate redox center in PSI, oxidizes A_0^-. A_0 is a chlorophyll a monomer and A_1 is a phylloquinone (vitamin K1) molecule (11). The axial ligands of the chlorophyll molecules that are assumed to be A_0 in the PSI structure are unusual; they are provided by the sulfur atoms of methionine residues in PsaA and PsaB (26). In addition, the keto oxygens of rings V of these chlorophyll molecules form H-bonds with the hydroxyl groups of Tyr in PsaA and PsaB. Substitution of one of these Tyr residues with Phe influences spectral and kinetic properties of A_0 (X Wu, S Saviknin, W Struve, & PR Chitnis, unpublished results), confirming the assignment of A_0 in the crystal structure (26).

Direct measurements of the E_m of A_1 are lacking, but indirect estimations have given a value of -755 to -785 mV for A_1^-/A_1 (56, 111). E_m of phylloquinone in dimethyl formamide is only approximately -465 mV versus normal hydrogen electrode (56). Therefore, protein interactions lower the E_m by 300 mV. When the A_1 sites in PSI of the phylloquinone-less mutants of *Synechocystis* are occupied by plastoquinone, the redox potential is estimated to be between -580 to -663 (111). Thus, in the phylloquinone-less cells, plastoquinone is functioning at three different redox potentials (-130 mV in Q_A site of PSII, -40 mV in Q_B of PSII, and -630 mV in A_1). The redox potential of plastoquinone in dimethylformamide is -369 mV versus normal hydrogen electrode. This is a dramatic example of how the protein environment determines the redox properties of cofactors. The A_1 site reduces the redox potential of a quinone (phylloquinone or plastoquinone) by ~300 mV. The structural basis for the altered redox potential of A_1 is not known. The phylloquinone-binding A_1 pockets in PsaA and PsaB show many common structural features. Consistent with the EPR results (76, 126), the crystal structure of PSI shows that a conserved Trp in each pocket lies parallel to the phylloquinone rings, forming strong pi interactions. In both phylloquinones of PSI, only one of the two carbonyl oxygens forms H-bonds with the amide group in the peptide backbone of the protein (26). The presence of only one H-bond is remarkable compared to quinones in other systems and may contribute to the very low redox potential of quinones in PSI. Another possible cause of low redox potential of A_1 could be the electrostatic fields in and around the A_1 sites. The charged residues and lipid molecules near the A_1 sites may also be critical determinants of long-range electrostatic interactions near the A_1 site.

Kinetics of electron transfer from A_0 to A_1 to F_X have been studied using high-resolution spectroscopy and resolution biochemistry. The rate constant for the electron transfer from A_0 to A_1 has been estimated to be 20–35 ps (11).

However, this number may represent an overestimate, and the rate constant for A_0 to A_1 electron transfer could be as fast as ~5 ps, which would be consistent with the distance between these redox centers (W Struve, personal communication). Forward electron transfer at room temperature from A_1 to F_X can be studied using transient EPR spectroscopy and time-resolved UV spectroscopy. This step of electron transfer takes place with a lifetime of ~280 ns in spinach and cyanobacterial PSI complexes (11).

Electron Transfer Involving Fe-S Clusters

PSI contains three Fe-S clusters, which have been studied extensively using EPR techniques. The EPR signal from the reduced F_X has characteristic g-values of 2.04, 1.88, and 1.78. This signal is highly temperature sensitive, only detectable at cryogenic temperatures. F_X is identified clearly in the crystal structure because of its high electron density. It is located near the stromal surface at the edge of the membrane plane (70, 110). The central position of F_X coincides with the twofold axis. F_X is a [4Fe-4S] cluster ligated by two cysteinyl residues, each from PsaA and PsaB. Site-directed conversion of Cys556 or Cys565 to serine in *Synechocystis* PsaB results in the assembly of [3Fe-4S] and [4Fe-4S] clusters in F_X. The mixed-ligand [4Fe-4S] cluster in this mutant can transfer electrons to the Fe-S clusters in PsaC (134), but overall quantum efficiency of electron transfer is decreased (130).

The F_A and F_B centers of PSI are two [4Fe-4S] clusters that are bound to the PsaC protein. The F_A and F_B clusters have characteristically low-temperature EPR spectra, with g-values of 2.05, 1.94, and 1.86 for the reduced F_A and 2.05, 1.92, and 1.89 for the reduced F_B. The electron is transferred from F_X to one of the [4Fe-4S] clusters of PsaC; and within 100 μs, both F_A and F_B clusters are partially reduced at room temperature because of fast electron exchange between the two clusters (5). F_A and F_B clusters are liganded by eight of the nine conserved Cys residues in PsaC. The F_A cluster is ligated by the cysteinyl residues Cys21, Cys48, Cys51, and Cys54, whereas the cysteinyl residues Cys11, Cys14, Cys17, and Cys58 provide ligands to the F_B cluster (149). The ninth cysteine Cys34 does not participate in ligating either F_A or F_B. It is now generally accepted that electrons flow from F_X to F_A to F_B to ferredoxin (31). This sequence of redox centers means that the electron transfer involves a small uphill electron transfer from F_A to F_B (Figure 2). Because the electron transfer in PSI depends on a large negative free-energy change, the small uphill transfer is believed to be inconsequential for the overall electron transport in PSI.

ELECTRON TRANSFER TO AND FROM PSI

P700 Reduction by Plastocyanin

On the lumenal side of thylakoid membranes, PSI accepts electrons from plastocyanin (Figure 3). In cyanobacteria and algae, cytochrome c_6 can serve as an alternate electron donor to the P700 reaction center. The electron transfer

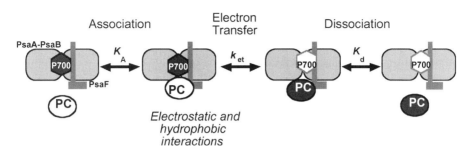

Figure 3 Interaction between PSI and plastocyanin. The steps are based on the electron transfer kinetics. Only PsaA, PsaB, and PsaF are included in the figure. Other PSI proteins, with the exception of PsaN, are not known to interact with plastocyanin.

from algal or plant donors to P700 takes place with a two- or three-step kinetic mechanism that involves complex formation, reorientation, and electron transfer (Figure 3) (22, 48, 81). In contrast, cytochrome c_6 and plastocyanin oxidation by the *Synechocystis* PSI complexes show the absence of the fast reduction phase, suggesting an apparent one-step bimolecular collision mechanism (142). The structural basis for these different electron transfer mechanisms relies on the presence of appropriate docking residues in the PsaF protein of PSI. The PsaF-less PSI of a *C. reinhardtii* mutant is defective in the fast phase of electron transfer to $P700^+$ (51). In contrast, the PsaF-deficient mutant strains of *Synechocystis* sp. PCC 6803 do not show any defect in their photoautotrophic growth, cytochrome c_6-dependent $NADP^+$ photoreduction, or $P700^+$ rereduction kinetics (16, 141, 142). Plastocyanin can be cross-linked to the N-terminal lysine-rich region of chloroplast PsaF (53), which is not found in the cyanobacterial PsaF. When four Lys residues in the N-terminal domain of PsaF were mutated to uncharged residues, the mutant PSI complexes showed different effects on the electron transfer rate constants and dissociation constants, suggesting the existence of a precise recognition site for electrostatic interactions (52). The lack of a basic N-terminal domain in the cyanobacterial PsaF protein is one of the factors responsible for the absence of a fast phase in $P700^+$ reduction in some cyanobacteria.

The PsaN subunit of PSI is present in the lumen of chloroplast thylakoids. Removal of spinach PsaN with salt washing does not influence steady-state electron transfer activity of PSI (43). Transgenic Arabidopsis plants that lack detectable levels of PsaN are capable of photoautotrophic growth and contain assembled and functional PSI complexes (37). The second-order rate constant for electron transfer from plastocyanin to P700 and steady-state $NADP^+$ reduction are decreased by ~50%. Therefore, this protein may play a plastocyanin-docking role similar to the lumenal domain of PsaF.

In addition to the electrostatic interactions with the lumenal domain of PsaF, and possibly with PsaN, plastocyanin interacts with the core proteins of PSI. Two α-helices lie parallel to the membrane plane near the P700 chlorophyll dimer. Site-directed mutations in the hydrophobic surface of the parallel helix of PsaB influence the interaction between plastocyanin and PSI, showing that the parallel lumenal helices provide a hydrophobic region for interaction with the hydrophobic surface of plastocyanin (123). Thus, the recognition between PSI and plastocyanin includes initial electrostatic interactions between the N-terminal domain of PsaF and the conserved negative patches of plastocyanin, followed by accurate docking of plastocyanin through hydrophobic interaction with the PSI core proteins.

Ferredoxin Reduction by PSI

Ferredoxin, a soluble protein with one [2Fe-2S] cluster, accepts electrons from the F_B cluster on the stromal side of the PSI complex (Figure 4). When grown under iron-depleted conditions, cyanobacteria synthesize flavodoxin that functionally replaces ferredoxin in most, but not all, reactions (91). The electron transfer involves three different first-order components with $t_{1/2}$ of ~500 ns, 13–20 μs, and 100–123 μs (112, 113). The 500-ns phase corresponds to electron transfer from F_A/F_B to ferredoxin. Based on kinetic arguments, it has been proposed that the PsaE-dependent transient ternary complex that contains PSI, ferredoxin, and ferredoxin-NADP$^+$ oxidoreductase is formed during linear electron transport (127).

The interactions between PSI and ferredoxin are electrostatic in nature. Spectroscopic study of ferredoxin reduction by PSI suggests that complex formation precedes electron transfer, and the rate constants for complex formation depend on ionic concentration, especially Mg^{2+} (47, 112). Based on chemical cross-linking and mutational analysis, researchers now accept that PsaD and PsaE form a docking site for ferredoxin and flavodoxin (77). Several mutagenesis studies have attempted to identify details of the interaction between PSI and ferredoxin (2, 19, 20, 39). The interaction between the PsaE-less PSI complexes and ferredoxin shows an increase in the dissociation constant by two orders of magnitude. The neutral substitution, Arg39, of the PsaE protein of *Synechocystis* leads to only a threefold increase in the association constant but a 250-fold increase of the dissociation

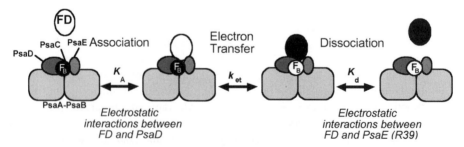

Figure 4   Interaction between PSI and ferredoxin. The steps are based on the electron transfer kinetics. All proteins of PSI are not shown. PsaD is involved in the docking of ferredoxin, whereas the Arg39 residue in PsaE has a critical role in dissociation. PsaH, which is not included in this figure, may also interact with ferredoxin in plants and algae.

constant, K_d, for the PSI-ferredoxin complex. The charge on the sidechain and pH influence the dissociation constant. Therefore, investigators have proposed that a major contribution of PsaE is to provide a prominent positive charge at position 39 that controls the electrostatic interaction and lifetime of the complex with ferredoxin.

In contrast to the phenotype of the PsaE-less PSI, the dissociation constant for the complex between the PsaD-less PSI and ferredoxin at pH 8 is increased 25 times as compared to the wild type (3). The second-order rate constant of ferredoxin reduction is lowered tenfold for PsaD-less PSI. Assuming a simple binding equilibrium between PSI and ferredoxin, PsaD may be important for the guiding of ferredoxin to its binding site (main effect on the association rate) (3). Because single site–directed mutations in the basic residues of PsaD do not alter electron transfer significantly (19, 39), the interaction between PsaD and ferredoxin may contain several alternative components, or an overall electrostatic field may be more important than specific interactions between charged residues.

PsaH, a peripheral protein that is absent in cyanobacteria, may also be involved in an interaction with ferredoxin (57). Arabidopsis plants with reduced PsaH have decreased $NADP^+$ photoreduction activity compared with wild type (98). However, these plants also contain reduced levels of PsaL, which may also contribute to the phenotype. Therefore, additional evidence is needed to demonstrate a direct role for PsaH in the docking of ferredoxin.

Cyclic Electron Transfer

Under most circumstances, electrons through PSI follow a noncyclic path from plastocyanin to ferredoxin and then to reduction of other compounds, including $NADP^+$. However, under some conditions, electrons from PSI are recycled via cytochrome $b_6 f$ complex. This cyclic pathway around PSI is independent of PSII and increases the level of ATP synthesis relative to that of NADPH, thus permitting a cell to adjust the production of these two chemicals according to its need (77). The mechanism that apportions electrons between the cyclic and linear pathways is unknown. In intact cells of *Synechococcus* sp. PCC 7942 grown under different light intensities, the light-saturated capacity for PSI cyclic electron transport increases relative to chlorophyll concentration, PSI concentration, and linear electron transport capacity as growth-light intensity is raised (46). Thus, the physiology of a cell dictates the importance of cyclic electron transport to the energy metabolism. No physiological condition has yet been identified in which cyclic electron flow is absolutely necessary.

Recent experiments with barley thylakoid membranes suggest that there are two parallel pathways of cyclic electron transport under anaerobic conditions (108). These pathways can be distinguished based on their antimycin sensitivity. An antimycin-binding site is associated with PSI, but not in pure PSI preparation (90). The proposed pathways of cyclic electron transfer involve electron shuttling by ferredoxin. The PsaE subunit of PSI has been implicated in cyclic electron flow. Growth and P700 reduction analysis in the PsaE-less mutant of *Synechococcus* sp. PCC 7002 indicate that photoreduction of ferredoxin has been decreased because of reduced cyclic electron flow (147. The PsaE-less mutants are capable of partial ferredoxin reduction activity, but they completely lack cyclic electron transfer. Therefore, PsaE may have a direct and specific role in the cyclic electron transfer rather than influencing cyclic electron transfer by decreasing ferredoxin reduction. The inhibitors of cytochrome $b_6 f$ function also abolish the ferredoxin-catalyzed cyclic electron transfer, indicating involvement of cytochrome $b_6 f$ complex in cyclic electron transfer. Both the NAD(P)H dehydrogenase complex and ferredoxin-NADP oxidoreducatse contribute independently to the quinone cytochrome $b_6 f$ reductase step in PSI-dependent cyclic electron transfer (128).

PHYSIOLOGY AND DYNAMICS OF PSI

In the mid-1990s, two reports by Greenbaum and colleagues questioned the Z-scheme of photosynthetic electron transport and argued that the function of PSI is dispensable for photosynthesis under certain conditions (34, 73). These studies showed that some mutants of the alga *C. reinhardtii* are capable of CO_2 fixation, H_2 photoevolution, and photoautotrophic growth (34, 73). These findings challenged the conventional view of photosynthesis and bioenergetics. Subsequent experiments by other researchers found no evidence for a PS-less strain that can perform photosynthetic CO_2 fixation (7, 21, 101). It is now generally accepted that the authors of the original papers (34, 73) did not detect or acknowledge a significant level of functional PSI complexes in the mutant strains that were used in their work. The maturation of the *psaA* mRNA is defective in these strains, but it does not completely eliminate functional PSI from the cells (101).

Regulation of the Relative Level of PSI

Changes in PSI activity and abundance have far-reaching physiological consequences. The reducing power handled in photosynthesis is a useful commodity, but excess unused reductants can generate harmful radicals. Therefore, it is imperative to adjust the rate of photosynthetic electron transport, depending on the need for the photosynthetic products. The cellular level of PSI is controlled to avoid excessive accumulation of the reductants produced by PSII. Cyanobacterial and algal mutants that lack active PSI cannot grow in continuous light (114, 117, 118, 124). Reduction in PSI activity in site-directed or subunit-deficient mutants of *Synechocystis* (144), *C. reinhardtii* (50, 62), Arabidopsis (129), or maize (44) also leads to a light-sensitive phenotype. Therefore, plants, algae, and cyanobacteria must maintain their photosystems in a proper ratio.

Changes in the environment could affect photosynthetic processes (e.g. light quality or intensity) or chloroplast metabolism (e.g. temperature). Thus, modulation of photosynthetic rates is critical in the adaptation of plants to environmental stress conditions (55, 84, 85). Short-term modulation of photosynthesis involves adjustment of antenna size and the function of PSII. This is a rapid means to funnel light energy toward or away from the reaction centers. In long-term adaptation, plants change a number of photosynthetic complexes and their proportion. Photosystem stoichiometry is modulated by environmental factors. Light intensity and quality are the major environmental factors that influence photosystem stoichiometry (84). In general, the antenna size of PSII is variable in both cyanobacteria and chloroplasts, whereas that of PSI is unchanged under various light conditions (84). Under low-light intensity, the photosystem stoichiometry is optimized based on antenna sizes, whereas high-intensity light requires that the stoichiometry be kept near unity irrespective of the antenna size. Thus, organisms must balance electron flow between two photosystems by modulating both antenna size and photosystem stoichiometry. Chloroplasts typically contain equimolar amounts of active photosystems. This ratio is determined by the growth conditions (e.g. light quality and intensity). The adaptation by changing photosystem stoichiometry is more often seen in young plants than in old ones. The blue photoreceptor in plants may be involved in these processes (132).

Cyanobacteria modulate the PSI to PSII ratio in response to light quality, light intensity, CO_2 availability, and stress conditions (27, 28). When grown under fluorescent light (which is absorbed mainly by phycobilisomes), different cyanobacterial species contain 2–5 times more PSI than PSII (95). *Synechocystis* cells change the PSI to PSII ratio, depending on the light intensity (49). These changes in PSI PSI:PSII stoichiometry are mainly a result of the alteration of the cellular PSI content in cyanobacteria by modulating both synthesis/assembly and degradation rates of the PSI complexes (93, 94). Synthesis or assembly of PSI is accelerated when cells are grown under PSII light, whereas synthesis is suppressed under PSI light (93, 94). PSII synthesis rates do not change under either condition. Similar to cyanobacteria, young pea leaves (28) and *C. reinhardtii* (87) change PSI levels in response to light quality or intensity. Therefore, changes in photosystem stoichiometry involve modulation of PSI levels in the thylakoids.

The signal for modulating PSI levels could be derived from the redox status of the cell or chloroplast. The ratio of ATP and NADPH could signal a change in PSI amounts (84). Another candidate for a signal could be the redox state of an electron transport component between two photosystems (plastoquinone or cytochrome $b_6 f$ complex, or both). The downstream components in this signal transduction mechanism are even more obscure. How the signal is sensed or transduced to the site of action remains to be discovered. What stage of PSI assembly is regulated by the stoichiometry-sensing signal transduction pathway is also unknown. The photosystem ratio may be regulated in the chlorophyll biosynthetic pathway, as chlorophyll *a* is preferentially incorporated in PSII (29).

Inactivation and degradation of PSII under stress conditions has been studied extensively (86). Until recently, researchers generally believed that PSI was not targeted for inactivation by stress factors (13). However, now it is becoming evident that PSI is the primary target for inactivation under some stress conditions. Under chilling conditions, PSI is an early site of damage of photoinhibition in barley (125) and cucumbers (121). The PSI electron acceptor chain is damaged progressively, starting with the terminal electron donors (F_A and F_B) (125). Light-induced PSI damage is also evident from partial degradation of the core proteins of PSI (120).

PSI Biogenesis

The structure and function of PSI is understood in great detail, but our understanding of its biogenesis and regulation is poor. The lifecycle of a PSI complex includes coordinated production of proteins and cofactors, assembly of the complexes, regulation of PSI function, and finally, disassembly and degradation. Here we focus on the assembly of complexes, as very little is known about regulation and degradation. The assembly sequence of different PSI subunits can be inferred from the studies on PSI assembly during light-induced chloroplast development, from in vitro reconstitution experiments, and from the presence of different PSI proteins in subunit-deficient mutants (14). The initial event in PSI assembly is the formation of a heterodimeric core of PsaA and PsaB (119). The PsaB- or PsaA-less mutants of *Synechocystis* (114, 117, 119), *Synechococcus 7002* (115), and *C. reinhardtii* (101, 136) do not show any evidence for the presence of monomeric or homodimeric chlorophyll protein complexes from PsaA or PsaB. Assembly of a proper F_X cluster is a critical requirement for the stability of the PSI core (131, 134). Once the core is assembled, the PsaC protein is expected to associate with the core, immediately followed by the other peripheral proteins (PsaC and PsaD). The PsaC-less mutants lack PsaC and PsaD (78, 145), whereas PsaD is required for the stable assembly of PsaC (74). Assembly of small integral membrane proteins of PSI could proceed in parallel to the assembly of the peripheral proteins. Some integral membrane proteins, such as PsaF, integrate into the membrane independent of the presence of the PSI core. PsaA- and PsaB-less cyanobacterial mutants often contain PsaF in the membrane (115).

In recent years, the availability of overproduced peripheral proteins has allowed structural investigations on soluble proteins before their assembly into PSI. These studies allow an understanding of the structural adaptations that are needed during assembly. When the assembly of PsaD was studied using microcalorimetry, researchers could determine the thermodynamic parameters associated with the assembly of this protein into PSI (60). Similar studies with other PSI proteins could provide valuable insight into the energetics of the assembly process. The unassembled PsaD protein of *Nostoc* sp. contains a central structured region and unstructured C and N termini (140). Therefore, assembly of PsaD into PSI complex confers structural rigidity to the protein through extensive interprotein interactions with the PsaA, PsaB, PsaL, PsaM, and PsaC proteins. Because of the high proportion of unstructured regions in PsaD, the attempts to determine its solution structure have proved futile. In contrast, the PsaC and PsaE proteins have a stable tertiary structure in solution (1, 5, 80). Comparison of soluble PSI proteins with their structures in complexes and further biophysical studies on protein interactions will give structural and mechanistic insights into the assembly of PSI proteins into the complex.

Cofactors play an important role in PSI assembly. Chlorophyll a is an absolute requirement for accumulation of PSI proteins in thylakoids. Fe-S clusters are required for stable assembly of PSI. Without a properly formed F_X cluster, PsaC does not assemble into the PSI complex. Similarly, the folding and assembly of the PsaC protein depends on the presence of both Fe-S clusters in this protein, both in vitro (82, 146) and in vivo (144). Phylloquinone-less mutants of *Synechocystis* contain PSI complexes that contain plastoquinone in the A_1 site (62); however, whether PSI can assemble without any quinone is unknown. The level of PSI complexes in the phylloquinone-less mutants is decreased to ~70% of the wild-type levels (62). Because the stability of the assembled complexes is not affected in these mutants, the presence of some quinone in the binding site may be essential during the assembly of the complex. Assembly of pigments and other cofactors in PSI may be mediated by protein factors. Some of these proteins are being identified from mutant analyses. In the past few years, researchers have isolated many cyanobacterial and algal mutants that have an altered abundance of PSI in the membranes (Table 3). In many of these mutants, the exact function of the mutated gene in PSI biogenesis is not known. Detailed analyses of the mutants, overproduced factors, and in vitro reconstitution assays are needed to identify the exact roles of the factors defined by these mutants.

CONCLUDING REMARKS

During the past ten years, advances in spectroscopy, crystallography, and molecular genetics have fueled research on PSI. Elegant combinations of these techniques have unraveled details of architecture and function of the PSI complex. We now know how this complex is organized and what the functions of its protein and cofactor components are. The knowledge of PSI structure has not provided answers to some questions about PSI function, but it has raised many more questions. How do proteins modulate function and properties of redox centers? This is particularly important in understanding the redox properties of quinones in PSI and in determining the special geometry and characters of the reaction center–chlorophyll pair. Excitation and early electron transfer events are still not completely understood. Do the chlorophylls in the electron transfer pathway participate in excitation transfer? What is the role of accessory chlorophylls? Do they participate directly in the early events? The PSI complex is an amazing enzyme. It is stable, efficient, and fast. The structural information will allow researchers to unlock secrets of the functional marvel of PSI.

With a solid base in structural and functional knowledge, attention will also shift to the understanding of PSI dynamics in thylakoid membranes. How is the level of

TABLE 3 Proteins that are known to regulate levels of PSI

Protein	Function	Evidence
BtpA	Stabilization of PSI	Rapid degradation of PSI in the BtpA-less mutants of *Synechocystis* when grown at low temperature (4, 148)
FtsH	Not understood	Targeted mutants in a FtsH homologue (slr0228) of *Synechocystis* contain 60% less PSI
Crd1	Thought to affect PSI accumulation indirectly by influencing iron metabolism	*C. reinhardtii* mutants fail to accumulate PSI and LHCI, and they contain reduced amounts of LHCII (92)
Ycf3	PSI assembly; may function as a member of a multiprotein complex	Complete loss of PSI in the Ycf3-less mutants of *C. reinhardtii* (8), tobacco (104), and *Synechocystis*
Ycf4	PSI assembly	Mutants of *C. reinhardtii* completely lack PSI, whereas cyanobacterial mutants have reduced PSI levels (8, 139)
Rubredoxin homologue	Fe-S cluster assembly	Cyanobacterial *rubA⁻* mutants contain PSI without F_X, F_A, F_B, and peripheral proteins (DA Bryant & JH Golbeck, personal communication)
PmgA	Possibly an indirect effect by decreasing chlorophyll synthesis, or a defect in incorporating chlorophyll into PSI	Less PSI complexes and less chlorophyll in the *pmgA⁻* mutant of *Synechocystis* (49)

PSI regulated in the membranes? How are different PSI genes controlled to avoid the wastage due to unassembled proteins? How does feedback inhibition modulate PSI activity? Questions related to regulatory mechanisms can be now addressed through application of systems biology approaches in which global changes in the gene expression are studied at the genomic level. Advances in functional genomics and proteomics should be instrumental in understanding the essential and amazing processes in photosynthesis.

ACKNOWLEDGMENTS

The author thanks Robert Blankenship, John H Golbeck, Gary Hastings, Kevin Redding, Walter Struve, Gerry Small, and Andrew Webber for reprints and discussions. He also acknowledges insightful discussions with N Krauss, P Jordan, and P Fromme of the PSI structure group in Berlin. The author's research on PSI has been supported by grants from NSF, USDA, and NIH. The work is also supported by the Hatch Act and State of Iowa funds. This is Journal Paper No. J-19152 of the

Iowa Agriculture and Home Economics Experiment Station, Ames, Iowa, Project No. 3416.

Visit the Annual Reviews home page at www.AnnualReviews.org

LITERATURE CITED

1. Antonkine ML, Bentrop D, Bertini I, Luchinat C, Shen G, et al. 2000. Paramagnetic ^{1}H NMR spectroscopy of the reduced, unbound photosystem I subunit PsaC: sequence-specific assignment of contact-shifted resonances and identification of mixed- and equal-valence Fe-Fe pairs in [4Fe-4S] centers F_A and F_B. *J. Biol. Inorg. Chem.* 5:381–92

2. Barth P, Guillouard I, Setif P, Lagoutte B. 2000. Essential role of a single arginine of photosystem I in stabilizing the electron transfer complex with ferredoxin. *J. Biol. Chem.* 275:7030–36

3. Barth P, Lagoutte B, Setif P. 1998. Ferredoxin reduction by photosystem I from *Synechocystis* sp. PCC 6803: toward an understanding of the respective roles of subunits PsaD and PsaE in ferredoxin binding. *Biochemistry* 37:16233–41

4. Bartsevich VV, Pakrasi HB. 1997. Molecular identification of a novel protein that regulates biogenesis of photosystem I, a membrane protein complex. *J. Biol. Chem.* 272:6382–87

5. Bentrop D, Bertini I, Luchinat C, Nitschke W, Muhlenhoff U. 1997. Characterization of the unbound 2[Fe$_4$S$_4$]-ferredoxin-like photosystem I subunit PsaC from the cyanobacterium *Synechococcus elongatus*. *Biochemistry* 36:13629–37

6. Bittl R, Zech SG, Fromme P, Witt HT, Lubitz W. 1997. Pulsed EPR structure analysis of photosystem I single crystals: localization of the phylloquinone acceptor. *Biochemistry* 36:12001–4

7. Boichenko VA. 1998. Photosynthetic generation of O$_2$ and H$_2$ by photosystem I-deficient *Chlamydomonas* mutants. *Biochemistry* (Moscow) 63:164–70

8. Boudreau E, Takahashi Y, Lemieux C, Turmel M, Rochaix JD. 1997. The chloroplast ycf3 and ycf4 open reading frames of *Chlamydomonas reinhardtii* are required for the accumulation of the photosystem I complex. *EMBO J.* 16:6095–104

9. Breton J, Ikegami I. 1989. Orientation of photosystem I pigments: low temperature linear dichroism spectroscopy of a highly-enriched P700 particle isolated from spinach. *Photosynth. Res.* 21:27–36

10. Breton J, Nabedryk E, Leibl W. 1999. FTIR study of the primary electron donor of photosystem I (P700) revealing delocalization of the charge in P700$^+$ and localization of the triplet character in ^{3}P700. *Biochemistry* 38:11585–92

11. Brettel K. 1997. Electron transfer and arrangement of the redox cofactors in photosystem I. *Biochim. Biophys. Acta* 1318:322–73

11a. Bryant DA, ed. 1994. *The Molecular Biology of Cyanobacteria*. Dordrecht: Kluwer

12. Byrdin M, Rimke I, Schlodder E, Stehlik D, Roelofs TA. 2000. Decay kinetics and quantum yields of fluorescence in photosystem I from *Synechococcus elongatus* with P700 in the reduced and oxidized state: Are the kinetics of excited state decay trap-limited or transfer-limited? *Biophys. J.* 79:992–1007

13. Chitnis PR. 1996. Photosystem I. *Plant Physiol.* 111:661–69

14. Chitnis PR. 1997. Import, assembly and degradation of chloroplast proteins. In *Photosynthesis: A Comprehensive Treatise*, ed. AS Raghavendra, pp. 58–71. Cambridge, UK: Cambridge Univ. Press

15. Chitnis PR, Chitnis VP, Xu Q, Jung Y-S, Yu L, Golbeck JH. 1995. Mutational

analysis of photosystem I polypeptides. In *Photosynthesis: From Light to Biosphere*, ed. P Mathis, pp. 17–22. Dordrecht: Kluwer

16. Chitnis PR, Purvis D, Nelson N. 1991. Molecular cloning and targeted mutagenesis of the gene psaF encoding subunit III of photosystem I from the cyanobacterium *Synechocystis* sp. PCC 6803. *J. Biol. Chem.* 266:20146–51

17. Chitnis PR, Xu Q, Chitnis VP, Nechushtai R. 1995. Function and organization of photosystem I polypeptides. *Photosynth. Res.* 44:23–40

18. Chitnis VP, Chitnis PR. 1993. PsaL subunit is required for the formation of photosystem I trimers in the cyanobacterium *Synechocystis* sp. PCC 6803. *FEBS Lett.* 336:330–34

19. Chitnis VP, Jung Y-S, Albee L, Golbeck JH, Chitnis PR. 1996. Mutational analysis of photosystem I polypeptides: role of PsaD and the lysyl 106 residue in the reductase activity of photosystem I. *J. Biol. Chem.* 271:11772–80

20. Chitnis VP, Ke A, Chitnis PR. 1997. The PsaD subunit of photosystem I. Mutations in the basic domain reduce the level of PsaD in the membranes. *Plant Physiol.* 115:1699–705

21. Cournac L, Redding K, Bennoun P, Peltier G. 1997. Limited photosynthetic electron flow but no CO_2 fixation in *Chlamydomonas* mutants lacking photosystem I. *FEBS Lett.* 416:65–68

22. Diaz A, Hervas M, Navarro JA, De la Rosa MA, Tollin G. 1994. A thermodynamic study by laser-flash photolysis of plastocyanin and cytochrome c_6 oxidation by photosystem I from the green alga *Monoraphidium braunii. Eur. J. Biochem.* 222:1001–7

23. DiMagno L, Chan CK, Jia Y, Lang MJ, Newman JR, et al. 1995. Energy transfer and trapping in photosystem I reaction centers from cyanobacteria. *Proc. Natl. Acad. Sci. USA* 92:2715–19

24. Fischer N, Boudreau E, Hippler M, Drepper F, Haehnel W, Rochaix JD. 1999. A large fraction of PsaF is nonfunctional in photosystem I complexes lacking the PsaJ subunit. *Biochemistry* 38:5546–52

25. Fromme P. 1999. Structure of photosystem I. See Ref. 116a, pp. 212–51

26. Fromme P, Jordan P, Krauss N. 2001. Structure of photosystem I. *Biochem. Biophys. Acta.* In press

27. Fujita Y. 1991. Regulation of stoichiometry among thylakoid components. See Ref. 90a, pp. 29–42

28. Fujita Y, Murakami A, Aizawa K, Ohki K. 1994. Short-term and long-term adaptation of the photosynthetic apparatus: homeostatic properties of thylakoids. See Ref. 11a, pp. 677–92

29. Fujita Y, Murakami A, Ohki K. 1990. Regulation of the stoichiometry of thylakoid components in the photosynthetic system of cyanophytes: Model experiments showing that control of the synthesis or supply of Chl *a* can change the stoichiometric relationship between the two photosystems. *Plant Cell Physiol.* 31:145–53

30. Golbeck JH. 1994. Photosystem I in cyanobacteria. See Ref. 11a, pp. 179–220

31. Golbeck JH. 1999. A comparative analysis of the spin state distribution of in vitro and in vivo mutants of PsaC. A biochemical argument for the sequence of electron-transfer in photosystem I as F_X to F_A to F_B to ferredoxin/flavodoxin. *Photosynth. Res.* 61:107–44

32. Gomez S, Chitnis PR. 2000. Light-harvesting antennas in plants. In *Probing Photosynthesis: Mechanism, Regulation and Adaptation*, ed. M Yunus, U Pathre, P Mohanty, pp. 51–69. London: Taylor & Francis

33. Green BR, Durnford DG. 1996. The chlorophyll-carotenoid proteins of oxygenic photosynthesis. *Annu. Rev. Plant Physiol. Plant Mol. Biol.* 47:685–714

34. Greenbaum E, Lee JW, Tevault CV, Blankinship SL, Mets LJ. 1995. CO_2 fixation and

photoevolution of H_2 and O_2 in a mutant of *Chlamydomonas* lacking photosystem I. *Nature* 376:438–41

35. Guergova-Kuras M, Boudreaux B, Joliot A, Joliot P, Redding K. 2001. Two active branches for electron transfer in photosystem I. *Proc. Natl. Acad. Sci. USA.* Submitted

36. Haehnel W, Jansen T, Gause K, Klosgen RB, Stahl B, et al. 1994. Electron transfer from plastocyanin to photosystem I. *EMBO J.* 13:1028–38

37. Haldrup A, Naver H, Scheller HV. 1999. The interaction between plastocyanin and photosystem I is inefficient in transgenic Arabidopsis plants lacking the PSI-N subunit of photosystem I. *Plant J.* 17:689–98

38. Haldrup A, Simpson DJ, Scheller HV. 2000. Down-regulation of the PSI-F subunit of photosystem I in *Arabidopsis thaliana*. The PSI-F subunit is essential for photoautotrophic growth and antenna function. *J. Biol. Chem.* 275:31211–18

39. Hanley J, Setif P, Bottin H, Lagoutte B. 1996. Mutagenesis of photosystem I in the region of the ferredoxin cross-linking site: modifications of positively charged amino acids. *Biochemistry* 35:8563–71

40. Hastings G, Hoshina S, Webber AN, Blankenship RE. 1995. Universality of energy and electron transfer processes in photosystem I. *Biochemistry* 34:15512–22

41. Hastings G, Kleinherenbrink FA, Lin S, Blankenship RE. 1994. Time-resolved fluorescence and absorption spectroscopy of photosystem I. *Biochemistry* 33:3185–92

42. Hastings G, Kleinherenbrink FA, Lin S, McHugh TJ, Blankenship RE. 1994. Observation of the reduction and reoxidation of the primary electron acceptor in photosystem I. *Biochemistry* 33:3193–200

43. He WZ, Malkin R. 1992. Specific release of a 9-kDa extrinsic polypeptide of photosystem I from spinach chloroplasts by salt washing. *FEBS Lett.* 308:298–300

44. Heck DA, Miles D, Chitnis PR. 1999. Char-

acterization of two photosynthetic mutants of maize. *Plant Physiol.* 120:1129–36

45. Heller BA, Holten D, Kirmaier C. 1995. Control of electron transfer between the L- and M-sides of photosynthetic reaction centers. *Science* 269:940–45

46. Herbert SK, Martin RE, Fork DC. 1995. Light adaptation of cyclic electron transport through photosystem I in the cyanobacterium *Synechococcus* sp. PCC 7942. *Photosynth. Res.* 46:277–85

47. Hervas M, Navarro J, Tollin G. 1992. A laser-flash spectroscopy study of the kinetics of electron transfer from spinach photosystem I to spinach and algal ferredoxins. *Photochem. Photobiol.* 56:319–24

48. Hervas M, Navarro JA, Diaz A, De la Rosa MA. 1996. A comparative thermodynamic analysis by laser-flash absorption spectroscopy of photosystem I reduction by plastocyanin and cytochrome c_6 in *Anabaena* PCC 7119, *Synechocystis* PCC 6803 and spinach. *Biochemistry* 35:2693–98

49. Hihara Y, Sonoike K, Ikeuchi M. 1998. A novel gene, *pmgA*, specifically regulates photosystem stoichiometry in the cyanobacterium *Synechocystis* species PCC 6803 in response to high light. *Plant Physiol.* 117:1205–16

50. Hippler M, Biehler K, Krieger-Liszkay A, van Dillewjin J, Rochaix JD. 2000. Limitation in electron transfer in photosystem I donor side mutants of *Chlamydomonas reinhardtii*. Lethal photo-oxidative damage in high light is overcome in a suppressor strain deficient in the assembly of the light-harvesting complex. *J. Biol. Chem.* 275:5852–59

51. Hippler M, Drepper F, Farah J, Rochaix JD. 1997. Fast electron transfer from cytochrome c_6 and plastocyanin to photosystem I of *Chlamydomonas reinhardtii* requires PsaF. *Biochemistry* 36:6343–49

52. Hippler M, Drepper F, Haehnel W, Rochaix JD. 1998. The N-terminal domain of PsaF: precise recognition site for binding and fast

electron transfer from cytochrome c_6 and plastocyanin to photosystem I of *Chlamydomonas reinhardtii*. *Proc. Natl. Acad. Sci. USA* 95:7339–44

53. Hippler M, Reichert J, Sutter M, Zak E, Altschmied L, et al. 1996. The plastocyanin binding domain of photosystem I. *EMBO J.* 15:6374–84

54. Holzwarth AR, Schatz G, Brock H, Bittersmann E. 1993. Energy transfer and charge separation kinetics in photosystem I. Part 1: picosecond transient absorption and fluorescence study of cyanobacterial photosystem I particles. *Biophys. J.* 64:1813–26

55. Horton P, Ruban AV, Walters RG. 1996. Regulation of light-harvesting in green plants. *Annu. Rev. Plant Physiol. Plant Mol. Biol.* 47:655–84

56. Iwaki M, Itoh S. 1994. Reaction of reconstituted acceptor quinone and dynamic equilibration of electron transfer in the photosystem I reaction center. *Plant Cell Physiol.* 35:983–93

57. Jansson S, Anderson B, Scheller HV. 1996. Nearest neighbour analysis of higher plant photosystem I holocomplex. *Plant Physiol.* 112:409–20

58. Jensen PE, Gilpin M, Knoetzel J, Scheller HV. 2000. The PSI-K subunit of photosystem I is involved in the interaction between light-harvesting complex I and the photosystem I reaction center core. *J. Biol. Chem.* 275:24701–8

59. Jia Y, Jean JM, Werst MM, Chan CK, Fleming GR. 1992. Simulations of the temperature dependence of energy transfer in the PSI core antenna. *Biophys. J.* 63:259–73

60. Jin P, Sun J, Chitnis PR. 1999. Structural features and assembly of the soluble overexpressed PsaD subunit of photosystem I. *Biochim. Biophys. Acta* 1410:7–18

61. Johnson TW. 2000. *Recruitment of foreign quinones in photosytem I*. PhD thesis. Iowa State Univ., Ames. 200 pp.

62. Johnson TW, Shen G, Zybailov B, Kolling D, Reategui R, et al. 2000. Recruitment of a foreign quinone into the A_1 site of photosystem I. Genetic and physiological characterization of phylloquinone biosynthetic pathway mutants in *Synechocystis* sp. PCC 6803. *J. Biol. Chem.* 275:8523–30

63. Joliot P, Joliot A. 1999. In vivo analysis of the electron transfer within photosystem I: Are the two phylloquinones involved? *Biochemistry* 38:11130–36

64. Kass H, Lubitz W. 1996. Quadrupole parameters of nitrogen nuclei in the cation radical $P700^+$ determined by ESEEM of single crystals of photosystem I. *Chem. Phys. Lett.* 251:193–203

65. Kleinherenbrink FA, Hastings G, Wittmerhaus BP, Blankenship RE. 1994. Delayed fluorescence from Fe-S type photosynthetic reaction centers at low redox potential. *Biochemistry* 33:3096–105

66. Klukas O, Schubert WD, Jordan P, Krauss N, Fromme P, et al. 1999. Localization of two phylloquinones, QK and QK', in an improved electron density map of photosystem I at 4-Å resolution. *J. Biol. Chem.* 274:7361–67

67. Klukas O, Schubert WD, Jordan P, Krauss N, Fromme P, et al. 1999. Photosystem I, an improved model of the stromal subunits PsaC, PsaD, and PsaE. *J. Biol. Chem.* 274:7351–60

68. Knoetzel J, Bossmann B, Grimme LH. 1998. Chlorina and viridis mutants of barley (*Hordeum vulgare* L.) allow assignment of long-wavelength chlorophyll forms to individual Lhca proteins of photosystem I in vivo. *FEBS Lett.* 436:339–42

69. Krabben L, Schlodder E, Jordan R, Carbonera D, Giacometti G, et al. 2000. Influence of the axial ligands on the spectral properties of P700 of photosystem I: a study of site-directed mutants. *Biochemistry* 39:13012–25

70. Krauss N, Schubert W-D, Klukas O, Fromme P, Witt HT, Saenger W. 1996. Photosystem I at 4 Å resolution represents the

first structural model of a joint photosynthetic reaction centre and core antenna system. *Nat. Struct. Biol.* 3:965–73

71. Kuhlbrandt W, Wang DN, Fujiyoshi Y. 1994. Atomic model of plant light-harvesting complex by electron crystallography. *Nature* 367:614–21

72. Laible PD, Zipfel W, Owens TG. 1994. Excited state dynamics in chlorophyll-based antennae: the role of transfer equilibrium. *Biophys. J.* 66:844–60

73. Lee JW, Tevault CV, Owens TG, Greenbaum E. 1996. Oxygenic photoautotrophic growth without photosytem I. *Science* 273:364–67

74. Li N, Zhao J, Warren PV, Warden JT, Bryant DA, Golbeck JH. 1991. PsaD is required for the stable binding of PsaC to the photosystem I core protein of *Synechococcus* sp. PCC 6301. *Biochemistry* 30:7863–72

74a. Lunde C, Jensen PE, Haldrup A, Knoetzel J, Scheller HV. 2000. The PSI-H subunit of photosystem I is essential for state transitions in plant photosynthesis. *Nature* 408:613–15

75. Mac M, Tang X-S, Diner BA, McCracken J, Babcock GT. 1996. Identification of histidine as an axial ligand to P700. *Biochemistry* 35:13288–93

76. MacMillan F, Hanley J, van der Weerd L, Knupling M, Un S, Rutherford AW. 1997. Orientation of the phylloquinone electron acceptor anion radical in photosystem I. *Biochemistry* 36:9297–303

77. Manna P, Chitnis PR. 1999. Function and molecular genetics of photosystem I. See Ref. 116a, pp. 212–51

78. Mannan RM, Pakrasi HB, Sonoike K. 1994. The PsaC protein is necessary for the stable association of the PsaD, PsaE, and PsaL proteins in the photosystem I complex: analysis of a cyanobacterial mutant strain. *Arch. Biochem. Biophys.* 315:68–73

79. Margus R, Johnson W, Chitnis PR, Small GJ. 2000. The red-absorbing chlorophyll

a antenna states of photosystem I: a hole-burning study of *Synechocystis* sp. pcc6803 and its mutants. *J. Phys. Chem.* 104:836–47

80. Mayer KL, Shen G, Bryant DA, Lecomte JT, Falzone CJ. 1999. The solution structure of photosystem I accessory protein E from the cyanobacterium *Nostoc* sp. strain PCC 8009. *Biochemistry* 38:13736–46

81. Medina M, Diaz A, Hervas M, Navarro JA, Gomez-Moreno C, et al. 1993. A comparative laser-flash absorption spectroscopy study of *Anabaena* PCC 7119 plastocyanin and cytochrome c_6 photooxidation by photosystem I particles. *Eur. J. Biochem.* 213:1133–38

82. Mehari T, Qiao F, Scott MP, Nellis DF, Zhao J, et al. 1995. Modified ligands to F_A and F_B in photosystem I. Structural constraints for the formation of iron-sulfur clusters in free and rebound PsaC. *J. Biol. Chem.* 270:28108–17

83. Meimberg K, Lagoutte B, Bottin H, Muhlenhoff U. 1998. The PsaE subunit is required for complex formation between photosystem I and flavodoxin from the cyanobacterium *Synechocystis* sp. PCC 6803. *Biochemistry* 37:9759–67

84. Melis A. 1991. Regulation of photosystem stoichiometry in oxygenic photosynthesis. See Ref. 90a, pp. 9–28

85. Melis A. 1996. Excitation energy transfer: functional and dynamic aspects of Lhc (cab) proteins. See Ref. 98a, pp. 523–38

86. Melis A. 1999. Photosystem-II damage and repair cycle in chloroplasts: What modulates the rate of photodamage? *Trends Plant Sci.* 4:130–35

87. Melis A, Murakami A, Nemson JA, Aizawa K, Ohki K, Fujita Y. 1996. Chromatic regulation in *Chlamydomonas reinhardtii* alters photosystem stoichiometry and improves the quantum efficiency of photosynthesis. *Photosynth. Res.* 47:253–65

88. Melkozernov AN, Lin S, Schmid VH, Paulsen H, Schmidt GW, Blankenship RE.

2000. Ultrafast excitation dynamics of low energy pigments in reconstituted peripheral light-harvesting complexes of photosystem I. *FEBS Lett.* 471:89–92

89. Melkozernov AN, Schmid VH, Schmidt GW, Blankenship RE. 1998. Energy redistribution in heterodimeric light-harvesting complex LHC I-730 of photosystem I. *J. Phys. Chem.* 102:8183–89

90. Mills JD, Slovacek RE, Hind G. 1978. Cyclic electron transport in isolated intact chloroplasts. Further studies with antimycin. *Biochim. Biophys. Acta* 504:298–309

90a. Miyachi S, Kanai R, Katoh S, eds. 1991. *Regulation of Photosynthetic Processes.* Tokyo: Bot. Soc. Jpn.

91. Morand LZ, Cheng L, Krogmann DW, Ho KK. 1994. Soluble electron transfer catalysts of cyanobacteia. See Ref. 11a, pp. 381–407

92. Moseley J, Quinn J, Eriksson M, Merchant S. 2000. The Crd1 gene encodes a putative di-iron enzyme required for photosystem I accumulation in copper deficiency and hypoxia in *Chlamydomonas reinhardtii. EMBO J.* 19:2139–51

93. Murakami A, Fujita Y. 1991. Regulation of photosystem stoichiometry in the photosynthetic system of the cyanophyte *Synechocystis* PCC 6714 in response to light intensity. *Plant Cell Physiol.* 32:223–30

94. Murakami A, Fujita Y. 1991. Steady state of photosynthetic electron transport in cells of the cyanophyte *Synechocystis* PCC 6714. *Plant Cell Physiol.* 32:231–22

95. Murakami A, Kim SJ, Fujita Y. 1997. Changes in photosystem stoichiometry in response to environmental conditions for cell growth observed with the cyanophyte *Synechocystis* PCC 6714. *Plant Cell Physiol.* 38:392–97

96. Naithani S, Hou JM, Chitnis PR. 2000. Targeted inactivation of the *psaK1, psaK2* and *psaM* genes encoding subunits of photosystem in the cyanobacterium *Synechocystis* sp. PCC 6803. *Photosynth. Res.* 63:225–36

97. Nakamoto H, Hasegawa M. 1999. Targeted inactivation of the gene *psaK* encoding a subunit of photosystem I from the cyanobacterium *Synechocystis* sp. PCC 6803. *Plant Cell Physiol.* 40:9–16

98. Naver H, Haldrup A, Scheller HV. 1999. Cosuppression of photosystem I subunit PSI-H in *Arabidopsis thaliana.* Efficient electron transfer and stability of photosystem I is dependent upon the PSI-H subunit. *J. Biol. Chem.* 274:10784–89

98a. Ort DR, Yocum CF, eds. 1996. *Oxygenic Photosynthesis: The Light Reactions.* Dordrecht: Kluwer

99. Palsson LO, Flemming C, Gobets B, van Grondelle R, Dekker JP, Schlodder E. 1998. Energy transfer and charge separation in photosystem I: P700 oxidation upon selective excitation of the long-wavelength antenna chlorophylls of *Synechococcus* elongatus. *Biophys. J.* 74:2611–22

100. Pichersky E, Jansson S. 1996. The light-harvesting chlorophyll a/b-binding polypeptides and their genes in angiosperm and gymnosperm species. See Ref. 98a, pp. 507–21

101. Redding K, Cournac L, Vassiliev IR, Golbeck JH, Peltier G, Rochaix JD. 1999. Photosystem I is indispensable for photoautotrophic growth, CO_2 fixation, and H_2 photoproduction in *Chlamydomonas reinhardtii. J. Biol. Chem.* 274:10466–73

102. Redding K, MacMillan F, Leibl W, Brettel K, Hanley J, et al. 1998. A systematic survey of conserved histidines in the core subunits of photosystem I by site-directed mutagenesis reveals the likely axial ligands of P700. *EMBO J.* 17:50–60

103. Rigby SE, Nugent JH, O'Malley PJ. 1994. ENDOR and special triple resonance studies of chlorophyll cation radicals in photosystem 2. *Biochemistry* 33:10043–50

104. Ruf S, Kossel H, Bock R. 1997. Targeted inactivation of a tobacco intron-containing open reading frame reveals a novel chloroplast-encoded photosystem I-related gene. *J. Cell Biol.* 139:95–102

105. Rutherford AW, Setif P. 1990. Orientation of P700, the primary electron donor of photosystem I. *Biochim. Biophys. Acta* 1019:128–32

106. Savikhin S, Xu W, Chitnis PR, Struve WS. 2000. Ultrafast primary processes in PSI from *Synechocystis* sp. PCC 6803: roles of P700 and A$_0$. *Biophys. J.* 79:573–86

107. Savikhin S, Xu W, Soukoulis V, Chitnis PR, Struve WS. 1999. Ultrafast primary processes in photosystem I of the cyanobacterium *Synechocystis* sp. PCC 6803. *Biophys. J.* 76:3278–88

108. Scheller HV. 1996. In vitro cyclic electron transport in barley thylakoids follows two independent pathways. *Plant Physiol.* 110:187–94

109. Schluchter WM, Shen G, Zhao J, Bryant DA. 1996. Characterization of psaI and psaL mutants of *Synechococcus* sp. strain PCC 7002: a new model for state transitions in cyanobacteria. *Photochem. Photobiol.* 64:53–66

110. Schubert WD, Klukas O, Krauss N, Saenger W, Fromme P, Witt HT. 1997. Photosystem I of *Synechococcus elongatus* at 4 Å resolution: comprehensive structure analysis. *J. Mol. Biol.* 272:741–69

111. Semenov AY, Vassiliev IR, van der Est A, Mamedov MD, Zybailov B, et al. 2000. Recruitment of a foreign quinone into the A$_1$ site of photosystem I. Altered kinetics of electron transfer in phylloquinone biosynthetic pathway mutants studied by time-resolved optical, EPR, and electrometric techniques. *J. Biol. Chem.* 275:23429–38

112. Setif PQ, Bottin H. 1994. Laser flash absorption spectroscopy study of ferredoxin reduction by photosystem I in *Synechocystis* sp. PCC 6803: evidence for sub-microsecond and microsecond kinetics. *Biochemistry* 33:8495–504

113. Setif PQ, Bottin H. 1995. Laser flash absorption spectroscopy study of ferredoxin reduction by photosystem I: spectral and kinetic evidence for the existence of several photosystem I-ferredoxin complexes. *Biochemistry* 34:9059–70

114. Shen G, Boussiba S, Vermaas WF. 1993. *Synechocystis* sp. PCC 6803 strains lacking photosystem I and phycobilisome function. *Plant Cell* 5:1853–63

115. Shen G, Bryant DA. 1995. Characterization of *Synechococcus* sp. strain PCC 7002 mutant lacking photosystem I. Protein assembly and energy distribution in the absence of the photosystem I reaction center core complex. *Photosynth. Res.* 44:41–53

116. Simpson DJ, Knoetzel J. 1996. Light-harvesting complexes of plants and algae. See Ref. 98a, pp. 493–506

116a. Singhal GS, Renger G, Sapory SK, Irrgang K-D, Govindjee, eds. 1999. *Concepts in Photobiology: Photosynthesis and Photomorphogenesis.* Dordrecht: Kluwer

117. Smart LB, Anderson SL, McIntosh L. 1991. Targeted genetic inactivation of the photosystem I reaction center in the cyanobacterium *Synechocystis* sp. PCC 6803. *EMBO J.* 10:3289–96

118. Smart LB, Bowlby NR, Anderson SL, Sithole I, McIntosh L. 1994. Genetic manipulation of the cyanobacterium *Synechocystis* sp. PCC 6803: development of strains lacking photosystem I for the analysis of mutations in photosystem II. *Plant Physiol.* 104:349–54

119. Smart LB, Warren PV, Golbeck JH, McIntosh L. 1993. Mutational analysis of the structure and biogenesis of the photosystem I reaction center in the cyanobacterium *Synechocystis* sp. PCC 6803. *Proc. Natl. Acad. Sci. USA* 90:1132–36

120. Sonoike K. 1996. Degradation of psaB gene product, the reaction center subunit of photosystem I, is caused by photoinhibition of photosystem I: possible involvement of active oxygen species. *Plant Sci.* 115:157–64

121. Sonoike K, Terashima I. 1994. Mechanism of the photosystem I photoinhibition in leaves of *Cucumis sativus* L. *Planta* 194:287–93

122. Soukoulis V, Savikhin S, Xu W, Chitnis PR, Struve WS. 1999. Electronic spectra of PSI mutants: the peripheral subunits do not bind red chlorophylls in *Synechocystis* sp. PCC 6803. *Biophys. J.* 76:2711–15

123. Sun J, Xu W, Hervas M, Navarro JA, Rosa MA, Chitnis PR. 1999. Oxidizing side of the cyanobacterial photosystem I. Evidence for interaction between the electron donor proteins and a luminal surface helix of the PsaB subunit. *J. Biol. Chem.* 274:19048–54

124. Takahashi Y, Goldschmidt-Clermont M, Soen S-Y, Franzen LG, Rochaix J-D. 1991. Directed chloroplast transformation in *Chlamydomonas reinhardtii*: insertional inactivation of the *psaC* gene encoding the iron sulfur protein destabilizes photosystem I. *EMBO J.* 10:2033–40

125. Tjus SE, Moller BL, Scheller HV. 1998. Photosystem I is an early target of photoinhibition in barley illuminated at chilling temperatures. *Plant Physiol.* 116:755–64

126. van der Est A, Bock C, Golbeck J, Brettel K, Setif P, Stehlik D. 1994. Electron transfer from the acceptor A_1 to the iron-sulfur centers in photosystem I as studied by transient EPR spectroscopy. *Biochemistry* 33:11789–97

127. van Thor JJ, Geerlings TH, Matthijs HC, Hellingwerf KJ. 1999. Kinetic evidence for the PsaE-dependent transient ternary complex photosystem I/ferredoxin/ferredoxin:$NADP^+$ reductase in a cyanobacterium. *Biochemistry* 38:12735–46

128. van Thor JJ, Jeanjean R, Havaux M, Sjollema KA, Joset F, et al. 2000. Salt shock-inducible photosystem I cyclic electron transfer in *Synechocystis* PCC 6803 relies on binding of ferredoxin:$NADP^+$ reductase to the thylakoid membranes via its CpcD phycobilisome-linker homologous N-terminal domain. *Biochim. Biophys. Acta* 1457:129–44

129. Varotto C, Pesaresi P, Meurer J, Oelmuller R, Steiner-Lange S, et al. 2000. Disruption of the Arabidopsis photosystem I gene *psaE1* affects photosynthesis and impairs growth. *Plant J.* 22:115–24

130. Vassiliev IR, Jung YS, Smart LB, Schulz R, McIntosh L, Golbeck JH. 1995. A mixed-ligand iron-sulfur cluster (C556SPsaB or C565SPsaB) in the F_X-binding site leads to a decreased quantum efficiency of electron transfer in photosystem I. *Biophys. J.* 69:1544–53

131. Vassiliev IR, Yu J, Jung YS, Schulz R, Ganago AO, et al. 1999. The cysteine-proximal aspartates in the Fx-binding niche of photosystem I. Effect of alanine and lysine replacements on photoautotrophic growth, electron transfer rates, single-turnover flash efficiency, and EPR spectral properties. *J. Biol. Chem.* 274:9993–10001

132. Walters RG, Rogers JJ, Shephard F, Horton P. 1999. Acclimation of *Arabidopsis thaliana* to the light environment: the role of photoreceptors. *Planta* 209:517–27

133. Warren PV, Golbeck JH, Warden JT. 1993. Charge recombination between $P700^+$ and A_1^- occurs directly to the ground state of P700 in a photosystem I core devoid of F_X, F_B, and F_A. *Biochemistry* 32:849–57

134. Warren PV, Smart LB, McIntosh L, Golbeck JH. 1993. Site-directed conversion of cysteine-565 to serine in PsaB of photosystem I results in the assembly of [3Fe-4S] and [4Fe-4S] clusters in F_X. A mixed-ligand [4Fe-4S] cluster is capable

of electron transfer to F_A and F_B. *Biochemistry* 32:4411–19

135. Watanabe T, Kobayashi M, Hongu A, Nakazato M, Hiyama T, Murata N. 1985. Evidence that a chlorophyll a' dimer constitutes the photochemical reaction centre I (P700) in photosynthetic apparatus. *FEBS Lett.* 191:252–56

136. Webber AN, Gibbs PB, Ward JB, Bingham SE. 1993. Site-directed mutagenesis of the photosystem I reaction center in chloroplasts. The proline-cysteine motif. *J. Biol. Chem.* 268:12990–95

137. Webber AN, Su H, Bingham SE, Kass H, Krabben L, et al. 1996. Site-directed mutations affecting the spectroscopic characteristics and midpoint potential of the primary donor in photosystem I. *Biochemistry* 35:12857–63

138. White NT, Beddard GS, Thorne JR, Feehan TM, Keyes TE, Heathcote P. 1996. Primary charge separation and energy transfer in the photosystem I reaction center of higher plants. *J. Phys. Chem.* 100:12086–99

139. Wilde A, Hartel H, Hubschmann T, Hoffmann P, Shestakov SV, Borner T. 1995. Inactivation of a *Synechocystis* sp. strain PCC 6803 gene with homology to conserved chloroplast open reading frame 184 increases the photosystem II–to–photosystem I ratio. *Plant Cell* 7:649–58

140. Xia Z, Broadhurst RW, Laue ED, Bryant DA, Golbeck JH, Bendall DS. 1998. Structure and properties in solution of PsaD, an extrinsic polypeptide of photosystem I. *Eur. J. Biochem.* 255:309–16

141. Xu Q, Jung YS, Chitnis VP, Guikema JA, Golbeck JH, Chitnis PR. 1994. Mutational analysis of photosystem I polypeptides in *Synechocystis* sp. PCC 6803. Subunit requirements for reduction of $NADP^+$ mediated by ferredoxin and flavodoxin. *J. Biol. Chem.* 2693:21512–18

142. Xu Q, Yu L, Chitnis VP, Chitnis PR. 1994.

Function and organization of photosystem I in a cyanobacterial mutant strain that lacks PsaF and PsaJ subunits. *J. Biol. Chem.* 269:3205–11

143. Yang F, Shen G, Schluchter WM, Zybailov BL, Ganago AO, et al. 1998. Deletion of the PsaF polypeptide modifies the environment of the redox-active phylloquinone A_1. Evidence for unidirectionality of electron transfer in photosystem I. *J. Phys. Chem. B* 102:8288–99

144. Yu J, Vassiliev IR, Jung YS, Golbeck JH, McIntosh L. 1997. Strains of *Synechocystis* sp. PCC 6803 with altered PsaC. I. Mutations incorporated in the cysteine ligands of the two [4Fe-4S] clusters F_A and F_B of photosystem I. *J. Biol. Chem.* 272:8032–39

145. Yu L, Smart LB, Jung YS, Golbeck J, McIntosh L. 1995. Absence of PsaC subunit allows assembly of photosystem I core but prevents the binding of PsaD and PsaE in *Synechocystis* sp. PCC 6803. *Plant Mol. Biol.* 29:331–42

146. Yu L, Vassiliev IR, Jung YS, Bryant DA, Golbeck JH. 1995. Modified ligands to F_A and F_B in photosystem I. II. Characterization of a mixed ligand [4Fe-4S] cluster in the C51D mutant of PsaC upon rebinding to P700-F_X cores. *J. Biol. Chem.* 270:28118–25

147. Yu L, Zhao J, Mühlenhoff U, Bryant DA, Golbeck JH. 1993. PsaE is required for in vivo cyclic electron flow around photosystem I in the cyanobacterium *Synechococcus* sp. PCC 7002. *Plant Physiol.* 103:171–80

148. Zak E, Pakrasi HB. 2000. The BtpA protein stabilizes the reaction center proteins of photosystem I in the cyanobacterium *Synechocystis* sp. PCC 6803 at low temperature. *Plant Physiol.* 123:215–22

149. Zhao J, Li N, Warren PV, Golbeck JH, Bryant DA. 1992. Site-directed conversion of a cysteine to aspartate leads to the assembly of a [3Fe-4S] cluster in PsaC

of photosystem I. The photoreduction of F_A is independent of F_B. *Biochemistry* 31:5093–99

150. Zybailov B, van der Est A, Zech SG, Teutloff C, Johnson TW, et al. 2000. Recruitment of a foreign quinone into the A_1 site of photosystem I. II. Structural and functional characterization of phylloquinone biosynthetic pathway mutants by electron paramagnetic resonance and electron-nuclear double resonance spectroscopy. *J. Biol. Chem.* 275:8531–39

Annu. Rev. Plant Physiol. Plant Mol. Biol. 2001. 52:627–58

GUARD CELL SIGNAL TRANSDUCTION

Julian I Schroeder, Gethyn J Allen, Veronique Hugouvieux, June M Kwak, David Waner

University of California, San Diego, Division of Biology, Cell and Developmental Biology Section and Center for Molecular Genetics, La Jolla, California 92093-0116; e-mail: julian@biomail.ucsd.edu

Key Words stomatal movement, gas exchange, abscisic acid, ion channel, cytosolic calcium

■ **Abstract** Guard cells surround stomatal pores in the epidermis of plant leaves and stems. Stomatal pore opening is essential for CO_2 influx into leaves for photosynthetic carbon fixation. In exchange, plants lose over 95% of their water via transpiration to the atmosphere. Signal transduction mechanisms in guard cells integrate hormonal stimuli, light signals, water status, CO_2, temperature, and other environmental conditions to modulate stomatal apertures for regulation of gas exchange and plant survival under diverse conditions. Stomatal guard cells have become a highly developed model system for characterizing early signal transduction mechanisms in plants and for elucidating how individual signaling mechanisms can interact within a network in a single cell. In this review we focus on recent advances in understanding signal transduction mechanisms in guard cells.

CONTENTS

1040-2519/01/0601-0627$14.00

INTRODUCTION

Opening and closing of stomatal pores is mediated by turgor and volume changes
in guard cells. During stomatal opening guard cells accumulate potassium, anions,
and sucrose (130, 162, 198). Osmotic water uptake leads to guard cell swelling and
stomatal opening. Stomatal closing is mediated by potassium and anion efflux from
guard cells, sucrose removal, and metabolism of malate to osmotically inactive
starch. Guard cells have become a popular system for dissecting the functions of
individual genes and proteins within signaling cascades for the following reasons.

1. Guard cells control CO_2 influx and water loss and thus critically affect
   whole plant growth and physiology.

2. Guard cells respond cell-autonomously to well-known plant physiological
   signals, including red and blue light (215), CO_2, plant pathogens, the
   hormones abscisic acid, auxin, cytokinin and gibberellins, and other
   environmental signals. Thus many specific receptors and early signaling
   mechanisms function at the single-cell level in guard cells.

3. Models for roles of guard cell ion channels (177, 178) and cytosolic [Ca^{2+}]
   changes (134) during stomatal movements provide a basis for analyzing
   individual mechanisms that contribute to signal transduction. These ion

channels are targets of early signaling branches and provide molecular probes to identify upstream regulators.

4. Hypotheses for mechanisms affecting signal transduction can be easily tested by analyzing stomatal opening and closing in response to various stimuli. Furthermore, several powerful approaches have been adapted to guard cell signaling analyses allowing interdisciplinary time-resolved cell biological, biophysical, molecular genetic, second-messenger imaging, physiological, and newly arising postgenomic analyses.

The central role of guard cells in regulating gas exchange is of importance for ecological and biotechnological applications. Agricultural and horticultural use of plants in climates to which these plants are not adapted, as well as short-term climate changes, lead to dramatic crop losses or freshwater consumption under stress conditions such as drought. Recent studies in *Arabidopsis* have demonstrated that stomatal responses can be manipulated by modifying guard cell signal transduction elements to reduce transpirational water loss and dessication during drought periods (53, 75, 154).

One might ask: Are guard cells different from many other plant cell types (aside from the obvious specializations) in terms of harboring many signal receptors in a single cell? Most likely not, because most individual plant cells respond to many classical hormones, pathogens, and light signals. The combination of the above-listed attributes (1 to 4), however, renders guard cells a well-developed model system for interdisciplinary and time-resolved characterizations of mechanisms or segments of early plant signaling cascades.

In the present review we focus mainly on recent dissections of signaling transduction mechanisms in guard cells. Of further importance for stomatal movements is signal-dependent modulation of starch-malate metabolism. The mechanisms by which signaling cascades described here tie into metabolic networks is an important frontier of future research and recent reviews on guard cell metabolic pathways can be found elsewhere (88, 149, 198). Furthermore, several reviews on aspects of guard cell signal transduction have appeared in recent years (8, 12, 13, 21, 113, 132, 136, 145, 180, 182, 207, 214).

LIGHT SIGNAL TRANSDUCTION AND STOMATAL OPENING

Stomatal opening is driven by H^+ extrusion through plasma membrane H^+-ATPases that are activated by auxins (124), red light (189), and blue light (14, 193). Cell-autonomous light receptors in guard cells induce stomatal opening (215). Light-induced stomatal opening requires activation of plasma membrane proton (H^+)-ATPases (14, 52, 94, 188, 193), causing plasma membrane hyperpolarization proposed to drive K^+ uptake into guard cells via inward-rectifying K^+ (K_{in}^+) channels (181, 202). Anion (Cl^-) influx into stomatal guard cells is thought to occur via H^+/anion symporters or anion/OH^- antiporters in the plasma membrane. In parallel, starch metabolism leads to accumulation of osmotically active malate in guard cells. In addition, sucrose levels in guard cells increase during light-induced stomatal opening (125, 159, 165, 197, 198). Studies with intact leaves show that the main solute supporting stomatal opening at the beginning of a daily cycle was K^+, whereas sucrose became predominant later in the daily cycle as guard cell K^+ content decreased (197, 198).

Early Events in Blue Light Signal Transduction

Cytosolic Ca^{2+} elevation reversibly inhibits blue light activation of the H^+-ATPases (92) ($K_{1/2} = 0.3$ μM Ca^{2+}) (Figure 1; see color insert). Furthermore, inhibitors of PP1- or PP2A-type (PP1/PP2A) protein phosphatases such as calyculin A and okadaic acid inhibited blue light–dependent H^+ pumping and light-induced stomatal opening in *Vicia*, suggesting that PP1/PP2A phosphatases are positive regulators of light-induced stomatal opening (93) (Figure 1). Abscisic acid (ABA) also inhibits blue light–dependent H^+ pumping activity of *Vicia* guard cell protoplasts (52, 169, 193). ABA inhibition of apoplastic acidification was not observed in the ABA-insensitive *Arabidopsis* mutants *abi1-1* and *abi2-1* (Figure 1). Interestingly, the PP1/PP2A inhibitor okadaic acid partially restored ABA inhibition of proton pumping in *abi1-1* guard cells, whereas the protein kinase inhibitor *K-252a* partially restored ABA inhibition of proton pumping in *abi2-1* guard cells (169).

14-3-3 proteins bind directly to the C-terminal domain and thus activate H^+-ATPases, and fusiccocin stabilizes the 14-3-3–H^+-ATPase complex (16, 49, 86). The direct mechanism of guard cell plasma membrane H^+-ATPase regulation was characterized in an elegant biochemical study. Blue light activates H^+-ATPases via phosphorylation of the C terminus (94). Coprecipitation of H^+-ATPases with endogenous guard cell 14-3-3 proteins and binding of recombinant 14-3-3 proteins only to the phosphorylated H^+-ATPase C terminus provide evidence for a role of 14-3-3 proteins as a positive regulator in physiological blue light signal transduction (Figure 1).

Although two different types of blue light receptors, CRY proteins and NPH1, have been isolated from plants (1a, 28, 29), the blue light receptors in guard cells have been proposed to include unique components. Stomata from the zeaxanthin-deficient *Arabidopsis* mutant, *npq1* (150), are impaired in blue light–induced stomatal opening (47), and stomata from the blue light photoreceptor mutants, *cry1*, *cry2*, *nph1*, *nph3*, *nph4*, *cry1cry2*, and *nph1cry1*, showed a wild-type blue light response (47, 101). These results have led to the proposal of a model in which zeaxanthins function as blue light receptors or receptor pigments in guard cells (47).

Cytosolic Factors That Regulate Inward-Rectifying K_{in}^+ Channels

K_{in}^+ channels in guard cells have been proposed to contribute to K^+ uptake during stomatal opening (178, 181). Reviews on the role of K_{in}^+ channels in guard cells and on the structure and function of these K^+ channels have appeared elsewhere (35, 42, 65, 128, 183). Extracellular acidification increases the activity of guard cell K_{in}^+ channels (20) and of cloned plant K_{in}^+ channels expressed in *Xenopus* oocytes (74, 78, 146, 204). Cytosolic Ca^{2+} ($[Ca^{2+}]_{cyt}$) elevation inhibits K_{in}^+ channels, thus limiting K^+ uptake (108, 175) (Figure 1). Almost complete inhibition of K_{in}^+ channels has been measured in *Vicia* guard cells when $[Ca^{2+}]_{cyt}$ was buffered to $\approx 1 \ \mu M$ (54, 57, 90, 108, 175), or when $InsP_3$ is uncaged in the guard cell cytoplasm to raise $[Ca^{2+}]_{cyt}$ (23) (Figure 1). Interestingly, in *Vicia*, K_{in}^+ channels in abaxial guard cells were $[Ca^{2+}]_{cyt}$ inhibited and stomatal movements were modulated by external Ca^{2+} and ABA, whereas K_{in}^+ channels in adaxial guard cells were insensitive to $[Ca^{2+}]_{cyt}$ and stomatal movements were less sensitive to external Ca^{2+} and ABA (206).

In addition, protein phosphorylation has been suggested to play an important role in modulation of K_{in}^+ channel activity. Inhibitors of calcineurin (PP2B), a calcium-dependent protein phosphatase, maintained K_{in}^+ channel activity in spite of elevated $[Ca^{2+}]_{cyt}$ in *Vicia* guard cells (126) (Figure 1). Cyclosporin A, an inhibitor of animal PP2B-type phosphatases, inhibits stomatal closure and reduces ABA inhibition of stomatal opening in *Pisum*, suggesting that PP2Bs might be negative regulators of stomatal opening (70) (Figure 1). Note that *PP2B* homologs have not yet been identified in plants. In contrast to PP2B inhibitors, inhibitors of PP1/PP2A protein phosphatases downregulate K_{in}^+ channel activity in guard cells, suggesting that PP1 or PP2As are positive regulators of K_{in}^+ channels (121, 201) (Figure 1). Biochemical approaches identified a *Vicia* guard cell Ca^{2+}-dependent protein kinase (CDPK) that phosphorylates the *Arabidopsis* guard cell K_{in}^+ channel subunit KAT1 (118), and heterologous expression of *KAT1* and a soybean CDPK in *Xenopus* oocytes shows a reduction in KAT1-mediated K^+ currents (17), suggesting a role of CDPK in Ca^{2+}-mediated K_{in}^+ channel inhibition (Figure 1). Combined genetic and cell biological analyses will be required to identify the kinases that regulate K_{in}^+ channels.

Stomatal aperture measurements show that linolenic acid and arachidonic acid promote stomatal opening and inhibit stomatal closing (106). Furthermore, patch-clamp analyses show that these fatty acids activate K_{in}^+ currents and inhibit outward-rectifying K_{out}^+ currents (106). These results are interesting as only a few agents have been found that enhance K_{in}^+ channel activity in guard cells. Furthermore, phospholipase A_2 inhibitors decrease stomatal responses to light (196). Together these data suggest that phospholipase A_2 may be a positive regulator of the guard cell light response pathway (Figure 1).

Role of Actin Filaments in Stomatal Movements

Cytochalasin D, an actin filament-depolymerizing agent, activates K_{in}^+ channels and enhances light-induced stomatal opening (76). In contrast, inhibition of K_{in}^+ channel currents and light-induced stomatal opening was observed when an actin filament stabilizer, phalloidin, was tested (76). These results imply a possible interaction of the actin cytoskeleton with guard cell plasma membrane K_{in}^+ channels in signal transduction (Figure 1).

ABA treatments reorganize the actin structure from a radial pattern to a randomly oriented and short-fragmented pattern (44). A small GTP-binding protein, AtRac1, can function as a negative regulator in ABA-induced actin reorganization (107). ABA causes AtRac1 inactivation (Figure 3, see color insert). This ABA response was impaired in *abi1-1* (107). In addition, transgenic *Arabidopsis* plants expressing a dominant negative AtRac1 mutant mimic constitutive ABA-induced actin reorganization in guard cells and increase ABA sensitivity of stomatal closure (107), suggesting that inactivation of AtRac1 is required for actin reorganization and stomatal closure. Together these studies show important roles of actin and small G-proteins in stomatal movements.

Cloned Guard Cell K_{in}^+ Channel Genes

The *Arabidopsis* K_{in}^+ channel gene *KAT1* was cloned by complementation of a yeast mutant defective in K^+ transport (10) and shown to mediate K^+ currents in *Xenopus* oocytes with typical properties of plant K_{in}^+ currents (67, 73, 78, 173, 204). Expression studies with *Arabidopsis KAT1* and the potato ortholog *KST1* show that these plant K_{in}^+ channel genes are predominantly expressed in guard cells (146, 148). In animals, functional K^+ channel proteins are composed of four α–subunits (87) and additional regulatory β–subunits (45). An *Arabidopsis* cDNA encoding a β–subunit homolog of K^+ channels has been isolated and binding to KAT1 has been reported (199).

The model that K_{in}^+ channels contribute to K^+ uptake during stomatal opening (181) has been analyzed using molecular genetic approaches. In a study with transgenic *Arabidopsis* expressing *KAT1* mutants with a reduced sensitivity to Cs^+ block, transgenic plants exhibited partial light-induced stomatal opening in the presence of Cs^+ concentrations that inhibit stomatal opening in wildtype (77). In another study, transgenic *Arabidopsis* expressing a dominant negative mutant form of the guard cell K_{in}^+ channel KAT1 showed 75% reduction in the activity of guard cell K_{in}^+ channel currents and a reduction in light-induced stomatal opening (100). As redundancy likely exists in K^+ channel subunits in guard cells, these data show that dominant negative *kat1* can disrupt K_{in}^+ channels. These data support the model that K^+ channels constitute a central mechanism for K^+ uptake during stomatal opening (178, 181). These studies do not exclude the likely model that other partially redundant (183) K^+ uptake transporters function in parallel in guard cells. For example, there are >12 isoforms of the *KT-KUP-HAK* K^+ transporter gene family (48, 91, 161, 172) in the *Arabidopsis* genome and some of these are likely to be expressed in guard cells. Furthermore, patch-clamp studies have shown the activity of additional inward-conducting cation channels (69, 205, 212). In conclusion, many positive and negative regulators of H^+ pumps, K_{in}^+ channels, and stomatal opening have been found (Figure 1). A combination of genetic, cell biological, and biochemical studies will allow further testing and expansion of these models.

MULTIPLE PHYSIOLOGICAL AND ABIOTIC STIMULI INDUCE STOMATAL CLOSING

Abscisic acid, produced in response to water deficit, causes stomatal closing. Furthermore, in C3 and C4 plants stomatal closing is induced by darkness and by elevated CO_2 concentrations in the intercellular spaces in leaves, arising from respiration (12, 133). Stomatal closing and reduced transpiration also leads to elevated temperatures inside leaves. Pathogen elicitors also cause stomatal closing, enabling plants to reduce access of pathogens to the inside of leaves (104). Aerial pollutants such as ozone and sulfur dioxide cause stomatal closing at high concentrations (203), thus reducing further damage of leaf tissues by these pollutants. Thus multiple stimuli elicit stomatal closing. Although the reception mechanisms for these stimuli remain unknown, the signaling pathways need to converge on central guard cell ion channel and metabolic pathways.

Model for Roles of Ion Channels in ABA-Induced Stomatal Closing

Stomatal closing requires ion efflux from guard cells. Models for roles of ion channels during ABA-induced stomatal closing have been used as a basis for dissecting upstream ABA signal transduction mechanisms (132, 175, 177, 207). In brief, ABA induces cytosolic Ca^{2+} increases (134) (Figure 2; see color insert). Cytosolic calcium elevations, in turn, inhibit plasma membrane proton pumps (92) and K_{in}^+ channels and activate two types or modes (39) of plasma membrane anion channels that mediate anion release from guard cells (89, 175) (Figure 2). One of these anion channels shows s̲low and s̲ustained activation (S-type anion channels) (122, 175, 179), whereas the other anion channel shows r̲apid transient activation (R-type or GCAC anion channels) (64). Channel-mediated anion efflux from guard cells causes either transient or sustained anion efflux and depolarization (Figure 2). Depolarization, in turn, deactivates inward-rectifying K^+ (K_{in}^+) channels and activates outward-rectifying K^+ (K_{out}^+) channels (181), resulting in K^+ efflux from guard cells (Figure 2). The ensuing long-term efflux of both anions and K^+ from guard cells contributes to loss of guard cell turgor and to stomatal closing (175) (Figure 2). Recent studies have shown a requirement for rapid ABA-induced Ca^{2+} influx and S-type anion channel activation for *RAB18* expression in *Arabidopsis* suspension culture cells (49b, 49c) indicating that these mechanisms (Figure 2) are of general importance for early ABA signaling in other cell types.

Most ions released across the plasma membrane of guard cells need first to be released into the cytosol from guard cell vacuoles (8, 130, 131, 207, 208). Models for the roles of vacuolar K^+ and anion channels during stomatal regulation have been proposed previously and are described elsewhere (7, 8, 131, 157, 207, 208). However, these models have not yet been tested as stringently as those for plasma membrane ion channels. Combined molecular genetic (e.g. gene disruption) and cell biological approaches are needed to directly analyze these vacuolar ion channel models.

CO$_2$-Induced Stomatal Closing

Elevated CO$_2$ concentrations arising from respiration in darkness stimulate stomatal closing (133). Increases in atmospheric CO$_2$ concentrations are also predicted to reduce stomatal apertures and affect gas exchange (12, 41). CO$_2$ signaling mechanisms in guard cells have been reviewed recently (12, 41). Here, we briefly summarize some recent findings and signaling models. Elevated CO$_2$ concentrations trigger rises in [Ca^{2+}]$_{cyt}$ (209), activate S-type anion and outward-rectifying K$^+$ channel currents (24), and modulate R-type anion channels (K Raschke, personal communication). These data show that the ion channel targets of early CO$_2$ signaling are to a degree shared with ABA signaling (Figure 2). However, upstream CO$_2$ sensing and transduction mechanisms have been reported to differ from ABA signaling, because the *abi1-1* and *abi2-1* mutants show wild-type CO$_2$-induced stomatal closing (116). A CO$_2$-induced increase in cell wall malate concentration has been proposed to cause stomatal closing (66). However, >20 mM external malate was required to produce stomatal closing in two independent studies under the same experimental conditions as the above study (31, 43). Furthermore, external malate counteracted CO$_2$-induced stomatal closing (31), thus calling into question the malate as CO$_2$ sensor hypothesis. An alternative hypothesis suggests that the CO$_2$ sensor is located in guard cell chloroplasts and functions via a CO$_2$-induced decrease in zeaxanthin levels (216). Further understanding of CO$_2$ sensing and signaling in guard cells will help in finding crucial links between the signaling pathways reviewed here and guard cell metabolic pathways. Foremost, future research should have important implications for manipulating gas exchange and carbon fixation in the face of rising atmospheric CO$_2$ levels.

STIMULI THAT INCREASE CYTOSOLIC CALCIUM IN GUARD CELLS

Roles of [Ca^{2+}]$_{cyt}$ in Stomatal Closing

Many stimuli that result in a change in stomatal aperture have been shown, at least in part, to utilize signal transduction pathways involving changes in guard cell [Ca^{2+}]$_{cyt}$. ABA-induced stomatal closing is Ca^{2+}-dependent (37, 51, 175, 186). Note that a Ca^{2+}-independent pathway appears to also exist (2). ABA induces repetitive, transient increases or oscillations in guard cell [Ca^{2+}]$_{cyt}$ (5, 50, 56, 135, 176, 195). Genetic support for the importance of ABA-induced [Ca^{2+}]$_{cyt}$ elevations in guard cells has been obtained recently, as the ABA-insensitive *Arabidopsis* mutants *abi1-1* and *abi2-1* show greatly reduced ABA-induced [Ca^{2+}]$_{cyt}$ elevations, and the *abi* anion channel regulation and stomatal movement phenotypes are suppressed by experimentally elevating [Ca^{2+}]$_{cyt}$ (4). Stomatal closure and guard cell [Ca^{2+}]$_{cyt}$ oscillations can also be induced by increases in external (apoplastic) [Ca^{2+}] (4, 5, 139). These Ca^{2+}-induced [Ca^{2+}]$_{cyt}$ oscillations include a repetitive Ca^{2+} influx across the plasma membrane coupled to Ca^{2+} release from intracellular stores for each separate Ca^{2+} transient (56, 139). Why $[Ca^{2+}]_{cyt}$ regulation is so sensitive to changes in apoplastic Ca^{2+} is not fully understood, although many species limit Ca^{2+} accumulation in the apoplast surrounding guard cells to prevent aberrant stomatal regulation (38, 171). Increases in CO_2 cause stomatal closure and $[Ca^{2+}]_{cyt}$ elevations (209). Cold shock (3, 211a) and oxidative stress, induced by application of H_2O_2 or methyl viologen, increase $[Ca^{2+}]_{cyt}$ and result in stomatal closure (137, 156). The removal of extracellular Ca^{2+} using EGTA abolishes CO_2- and H_2O_2-induced $[Ca^{2+}]_{cyt}$ elevations, indicating that plasma membrane Ca^{2+} influx occurs (156, 209).

Roles of $[Ca^{2+}]_{cyt}$ in Stomatal Opening

Interestingly, stimuli that result in stomatal opening also induce $[Ca^{2+}]_{cyt}$ elevations. Auxin promotes stomatal opening and direct $[Ca^{2+}]_{cyt}$ measurements (80), and pharmacological studies (32) suggest a role for $[Ca^{2+}]_{cyt}$ elevations. Furthermore, Ca^{2+}-dependent protein kinases (CDPK) activate guard cell vacuole Cl^- channels and malate uptake currents that have been implicated in vacuolar anion uptake during stomatal opening (157). Blue light promotes stomatal opening, and pharmacological experiments suggest the involvement of $[Ca^{2+}]_{cyt}$/calmodulin as a second messenger in this process (33, 194). However, increasing external Ca^{2+} can inhibit light-induced stomatal opening (4, 152, 192) (Figure 1). Cyclic nucleotides may also act in a Ca^{2+}-dependent stomatal opening pathway as stomatal opening can be stimulated by cAMP (33) or the membrane-permeable cGMP analog 8-Br-cGMP (32). Cyclic GMP-induced stomatal opening is inhibited by chelation of external Ca^{2+} or by inhibitors of intracellular Ca^{2+} release (32).

How a single second messenger such as $[Ca^{2+}]_{cyt}$ can control many diverse and opposing responses in a single cell type remains unknown but likely depends on the Ca^{2+} channels and Ca^{2+} regulatory systems activated by each stimulus, the downstream response elements expressed at a given time, and the characteristics and dynamics of the elicited $[Ca^{2+}]_{cyt}$ change (the Ca^{2+} signature) (138). The recent demonstration that GFP-based "cameleon" calcium indicators (142, 143) function in *Arabidopsis* will allow addressing of these questions by combined genetic and $[Ca^{2+}]_{cyt}$ signaling studies (5).

SECOND MESSENGER SYSTEMS REGULATING $[Ca^{2+}]_{cyt}$ IN GUARD CELLS

Cyclic ADP-Ribose and Vacuolar Ca^{2+} Release

Recent experiments have implicated several second messenger systems in ABA and $[Ca^{2+}]_{cyt}$ signaling in guard cells (Figure 3; see color insert). In animal cells, cyclic ADP ribose (cADPR) is produced from NAD via the action of the enzyme ADP-Ribosyl cyclase, and it mobilizes Ca^{2+} from intracellular stores by activation of an endomembrane ion channel known as the ryanodine receptor

(RYR) (103). In plant vacuoles, nanomolar cADPR concentrations can activate a Ca^{2+} permeable current (6). Microinjection of cADPR into tomato hypocotyl cells shows that cADPR can function in ABA signaling (213). In *Commelina* guard cells cADPR causes $[Ca^{2+}]_{cyt}$ increases and elicits stomatal closing (102). However, microinjection of the inactive cADPR analog 8-NH_2-cADPR or noncyclic ADPR does not elicit $[Ca^{2+}]_{cyt}$ increases or guard cell turgor loss. Ryanodine treatment of guard cells also reduces $[Ca^{2+}]_{cyt}$ increases (57). Note that ABA-induced stomatal closure is only partly inhibited by either microinjection of 8-NH_2-cADPR (102) or by nicotinamide, an inhibitor of cADPR production (85, 102), suggesting that additional parallel $[Ca^{2+}]_{cyt}$ elevation mechanisms are needed in the ABA signaling cascade.

Phospholipase C and Inositol 1,4,5 Trisphosphate

Various lines of evidence suggest that phospholipase C (PLC) is a component of ABA signal transduction in guard cells. Early experiments showed that release of caged $InsP_3$ into the cytosol of guard cells could cause $[Ca^{2+}]_{cyt}$ increases and stomatal closure (51) and inhibit K_{in}^+ channels (23). Treating guard cell protoplasts with ABA slightly elevates $InsP_3$ levels (105, 151). Additionally, the PLC inhibitor U-73122 (but not the inactive analog U-73343) inhibits the activity of recombinant PLC from tobacco (195). ABA-induced stomatal closure was also inhibited by U-73122, but only by 20% (195). However, complete inhibition of ABA-induced stomatal closure can be achieved by treating stomata with a combination of U-73122 and nicotinamide (85, 132a), suggesting that both cADPR and PLC signaling systems function in ABA signaling (Figure 3).

Note that other inositol-phosphates can also act as second messengers in ABA signal transduction in guard cells. In a recent study, myo-inositol hexakisphosphate ($InsP_6$) was identified as an intermediary of guard cell signal transduction. ABA stimulates production of $InsP_6$ in guard cells, and $InsP_6$ perfused into the cytosol via a patch pipette inhibited K_{in}^+ channels in potato guard cell protoplasts in a Ca^{2+}-dependent manner. These data suggest that $InsP_6$ production is also an important component of ABA signaling (109) (Figures 1, 3; see color insert).

Phospholipase D and Phosphatidic Acid

Phospholipase D (PLD) has been implicated in ABA signaling in aleurone cells (164) and in guard cells (85). PLD generates phosphatidic acid (PtdOH), and ABA treatment of *Vicia* guard cells caused PtdOH levels to transiently increase 2.5-fold (85). PtdOH also promotes stomatal closure and inactivates K_{in}^+ currents. Guard cell $[Ca^{2+}]_{cyt}$ did not increase following PtdOH treatment, suggesting that PLD acts in a parallel pathway or downstream of Ca^{2+} mobilizing second messenger systems (Figure 3). An inhibitor of PLD activity, 1-butanol, caused only a partial inhibition of ABA-induced stomatal closure whereas near-complete inhibition of stomatal closure resulted from adding 1-butanol together with nicotinamide (85), suggesting a parallel action of PLD to the cADPR-mediated pathway.

Amplifying Calcium Signals by Calcium-Induced Calcium Release

Release of caged Ca^{2+} into the guard cell cytosol can induce $[Ca^{2+}]_{cyt}$ increases or oscillations that are larger than can be accounted for solely by the Ca^{2+} released by photolysis (51, 139), suggesting that a $[Ca^{2+}]_{cyt}$-induced calcium release (CICR) mechanism exists in guard cells. Ca^{2+}-permeable SV channels have been proposed to amplify and propagate $[Ca^{2+}]_{cyt}$ signals in guard cells by CICR from vacuoles (208). Cytosolic Mg^{2+} sensitizes SV channels to physiological $[Ca^{2+}]_{cyt}$ elevations (158) and shifts the voltage-dependence of SV channels (27) such that SV channel activity is enhanced. The ability of the SV channel to mediate CICR has been questioned because in mesophyll vacuoles increasing the transvacuolar Ca^{2+} gradient shifts the voltage-dependence to prevent channel opening under conditions that would otherwise allow Ca^{2+} to enter the cytosol (160). However, the voltage-dependence and pharmacology of radiolabeled Ca^{2+} release in vitro from vacuolar vesicles suggests that CICR can be mediated by SV channels (18). The role of SV channels in CICR in guard cells remains an important issue in signal transduction, analysis of which best requires manipulation of SV channel genes.

Plasma Membrane Calcium Channels and Calcium Influx in Guard Cells

Experimental application of repeated hyperpolarizations negative of -120 mV induced repetitive $[Ca^{2+}]_{cyt}$ transients in guard cells (56). ABA application shifted the threshold of hyperpolarization-activated Ca^{2+} elevations to -80 mV, indicating that an early event in ABA signaling is the sensitization of Ca^{2+} influx to membrane potential. Furthermore, in 50 mM KCl buffers [in which the cells are depolarized (168, 202)] ABA only induces $[Ca^{2+}]_{cyt}$ increases in 30–60% of guard cells (2, 4, 50, 135, 176). Transient ABA activation of Ca^{2+}-permeable channels was found during depolarizations in 37% of guard cells (176), which could contribute to ABA-induced $[Ca^{2+}]_{cyt}$ elevations in depolarized guard cells. Interestingly, in cells maintained in 5 mM KCl, guard cells are hyperpolarized and ABA induces repetitive $[Ca^{2+}]_{cyt}$ transients or oscillations in a higher proportion of cells (80–90%) (5, 56, 195). These data indicate that changes in plasma membrane potential are a central component in ABA signaling.

The upstream second messenger mechanisms that activate guard cell plasma membrane Ca^{2+} channels remained unknown. A recent study in *Arabidopsis* guard cells shows that reactive oxygen species (ROS) can activate a hyperpolarization-activated Ca^{2+} influx current (I_{Ca}) and that ROS can act as a second messenger in ABA signaling. ABA treatment enhances ROS production in *Arabidopsis* guard cells (156). Interestingly, ABA activates guard cell I_{Ca} (156) only when NADPH is present in the cytosol, implicating NADPH oxidases in ABA signaling (Y Murata & J Schroeder, unpublished). Activation of I_{Ca} by hydrogen peroxide is impaired in the recessive ABA-insensitive mutant *gca2*, whereas ABA-induced ROS production remains intact in *gca2* (156), providing genetic evidence for roles of ROS and I_{Ca} in ABA signaling. These data lead to a model in which ROS production, GCA2, and Ca^{2+} channel activation represent a new signaling "cassette" in guard cells (Figure 3, see color insert). A study in maize embryos has also shown that ABA enhances ROS production (60), indicating that ROS may be universal second messengers in plant ABA signaling.

Single channel recordings in *Vicia* guard cell protoplasts have identified a Ca^{2+} channel that is hyperpolarization-activated and shows a 250-fold increased open probability following addition of 20 μM ABA (61). Currents exhibited by this channel are very similar to I_{Ca}. The activation by ABA occurs in isolated patches, suggesting that ABA perception and channel activation are closely associated in *Vicia*. Interestingly, the single channel open probability was reduced tenfold when buffering $[Ca^{2+}]_{cyt}$ from 200 nM to 2 μM, indicating that the channel is down-regulated during $[Ca^{2+}]_{cyt}$ elevation and is therefore subject to negative feedback control during $[Ca^{2+}]_{cyt}$ signaling (61).

Both at the single-channel level (61) and in whole cells (156), the activity of the Ca^{2+} influx channel can show spontaneous oscillatory behavior without exogenous ABA addition. Background I_{Ca} activity was inhibited by addition of 0.1 mM DTT in *Arabidopsis* guard cells (156). The spontaneous I_{Ca} activity may contribute to spontaneous $[Ca^{2+}]_{cyt}$ elevations found in hyperpolarized guard cells (5, 56, 195). Because I_{Ca} channels are regulated by ROS, various stress signals may control Ca^{2+} influx by regulating the oxidative state of guard cells. For example, pathogen elicitors trigger ROS production in guard cells and stomatal closing (104), and ozone, which closes stomatal pores (203), might modulate I_{Ca}. In this regard, ROS production and I_{Ca} have been proposed to function as a shared "signaling cassette" of multiple stress signaling pathways (156).

Additional Ca^{2+} influx pathways may be provided by plasma membrane stretch-activated Ca^{2+} permeable channels (30) or via a Ca^{2+} permeability of transient and sustained K^+_{out} channels (153, 170). Clearly, Ca^{2+} influx, Ca^{2+} release, and second messengers are integrated in guard cells to produce a $[Ca^{2+}]_{cyt}$ signal that controls stomatal movements. How these separate processes may be integrated to produce $[Ca^{2+}]_{cyt}$ signals that encode information necessary for stomatal closure is an important focus of ongoing studies (see 132a).

Cytosolic $[Ca^{2+}]$ Oscillations Are Necessary for Stomatal Closing in Guard Cells

In a few cases in animal cells, the frequency of $[Ca^{2+}]_{cyt}$ oscillations has been shown to control the efficiency and specificity of cellular responses (36, 40, 120). In plants, it remains to be investigated whether Ca^{2+} oscillations are an absolute requirement for eliciting physiological responses. Models for membrane potential oscillations in guard cells have been generated (26, 59, 96) to analyze different mechanisms that may contribute to generation of $[Ca^{2+}]_{cyt}$ oscillations. Using guard cells of the *Arabidopsis* V-ATPase mutant *de-etiolated 3* (*det3*) (185), which has reduced endomembrane proton pumping and energization, external Ca^{2+} and oxidative stress elicited prolonged Ca^{2+} increases (plateaus) that did not oscillate, whereas wild-type cells show $[Ca^{2+}]_{cyt}$ oscillations (3). Unexpectedly, steady state stomatal closure was inhibited in *det3* in response to these stimuli. Conversely, cold and ABA elicited Ca^{2+} oscillations in *det3*, and stomatal closures were not impaired (3). Moreover, in *det3* guard cells, experimentally imposing external Ca^{2+}-induced oscillations rescued steady state stomatal closure in response to external Ca^{2+}, and imposing Ca^{2+} plateaus in wild-type guard cells prevented steady-state stomatal closing. These data provide genetic evidence that stimulus-specific Ca^{2+} oscillations, rather than a mere plateau of $[Ca^{2+}]_{cyt}$, are necessary for long-term stomatal closure (3). These findings suggest that guard cells may provide an excellent genetic system to study $[Ca^{2+}]_{cyt}$ pattern-dependent responses.

ABA-INSENSITIVE PP2C MUTANTS

Genetic screens for *Arabidopsis* mutants insensitive to ABA inhibition of seed germination yielded two dominant mutants that are impaired in ABA-induced stomatal closure (97). The corresponding genes, *ABI1* and *ABI2*, both encode type 2C protein phosphatases and the dominant mutant alleles *abi1-1* and *abi2-1* have point mutations altering a conserved amino acid (112, 114, 140, 166). Several downstream responses to ABA are impaired in these *Arabidopsis* mutants including K_{out}^{+} and K_{in}^{+} channel regulation (11) and anion channel activation (155). These mutations also impair ABA-induced $[Ca^{2+}]_{cyt}$ increases (4). Furthermore, experimental elevation in $[Ca^{2+}]_{cyt}$ causes anion channel activation and stomatal closure in *abi1-1* and *abi2-1*, thus bypassing the effects of the *abi1-1* and *abi2-1* mutations (4). These data demonstrate that the dominant *abi* PP2C mutants interfere with very early ABA signaling events that act upstream of $[Ca^{2+}]_{cyt}$ (4) (Figure 3).

Because the only known alleles of these genes were dominant mutations, it has been unclear whether the ABI1 and ABI2 phosphatases are positive or negative regulators of ABA signaling or indeed whether they affect ABA signaling at all in wildtype. Recently, however, intragenic revertants of the *abi1-1* and *abi2-1* mutants were isolated and shown to have reduced or no phosphatase activity in vitro (53, 139a). Because a double mutant of both revertants shows hypersensitivity to ABA, ABI1 and ABI2 are likely negative regulators of ABA signaling (139a). In correlation, overexpression of wild-type ABI1 in maize mesophyll protoplasts blocks ABA regulation of gene expression (191). In spite of these advances, *ABI1* and *ABI2* gene deletion or silencing mutants would be useful for a stringent test of their functions, because all intragenic revertant mutations lie downstream of the dominant mutant site (53, 139a), which might form an attachment to an essential signaling protein.

ANION CHANNELS AND ABA-INDUCED STOMATAL CLOSURE

Anion channel activation at the plasma membrane of guard cells has been proposed as an essential step during stomatal closure (Figure 2) (64, 175, 179). S-type anion channel currents in guard cells are activated by increases in $[Ca^{2+}]_{cyt}$ in *Vicia* (175) and *Arabidopsis* (4). R-type anion currents are activated following an increase in external Ca^{2+} (64). Whether ABA regulates R-type anion channels remains to be determined. ABA activation of S-type anion channels in the plasma membrane of guard cells has now been demonstrated in *Arabidopsis* (155), tobacco (58), and *Vicia* (111, 119, 187) (Figure 3). This response is disrupted in the *Arabidopsis abi1-1* and *abi2-1* mutants, providing genetic evidence that activation of S-type channels contributes to stomatal closure (155). Putative anion channel genes have been cloned from tobacco (127) and *Arabidopsis* (62) based on sequence homology with the animal voltage-dependent CLC chloride channels [for review see (15)]. Further work is needed to determine whether these genes encode components of native plant plasma membrane anion channels.

Regulation of Guard Cell ABA Signaling by ABC Proteins

Pharmacological studies have led to the model that guard cell S-type anion channels may be encoded by or regulated by ATP binding cassette (ABC) proteins (110, 111) (Figure 3). ABC proteins comprise a large family of membrane proteins that actively translocate a wide spectrum of substrates. In addition, ABC proteins regulate the activity of other unrelated transporters. ABC proteins such as CFTR (cystic fibrosis transmembrane conductance regulator) or SUR (sulfonylurea receptor) show Cl^- channel activity and/or regulate other channels [for review see (200)]. Inhibitors of SUR, such as glibenclamide, prevent ABA-induced stomatal closure in *Vicia* and *Commelina*. Furthermore, the ABC protein inhibitors DPC and glibenclamide block slow anion currents in *Vicia* guard cells (111). In contrast, cromakalin, an antagonist of glibenclamide, triggers stomatal closing in *Commelina* and reverses the inhibition of glibenclamide on S-type anion currents in *Vicia* guard cells (111).

Protein Kinases Function in ABA Signaling and Anion Channel Regulation

Pharmacological approaches, using the serine/threonine protein kinase inhibitor K252a and cytosolic replacement of ATP, showed that phosphorylation events are central positive regulators in ABA-induced stomatal closure in *Vicia* (174), as well as in *Commelina* (43), *Pisum* (70), and *Arabidopsis* (4). K252a abolishes both

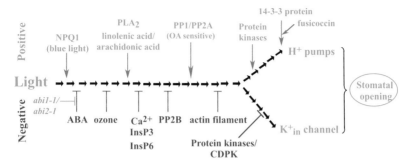

Figure 1 A simplified working model for proposed functions of positive and negative regulators in light-induced stomatal opening. Positive (in green, *top*) and negative regulators (in red, *bottom*) of light signaling in guard cells are shown. The sequence of events and epistasis among regulators remain largely unknown and requires further genetic, biochemical, and cellular signaling analyses. For simplicity, parallel signaling branches are not included here (see text for details).

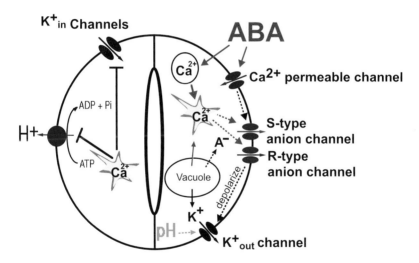

Figure 2 A guard cell model, illustrating the proposed functions of ion channels in ABA signaling and stomatal closing (177). The right cell of the stomate shows ion channels and regulators that mediate ABA-induced stomatal closing. The left cell shows the parallel effects of ABA-induced $[Ca^{2+}]_{cyt}$ increases that inhibit stomatal opening mechanisms. [Modified with permission from Schroeder et al, 2001 (180)]

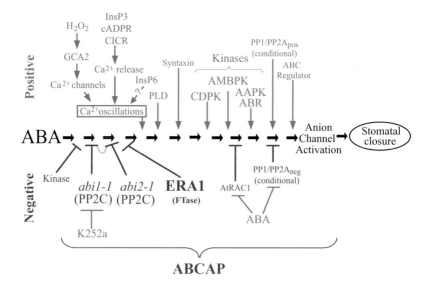

Figure 3 A working model for the proposed functions of positive and negative regulators of ABA-induced stomatal closing and of S-type anion channels in guard cells. Positive transducers are shown at top and/or in green and negative regulators are shown below in red. The sequence of events and epistasis among regulators remains largely unknown and requires further analysis. For simplicity, parallel signaling branches are not shown. Note that some of the ABA signaling "casettes" (*top*, vertical cascades) may be activated by ABA in parallel (see text for details).

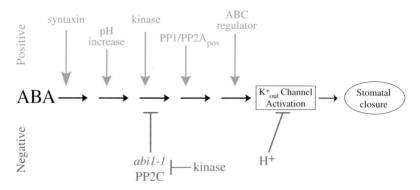

Figure 4 A working model for the proposed functions of positive transducers and negative regulators of K^+_{out} channels in guard cells. Positive transducers (green, *top*) and negative regulators (red, *bottom*) are shown.

anion channel activity and ABA-induced stomatal closing (174). In correlation with these results, ABA induction of gene expression (*RD29a* and *KIN2*) in tomato hypocotyls is inhibited by K252a (213), together with other studies, indicating that kinase-dependent transduction of ABA signaling (174) is of general significance (95, 190, 213). Note that the R-type anion currents are not regulated by phosphorylation events but that nucleotide binding activates these anion channels (64, 184).

Biochemical approaches led to the characterization of a Ca^{2+}-independent, ABA inducible 48-kDa kinase (non-MAP kinase) in *Vicia* guard cells (117, 144). The kinase activity was named AAPK or ABR. Recently, an *AAPK* gene was cloned (119). Transient expression of a dominant negative allele of AAPK, which abolished kinase activity, prevents ABA activation of S-type anion currents and stomatal closing. In correlation with these findings, in *Vicia* S-type anion currents are activated at low $[Ca^{2+}]_{cyt}$ and high ATP concentrations, suggesting that a final phosphorylation event in anion channel activation can be Ca^{2+} independent (187) (Figure 3). Recessive loss-of-function mutations in AAPK will allow further analysis of AAPK function in guard cells.

Two Ca^{2+}-dependent protein kinases of 53 kDa and 58 kDa have been characterized in *Vicia* guard cells (118, 144). Removal of Ca^{2+} with BAPTA in *Vicia* guard cell protoplast suspensions prevents ABR kinase activation and indicates that Ca^{2+} is required upstream for ABR activation (144) (Figure 3). These data and overexpression studies on maize protoplasts suggest that CDPKs may be positive regulators in ABA signal transduction (190).

In addition, MAP kinases have been reported to positively control ABA-induced stomatal closure in *Pisum* (25). ABA causes a transient activation of a 43-kDa MAP kinase named AMBPK. AMBPK exhibits all fundamental MAP kinase properties, including tyrosine phosphorylation (25). The MAPK kinase inhibitor PD98059 abolished ABA-induced stomatal closing (Figure 3) and ABA induction of dehydrin mRNA (25). ABA activation of MAP kinases in barley aleurone was previously reported (68, 95).

In parallel to the above kinases that transduce ABA signals, other protein kinases have been suggested to act as negative regulators of ABA signaling in tobacco and *Arabidopsis* guard cells in the *abi1-1* background (11, 155). Application of kinase inhibitors partially restores ABA activation of anion channels and regulation of K^+ channels and stomatal closing in *abi1-1* backgrounds (11, 155) (Figures 3 and 4; see color insert).

Okadaic Acid–Sensitive Phosphatases Regulate Anion Channels and ABA Signaling

Inhibitors of PP1 and PP2A protein phosphatases such as okadaic acid (OA) were found to enhance S-type anion currents and ABA-induced stomatal closure in *Vicia* (174, 187), as well as in tobacco (58), *Commelina* (43), and *Pisum* (70), and enhance ABA-induced gene expression in tomato hypocotyls (213), suggesting that

PP1s or PP2As act as negative regulators in ABA signaling (Figure 3; PP1/PP2A$_{neg}$). Note that PP1/PP2A$_{neg}$ in Figure 3 and the PP1/PP2A shown in Figure 1 both promote stomatal opening and therefore might be encoded by the same genes. In *Vicia*, either OA or ABA maintain anion current activation without cytosolic ATP, indicating that ABA may indeed downregulate a PP1/PP2A$_{neg}$ (187) (Figure 3).

In addition to negatively regulating PP1/PP2As, evidence suggests that other PP1/PP2As can also act as positive regulators in ABA signaling (Figure 3; PP1/-PP2A$_{pos}$). In *Arabidopsis*, OA partially inhibited ABA activation of S-type anion channels and stomatal closing (155). A similar inhibitory effect of OA was also observed on ABA signaling during stomatal opening and ABA induction of dehydrin mRNA in *Pisum* epidermal peels (70). OA also inhibits ABA-induced expression of the *PHAV1* gene in barley aleurone (99). Experiments in *Pisum* show that the activity of either PP1/PP2A$_{pos}$ or PP1/PP2A$_{neg}$ can be resolved depending on the aperture of stomates (70) (Figure 3).

These different studies bring to light that a complex phosphorylation and dephosphoryation network exists in guard cells (Figure 3) and that significant differences can occur in ABA signaling depending on the physiological state of guard cells.

ACTIVITY OF PLASMA MEMBRANE K$^+_{out}$ CHANNELS IN STOMATAL MOVEMENTS

Efflux of K$^+$ from the cell during stomatal closing has been proposed to occur through outward rectifying K$^+$ (K$^+_{out}$) channels that are activated by membrane depolarization (181). Guard cells respond to ABA by enhancing K$^+_{out}$ and reducing K$^+_{in}$ channel currents (19, 22). Unlike K$^+_{in}$ channels, however, K$^+_{out}$ channels are largely insensitive to increases in [Ca^{2+}]$_{cyt}$ that occur during ABA signaling (108, 175). A guard cell-expressed *SKOR* K$^+$ channel cDNA homologue, named *GORK*, was isolated that when expressed in *Xenopus* oocytes produces outward-rectifying K$^+$ channels with properties similar to K$^+_{out}$ channels (1).

ABA induces an increase in the cytosolic pH of guard cells (22, 54, 80). Experiments in *Vicia* guard cells show that K$^+_{out}$ currents are enhanced by increased cytoplasmic pH (20). The pH stimulation of K$^+_{out}$ channels occurs in isolated membrane patches and is thus membrane delimited (141). ABA-induced increases in K$^+_{out}$ currents can be inhibited by acidification or buffering of the guard cell cytoplasmic pH, showing that cytosolic pH has a functional role in ABA signal transduction (22) (Figure 4; see color insert).

Regulation of K$^+_{out}$ by Phosphorylation

Several lines of evidence suggest that protein phosphorylation plays a role in modulation of K$^+_{out}$ channel activity. Guard cells from tobacco plants transformed with the dominant phosphatase mutant allele *abi1-1* from *Arabidopsis* show K$^+_{out}$ currents that are two- to fourfold lower than wild type, and both K$^+_{in}$ and K$^+_{out}$

currents are insensitive to modulation by ABA, suggesting a role for PP2Cs in guard cell signaling (11). Despite the ABA insensitivity of K_{out}^+ channels in the *abi1-1*-transformed guard cells, concurrent measurements of intracellular pH show normal pH increases in response to ABA (55). This suggests that the *abi1-1* phosphatase acts downstream of, or parallel to, the cytosolic pH changes (Figure 4). If cytosolic pH directly modulates K_{out}^+ channels (141), then *abi1-1* must act in a parallel pathway to alter the responsiveness of the K_{out}^+ channel to pH.

In addition to the PP2C phosphatases identified genetically, experiments using the phosphatase inhibitor OA implicate PP1- or PP2A-type protein phosphatases in the regulation guard cell K_{out}^+ channels. OA downregulates both K_{in}^+ and K_{out}^+ channel currents in *Vicia* (201). However, another study showed that OA downregulated only K_{in}^+, and not K_{out}^+, currents (121). Despite the experimental differences, one study indicates a putative role for PP1- and/or PP2A-phosphatases as positive regulators of K_{out}^+ channel activity in guard cells [(Figure 4); possibly related to PP1/PP2A$_{pos}$ in (Figure 3)].

Syntaxins and ABA Signaling

Syntaxins play important roles in membrane fusion. A tobacco cDNA encoding a homolog of human and yeast syntaxin (*NtSyr1*) was isolated using heterologous expression of drought-stressed tobacco leaf mRNA in *Xenopus* oocytes (115). Expression of mRNA pools show ABA activation of endogeneous Ca^{2+}-activated Cl^- currents in oocytes (115) and ABA downregulation of KAT1-mediated K_{in}^+ channels in oocytes (196a), suggesting that oocytes will provide an approach for isolating and analyzing putative ABA receptor cDNAs. By subfractionation the *NtSyr1* mRNA was isolated, which when expressed in oocytes constitutively activated the Cl^- currents without addition of ABA (115). Whether *NtSyr1* contributes to the ABA response in oocytes remains to be determined (115). Voltage clamp recordings in tobacco guard cells provide pharmacological evidence for a role of syntaxins in ABA regulation of K^+ channels and S-type anion channels. These data suggest that syntaxin acts as a positive regulator of ABA signaling in guard cells (115) (Figures 3 and 4). Guard cell volume is changed during stomatal movements and is accompanied by changes in membrane surface area (72, 98). Syntaxins may link ABA signaling to membrane trafficking.

Osmolarity and Temperature Sensitivity

Guard cell measurements of $^{86}Rb^+$ efflux kinetics show that whereas a rapid transient K^+ release response to ABA was dependent on the concentration of ABA and duration of exposure, the end-state or final internal $^{86}Rb^+$ concentration reached was not (131). This led to the suggestion that guard cells have some means of sensing their internal osmolarity that is linked to regulation of K^+ efflux channels. *Vicia* guard cell plasma membrane patches exposed to osmotic gradients show K_{out}^+ channels that are inactivated by hypotonic (guard cell swelling) conditions and activated by hypertonic (guard cell shrinking) conditions (123).

Recent work has suggested that K_{out}^+ channels may be involved in the response of guard cells to another environmental stimulus: temperature. At moderate temperatures ($13°$ to $20°C$), both K_{in}^+ and K_{out}^+ channel conductances in *Vicia* increase with increasing temperature. At temperatures from $20°$ to $28°C$, K_{out}^+ conductance decreases with increasing temperature, whereas K_{in}^+ conductance continues to increase (79). This difference in temperature response between K_{in}^+ and K_{out}^+ channels at higher temperatures would favor K^+ influx and stomatal opening and thus could allow increased transpirational cooling of leaves (79).

Transient K^+ Efflux Currents

In addition to the slow activating K_{out}^+ channels discussed above, a rapidly activated transient outward K^+ current, (I_{AP}), has been observed in *Arabidopsis* and tobacco guard cells (11, 153, 167). In addition to being the first inactivating K_{out}^+ current characterized in plants, I_{AP} has several unusual characteristics. In contrast to the slow K_{out}^+ channels that are activated by alkaline cytosolic pH (20), I_{AP} is slightly inhibited by alkaline pH_{cyt} (153). I_{AP} is also inhibited by increased $[Ca^{2+}]_{cyt}$ (153), whereas guard cell K_{out}^+ channels are not regulated by small cytoplasmic Ca^{2+} changes. I_{AP} channels show a significant Ca^{2+} permeability (153). The physiological role of this transient current is unknown, but I_{AP} may contribute to shorter-term adjustments in stomatal aperture or to membrane potential oscillations observed in guard cells (59, 202).

NEW GUARD CELL SIGNALING MUTANTS AND GENETIC APPROACHES

Quantitative and mechanistic characterization (4, 155) of new *Arabidopsis* guard cell signaling mutants is paramount to achieve a molecular understanding of the ABA signaling cascade. Furthermore genes for many of the above proposed cell biologically and pharmacologically derived mechanisms have not yet been identified.

Loss-of-function mutations in the *Arabidopsis* ERA1 farnesyltransferase β subunit cause an enhanced response to ABA in seeds (34). Moreover, the *era1* mutant shows ABA hypersensitive stomatal closing and ABA hypersensitive activation of S-type anion currents (154). Furthermore, *era1* plants show reduced water loss during drought (154). Application of farnesyltransferase inhibitors to wild-type stomata mimics the *era1* phenotype, suggesting that ERA1 functions in early guard cell signaling and illustrating the complementarity of "steady-state" gene knockouts and "short-term" inhibitor applications. In mammals and yeast, farnesylation of signaling proteins promotes their membrane location and protein-protein interactions, suggesting that a negative regulator of guard cell ABA signaling is targeted via farnesylation (154) (Figure 3). ABA hypersensitive $[Ca^{2+}]_{cyt}$ elevations in *era1* show that ERA1 functions upstream of $[Ca^{2+}]_{cyt}$ elevations (G Allen, Y Murata, & J Schroeder, unpublished) (Figure 3).

A new ABA hypersensitive loss-of-function mutant, *abcap*, was isolated and characterized by screening for ABA hypersensitivity in seed germination in a primary screen and identifying the subset of mutations that affect guard cell signaling in a secondary screen (75). Stomatal closing is hypersensitive to ABA in *abcap* and, consistent with this phenotype, ABA-induced $[Ca^{2+}]_{cyt}$ elevations and guard cell plasma membrane anion currents are enhanced and K_{in}^{+} currents are reduced in *abcap*. Suprisingly, *ABCAP* encodes a subunit of a nuclear RNA cap binding complex (75) previously described in mammals and yeast, which regulates RNA processing and growth factor signal transduction (83, 84, 211). ABCAP may control the strength of ABA signaling by modulating the expression of an early ABA signal transduction element(s) (Figure 3).

New Genetic Screens and Reverse Genetics

To date, most of the ABA-insensitive mutations identified in guard cell signaling (*abi1-1*, *abi2-1*, and *aapk*) are dominant (46, 114, 119). This suggests that redundancy in phosphatase and kinase activities may limit the isolation of recessive mutations in such genes. Dominant mutations can also be generated in *Arabidopsis* by activation tagging or the random overexpression of wild-type genes (210). Such mutants can aid in identifying and isolating redundant genes involved in guard cell signaling pathways. However, dominant mutations can result from interactions with unnatural partners, causing neomorphic responses. To identify unequivocally the functions of such genes, it will be important to isolate loss-of-function mutants (71). Disruption or silencing of homologous redundant genes expressed in guard cells may allow more direct characterizations of in vivo functions of redundant genes.

Isolating guard cell signaling mutants is not trivial, owing to the lack of easily scorable phenotypes or markers, and is more difficult than isolating stomatal development mutants, which include cell-to-cell signaling mechanisms (16a, 49a). Thus the *era1* and *abcap* guard cell phenotypes were identified in secondary stomatal movement screens (75, 154). A highly elegant stomatal movement screen has been developed in which small differences in leaf temperature [due to stomatal transpiration (163)] were used to isolate new *Arabidopsis* guard cell signaling mutants (J Giraudat & S Merlot, personal communication; 139a). In a different approach, mutations that affect circadian control of stomatal movements were identified by selecting *Arabidopsis* mutants with an enhanced sensitivity to sulfur dioxide at specific times of day (R McClung, personal communication). This screen has led to isolation of circadian timing-defective (*ctd*) and out-of-phase (*oop*) mutants. In another screen using luciferase as a reporter, many mutants were isolated that are affected in osmotic, ABA, and cold stress–induced signal transduction (81). A subset of these mutations will likely affect guard cell signaling. Use of novel creative genetic screens will lead to identification of many new mechanisms affecting guard cell signaling. For example, new guard cell signaling mutants in stomatal responses could be isolated based on variation in responses among *Arabidopsis* ecotypes and use of recombinant inbred lines to map quantitative trait loci (9) that affect guard cell signaling.

Note that many *Arabidopsis* light and hormone signaling mutants have been isolated based on whole-plant or whole-tissue phenotypes, which can lead to isolation of genes that indirectly affect a signaling pathway via crosstalk or indirect feedback among signaling cascades. Analyses of ion channel regulation and $[Ca^{2+}]_{cyt}$ signaling in mutants allows one to closely associate mutations with specific elements in early signaling (4, 154, 155).

The completion of the *Arabidopsis* genome sequence will lead to reverse genetic functional characterizations of new guard cell signaling components using biophysical cell biological (4, 5, 155) and genomic methods developed and adapted to *Arabidopsis* guard cells. The identification of the full complement of guard cell–expressed genes is now possible using DNA array and chip technologies, which will have profound influence on future research. Reverse genetic analyses of guard cell–expressed genes will be needed to identify genes and test the function and relative contribution of the many proposed signal transducers reviewed here (Figures 1 to 4). Furthermore, many of the signal transducers reviewed here likely form signal transduction complexes consisting of many proteins. Proteomic approaches (119) will play an increasingly important role for identifying members of guard cell signaling complexes.

FUTURE OUTLOOK

Guard cell research has revealed many new signal transduction components and led to models of early signal transduction elements and signaling cassettes in plants. Many of the proposed mechanisms summarized in this review can now be directly tested by reverse genetics. Furthermore, this research has led to an initial understanding of how a large number of signaling mechanisms can interact in concert to produce a rapid physiological response. Future research on mutants will define molecular junction points of an integrated network comprising Figures 1 to 4. As discussed in the introduction, most plant cells respond to the classically known hormones and light signals in specific ways. In this sense, each plant cell contains a microcosm of plant signaling cascades with intricate crosstalk and specificity mechanisms. The guard cell system lends itself to functional characterization of many new unknown early signaling mechanisms (see 1 to 4 in Introduction). Interdisciplinary studies using cell biological, genomic, molecular genetic, biophysical, reverse genetic, and proteomic approaches will define much of the future research in this field.

Initial examples have shown that manipulation of guard cell signaling genes in *Arabidopsis* can affect stomatal movements, leading to reduced water loss and slowing of dessication during transitory drought periods (53, 75, 154). Future research in this area combined with inducible guard cell-specific gene expression or cell-specific gene silencing will lead to identification of mechanisms for engineering improved gas exchange in response to drought, elevated atmospheric CO_2, and other environmental stresses (180). In this respect, guard cell signaling research holds much promise at addressing major environmental and agricultural problems of the twenty-first century.

ACKNOWLEDGMENTS

We thank many colleagues for communicating new and unpublished findings. Majid Ghassemian, Nathalie Leonhardt, Pascal Mäser, Jared Young, and other members of the Schroeder lab are gratefully acknowledged for comments on the manuscript. Research in the authors' laboratory was supported by NSF, NIH, and DOE grants.

Visit the Annual Reviews home page at www.AnnualReviews.org

LITERATURE CITED

1. Ache P, Becker D, Ivashikina N, Dietrich P, Roelfsema MRG, Hedrich R. 2000. GORK, a delayed outward rectifier expressed in guard cells of *Arabidopsis thaliana*, is a K^+-selective K^+-sensing ion channel. *FEBS Lett.* 486:93–98

1a. Ahmad M, Cashmore AR. 1993. HY4 gene of *A. thaliana* encodes a protein with characteristics of a blue-light photoreceptor. *Nature* 366:162–66

2. Allan AC, Fricker MD, Ward JL, Beale MH, Trewavas AJ. 1994. Two transduction pathways mediate rapid effects of abscisic acid in *Commelina* guard cells. *Plant Cell* 6:1319–28

3. Allen GJ, Chu SP, Schumacher K, Shimazaki C, Vafeados D, et al. 2000. Alteration of stimulus-specific guard cell calcium oscillations and stomatal closing in *Arabidopsis det3* mutant. *Science* 289:2338–42

4. Allen GJ, Kuchitsu K, Chu SP, Murata Y, Schroeder JI. 1999. *Arabidopsis abi1-1* and *abi2-1* mutations impair abscisic acid induced cytosolic calcium rises in guard cells. *Plant Cell* 11:1785–98

5. Allen GJ, Kwak JM, Chu SP, Llopis J, Tsien RY, et al. 1999. Cameleon calcium indicator reports cytoplasmic calcium dynamics in *Arabidopsis* guard cells. *Plant J.* 19:735–47

6. Allen GJ, Muir SR, Sanders D. 1995. Release of Ca^{2+} from individual plant vacuoles by both InsP3 and cyclic ADP-ribose. *Science* 268:735–37

7. Allen GJ, Sanders D. 1996. Control of ionic currents guard cell vacuoles by cytosolic and luminal calcium. *Plant J.* 10:1055–69

8. Allen GJ, Sanders D. 1997. Vacuolar ion channels of higher plants. *Adv. Bot. Res.* 25:217–52

9. Alonso-Blanco C, El-Assal SE-D, Coupland G, Koornneef M. 1998. Analysis of natural allelic variation at flowering time loci in the Landsberg erecta and Cape Verde Islands ecotypes of *Arabidopsis thaliana*. *Genetics* 149:749–64

10. Anderson JA, Huprikar SS, Kochian LV, Lucas WJ, Gaber RF. 1992. Functional expression of a probable *Arabidopsis thaliana* potassium channel in *Saccharomyces cerevisiae*. *Proc. Natl. Acad. Sci. USA* 89:3736–40

11. Armstrong F, Leung J, Grabov A, Brearley J, Giraudat J, Blatt MR. 1995. Sensitivity to abscisic acid of guard-cell K^+ channels is suppressed by *abi1-1*, a mutant *Arabidopsis* gene encoding a putative

protein phosphatase. *Proc. Natl. Acad. Sci. USA* 92:9520–24

12. Assmann SM. 1999. The cellular basis of guard cell sensing of rising CO_2. *Plant Cell Environ.* 22:629–37

13. Assmann SM, Shimazaki K-I. 1999. The multisensory guard cell. Stomatal responses to blue light and abscisic acid. *Plant Physiol.* 119:809–15

14. Assmann SM, Simoncini L, Schroeder JI. 1985. Blue light activates electrogenic ion pumping in guard cell protoplasts of *Vicia faba*. *Nature* 318:285–87

15. Barbier-Brygoo H, Vinauger M, Colcombet J, Ephritikhine G, Frachisse J-M, Maurel C. 2000. Anion channels in higher plants: functional characterization, molecular structure and physiological role. *Biochim. Biophys. Acta* 1465:199–218

16. Baunsgaard L, Fuglsang AT, Jahn T, Korthout HAAJ, De Boer AH, Palmgren MG. 1998. The 14-3-3 proteins associate with the plant plasma membrane H^+-ATPase to generate fusicoccin binding complex and a fusicoccin responsive system. *Plant J.* 13:661–71

16a. Berger D, Altmann T. 2000. A subtilisin-like serine protease involved in the regulation of stomatal density and distribution in *Arabidopsis thaliana*. *Genes Dev.* 14:1119–31

17. Berkowitz G, Zhang X, Mercier R, Leng Q, Lawton M. 2000. Co-expression of calcium-dependent protein kinase with the inward rectified guard cell K^+ channel KAT1 alters current parameters in *Xenopus laevis* oocytes. *Plant Cell Physiol.* 41:785–90

18. Bewell MA, Maathuis FJM, Allen GJ, Sanders D. 1999. Calcium-induced calcium release mediated by a voltage-activated cation channel in vacuolar vesicles from red beet. *FEBS Lett.* 458:41–44

19. Blatt MR. 1990. Potassium channel currents in intact stomatal guard cells: rapid enhancement by abscisic acid. *Planta* 180:445–55

20. Blatt MR. 1992. K^+channels of stomatal guard cells: characteristics of the inward-rectifier and its control by pH. *J. Gen. Physiol.* 99:615–44

21. Blatt MR. 1999. Reassessing roles for Ca^{2+} in guard cell signalling. *J. Exp. Bot.* 50:989–99

22. Blatt MR, Armstrong F. 1993. K^+ channels of stomatal guard cells: abscisic-acid-evoked control of the outward-rectifier mediated by cytoplasmic pH. *Planta* 191:330–41

23. Blatt MR, Thiel G, Trentham DR. 1990. Reversible inactivation of K^+ channels of *Vicia* stomatal guard cells following the photolysis of caged 1,4,5-trisphosphate. *Nature* 346:766–69

24. Brearley J, Venis MA, Blatt MR. 1997. The effect of elevated CO_2 concentrations on K^+ and anion channels of *Vicia faba* L. guard cells. *Planta* 203:145–54

25. Burnett EC, Desikan R, Moser RC, Neill SJ. 2000. ABA activation of an MBP kinase in *Pisum sativun* epidermal peels correlates with stomatal responses to ABA. *J. Exp. Bot.* 51:197–205

26. Buschmann P, Gradmann D. 1997. Minimal model for oscillations of membrane voltage in plant cells. *J. Theor. Biol.* 188:323–32

27. Carpaneto A, Cantu AM, Gambale F. 2001. Effects of cytoplasmic Mg^{2+} on the slowly activating channels in isolated vacuoles of *Beta vulgaris. Planta.* In press

28. Cashmore AR, Jarillo JA, Wu Y-J, Liu D. 1999. Cryptochromes: blue light receptors for plants and animals. *Science* 284:760–65

29. Christie JM, Reymond P, Powell GK, Bernasconi P, Raibekas AA, et al. 1998. *Arabidopsis* NPH1: a flavoprotein with the properties of a photoreceptor for phototropism. *Science* 282:1698–701

30. Cosgrove DJ, Hedrich R. 1991. Stretch-activated chloride, potassium, and calcium channels co-existing in the plasma

membranes of guard cells of *Vicia faba* L. *Planta* 186:143–53

31. Cousson A. 2000. Analysis of the sensing and transducing processes implicated in the stomatal responses to carbon dioxide in *Commelina communis* L. *Plant Cell Environ.* 23:487–95

32. Cousson A, Vavasseur A. 1998. Putative involvement of cytosolic Ca^{2+} and GTP-binding proteins in cyclic-GMP-mediated induction of stomatal opening by auxin in *Commelina communis* L. *Planta* 206:308–14

33. Curvetto N, Darjania L, Delmastro S. 1994. Effect of two cAMP analogs on stomatal opening in *Vicia faba*: possible relationship with cytosolic calcium concentration. *Plant Physiol. Biochem.* 32:365–72

34. Cutler S, Ghassemian M, Bonetta D, Cooney S, McCourt P. 1996. A protein farnesyl transferase involved in abscisic acid signal transduction in *Arabidopsis*. *Science* 273:1239–41

35. Czempinski K, Gaedeke N, Zimmermann S, Muller-Rober B. 1999. Molecular mechanisms and regulation of plant ion channels. *J. Exp. Bot.* 50:955–66

36. DeKoninck P, Schulman H. 1998. Sensitivity of CaM kinase II to the frequency of Ca^{2+} oscillations. *Science* 279:227–30

37. DeSilva DLR, Hetherington AM, Mansfield TA. 1985. Synergism between calcium ions and abscisic acid in preventing stomatal opening. *New Phytol.* 100:473–82

38. DeSilva DLR, Hetherington AM, Mansfield TA. 1998. The regulation of apoplastic calcium in relation to intracellular signalling in stomatal guard cells. *Z. Pflanzenernaehr. Bodenkd.* 161:533–39

39. Dietrich P, Hedrich R. 1994. Interconversion of fast and slow gating modes of GCAC1, a guard cell anion channel. *Planta* 195:301–4

40. Dolmetsch RE, Xu K, Lewis RS. 1998. Calcium oscillations increase the efficiency and specificity of gene expression. *Nature* 392:933–36

41. Drake BG, Gonzalez-Meler MA, Long SP. 1997. More efficient plants: a consequence of rising atmospheric CO_2? *Annu. Rev. Plant Physiol. Plant Mol. Biol.* 48:609–39

42. Dreyer I, Horeau C, Lemaillet G, Zimmermann S, Bush DR, et al. 1999. Identification and characterization of plant transporters using heterologous expression systems. *J. Exp. Bot.* 50:1073–87

43. Esser JE, Liao Y-J, Schroeder JI. 1997. Characterization of ion channel modulator effects on ABA- and malate-induced stomatal movements: strong regulation by kinase and phosphatase inhibitors, and relative insensitivity to mastoparans. *J. Exp. Bot.* 48:539–50

44. Eun S-O, Lee Y. 1997. Actin filaments of guard cells are reorganized in response to light and abscisic acid. *Plant Physiol.* 115:1491–98

45. Fink M, Deuprat F, Lesage F, Heurteaux C, Romey G, et al. 1996. A new K^+ channel beta subunit to specifically enhance Kv2.2 (CDRK) expression. *J. Biol. Chem.* 271:26341–48

46. Finkelstein RR, Somerville CR. 1990. Three classes of abscisic acid (ABA)-insensitive mutations of *Arabidopsis* define genes that control overlapping subsets of ABA responses. *Plant Physiol.* 94:1172–79

47. Frechilla S, Zhu J, Talbott LD, Zeiger E. 1999. Stomata from *npq1*, a zeaxanthin-less *Arabidopsis* mutant, lack a specific response to blue light. *Plant Cell Physiol.* 40:949–54

48. Fu H-H, Luan S. 1998. AtKUP1: a dual-affinity K^+ transporter from *Arabidopsis*. *Plant Cell* 10:63–73

49. Fullone MR, Visconti S, Marra M, Fogliano V, Aducci P. 1998. Fusicoccin effect on the in vitro interaction between plant 14-3-3 proteins and plasma membrane H^+-ATPase. *J. Biol. Chem.* 273:7698–702

49a. Geisler M, Nadeau J, Sack FD. 2000.

Oriented asymmetric divisions that generate the stomatal spacing pattern in *Arabidopsis* are disrupted by the too many mouths mutation. *Plant Cell* 12:2075–86

49b. Ghelis T, Dellis O, Jeannette E, Bardat F, Cornel D, et al. 2000. Abscisic acid specific expression of *RAB18* involves activation of anion channels in *Arabidopsis thaliana* suspension cells. *FEBS Lett.* 474:43–47

49c. Ghelis T, Dellis O, Jeannette E, Bardat F, Miginiac E, Sotta B. 2000. Abscisic acid plasmalemma perception triggers a calcium influx essential for *RAB18* gene expression in *Arabidopsis thaliana* suspension cells. *FEBS Lett.* 483:67–70

50. Gilroy S, Fricker MD, Read ND, Trewavas AJ. 1991. Role of calcium in signal transduction of *Commelina* guard cells. *Plant Cell* 3:333–44

51. Gilroy S, Read ND, Trewavas AJ. 1990. Elevation of cytoplasmic Ca^{2+} by caged calcium or caged inositol triphosphate initiates stomatal closure. *Nature* 346:769–71

52. Goh C-H, Kinoshita T, Oku T, Shimazaki K-I. 1996. Inhibition of blue light-dependent H^+ pumping by abscisic acid in *Vicia* guard-cell protoplasts. *Plant Physiol.* 111:433–40

53. Gosti F, Beaudoin N, Serizet C, Webb ARR, et al. 1999. ABI1 protein phosphatase 2C is a negative regulator of abscisic acid signaling. *Plant Cell* 11:1897–910

54. Grabov A, Blatt MR. 1997. Parallel control of the inward-rectifier K^+ channel by cytosolic free Ca^{2+} and pH in *Vicia* guard cells. *Planta* 201:84–95

55. Grabov A, Blatt MR. 1998. Co-ordination of signalling elements in guard cell ion channel control. *J. Exp. Bot.* 49:351–60

56. Grabov A, Blatt MR. 1998. Membrane voltage initiates Ca^{2+} waves and potentiates Ca^{2+} increases with abscisic acid in stomatal guard cells. *Proc. Natl. Acad. Sci. USA* 95:4778–83

57. Grabov A, Blatt MR. 1999. A steep dependence of inward-rectifying potassium channels on cytosolic free calcium concentration increase evoked by hyperpolarization in guard cells. *Plant Physiol.* 119:277–87

58. Grabov A, Leung J, Giraudat J, Blatt MR. 1997. Alteration of anion channel kinetics in wild-type and *abi1-1* transgenic *Nicotiana benthamiana* guard cells by abscisic acid. *Plant J.* 12:203–13

59. Gradmann D, Blatt MR, Thiel G. 1993. Electrocoupling of ion transporters in plants. *J. Memb. Biol.* 136:327–32

60. Guan LQM, Zhao J, Scandalios JG. 2000. Cis-elements and trans-factors that regulate expression of the maize Cat1 antioxidant gene in response to ABA and osmotic stress: H_2O_2 is the likely intermediary signaling molecule for the response. *Plant J.* 22:87–95

61. Hamilton DWA, Hills A, Köhler B, Blatt MR. 2000. Ca^{2+} channels at the plasma membrane of stomatal guard cells are activated by hyperpolarization and abscisic acid. *Proc. Natl. Acad. Sci. USA* 97:4967–72

62. Hechenberger M, Schwappach B, Fischer WN, Frommer WB, Jentsch TJ, Steinmeyer K. 1996. A family of putative chloride channels from *Arabidopsis* and functional complementation of a yeast strain with a CLC gene disruption. *J. Biol. Chem.* 271:33632–38

63. Hedrich R, Becker D. 1994. Green circuits: the potential of plant specific ion channels. *Plant Mol. Biol.* 26:1637–50

64. Hedrich R, Busch H, Raschke K. 1990. Ca^{2+} and nucleotide dependent regulation of voltage dependent anion channels in the plasma membrane of guard cells. *EMBO J.* 9:3889–92

65. Hedrich R, Dietrich P. 1996. Plant K^+ channels: similarity and diversity. *Bot. Acta* 109:94–101

66. Hedrich R, Marten I, Lohse G, Dietrich P, Winter H, et al. 1994. Malate-sensitive anion channels enable guard cells to sense

changes in the ambient CO_2 concentration. *Plant J.* 6:741–48

67. Hedrich R, Moran O, Conti F, Busch H, Becker D, et al. 1995. Inward rectifier potassium channels in plants differ from their animal counterparts in response to voltage and channel modulators. *Eur. Biophys. J.* 24:107–15

68. Heimovaara-Dijkstra S, Testerink C, Wang M. 2000. Mitogen-activated protein kinase and abscisic acid signal transduction. *Results Probl. Cell Differ.* 27:131–44

69. Henriksen GH, Taylor AR, Brownlee C, Assmann SM. 1996. Laser microsurgery of higher plant cell walls permits patch-clamp access. *Plant Physiol.* 110:1063–68

70. Hey SJ, Bacon A, Burnett E, Neill SJ. 1997. Abscisic acid signal transduction in epidermal cells of *Pisum sativum L. Argenteum*: Both dehydrin mRNA accumulation and stomatal responses require protein phosphorylation and dephosphorylation. *Planta* 202:85–92

71. Himmelbach A, Iten M, Grill E. 1998. Signalling of abscisic acid to regulate plant growth. *Philos. Trans. R. Soc. London Ser. B* 353:1439–44

72. Homann U. 1998. Fusion and fission of plasma-membrane material accommodates for osmotically induced changes in the surface area of guard-cell protoplasts. *Planta* 206:329–33

73. Hoshi T. 1995. Regulation of voltage-dependence of the *KAT1* channel by intracellular factors. *J. Gen. Physiol.* 105:309–28

74. Hoth S, Dreyer I, Dietrich P, Becker D, Müller-Röber B, Hedrich R. 1997. Molecular basis of plant-specific acid activation of K^+ uptake channels. *Proc. Natl. Acad. Sci. USA* 94:4806–10

75. Hugouvieux V, Kwak JM, Murata Y, Schroeder JI. 2001. A nuclear mRNA cap binding protein, ABCAP, modulates early abscisic acid signal transduction in *Arabidopsis*. Submitted

76. Hwang J-U, Suh S, Yi H, Kim J, Lee Y.

1997. Actin filaments modulate both stomatal opening and inward K^+-channel activities in guard cells of *Vicia faba* L. *Plant Physiol.* 115:335–42

77. Ichida AM, Pei Z-M, Baizabal-Aguirre VM, Turner KJ, Schroeder JI. 1997. Expression of a Cs^+-resistant guard cell K^+ channel confers Cs^+-resistant, light-induced stomatal opening in transgenic *Arabidopsis*. *Plant Cell* 9:1843–57

78. Ichida AM, Schroeder JI. 1996. Increased resistance to extracellular cation block by mutation of the pore domain of the *Arabidopsis* inward-rectifying K^+ channel KAT1. *J. Memb. Biol.* 151:53–62

79. Ilan N, Moran N, Schwartz A. 1995. The role of potassium channels in the temperature control of stomatal aperture. *Plant Physiol.* 108:1161–70

80. Irving HR, Gehring CA, Parish RW. 1992. Changes in cytosolic pH and calcium of guard cells precede stomatal movements. *Proc. Natl. Acad. Sci. USA* 89:1790–94

81. Ishitani M, Xiong LM, Stevenson B, Zhu J-K. 1997. Genetic analysis of osmotic and cold stress signal transduction in *Arabidopsis*: interactions and convergence of abscisic acid-dependent and abscisic acid-independent pathways. *Plant Cell* 9:1935–49

82. Deleted in proof

83. Izaurralde E, Lewis J, Gamberi C, Jarmolowski A, McGuigan C, Mattaj IW. 1995. A cap-binding protein complex mediating U snRNA export. *Nature* 376:709–12

84. Izaurralde E, Lewis J, McGuigan C, Jankowska M, Darynkiewicz E, Mattaj IW. 1994. A nuclear cap binding protein complex involved in pre-mRNA splicing. *Cell* 78:657–68

85. Jacob T, Ritchie S, Assmann SM, Gilroy S. 1999. Abscisic acid signal transduction in guard cells is mediated by phospholipase D activity. *Proc. Natl. Acad. Sci. USA* 96:12192–97

86. Jahn T, Fuglsang AT, Olsson A, Bruntrup IM, Collinge DB, et al. 1997. The 14-3-3 protein interacts directly with the C-terminal region of the plant plasma membrane H^+-ATPase. *Plant Cell* 9:1805–14

87. Jan LY, Jan YN. 1992. Structural elements involved in specific K^+ channel functions. *Annu. Rev. Physiol.* 54:537–55

88. Jarvis AJ, Davies WJ. 1998. The coupled response of stomatal conductance to photosynthesis and transpiration. *J. Exp. Bot.* 49:399–406

89. Keller BU, Hedrich R, Raschke K. 1989. Voltage-dependent anion channels in the plasma membrane of guard cells. *Nature* 341:450–53

90. Kelly WB, Esser JE, Schroeder JI. 1995. Effects of cytosolic calcium and limited, possible dual, effects of G protein modulators on guard cell inward potassium channels. *Plant J.* 8:479–89

91. Kim EJ, Kwak JM, Uozumi N, Schroeder JI. 1998. *AtKUP1*: an arabidopsis gene encoding high-affinity potassium transport activity. *Plant Cell* 10:51–62

92. Kinoshita T, Nishimura M, Shimazaki K-I. 1995. Cytosolic concentration of Ca^{-2+} regulates the plasma membrane H^+-ATPase in guard cells of fava bean. *Plant Cell* 7:1333–42

93. Kinoshita T, Shimazaki K-I. 1997. Involvement of calyculin A- and okadaic acid-sensitive protein phosphatase in the blue light response of stomatal guard cells. *Plant Cell Physiol.* 38:1281–85

94. Kinoshita T, Shimazaki K-I. 1999. Blue light activates the plasma membrane H^+-ATPase by phosphorylation of the C terminus in stomatal guard cells. *EMBO J.* 18:5548–58

95. Knetsch MLW, Wang M, Snaar-Jagalska BE, Heimovaara-Dijkstra S. 1996. Abscisic acid induces mitogen-activated protein kinase activation in barley aleurone protoplasts. *Plant Cell* 8:1061–67

96. Kolb HA, Marten I, Hedrich R. 1995. Hodgkin-Huxley analysis of a GCAC1

anion channel in the plasma membrane of guard cells. *J. Memb. Biol.* 146:273–82

97. Koornneef M, Reuling G, Karssen CM. 1984. The isolation of abscisic acid-insensitive mutants of *Arabidopsis thaliana*. *Physiol. Plant* 61:377–83

98. Kubitscheck U, Homann U, Thiel G. 2000. Osmotically evoked shrinking of guard-cell protoplasts causes vesicular retrieval of plasma membrane into the cytoplasm. *Planta* 210:423–31

99. Kuo A, Cappelluti S, Cervantes-Vervantes M, Rodriguez M, Bush DS. 1996. Okadaic acid, protein phosphatase inhibitor, blocks calcium changes, gene expression and cell death induced by gibberellin in wheat aleurone cells. *Plant Cell* 8:259–69

100. Kwak JM, Murata Y, Baizabal-Aguirre VM, Merrill J, Wang M, et al. 2001. Dominant negative guard cell K^+ channel mutants reduce inward rectifying K^+ currents and light-induced stomatal opening in *Arabidopsis*. Submitted

101. Lascève G, Leymarie J, Olney MA, Liscum E, Christie JM, et al. 1999. *Arabidopsis* contains at least four independent blue-light-activated signal transduction pathways. *Plant Physiol.* 120:605–14

102. Leckie CP, McAinsh MR, Allen GJ, Sanders D, Hetherington AM. 1998. Abscisic acid-induced stomatal closure mediated by cyclic ADP-ribose. *Proc. Natl. Acad. Sci. USA* 95:15837–42

103. Lee HC. 1997. Mechanisms of calcium signaling by cyclic ADP-ribose and NAADP. *Physiol. Rev.* 77:1133–64

104. Lee S, Choi H, Suh S, Doo I-S, Oh K-Y, et al. 1999. Oligogalacturonic acid and chitosan reduce stomatal aperture by inducing the evolution of reactive oxygen species from guard cells of tomato and *Commelina communis*. *Plant Physiol.* 121:147–52

105. Lee Y, Choi YB, Suh S, Lee J, Assmann SM, et al. 1996. Abscisic acid-induced phosphinositide turn over in guard cell

protoplasts of *Vicia faba. Plant Physiol.* 110:987–96

106. Lee Y, Lee HJ, Crain RC, Lee A, Korn SJ. 1994. Polyunsaturated fatty acids modulate stomatal aperture and two distinct K^+ channel currents in guard cells. *Cell. Signal.* 6:181–86

107. Lemichez E, Wu Y, Sanchez JP, Chua N-H. 2000. Abscisic acid regulates stomatal closure through the inactivation of p21-Rac. *6th Int. Congr. Plant Mol. Biol.*

108. Lemtiri-Chlieh F, MacRobbie EAC. 1994. Role of calcium in the modulation of *Vicia* guard cell potassium channels by abscisic acid—a patch-clamp study. *J. Memb. Biol.* 137:99–107

109. Lemtiri-Chlieh F, MacRobbie EAC, Brearley CA. 2000. Inositol hexakisphosphate is a physiological signal regulating the K^+-inward rectifying conductance in guard cells. *Proc. Nat. Acad. Sci. USA* 97:8687–92

110. Leonhardt N, Marin E, Vavasseur A, Forestier C. 1997. Evidence for the existence of a sulfonylurea-receptor-like protein in plants: modulation of stomatal movements and guard cell potassium channels by sulfonylureas and potassium channel openers. *Proc. Natl. Acad. Sci. USA* 94:14156–61

111. Leonhardt N, Vavasseur A, Forestier C. 1999. ATP binding cassette modulators control abscisic acid-regulated slow anion channels in guard cells. *Plant Cell* 11:1141–52

112. Leung J, Bouvier-Durand M, Morris P-C, Guerrier D, Chefdor F, Giraudat J. 1994. *Arabidopsis* ABA response gene *ABI1*—features of a calcium-modulated protein phosphatase. *Science* 264:1448–52

113. Leung J, Giraudat J. 1998. Abscisic acid signal transduction. *Annu. Rev. Plant Physiol. Plant Mol. Biol.* 49:199–222

114. Leung J, Merlot S, Giraudat J. 1997. The *Arabidopsis* abscisic acid-insensitive (*ABI2*) and *ABI1* genes encode homologous protein phosphatases 2C involved in abscisic acid signal transduction. *Plant Cell* 9:759–71

115. Leyman B, Geelen D, Quintero FJ, Blatt MR. 1999. A tobacco syntaxin with a role in hormonal control of guard cell ion channels. *Science* 283:537–40

116. Leymarie J, Vavasseur A, Lasceve G. 1998. CO_2 sensing in stomata of *abi1-1* and *abi2-1* mutants of *Arabidopsis thaliana. Plant Physiol. Biochem.* 36:539–43

117. Li J, Assmann SM. 1996. An abscisic acid-activated and calcium-independent protein kinase from guard cells of fava bean. *Plant Cell* 8:2359–68

118. Li J, Lee Y-RJ, Assmann SM. 1998. Guard cells possess a calcium-dependent protein kinase that phosphorylates the KAT1 potassium channel. *Plant Physiol.* 116:785–95

119. Li J, Wang XQ, Watson MB, Assmann SM. 2000. Regulation of abscisic acid-induced stomatal closure and anion channels by guard cell AAPK kinase. *Science* 287:300–3

120. Li W-H, Llopis J, Whitney M, Zlokarnik G, Tsien RY. 1998. Cell-permeant caged InsP3 ester shows that Ca^{2+} spike frequency can optimize gene expression. *Nature* 392:936–41

121. Li WW, Luan S, Schreiber SL, Assmann SM. 1994. Evidence for protein phosphatase and 2A regulation of K^+ channels in two types of leaf cells. *Plant Physiol.* 106:963–70

122. Linder B, Raschke K. 1992. A slow anion channel in guard cells, activation at large hyperpolarization, may be principal for stomatal closing. *FEBS Lett.* 313:27–30

123. Liu K, Luan S. 1998. Voltage-dependent K^+ channels as targets of osmosensing in guard cells. *Plant Cell* 10:1957–70

124. Lohse G, Hedrich R. 1992. Characterization of the plasma membrane H^+ ATPase from *Vicia faba* guard cells; modulation by extracellular factors and seasonal changes. *Planta* 188:206–14

125. Lu P, Zhang SQ, Outlaw WH, Riddle

KA. 1995. Sucrose: a solute that accumulates in the guard cell apoplast and guard cell symplast of open stomata. *FEBS Lett.* 362:180–84

126. Luan S, Li W, Rusnak F, Assmann SM, Schreiber SL. 1993. Immunosuppressants implicate protein phosphatase regulation of K^+ channels in guard cells. *Proc. Natl. Acad. Sci. USA* 90:2202–6

127. Lurin C, Geelen D, Barbier-Brygoo H, Guern J, Maurel C. 1996. Cloning and functional expression of a plant voltage-dependent chloride channel. *Plant Cell* 8:701–11

128. Maathuis FJM, Ichida AM, Sanders D, Schroeder JI. 1997. Roles of higher plant K^+ channels. *Plant Physiol.* 114:1141–49

129. MacRobbie EAC. 1981. Effects of ABA on "isolated" guard cells of *Commelina communis* L. *J. Exp. Bot.* 32:563–72

130. MacRobbie EAC. 1983. Effects of light/dark on cation fluxes in guard cells of *Commelina communis* L. *J. Exp. Bot.* 34:1695–710

131. MacRobbie EAC. 1995. ABA-induced ion efflux in stomatal guard cells: multiple actions of ABA inside and outside the cell. *Plant J.* 7:565–76

132. MacRobbie EAC. 1998. Signal transduction and ion channels in guard cells. *Philos. Trans. R. Soc. London Ser. B* 353:1475–88

132a. MacRobbie EAC. 2000. ABA activates multiple Ca^{2+} fluxes in stomatal guard cells, triggering vacuolar $K^+(Rb^+)$ release, *Proc. Natl. Acad. Sci. USA* 97:12361–68

133. Mansfield TA, Hetherington AM, Atkinson CJ. 1990. Some current aspects of stomatal physiology. *Annu. Rev. Plant Physiol. Plant Mol. Biol.* 41:55–75

134. McAinsh MR, Brownlee C, Hetherington AM. 1990. Abscisic acid-induced elevation of guard cell cytosolic Ca^{2+} precedes stomatal closure. *Nature* 343:186–88

135. McAinsh MR, Brownlee C, Hetherington AM. 1992. Visualizing changes in cytosolic-free Ca^{2+} during the response of stomatal guard cells to abscisic acid. *Plant Cell* 4:1113–22

136. McAinsh MR, Brownlee C, Hetherington AM. 1997. Calcium ions as second messengers in guard cell signal transduction. *Physiol. Plant.* 100:16–29

137. McAinsh MR, Clayton H, Mansfield TA, Hetherington AM. 1996. Changes in stomatal behavior and guard cell cytosolic free calcium in response to oxidative stress. *Plant Physiol.* 111:1031–42

138. McAinsh MR, Hetherington AM. 1998. Encoding specificity in Ca^{2+} signalling systems. *Trends Plant Sci.* 3:32–36

139. McAinsh MR, Webb AR, Taylor JE, Hetherington AM. 1995. Stimulus-induced oscillations in guard cell cytosolic free calcium. *Plant Cell* 7:1207–19

139a. Merlot S, Gosti F, Guerrier D, Vavasseur A, Giraudat J. 2001. The ABI1 and ABI2 protein phosphatases 2C act in a negative feedback regulatory loop of the abscisic acid signalling pathway. *Plant J.* 25:1–10

140. Meyer K, Leube MP, Grill E. 1994. A protein phosphatase 2C involved in ABA signal transduction in *Arabidopsis thaliana*. *Science* 264:1452–55

141. Miediema H, Assmann SM. 1996. A membrane-delimited effect of internal pH on the K+ outward rectifier of *Vicia faba* guard cells. *J. Memb. Biol.* 154:227–37

142. Miyawaki A, Griesbeck O, Heim R, Tsien RY. 1999. Dynamic and quantitative Ca^{2+} measurements using improved cameleons. *Proc. Natl. Acad. Sci. USA* 96:2135–40

143. Miyawaki A, Llopis J, Heim R, McCaffery JM, Adams JM, et al. 1997. Fluorescent indicators for Ca^{2+} based on green fluorescent proteins and calmodulin. *Nature* 388:882–87

144. Mori I, Muto S. 1997. Abscisic acid

activates a 48-kilodalton protein kinase in guard cell protoplasts. *Plant Physiol.* 113:833–40

145. Müller-Röber B, Ehrhardt T, Plesh G. 1998. Molecular features of stomatal guard cells. *J. Exp. Bot.* 49:293–304

146. Müller-Röber B, Ellenberg N, Provart N, Willmitzer L, Busch H, et al. 1995. Cloning and electrophysiological analysis of KST1, an inward rectifying K$^+$ channel expressed in potato guard cells. *EMBO J.* 14:2409–16

147. Deleted in proof

148. Nakamura RL, McKendree WL, Hirsch RE, Sedbrook JC, Gaber RF, Sussman MR. 1995. Expression of an *Arabidopsis* potassium channel gene in guard cells. *Plant Physiol.* 109:371–74

149. Netting AG. 2000. pH, abscisic acid and the integration of metabolism in plants under stressed and non-stressed conditions: cellular responses to stress and their implication for plant water relations. *J. Exp. Bot.* 51:147–58

150. Niyogi KK, Grossman AR, Bjorkman O. 1998. *Arabidopsis* mutants define a central role for the xanthophyll cycle in the regulation of photosynthetic energy conversion. *Plant Cell* 10:1121–34

151. Parmar PN, Brearley CA. 1995. Metabolism of 3- and 4-phosphorylated phosphatidylinositols in stomatal guard cells of *Commelina communis* L. *Plant J.* 8:425–33

152. Parvathi K, Raghavendra AS. 1997. Blue light-promoted stomatal opening in abaxial epidermis of *Commelina benghalensis* is maximal at low calcium. *Physiol. Plant* 101:861–64

153. Pei Z-M, Baizabal-Aguirre VM, Allen GJ, Schroeder JI. 1998. A transient outward-rectifying K$^+$ channel current down-regulated by cytosolic Ca^{2+} in *Arabidopsis thaliana* guard cells. *Proc. Natl. Acad. Sci. USA* 95:6548–53

154. Pei Z-M, Ghassemian M, Kwak CM,

McCourt P, Schroeder JI. 1998. Role of farnesyltransferase in ABA regulation of guard cell anion channels and plant water loss. *Science* 282:287–90

155. Pei Z-M, Kuchitsu K, Ward JM, Schwarz M, Schroeder JI. 1997. Differential abscisic acid regulation of guard cell slow anion channels in *Arabdiopsis* wild-type and *abi1* and *abi2* mutants. *Plant Cell* 9:409–23

156. Pei Z-M, Murata Y, Benning G, Thomine S, Klüsener B, et al. 2000. Calcium channels activated by hydrogen peroxide mediate abscisic acid signalling in guard cells. *Nature* 406:731–34

157. Pei Z-M, Ward JM, Harper JF, Schroeder JI. 1996. A novel chloride channel in *Vicia faba* guard cell vacuoles activated by the serine/threonine kinase, CDPK. *EMBO J.* 15:6564–74

158. Pei Z-M, Ward JM, Schroeder JI. 1999. Magnesium sensitizes slow vacuolar channels to physiological cytosolic calcium and inhibits fast vacuolar channels in faba bean guard cell vacuoles. *Plant Physiol.* 121:977–86

159. Poffenroth M, Green DB, Tallman G. 1992. Sugar concentrations in guard cells of *Vicia faba* illuminated with red or blue light: analysis by high performance liquid chromatography. *Plant Physiol.* 98:1460–71

160. Pottosin II, Tikhonova LI, Hedrich R, Schoenknecht G. 1997. Slowly activating vacuolar channels can not mediate Ca^{2+}-induced Ca^{2+} release. *Plant J.* 12:1387–98

161. Quintero F, Blatt M. 1997. A new family of K$^+$ transporters from *Arabidopsis* that are conserved across phyla. *FEBS Lett.* 415:206–11

162. Raschke K. 1979. Movements of stomata. In *Encyclopedia of Plant Physiology*, ed. W Hale, E Feinleib, pp. 384–441. Berlin: Springer-Verlag

163. Raskin I, Ladyman JAR. 1988. Isolation and characterization of a barley mutant

with abscisic-acid-insensitive stomata. *Planta* 173:73–78

164. Ritchie S, Gilroy S. 1998. Abscisic acid signal transduction in the barley aleurone is mediated by phospholipase D activity. *Proc. Nat. Acad. Sci. USA* 95:2697–702

165. Ritte G, Rosenfeld J, Rohrig K, Raschke K. 1999. Rates of sugar uptake by guard cell protoplasts of *Pisum sativun* L. related to the solute requirement for stomatal opening. *Plant Phsyiol.* 121:647–55

166. Rodriguez PL, Benning G, Grill E. 1998. ABI2, a second protein phosphatase 2C involved in abscisic acid signal transduction in *Arabidopsis*. *FEBS Lett.* 421:185–90

167. Roelfsema MRG, Prins HBA. 1997. Ion channels in guard cells of *Arabidopsis thaliana* (L) Heynh. *Planta* 202:18–27

168. Roelfsema MRG, Prins HBA. 1998. The membrane potential of *Arabidopsis thaliana* guard cells: depolarizations induced by apoplastic acidification. *Planta* 205:100–12

169. Roelfsema MRG, Staal M, Prins HBA. 1998. Blue light-induced apoplastic acidification of *Arabidopsis thaliana* guard cells: inhibition by ABA is mediated through protein phosphates. *Physiol. Plant.* 103:466–74

170. Romano LA, Miedema H, Assmann SM. 1998. Ca^{2+}-permeable, outwardly-rectifying K^+ channels in mesophyll cells of *Arabidopsis thaliana*. *Plant Cell Physiol.* 39:1133–44

171. Ruiz LP, Mansfield TA. 1994. A postulated role for calcium oxalate in the regulation of calcium ions in the vicinity of stomatal guard cells. *New Phytol.* 127:473–81

172. Santa-Maria GE, Rubio F, Dubcovsky J, Rodriguez-Navarro A. 1997. The HAK1 gene of barley is a member of a large gene family and encodes a high-affinity potassium transporter. *Plant Cell* 9:2281–89

173. Schachtman DP, Schroeder JI, Lucas WJ, Anderson JA, Gaber RF. 1992. Expression of an inward-rectifying potassium channel by the *Arabidopsis KAT1* cDNA. *Science* 258:1654–58

174. Schmidt C, Schelle I, Liao YJ, Schroeder JI. 1995. Strong regulation of slow anion channels and abscisic acid signaling in guard cells by phosphorylation and dephosphorylation events. *Proc. Natl. Acad. Sci. USA* 92:9535–39

175. Schroeder JI, Hagiwara S. 1989. Cytosolic calcium regulates ion channels in the plasma membrane of *Vicia faba* guard cells. *Nature* 338:427–30

176. Schroeder JI, Hagiwara S. 1990. Repetitive increases in cystolic Ca^{2+} of guard cells by abscisic acid activation of non-selective Ca^{2+}-permeable channels. *Proc. Natl. Acad. Sci. USA* 87:9305–9

177. Schroeder JI, Hedrich R. 1989. Involvement of ion channels and active transport in osmoregulation and signaling of higher plant cells. *Trends Biochem. Sci.* 14:187–92

178. Schroeder JI, Hedrich R, Fernandez JM. 1984. Potassium-selective single channels in guard cell protoplasts of *Vicia faba*. *Nature* 312:361–62

179. Schroeder JI, Keller BU. 1992. Two types of anion channel currents in guard cells with distinct voltage regulation. *Proc. Natl. Acad. Sci. USA* 89:5025–29

180. Schroeder JI, Kwak JM, Allen GJ. 2000. Guard cell abscisic acid signal transduction network and engineering of plant drought hardiness. *Nature*. In press

181. Schroeder JI, Raschke K, Neher E. 1987. Voltage dependence of K^+ channels in guard cell protoplasts. *Proc. Natl. Acad. Sci. USA* 84:4108–12

182. Schroeder JI, Schwarz M, Pei Z-M. 1998. Protein kinase and phosphatase regulation during abscisic acid signaling and ion channel regulation in guard cells. In *Cellular Integration of Signaling Pathways in Plant Development*, ed. RLF Schiavo, G Morelli, N Raikhel, pp. 59–69. Heidelberg: Springer-Verlag

183. Schroeder JI, Ward JM, Gassmann W. 1994. Perspectives on the physiology and structure of inward-rectifying K$^+$ channels in higher plants: biophysical implications for K$^+$ uptake. *Annu. Rev. Biophys. Biomol. Struct.* 23:441–71

184. Schulz-Lessdorf B, Lohse G, Hedrich R. 1996. GCAC1 recognizes the pH gradient across the plasma membrane: a pH-sensitive and ATP-dependent anion channel links guard cell membrane potential to acid and energy metabolism. *Plant J.* 10:993–1004

185. Schumacher K, Vafeados D, McCarthy M, Sze H, Wilkins T, Chory J. 1999. The *Arabidopsis det3* mutant reveals a central role for the vacuolar H(+)-ATPase in plant growth and development. *Genes Dev.* 13:3259–70

186. Schwartz A. 1985. Role of calcium and EGTA on stomatal movements in *Commelina communis*. *Plant Physiol.* 79:1003–5

187. Schwarz M, Schroeder J. 1998. Abscisic acid maintains S-type anion channel activity in ATP-depleted *Vicia faba* guard cells. *FEBS Lett.* 428:177–82

188. Serrano EE, Zeiger E, Hagiwara S. 1988. Red light stimulates an electrogenic proton pump in *Vicia* guard cell protoplasts. *Proc. Natl. Acad. Sci. USA* 85:436–40

189. Serrano R. 1988. Structure and function of proton translocation ATPase in plasma membranes of plants and fungi. *Biochim. Biophys. Acta* 947:1–28

190. Sheen J. 1996. Ca^{2+}-dependent protein kinases and stress signal transduction in plants. *Science* 274:1900–2

191. Sheen J. 1998. Mutational analysis of protein phosphatase 2C involved in abscisic acid signal transduction in higher plants. *Proc. Natl. Acad. Sci. USA* 95:975–80

192. Shimazaki K, Goh C-H, Kinoshita T. 1999. Involvement of intracellular Ca^{2+} in blue light-dependent proton pumping in guard cell protoplasts from *Vicia faba*. *Physiol. Plant* 105:554–61

193. Shimazaki K, Iino M, Zeiger E. 1986. Blue light-dependent proton extrusion by guard-cell protoplasts of *Vicia faba*. *Nature* 319:324–26

194. Shimazaki K, Kinoshita T, Nishimura M. 1992. Involvement of calmodulin and calmodulin-dependent myosin light chain kinase in blue light-dependent H$^+$ pumping by guard cell protoplasts from *Vicia faba* L. *Plant Physiol.* 99:1416–21

195. Staxen I, Pical C, Montgomery LT, Gray JE, Hetherington AM, McAinsh MR. 1999. Abscisic acid induces oscillations in guard-cell cytosolic free calcium that involve phosphoinositide-specific phospholipase C. *Proc. Natl. Acad. Sci. USA* 96:1779–84

196. Suh S, Park J-G, Lee Y. 1998. Possible involvement of phospholipase A2 in light signal transduction of guard cells of *Commelina communis*. *Physiol. Plant.* 104:306–10

196a. Sutton F, Paul SS, Wang XQ, Assmann SM. 2000. Distinct abscisic acid signaling pathways for modulation of guard cell versus mesophyll cell potassium channels revealed by expression studies in *Xenopus laevis* oocytes. *Plant Physiol.* 124:223–30

197. Talbott LD, Zeiger E. 1996. Central roles for potassium and sucrose in guard cell osmoregulation. *Plant Physiol.* 111:1051–57

198. Talbott LD, Zeiger E. 1998. The role of sucrose in guard cell osmoregulation. *J. Exp. Bot.* 49:329–37

199. Tang HX, Vasconcelos AC, Berkowitz GA. 1996. Physical association of KAB1 with plant K$^+$ channel alpha subunits. *Plant Cell* 8:1545–53

200. Theodoulou FL. 2000. Plant ABC transporters. *Biochim. Biophys. Acta* 1465:79–103

201. Thiel G, Blatt MR. 1994. Phosphatase antagonist okadaic acid inhibits steady-state K$^+$ currents in guard cells of *Vicia faba*. *Plant J.* 5:727–33

202. Thiel G, MacRobbie EAC, Blatt MR. 1992. Membrane transport in stomatal guard cells: the importance of voltage control. *J. Memb. Biol.* 126:1–18

203. Torsethaugen G, Pell EJ, Assmann SM. 1999. Ozone inhibits guard cell K$^+$ channels implicated in stomatal opening. *Proc. Natl. Acad. Sci. USA* 96:13577–82

204. Véry A-A, Gaymard F, Bosseux C, Sentenac H, Thibaud J-B. 1995. Expression of a cloned plant K$^+$ channel in *Xenopus* oocytes: analysis of macroscopic currents. *Plant J.* 7:321–32

205. Véry A-A, Robinson MF, Mansfield TA, Sanders D. 1998. Guard cell cation channels are involved in Na$^+$-induced stomatal closure in a halophyte. *Plant J.* 14:509–21

206. Wang XQ, Wu W-H, Assmann SM. 1998. Differential responses of abaxial and adaxial guard cells of broad bean to abscisic acid and calcium. *Plant Physiol.* 118:1421–29

207. Ward JM, Pei Z-M, Schroeder JI. 1995. Roles of ion channels in initiation of signal transduction in higher plants. *Plant Cell* 7:833–44

208. Ward JM, Schroeder JI. 1994. Calcium-activated K$^+$ channels and calcium-induced calcium release by slow vacuolar ion channels in guard cell vacuoles implicated in the control of stomatal closure. *Plant Cell* 6:669–83

209. Webb AAR, McAinsh MR, Mansfield TA, Hetherington AM. 1996. Carbon dioxide induces increases in guard cell cytosolic free calcium. *Plant J.* 9:297–304

210. Weigel D, Ahn JH, Blazquez MA, Borevitz JO, Christensen SK, et al. 2000. Activation tagging in *Arabidopsis*. *Plant Physiol.* 122:1003–13

211. Wilson KF, Fortes P, Singh US, Ohno M, Mattaj IW, Cerione RA. 1999. The nuclear cap-binding complex is a novel target of growth factor receptor-coupled signal transduction. *J. Biol. Chem.* 274:4166–73

211a. Wood NT, Allan AC, Haley A, Viry-Moussaïd M, Trewavas AJ. 2000. The characterization of differential calcium signalling in tobacco guard cells. *Plant J.* 24:335–44

212. Wu W-H. 1995. A novel cation channel in *Vicia faba* guard cell plasma membrane. *Acta Phytopathol. Sin.* 21:347–54

213. Wu Y, Kuzma J, Marechal E, Graeff R, Lee HC, et al. 1997. Abscisic acid signaling through cyclic ADP-ribose in plants. *Science* 278:2126–30

214. Zeiger E. 2000. Sensory transduction of blue light in guard cells. *Trends Plant Sci.* 5:183–84

215. Zeiger E, Hepler PK. 1977. Light and stomatal function: blue light stimulates swelling of guard cell protoplasts. *Science* 196:887–89

216. Zhu J, Talbott LD, Jin X, Zeiger E. 1998. The stomatal response to CO$_2$ is linked to changes in guard cell zeaxanthin. *Plant Cell Environ.* 21:813–20

Annu. Rev. Plant Physiol. Plant Mol. Biol. 2001. 52:659–88

TRANSPORTERS RESPONSIBLE FOR THE UPTAKE AND PARTITIONING OF NITROGENOUS SOLUTES

LE Williams

University of Southampton, School of Biological Sciences, Bassett Crescent East, Southampton, SO16, 7PX, United Kingdom; e-mail: lew@soton.ac.uk

AJ Miller

Biochemistry and Physiology Department, IARC-Rothamsted, Harpenden, Herts AL5 2JQ, United Kingdom; e-mail: tony.miller@bbsrc.ac.uk

Key Words   amino acids, ammonium, membrane, nitrate, peptides

■ **Abstract**   The acquisition and allocation of nitrogenous compounds are essential processes in plant growth and development. The huge economic and environmental costs resulting from the application of nitrogen fertilizers make this topic very important. A diverse array of transporters varying in their expression pattern and also in their affinity, specificity, and capacity for nitrogenous compounds has been identified. Now the future challenge is to define their individual contribution to nitrogen nutrition and signalling processes. Here we have reviewed recent advances in the identification and molecular characterization of these transporters, concentrating on mechanisms existing at the plasma membrane. The review focuses on nitrate, ammonium, and amino acid transporter familes, but we also briefly describe what is known at the molecular level about peptide transporters and a recently identified family implicated in the transport of purines and their derivatives.

CONTENTS

1040-2519/01/0601-0659$14.00

659

INTRODUCTION

Of all the mineral elements required by plants, nitrogen is needed in the greatest amount and most often limits growth. It is a constituent of proteins, nucleic acids, and many other important cellular components including chlorophyll and several plant hormones. Deficiency results in reduced plant growth, a gradual chlorosis of older leaves, followed by abscission. Often anthocyanins are synthesized in the stems, petioles, and leaf veins from excess carbohydrates that have accumulated because of reduced nitrogen metabolism.

Nitrogen is available to plants in the soil in a variety of forms including ammonium (as both NH_3 and NH_4^+), nitrate, amino acids, soluble peptides, and complex insoluble nitrogen-containing compounds. Plant species differ in their preferred N source, absorbing it via the roots primarily in an inorganic form as nitrate or ammonium (Figure 1, see color insert). Amino acids (and here we also include amides and ureides), which also occur in abundance in certain soils, can also be an important source of N (34, 50). Where symbiotic associations occur with nitrogen-fixing bacteria, the ammonia released by the bacteroid is assimilated in the cytoplasm of the infected cells, and the assimilated nitrogen (mainly amides and ureides) is translocated out of the nodules to other parts of the plant (132). Ectomycorrhizal fungi make a valuable contribution to the nitrogen nutrition of their host by absorbing, assimilating, and translocating simple nitrogenous compounds from the soil to the root and also by converting complex N sources in the soil into more readily utilizable forms (73). Once assimilated, N transfer between the fungus and host is thought to occur predominantly in the form of amino acids (73). Some plants can even supplement their nitrogen requirement by carnivory (110).

Following uptake, inorganic nitrogen is first reduced to ammonia before it is incorporated into the amino acids glutamine and glutamate. Ammonium assimilation usually occurs in the roots whereas nitrate assimilation can occur both in roots and in leaves, depending on species and environmental conditions (Figure 1). Transport to the leaves occurs via the xylem whereas redistribution from the leaves to other nitrogen-requiring organs occurs predominantly in the form of amino acids via the phloem (Figure 1). This redistribution is essential for supplying tissues that do not participate in nitrogen assimilation. When nitrogen assimilation occurs in the root, amino acids are transported to the mature leaves in the transpiration stream through the xylem. A high proportion of amino acids arriving in the mature leaves is cycled from the xylem into the phloem for redistribution to nitrogen sinks. When assimilation occurs predominantly in the shoot, it is essential that cycling of amino acids take place to cover the demand of the roots for these nutrients (72). In the root, excess amino acids can move from the phloem to the xylem for recycling (15, 61). Nitrogen can also be transported across the plasma membrane of certain cells in other forms such as small peptides (122) and purine and pyrimidine bases and their derivatives (32).

Nitrogen uptake and partitioning is achieved through a panoply of differentially regulated transporters, differing in their specificity, affinity, and capacity, to allow growth and development under a variety of environmental conditions. Here we concentrate on recent advances in the molecular characterization of plant membrane transporters for nitrogenous compounds, focusing on the plasma membrane but also briefly discussing transport at the vacuole.

NITRATE TRANSPORTERS

Identification of Nitrate Transport Systems

Physiologicial studies investigating nitrate uptake into roots indicate that at least three distinct nitrate uptake systems exist. One is a low-affinity transport system (LATS) and the other two are high-affinity transport systems (HATS), defined according to the external concentrations over which the transport systems operate (117). The HATS are distinguished by whether they are substrate induced (iHATS) or constitutively active (cHATS) (1). Uptake kinetics were obtained by measuring depletion from the bathing solution or by the uptake of ^{13}N-labeled NO_3^-, and the borderline between the high- and low-affinity systems is species dependent but is usually around 0.5 mM. Considerable effort has been invested in trying to isolate the transporters responsible for the three systems observed in physiological studies. Although yeast complementation has advanced the molecular characterization of other plant transporters, this strategy has not been possible for the isolation of genes encoding nitrate transporters because the yeasts most amenable for transformation do not utilize nitrate as a nitrogen source. Alternative strategies for cloning nitrate transporters have involved screening for plant mutants deficient in nitrate transport using their resistance to chlorate, the toxic nitrate homologue. However, the identification of a nitrate transporter gene in the yeast *Hansenula polymorpha* and its disruption to give a mutant that is unable to grow with nitrate as the nitrogen source (97) may offer the possibility for functional complementation cloning of plant nitrate transporters (23).

The lack of a convenient tracer for assaying nitrate transport is also a problem. The access to a supply of ^{13}N-labeled nitrate has limited the use of this technique, although when available a wealth of information has been obtained (e.g. 115, 116, 128). The improvements in mass spectrometers have enabled ^{15}N-enrichment studies to assay transport of nitrogenous solutes (14, 30). In addition, electrophysiological measurements have been successfully used to assay for nitrate transporter activity (33, 77), and these measurements have been used to characterize mutants with altered transport properties (44, 139).

Nitrate Transporter Families

Two families of membrane proteins have been identified that can mediate the active transport of nitrate, presumably by symport with protons, across the plasma membrane: the nitrate-nitrite porters (NNP) and the peptide transporter (PTR) family. Both families have prokaryotic and eukaryotic members and have been assigned to the Major Facilitating Superfamily (95). Both families share the usual features of the superfamily in having two sets of six transmembrane domains linked by a longer cytoplasmic loop. The molecular identity of these two transport systems was recently reviewed (23), so only background and new information is given here.

Peptide Transporter (PTR) Family   The PTR family includes members that transport a wide range of nitrogen-containing substrates, including amino acids, peptides, and nitrate (96). The family has also been called the proton-dependent oligopeptide transporters or POT (121), although this name may be less appropriate as proton-dependence has not been unanimously demonstrated. A phylogenetic analysis indicates that there are four clearly distinguishable clusters with bacterial proteins in cluster I, animal proteins in cluster II, yeast and one plant protein, AtPtr2-A, in cluster III, and the remaining plant proteins in cluster IV (109). All members of this family have two characteristic conserved motifs, one between transmembrane domains 2 and 3, and the other within the fifth (96). Many members also have a protein kinase C recognition motif at the beginning of the central cytoplasmic loop.

The first plant nitrate transporter gene to be cloned, *AtNRT1.1* (formerly called *CHL1*), belongs to the PTR family (130). The *Arabidopsis* gene was isolated by T-DNA tagging in 1993, but the mutant phenotype was described much earlier and had been selected by resistance to the toxic nitrate homologue, chlorate (18). In *Arabidopsis*, many new family members have been identified from the EST (expressed sequence tag) database or the genome sequencing program but the transported substrates have yet to be identified (23). Assigning substrates to the PTR family members is difficult because the family can transport such a diverse range of nitrogen-containing solutes. Two members that exhibit less than 40% identity to *AtNRT1.1* have been identified as oligopeptide transporters (120; see section on peptide transporters), and one family member transports both nitrate and basic amino acids (147).

The original chlorate-selected mutant of *AtNRT1.1* was initially shown to be defective in only LATS (18), an observation later confirmed by $^{13}NO_3$ uptake measurements (43, 128). However, the decreased nitrate uptake was sometimes observed only in plants grown with a mixed ammonium and nitrate nitrogen source (128). It has been suggested that there may be an additional component of LATS that can compensate under one set of conditions but is downregulated under others [for example, when grown under NH_4^+ (23)]. A possible candidate is AtNRT1.2, which has an affinity in the LATS range, although it is also constitutively expressed (44, 66). Attempts to match the expression of the transporter genes to the transport systems (HATS, LATS) have become further complicated by the fact that At-NRT1.1 can show biphasic uptake kinetics, with K_m values in both the LATS and HATS ranges, suggesting it is a dual-affinity transporter (66, 140).

Both *AtNRT1* genes are expressed mainly in roots, with the mRNA localized in the root tips and epidermis; in the more mature parts of the root, *AtNRT1.1* was expressed in the cortex and endodermis (43, 44). Root hair expression of *At-NRT1.2* was also shown (44). In tomato, two other *NRT1* genes showed differing patterns of expression; mRNA for the nitrate-inducible *LeNRT1.2* was present only in root hairs, whereas the constitutively expressed *LeNRT1.1* was more generally distributed in the root (62). Most *NRT1* genes are nitrate inducible and sub-mM concentrations can be used (147); the constitutively expressed examples are *LeNRT1.1*, *AtNRT1.2*, and *OsNRT1* (44, 62, 65). The expression and function of *AtNRT1* was also linked to changes in pH; *AtNRT1.1* mRNA abundance was increased at a more acidic external pH in the absence of nitrate (130). Furthermore, the *AtNRT1.1*-deficient mutant had a more acidic cytoplasmic pH in the dark and absence of nitrate (79), whereas the HATS activity of the mutant was most evident at a more acidic external pH (140). The significance of the link between pH and nitrate transport remains to be determined, but the importance of the relationship between nitrogen supply and pH homeostasis has long been recognized (101).

Nitrate-Nitrite Porter (NNP) Family   The first members of this family were identified in *Escherichia coli*, and one was shown to mediate nitrite efflux (107). Like the PTR family, the NNPs also have a conserved signature sequence (23, 95). Mutants with defective nitrate uptake systems in both fungal and algal cells led to the genetic isolation of other eukaryotic members of this family. In *Aspergillus nidulans*, the *crnA* gene (133) was isolated from a mutant obtained by selection using chlorate. This gene encodes a functional nitrate/nitrite transporter that has been characterized by expressing the protein in *Xenopus* oocytes (148). In the green alga, *Chlamydomonas reinhardtii*, a group of genes related to *crnA* have been identified that are involved in the high-affinity uptake of nitrate and nitrite (29, 98, 99). The nitrite transport systems are regulated by nitrogen and carbon supply, and a regulatory gene has been identified (106). For one of these HATS, the requirement for two mRNAs, *CrNRT2.1*, and *nar2* to give nitrate transport was confirmed by *Xenopus* oocyte expression (146). A third *crnA*-related gene encodes a nitrite-specific transport system (29).

Sequence homology to crnA was used to clone genes from higher plants, and now a large family has been identified and classified as the *NRT2*s. In *Arabidopsis*, there are at least seven *NRT2* genes, of which several have been cloned (20, 149), as have four in barley (129, 135). Differences in the predicted two-dimensional structure within the NNP family was the basis for subdivision into three groups: prokaryotes, fungal, and algal/plants (23). The fungal members have a long central loop of around 90 amino acids between transmembrane domains 6 and 7. The *Chlamydomonas* and plant family members all have long C-terminal domains of around 70 amino acids that extend into the cytoplasm, and these members can be further subdivided based on the presence or absence of a conserved N-terminal sequence (23).

Heterologous expression of the higher plant transporters in oocytes seems to be difficult as attempts to express genes from barley, *Arabidopsis*, and *Lotus* have failed to give nitrate transport activity (JJ Zhou, LJ Trueman, BG Forde, & AJ Miller, unpublished results). This lack of success may be due to the requirement for a second gene product, equivalent to the *Chlamydomonas nar2* that has yet to be isolated from higher plants.

Regulation of Nitrate Transporters   Like the nitrate-assimilatory enzymes (123), nitrate-induction of *NRT2* transcripts has been demonstrated for many different plant species and the maximal rates of uptake are usually observed several hours after supplying nitrate, with a subsequent decline in transport activity (23). Low (10 μM) but not higher concentrations of nitrite can also induce iHATS (2, 135, 149). In barley roots, the *HvNRT2* transcripts of four closely related genes were undetectable in nitrate-starved plants, but treatment with nitrate and nitrite gave a rapid increase in abundance and a parallel increase in $^{13}NO_3^-$ uptake (135). Furthermore, after 6 to 12 h there was a subsequent decrease in transcripts of three of the genes and only *HvNRT2.4* remained highly expressed. Increasing the external nitrate concentration from 50 to 500 μM or supplying ammonium decreased the amount of expression of these transporters (135). Indirect evidence of NRT2 function was provided by the close correlation between high-affinity influx of $^{15}NO_3^-/^{13}NO_3^-$ and the time course of *NRT2* mRNA abundance (63, 135, 149). The decrease in iHATS that is associated with longer exposures to nitrate is generally accepted to be feedback repression presumed to result from the accumulation of nitrate (51) or some downstream metabolites of nitrate assimilation, such as amino acids (85). *NRT2* transcripts were decreased after the direct application of these metabolites (135, 136, 149) or by some chemical or genetic manipulation to modify these pools in the plant (20, 53, 136, 149). A recent model that has brought together all this information on the regulation of iHATS activity suggests that glutamine is the main downregulator of *HvNRT2* transcripts (136).

In most plants, the *NRT2*s are more strongly expressed in the roots than in the shoots (23, 100, 149) although transcripts were detected in leaves, flowers, petioles, and seeds (100). In root tips of *N. plumbaginifolia*, (*NpNRT2*) is expressed most strongly in epidermal and endodermal cells, whereas in mature root tissue it is highest in epidermis and in lateral root primordia (53). In *Arabidopsis*, expression of *AtNRT2.1* mRNA was developmentally and diurnally regulated, with higher expression occurring at day 10 compared to day 15 (149) and during the light period (63). Furthermore, transcript abundance was delayed by supplying sucrose to plants providing a link between C and N metabolism (63).

When the PTR and NNP families were compared, the induction by treatment with 50 μM nitrate gave stronger mRNA expression of *AtNRT2.1* compared with *AtNRT1.1* (20). Comparison of the diurnal pattern of expression of *NRT1* and *NRT2* genes was very similar for both *Arabidopsis* (63) and tomato (90). Within the diurnal changes in transcript level, other more subtle changes in expression could be measured, suggesting that regulation may be mediated by several factors, including phytochrome, N metabolites, and C supply (90).

A recent study has demonstrated that *NpNRT2.1* is a limiting element of iHATS in tobacco and also that post-transcriptional regulation by a reduced nitrogen source occurs (24b). Transgenic plants, constitutively expressing this transporter, showed decreased $^{15}NO_3^-$ influx following exposure to ammonium, suggesting that a repressive effect on influx can occur post-transcriptionally. Conserved protein kinase recognition motifs have been identified in both NRT2 and NRT1 transporters, indicating that their activity may be regulated by phosphorylation/dephosphorylation (23). Results obtained by expressing the proteins in oocytes suggests that phosphorylation can change the kinetic properties of the transporters (JJ Zhou & AJ Miller, unpublished).

Nitrate Efflux Systems   Nitrogenous compounds are also effluxed from plant cells, a process that usually occurs during conditions of excess supply (24). Nitrogen can be lost from roots as nitrate, amino acids, and ammonium (although ammonia may be the actual chemical form effluxed from the cell). The evidence for the energetically wasteful process of nitrate efflux is well established, and the process is nitrate inducible (3) and stimulated by ammonium (54) but not exogenously applied amino acids (84). Under most environmental conditions, an open anion channel can mediate efflux from the cytoplasm, but such a mechanism should rapidly deplete the cytoplasmic nitrate pool. Patch-clamp measurements of root cells have not yet revealed such a channel in the plasma membrane (117), although a passive nitrate transport system was shown in inside-out plasma membrane vesicles obtained from corn root cells (35). This efflux system was saturable with a K_m of 5 mM, which is close to the values reported for the cytoplasmic concentration (81). Recently, a nitrate selective channel has been identified at the plasma membrane of hypocotyl cells, and it was suggested that it may be involved in long-term anion efflux, which, when associated with potassium efflux, could regulate the osmotic pressure of these cells (24a).

Endomembrane Nitrate Transport   Thermodynamic arguments would suggest that plant cells require an active transport system in the tonoplast when nitrate accumulates above $\sim$12 mM (80), and nitrate-inducible protein bands have been identified in tonoplast membrane preparations (78, 87). A proton antiport mechanism driving active nitrate accumulation in the vacuole has been proposed (80, 111). Plant members of the voltage-dependent chloride channel family (CLC) have been identified (68), and these appear to be located in endomembranes (36). The remobilization of vacuolar stored nitrate (134) is likely to be channel mediated, and an *Arabidopsis* knock-out mutant for one of these CLC genes was shown to have a decreased ability for vacuolar nitrate accumulation (31). Nitrite transport at the chloroplast also appears to be proton coupled (114), and a putative plastid nitrite transporter belonging to the NNP family has been identified in rice (23).

AMMONIUM TRANSPORTERS

Ammonium Transport Systems

The physicochemical similarities between NH_4^+ and K^+ suggest that the same thermodynamic arguments apply to the uptake of the two ions: active transport (most likely proton-coupled) at low external concentrations and passive transport through channels at high external concentrations. The threshold for these two mechanisms depends on the cytosolic ammonium concentrations, and a wide range of values exist for this parameter that seem to depend on the external concentration (55). Both $^{13}NH_4^+$ uptake and electrophysiological measurements have provided evidence for separate high- and low-affinity uptake systems (56, 141). Low-affinity uptake of NH_4^+ is likely mediated primarily by channels, and examples that can mediate NH_4^+ entry have been identified (16, 109). High-affinity transport (K_m in the range 10–200 μM) is thought to occur via H^+-coupled NH_4^+ transporters that show little affinity for K^+ (see below). It will be important to determine the capacity of these different systems to help establish their relative contribution to NH_4^+ uptake in vivo.

Ammonium Transporter (AMT) Family

A large family of ammonium transporters is present in prokaryotes and eukaryotes. This was first called the methylammonium permease family (MEP) because this substrate was conveniently used to study the activity. Recently the family has become known more appropriately as the ammonium transporter family (AMT), as at least one member of the family can transport ammonium but not methylammonium (118). Functional complementation of yeast mutants defective in two ammonium uptake systems (*mep1-1*, *mep2-1*) led to the cloning of a plant ammonium transporter, *AtAMT1;1* (89). *AtAMT1;1* encodes a 53-kD protein, and kinetic analysis suggests that it is a high-affinity NH_4^+ cotransporter (89). Further work is required to determine whether it functions as an H^+ cotransporter or a uniporter driven by $\Delta\Psi$. Additional family members have been identified by screening DNA libraries and PCR, with at least eight identified in *Arabidopsis* (30, 118, 137). At least one of these, AtAMT2;1, is structurally more similar to the yeast MEPs and may belong to a new subfamily exhibiting specific functions (118). Other *AMTs* have been isolated from rice and tomato (62, 138). Structural differences in one of the tomato genes, *LeAMT1;3*, has led to speculation that it may have a different functional role (137, 138).

All the AMTs are predicted to have 11 *trans*-membrane domains, with the N terminus located on the exterior face of the membrane (127). The properties of the *Arabidopsis* genes cloned to date have been determined following expression in yeast by using uptake of ^{14}C-labeled methylammonium and competition with ammonium (30). The AMT1s showed distinct substrate affinities that allow the plant to take up ammonium over a wide concentration range. The K_ms for methylammonium were 8 μM, 24 μM, and 11 μM for AtAMT1;1, AtAMT1;2, and

AtAMT1;3, respectively. AtAMT1;1 showed selectivity for NH_4^+ over methylammonium (50% inhibition of methylammonium by ≤ 0.5 μM NH_4^+), but the other two transporters showed little discrimination. When expressed in yeast, AtAMT1.1 showed little transport of di- and trimethylammonium and other monovalent cations, including K^+ (89). In both yeast and plants, treatments with protonophores and ATPase inhibitors can decrease the uptake of methylammonium and NH_4^+ (89, 141). The membrane potential depolarizations elicited by treatment with NH_4^+ (4, 141) could be occurring as a result of cotransport with protons or passive entry through a channel. A detailed characterization of these carriers requires expression in a heterologous system such as *Xenopus* oocytes (82).

Physiological Function of AMTs   AtAMT1;1 is expressed in roots and leaves, suggesting that AtAMT1;1 not only functions in uptake of NH_4^+ from the soil but may also be involved in the recovery of NH_3 that has effluxed from the cytoplasm to the extracellular space, where it becomes protonated (89). LeAMT1;1 is specifically expressed in roots, consistent with a role in high-affinity NH_4^+ uptake from the soil. In leaves, NH_3 is released during photorespiration, and in both shoots and roots, it is generated by the breakdown of amino acids (19). Furthermore, in leaves the photorespiratory generation of ammonium and the location of glutamine synthetase would argue that a retrieval system is required in the chloroplast envelope. Evidence for this role of ammonium transporters in retrieval is shown by the triple yeast mutant (*mep1-1, mep2-1, mep3-1*) because it shows poor growth on any nitrogen source and continuously effluxes NH_4^+/NH_3 (70).

In root nodules, NH_4^+ is transported across the symbiosome membrane that separates the N-fixing bacteroids from the plant cytoplasm. The ammonium concentration was estimated to be 50 times lower in the plant cytosol than that in the bacteroids (124). Patch-clamp analysis of the symbiosome membrane from soybean nodules has identified a cation channel with preference for NH_4^+ (131), and a candidate cDNA for this transporter was identified, *GmSAT1*, using the yeast double-mutant (*mep1-1, mep2-1*) (49). However, more recent data suggest that because GmSAT1 was unable to complement the triple mutant (*mep1-1, mep2-1, mep3-1*), it is probably not a functional transporter but rather has an effect on posttranslational regulation of the yeast endogenous transporter Mep3 (71). The permeation of NH_4^+ through K^+ channels (109) suggests that the channel mediating this transport in the symbiosome membrane could be closely related to known K^+ channels. It has also been suggested that NH_3 may cross the membrane through aquaporins (41), and the membrane permeation of NH_3 was recently demonstrated (88).

Regulation of AMTs   After two days of N-starvation the $^{15}NH_4^+$ influx rate rapidly increases, a pattern that coincides with an increase in expression of *AtAMT1.1*, the transcript of the other two genes (*AtAMT1;2* and *AtAMT1;3*) remaining fairly constant (30). Thus the highest affinity transporter is induced during N-deficiency. When plants were resupplied with N, *AtAMT1.1* mRNA levels rapidly decline, as does uptake of ammonium (30). Only when glutamine concentration was increased in the root (by methionine sulfoximine treatment) does this pattern change (102). In *Arabidopsis* and tomato, a negative correlation between influx and glutamine accumulation in roots suggests that this amino acid might be the feedback signal for repression of influx and *AtAMT1.1* expression (102, 137). However, this feedback may also occur directly by ammonium accumulation in the cells because the influx changes more rapidly than the *AtAMT1.1* mRNA levels (102).

Tomato root hairs preferentially express two AMT genes (*LeAMT1;1* and *LeAMT1;2*), but only *LeAMT1.1* mRNA is most abundant during N-starvation, which suggests that it may be the tomato equivalent of *AtAMT1.1*. In contrast, *LeAMT1.2* is induced by the supply of ammonium and nitrate (62, 138). These transporters may therefore have different roles in the uptake of ammonium, depending on the N-status of the soil.

A diurnal pattern of ammonium uptake is seen (30), and the mRNA levels for all three *AtAMT1* genes show diurnal variation; however, only *AtAMT1.3* transcripts peaked at the same point as ammonium influx, at the end of the light period (30). These results suggest that this gene product may provide a link between carbon supply to roots and ammonium uptake (30). As light and N starvation have differential effects on the expression of *AtAMT1* genes, regulation of ammonium uptake in response to changes in N or C status may not be mediated by a common signalling/sensing mechanism (137).

In tomato, two of the *AMT1* genes are diurnally regulated in leaves. The expression of *LeAMT1.2* and *LeAMT1.3* showed reciprocal diurnal patterns of expression, the latter showing maximum expression during the dark period, whereas the former has a maximum in the light period (138). These expression patterns may indicate that LeAMT1.2 is involved in the retrieval of photorespiratory-generated ammonium or uptake of xylem-derived ammonium (137), whereas LeAMT1.3 may be required for the retrieval of ammonium from light-repressed enzymes, such as glutamate dehydrogenase and aparagine synthetase (60, 137).

AMINO ACID TRANSPORTERS

Amino Acid Transporter Families

Plants possess a multiplicity of amino acid transporters or permeases that exhibit different properties with respect to tissue distribution, substrate specificity, affinity, and capacity and also in their regulation. Members of two main families of amino acid transporters have been identified so far: the APC superfamily (amino acid, polyamine, and choline transporter) and the AAAP family (Amino Acid/Auxin:Permease family) (144). The plant permeases represent a subfamily of the AAAPs and have been referred to as the ATF family (amino acid transporter family) (21). Preliminary evidence suggests that proteins of the eukaryotic-specific AAAP family are very distantly related to proteins of the large ubiquitous APC family as well as to those of two small bacterial amino acid transporter families, the aromatic amino acid permease (ArAAP) family, and the serine/threonine permease (STP) family (144).

The plant APCs have been subdivided into two subgroups: the CATs (cationic amino acid transporters) and the GABA (4-aminobutyrate) permease-related family (21). The only transporter of the APC family to have been characterized in any detail is AtCAT1 (see below). Much more is known about members of the ATF family, and to date four subclasses have been defined: the AAPs (amino acid permeases), the LHTs (lysine, histidine transporters), the ProTs (proline transporters), and the AUXs (putative auxin transporters).

APC Family   AtCAT1 (previously called AtAAT1) is in the CAT family, which also contains mammalian CATs, e.g. CAT-1, the murine leukemia virus receptor, a system y^+ high-affinity basic amino acid transporter (94). It is the only plant member of this family to have been characterized in detail (27), although sequence database analysis indicates that other CATs exist. AtCAT1 has 533 amino acids (58 kDa), and hydrophobicity analysis suggests that, like other members of this family, it is composed of 14 *trans*-membrane domains. Transport studies in yeast suggest that AtCAT1 is a high-affinity transporter for basic amino acids (K_m 35 μM for histidine), although it is able to transport other amino acids with lower affinity.

AtCAT1 is expressed in a broad range of organs; analysis of tobacco transformed with promoter-GUS constructs indicated that this gene is expressed in various floral tissues and also in the major veins of leaves and roots (27). Expression in the vascular tissue indicates a role in long-distance translocation possibly also serving a role in xylem/phloem interchange of amino acids, whereas expression in the ovaries indicates a possible role in supplying developing embryos with basic amino acids (27).

There are plant sequences in the databases related to the GABA-permeases (approximately 25% identities at the amino acid level) and putative polyamine transporters described in yeast, but these have not yet been functionally characterized. *Arabidopsis thaliana* can grow on GABA as the sole nitrogen source, but this may be due to the uptake of this nonprotein amino acid by members of the AAP and ProT family (9; see below).

AAAP Family   The plant AAAPs, classed as part of the ATF family, are further divided into four subfamilies: AAPs, LHTs, ProTs, and the AUXs. These subfamilies share a high degree of similarity within a group but are only distantly related to each other (103)

AtAAP1, a member of the AAPs, was the first amino acid permease cDNA to be isolated from plants, and this was achieved using yeast complementation (26, 42). Subsequently, five related permeases (*AtAAP2-6*) were reported in *Arabidopsis* (22, 58, 104), and additional *Arabidopsis* sequences in this class are in the sequence databases. Furthermore, three AAPs have been reported in *Ricinus communis*, RcAAP1-3 (6, 76, 86), and in the carnivorous plant *Nepentes alata*, NaAAP1-3 (110). Several cDNAs (both full-length and partial sequences) were isolated from *Vicia faba [VfAAP2, VfAAPa, VfAAPb,* VfAAPc (83)] and *Pisum sativum [PsAAP1* and 2 (126)] and other related sequences are in the database for *Solanum tuberosum* (*StAAP1* and 2) and *Nicotiana sylvestris* (*NsAAP1*). Each plant species likely has several AAPs, although this remains to be formally demonstrated.

The AAPs are similar in size (51-56 kDa) and predicted topology. Hydropathy analysis indicates that they contain 10–12 membrane-spanning regions (26, 42, 58) and experimental data for AtAAP1 are consistent with an 11-*trans*-membrane domain model with the NH_2-terminus in the cytoplasm and COOH-terminus facing outside of the cell (11). AAPs recognize a wide spectrum of amino acids as determined from competition studies following expression in yeast. The *Arabidopsis* AAPs, AtAAP1, AtAAP2, AtAAP4, and AtAAP6 show a preference for neutral and acidic amino acids, whereas AtAAP3 and AtAAP5 transport all classes of amino acids, with high efficiency for basic amino acids (7, 8, 21, 22). RcAAP3 from *Ricinus communis* is a broad-substrate permease that can transport neutral and basic amino acids and has a lower affinity for acidic amino acids. In contrast, RcAAP1 has a higher specificity for basic amino acids (76). The broad bean amino acid permease, VfAAP2, shows higher specificity for neutral and acidic amino acids (83), and the pea amino acid permease, PsAAP1, recognizes neutral, acidic, and basic amino acids (126). Studies in oocytes will be required to distinguish between binding and actual transport for the full range of AAPs to allow the substrate specificity to be precisely determined.

Detailed expression studies for the AAPs are limited. Northern analysis indicates that every organ has at least one AAP in *Arabidopsis*. AtAAP3 is restricted to roots, AtAAP6 is sink specific (roots, sink, and cauline leaves), but certain AtAAPs, e.g. AtAAP5, have a more general distribution. Promoter-GUS fusions showed *AtAAP1* and *AtAAP2* are strongly induced in immature siliques of *Arabidopsis*, at the heart stage of embryogenesis (39). Their expression is nonoverlapping: *AtAAP1* is expressed in the endosperm and cotyledons whereas *AtAAP2* is expressed in the vascular strands of siliques and in funiculi, indicating that these permeases serve distinct physiological roles in supplying organic nitrogen to the developing seed. A model was presented in which AtAAP2 may function in efficient exchange of amino acids between the xylem and phloem (amino acids are imported into seeds mainly via the phloem), whereas AtAAP1 is responsible for amino acid uptake into the endosperm and subsequently into the cotyledons of the developing embryo (39). The induction of these AAPs preceded that of storage protein genes, suggesting that amino acid transporters might play a role in regulating storage protein biosynthesis (39).

RcAAP1 and 2 are predominantly expressed in the cotyledons of the germinating *Ricinus* seedling, to a lower but appreciable extent in the root, and at low levels in the endosperm, hypocotyl, and source and sink leaves of mature plants (6). A high expression in the cotyledons is consistent with the important role that these organs play in the active loading of amino acids released from the endosperm during germination. In situ hybridization showed that *RcAAP1* is expressed in many cells of the root but particularly within the stele in four regions adjacent to the protoxylem poles (6). These may represent specialized cells that actively accumulate amino acids for subsequent transfer to the xylem (6). Lateral roots also develop from these regions farther up the root, and thus RcAAP1 may be involved in accumulating amino acids required for active protein synthesis necessary to initiate organogenesis (6). Northern analysis indicates that *RcAAP3* shows a pattern of expression distinct from that of *RcAAP1* and *2*, being widely expressed in source and sink tissues. The cellular expression pattern remains to be determined.

The expression of various transporters for nitrogenous compounds has been studied in the insect-trapping pitchers of the carnivorous plant, *Nepenthes alata* (110). Movement of nutrients from the pitcher fluid to the phloem involves several steps where plasma membrane transporters may be required, e.g. uptake into the digestive gland cells and transport from cortical cells beneath the gland to the vascular tissue. *NaAAP1* was localized to bundle sheath cells of the pitcher. Because symplastic connections between cortical cells of the pitcher and vascular bundles were lacking, NaAAP1 may function in loading amino acids into vascular tissue (110).

Amino acid transport in legumes has received considerable attention because they accumulate large amounts of proteins in seeds of economic interest and also because they can use either soil nitrogen or organic compounds arising from symbiotic associations (83). The expression pattern for the broad bean amino acid permease genes differs; *VfAAP2* is expressed most strongly in the stem and at a lower level in sink leaves and pods, whereas *VfAAPa, b,* and *c* are all strongly expressed in the flower (83). The exact function of each of these transporters in these locations requires further investigation. In pea seeds, *PsAAP1* is predominantly expressed in epidermal transfer cells forming the outer surface of cotyledons. Since these cells abut the seed coat this transporter may play a role in the uptake of amino acids released from the seed coat (126). This transporter is not confined to seeds and is also expressed in vegetative organs.

AtLHT1 is the only member of the LHT subfamily to be functionally characterized, although there are related sequences in the databases. AtLHT1 is 446 amino acids (50.5 kD), with 9–10 predicted transmembrane domains (12). This permease transports histidine and lysine but not arginine. The lack of arginine transport clearly differentiates it from the other basic amino acid transporter, AtCAT1 (12, 22). From northern analysis, *AtLHT1* was shown to be expressed most strongly in flowers, siliques, and young leaves, although whole mount, in situ hybridization revealed that expression was localized on the surface of roots in young seedlings and in pollen. This expression pattern appears to complement the expression of *AtCAT1* (27), and therefore AtLHT1 may function in amino acid acquisition in sink tissues, whereas AtCAT1 may be involved in long-distance transport (10).

Members of the Prot subclass have been identified in *Arabidopsis* (AtProT1 and 2) and tomato (LeProT1,2 and 3) (104, 112). Nine transmembrane domains have been proposed for this family (112). Functional studies in yeast indicated that AtProT1 and 2 and LeProT1 are fairly specific for proline with K_ms of 360 μM for AtProT1 and 2 and 1.9 mM for LeProT1 (104, 112). No transport activity has been reported as yet for LeProT2 and 3. The ProTs are also able to transport GABA, and LeProt1 has a higher affinity for glycine betaine than for proline

(K_m 110 μM), although the physiological relevance of this is not clear insofar as tomato seems not to accumulate glycine betaine (112).

The ProTs may facilitate the transport of a variety of stress-related compounds that could act as osmolytes, free radical scavengers, and protein stabilizers (9). AtProt2, but not AtProt1, is strongly induced in leaves under both water and salt stress and thus may be important in nitrogen distribution under osmotic stress (104). Different members of this subclass may have different functions; in addition to roles in water and salt stress responses, roles in pollen nutrition and floral induction have been suggested (104, 112). AtProts are found at low levels in all organs of *Arabidopsis*. In the flower, *AtProT1* is expressed in the medial vascular strands of the carpels and also in the phloem of the pedicel and inflorescence stem (104). Proline represents a higher proportion of total free amino acids in reproductive tissue than in vegetative tissues in *Arabidopsis* and tomato (13, 112), and in some species proline accumulates with the onset of flowering. AtProT1 may therefore play a role in flower induction and development (104). LeProT1 is a pollen-specific transporter, and the mRNA accumulates late in pollen development, suggesting a possible role in proline accumulation from anther tissue and also in germination. Proline may serve as an important energy source when the pollen tube is undergoing rapid elongation and serve as a compatible solute when pollen is undergoing dehydration during maturation (112).

AtAUX1, a member of the AUX subfamily, was identified using a gene-tagging procedure in screens for agravitropic root mutants. *AtAUX1* encodes a protein of 485 amino acids with a predicted molecular mass of 54.1 kDa (5). Direct auxin transport has not yet been demonstrated categorically for *AtAUX1*. However, *AtAUX1* is proposed to encode a transmembrane component of the auxin influx carrier, based on the observations that (*a*) in root elongation bioassays, *Arabidopsis aux1* mutants exhibit a reduced response to auxins requiring carrier-mediated uptake (IAA and 2,4-D) yet retain a wild-type sensitivity toward 1-NAA, which enters the cell via diffusion; (*b*) root segments from *aux1* mutants accumulated twofold less ^{14}C-labeled 2,4-D than those from wild-type plants; and (*c*) the agravitropic phenotype of *aux1* roots can be rescued with 1-NAA but not with 2,4-D (69). Because auxins are structurally very similar to tryptophan, it has been proposed that AUX1 and AAPs may have shared a common ancestry. Preliminary data for AtANT1 (aromatic and neutral amino acid transporter), another member of the family, suggest that it can transport aromatic amino acids, neutral amino acids, arginine, and auxin (91).

Physiological Function of Amino Acid Transporters

Various physiological roles have been suggested for amino acid permeases (28). For example, in the root, amino acid transporters may be involved in uptake of amino acids from the soil, transfer of amino acids to the xylem for mobilization from the root, unloading of amino acids from the phloem in the root, and possibly direct transfer between the phloem and xylem for recycling. In leaves, amino acid transporters are necessary for transfer from mesophyll cells to the apoplast and

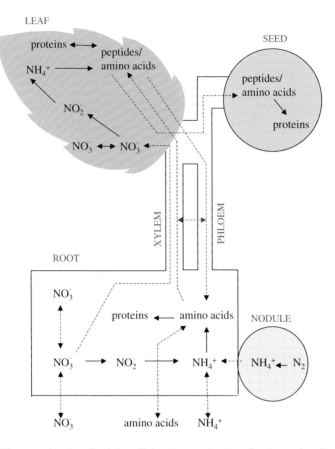

Figure 1 Diagram showing the intercellular transport routes for the main nitrogenous solutes in a generalized plant. For the arrows, full lines show chemical conversion and dashed lines indicate transport steps, with the red arrow showing exchange between xylem and phloem. Adapted from (62a).

for uptake from the apoplast into the phloem; there may also be a system for taking up amino acids from the pool delivered in the xylem and for retrieval of amino acids from senescing leaves. Transporters are also required to supply the embryonic tissues in developing seeds and also to obtain amino acids released from the endosperm or other storage tissue during germination.

Adjusting nitrogen transport in response to environmental perturbations is very important, and such regulation has been observed in the case of the proline transporter AtProT2, which is strongly induced under conditions of water and salt stress (104). In contrast, the amino acid transporters, *AtAAP4* and *AtAAP6*, were strongly repressed during desiccation. Because osmotically active compounds such as proline, glycinebetaine, and sugar alcohols may accumulate under conditions of drought or salt stress (125), the downregulation of broad specificity amino acid transporters and upregulation of proline translocators may enhance the transport of proline under stress conditions (104). The concentration of GABA also increases dramatically in xylem sap during drought conditions (113), and the ability of AtProT2 to transport this amino acid and its upregulation under such conditions could therefore be physiologically significant (9). Compatible solutes, e.g. proline, and glycine betaine also accumulate in plant tissues that dehydrate during their maturation, e.g. pollen and seeds. The uptake and accumulation of proline in developing and germinating tomato pollen correlated with the induction of LeProt1, a pollen-specific member of the ProT family (112).

Most of the amino acid transporters isolated to date have a relatively broad specificity. They may predominantly transport particular amino acids but also have lower affinity for a range of other amino acids. Therefore, although kinetic studies in yeast and oocytes are useful for indicating the ability to transport particular amino acids, they do not provide conclusive evidence for the role of the transporter in vivo. For example, the amino acid transporter AtCAT1 predominantly transports basic amino acids but also has affinities for a wide spectrum of other amino acids. Depending on where it is expressed, the levels of neutral and acidic amino acids may be much higher than those of basic amino acids, and therefore this transporter may actually function in transporting those amino acids that are present at higher concentrations. This has been put forward as an explanation as to why, for example, many seeds have a very low lysine content (27).

The presence of multiple amino acid transporters, some with overlapping specificities, might at first sight suggest functional redundancy; however, each appears to be expressed in widely different tissues, and some show developmental and environmental regulation. More information is still needed on the actual tissue and cellular expression pattern of all of the amino acid transporters, but preliminary data indicate that although many do show similar substrate specificities, they function in quite different cells and are tailored so that the cell can carry out its particular function. The use of PCR-based screening of T-DNA or transposon-tagged populations could feasibly lead to the isolation of knockout mutants for the full range of amino acid transporters that have now been identified. This will be important in assessing their physiological role. Mutants isolated to date have been obtained mainly following exposure to toxic concentrations of certain amino acids or to toxic analogues (reviewed in 21; 10). Although defects in particular components of amino acid uptake have been detected, further work is required to determine whether the transport activities revealed in the kinetic analysis of the mutants can be attributed to any of the amino acid permeases identified to date.

Mechanism of Amino Acid Transporters

The reaction mechanism of individual amino acid transporters has only been investigated in detail in two cases (AtAAP1 and AtAAP5). For these experiments the permeases were expressed in *Xenopus* oocytes and transport was characterized using electrophysiological and radiotracer flux methods. The data indicate that AtAAP1 operates as a proton-coupled amino acid symporter; both ligands (H^+ and amino acid) bind randomly to AtAAP1 and are transported simultaneously (8). AtAAP1 transports neutral, basic, and acidic amino acids, and the analysis suggested that the transport mechanism appeared to be the same for glutamine, histidine, and glutamate (8). It was assumed that these amino acids are transported in their zwitterionic form. Thus, the concentration of the zwitterionic form should be determined when calculating the contribution of an individual carrier to the transport of a particular amino acid. Kinetic parameters are often calculated for total amino acid concentration (i.e. all species), and this can be misleading. A detailed analysis of AtAAP5 demonstrated that the stoichiometry was one proton per amino acid (7). Consistent with earlier analyses using purified membrane vesicles to examine which groups are important determinants of substrate specificity (64), α-amino and carboxyl groups as well as the β-carbon were important for substrate recognition in AtAAP5 (7). AtAAP5 had a reduced affinity for amino acids branching at the β-carbon, e.g. proline, valine, and isoleucine. For this permease, lysine was transported in its cationic form whereas histidine and glutamate were transported as neutral species.

Mechanistic studies in *Ricinus communis* plasma membrane vesicles detected a transport activity for the basic amino acids, lysine and arginine, that was not due to H^+ cotransport but was instead driven by the negative membrane potential (143). It will be interesting to determine the transport mechanism for the LHTs and CATs following expression in *Xenopus* oocytes as one of these family members may be contributing to the activity determined in *Ricinus communis* vesicles.

Site-directed and random mutagenesis should help reveal residues that are important in substrate-binding and translocation. Preliminary studies indicate that H47 and H337, two histidine residues in AtAAP1 that are conserved in the AAP family, are critical for function because substitutions have a dramatic impact on substrate binding or protein stabilization (91). Two other residues in this transporter, D252 and A254, thought to be associated with membrane spanning domains, have been implicated in substrate binding (91).

Regulation of Amino Acid Transporters

Although very little is known about the regulation of amino acid transporters in plants, they clearly are regulated by endogenous and environmental signals.

Evidence for regulation at the gene level is seen by the distinct tissue and cellular expression pattern of many of the transporters, e.g. *AtAAP1* and *2* are expressed in different cell types in the immature silique (39). Evidence has been presented indicating that amino acid uptake is sensitive to regulation in response to the N or C status of the plant (reviewed in 34). It will be important to determine the nature of the regulation and which amino acid permeases are involved.

There are preliminary reports that *AtAAP1* transcripts increase within 6 h in dark-adapted plants exposed to light and in dark-adapted plants fed sucrose as an exogenous carbon source (91). Whether this is due to a direct light signal or changes in the C/N ratio is not yet clear (91). *AtAAP1* transcripts also increased several fold in plants that were fed 50 mM KNO_3 after being starved of nitrogen for 7 days (91). There may be a global regulatory system controlling the expression of nitrate uptake, nitrogen assimilation, and long-distance transport genes allowing the plant to respond efficiently to changes in nitrogen availability (91). Interestingly, the *AtAAP1* promoter has a nitrate response element that is commonly found in the promoter regions of nitrogen-assimilatory enzymes from various species (45, 91).

Amino Acid Transporters at the Vacuole

It still remains to be investigated whether any of the genes already cloned encode vacuolar transporters as most have not been localized at the membrane level. There is biochemical evidence for at least three different systems at the tonoplast (74). A system transporting aromatic amino acids that is stimulated by MgPPi and MgATP and is sensitive to nitrate and uncouplers has been identifed (40). Whether this is an energized system has not been demonstrated unequivocally (74). A broad-specificity transporter, regulated but not energized by ATP/MgATP, is also present and may function to allow a steady flux between the vacuole and cytosol for maintaining cytosolic homeostasis (74). A third system transporting basic amino acids, which is not dependent on ATP, has also been demonstrated (75).

PEPTIDE TRANSPORTERS

In addition to amino acid transporters, plant cells also contain peptide transporters. These are saturable carriers that transport small peptides ($\geq$6 amino acids) across a membrane (122). Peptide transport is often associated with tissues showing rapid protein hydrolysis, such as germinating seeds and senescing leaves. Initial studies of peptide uptake were carried out on the scutellum of barley and other cereals (for a review see 37). On germination, peptides resulting from seed protein hydrolysis in the starchy endosperm are transferred to the embryo via the scutellum (modi-fied cotyledon). Together with amino acids, they represent an important nitrogen source for the developing embryo. Later it was shown that peptide uptake systems occur more generally, e.g. in mature leaves (47). Following transport, intracellular peptidases hydrolyze peptides to amino acids and thus serve as important sources of amino acids, carbon or nitrogen (120). In addition to their possible nutritional roles, other functions have been postulated (see 120 for details). These include the regulation of plant hormone activity by transporting hormone-peptide conjugates (38). In addition, peptide transporters may be responsible for taking up small peptide phytotoxins produced by plant pathogens. The affinity for such compounds could be tested in the heterologous yeast expression system.

Two oligopeptide transporters have been isolated from *Arabidopsis* using a yeast complementation approach, AtPTR2A (122) and AtNTR1 (25, 105). The latter was also subsequently isolated independently and named AtPTR2-B (120). *AtPTR2A* and *AtNTR1/AtPTR2B* encode proteins of 67.5 and 64.5 kDa, respectively (25, 120). A peptide transporter gene, *HvPTR1*, was also isolated from barley. These three transporters belong to the Peptide Transporter (PTR) family discussed previously. Both AtPTR2-A and AtPTR2-B appear to transport di- and tripeptides but not peptides four residues or longer (120, 122). The K_ms for dileucine transport were 50 μM and 14 μM for AtPTR2-A and AtPTR2-B, respectively. These appear to be broad-specificity peptide transporters that favor highly hydrophobic peptides. AtPTR2-B also showed a lower affinity for toxic peptides than AtPTR2-A (120). The low selectivity of these peptide transporters ensures efficient transport of a whole range of peptides, which would be released if proteolysis is the peptide source. Although *HvPTR1* was functionally expressed in oocytes, its substrate specificity was not investigated in detail (142).

The expression patterns of the peptide transporters differ. *AtPTR2-A* could not be detected by northern analysis but was detected in flower, stem leaf, and roots after PCR amplification. There is some discrepancy in the distribution reported by two different groups for *AtPTR2-B/AtNTR1*. In one study it was reported that *AtPTR2B* was expressed at reasonably high levels (detectable by northern analysis) in all organs examined, suggesting that this transporter supplies the plant with a basal level of peptide uptake capacity (120). However, expression analysis of the same gene by another group showed a high level of expression in developing pods, an intermediate level in leaves, and low levels in other tissues examined (27). It was suggested that AtPTR2-B/AtNTR1 might be involved in transport of nitrogenous compounds from the vascular system to the developing embryo and might subsequently play a role in the mobilization of stored nitrogen during germination. Consistent with this hypothesis was the observation that *AtPTR2-B/AtNTR1* showed high expression in the embryo of developing seeds when siliques were analyzed by in situ hybridization (105). Antisense lines for *AtPTR2-B/AtNTR1* exhibited significant phenotypic changes (119). These included a 7- to 15-day delay in flowering and larger rosette leaves prior to flowering. These changes may be due to lower nutrient transfer, although a more specific role in regulating transition to flowering cannot be excluded (119). The transgenic plants were not affected in silique formation and growth, but the seed number was significantly less than wild type even though the seeds were larger (119). This suggests that there was a similar import of nutrients into transgenic and control lines but that the antisense lines used this nutrient source to produce fewer, larger seeds. About half of the seeds in the antisense plants were arrested in development apparently after the heart or torpedo stage of embryo development, which suggests that AtPTR2-B/AtNTR may be involved in the import of nitrogen into the embryo that occurs mainly during the maturation stage of seed development.

In the carnivorous plant, *Nepentes alata*, a putative peptide transporter gene, *NaNTR1*, was expressed at highest levels in the pitchers but was also detectable in leaves and petioles (110). In the pitcher, it was exclusively localized in the phloem tissue in the bottom part of the pitcher, suggesting that it may play a significant role in exporting nitrogen from pitchers to other plant tissue (110). It will be important to determine whether this is a more general phenomenon in other plants that export high amounts of nitrogen from their leaves. The uptake of various dipeptides in broad bean leaf discs resulted in a concentration-dependent pH rise of the medium; a transient depolarization of the transmembrane potential difference was also observed upon the addition of Gly-Gly (47). These results are consistent with a proton-peptide cotransport uptake mechanism. It remains to be determined whether the peptide transporters isolated to date function as proton-coupled carriers, although the inhibition of dileucine uptake by the protonophore CCCP in yeast expressing *AtNTR1/AtPTR2B* would support this mechanism (105).

PURINE AND PURINE-DERIVATIVE TRANSPORTERS

Nucleic acid bases, nucleotides, and nucleosides contain a high proportion of nitrogen in their structure. The bases are required not only for nucleic acid synthesis but, together with their derivatives, for a variety of metabolic processes with potential roles in energization, cell division, senescence, and defense responses (32). Several studies have demonstrated transport processes for nucleic acid bases and derivatives, for example, in pollen and in germinating seeds (48, 52). Recently, a new family (PUP) of high-affinity transporters for purine bases and derivatives has been identified in *Arabidopsis* (32). *AtPUP1* (for *Arabidopsis thaliana* purine permease 1) was isolated by its ability to complement a yeast mutant defective in adenine and cytosine uptake (32). *AtPUP1* encodes a protein of 356 amino acids with a calculated molecular mass of 39 kD; hydrophobicity analysis suggests that it has 10 putative membrane-spanning domains (32). Fourteen putative sequences were identified in the genome database for *Arabidopsis*, ranging from 17% to 64% identity to AtPUP1 (32). Thus there is a multigene family encoding a range of small integral membrane proteins that may function in the transport of nucleic acid bases and their derivatives (32).

AtPUP1 has a K_m of 30 μM for adenine; uptake was sensitive to protonophores and increased at acidic pH, indicating proton-coupled transport (32). In competition assays with a range of purine derivatives, phytohormones, and alkaloids, the order of inhibition was adenine/kinetin/caffeine≥cytosine/zeatin/hypoxanthine>cytidine/nicotine>kinetin riboside/adenosine/zeatin riboside>thymine. Nucleotides did not compete for adenine uptake. Inhibition of adenine uptake by cytosine and by the cytokinins, kinetin and zeatin, was competitive, indicating that they may serve as transported substrates. However, a physiological function for AtPUP1 in cytokinin transport remains to be shown. Northern analysis showed that *AtPUP1* expression was greatest in leaves, stems, and flowers; lower expression was observed in developing siliques, but no expression was detected in roots (32). This suggests that AtPUP1 may serve as an uptake system for root-derived nucleic acid base derivatives in shoots or as a system for export from shoots via the phloem (32). The physiological function for members of the PUP protein family can only be speculated upon at this stage, but as well as roles in the transport of nucleic acid bases, nucleosides, and cytokinins, the transport of secondary metabolites such as caffeine and nicotine have also been suggested as worthy of investigation (32).

A cDNA encoding a putative nucleoside transporter has been cloned from *Arabidopsis* (63a) AtENT1 is not a member of the PUP family but is instead related to the equilibrative nucleoside transporters (ENTs) found in protozoan parasites and mammals (20–30% identity). AtENT1 encodes a protein of 428 amino acids and hydrophobicity analysis predicts 11 transmembrane domains (63a). A related gene (50% identity) is present in the *Arabidopsis* genome. Further work is required to determine the substrate(s) transported by AtENT1 and its physiological function.

FUTURE PERSPECTIVES

Sequencing of the *Arabidopsis* genome is now complete and sequences for all the genes required for nitrogen transport in a higher plant are available. This information is important but it may be dangerous to assign gene function solely on the basis of sequence similarity; the PTR family may not be unique in having members that can transport a range of different substrates. Functional studies are therefore essential, and biochemical properties (e.g. substrate specificity, affinity, and transport mechanism) can be obtained by expressing the genes in heterologous systems. It is advisable not to be too conservative when testing the substrate range. In addition, estimating the capacity for particular substrates is also important. Although many systems identified to date appear to be secondary transporters, other mechanisms may exist for the membrane transfer of nitrogenous compounds, e.g. ABC transporters may have a role.

Sequence information can also be used for PCR-based screening of insertional mutants that are defective in the expression of individual transporter genes. The physiological, cytological, and biochemical data from these plants can be combined with information from the heterologous systems to help define the role that each transporter plays in the uptake and distribution of nitrogen throughout the plant.

Further details concerning membrane localization of individual transporters are also required. Since many of the transporters isolated to date can complement nutrient-uptake-deficient yeast mutants, it is assumed they are targeted to the plasma membrane. However, immunogold labeling and localization of GFP fusions are required to prove their cellular location within the plant. Evidence has been provided for targeting of the sucrose transporter *SUT1* mRNA and possibly the protein through the plasmodesmata connecting companion cells and sieve elements of the phloem (57). It will be interesting to determine whether such a phenomenon is observed for amino acid transporters since amino acids, like sucrose, are major components of the phloem sap. It will be useful to correlate information now accumulating on both the cellular distribution and apparent affinities/capacities of the various transporters in *Arabidopsis* with data on the abundance of nitrogenous solutes in this plant at various stages of development and under various growth conditions. This would allow us to assess more clearly their individual contribution to nitrogen distribution.

There are important biotechnological applications for nitrogen nutrition but the strategies implemented must be carefully chosen. For example, simply increasing the expression of a plasma membrane influx carrier may have little effect on improving nitrogen nutrition. Coordination with other activities may be required, such as increasing the flux across the tonoplast to allow storage in the vacuole or targeting expression to particular storage tissues. Constitutive expression of inducible systems would be interesting but this may lead merely to increased efflux; thus, further information on the molecular mechanisms of this process is required. The manipulation of amino acid transport in plants has significant promise. For example, increasing the lysine content in harvestable tissues such as cereal grain would be extremely beneficial in improving the nutritional value of crops (12). Improving crop yield under water stress conditions, e.g. by increasing the accumulation of compatible solutes, such as proline, would also be beneficial. It may be useful to clone transporters from a wider variety of plants for overexpression or alternatively express transporters from other organisms since some show a much narrower specificity and may help to increase the transport of particular amino acids that are normally limiting. Because of the importance of nitrogen in plant productivity and crop yield, many studies have concentrated on a few crop species and on the model plant *Arabidopsis*. Studies must be extended to a wider variety of plants that may differ in their preferred nitrogen source. For example, organic nitrogen seems to play a much more important role in the nitrogen economy of arctic plants (50); these may have novel transport systems or simply express a preponderance of amino acid transporters in their roots compared with those for inorganic sources of nitrogen. Understanding the relative contribution of various transporters in plants that have symbiotic associations is also important.

The possibilities for exploiting the plant peptide transporters for delivering toxic or growth-promoting substances to plants have been discussed (122). Since a number of plant pathogens secrete toxic peptides, modifying the peptide transport system of important crop species could provide the necessary resistance to these pathogens (122).

Undoubtedly, we need to know more about the regulatory mechanisms involved in nitrogen transport and assimilation. An important challenge for the future is to understand how the nitrogen status of the plant is sensed and which are the signalling pathways involved in gene induction by nitrogenous solutes. To help elucidate nitrate regulatory mechanisms further, a microarray analysis of nitrate-induced gene expression has recently been performed and has shown that nitrate induces many diverse responses at the mRNA level (141a). Genes involved directly or indirectly with nitrite reduction were the most highly induced by nitrate. The nitrate transporter *AtNRT1* appeared to be high on the list of nitrate-induced genes whereas the ammonium transporter, *AMT1;1*, was repressed by higher nitrate concentrations (141a).

In yeast, transporters are implicated in sensing sugars and ammonium, e.g. the presence of the yeast ammonium transporter, Mep2, is essential for the development of pseudohyphae in the nitrogen-starvation response (67). Similar mechanisms may exist in higher plants, for example, changes in root morphology in response to nitrate (145) may be a suitable model to test for nitrogen sensors in higher plants using knock-out lines. Very little is known about the regulation of amino acid transporters in response to nitrogen status, but there have been some interesting recent findings in *Saccharomyces cerevisiae*. A permease-like sensor Ssy1 appears to control the expression of a range of other amino acid and peptide transporter genes in response to various amino acids (17, 46), and transcriptional induction was observed in response to extracellular rather than intracellular amino acids (46). It was proposed that Ssy1 detects external amino acids and activates a transduction pathway leading to transcriptional activation of several permease genes. Interestingly, Ssy1 displays structural features reminiscent of those displayed by Snf3 and Rgt2, glucose sensors that have extended cytoplasmic C-terminal domains essential for the glucose sensing function (92, 93). In Ssy1, it was suggested that the large N-terminal domain might play an important role in generating the amino acid signal (46). Also in relation to sensing mechanisms, a family of genes with homology to glutamate receptors has been identified (59), although the functional significance of these in relation to signalling has not yet been investigated. Thus we are entering a very exciting era in the field of nitrogen transport, and we have many of the molecular tools necessary to unravel the nutritional, osmotic, and signalling roles of nitrogenous solutes in plants.

ACKNOWLEDGMENTS

Work in LEW's laboratory was funded by the Royal Society and Biotechnology and Biological Sciences Research Council of the UK. Work in AJM's laboratory was funded by European Union (BIO4-CT97-2310) and IACR receives grant-aided support from the Biotechnology and Biological Sciences Research Council of the UK.

Visit the Annual Reviews home page at www.AnnualReviews.org

LITERATURE CITED

1. Aslam M, Travis RL, Huffaker RC. 1992. Comparative kinetics and reciprocal inhibition of nitrate and nitrite uptake in roots of uninduced and induced barley (*Hordeum-vulgare* l) seedlings. *Plant Physiol.* 99: 1124–33

2. Aslam M, Travis RL, Huffaker R. 1993. Comparative induction of nitrate and nitrite uptake and reduction systems by ambient nitrate and nitrite in intact roots of barley (*Hordeum vulgare* L.) seedlings. *Plant Physiol.* 102:811–19

3. Aslam M, Travis RL, Rains D. 1996. Evidence for substrate induction of a nitrate

efflux system in barley roots. *Plant Physiol.* 112:67–175

4. Ayling SM. 1993. The effect of ammonium ions on membrane potential and anion flux in roots of barley and tomato. *Plant Cell Environ.* 16:297–303

5. Bennett MJ, Marchant A, Green HG, May ST, Ward SP, et al. 1996. The *Arabidopsis AUXI* gene: a permease-like regulator of root gravitropism. *Science* 273:948–50

6. Bick J-A, Neelam A, Hall JL, Williams LE. 1998. Amino acid carriers of *Ricinus communis* expressed during seedling development: molecular cloning and expression analysis of two putative amino acid transporters, *RcAAP1* and *RcAAP2*. *Plant Mol. Biol.* 36:377–85

7. Boorer KJ, Fischer WN. 1997. Specificity and stoichiometry of the *Arabidopsis* H$^+$/amino acid transporter AAP5. *J. Biol. Chem.* 272:13040–46

8. Boorer KJ, Frommer WB, Bush DR, Kreman M, Loo DDF, et al. 1996. Kinetics and specificity of a H$^+$/amino acid transporter from *Arabidopsis thaliana*. *J. Biol. Chem.* 271:2213–20

9. Breitkreuz KE, Shelp BJ, Fischer WN, Schwacke R, Rentsch D. 1999. Identification and characterization of GABA, proline and quaternary ammonium compound transporters from *Arabidopsis thaliana*. *FEBS Lett.* 450:280–84

10. Bush DR. 1999 Amino acid transport. In *Plant Amino Acids*, ed. BK Singh, pp. 305–18. New York/Basel/Hong Kong: Marcel Dekker

11. Chang HC, Bush DR. 1997. Topology of NAT2: a prototypical example of a new family of amino acid transporters. *J. Biol. Chem.* 272:30552–57

12. Chen L, Bush DR. 1997. LHT1, a lysine- and histidine-specific amino acid transporter in *Arabidopsis*. *Plant Physiol.* 115:1127–34

13. Chiang H-H, Dandekar AM. 1995. Regulation of proline accumulation in *Arabidopsis thaliana* (L.) Heynh during develop-ment in response to desiccation. *Plant Cell Environ.* 18:1280–90

14. Clarkson DT, Gojon A, Saker LR, Wiersema PK, Purves JV, et al. 1996. Nitrate and ammonium influxes in soybean (*Glycine max*) roots: direct comparison of ^{13}N and ^{15}N tracing. *Plant Cell Environ.* 19:859–68

15. Cooper HD, Clarkson DT. 1989. Cycling of amino nitrogen and other nutrients between shoots and roots in cereals: a possible mechanism integrating shoot and root in the regulation of nutrient uptake. *J. Exp. Bot.* 40:753–62

16. Davenport RJ, Tester M. 2000. A weakly voltage-dependent, nonselective cation channel mediates toxic sodium influx in wheat. *Plant Physiol.* 122:823–34

17. Didion T, Regenberg B, Jørgensen MU, Kielland-Brandt MC, Anderson HA. 1998. The permease homologue Ssy1p controls the expression of amino acid and peptide transporter genes in *Saccharomyces cerevisiae*. *Mol. Microbiol.* 27:643–50

18. Doddema H, Telkamp GP. 1979. Uptake of nitrate by mutants of *Arabidopsis thaliana*, disturbed in uptake or reduction of nitrate. II. Kinetics. *Physiol. Plant.* 45:332–38

19. Feng JN, Volk RJ, Jackson WA. 1998. Source and magnitude of ammonium generation in maize roots. *Plant Physiol.* 118:835–41

20. Filleur S, Daniel-Vedele F. 1999. Expression analysis of a high-affinity nitrate transporter isolated from *Arabidopsis thaliana* by differential display. *Planta* 207:461–69

21. Fischer WN, Andre B, Rentsch D, Krolkiewicz S, Tegeder M, et al. 1998. Amino acid transport in plants. *Trends Plant Sci.* 3:188–95

22. Fischer WN, Kwart M, Hummel S, Frommer WB. 1995. Substrate specificity and expression profile of amino acid transporters (AAPs) in *Arabidopsis*. *J. Biol. Chem.* 270:16315–20

23. Forde BG. 2000. Nitrate transporters in

plants: structure, function and regulation. *Biochim. Biophys. Acta* 1465:219–35

24. Forde BG, Clarkson DT. 1999. Nitrate and ammonium nutrition of plants: physiological and molecular perspectives. *Adv. Bot. Res.* 30:1–90

24a. Frachisse JM, Colcombet J, Guern J, Barbier-Brygoo H. 2000. Characterization of a nitrate-permeable channel able to mediate sustained anion efflux in hypocotyl cells from *Arabidopsis thaliana. Plant J.* 21:361–71

24b. Fraisier V, Gojon A, Tillard P, Daniel-Vedele F. 2000. Constitutive expression of a putative high-affinity transporter in *Nicotiana plumbaginifolia*: evidence for post-transcriptional regulation by a reduced nitrogen source. *Plant J.* 23:489–96

25. Frommer WB, Hummel S, Rentsch D. 1994. Cloning of an *Arabidopsis* histidine transporting protein related to nitrate and peptide transporters. *FEBS Lett.* 347:185–89

26. Frommer WB, Hummel S, Riesmeier JW. 1993. Expression cloning in yeast of a cDNA encoding a broad specificity amino acid permease from *Arabidopsis thaliana. Proc. Natl. Acad. Sci. USA* 90:5944–48

27. Frommer WB, Hummel S, Unseld M, Ninnemann O. 1995. Seed and vascular expression of a high affinity transporter for cationic amino acids in *Arabidopsis. Proc. Natl. Acad. Sci. USA* 92:12036–40

28. Frommer WB, Kwart M, Hirner B, Fischer WN, Hummel S, et al. 1994. Transporters for nitrogenous compounds in plants. *Plant Mol. Biol.* 26:1651–70

29. Galván A, Quesada A, Fernández E. 1996. Nitrate and nitrite are transported by different specific transport systems and by a bispecific transporter in *Chlamydomonas reinhardtii. J. Biol. Chem.* 271:2088–92

30. Gazzarrini S, Lejay L, Gojon A, Ninnemann O, Frommer WB, et al. 1999. Three functional transporters for constitutive, diurnally regulated, and starvation-induced uptake of ammonium into *Arabidopsis* roots. *Plant Cell* 11:937–47

31. Geelen D, Lurin C, Bouchez D, Frachisse JM, Lelievre F, et al. 2000. Disruption of putative anion channel gene *AtCLC-a* in *Arabidopsis* suggests a role in the regulation of nitrate content. *Plant J.* 21:259–67

32. Gillissen B, Burkle L, André B, Kühn C, Rentsch D, et al. 2000. A new family of high affinity transporters for adenine, cytosine and purine derivatives in *Arabidopsis. Plant Cell* 12:291–300

33. Glass ADM, Shaff J, Kochian LV. 1992. Studies of the uptake of nitrate in barley. IV. Electrophysiology. *Plant Physiol.* 99:456–63

34. Glass ADM, Siddiqi MY. 1995. Nitrogen absorption by plant roots. In *Nitrogen Nutrition in Higher Plants*, ed. HS Srivastava, RP Singh, pp. 21–56. New Delhi: Associated Publ.

35. Grouzis JP, Pouliquin P, Rigaud J, Grignon C, Gibrat R. 1997. In vitro study of passive nitrate transport by native and reconstituted plasma membrane vesicles from corn root cells. *Biochim. Biophys. Acta* 1325:329–42

36. Hechenberger M, Schwappach B, Fischer WN, Frommer WB, Jentsch TJ, et al. 1996. A family of putative chloride channels from *Arabidopsis* and functional gene complementation of a yeast strain with a CLC gene disruption. *J. Biol. Chem.* 271:33632–38

37. Higgins CF, Payne JW. 1980. Transport and utilization of amino acids and peptides by higher plants. In *Microorganisms and Nitrogen Sources*, ed. JW Payne, 609–39. New York: Wiley.

38. Higgins CF, Payne JW. 1982. Plant peptides. *Encycl. Plant Physiol.* 14A:438–58

39. Hirner B. Fischer WN, Rentsch D, Kwart M, Frommer WB. 1998. Developmental control of H^+/amino acid permease gene expression during seed development of *Arabidopsis. Plant. J.* 14:535–44

40. Homeyer U, Litek K, Huchzermeyer B,

Schultz G. 1989. Uptake of phenylalanine into isolated barley vacuoles is driven by both tonoplast adenosine-triphosphatase and pyrophosphatase-evidence for a hydrophobic L-amino acid carrier system. *Plant Physiol.* 89:1388–93

41. Howitt SM, Udvardi MK. 2000. Structure, function and regulation of ammonium transporters in plants. *Biochim. Biophys. Acta* 1465:152–70

42. Hsu LC, Chiou TJ, Chen L, Bush DR. 1993. Cloning a plant amino acid transporter by functional complementation of a yeast amino acid transport mutant. *Proc. Natl. Acad. Sci. USA* 90:7441–45

43. Huang NC, Chiang CS, Crawford NM, Tsay YF. 1996. *CHL1* encodes a component of the low affinity nitrate uptake system in *Arabidopsis* and shows cell type-specific expression in roots. *Plant Cell* 8:2183–91

44. Huang NC, Liu KH, Lo HJ, Tsay YF. 1999. Cloning and functional characterization of an *Arabidopsis* nitrate transporter gene that encodes a constitutive component of low-affinity uptake. *Plant Cell* 11:1381–92

45. Hwang CF, Lin Y, D'Souza T, Cheng CL. 1997. Sequences necessary for nitrate-dependent transcription of *Arabidopsis* nitrate reductase genes. *Plant Physiol.* 113:853–62

46. Iraqui I, Vissers S, Bernard F, De Craene JO, Boles E, et al. 1999. Amino acid signaling in *Saccharomyces cerevisiae*: a permease-like sensor of external amino acids and F-box protein Grr1p are required for transcriptional induction of the *AGP1* gene, which encodes a broad-specificity amino acid permease. *Mol. Cell Biol.* 19:989–1001

47. Jamai A, Chollet J-F, Delrot S. 1994. Proton-peptide co-transport in broad bean leaf tissues. *Plant Physiol.* 106: 1023–31

48. Kamboj RK, Jackson JF. 1987. Purine nucleoside transport in *Petunia* pollen is an active, carrier-mediated system not sensitive to nitrobenzylthioinosine and not renewed during pollen tube growth. *Plant Physiol.* 84:688–91

49. Kaiser BN, Finnegan PN, Tyerman SD, Whitehead LF, Bergersen FJ, et al. 1998. Characterization of ammonium transport from the peribacteroid membrane of soybean nodules. *Science* 281:1202–6

50. Kielland K. 1994. Amino acid absorption by arctic plants: implications for plant nutrition and nitrogen cycling. *Ecology* 75:2373–83

51. King BJ, Siddiqi MY, Ruth TJ, Warner RL, Glass ADM. 1993. Feedback regulation of nitrate influx in barley roots by nitrate, nitrite, and ammonium. *Plant Physiol.* 102:1279–86

52. Kombrink E, Beevers H. 1983. Transport of purine and pyrimidine bases and nucleosides from endosperm to cotyledons in germinating castor bean seedlings. *Plant Physiol.* 73:370–76

53. Krapp A, Fraisier V, Scheible WR, Quesada A, Gojon M, et al. 1998. Expression studies of *Nrt2:1Np*, a putative high-affinity nitrate transporter: evidence for its role in nitrate uptake. *Plant J.* 14:723–32

54. Kronzucker HJ, Glass ADM, Siddiqi MY. 1999. Inhibition of nitrate uptake by ammonium in barley. Analysis of component fluxes. *Plant Physiol.* 120:283–91

55. Kronzucker HJ, Siddiqi MY, Glass ADM. 1995. Compartmentation and flux characteristics of ammonium in spruce. *Planta* 196:691–98

56. Kronzucker HJ, Siddiqi MY, Glass ADM. 1996. Kinetics of NH_4^+ influx in spruce. *Plant Physiol.* 110:773–79

57. Kühn C, Francheschi VR, Schulz A, Lemoine R, Frommer WB. 1997. Macromolecular trafficking indicated by localization and turnover of sucrose transporters in enucleate sieve elements. *Science* 275:1298–300

58. Kwart M, Hirner B, Hummel S, Frommer WB. 1993. Differential expression of two related amino acid transporters with

differing substrate specificity in *Arabidopsis thaliana. Plant J.* 4:993–1002

59. Lam HM, Chiu J, Hsieh MH, Meise L, Oliveira IC, et al. 1998. Glutamate-receptor genes in plants. *Nature* 396:125–26

60. Lam HM, Hsieh MH, Corruzzi G. 1998. Reciprocal regulation of distinct asparagine synthetase genes by light and metabolites in *Arabidopsis thaliana. Plant J.* 16:345–53

61. Larsson CM, Larsson M, Purves JV, Clarkson DT. 1991. Translocation and cycling through roots of recently absorbed nitrogen and sulfur in wheat (*Triticum aestivum*) during vegetative and generative growth. *Physiol. Plant.* 82:345–52

62. Lauter FR, Ninnemann O, Bucher M, Riesmeier JW, Frommer WB. 1996. Preferential expression of an ammonium transporter and of two putative nitrate transporters in root hairs of tomato. *Proc. Natl. Acad. Sci. USA* 93:8139–44

62a. Lea PJ. 1993. Nitrogen metabolism. In *Plant Biochemistry and Molecular Biology*, ed. PJ Lea, RC Leegood, pp. 155–80. England: Wiley

63. Lejay L, Tillard P, Domingo-Olive F, Lepetit M, Olive FD, et al. 1999. Molecular and functional regulation of two NO_3^--uptake systems by N- and C-status of *Arabidopsis* plants. *Plant J.* 18:509–19

63a. Li J, Wang D. 2000. Cloning and in vitro expression of the cDNA encoding a putative nucleoside transporter from *Arabidopsis thaliana.* Plant Sci. 157:23–32

64. Li ZC, Bush DR. 1992. Structural determinants in substrate recognition by proton-amino acid symports in plasma membrane vesicles isolated from sugar beet leaves. *Arch. Biochem. Biophys.* 294:519–26

65. Lin CM, Koh S, Stacey G, Yu SM, Lin TY, et al. 2000. Cloning and functional characterization of a constitutively expressed nitrate transporter gene, OsNRT1, from rice. *Plant Physiol.* 122:379–88

66. Liu K-H, Huang C-H, Tsay Y-F. 1999.

CHL1 is a dual-affinity nitrate transporter of *Arabidopsis* involved in multiple phases of nitrate uptake. *Plant Cell* 11:865–74

67. Lorenz M, Heitman J. 1998. The MEP2 ammonium permease regulates pseudohyphal differentiation in *Saccharomyces cerevisiae. EMBO J.* 17:1236–47

68. Lurin C, Geelen D, Barbier-Brygoo H, Guern J, Maurel C. 1996. Cloning and functional expression of a plant voltage-dependent chloride channel. *Plant Cell* 8:701–11

69. Marchant A, Kargul J, May ST, Muller P, Delbarre A, et al. 1999. AUX1 regulates root gravitropism in *Arabidopsis* by facilitating auxin uptake within root apical tissues. *EMBO J.* 18:2066–73

70. Marini AM, Soussi-Boudekou S, Vissers S, André B. 1997. A family of ammonium transporters in *Saccharomyces cerevisiae. Mol. Cell Biol.* 17:4282–93

71. Marini AM, Springael JY, Frommer WB, André B. 2000. Cross-talk between ammonium transporters in yeast and interference by the soybean SAT1 protein. *Mol. Microbiol.* 35:378–85

72. Marschner H, Kirkby EA, Engels C. 1997. Importance of cycling and recycling of mineral nutrients within plants for growth and development. *Bot. Acta* 4:265–74

73. Martin F, Botton B. 1993. Nitrogen metabolism of ectomycorrhizal fungi and ectomycorrhiza. *Adv. Bot. Res.* 9:83–102

74. Martinoia E, Ratajczak R. 1997. Transport of organic molecules across the tonoplast. *Adv. Bot. Res.* 25:365–400

75. Martinoia E, Thume M, Vogt E, Rentsch D, Dietz KJ. 1991. Transport of arginine and aspartic-acid into isolated barley mesophyll vacuoles. *Plant Physiol.* 97:644–50

76. Marvier AC, Neelam A, Bick JA, Hall JL, Williams LE. 1998. Cloning of an amino acid carrier from *Ricinus communis* (RcAAP1) by functional complementation in yeast: kinetic analysis, inhibitor sensitivity and substrate specificity. *Biochim. Biophys. Acta* 1373:321–31

77. McClure PR, Kochian LV, Spanswick RM, Shaff J. 1990. Evidence for cotransport of nitrate and protons in maize roots. I. Effects of nitrate on the membrane potential. *Plant Physiol.* 76:913–17

78. McClure PR, Omholt TE, Pace GM, Bouthyette PY. 1987. Nitrate-induced changes in protein synthesis and translation of RNA in maize roots. *Plant Physiol.* 84:52–57

79. Meraviglia G, Romani C, Beffagna N. 1996. The *chl Arabidopsis* mutant impaired in nitrate-inducible NO_3^-- transporter has an acidic intracellular pH in the absence of nitrate. *J. Plant Physiol.* 149:307–10

80. Miller AJ, Smith SJ. 1992. The mechanism of nitrate transport across the tonoplast of barley root cells. *Planta* 187:554–57

81. Miller AJ, Smith SJ. 1996. Nitrate transport and compartmentation in cereal root cells. *J. Exp. Bot.* 47:843–54

82. Miller AJ, Zhou JJ. 2000. *Xenopus* oocytes as an expression system for plant transporters. *Biochim. Biophys. Acta* 1465:343–58

83. Montamat F, Maurousset L, Tegeder M, Frommer W, Delrot S. 1999. Cloning and expression of amino acid transporters from broad bean. *Plant Mol. Biol.* 41:259–68

84. Muller B, Tillard P, Touraine B. 1995. Nitrate fluxes in soybean seedling roots and their response to amino acids: an approach using [15]N. *Plant Cell Environ.* 18:1267–79

85. Muller B, Touraine B. 1992. Inhibition of NO_3^-- uptake by various phloem-translocated amino acids in soybean seedlings. *J. Exp. Bot.* 43:617–23

86. Neelam A, Marvier AC, Hall JL, Williams LE. 1999. Functional characterization and expression analysis of the amino acid permease RcAAP3 from castor bean. *Plant Physiol.* 120:1049–56

87. Ni M, Beevers L. 1994. Nitrate-induced polypeptides in membranes from corn seedling roots *J. Exp. Bot.* 45:355–65

88. Niemietz CM, Tyerman SD. 2000. Channel-mediated permeation of ammonia gas through the peribacteroid membrane of soybean nodules. *FEBS Lett.* 465:110–14

89. Ninnemann O, Jauniaux JC, Frommer WB. 1994. Identification of a high affinity NH_4^+ transporter from plants. *EMBO J.* 13:3464–71

90. Ono F, Frommer WB, von Wirén N. 2000. Coordinated diurnal regulation of low-and high-affinity nitrate transporters in tomato. *Plant Biol.* 2:17–23

91. Ortiz-Lopez A, Chang HC, Bush DR. 2000. Amino acid transporters in plants. *Biochim. Biophys. Acta* 1465:275–80

92. Ozcan S, Dover J, Johnston M. 1998. Glucose sensing and signalling by two glucose receptors in the yeast *Saccharomyces cerevisiae*. *EMBO J.* 17:2566–73

93. Ozcan S, Dover J, Rosenwald AG, Wolfl S, Johnston M. 1996. Two glucose transporters in *Saccharomyces cerevisiae* are glucose sensors that generate a signal for induction of gene expression. *Proc. Natl. Acad. Sci. USA* 93:12428–32

94. Palacín M, Estévez R, Bertran J, Zorzano A. 1998. Molecular biology of mammalian plasma membrane amino acid transporters. *Physiol. Rev.* 78:969–1054

95. Pao SS, Paulsen IT, Saier MH. 1998. Major facilitator superfamily. *Microbiol. Mol. Biol. Rev.* 62:1–34

96. Paulsen IT, Skurray RA. 1994. The POT family of transport proteins. *Trends Biol. Sci.* 19:404

97. Perez M, Gonzalez C, Ávila J, Brito N, Siverio JM. 1997. The YNT1 gene encoding the nitrate transporter in the yeast *Hansenula polymorpha* is clustered with genes YNI1 and YNR1 encoding nitrite reductase and nitrate reductase, and its disruption causes inability to grow in nitrate. *Biochem. J.* 321:397–403

98. Quesada A, Galván A, Fernández E. 1994. Identification of nitrate transporter genes in *Chlamydomonas reinhardtii*. *Plant J.* 5:407–19

99. Quesada A, Hidalgo J, Fernández E. 1998. Three *Nrt2* genes are differentially regulated in *Chlamydomonas reinhardtii*. *Mol. Gen. Genet.* 258:373–77

100. Quesada A, Krapp A, Trueman LJ, Daniel Vedele F, Fernández E. 1997. PCR-identification of a *Nicotiana plumbaginifolia* cDNA homologous to the high-affinity nitrate transporters of the crnA family. *Plant Mol. Biol.* 34:265–74

101. Raven JA, Smith FA. 1976. Nitrogen assimilation and transport in vascular land plants in relation to intracellular pH regulation. *New Phytol.* 76:415–31

102. Rawat S, Silim S, Kronzucker HJ, Siddiqi MY, Glass ADM. 1999. AtAMT1 gene expression and NH_4^+ uptake in roots of *Arabidopsis thaliana*: evidence for regulation by root glutamine levels. *Plant J.* 19:143–52

103. Rentsch D, Boorer KJ, Frommer WB. 1998. Structure and function of plasma membrane amino acid, oligopeptide and sucrose transporters from higher plants. *J. Membr. Biol.* 162:177–90

104. Rentsch D, Hirner B, Schmelzer E, Frommer WB. 1996. Salt stress-induced proline transporters and salt stress-repressed broad specificity amino acid permeases identified by suppression of a yeast amino acid permease-targeting mutant. *Plant Cell* 8:1437–46

105. Rentsch D, Laloi M, Rouhara I, Schmelzer E, Delrot S, et al. 1995. *NTR1* encodes a high affinity oligopeptide transporter in *Arabidopsis*. *FEBS Lett.* 370:264–68

106. Rexach J, Montero B, Fernández E, Galván A. 1999. Differential regulation of the high affinity nitrite transport systems III and IV in *Chlamydomonas reinhardtii*. *J. Biol. Chem.* 274:27801–6

107. Rowe JJ, Ubbink-Kok T, Molenaar D, Konings WN, Driessen AJM. 1994. NarK is a nitrite-extrusion system involved in anaerobic nitrate respiration by *Escherichia coli*. *Mol. Microbiol.* 12:579–86

108. Saier MH Jr, Eng BH, Fard S, Garg J, Haggerty DA, et al. 1999. Phylogenetic characterization of novel transport protein families revealed by genome analyses. *Biochim. Biophys. Acta* 1422:1–56

109. Schroeder JI, Ward JM, Gassman W. 1994. Perspectives on the physiology and structure of inward-rectifying K^+ channels in higher plants: biophysical implications for K^+ uptake. *Annu. Rev. Biophys. Biomol. Struct.* 23:441–71

110. Schulze W, Frommer W, Ward JM. 1999. Transporters for ammonium, amino acids and peptides are expressed in pitchers of the carnivorous plant *Nepenthes*. *Plant J.* 17:637–46

111. Schumaker KS, Sze H. 1987. Decrease of pH gradients in tonoplast vesicles by NO_3^-- and Cl^- evidence for H^+-coupled anion transport. *Plant Physiol.* 83:490–96

112. Schwacke R, Grallath S, Breitkreuz KE, Stransky E, Stransky H, et al. 1999. LeProT1, a transporter for proline, glycine betaine, and gamma-amino butyric acid in tomato pollen. *Plant Cell* 11:377–91

113. Serraj R, Shelp BJ, Sinclair TR. 1998. Accumulation of gamma-aminobutyric acid in nodulated soybean in response to drought stress. *Physiol. Plant.* 102:79–86

114. Shingles R, Roh MH, McCarty RE. 1996. Nitrite transport in chloroplast inner envelope vesicles. I. Direct measurement of proton-linked transport. *Plant Physiol.* 112:1375–81

115. Siddiqi MY, Glass ADM, Ruth TJ. 1991. Studies of the uptake of nitrate in barley. III. Compartmentation of NO_3^-. *J. Exp. Bot.* 42:1455–63

116. Siddiqi MY, Glass ADM, Ruth TJ, Fernando M. 1989. Studies of the regulation of nitrate influx by barley seedlings using $^{13}NO_3$ *Plant Physiol.* 90:806–13

117. Skerrett M, Tyerman SD. 1994. A channel that allows inwardly directed fluxes of anions in protoplasts derived from wheat roots. *Planta* 192:295–305

118. Sohlenkamp C, Shelden M, Howitt S,

Udvardi M. 2000. Characterization of *Arabidopsis* AtAMT2, a novel ammonium transporter in plants. *FEBS Lett.* 467:273–78

119. Song W, Koh S, Czako M, Marton L, Drenkard E. 1997. Antisense expression of the peptide transport gene AtPTR2-B delays flowering and arrests seed development in transgenic *Arabidopsis* plants. *Plant Physiol.* 114:927–35

120. Song W, Steiner HY, Zhang L, Naider F, Stacey G, et al. 1996. Cloning of a second *Arabidopsis* peptide transport gene. *Plant Physiol.* 110:171–78

121. Steiner HY, Naider F, Becker JM. 1995. The PTR family: a new group of peptide transporters. *Mol. Microbiol.* 16:825–34

122. Steiner HY, Song W, Zhang L, Naider F, Becker JM, et al. 1994. An *Arabidopsis* peptide transporter is a member of a new class of membrane transport proteins. *Plant Cell* 6:1289–99

123. Stitt M. 1999. Nitrate regulation of metabolism and growth. *Curr. Opin. Plant Biol.* 2:178–86

124. Streeter J. 1989. Estimation of ammonium concentration in the cytosol of soybean nodules. *Plant Physiol.* 90:779–82

125. Tarczynski MC, Jensen RG, Bohnert HJ. 1993. Stress protection of transgenic tobacco by production of the osmolyte mannitol. *Science* 259:508–10

126. Tegeder M, Offler C, Frommer WB, Patrick JW. 2000. Amino acid transporters are localised to transfer cells of developing pea seeds. *Plant Physiol.* 122:319–25

127. Thomas GH, Mullins JGL, Merrick M. 2000. Membrane topology of the Mep/Amt family of ammonium transporters. *Mol. Microbiol.* 37:331–44

128. Touraine B, Glass ADM. 1997. NO_3^-- and ClO_3^--fluxes in the chl1-5 mutant of *Arabidopsis thaliana*—does the CHL1-5 gene encode a low-affinity NO_3^--transporter? *Plant Physiol.* 114:137–44

129. Trueman LJ, Richardson A, Forde BG.

1996. Molecular cloning of higher plant homologues of the high-affinity nitrate transporters of *Chlamydomonas reinhardtii. Gene* 175:223–31

130. Tsay YF, Schroeder JI, Feldmann KA, Crawford NM. 1993. The herbicide sensitivity gene *CHL1* of *Arabidopsis* encodes a nitrate-inducible nitrate transporter. *Cell* 72:705–13

131. Tyerman SD, Whitehead LF, Day DA. 1995. A channel-like transporter for NH_4^+ on the symbiotic interface of N_2^--fixing plants. *Nature* 378:629–32

132. Udvardi MK, Day DA. 1997. Metabolite transport across symbiotic membranes of legume nodules. *Annu. Rev. Plant Physiol. Plant Mol. Biol.* 48:493–523

133. Unkles SE, Hawker KL, Grieve C, Campbell EI, Montague P, et al. 1991. *crnA* encodes a nitrate transporter in *Aspergillus nidulans. Proc. Natl. Acad. Sci. USA* 88:204–8

134. van der Leij M, Smith SJ, Miller AJ. 1998. Remobilisation of vacuolar stored nitrate in barley root cells. *Planta* 205:64–72

135. Vidmar JJ, Zhuo D, Siddiqi MY, Glass ADM. 2000. Isolation and characterization of *HvNRT2.3* and *HvNRT2.4*, cDNAs encoding high-affinity nitrate transporters from roots of barley. *Plant Physiol.* 122:783–92

136. Vidmar JJ, Zhuo D, Siddiqi MY, Schjoerring JK, Touraine B. 2000. Regulation of high-affinity nitrate transporter genes and high-affinity nitrate influx by nitrogen pools in roots of barley. *Plant Physiol.* 123:307–18

137. von Wirén N, Gazzarrini S, Gojon A, Frommer WB. 2000. The molecular physiology of ammonium uptake and retrieval. *Curr. Opin. Plant Biol.* 3:254–61

138. von Wirén N, Lauter FR, Ninnemann O, Gillisen B, Walch-Liu P, et al. 2000. Differential regulation of three functional ammonium transporter genes by nitrogen in root hairs and by light in leaves of tomato. *Plant J.* 21:167–75

139. Wang R, Crawford NM. 1996. Genetic identification of a gene involved in constitutive, high affinity nitrate transport in higher plants. *Proc. Natl. Acad. Sci. USA* 93:9297–301

140. Wang H, Fei YJ, Ganapathy V, Leibach FH. 1998. Electrophysiological characteristics of the proton-coupled peptide transporter PEPT2 cloned from rat brain. *Am. J. Physiol.* 44:C967–75

141. Wang MY, Glass ADM, Shaff JE, Kochian LV. 1994. Ammonium uptake by rice roots. III. Electrophysiology. *Plant Physiol.* 104:899–906

141a. Wang R, Guegler K, LaBrie ST, Crawford NM. 2000. Genomic analysis of a nutrient response in *Arabidopsis* reveals diverse expression patterns and novel metabolic and potential regulatory genes induced by nitrate. *Plant Cell* 12:1491–509

142. West CE, Waterworth WM, Stephens SM, Smith CP, Bray CM. 1998. Cloning and functional characterisation of a peptide transporter expressed in the scutellum of barley grain during the early stages of germination. *Plant J.* 15:221–29

143. Weston K, Hall JL, Williams LE. 1995. Characterisation of amino acid transport in *Ricinus communis* roots using isolated membrane vesicles. *Planta* 196:166–73

144. Young GB, Jack DL, Smith DW, Saier MH. 1999. The amino acid/auxin:proton symport permease family. *Biochim. Biophys. Acta* 1415:306–22

145. Zhang H, Forde BG. 1998. An *Arabidopsis* MADS box gene that controls nutrient-induced changes in root architecture. *Science* 279:407–9

146. Zhou JJ, Fernández E, Galván A, Miller AJ. 2000. A high affinity nitrate transport system from *Chlamydomonas* requires two gene products. *FEBS Lett* 466:225–27

147. Zhou JJ, Theodoulou FL, Muldin I, Ingemarsson B, Miller AJ. 1998. Cloning and functional characterization of a *Brassica napus* transporter that is able to transport nitrate and histidine. *J. Biol. Chem.* 273:12017–23

148. Zhou JJ, Trueman LJ, Boorer KJ, Theodoulou FL, Forde BG, Miller AJ. 2000. A high affinity fungal nitrate carrier with two transport mechanisms. *J. Biol. Chem.* 275:39894–99

149. Zhuo DG, Okamoto M, Vidmar JJ, Glass ADM. 1999. Regulation of a putative high-affinity nitrate transporter (*Nrt2;1At*) in roots of *Arabidopsis thaliana*. *Plant J.* 17:563–68

NOTE ADDED IN PROOF

It has now been found that *AtPTR2-A* is not a bona fide *Arabidopsis* gene but more likely is derived from a fungal contaminant (information from Correction. *Plant Cell.* 2000. 12:2295).

Annu. Rev. Plant Physiol. Plant Mol. Biol. 2001. 52:689–724

DEFENSIVE RESIN BIOSYNTHESIS IN CONIFERS

Susan Trapp and Rodney Croteau
*Institute of Biological Chemistry, Washington State University, Pullman,
Washington 99164-6340; e-mail: croteau@mail.wsu.edu, sctrapp@mail.wsu.edu*

Key Words   bark beetles, turpentine, rosin, monoterpenes, sesquiterpenes,
diterpenes, metabolism, regulation, molecular genetics

■ **Abstract**   Tree killing bark beetles and their vectored fungal pathogens are the
most destructive agents of conifer forests worldwide. Conifers defend against attack
by the constitutive and inducible production of oleoresin, a complex mixture of mono-,
sesqui-, and diterpenoids that accumulates at the wound site to kill invaders and both
flush and seal the injury. Although toxic to the bark beetle and fungal pathogen, oleoresin also plays a central role in the chemical ecology of these boring insects, from host
selection to pheromone signaling and tritrophic level interactions. The biochemistry of
oleoresin terpenoids is reviewed, and the regulation of production of this unusual plant
secretion is described in the context of bark beetle infestation dynamics with respect to
the function of the turpentine and rosin components. Recent advances in the molecular genetics of terpenoid biosynthesis provide evidence for the evolutionary origins of
oleoresin and permit consideration of genetic engineering strategies to improve conifer
defenses as a component of modern forest biotechnology.

CONTENTS

INTRODUCTION

Conifers are an ancient group of woody plants that arose at least 200 million years ago (34) and include the oldest living organisms (yew, bristlecone pine, redwood) with life spans of thousands of years (100). Over 600 species of conifers (order Coniferales) of seven families (Pinaceae, Podocarpaceae, Araucariaceae, Taxodiaceae, Cephalotaxaceae, Taxaceae, Cupressaceae) (49) dominate large regions of temperate forest, especially in Western North America, Eastern Asia, and parts of Australia and New Zealand (100). The Pinaceae are the most abundant and widespread of these families, particularly in the Northern Hemisphere where firs (*Abies*), spruces (*Picea*), and pines (*Pinus*) predominate. Like all plants, conifers are subject to predation by a wide range of herbivores and pathogens (but over an uncommonly long life span), with the most serious destruction worldwide resulting from the infestation by tree killing bark beetles and their symbiotic fungal pathogens. The great success of the conifers rests in part on their evolution of complex defense mechanisms to deter such herbivore and pathogen predation. A principal, and unique, chemical and physical defense of conifers is comprised of the constitutive and inducible production of oleoresin (often simply termed resin or pitch). The viscous oleoresin secretion is composed of a complex mixture of terpenoids, consisting of roughly equal parts of volatile turpentine [mostly monoterpene (C_{10}) olefins with some sesquiterpenes (C_{15}), including oxygenated types] and rosin [diterpene (C_{20}) resin acids] (Figure 1) (29, 63, 82, 85). Accumulated resin is released upon tissue injury and/or produced locally at the site of infestation, with the consequence that the beetle and associated fungal pathogen(s) are killed, encased in resin, and expelled from the bore hole point of entry. This process is called pitching out (Figure 2*B*, see color insert), and it results in not only killing the attackers and flushing the wound site but also moving the oleoresin to the trunk surface where the turpentine evaporates to permit the resin acids to form a formidable physical barrier that seals the wound (29, 52).

With the advent of large-scale commercial lumbering of softwoods at the turn of the century and the replanting of clearcuts with a single conifer species, accompanied by the prevention of forest fires as a natural control agent, predation by bark beetles has become a serious, and occasionally epidemic, problem in monocultural forestry. For these reasons, the biology of bark beetles and their microbial associates as well as their attack strategies and dynamics have become the focus of considerable study. The response of the host conifer, especially the physiological and environmental conditions that result in susceptibility and resistance, and the physical and chemical character of the defensive secretion have also been subjected to substantial investigation. For many such predator-host systems, the players are now well understood, and the chemical bases of the interaction (largely in the context of bark beetle chemical ecology) have been defined. Much recent work has focused on a more refined analysis of conifer resin production, and it is these biochemical, physiological, and molecular advances that

Monoterpenes

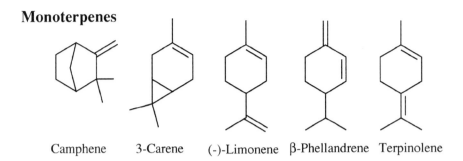

Camphene   3-Carene   (-)-Limonene   β-Phellandrene   Terpinolene

Sesquiterpenes

β-Caryophyllene   γ-Humulene   δ-Selinene

Diterpene resin acids

Abietic acid   Neoabietic acid   Dehydroabietic acid

Figure 1   Structures of typical resin components.

are emphasized in this overview of the topic. The evolutionary origins of oleoresin are also briefly described as are the prospects for biotechnological applications using these newer molecular tools. The latter assumes some significance,
because there are very few traditional pest control strategies applicable to large-
scale forestry.

CONIFER-BARK BEETLE INTERACTIONS

Although conifers encounter a range of pests and pathogens, including insect defoliators (101), root feeders (84), and nematodes (48), bark boring beetles (Coleoptera:Scolytidae) are the most destructive agent of coniferous forests worldwide with annual losses in the United States alone exceeding five million board feet of lumber (8). Most bark beetles live and feed on dead trees; however, aggressive species of *Dendroctonus*, *Ips*, *Scolytus*, and *Dryocoetes* attack living trees exclusively and must kill the host in order to reproduce (8, 118). Bark beetle outbreaks are generally episodic and can rapidly spread over hundreds of square miles of forest before abating. The origins and dynamics of such outbreaks are not yet fully understood, although it is clear that the underlying interactions between the bark beetle and its conifer host involve a very high degree of specialization. This selectivity, wherein a given beetle species will attack only one or two conifer species, reflects the extended period of coevolution between insect and host (112). The biology, behavior, and ecology of bark beetles and their unusual mutualistic relationship with the pathogenic fungi they carry as well as the role of host resin production in resistance against attack have been described for a range of specific beetle-conifer interactions (8, 24, 94, 104, 105), which permit a generalized description for the purpose of this review.

Bark Beetle Life Cycle

The details of the bark beetle life cycle vary with species and geographic location; however, four major phases can be defined as multiplication, development, dispersal, and concentration (8, 105). Adult beetles mass attack the selected host by boring through the bark (Figure 2C, see color insert), where they mate and lay eggs in tunnels (brood galleries) excavated in the phloem, cambium, and sapwood of the dying tree (Figures 2F, G, see color insert). In the process of colonization, which has the effect of girdling the tree, the ailing host is also infected with pathogenic fungi carried by the beetles in specialized anatomical structures called mycangia (Figure 2A, see color insert) or on other external, invaginated body parts (5, 43), whereupon the fungi assist in tree killing by invasive growth and toxin production in the conducting elements. The larvae hatch, feed in the tunnels that they construct (Figures 2F, G), develop, and then pupate and overwinter. In the dispersal phase, young adults emerge from the dead host by boring exit holes and then seek new living hosts by utilizing a variety of visual, tactile, and olfactory cues (122). Once a suitable host is located, often a physically damaged or physiologically compromised tree, pioneer beetles signal for mass attack (Figure 2C), via aggregation or sex attracting pheromones (see below), in an attempt to overcome host defenses (7, 97, 122). This concentrated attack often results in the death of the tree in which the annual cycle of multiplication, development, dispersal, and concentration is repeated.

Bark Beetle Microbial Symbiosis

The bark beetle–microbe-tree ecosystem has been described as a supra-organism (6) in which bark beetles associate in a generally mutualistic relationship with a variety of microorganisms (fungi, yeasts, bacteria, and protozoans) borne on and in their bodies (118). As early as the turn of the century, investigators proposed that bark beetles transmit pathogenic fungi to their conifer hosts; however, not until 1929 did experiments show that *Dendroctonus* and *Ips* species vector blue-stain fungi (83). Pathogenic fungi are often designated as blue- or black-staining because they typically discolor the infected wood and reduce its lumber value.

All bark beetle species appear to vector pathogenic fungi, the most common associative types belonging to the genera *Ophiostoma* (formerly *Ceratocystis*), *Leptographium*, *Graphium*, and *Trichosporium*. These vectored fungi, as a consequence of beetle excavation of the host, assist in tree killing; pathogenicity is clearly conditional on entry provided by the wood-boring insect. Not all mutualists are carried externally in the mycangia, as are fungal spores, and the benefits provided to and by these associates are less clear (43, 118). Vectored yeasts may serve as food sources for beetles and their broods (118).

Bark Beetle Chemical Ecology

The volatile monoterpene constituents of conifer oleoresin serve diverse roles in bark beetle chemical ecology, including host recognition and selection; pheromone signaling, which directs beetle aggregation and colonization; and tritrophic level interactions that involve signaling of beetle predators and parasitoids (52, 87, 89, 94, 122). In spite of their toxicity toward bark beetles, resin monoterpenes provide a species-specific chemical signature and thus function as olfactory cues in host location (122); visual cues and gustatory (textural and compositional) features of the bark also serve in final host selection (94). The monoterpene air plume derived from freshly exposed oleoresin resulting from tree damage (lightning strike, wind fall, lumbering activity) is generally attractive to pioneer beetles, as are the emissions from physiologically compromised individuals (e.g. victims of drought stress) (8, 52, 77). Such sites often provide the focus for infestation and subsequent outbreaks by attracting many host-seeking pioneers, which leads to the aggregation and colonization phases of host attack.

The essential advantage of a focused attack, wherein beetles initially aggregate upon a small number of trees, is that the host is unable to respond to the sheer number of invaders. The production of sex attractants and aggregation pheromones (to which both sexes respond) is the critical determinant in the success of a concentrated attack on the selected host (16) and often leads to the colonization of adjacent healthy trees that were not the object of the original pioneers. Many bark beetle species synthesize aggregation pheromones from turpentine components of host oleoresin.

cis-Verbenol, (+)-ipsdienol and (−)-ipsdienol (Figure 3), produced by *Ips para-confusus*, were the first scolytid aggregation pheromones identified. *I. paracon-fusus* converts the acyclic monoterpene myrcene to either enantiomer of ipsdienol, both of which appear to be important in communication in this beetle genus (16). (+)-Ipsdienol acts as an aggregation pheromone for *I. paraconfusus*, whereas (−)-ipsdienol acts as an aggregation inhibitor to regulate attack density and direct colonization to adjacent host trees. In the case of the pine engraver (*Ips pini*), the signaling pattern is reversed (10); the complementary adaptation between these two co-occurring beetle species is thought to regulate interspecific competition (69, 81). The chiral preferences of *I. pini* may also depend upon geographical lo-cation because eastern populations of this insect are most strongly attracted by a mixture of both ipsdienol enantiomers (96).

Ips typographus produces (+)-*cis*-verbenol and (+)-*trans*-verbenol (Figure 3) by oxygenation of the monoterpene precursors (+)-α-pinene and (−)-α-pinene, respectively, obtained from the Norway spruce (*Picea abies*) host. *I. typographus*, however, recognizes only (+)-*cis*-verbenol as an aggregation pheromone (69). Host production of both α-pinene enantiomers consequently undermines the effective-ness of pheromonal communication because the beetle transforms both antipodes to the corresponding verbenol isomers with nearly equal efficiency. The verbenols can be further oxidized to the corresponding ketones (+)-verbenone and (−)-verbenone (Figure 3), which act as anti-aggregation (dispersal) pheromones (16). As indicated above, pheromone-based dispersal regulates attack density, such that once a host has been successfully colonized by mass attack, incoming beetles are directed to broaden the offensive to adjacent trees (16, 122). In many *Dendroctonus* species, (+)-*trans*-verbenol is a strong attractant that often acts synergistically with other pheromones or host monoterpenes (58, 92). In the case of the mountain pine beetle (*Dendroctonus ponderosae*), *trans*-verbenol is ineffective as an attractant, unless presented in combination with host monoterpenes (9, 91).

Although the involvement of bark beetles in the production of pheromones is clear, the biosynthetic origin of these signaling compounds is still at issue. Some fungal symbionts and insect gut microorganisms are able to oxidize the host monoterpenes α-pinene and myrcene to the corresponding pheromones (17, 18, 59, 70, 71). However, the production of (+)- and (−)-ipsdienol by *Ips* species, in the absence of the myrcene precursor, has been reported (19, 103), indicating that at least some bark beetle species have the capacity to synthesize pheromones de novo. Francke & Vité (42) have hypothesized that the oxidative modification of host monoterpenes by bark beetles may have arisen as a detoxification mechanism. The ultimate exploitation of these detoxification products in pheromone signaling would thus represent a most unusual and interesting evolutionary adaptation.

Insect predators and parasitoids of bark beetles also respond to bark beetle pheromones and to conifer monoterpenes, but the specificity of these responses is not well understood, in part because these insects, especially predatory beetles, tend to feed on a wide range of prey and may exploit a broad range of chemical signals (87). An illustrative example of these complex interactions is provided by

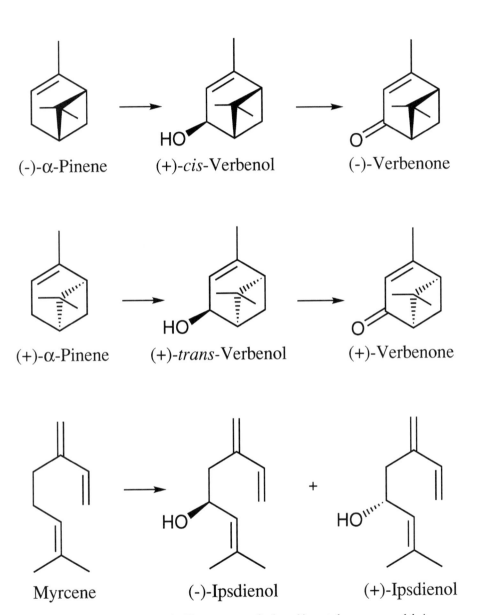

Figure 3   Pheromone biosynthesis. The structures of selected insect pheromones and their corresponding monoterpene olefin precursors are shown. Transformations occur typically in the hindgut of the bark beetle and have been attributed to associated microorganisms. Depending on the species, pheromones may signal aggregation or dispersal, and they may also attract beetle predators and parasitoids (adapted from Gijzen et al; 8).

three trophic levels of Norway spruce (*Picea abies*), the European spruce bark beetle (*Dendroctonus micans*), and the predatory beetle (*Rhizophagus grandis*). Within this interaction, resin monoterpenes attract both bark beetles and predator beetles to mediate host location and bark beetle aggregation, as well as long-range prey location and oviposition stimulation of the *Rhizophagus* predator (54). In this complex ecological context, the selection pressure on the host to alter resin chemistry is clearly multidimensional, and it involves considerations of attraction or repulsion, toxicity, pheromone signaling, and tritrophic level interactions (89, 122).

Raffa & Klepzig (96) have suggested that the chirality of ipsdienol beetle pheromones has evolved as a response to predator recognition. Thus, two species of predatory beetles that feed on *Ips pini* are drawn to the mixture of ipsdienol antipodes produced by the prey; however, the mixture of stereoisomers that is optimally attractive for the predators differs from that which is most attractive to *I. pini*. Such allomonal (signals that benefit the emitter) and kairomonal (signals that benefit the receiver) effects may impose strong selective pressures favoring the use of one or the other enantiomer in chemical signaling (52, 87, 96, 122).

Although it is paradoxical that bark beetles are attracted to and exploit monoterpenes that are both toxic and signal predators, the benefits to the beetle of utilizing specific semiochemical cues to locate a suitable host must outweigh the disadvantages. These interactions illustrate the complexity of the evolutionary relationships between conifer host and insect herbivores, causing selection over many generations to produce bark beetles that are highly adapted to a particular host and conifers that produce highly diverse chemical defenses (36, 52). Most information bearing on resin-based defenses concerns interactions with bark beetles; however, it is important to note that oleoresin also provides the basis of complex interactions with numerous other conifer pests and pathogens, including insect defoliators (101), root feeders (84), nematodes (48), and even mammalian and avian herbivores (31, 56).

CONIFER RESIN PRODUCTION

The term terpene (or terpenoid) derives from the German word for turpentine (Terpentin) from which the first members of this class of natural products were isolated and their structures determined. Historically, the study of conifer resin components is entwined with the development of classical organic chemistry and biogenetic theory (27), and the processing of oleoresin once formed the basis of a substantial "naval stores" industry. With the passing of wooden sailing ships and the growing use of petroleum, the naval stores industry collapsed by the turn of the century, although oleoresin still finds use in the commercial production of turpentine and rosin and as starting chemicals in the preparation of flavorings, adhesives, sealants, and materials for the printing industry (33, 124). As a consequence of this historical legacy, the chemistry of oleoresin terpenes is very well understood. More

Figure 2 Physical and ecological aspects of bark beetle-conifer interactions. (*A*) Scanning electron micrograph of a Southern pine beetle depicting the mycangia (M), a specialized anatomical structure employed to vector fungal spores (adapted from Barras (5). (*B*) "Pitching out" of a pair of mountain pine beetles (*D. ponderosae*) on ponderosa pine (*P. ponderosa*). (*C*) Mass attack by mountain pine beetles (*D. ponderosae*) on a lodgepole pine (*P. contorta*) bole. Each white spot on the trunk represents a beetle entry point. (*D*) Photomicrograph of a resin duct (transverse section) from Jeffery pine (*P. jeffreyi*) showing lumen (L), secretory cells (S); sheath cells (Sh); and xylem cells (X). (*E*) Photomicrograph of a resin duct (radial section, safranin-fast green stained) from *Pinus sylvestris* stem showing resin duct (r) length and parenchyma cells (p) (courtesy of Vincent Franceschi). (*F*) Forked tunnel beetle galleries typical of *Scolytus* spp. [redrawn from Stark (105)]. (*G*) Fir engraver (*Scolytus ventralis*) galleries below the bark of a colonized grand fir (*Abies grandis*). Note that the galleries are filled with mycelia of the symbiotic fungal pathogen *Trichosporium symbioticum*. (Figures 2B, 2C, 2D and 2G are from the authors' laboratory.)

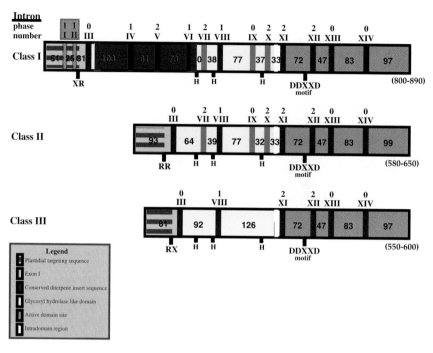

Figure 9 General structural features and organization of plant terpene synthase genes. The generic class I, II, and III terpene synthase (Tps) gene illustrations are based upon defined Tps templates (gA*gggabi*, gA*ggglim*, and Pf*glim*, respectively). General domains pertaining to primary or secondary structure are depicted by colored boxes as described in the legend box. The DDXXD and RR motifs are shown in bold; RX is used where an alternate residue sometimes occurs. Introns I-XIV, represented by colored vertical bars indicating sequential loss during evolution, are indicated as follows: introns I and II (pink bars) are found only in two class I terpene synthase genes gA*gggabi* and gAt*ggcopp1*; introns I and II are also boxed in peach to indicate that their presence is not a class I Tps gene requirement; introns IV,V, and VI (purple bars); introns VII, IX, X (green bars), introns III, VIII, XI, XII, XIII, XIV (brown bars); the later set of introns (brown) are conserved in all plant terpene synthases. The number above the intron number represents the intron phase number (see text). Each block separated by vertical bars represents an exon with the typical amino acid length specified. Class I Tps genes contain 12 to 15 exons; class II and III genes contain 9 and 7 exons, respectively. Exon 12 (last exon) of gCc*gLINOH1* and gA*gfEαbis* is 175 aa and 181 aa in length, respectively (gA*gfEαbis* has lost intron XIV). The gray box labeled exon I varies in size; monoterpene and diterpene synthases comprise an exon size of 80-107 aa, whereas sesquiterpene synthases comprise an exon I size of 30-50 aa due to the absence of a plastidial targeting sequence. The glycosyl hyrdolase-like domain (yellow), the catalytic domain (orange), and the intradomain region (white) are predicted (13, 32) based upon the crystal structure of NtfeARI4 (106).

recent studies in the context of resin production have focused on those properties most relevant to host defense function (insect toxicity and solvation properties of turpentine components as well as viscosity, crystallinity, and oxidative polymerization properties of rosin components) and on the biological origins of this unique plant secretion.

Copious resin production responsible for the killing and encasing of bark beetles and fungal associates, i.e. the phenomenon of "pitching out" (Figure 2B, see color insert), is the most important chemical defense of the host in repelling initial invasion. Depending on the species, resin production may be largely constitutive (primary resin), composed of material produced and stored in specialized secretory structures, or induced (secondary resin) as the result of injury. Most conifers rely on some combination of preformed and inducible resin defenses, but there is a fairly clear correlation between the anatomical complexity of the specialized resin secretory structures and the reliance on constitutive defenses (76).

Sites of Resin Production and Accumulation

The simplest type of compartmentalized structures are resin cells, isolated cells containing oleoresin that are scattered throughout the stems of certain conifer species, including western red cedar (*Thuja plicata*; Cupressaceae). Other conifer species exhibit a higher degree of anatomical organization in their resin secretory structures. California redwood (*Sequoia sempervirens*; Taxodiaceae) and true firs, such as grand fir (*Abies grandis*; Pinaceae), accumulate oleoresin in resin blisters (often with scattered resin cells also present in the xylem). Resin blisters (or cysts), located in the wood and bark, are oleoresin-containing, multicellular sacklike structures surrounded by a layer of epithelial cells (4). During development, the walls of the epithelial cells thicken and lignify, and presumably die during the year of origin (88). Douglas Fir (*Pseudotsuga menziesii*), western larch (*Larix occidentalis*), and Colorado blue spruce (*Picea pungens*) display an even higher order of organization in which a network of constricted resin passages and ducts reside throughout the trunk. The toxic oleoresin is accumulated within the lumen of these structures, which are surrounded by a layer of thin walled epithelial cells, that presumably remain biologically active for several years (88). Pine species (*Pinus*) contain the most elaborate network of interconnected nonconstricted resin ducts (Figures 2D, E, see color insert) located throughout the wood and bark (39, 117). The longevity of the secretory epithelial cells that produce the oleoresin is also loosely correlated with anatomy; thus, the more complex the resin secretory system, as in pines, the more long-lived are the epithelial cells (60).

If a bark beetle severs a resin passage or duct system of a pine or spruce in the process of establishing a gallery, it is often overwhelmed by the rapid and copious exudation of resin, which results in sudden death (Figure 2B, see color insert) (20, 26, 104). The efficacy of the process is primarily dependent upon the composition and amount of oleoresin that may flow under pressure to the site of attack (reaction zone) by emptying connected resin passages along several meters of the trunk (Figure 2E, see color insert). The response to an individual boring insect depends on attack density and the overall physiological condition of the tree (52). Only conifer species with substantial constitutive reservoir systems (pines and spruces) can depend upon such preformed resistance as a primary defense strategy (8). A secondary response involving the induced production of resin can often be distinguished in these species (28), but the amount is small compared with the initial resin flow.

Bark beetles occasionally penetrate resin cells and blisters in their excavation; however, the scattered nature of these structures in the trunk limits their utility in primary defense. Species lacking extensive resin ducts or passages (*Abies*, *Tsuga*, *Cedrus*, etc) must rely on induced (secondary) oleoresin production as a defense against bark beetle infestation, and this localized response is usually part of a more generalized hypersensitive reaction at the site of injury (8). Induced resin production is not carried out by epithelial cells of secretory structures but rather by parenchyma cells (Figure 2E) surrounding the site of injury. Secondary resin can usually be distinguished from primary resin by chemical composition, and studies with grand fir (*Abies grandis*) have indicated that de novo resin biosynthesis is much the same whether induction results from beetle penetration or other physical trauma, with the level of production reflecting the extent of injury (72). Although induced resin production is necessarily a slower process than the immediate flow of stored resin to a wound site, de novo resin production at the site of injury in a healthy response nevertheless can create a formidable barrier to beetle excavation.

Conifers, such as firs, that lack an interconnected duct system often respond to wounding by forming traumatic resin ducts, which are normally absent in uninjured tissue (39, 40, 67). These cyst-like structures accumulate resin but lack epithelial cells. By contrast, pines respond to wounding by forming more resin ducts that are anatomically indistinguishable from normal ducts but are often improperly called traumatic resin ducts (41).

Resin Biosynthesis

Like all terpenoids, oleoresin terpenes arise from the fundamental precursor isopentenyl diphosphate, which in plants arises at one of two subcellular locations. The classic acetate/mevalonate pathway (21) operates in the cytosol compartment in which sesquiterpenes and triterpenes are formed, whereas the mevalonate-independent pathway (initiated from pyruvate and glyceraldehyde 3-phosphate) operates in the plastids to provide the monoterpenes, diterpenes, and tetraterpenes (37, 78). Following production of isopentenyl diphosphate and its isomerization to dimethylallyl diphosphate by isopentenyl diphosphate isomerase, the latter is condensed with one, two, or three units of isopentenyl diphosphate by specific prenyltransferases at the corresponding subcellular locales to give the respective precursors of the monoterpenes (geranyl diphosphate), sesquiterpenes (farnesyl diphosphate), and diterpenes (geranylgeranyl diphosphate) (Figure 4).

The terpenoid synthases next convert the respective acyclic precursors, geranyl, farnesyl, and geranylgeranyl diphosphate, to the various parent structural derivatives of the different terpene families and so represent the committed enzymes of these pathways (32). These enzymes are often called cyclases because most of the products derived from the three central acyclic precursors are cyclic. Terpenoid synthases have been isolated and characterized from several conifer species, but the bulk of this work has been carried out with grand fir (*A. grandis*), a common and widespread species in the Pacific Northwest. The plant is easily raised in the greenhouse, and oleoresin production is wound-inducible, which mimics bark beetle attack (73), thereby offering significant advantage for biochemical and molecular study.

The monoterpene synthases of grand fir are very similar to each other (50), and they differ little in their properties from their counterparts isolated from pine species (99). All are operationally soluble proteins with native (monomeric) sizes in the 50–70 kDa range, pI values around pH 6, and pH optima in the pH 6.8 to 7.8 range (generally higher than angiosperm synthases) (13, 32, 121). They require a divalent metal ion for catalysis (Mg^{2+}, Mn^{2+}, or Fe^{2+}), and activity is stimulated by monovalent cations (preferably K^+) (99); this latter property is not shared by angiosperm synthases. Michaelis constants for the prenyl diphosphate substrate rarely exceed 10 μM, and turnover rates typically range from 0.02 to 0.2 s^{-1} (121). The inducible turpentine of grand fir differs in composition from that of the constitutive oleoresin, and these differences are reflected by the differing product outcomes of the inducible monoterpene synthases. In general properties, however, the constitutive and inducible synthases are indistinguishable. All conifer monoterpene synthases appear to arise as preproteins targeted to the plastids (see below), consistent with the origin of the essential geranyl precursor at this locale.

All conifer monoterpene synthases examined thus far produce acyclic or cyclic olefins as products (121), consistent with the composition of turpentine in which oxygenated monoterpenes only make up trace components. As indicated previously, host monoterpene olefins do serve as the precursors of several oxygenated derivatives produced and employed by bark beetles as pheromones (Figure 3). The monoterpene synthase reaction involves the initial, metal ion–assisted ionization of the substrate to the corresponding carbocation-diphosphate anion pair, which may undergo direct deprotonation at various positions to yield the acyclic monoterpenes, such as myrcene (Figure 5). Alternatively, and more commonly, the ionized geranyl precursor may collapse to the corresponding tertiary allylic isomer linalyl diphosphate (Figure 5). The effect of this tightly coupled isomerization step is to convert the original *trans*-C2,C3-double bond of the geranyl substrate (which sterically prohibits direct cyclization) to a single bond of the linalyl intermediate, such that, following transoid to cisoid rotation then ionization, cyclization to the α-terpinyl carbocation is allowed from which all cyclic monoterpenes are subsequently derived (Figure 5). The α-terpinyl cation may suffer direct deprotonation to give, for example, limonene, or it may undergo a range of internal additions to the remaining double bond, hydride shifts, or other rearrangements before the

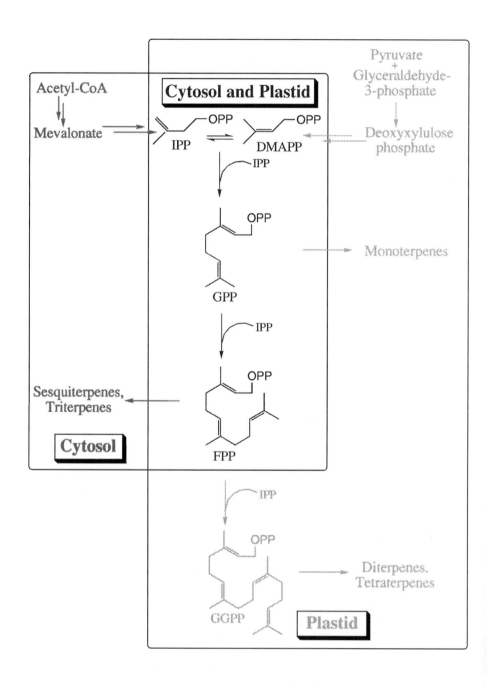

terminating deprotonation to yield any of several possible bicyclic olefins. The cyclizations to $(-)$-α-pinene and $(-)$-β-pinene are illustrative of this reaction type (Figure 5). Many monoterpene synthases essentially produce a single product, but there are several examples of these enzymes that produce multiple products from the geranyl substrate. The inducible pinene synthase from grand fir (74) and the constitutive pinene synthases from several pine species (90, 99), for example, produce substantial amounts of both $(-)$-α-pinene and $(-)$-β-pinene by simple variations on the same reaction mechanism. The similarity in properties, and also in primary sequence (see below), of these enzymes indicates that rather subtle differences in structure and mechanism can result in very different product outcomes.

Relatively few sesquiterpene synthases from conifers have been examined thus far. However, it is clear from this work that these cytosolic enzymes resemble the plastidial monoterpene synthases in general properties, although the divalent cation requirement may differ and monovalent cations have no influence on reaction rate. In the case of the sesquiterpene synthases, the longer chain length and additional double bond of the farnesyl substrate permit far greater flexibility in the construction of different carbon skeletons by the same type of electrophilic cyclization mechanisms, involving initial ionization of the diphosphate ester. This great range in mechanistic flexibility is exploited by two constitutive sesquiterpene synthases from grand fir, δ-selinene synthase and γ-humulene synthase, which each produces in excess of 30 different sesquiterpene olefin products from the farnesyl diphosphate substrate (107). These two very prolific enzymes may represent evolutionary adaptations for maximizing chemical diversity with the minimum genetic and enzymatic machinery. A contrasting example is provided by the wound-inducible (E)-α-bisabolene synthase from grand fir, which produces this single olefin as product. It is significant to note that (E)-α-bisabolene is efficiently converted to todomatuic acid and juvabione by subsequent oxidative metabolism in grand fir and related species (Figure 6) (11). These oxygenated sesquiterpenes are mimics of juvenile hormone III and can disrupt insect reproduction and/or larval development. The production of these modified sesquiterpenes by true firs (*Abies*) might represent a second line of defense directed to insect fecundity, should the initial resinosis response be overcome and successful infestation of the host occur (11, 89).

Figure 4   Intracellular compartmentalization of the mevalonate and mevalonate-independent pathways for the production of isopentenyl diphosphate (IPP), dimethylallyl diphosphate (DMAPP), and associated terpenoids in higher plants. The cytosolic pool of IPP, which serves as a precursor of farnesyl diphosphate (FPP) and, ultimately, the sesquiterpenes and triterpenes, is derived from mevalonic acid. The plastidial pool of IPP is derived from the glycolytic intermediates pyruvate and glyceraldehyde-3-phosphate, and it provides the precursor of geranyl diphosphate (GPP) and geranylgeranyl diphosphate (GGPP) and, ultimately, the monoterpenes, diterpenes, and tetraterpenes. Reactions common to both pathways are enclosed by both boxes, although separate prenyltransferases are responsible for catalyzing these reactions in each compartment.

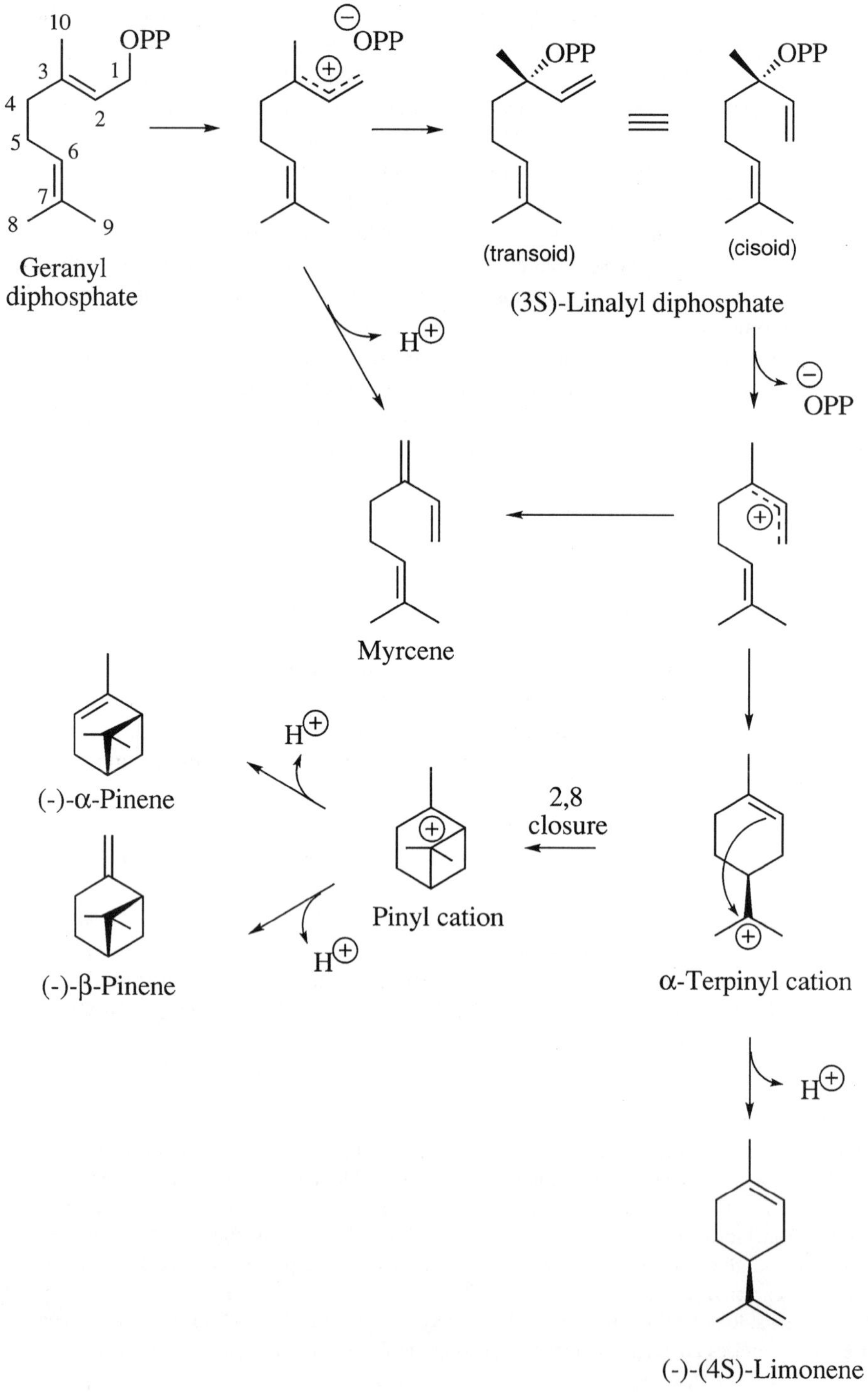

Geranyl
diphosphate

(transoid)   (cisoid)

(3S)-Linalyl diphosphate

Myrcene

(-)-α-Pinene

(-)-β-Pinene

Pinyl cation

2,8
closure

α-Terpinyl cation

(-)-(4S)-Limonene

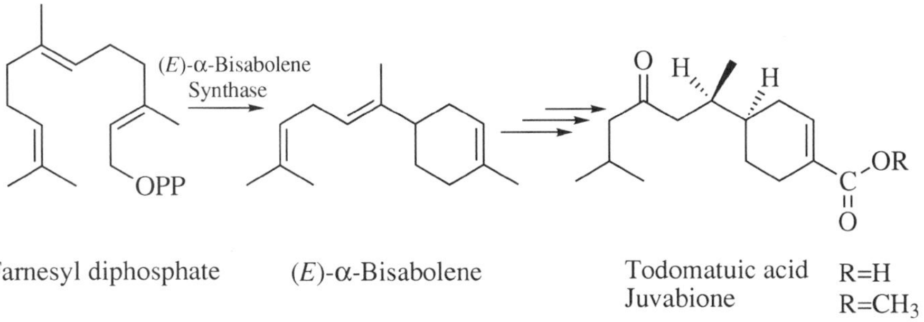

Farnesyl diphosphate   (E)-α-Bisabolene   Todomatuic acid   R=H
                                                     Juvabione   R=CH₃

Figure 6 Biosynthesis of the sesquiterpenoid insect juvenile hormone mimics todomatuic acid and juvabione. The sesquiterpene (E)-α-bisabolene is derived from farnesyl diphosphate by (E)-α-bisabolene synthase of grand fir (A. *grandis*) and is further modified through a series of redox transformations to products that simulate the action of juvenile hormone III, an insect molting hormone.

Although conifer diterpene synthases appear to resemble monoterpene synthases and sesquiterpene synthases in general properties, the cyclization reactions leading to the diterpene olefin precursors of the resin acids are fundamentally different from those of the monoterpene and sesquiterpene series. In these two-step reactions, a proton-initiated cyclization of geranylgeranyl diphosphate leads first to the bicyclic, enzyme-bound intermediate copalyl diphosphate (Figure 7). A second reaction, involving the more typical ionization of the diphosphate ester, allows formation of the third ring that, with or without a methyl migration step and a terminating deprotonation, provides the various pimarane or abietane precursors. These various olefin isomers, differing in the substituents on the third ring and in the positions of the double bonds, undergo oxidative conversion of the C18 methyl to a carboxyl to yield the corresponding resin acid (68). In the case of abietic acid, one of the most common resin acids and the most prone to polymerization, the abietadiene precursor is oxidized in three distinguishable steps to the resin acid by two cytochrome P450 hydroxylases and a dehydrogenase (46). The constitutive and inducible forms of abietadiene synthase from grand fir appear to be indistinguishable and to carry out both of the coupled cyclization steps without the formation of free intermediates (68, 115a). Like the monoterpene synthases, abietadiene synthase arises as a preprotein bearing an

Figure 5 Mechanism of the monoterpene synthase reaction. The formation of myrcene, (−)-(4S)-limonene, (−)-α-pinene, and (−)-β-pinene from the precursor geranyl diphosphate are shown, illustrating the initial isomerization step, which is necessary to overcome the geometric impediment to direct cyclization of the geranyl precursor. Subsequent internal additions in the α-terpinyl cation, methyl migrations, and hydride shifts may also occur, with the ultimate outcome depending on the specific substrate and intermediate folding conformations allowed by the particular synthase.

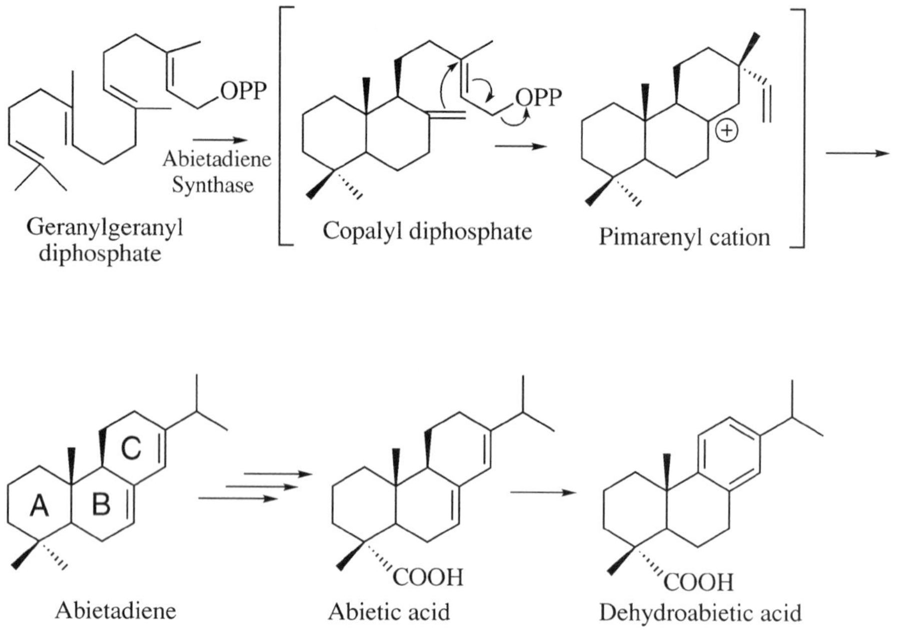

Figure 7   Biosynthesis of the diterpenoid resin acids, abietic acid and dehydroabietic acid. The formation of abietadiene from geranylgeranyl diphosphate is catalyzed by (−)-abietadiene synthase from grand fir (*A. grandis*) via the bound intermediate (+)-copalyl diphosphate. The subsequent oxidations of the olefin are catalyzed by two cytochrome P450-dependent oxygenases and an NAD⁺-dependent dehydrogenase.

N-terminal plastidial targeting sequence for localization to the site of diterpene biosynthesis.

Regulation

Because of the wound-inducibility of oleoresin production in grand fir saplings under laboratory conditions, this species has been developed as a model for studying the regulation of conifer defense. The time course of the response was initially investigated at the level of resin chemistry by monitoring the levels of the relevant monoterpene, sesquiterpene, and diterpene biosynthetic enzymes (47, 109). The response time is slower than that typical of phytoalexin production in angiosperms but is sustained for several weeks, as is appropriate to the longer time frame involved in beetle colonization and attendant bark boring and tunnel mining activity (Figure 8). The production of induced oleoresin monoterpenes, sesquiterpenes, and diterpenes is coordinated to accomplish a range of defense goals; the first of which is the localized generation of large quantities of sticky, semi-fluid toxic material to physically impede the progress of beetle mining and to poison the invaders. The turpentine components provide the principal toxins (26, 86, 95) and the solvent for mobilization of the resin acids. Solvation properties of the turpentine components and the composition of the rosin fraction (in terms of crystallinity and susceptibility to oxidative polymerization) are important considerations in producing a sufficiently viscous oleoresin to deter beetle progress. Yet, this material must also be sufficiently mobile to flush the wound and permit flow to the trunk surface, whereupon the turpentine evaporates to deposit a semi-crystalline mass of resin acids that upon exposure to air and UV light polymerizes to form a hardened plastic coating to seal the wound site (29). The cytochrome P450 oxygenases involved in resin acid biosynthesis are upregulated in coordination with the terpene synthases (47); however, timing in the appearance of the enzymatic machinery involved in the oxidative conversion of (E)-α-bisabolene to todomatuic acid and juvabione has not yet been evaluated.

Given the complexity of the bark beetle-host interaction, and the many functions of the oleoresin, it is not a trivial exercise (aside from a few broad generalizations, see below) to consider what a chemically and physically optimized resin should contain. Little guidance is provided by an assessment of the induced response among a native population of grand fir in which investigators observed wide variation, especially in the composition of monoterpene production (64). This evidence suggests that there is no single best strategy to deter beetle attack. Studies with water-stressed and light-stressed trees have demonstrated that, regardless of compositional variations in induced oleoresinosis, such stresses delay and/or diminish the response and ultimately eliminate it entirely (75). These results are consistent with field observations indicating that physiologically compromised trees are most readily overwhelmed by massed beetle attacks and often provide the focus for wider spread infestation.

With the availability of cDNA clones that encode several of the monoterpene, sesquiterpene, and diterpene synthases of grand fir (see below) and of polyclonal antibodies directed against some of the corresponding native or recombinant enzymes, researchers are able to examine the defense response in greater detail and demonstrate that induced oleoresinosis arises via the differential transcriptional control of the synthase genes in response to wounding (108). A more precise time course evaluation of the relevant enzyme activities indicates that the monoterpene synthases appear first and proceed to accumulate (Figure 8B), correlating closely with the results of immunoblot experiments using broadly crossreacting polyclonal antibodies directed against (−)-pinene synthase (51). RNA-blot hybridization analysis over the same induction time course, using terpene synthase class-specific probes, again indicates that the monoterpene synthases arise first (transcripts detectable in 2 h, reaching a maximum steady-state abundance in 2–4 days) and are followed by a coordinated increase in sesquiterpene and diterpene synthase transcripts (transcription beginning on day 3 or 4 and reaching maximum steady-state abundance at 13–14 days) (Figure 8A) (108).

Evaluation of the products of the inducible monoterpene synthases indicate that limonene, a prominent constitutive monoterpene, is the principal monoterpene generated at day 1 after wounding but is replaced by α-pinene and β-pinene

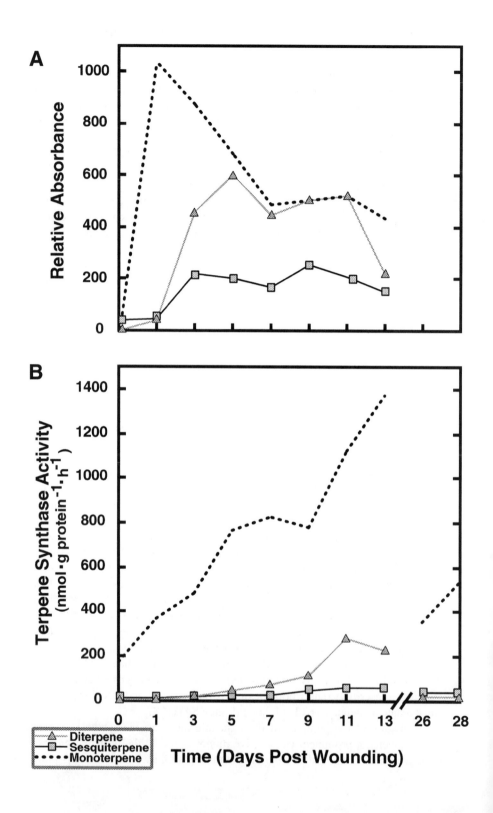

A

Relative Absorbance

B

Terpene Synthase Activity
(nmol·g protein^{-1}·h^{-1})

△ Diterpene
□ Sesquiterpene
▪▪▪ Monoterpene

Time (Days Post Wounding)

as principal constituents by day 7 after wounding. This dynamic alteration is consistent with the notion that the production of toxic monoterpenes (e.g. limonene) is first upregulated, then followed by the production of monoterpenes that are more notable for their solvent properties [e.g. pinenes (66)] in dissolving resin acids. For all terpene synthase types, enzyme activity levels continue to rise after steady-state mRNA levels are reached, suggesting that the terpene synthases are quite stable in vivo and are not turned over until several weeks later. The time delay in production of diterpene resin acids following the initiation of monoterpene biosynthesis might result from the need to first generate the solvent for rosin mobilization (108), and it fits the time-frame of beetle attack, involving many days, thereby maximizing entrapment of boring beetles and minimizing the possibility of withdrawal to establish a brood elsewhere (89). Although the sesquiterpenes make up only a small portion of conifer oleoresin (about 15% of the turpentine of grand fir), the mixture of constitutive sesquiterpenes is exceedingly complex, and it is now clear that wounding does induce sesquiterpene synthesis as well, suggesting that these resin components may be more important in defense than previously appreciated (11). The wound-inducible sesquiterpene synthases of grand fir, (E)-α-bisabolene synthase and δ-cadinene synthase, produce single products with high fidelity, but neither of these olefins accumulates. (E)-α-Bisabolene is transformed through a series of steps to the juvenile hormone mimics todomatuic acid and juvabione, whereas δ-cadinene is efficiently converted to oxygenated metabolites of as yet unknown structure. In contrast to diterpene synthase gene expression, (E)-α-bisabolene synthase mRNA levels continually increase to a maximum, which is reached at about 12 days after wounding (11), suggesting that the delayed de novo biosynthesis of the juvenile hormone analogs is designed to interfere with insect development as a second line of defense should infestation of the host succeed. Researchers have shown the wound induced accumulation of juvenile hormone analogs in intact fir (93), but they have not evaluated the direct influence of this phenomenon on insect fecundity.

Molecular Genetics

Much progress in understanding the molecular genetics of terpenoid formation has been made with angiosperms as genes encoding a monoterpene synthase (25), a sesquiterpene synthase (38), and a diterpene synthase (79) were first isolated from these species. Each of these initial genes was isolated using tools developed

Figure 8   Regulation of terpene synthases in grand fir saplings in response to wounding. (A). Changes in terpenoid synthase mRNA levels. (B). Corresponding changes in terpene synthase enzymatic activities. Developmental Northern blots of total mRNA with respective probes are described in Steele et al 1998 (108). Enzyme activities for monoterpene synthases (dotted line), sesquiterpene synthases (squares), and diterpene synthases (triangles) are plotted as a function of time after wounding (replotted from Steele et al 1998) (108).

from the corresponding protein. The first terpenoid synthase cDNA acquired from a conifer (the diterpene cyclase abietadiene synthase from grand fir) was also obtained by the reverse genetic approach (115a). However, because gymnosperm terpene synthases resemble in primary sequence their angiosperm counterparts, most recent cloning efforts have involved homology-based approaches (13, 109) with which seven monoterpene synthase genes (14, 15), three sesquiterpene synthase genes (11, 107), and two diterpene synthase genes (115a, 119) have been isolated and confirmed by functional heterologous expression. All these genes have been obtained from grand fir with the exception of one, the diterpene cyclase taxadiene synthase from yew (*Taxus*) that catalyzes the first committed step in the biosynthesis of the anti-cancer drug Taxol (119).

Nearly 40 cDNAs encoding gymnosperm and angiosperm terpene synthases have now been acquired, consisting of six phylogenic families. Based on sequence similarity, the conifer synthases are clustered in the *Tpsd* gene family. The monoterpene synthases and diterpene synthases are encoded as preproteins bearing plastidial transit peptides, whereas the sesquiterpene synthases bear no obvious N-terminal targeting information befitting their cytosolic localization. The sequences of all conifer terpenoid synthase types thus far examined contain conserved elements, including the DDXXD motif involved in substrate binding and aromatic residues that may be involved in stabilizing carbocation intermediates of the reaction sequence (13, 121). Tandem arginines near the N terminus of mature monoterpene synthases appear to play a role in the isomerization step required by most enzymes of this class (120). Although no crystal structures of conifer terpene synthases are yet available, modeling studies based upon the structure of *epi*-aristolochene synthase from tobacco (106) suggest that all terpenoid synthases may share a similar overall folding pattern.

A wide range of nomenclatures has been applied to the terpenoid synthases, none of which is systematic. Here we use a unified and specific nomenclature system in which the Latin binomial (two letters), substrate (one to four letter abbreviation), and product (three letters) are specified. Thus, *ag22*, the original cDNA designation for abietadiene synthase from *A. grandis* (a *Tpsd* subfamily member), becomes AgggABI for the protein and Aggg*abi* for the gene; the remaining conifer synthases (and other selected genes) are described accordingly (Table 1).

Protein-Based Phylogenetics

Amino acid sequence comparison of 12 conifer terpene synthases enabled researchers to identify common structural features of this enzyme class (12, 13, 32). Terpene synthase cDNAs encode proteins of 550–850 amino acids (aa) (13), in agreement with observed native molecular masses in the 50–100 kDa range. In general, sesquiterpene synthases are 580–650 aa in length and are 50–70 aa shorter than monoterpene and diterpene synthases due to the absence of the N-terminal plastidial transit peptide (Figure 9, see color insert) (12). Although conifer monoterpene and diterpene synthases lack significant primary sequence similarity in the transit peptide region, these targeting sequences characteristically contain a high content of serine and threonine residues and a low content of acidic residues (65). Sequence conservation begins just downstream of an RR (tandem arginine residues) motif of the monoterpene synthases, suggesting that the approximate cleavage site of the transit peptide may be defined by this RR element (Figure 9) (120). Truncation studies with limonene synthase have demonstrated that residues upstream of the tandem arginine element are not required for activity and that the RR motif plays an important role in the isomerization step of the monoterpene cyclization reaction (120). The conifer diterpene synthases AgggABS and TbggTAX (115a, 119) are approximately 210 aa longer than the monoterpene synthases. This difference in length is accounted for by an additional internal sequence element, termed the conifer diterpene internal sequence (CDIS) element (Figure 9), that is conserved in both sequence and position regardless of the type of cyclization catalyzed by these enzymes (13). This CDIS element is also observed in the grand fir sesquiterpene synthase (E)-α-bisabolene synthase, AgfEαBIS (11), and in the angiosperm monoterpene synthase linalool synthase from *Clarkia* (30, 35). The CDIS element in these two synthases may be relictual and alludes to their evolutionary origins. No function has been assigned to this element and, based upon the location and distance from the active site, the CDIS element is suspected to serve a purpose other than a catalytic function (13). Based upon modeling from the crystal structure of aristolochene synthase (106), investigators found that conifer terpene synthases, like other terpene synthases, are composed of two distinct structural domains, a C-terminal active site domain and an N-terminal domain that structurally resembles the catalytic cores of glycosyl hydrolases (13) (Figure 9).

The phylogenetic reconstruction based upon amino acid sequence comparison of 33 plant terpene synthases indicates that conifer monoterpene, sesquiterpene, and diterpene synthases are more closely related to each other than they are to their respective, mechanism-based counterparts of angiosperm origin (13), as exemplified by their grouping in the Tpsd family. Additionally, conifer synthases within each class of the same species (producing mono-, sesqui-, or diterpenes) are more closely related to each other than they are to the same cyclase type of other conifers. Prior to phylogenetic analysis, immunochemical studies (51) had indicated that pinene synthase from grand fir is more closely related to other monoterpene synthases from grand fir than to pinene synthases from related conifer species. Consistent with this observation, the six monoterpene synthases (Table 1) from grand fir share 60% or greater sequence identity and form a subgroup within the Tpsd family. The similarity of these six synthases may indicate that they have arisen by multiple gene duplications (13).

The terpene synthases of gymnosperms and angiosperms are divided into six gene families, designated Tpsa through Tpsf, with the groupings based upon a minimum amino acid sequence identity of 40% (13). Terpenoids involved in primary metabolism (e.g. phytosterols, carotenoids, gibberellins, and brassinosteroids) are essential for viability, whereas those derived from secondary metabolism are not. The majority of terpene synthases analyzed to date produce secondary metabolites

TABLE 1 Conifer and other selected terpene synthases

Terpene synthase (products)	Species	Former gene name	Enzyme name	cDNA/gene name	cDNA/mRNA Acc #	gDNA Acc #
Abietadiene	A. grandis	ag22	AgggABI	Agggabi	U50765 (81)	upub
(E)-α-Bisabolene	A. grandis	ag1	AgfEαBIS	AgfEαbis	AF006195 (78)	upub
(−)-Camphene	A. grandis	ag6	Agg-CAM	Agg-cam	U87910 (96)	-----
γ-Humulene	A. grandis	ag5	AgfγHUM	Agfγhum	U92267 (77)	-----
(−)-4S-Limonene	A. grandis	ag10	Agg-LIM1	Agg-lim	AF006193 (95)	upub
Myrcene	A. grandis	ag2	AggMYR	Aggmyr	U87908 (95)	-----
(−)-(1S,5S)-Pinene	A. grandis	ag3	Agg-PIN1	Agg-pin1	U87909 (95)	upub
(−)-α-Pinene/(−)-limonene	A. grandis	ag11	Agg-PIN2	Agg-pin2	AF139207 (96)	-----
(−)-β-Phellandrene	A. grandis	ag8	Agg-βPHE	Agg-βphe	AF139205 (96)	-----
δ-Selinene	A. grandis	ag4	AgfδSEL1 AgfδSEL2	Agfδsel1 Agfδsel2	U92266 (77)	upub upub
Taxadiene	T. brevifolia	Tb1	TbggTAX	Tbggtax	U48796 (97)	upub
Terpinolene	A. grandis	ag9	AggTEO	Aggteo	AF139206 (96)	-----

5-*epi*-Aristolochene	*N. tabacum*	TEAS3	NtfeARI3	*Ntfeari3*	L04680 (93)	L04680 (74)
		TEAS4	NtfeARI4	*Ntfeari4*	L04680 (93)	L04680 (74)
δ-Cadinene	*G. arboreum*	CAD1-A	GafδCAD1A	*Gafδcad1a*	X96429 (121)	Y18484[dcr]
Casbene	*R. communis*	cas	RcggCAS	*Rcggcas*	L32134 (94)	na[pc]
(−)-Copalyl diphosphate[b]	*A. thaliana*	GA1	Atgg-COPP1	*Atgg-copp1*	U11034 (122)	na (123)
						AC004004[p]
ent-Kaurene[b]	*A. thaliana*	GA2	Atgg-KAU	*Atgg-kau*	443904 (124)	AC007202[dcr]
(4S)-Limonene	*M. spicata*	LMS	Msg-LIM	*Msg-lim*	L13459 (92)	------
(S)-Linalool	*C. concinna*	LIS	CcgLINOH	*Ccglinoh*	------	AF067602 (103)
Vetispiradiene	*H. muticus*	CVS1	HmfVET1	*Hmfvet1*	U20188 (104)	na[pc] (104)

[a]Abbreviations are: Acc #, EMBL Accession number; upub, genomic sequences by Trapp & Croteau (in press); na, sequences unavailable in the public databases but discussed in journal reference; pc, sequences obtained by personal communications; dcr, sequences in public database but not published; p, sequences in database with putative function; dotted line (--), no former gene name or accession number. Species names are: *Abies grandis, Arabidopsis thaliana, Clarkia concinna, Gossypium arboreum, Hyoscyamus muticus, Mentha spicata, Nicotiana tabacum, Ricinus communis, Taxus brevifolia.*

[b]Former names for (−)-copalyl diphosphate and *ent*-kaurene sythase were *ent*-kaurene sythase A and *ent*-kaurene sythase B, respectively.

[c]Nomenclature architecture is specified as follows: The latin binomial two letter abbreviations (abbrev.) are in spaces 1–2. The substrate and product (1–4 letters abbrev.) are in spaces 3–6, consisting of 1–2 letter abbrev. for substrate utilized in bold (e.g. **g**, geranyl diphosphate; **f**, farnesyl diphosphate; **gg**, geranylgeranyl diphosphate; **c**, copalyl diphosphate; **ch**, chrysanthemyl diphosphate in lower case) followed by product stereochemistry and/or isomer definition (e.g. α, β, δ, γ, etc. followed by epi (e), E, Z, −, +, etc. followed by epi (e), E, Z, −, +, etc. The three-letter product abbrev. indicates the major product is an olefin, otherwise the quenching nucleophile is indicated (e.g. ABI, abietadiene synthase; BORPP, bornyl diphosphate synthase; CEDOH, cedrol synthase); the upper case specifies protein and the lower case specifies cDNA or gDNA. All letters except species names are in italics for cDNA and gDNA. Distinction between cDNA and gDNA must be stated or a "g" is added before the abbreviation (e.g. T*bggtax* cDNA and gT*bggtax*, or T*bggtax* gene. (Nomenclature system devised by S Trapp, E Davis, J Crock, & R Croteau).

(natural products) and are classified into three families, Tpsa (sesquiterpene and diterpene synthases from angiosperms), Tpsb (monoterpene synthases from angiosperms of the Lamiaceae), and Tpsd (11 gymnosperm mono-, sesqui-, and diterpene synthases from *A. grandis* and a diterpene synthase, TbggTAX, from *T. brevifolia*). The grouping into a single clade of other Tps families (Tpsc, Tpse, Tpsf) involved in primary metabolism (e.g. kaurene synthase and (−)-copalyl diphosphate synthase of gibberellin biosynthesis) suggests that the bifurcation of terpenoid synthases of primary and secondary metabolism occurred before the separation of angiosperms and gymnosperms. Furthermore, the pattern of branching between gymnosperm and angiosperm synthases and among specific synthase classes (monoterpene, sesquiterpene, and diterpene) from a common terpene synthase ancestor implies that independent functional specialization occurred after the separation of angiosperm and gymnosperm lineages. That two limonene synthases, MsgLIM and AggLIM, share only 35% identity reflects this independent specialization and indicates that limonene synthase evolved separately in mint and grand fir (13).

The conifer synthases analyzed thus far primarily represent those from a single species, and, although 33 terpene synthases were used for phylogenetic analysis, the sample size is too small to permit precise analysis. Furthermore, of the sequences analyzed, all but five terpene synthases are involved in secondary metabolism, indicating that synthases of primary metabolism are underrepresented; thus far, no conifer terpene synthases of primary metabolism are available. A variety of additional terpene synthase sequences from different gymnosperm species will be necessary to determine the accuracy of the present Tps phylogenetic scheme and its evolutionary significance.

Genomic Intron/Exon Organization

The examination of terpene synthase genomic (intron/exon) organization (S Trapp & R Croteau, unpublished data) generally supports the protein-based phylogenetic evaluation of this enzyme class (13). In addition, this genomic evaluation provides the first model for the history of the plant terpene synthase gene superfamily, including molecular evolutionary events and ancestral lineage. Until recently, the sequences of only a few angiosperm terpene synthase genes (Nt*fepiari*, Rc*ggcas*, Hm*fvet*) had been described, and these revealed very similar overall structure with six positionally conserved introns (3, 38, 79). The sequences for six conifer terpene synthase genes are now available (S Trapp & R Croteau, unpublished data), including a constitutive and an inducible monoterpene synthase (Ag*glim*, Ag*pin*), a constitutive and an inducible sesquiterpene synthase (Ag*fabis*, Ag*fδsel*), and two diterpene synthases (Ag*ggabi*, Tb*ggtax*). The genomic organization of these conifer terpene synthases was analyzed by alignment with seven defined angiosperm terpene synthases and eight putative terpene synthases from *Arabidopsis*. By examining patterns of intron and exon loss, CDIS domain loss, conservation of intron phase and placement, and conservation of exon size, investigators addressed evolutionary relationships among the plant terpene synthase genes involved in primary and secondary metabolism.

Three classes of terpene synthase genes were established based upon distinct exon/intron patterns (Figure 9, see color insert), and all conifer synthase genes fell into Class I or Class II. Class I comprises conifer diterpene synthase genes Ag*ggabi* and Tb*ggtax*, a sesquiterpene synthase Ag*fαbis*, and angiosperm synthase genes specifically involved in primary metabolism (At*gg-coppl* and Cc*glin*). Terpene synthase Class I genes contain 11–14 introns and 12–15 exons of characteristic size (Figure 9), including the CDIS domain made up of exons 4, 5, and 6; the first ~20 aa of exon 7; and introns 4, 5, and 6 (based upon Ag*ggabi* exon structure). Class II terpene synthases comprise only conifer monoterpene synthases and sesquiterpene synthases and contain 9 introns and 10 exons; introns 1 and 2, and the entire CDIS element, have been lost, including introns 4, 5, and 6. Class III terpene synthases contain only angiosperm monoterpene, sesquiterpene, and diterpene synthases involved in secondary metabolism, and these have 6 introns and 7 exons. Introns 1, 2, 7, 9, and 10 and the CDIS domain have been lost in the Class III type. The introns found in Class III terpene synthase genes (introns 3, 8, 11–14) have been conserved among all gymnosperm and angiosperm plant terpene synthase genes, with two exceptions; bisabolene synthase (Ag*fαbis*) has lost intron 14, and linalool synthase (Cc*glin*) has lost intron 3 (as well as introns 1 and 2).

The intron phases of introns 2 through 14 are conserved among gymnosperm and angiosperm terpene synthase genes (Figure 9), and this observation provides a novel means of evaluating the relatedness of genes of this type. Intron phase is defined as the placement of the intron before the first, second, or third nucleotide position of the codon and is referred to as phase 0, 1, and 2, respectively (for example, all terpene synthase genes that contain intron 3 have a phase of 0). The conservation of phases among introns indicates divergent evolutionary events. Conversely, if families of terpene synthase genes evolved by convergent evolution, it is unlikely that the introns would be so precisely placed and intron phase conserved. It is reasonably postulated that the ancestral terpene synthase gene most closely resembles a contemporary gene that contains the largest number of exons and introns because only intron loss would be anticipated (S Trapp & R Croteau, unpublished data). Limited by the sample size of 21 terpene synthase genes, the candidate gene is either At*gg-coppl* or Ag*ggabi* (because both contain 14 introns and 15 exons), with At*gg-copp* being most likely because it is involved in primary metabolism. Intron loss and CDIS domain loss data, presented in an evolutionary tree model of intron/exon structure (Figure 10), suggest that all angiosperm terpene synthases involved in secondary metabolic processes evolved from a gymnosperm ancestor that contained 9 introns and 10 exons. There are two exceptions to the general genomic organization pattern observed in plant terpene synthases. The sesquiterpene synthase bisabolene synthase (Ag*fαbis*) and the monoterpene synthase linalool synthase (Cc*glin*) gene structures are more similar to conifer diterpene synthase genes, all of which contain the CDIS element. Most likely, both of these are defunct

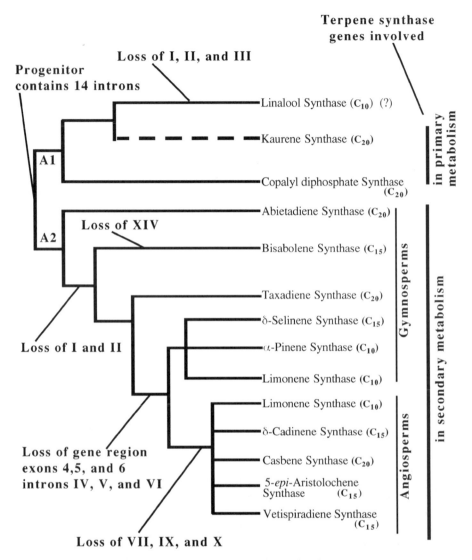

Figure 10 Model for the evolution of Tps gene intron and exon structure. The dendrogram represents an evolutionary tree based on two characters, loss of introns and loss of the CDIS domain (containing 3 exons and 3 introns). Only plant terpene synthase genes of defined function were used for the phylogenetic model (these are listed in Table I). The letters A1 and A2 represent the progeny of the duplicated ancestral gene, both containing a genome organization predicted to be similar to present day gymnosperm diterpene synthase gene-like structures with 14 introns and 15 exons. The question mark (?) symbolizes the uncertain placement of the linalool synthase gene within this scheme. The dotted line indicates prediction of placement in the model for an angiosperm or gymnosperm kaurene synthase gene for which a genomic structure has not yet been described. The symbols C_{10}, C_{15}, and C_{20} represent the enzyme class corresponding to monoterpene, sesquiterpene, and diterpene synthases, respectively.

diterpene synthases whose nondeleterious mutations have evolved to their present day enzymatic function.

Evolutionary Origins

Prior to the availability of any sequence conservation data and based on immuno-chemical evidence, the suggestion was made that multiple monoterpene synthase genes arose by gene duplication to provide a family of related catalysts for the synthesis of different monoterpene products (51). Limited sequence comparisons between other terpene synthases, based largely on conserved structural features such as the mechanistically relevant DDXXD motif, supported this general notion (3, 25, 38, 79). Ultimately, the protein-based phylogenetic analysis by Bohlmann et al (13) provided substantial evidence that all plant terpene synthases share a common evolutionary origin.

The conservation of genomic organization of plant terpene synthases provides further evidence that the terpene synthases from gymnosperms and angiosperms constitute a superfamily of genes derived from a single ancestor (S Trapp & R Croteau, unpublished results). Prior to the divergence of gymnosperms and angiosperms, during the carboniferous period about 300 million years ago (34), a single initial duplication of an ancestral terpene synthase gene, which most closely resembled a contemporary conifer diterpene synthase, occurred. The terpene synthase multigene family tree arose by subsequent duplication, then functional and structural specialization, by evolutionary processes now considered to be quite common (45, 62). One copy of the duplicated ancestral gene remained conserved in structure and function with little or no intron/exon loss, and this gene may have contemporary descendants in the terpene synthases involved in gibberellin biosynthesis. The second ancestral gene copy diverged in structure and function by adaptive evolutionary processes over millions of years to yield the large multi-gene superfamily of terpene synthases involved in secondary metabolic pathways. Although entirely speculative, it is plausible that terpene synthase ancestors were functionally less specialized and perhaps able to utilize multiple prenyl diphos-phate substrates for the production of multiple terpene types, the specialization into different classes having evolved much later.

The evolution of the extant large number of terpene synthase genes provides an example in which many functionally complementary and nonlethal gene duplication and divergence events were retained by natural selection to provide the great diversity in terpene chemistry as the foundation of conifer defense. Thus, terpene synthase genes evolved to produce new functions that through evolutionary adap-tation increased the fitness of the species to defend against predators, pathogens, and herbivores.

Pathway Organization

An important challenge for the immediate future is to identify and isolate all genes of oleoresin terpenoid biosynthetic pathways. The terpene synthases are presumed to catalyze rate-limiting steps in terpene biosynthesis (e.g. turpentine production) and thus are obvious targets for molecular genetic manipulation to improve tree resistance. Genes encoding enzymes for downstream pathway steps are also important targets. Thus, in the biosynthesis of the common resin acid abietic acid in firs and pines, the cyclization product abietadiene is sequentially oxidized at the C18 methyl group by two cytochrome P450 hydroxylases and a soluble aldehyde dehydrogenase to yield the corresponding carboxyl function (Figure 7) (46). Variations on the cyclization scheme, coupled to the same oxidation sequence, can account for the formation of essentially all of the labdane, pimarane, and abietane resin acids of conifers (68). Similar biosynthetic steps, involving cytochrome P450 and redox enzymes, are likely involved in the conversion of the cyclization product (E)-α-bisabolene to todomatuic acid (Figure 6) (11). Genes encoding cytochrome P450 oxygenases and redox enzymes can be isolated based on homology; however, the very large number of these genes makes the sorting of candidates by functional expression of the relevant activities arduous. Furthermore, the extremely large genome size of conifers ($\sim 10^{11}$ for pines versus $\sim 10^6$ for *Arabidopsis*) and their exceedingly long development cycles (98) effectively preclude mutagenesis-based approaches for identification of gene function by phenotype.

As an alternative to gene cloning via purification of the target protein, the clustering of secondary metabolic pathway genes may provide rapid access to these sequences. In maize, five genes are clustered on the short arm of chromosome IV that encode the enzymes responsible for the biosynthesis of 2,4-dihydroxy-7-methoxy-1,4-benzoxazin-3-one (44), an important hydroxamic acid defense compound of cereals (53). Clustering of fungal sesquiterpene biosynthetic genes for simple and macrocyclic trichothecene production exists in several fungal species (57, 115), and three putative sesquiterpene synthase genes, resembling cadinene synthase, vetispiradiene synthase, and *epi*-aristolochene synthase, are located adjacent to each other on chromosome IV of *Arabidopsis* (2). Whether genes encoding enzymes for the oxidative modification of cyclic terpene parent compounds reside in proximity to the corresponding terpene synthases is not presently known.

PROSPECTS FOR FOREST BIOTECHNOLOGY

The prospects for genetically engineering conifer defenses to improve resistance face the same constraints as for forest biotechnology in general. Although forests are internationally recognized as one of the most important of natural resources (102), the agricultural domestication of forest species as "crop plants" is still in its infancy, and the bulk of wood is still harvested from natural forests. Until now, genetic improvement in agroforestry has relied primarily on conventional breeding programs to alter characteristics such as resistance to pests and pathogens, growth rate and form, volume and yield, and quality of end product lumber and paper pulp [see review by Walter et al, (116)]. This approach is clearly limited by the generation time required for selection of improved trees. It is sobering to realize that even the most advanced forest tree-breeding programs are in their third generation, while maize and wheat have passed through many thousands of generations of cultivation and selective breeding (80).

A decade ago, the application of routine biotechnological techniques (transformation, regeneration, micropropagation) to engineer conifers presented formidable theoretical and practical barriers (80). However, more recently, these approaches, e.g. antisense technologies, are being applied to forest species (102, 116). The current understanding of what constitutes superior traits at the molecular level is still quite rudimentary and lags significantly behind other fields of agrobiotechnology (98). An important challenge is to rapidly acquire genes underpinning desirable traits and to do so without the immediate benefit of a highly revealing conifer genome project. Both poplar and pine expressed sequence tag and genome initiatives are progressing (1, 102, 110), but the large genome size of conifers—up to ten times larger than that of humans—puts these efforts in perspective (80). In addition to the long-term commitment required to make forest biotechnology a commercial reality (98), legitimate environmental concerns will also need to be addressed, and public education will be necessary to overcome the adverse perception of plant genetic engineering, especially when applied on the large-scale in the forest setting (61).

The ecological interactions between conifer hosts, pathogens, and bark beetles and their predators and parasitoids that are mediated by oleoresin terpenoids are exceedingly complex, yet they offer several possible avenues for improving tree resistance by manipulation of oleoresin composition. Understanding the molecular genetics, organization, and regulation of constitutive and inducible oleoresin formation underlies the ability to design protective and management strategies for providing sustainable forest products. Terpene synthases are conceptually attractive and obvious candidates for this purpose, and the recent cloning of a number of terpene synthase cDNAs now offers a biorational approach for improving conifer defenses by altering not only the mix of constitutive and inducible oleoresin but also the yield and composition of oleoresin itself via gene transfer technologies. These approaches to engineered manipulation of oleoresin formation include (*a*) improving the speed and level of the defense response at the critical early attack stages, (*b*) increasing the concentration of resin components that are particularly toxic to invaders by modulating promoter strength and copy number of extant genes, and (*c*) introducing new defense genes. Other more sophisticated strategies, some of which are in development (22, 89), involve (*a*) altering oleoresin chemistry to disguise the host and thereby confuse host selection, (*b*) promoting tritrophic level interactions through improved signaling to foster bark beetle predation or parasitism, (*c*) abolishing production or altering the stereochemistry of pheromone precursors to diminish or mask signaling and thereby disrupt massed attack, (*d*) engineering trees to produce disperal pheromones, and (*e*) improving (or introducing) the production of hormone analogs to disrupt insect reproduction and development.

There are still many aspects of oleoresin-based conifer defense that remain unexplored. No secretory cell-specific constitutive promoters for controlling primary resin formation, or wound/infection-specific promoters for controlling attack-dependent defense genes, have yet been defined, nor have transcription factors involved in these processes been described. Very little is known about the signaling cues and downstream cascade pathways that mediate the communication between host and pest or pathogen. No crystal structure for a conifer terpene synthase has, to date, been solved to provide information on the determinants of substrate specificity and product outcome that would permit the redesign of these catalysts. Advances in each of these areas can be expected to lead to new strategies for tree protection.

Finally, although this review focuses on specific means of eliminating forest destruction caused by insect pests and their microbial symbionts, we wish to leave the reader with the broader view of sustainable forest management advocated by the International Union of Forestry Research Organizations that is based on the promotion of biological diversity with minimum impact on the functioning equilibrium of the ecosystem. Most insects are not potential pests, and, in a typical forest, insects represent a biomass roughly twice that of vertebrates, with a far greater diversity of species and impact on the structure and function of the complex forest ecosystem (55). For these reasons, biotechnologically based pest management strategies, whether founded on natural defense mechanisms or introduced biopesticides, need to be explored incrementally, in both type and scale, to permit responsible, stepwise consideration of possible, unintended consequences.

Visit the Annual Reviews home page at www.AnnualReviews.org

LITERATURE CITED

1. Allona I, Quinn M, Shoop E, Swope K, Carlis J, et al. 1998. Analysis of xylem formation in pine by cDNA sequencing. *Proc. Natl. Acad. Sci. USA* 95:9693–98
2. Aubourg S, Takvorian A, Chéron A, Kreis M, Lechamy A. 1997. Structure, organization and putative function of the genes identified within a 23.9 kb fragment from *Arabidopsis thaliana* chromosome IV. *Gene* 199:241–53
3. Back K, Chappell J. 1995. Cloning and bacterial expression of a sesquiterpene cyclase from *Hyoscyamus muticus* and its molecular comparison to related terpene cyclases. *J. Biol. Chem.* 270:7375–81
4. Bannon M. 1936. Vertical resin ducts in the secondary wood of the Abietinae. *New Phytol.* 35:11–47
5. Barras SJ. 1975. Release of fungi from mycangia of southern pine beetles observed under a scanning electron microscope. *Z. Angew. Entomol.* 79:173–76
6. Barras SJ. 1979. Forest ecosystem approach to tree-pest interaction. *Proc. West. For. Insect Work Conf., March 7–9, Boise, ID.* Moscow, ID: Univ. Idaho
7. Bedard WE, Tilden PE, Wood DL, Silverstein RM, Brownlee RG, et al. 1969. Western pine beetle: field response to its sex pheromone and a synergistic host terpene, myrcene. *Science* 164:1284–85
8. Berryman AA. 1972. Resistance of conifers to invasion by bark beetle-fungus associations. *BioScience* 22:598–602
9. Billings RF, Gara RI, Hrutfiord BF. 1976. Influence of ponderosa pine resin volatiles on

the response of *Dendroctonus ponderosae* to synthetic *trans*-verbenol. *Environ. Entomol.* 5:171–79

10. Birch MC, Light DM, Wood DL, Browne LE, Silverstein RM, et al. 1980. Pheromonal attraction and allomonal interruption of *Ips pini* in California by the two enantiomers of ipsdienol. *J. Chem. Ecol.* 6:703–17

11. Bohlmann J, Crock J, Jetter R, Croteau R. 1998. Terpenoid-based defenses in conifers: cDNA cloning, characterization and functional expression of wound-inducible *(E)-α*-bisabolene synthase from grand fir *(Abies grandis)*. *Proc. Natl. Acad. Sci. USA* 95:6756–61

12. Bohlmann J, Croteau R. 1999. Diversity and variability of terpenoid defenses in conifers: molecular genetics, biochemistry and evolution of the terpene synthase gene family in grand fir. In *Insect-Plant Interactions and Induced Plant Defence*, 223:132–49. Chichester: Wiley

13. Bohlmann J, Meyer-Gauen G, Croteau R. 1998. Plant terpenoid synthases: molecular biology and phylogenetic analysis. *Proc. Natl. Acad. Sci. USA* 95:4126–33

14. Bohlmann J, Phillips M, Ramachandiran V, Katoh S, Croteau R. 1999. cDNA cloning, characterization, and functional expression of four new monoterpene synthase members of the *Tpsd* gene family from grand fir *(Abies grandis)*. *Arch. Biochem. Biophys.* 368:232–43

15. Bohlmann J, Steele CL, Croteau R. 1997. Monoterpene synthases from grand fir *(Abies grandis)*: cDNA isolation, characterization and functional expression of myrcene synthase, (−)-4*S*-limonene synthase and (−)-(1*S*,5*S*)-pinene synthase. *J. Biol. Chem.* 272:21784–92

16. Borden JH. 1984. Semiochemical-mediated aggregation and dispersion in the Coleoptera. In *Insect Communication*, ed. T Lewis, pp. 123–49. New York: Academic

17. Brand JM, Bracke JW, Britton LN, Markovetz AJ, Barras SJ. 1976. Bark beetle pheromones: production of verbenone by a mycangial fungus of *D. frontalis*. *J. Chem. Ecol.* 2:195–99

18. Brand JM, Schultz J, Barras SJ, Edson LJ, Payne TL, et al. 1977. Barkbeetle pheromones: enhancement of *Dendroctonus frontalis* (Coleoptera: Scolytidae) aggregation pheromone by yeast metabolites in laboratory bioassays. *J. Chem. Ecol.* 2:657–66

19. Byers JA, Birgersson G. 1990. Pheromone production in a bark beetle independent of myrcene precursor in host pine species. *Naturwissenschaften* 77:385–87

20. Cates RG, Alexander H. 1982. Host resistance and susceptibility. See Ref. 79a, pp. 212–63

21. Chappell J. 1995. Biochemistry and molecular biology of the isoprenoid biosynthetic pathway in plants. *Annu. Rev. Plant Physiol. Plant Mol. Biol.* 46:521–47

22. Charest P. 1996. Biotechnology in forestry: examples from the Canadian Forest Service. *For. Chron.* 72:37–42

23. Chen XY, Wang M, Chen Y, Davisson VJ, Heinstein P. 1996. Cloning and heterologous expression of a second (+)-delta-cadinene synthase from *Gossypium arboreum*. *J. Nat. Prod.* 59:944–51

24. Christiansen E, Waring RH, Berryman AA. 1987. Resistance of conifers to bark beetle attack: searching for general relationships. *For. Ecol. Manage.* 22:89–106

25. Colby SM, Alonso WR, Katahira EJ, McGarvey DJ, Croteau R. 1993. 4*S*-Limonene synthase from the oil glands of spearmint *(Mentha spicata)*: cDNA isolation, characterization and bacterial expression of the catalytically active monoterpene cyclase. *J. Biol. Chem.* 268:23016–24

26. Cook SP, Hain FP. 1988. Toxicity of host monoterpenes to *Dendroctonus frontalis* and *Ips calligraphus* (Coleoptera: Scolytidae). *J. Entomol. Sci.* 23:287–92

27. Croteau R. 1998. The discovery of terpenes. In *Discoveries in Plant Biology*, ed.

S-D Kung, S-F Yang, 1:329–43. Singapore: World Sci.

28. Croteau R, Gurkewitz S, Johnson MA, Fisk HJ. 1987. Biochemistry of oleoresinosis: monoterpene and diterpene biosynthesis in lodgepole pine saplings infected with *Ceratocystis clavigera* or treated with carbohydrate elicitors. *Plant Physiol.* 85:1123–28

29. Croteau R, Johnson MA. 1985. Biosynthesis of terpenoid wood extractives. In *Biosynthesis and Biodegradation of Wood Components*, ed. T Higuichi, pp. 379–439. New York: Academic

30. Cseke L, Dudareva N, Picherskey E. 1998. Structure and evolution of linalool synthase. *Mol. Biol. Evol.* 15:1491–98

31. Danell K, Gref R, Yazdani R. 1990. Effects of mono- and diterpenes in Scots pine needles on moose browsing. *Scand. J. For. Res.* 5:535–39

32. Davis EM, Croteau R. 2000. Cyclization enzymes in the biosynthesis of monoterpenes, sesquiterpenes and diterpenes. In *Topics in Current Chemistry: Biosynthesis*, ed. F Leeper, JC Vederas, 209:53–95. Heidelberg: Springer-Verlag

33. Dawson FA. 1994. The amazing terpenes. *Nav. Stores Rev.* March/April:6–12

34. Doyle JA. 1998. Phylogeny of vascular plants. *Annu. Rev. Ecol. Syst.* 29:567–99

35. Dudareva N, Cseke L, Blanc VM, Pichersky E. 1996. Evolution of floral scent in Clarkia: novel patterns of S-linalool synthase gene expression in *C. breweri* flower. *Plant Cell* 8:1137–48

36. Edmunds GF Jr, Alstad DN. 1978. Coevolution in insect herbivores and conifers. *Science* 199:941–45

37. Eisenreich W, Schwarz M, Cartayrade A, Arigoni D, Zenk MH, et al. 1998. The deoxyxylulose phosphate pathway of terpenoid biosynthesis in plants and microorganisms. *Chem. Biol.* 5:R221–23

38. Facchini PJ, Chappell J. 1992. Gene family for an elicitor-induced sesquiterpene cyclase in tobacco. *Proc. Natl. Acad. Sci. USA* 89:11088–92

39. Fahn A. 1979. *Secretory Tissues in Plants*, pp. 176–218. London: Academic

40. Fahn A, Werker E, Ben Tzur P. 1979. Seasonal effects of wounding and growth substances on development of traumatic resin ducts in *Cedrus libani*. *New Phytol.* 82:537–44

41. Fahn A, Zamski E. 1970. The influence of pressure, wind, wounding, and growth substances on rate of resin duct formation in *Pinus halepenis* wood. *Isr. J. Bot.* 19:429–46

42. Francke W, Vite JPZ. 1983. Oxygenated terpenes in pheromone systems of bark beetles [*Polygraphus poligraphus, Ips amitinus, Ips typographus*]. *Z. Angew. Entomol.* 96:146–56

43. Francke-Grosmann H. 1967. Ectosymbiosis in wood-inhabiting insects. In *Associations of Invertebrates, Birds, Ruminants, and Other Biota*, ed. SM Henry, 2:141–205. New York: Academic

44. Frey M, Chomet P, Glawischnig E, Stettner C, Grün S, et al. 1997. Analysis of a chemical plant defense mechanism in grasses. *Science* 277:696–99

45. Fryxell KJ. 1996. The coevolution of gene family trees. *Trends Genet.* 12:356–69

46. Funk C, Croteau R. 1994. Diterpenoid resin acid biosynthesis in conifers: characterization of two cytochrome P450–dependent monooxygenases and an aldehyde dehydrogenase involved in abietic acid biosynthesis. *Arch. Biochem. Biophys.* 308:258–66

47. Funk C, Lewinsohn E, Vogel BS, Steele CL, Croteau R. 1994. Regulation of oleoresinosis in grand fir (*Abies grandis*): coordinate induction of monoterpene and diterpene cyclases and two cytochrome P450–dependent diterpene hydroxylases by stem wounding. *Plant Physiol.* 106:999–1005

48. Futai K, Furano T. 1979. The variety of resistances among pine species to pine wood nematode *Bursaphelenchus lignicolus*. *Bull. Kyoto Univ. For.* 51:23–26

49. Gifford EM, Foster AS. 1988. Conifero-phyta. In *Morphology and Evolution of Vascular Plants*, pp. 401–53. New York: Freeman

50. Gijzen M, Lewinsohn E, Croteau R. 1991. Characterization of the constitutive and wound-inducible monoterpene cyclases of grand fir (*Abies grandis*). *Arch. Biochem. Biophys.* 289:267–73

51. Gijzen M, Lewinsohn E, Croteau R. 1992. Antigenic cross-reactivity among monoter-pene cyclases from grand fir and induc-tion of these enzymes upon stem wound-ing. *Arch. Biochem. Biophys.* 294:670–74

52. Gijzen M, Lewinsohn E, Savage TJ, Croteau RB. 1993. Conifer monoterpenes: biochemistry and bark beetle chemical ecology. In *Bioactive Volatile Compounds from Plants*, ed. R Teranishi, RG Buttery, H Sugisawa, pp. 8–22. Washington, DC: Am. Chem. Soc.

53. Gladwischnig E, Grün S, Frey M, Alfons G. 1999. Cytochrome P450 monoxyge-nases of DIBOA biosynthesis: specificity and conservation among grasses. *Phyto-chemistry* 50:925–30

54. Grégoire J-C, Couillien D, Krebber R, Konig WA, Meyer H, et al. 1992. Ori-entation of *Rhizophagus grandis* (Coleo-ptera:Rhizophagidae) to oxygenated mo-noterpenes in a species-specific predator-prey relationship. *Chemoecology* 3:14–18

55. Hervé J. 1996. *Trees and Forests: Living with Insects and Microorganisms*. http://www.ersac.umn.edu/iufro/publications

56. Hohf RS, Ratti JT, Croteau R. 1987. Exper-imental analysis of winter food selection by spruce grouse. *J. Wildl. Manage.* 51:159–67

57. Hohn TM, McCormick SP, Desjardins AE. 1993. Evidence for a gene cluster involving trichothecene pathway biosyn-thetic genes in *Fusarium sporotrichioides*. *Gene* 79:131–38

58. Hughes PR. 1973. *Dendroctonus* produc-tion of pheromones and related com-pounds in response to host monoterpenes. *Z. Angew. Entomol.* 73:294–312

59. Hunt DWA, Borden JH. 1990. Conver-sion of verbenols to verbenone by yeasts isolated from *Dendroctonus ponderosae* (Coleoptera: Scolytidae). *J. Chem. Ecol.* 16:1385–97

60. Jain KK. 1976. Evolution of wood struc-ture in Pinaceae. *Isr. J. Bot.* 25:28–33

61. James RR. 1997. Utilizing a social ethic to-ward the environment in assessing geneti-cally engineered insect-resistance in trees. *Agr. Hum. Values* 14:237–49

62. Jarvis BB, Miller JM. 1996. Natural prod-ucts, complexity, and evolution. In *Phy-tochemical Diversity and Redundancy in Ecological Interactions*, ed. J Romeo, pp. 265–93. New York: Plenum

63. Johnson MA, Croteau R. 1987. Biochem-istry of conifer resistance to bark beetles and their fungal symbionts. In *Ecology and Metabolism of Plant Lipids*, ed. G Fuller, WD Nes, pp. 76–92. Washington, DC: Am. Chem. Soc.

64. Katoh S, Croteau R. 1998. Individual vari-ation in constitutive and induced monoter-pene biosynthesis in grand fir (*Abies gran-dis*). *Phytochemistry* 47:577–82

65. Keegstra K, Olsen LJ, Theg SM. 1989. Chloroplastic precursors and their trans-port across the envelope membrane. *Annu. Rev. Plant Physiol. Plant Mol. Biol.* 40:471–501

66. Kelly MJ, Rohl AE. 1989. Pine oil and mis-cellaneous uses. See Ref. 124, pp. 560–72

67. Kuroda K, Shimaji K. 1983. Traumatic resin canal formation as a marker of xylem growth. *For. Sci.* 29:653–59

68. LaFever RE, Stofer Vogel B, Croteau R. 1994. Diterpenoid resin acid biosynthe-sis in conifers: enzymatic cyclization of geranylgeranyl pyrophosphate to abietadi-ene, the precursor of abietic acid. *Arch. Biochem. Biophys.* 313:139–49

69. Lanier GN, Claesson A, Stewart T, Pis-ton JJ, Silverstein RM. 1980. *Ips pini*: the basis for interpopulational differences in

pheromone biology. *J. Chem. Ecol.* 6:677–88

70. Leufven A, Birgensson G. 1987. Quantitative variation of different monoterpenes around galleries of *Ips typographus* (Coleoptera: Scolytidae) attacking Norway spruce. *Can. J. Bot.* 65:1038–44

71. Leufven A, Nehls L. 1986. Quantification of different yeasts associated with the bark beetle, *Ips typographus*, during its attack on a spruce tree. *Microb. Ecol.* 12:237–43

72. Lewinsohn E, Gijzen M, Croteau R. 1991. Defense mechanisms of conifers: differences in constitutive and wound-induced monoterpene biosynthesis among species. *Plant Physiol.* 96:44–49

73. Lewinsohn E, Gijzen M, Croteau R. 1992. Regulation of monoterpene biosynthesis in conifer defense. In *Regulation of Isopentenoid Metabolism*, ed. WD Nes, EJ Parish, JM Trzaskos, pp. 8–17. Washington, DC: Am. Chem. Soc.

74. Lewinsohn E, Gijzen M, Croteau R. 1992. Wound-inducible pinene cyclase from grand fir: purification, characterization, and renaturation after SDS-PAGE. *Arch. Biochem. Biophys.* 293:167–73

75. Lewinsohn E, Gijzen M, Muzika RM, Barton K, Croteau R. 1993. Oleoresinosis in grand fir (*Abies grandis*) saplings and mature trees: modulation of this wound response by light and water stresses. *Plant Physiol.* 101:1021–28

76. Lewinsohn E, Gijzen M, Savage TJ, Croteau R. 1991. Defense mechanisms of conifers: relationship of monoterpene cyclase activity to anatomical specialization and oleoresin monoterpene content. *Plant Physiol.* 96:38–43

77. Lewinsohn E, Katoh S, Croteau R. 1999. Conifer chemical defenses against bark beetles: the modulation of monoterpene biosynthesis by wounding, environmental stress, and ethylene. In *Plant Responses to Environmental Stresses: From Phytohormones to Genome Reorganization*, ed. HR Lerner, pp. 659–706. New York: Marcel Dekker

78. Lichtenthaler HK. 1999. The 1-deoxy-D-xylulose 5-phosphate pathway of isoprenoid biosynthesis in plants. *Annu. Rev. Plant Physiol. Plant Mol. Biol.* 50:47–66

79. Mau CJD, West CA. 1994. Cloning of casbene synthase cDNA: evidence for conserved structural features among terpenoid cyclases in plants. *Proc. Natl. Acad. Sci. USA* 91:8497–501

79a. Mitton JB, Sturgeon KB. 1982. *Bark Beetles in North American Conifers: A System for the Study of Evolutionary Biology*. Austin: Univ. Tex. Press

80. Moffat AS. 1996. Plant biotechnology: moving forest trees into the modern genetics era. *Science* 271:760–61

81. Mustaparta H, Angst ME, Lanier GN. 1980. Receptor discrimination of enantiomers of the aggregation pheromone ipsdienol in two species of *Ips*. *J. Chem. Ecol.* 6:689–701

82. Mutton DB. 1962. Wood resin. In *Wood Extractives*, ed. WE Hillis pp. 331–63. New York: Academic

83. Nelson RM, Beal JA. 1929. Experiments with bluestain fungi in southern pines. *Phytopathology* 19:1101–6

84. Nordlander G. 1990. Limonene inhibits attraction to α-pinene in the pine weevils *Hylobius abietis* and *H. pinastri*. *J. Chem. Ecol.* 16:1307–20

85. Norin T. 1972. Some aspects of the chemistry of the order pinales. *Phytochemistry* 11:1231–42

86. Payne TL. 1983. Nature of insect and host tree interactions. *Z. Angew. Entomol.* 96:105–9

87. Payne TL. 1989. Olfactory basis for insect enemies of allied species. In *Potential for Biological Control of Dendroctonus and Ips Bark Beetles*, ed. DL Kulhavy, MC Miller, pp. 55–69. Nacogdoches, TX: Stephen F. Austin Univ. Press

88. Penhallow RP. 1907. *A Manual of the North American Gymnosperms.* Boston, MA: Atheneaeums. 374 pp.

89. Phillips MA, Croteau R. 1999. Resin based defenses in conifers. *Trends Plant Sci.* 4:184–90

90. Phillips MA, Savage TJ, Croteau R. 1999. Monoterpene synthases of loblolly pine (*Pinus taeda*) produce pinene isomers and enantiomers. *Arch. Biochem. Biophys.* 372:197–204

91. Pitman GB. 1971. *Trans*-verbenol and *alpha*-pinene: their utility in manipulation of the mountain pine beetle. *J. Econ. Entomol.* 64:426–30

92. Pitman GB, Vite JP, Kinzer GW, Fentiman AF. 1968. Bark beetle attractants: *trans*-verbenol isolated from *Dendroctonus. Nature* 218:168–69

93. Puritch GS, Nijholt WW. 1974. Occurrence of juvabione-related compounds in grand fir [*Abies grandis*] and pacific silver fir [*Abies amabilis*] infested by balsam wooly aphid [*Adelges piceae*]. *Can. J. Bot.* 52:585–87

94. Raffa KF, Berryman AA. 1983. The role of host plant resistance in the colonization behavior and ecology of bark beetles. *Ecol. Monogr.* 53:27–49

95. Raffa KF, Berryman AA, Simasko J, Teal W, Wong BL. 1985. Effects of grand fir monoterpenes on the fir engraver, *Scolytus ventralis* (Coleoptera:Scolytidae) and its symbiotic fungus. *Environ. Entomol.* 14:552–56

96. Raffa KF, Klepzig DK. 1989. Chiral escape of bark beetles from predators responding to a bark beetle pheromone. *Oecologia* 80:566–69

97. Renwick JAA. 1970. Chemical aspects of bark beetle aggregation. *Boyce Thompson Inst. Contrib.* 24:337–41

98. Robinson C. 1999. Making forest biotechnology a commercial reality. *Nat. Biotechnol.* 17:27–29

99. Savage TJ, Hatch MW, Croteau R. 1994. Monoterpene synthases of *Pinus contorta*:

100. Scagel RF, Bandoni RJ, Rouse GE, Schofield WB, Stein JR, et al. 1965. *An Evolutionary Survey of the Plant Kingdom*, pp. 491–524. Belmont, CA: Wadsworth

101. Schopf R. 1986. The effect of secondary needle compounds on the development of phytophagous insects. *For. Ecol. Manage.* 15:55–64

102. Sederoff R. 1999. Building better trees with antisense. *Nat. Biotechnol.* 17:750–51

103. Seybold SJ, Quilici DR, Tillman JA, Vanderwel D, Wood DL, et al. 1995. *De novo* biosynthesis of aggregation pheromone components ipsenol and ipsdienol by the pine bark beetles *Ips paraconfusus* and *Ips pini* (Say) (Coleoptera:Scolytidae). *Proc. Natl. Acad. Sci. USA* 92:8993–97

104. Shrimpton DM. 1978. Resistance of lodgepole pine to mountain pine beetle infestation. In *Theory and Practice of Mountain Pine Beetle Management in Lodgepole Forests*, ed. AA Berryman, GD Amman, DL Kibbee, pp. 64–76. Moscow: Univ. Idaho For., Wildl. Range Exp. Stn.

105. Stark RW. 1982. Generalized ecology and life cycle of bark beetles. See Ref. 79a, pp. 21–45

106. Starks CM, Back K, Chappell J, Noel JP. 1997. Structural basis for cyclic terpene biosynthesis by tobacco 5–*epi*-aristolochene synthase. *Science* 277:1815–20

107. Steele CL, Bohlmann J, Crock JE, Croteau R. 1998. Sesquiterpene synthases from grand fir (*Abies grandis*): comparison of constitutive and wound-induced activities, and cDNA isolation, characterization, and bacterial expression of δ-selinene synthase and γ-humulene synthase. *J. Biol. Chem.* 273:2078–89

108. Steele CL, Katoh S, Bohlmann J, Croteau R. 1998. Regulation of oleoresinosis

a new class of terpenoid cyclase. *J. Biol. Chem.* 269:4012–20 in grand fir (*Abies grandis*). Differential transcriptional control of monoterpene, sesquiterpene and diterpene synthase genes in response to wounding. *Plant Physiol.* 116:1497–504

109. Steele CL, Lewinsohn E, Croteau R. 1995. Induced oleoresin biosynthesis in grand fir as a defense against bark beetles. *Proc. Natl. Acad. Sci. USA* 92:4164–68

110. Sterky F. 1998. Gene discovery in the wood-forming tissues of poplar: analysis of 5,692 expressed sequence tags. *Proc. Natl. Acad. Sci. USA* 95:13330–35

111. Deleted in proof

112. Sturgeon KB, Mitton JB. 1982. Evolution of bark beetle communities. See Ref. 79a, pp. 350–84

113. Sun T-P, Goodman HM, Ausubel FM. 1992. Cloning the Arabidopsis GA1 locus by genomic subtraction. *Plant Cell* 4:119–28

114. Sun T-P, Kamiya Y. 1994. The *arabidopsis* GA1 locus encodes the cyclase *ent*-kaurene synthetase A of gibberellin biosynthesis. *Plant Cell* 6:1509–18

115. Trapp SC, Hohn TM, McCormick SP, Jarvis BB. 1998. Characterization of the gene cluster for biosynthesis of macrocyclic trichothecenes in *Myrothecium roridum. Mol. Gen. Genet.* 257:421–32

115a. Vogel BS, Wildung MR, Vogel G, Croteau R. 1996. Abietadiene synthase from grand fir (*Abies grandis*): cDNA isolation, characterization and bacterial expression of a bifunctional diterpene cyclase involved in resin acid biosynthesis. *J. Biol. Chem.* 271:23262–68

116. Walter C, Carson SD, Menzies MI, Richardson T, Carson M. 1998. Application of biotechnology to forestry-molecular biology of conifers. *World J. Microbiol. Biotechnol.* 14:321–30

117. Werker E, Fahn A. 1969. Resin ducts of *Pinus halepensis* Mill. Their structure, development and pattern of arrangement. *Linn. Soc. London J. Bot.* 62:379–410

118. Whitney HS. 1982. Relationships between bark beetles and symbiotic organisms. See Ref. 79a, pp. 183–211

119. Wildung MR, Croteau R. 1996. A cDNA clone for taxadiene synthase, the diterpene cyclase that catalyzes the committed step of Taxol biosynthesis. *J. Biol. Chem.* 271:9201–4

120. Williams DC, McGarvey DJ, Katahira EJ, Croteau R. 1998. Truncation of limonene synthase preprotein provides a fully active 'pseudomature' form of this monoterpene cyclase and reveals the function of the amino-terminal arginine pair. *Biochemistry* 37:12213–20

121. Wise ML, Croteau R. 1999. Monoterpene biosynthesis. In *Comprehensive Natural Products Chemistry: Isoprenoids Including Steroids and Carotenoids*, ed. DE Cane, 2:97–153. Oxford: Elsevier Sci.

122. Wood DL. 1982. The role of pheromones, kairomones, and allomones in the host selection and colonization behavior of bark beetles. *Annu. Rev. Entomol.* 27:411–46

123. Yamaguchi S, Sun T-P, Kawaide H, Kamiya Y. 1998. The GA2 locus of *Arabidopsis thaliana* encodes *ent*-kaurene synthase of gibberellin biosynthesis. *Plant Physiol.* 116:1271–78

124. Zinkel DF, Russell J. 1989. *Naval Stores: Production, Chemistry, Utilization*, New York: Pulp Chem. Assoc.

Annu. Rev. Plant Physiol. Plant Mol. Biol. 2001. 52:725–49

MOLECULAR BIOLOGY OF FRUIT MATURATION AND RIPENING

Jim Giovannoni
USDA-ARS Plant, Soil and Nutrition Laboratory and Boyce Thompson Institute for Plant Research, Cornell University, Ithaca, New York 14853; e-mail: jjg33@cornell.edu

Key Words cell wall metabolism, ethylene signal transduction, light signal transduction, developmental regulation, gene expression

■ **Abstract** The development and maturation of fruits has received considerable scientific scrutiny because of both the uniqueness of such processes to the biology of plants and the importance of fruit as a significant component of the human diet. Molecular and genetic analysis of fruit development, and especially ripening of fleshy fruits, has resulted in significant gains in knowledge over recent years. Great strides have been made in the areas of ethylene biosynthesis and response, cell wall metabolism, and environmental factors, such as light, that impact ripening. Discoveries made in *Arabidopsis* in terms of general mechanisms for signal transduction, in addition to specific mechanisms of carpel development, have assisted discovery in more traditional models such as tomato. This review attempts to coalesce recent findings in the areas of fruit development and ripening.

CONTENTS

INTRODUCTION

In their constant effort to yield subsequent generations of viable and competitive progeny, plant species have evolved numerous mechanisms for seed dispersal. Fruit are an integral part of this endeavor and can be narrowly defined as mature carpels. This definition accurately describes the fruits of tomato, melons, and stone fruits, to name just a few. A more accurate and inclusive definition encompasses extracarpellary tissues that are included at the mature fruiting stage. Examples of such additional tissues in more complex fruits include the receptacle in strawberry and the bracts of pineapple. Fruits can be additionally separated into dehiscent, or dry, fruits and non-dehiscent, or fleshy, fruits. Examples of dehiscent fruits include the pods of legumes and the siliques of many of the Brassicaceae, including *Arabidopsis thaliana*. Analysis of floral development–related MADS-box genes in *Arabidopsis* has been particularly relevant toward initiating the dissection of the molecular basis of fruit development and make up a portion of the discussion here (for recent review, see 38).

The ripening process renders fruit attractive and palatable to a variety of seed-dispersing organisms and typifies non-dehiscent (fleshy) fruits. Because of the dual role of non-dehiscent fruits as both a unique aspect of plant development and the source of a large portion of the human diet, the molecular basis of development and ripening of fleshy fruits has received considerable scientific attention in recent years and constitutes the majority of this review. Previous reviews of the molecular regulation of fruit ripening have focused primarily on tomato, cell wall metabolism in particular, and the effects of the gaseous hormone ethylene (19, 46, 48, 52, 81, 161). The ripe phenotype is the summation of biochemical and physiological changes that occur at the terminal stage of fruit development and render the organ edible and desirable to seed-dispersing animals. Ripening also imparts value to fruit as agricultural commodities. These changes, although variable among species, generally include modification of cell wall ultrastructure and texture, conversion of starch to sugars, increased susceptibility to post-harvest pathogens, alterations in pigment biosynthesis and accumulation, and heightened levels of flavor and aromatic volatiles [for reviews on fruit physiology and biochemistry, see (116, 128)]. One of the key regulatory questions relative to the ripening process is, "How is the collection of otherwise unrelated pathways and processes coordinated to act efficiently and synchronously during this stage of fruit development?" Additionally, from a practical viewpoint, several ripening attributes translate to decreased shelf-life and high-input harvest, shipping, and storage practices, particularly as a result of changes in firmness and the overall decrease in resistance to microbial infection of ripe fruit. The 1990s have been a time of significant advances in our understanding of the molecular regulation of individual ripening parameters in which significant insights into their coordination have been revealed. The resulting knowledge has contributed to a more complete view of molecular ripening control and has produced the first molecular tools for addressing problems in fruit production and quality.

CLIMACTERIC AND NON-CLIMACTERIC RIPENING

Although most fruit display modifications in color, texture, flavor, and pathogen susceptibility during maturation, two major classifications of ripening fruit, climacteric and non-climacteric, have been utilized to distinguish fruit on the basis of respiration and ethylene biosynthesis rates. Climacteric fruit, such as tomato, cucurbits, avocado, banana, peaches, plums, and apples, are distinguished from non-climacteric fruits, such as strawberry, grape, and citrus, by their increased respiration and ethylene biosynthesis rates during ripening (81). Although non-climacteric fruits, such as citrus, may respond to ethylene (an example being ethylene-induced mRNA and pigment accumulation in the flavedo of orange; 5), ethylene is not required for fruit ripening from species in this classification. In contrast, ethylene is necessary for the coordination and completion of ripening in climacteric fruit via analysis of inhibitors of ethylene biosynthesis and perception (148, 157), in transgenic plants blocked in ethylene biosynthesis (69, 105, 113), and through examination of the *Never-ripe* (*Nr*) ethylene receptor mutant of tomato (77, 149, 155, 159). It is also important to note that, though not nearly as well characterized in this regard, plant hormones, in addition to ethylene, are likely to influence climacteric fruit ripening (28, 92).

COMMON GENETIC REGULATORY MECHANISMS

A clarification of the common genetic regulatory elements that are shared among climacteric and non-climacteric species is central to a full understanding of fruit ripening. Such primary regulators of fruit maturation might be shared by, or at least related to, those that regulate maturation of dehiscent fruit. Although such common regulatory elements remain elusive, *Arabidopsis* silique development genes, such as those from the MADS-box family of transcription factors (38), may represent starting points in a search for common control mechanisms. Indeed, although anti-sense repression had no obvious effect on fruit ripening (114), ectopic expression of the tomato *AGAMOUS* gene (*TAG1*) results in fleshy expansion, ripening-like cell wall metabolism, and carotenoid accumulation in the sepals of transgenic tomatoes (60). Though not conclusive, these results are consistent with a hypothesis in which TAG1 represents a redundant ripening control function. Alternatively, TAG1 may not regulate in vivo ripening, but it may be related to, and thus mimic, a similar regulatory gene when over-expressed in sepals. In addition to a further pursuit of candidate genes or gene families, investigators have identified a number of climacteric ripening mutants that fail to ripen in response to ethylene and represent an additional track toward identification of common ripening regulators (52).

PRACTICAL AND SCIENTIFIC IMPORTANCE

Fruit development and ripening are processes unique to plant species and, from this perspective, represent an opportunity for novel insights regarding plant developmental regulatory mechanisms. The development and maturation of fruit tissues represent a final phase of floral development typically proceeding and signaled by successful pollination (106). Although parthenocarpic (seedless) fruit development occurs, such phenomena typically result from either (A) genetic alterations (including gene mutations or changes in genome ploidy) or environmental and/or hormonal alterations that ultimately mimic and trigger the fruit developmental cascade (true parthenocarpy) or (B) premature embryo abortion that results in fruit with minimal residual seed tissue (95). Indeed, parthenocarpy is of considerable agricultural importance as a means of both consumer satisfaction and variety protection. Although much is known of the hormonal and physiological signals that trigger fruit development (39), maturation and ripening are aspects of late floral development for which the molecular regulatory signals remain largely unknown.

From the standpoint of agriculture, ripening confers both positive and negative attributes to the resulting commodity. Although ripening imparts desirable flavor, color, and texture, considerable expense and crop loss result from negative ripening characteristics. For example, ripening-related increase in fruit pathogen susceptibility is a major contributor to fruit loss both before and after harvest. This genetically regulated change in fruit physiology currently necessitates the use of pesticides, post-harvest fumigants, and controlled atmosphere storage and shipping mechanisms in attempts to minimize loss. In addition to being wasteful of energy and potentially harmful to the environment, such practices represent major expenses in fruit production.

Finally, it is important to reiterate that ripening imparts numerous quality and nutritional characteristics upon a significant component of the human diet, fruit. Ripening impacts various critical aspects of mature fruit, including fiber content and composition, lipid metabolism, and the levels of vitamins and various antioxidants (123). The ability to understand key control points in global ripening regulation or within specific ripening processes, such as carotenoid, flavonoid, vitamin, and flavor volatiles, will allow for manipulation of nutrition and quality characteristics associated with ripening. The most convincing argument for the promotion of safe plant–genetic engineering will be the development of products with direct consumer impact and appeal, such as quality and nutritionally enhanced fruits.

MODEL SYSTEMS FOR FRUIT DEVELOPMENT AND RIPENING

As the fruit of numerous plant species have been studied in terms of development, maturation, ripening, and associated quality and yield characteristics, several have emerged as model systems from which the majority of available information

Figure 1 Isolation of an *fw2.2*, a QTL regulating fruit mass. (*A*) Fruit of the wild tomato species *L. pennellii* (left) and a large cultivated variety of *L. esculentum* (right). A gene residing at a major QTL for fruit mass, designated *fw2.2*, was identified and isolated. The dominant *L. pennellii* allele of *fw2.2* was inserted into the genome of a relatively large fruited *L. esculentum* variety via T-DNA transfer resulting in a reduction in fruit weight and confirmation of isolation of the target gene (*B*). From Frary et al (44) with permission.

Figure 3 Ethylene insensitivity in tomato and petunia resulting from expression of a mutant *Arabidopsis* ethylene receptor. Expression of a mutant *Arabidopsis* ethylene receptor (ETR1-1) in tomato resulted in (*A*) seedlings that were insensitive to ACC in the growth medium, (*B*) petals that failed to senescence following pollination, and inhibition of fruit ripening at 0, 10, and 100 days post-mature green (*D, E, F*, respectively). Non-uniform expression of the transgene correlated with sectored ripening (*C*). Expression of the same gene in petunia resulted in delayed petal senescence. *G, H,* and *I* are transgenic petunia flowers at 0, 3, and 8 days post pollination, respectively. *J* and *K* are non-transformed controls at 0 and 3 days, respectively. Treatment of transgenic petunias with exogenous ethylene resulted in reduced senescence as compared to wild-type controls (*L*). WT, wild type; TR, transgenic. Reproduced from Wilkinson et al (153) with permission.

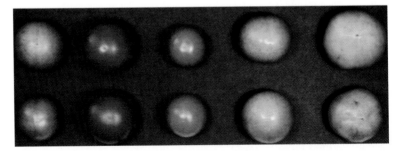

Figure 4 Tomato fruit ripening mutants. From left to right are mature green and ripe (mature green + 7 days) fruit from tomato *cultivar Ailsa Craig*. Following are fruit of identical age as the ripe control and from nearly isogenic lines homozygous for the *Nr* (*Never-ripe*), *rin* (*ripening-inhibitor*), and *nor* (*non-ripening*) mutations, respectively.

regarding the molecular regulation of development and ripening has been derived. Specifically, these include tomato, *Arabidopsis*, and important but to a significantly lesser extent, strawberry. Each of these model systems represents unique fruit development and maturation programs, and each has attributes reflective of a useful model system. All three, for example, can be utilized for direct assessment of gene function via stable integration of transgenes (27, 41, 93).

In large part due to its importance as a crop species, tomato has long served as the primary model for climacteric fruit ripening. This practical importance combined with diploid inheritance, ease of seed and clonal propagation, efficient sexual hybridization, a short generation period ($\sim$45–100 days, depending on variety and season), and year-round growth potential in greenhouses has made tomato the plant of choice for ripening research. From the standpoint of genetic and molecular investigations, tomato has the additional advantage of a relatively small genome (0.9 pg/haploid genome; 9) for which over 1000 molecular markers have been identified, with an average genetic spacing of less than 2 cM (138). The resulting genetic map has been especially useful in the identification and localization of quantititive trait loci (QTLs) that influence numerous fruit development, ripening, and quality loci (22, 34, 51, 74). High-molecular weight insert genomic libraries are available in both yeast artificial chromosome (17, 91, 101) and bacterial artificial chromosome (23, 43, 58) vector systems to facilitate positional cloning, and a limited number of characterized heterologous T-DNA insertion lines have been created (14, 70, 96, 107). A recently added tool to the repertoire of tomato and other plant science researchers is the National Science Foundation–sponsored development of a tomato expressesd sequence tag (EST) database. Over 20 cDNA libraries from various tissues have been created, followed by partial (single-pass 5′) sequencing of 2000–10,000 clones from each. The database will be at or near completion at the publication of this review and can be accessed prior to and following completion via the following URL, http://www.tigr.org/tdb/lgi/index.html. The finished database will include approximately 30,000 sequences derived from fruit at various stages of development, and a recent query indicated approximately 1000 non-redundant ESTs that are found exclusively in the subset of fruit libraries.

In addition to the molecular tools noted above, years of breeding and mutagenesis have resulted in a valuable germplasm resource, representing genes that influence multiple aspects of fruit development and ripening. QTL analysis has resulted in the identification of loci that regulate shape (74), size (51), and ripening time (34), while a variety of single gene mutants have been described that influence comprehensive ripening effects or subsets of ripening attributes, such as pigment accumulation (Table 1; 52, 54). In addition, Eshed & Zamir (36) created a series of introgressions of a wild tomato species (*Lycopersicon pennellii*) into cultivated tomato (*L. esculentum*), resulting in 50 introgression lines that span the tomato genome and yield variation in numerous phenotypes, including fruit development and ripening. The potential for further examination and discovery using this genetic resource remains considerable.

TABLE 1 Tomato germplasm altered in ripening. The dashed line separates mutants for which the corresponding gene has been cloned (1st tier) from those that have not (2nd tier). The third tier indicates transgenic lines altered in ethylene signaling

Genotype	Activity	Function	Reference
rin, ripening-inhibitor	Transcription factor	Comprehensive ripening	147*
nor, non-ripening	Transcription factor	Comprehensive ripening	147*
Nr, Never-ripe	C2H4 receptor	Ethylene signaling	155
hp-2, high-pigment-2	DET1 homolog	Light signaling	100
cr, crimson	Lycopene cyclase	Carotenoid metabolism	123
B, Beta	Lycopene cyclase	Carotenoid metabolism	123
r, Phytoene Synthase	Phytoene synthase	Carotenoid metabolism	45
- - - - - - - - - - - -	- - - - - - - - - - - -	- - - - - - - - - - - -	- - - - - - - - -
hp-1, high-pigment-1	NA	Light signaling	152, 160
alc, alcobaca	NA	Comprehensive ripening	72
Nr-2, Never-ripe-2	NA	Comprehensive ripening	65
Gr, Green-ripe	NA	Comprehensive ripening	64
Cnr, Clear non-ripening	NA	Comprehensive ripening	143
Gf	NA	Comprehensive ripening	3
t, tangerine	NA	Carotenoid metabolism	119
at, apricot	NA	Carotenoid metabolism	61
ACO	ACC oxidase	C2H4 biosynthesis	113
ACS	ACC synthase	C2H4 biosynthesis	105
ACD	ACC deaminase	C2H4 biosynthesis	69
LeETR4	Ethylene receptor	Ethylene signaling	146
TCTR1	Putative MAPKKK	Ethylene signaling	**

*Vrebalov, Ruezinsky, Padmanabhan, and Giovannoni, unpublished.
**Adams, Kannan, Barry, and Giovannoni, unpublished.

Arabidopsis remains unsurpassed as a model for dehiscent fruit development in particular and plant biology in general. At 0.15 pg/haploid genome, the *Arabidopsis* genome is small, gene-dense, and almost completely sequenced. Combined, these attributes make positional cloning strategies fairly straightforward (87). Numerous mutants have resulted from large-scale mutagenesis programs, with insertional mutagenesis efforts resulting in particularly powerful tools for ascertaining gene function (reviewed in 11, 71, 90, 108). With respect to genetic control of fruit development, recent functional analyses of *AGAMOUS*-like (*AGL*) genes has resulted in identification of several MADS-box genes that regulate fruit (silique) development and maturation (38).

Finally, although several non-climacteric species, including citrus (67) and grape (30, 139, 140), have received considerable attention as systems for molecular analysis of fruit maturation, strawberry has emerged as the most widely studied and tractable non-climacteric model system. Several differential screens have resulted in a number of novel ripening-related genes (89, 103, 154), and a strawberry fruit microarray has been developed for use in identifying genes associated with quality characters (2).

MOLECULAR ANALYSIS OF FRUIT DEVELOPMENT

Arabidopsis MADS-Box Genes

To date, molecular factors influencing fruit development have been best described via mutant and subsequent gene cloning in *Arabidopsis* and *Antirrhinum*. Classic floral homeotic genes, such as the *AGAMOUS* and *SQUAMOSA* MADS-box genes, represent molecular determinants necessary for the formation of floral organs, including carpels. However, these genes are not fruit specific in effects and thus are not the focus of this review (for recent reviews of floral development, see 97, 141). Nevertheless, recent analysis of *Arabidopsis* MADS genes (of which there are at least 45) (8) reveals several that have clear fruit-specific activities. MADS genes are defined by the presence of a highly conserved amino-terminal DNA-binding motif, denoted as the MADS-box, followed by less well conserved I, K, and C domains. The I and K domains may be involved in the formation of homo- and heterodimers, with additional MADS proteins, whereas the C domain is the most variable and likely to confer functional specificity (120).

Inactivation of the *FRUITFUL* MADS gene (*AGL8*) resulted in siliques that failed to fully expand, although that produced no discernable effect on seed development (55). Mutant siliques also fail to dehisce as a result of abnormal formation of valve-replum boundaries (38). In this latter regard, *FRUITFUL* does not seem to directly influence silique maturation per se. Rather, it does so indirectly because it mediates silique expansion and development processes that result in appropriate definition of valve-replum boundaries and normal formation of the dehiscence zone.

Two functionally redundant MADS-box genes (*AGL1* and *AGL5*) required for normal silique dehiscence–zone formation were also recently reported. The *AGL1* and *AGL5* MADS-box genes are highly homologous and demonstrate similar gene expression patterns. Inactivation of either gene yields no discernable phenotype. This fact, together with sequence and expression similarities, suggests the possibility of functional redundancy. To test this hypothesis, *AGL1/AGL5* double mutant lines were generated and were found to yield siliques that failed to dehisce but were otherwise normal (82, 83). *AGL1* and *AGL5* were renamed *SHATTERPROOF1* and *SHATTERPROOF2* (*SHP1, 2*), respectively, and are negatively regulated by *FRUITFUL* (37, 82). These results suggest that a cascade of MADS-box gene activities coordinate aspects of fruit development in *Arabidopsis* and possibly other species. As mentioned above, MADS-box genes have been correlated with the induced ripening of tomato sepals and have also been associated with development and ripening of additional fruit-bearing species, including apple (135, 136, 158), strawberry (125), and cucurbits (40). Although specific functions of MADS-box genes in the development of these fleshy fruits remain unknown, their expression in various stages of fruit development is consistent with possible roles in fruit development and expansion, as well as later stages of development that may include ripening and senescence.

Tomato Fruit Mass QTLs

Quantitative trait loci (QTLs) are responsible for the majority of important crop characteristics, including regulation of fruit development and ripening. Thus, the ability to isolate QTLs, though important, has been thwarted by their very nature as multiple locus traits. This recalcitrance to isolation results from the fact that genes revealed only by allelic variation (as is typical of QTLs), in the absence of additional biochemical or molecular clues, are typically targeted for isolation through positional cloning or insertion mutagenesis strategies. Both approaches are dependent on fully accurate target locus segregation analysis that can be confused by additional segregating loci.

Tomato fruit mass genes have been the proving ground for a strategy to isolate QTLs based on effective conversion of the target gene to a single gene trait. In summary, germplasm is developed through advanced backcross breeding to fix the genotype of all non-target QTLs while selecting nearly isogenic lines (NILs) for the target locus. The resulting NILs can be used simultaneously for both gene isolation and accurate assessment of the contribution of specific alleles at an individual locus to the trait in question. Advanced backcross breeding was initially used to genetically isolate a QTL that plays a major role in fruit mass variation between cultivated tomato and the considerably smaller fruited wild species *L. pennellii* (6). This locus was designated *fruit weight 2.2* (*fw2.2*). Once all other major fruit weight loci were fixed for genotype, a large segregating population could be accurately scored to permit high-resolution genetic mapping (7) as a prelude to eventual positional cloning (44). Gene isolation was eventually confirmed via transfer of the dominant (*L. pennellii*) allele to the recessive (*L. esculentum*) genotype via *Agrobacterium*-mediated T-DNA transfer (Figure 1, see color insert). This accomplishment represents the first targeted isolation of a QTL known only through phenotype.

The *fw2.2* sequence is only indicative of the route through which this gene influences fruit mass. Analysis of the predicted amino acid sequence indicates a similarity to a human oncogene RAS protein, thus suggestive of a possible role in developmental regulation. Additional clues stem from the facts that (*a*) variation in fruit mass can be at least partially attributable to a corresponding variation in pre-anthesis carpel cell number between NILs harboring the *L. esculentum* versus *L. pennellii* alleles of *fw2.2*, (*b*) a corresponding difference in cell size was not observed between the fruit of NILs, and (*c*) *fw2.2* is expressed in pre-anthesis floral organs at low levels, with highest expression in carpel tissues. These results suggest that *fw2.2* may regulate fruit mass through modulation of pre-anthesis carpel cell number. Furthermore, no obviously significant changes in coding sequence are observed between the *L. esculentum* and *L. pennellii* alleles of *fw2.2*, though mRNA accumulation was higher in pre-anthesis carpels of the *L. pennellii* NIL. This observation suggests that the dominance observed for the *L. pennellii* allele results from elevated expression (presumably due to promoter sequence variation). This observation supports a model in which the *fw2.2* gene product acts as a negative regulator of cell division during early carpel development (44), and selection for weaker alleles at the *fw2.2* locus may have occurred during domestication. Following a search of the EST and genome sequence databases, researchers identified *fw2.2* homologs in *Arabidopsis*. Whether any of these related genes influence fruit mass or additional aspects of fruit development, and how such genes may interact with MADS-box fruit development genes, should prove to be interesting lines of future investigation.

RIPENING OF FLESHY FRUITS

As mentioned above, climacteric fruits are distinguished from non-climacteric fruits by their increased respiration and ethylene biosynthesis rates during ripening (81). Using the tomato system, investigators have long known that ethylene is necessary for manifestation of ripening in climacteric fruit (148, 157). The critical role of ethylene in coordinating climacteric ripening at the molecular level was first observed via analysis of ethylene-inducible, ripening-related–gene expression in tomato (85, 94). Numerous fruit development–related genes were isolated using differential gene expression patterns and biochemical function in the late 1980s and early 1990s (reviewed in 53), with more recent screens focused on gene isolation strategies that are likely to detect less abundant mRNAs (162). The in vivo functions of fruit development– and ripening-related–genes, including HMG-CoA reductase, polygalacturonase (PG), pectin methylesterase, ACC synthase, ACC oxidase, phytoene synthase, and the *NR* ethylene receptor, have been tested via antisense gene repression and/or mutant complementation in tomato (52). This is demonstrated by the following examples: PG is necessary for ripening-related pectin depolymerization and pathogen susceptibility, yet it has little effect on fruit softening (49, 73, 131). Inhibition of phytoene synthase results in reduced carotenoid biosynthesis and reduction in fruit and flower pigmentation (45). Reduced ethylene evolution results in ripening inhibition of ACC synthase and ACC oxidase antisense lines (57, 105), whereas introduction of a dominant mutant allele of the *NR* ethylene receptor results in tomato plants that are inhibited in virtually every measurable ethylene response, including fruit ripening (155, 159).

Ethylene Signal Transduction

Analysis of *Arabidopsis* ethylene response mutants has yielded the clearest model for hormone signal transduction in plants (Figure 2) (35, 42, 62, 66, 134). Demonstration that the tomato *Nr* mutant represents a lesion in an ethylene receptor

Ethylene Biosynthesis and Signaling

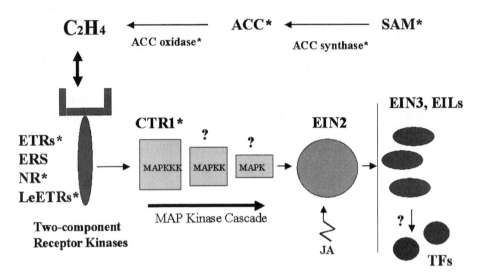

C₂H₄ ←——— ACC* ←——— SAM*

Figure 2   Model for ethylene synthesis and signal transduction. A composite model derived from the work of Yang (157) on ethylene biosynthesis and as reviewed in Stepanova & Ecker's research on ethylene signal transduction (134). Steps and intermediates designated with an asterisk have been targeted for transgene modification in ripening fruit. EIN3, EILs, and EREBPs are localized in the nucleus.

gene (155), combined with the isolation of additional fruit species homologues [tomato (80, 109, 163), cucurbits (126, 156), peach (13)], has permitted comparative analysis of ethylene receptor expression in several species, as well as functional analysis during fleshy fruit ripening in tomato. As would be predicted by the *Arabidopsis* model, mutation in the putative ethylene-binding domain of the tomato *NR* gene results in global ethylene insensitivity, including inhibition of ripening (77, 155). Genetic mapping of putative tomato ethylene receptor loci employing the *Arabidopsis ETR1* ethylene receptor as a probe suggested the presence of several tomato receptors in addition to *NR* (159). Corresponding loci have since been isolated and characterized for expression by several groups (80, 109, 163). *NR* and *LeETR4* demonstrated elevated expression during ripening and were thus targeted for antisense repression. In summary, repression of *NR* had no obvious effects on ethylene signaling other than elevated expression of *LeETR4*, suggesting a feedback mechanism resulting in compensation for missing *NR* with increased *LeETR4*. Repression of *LeETR4* did not elicit any alteration of *NR* expression but did result in leaf epinasty, premature floral senescence, and accelerated ripening suggestive of a negative regulatory role in ethylene signaling. Transgene mediated expression of *NR* in *LeETR4* repression lines resulted in complementation of the enhanced ethylene response phenotype, confirming functional redundancy (146).

Initially, this result seems odd as the inactivation of single *Arabidopsis* ethylene receptor genes has no obvious effect on ethylene signal transduction. An ethylene constitutive response phenotype analogous to tomato *LeETR4* repression was not observed until multiple *Arabidopsis* ethylene receptor loci were rendered inactive (59). One possible explanation for this result is that *LeETR4* may make a greater contribution to net receptor levels in tomato versus individual receptor genes in *Arabidopsis*. Inactivation of the remaining tomato ethylene receptors should confirm or deny this possibility and will provide insights into how evolution has tailored ethylene perception to suit the developmental programs deployed by these two species.

Analyses of gene knockouts and repression in *Arabidopsis* and tomato, respectively, do indicate clear functional redundancy in the ethylene receptor gene families of both species. Wilkinson et al (153) demonstrated that ethylene receptor function is also highly conserved across species boundaries. Specifically, expression of a mutated *Arabidopsis ETR1* transgene yielded a receptor gene product that was altered in its ability to bind ethylene (127) and resulted in ethylene insensitivity in *Arabidopsis* plants that harbored the normal complement of ethylene receptor genes. This result is consistent with a model in which ethylene phenotypes result from ethylene inactivation of receptors, thus allowing dominant mutant (active) receptors to continue repression of responses attributed to the recognition of ethylene (56). Wilkinson et al also expressed the mutated *Arabidopsis ETR1* transgene in petunia and tomato, resulting in similar repression of ethylene phenotypes (153). (Figure 3, see color insert) Both species demonstrated general ethylene insensitivity in response to transgene expression, though most notably in the agriculturally significant attributes of fruit ripening and floral senescence. This result demonstrates functional conservation across species and suggests that the mutant *Arabidopsis* receptor gene will have wide-range potential for modification of ethylene responses (such as climacteric fruit ripening) across diverse taxa.

Developmental Regulation

Further analysis of transgenic and mutant tomato lines that are inhibited in ethylene biosynthesis or perception demonstrates that climacteric ripening represents a combination of ethylene regulation and developmental control. Indeed, the gene encoding the rate limiting activity in ethylene biosynthesis, *ACC synthase*, is initially induced during ripening by an unknown developmental signaling system (12, 142).

Expression analysis of a number of additional ripening-related genes indicates that developmental or non-ethylene–mediated regulation of a subset of ripening-related genes is evident in climacteric fruits. Examples in tomato include members of the *ACO* and *ACS* gene families (12, 16, 84, 102, 142), the *NR* ethylene receptor (80, 109, 155), and E8 (32). Additional evidence for non-ethylene–mediated ripening control comes from analysis of gene expression in a number of ripening impaired mutants, such as *rin* (*ripening-inhibitor*) and *nor* (*non-ripening*), that fail to ripen in response to exogenous ethylene yet display signs of ethylene sensitivity and signaling, including induction of some ethylene-regulated genes (Figure 4, see color insert; 159). Other researchers and we have interpreted these results to indicate that additional regulatory constraints are placed on climacteric fruit maturation in addition to general ethylene biosynthesis and signaling. Such regulatory mechanisms could include fruit-specific regulation of certain subsets of ethylene-regulated genes or regulatory mechanisms that operate separately from and in addition to ethylene (Figure 5). Genes corresponding to both the *rin* and *nor* mutations have been recently cloned; although unrelated at the level of DNA or protein sequence, both have features suggestive of roles in regulation of gene transcription (Vrebalov, Ruezinsky, Padmanabhan, White, Noensie, & Giovannoni, unpublished data). Availability of these ripening regulatory genes should allow analysis of steps in the ripening regulatory hierarchy that precede ethylene. They should also permit

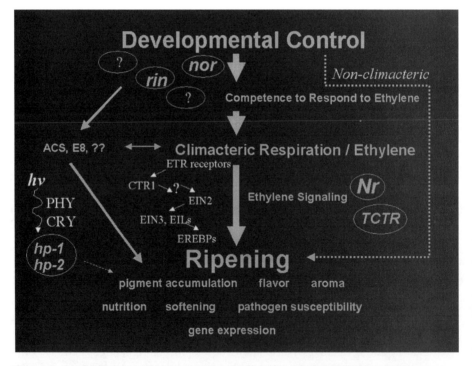

Figure 5   Model for interactions among developmental, hormonal, and light signaling systems that impact ripening. Developmental cues as represented via available tomato ripening mutants are required for climacteric ethylene biosynthesis and response. Studies in tomato also suggest that light is critical in normal pigment accumulation. A key question (dotted line) is whether common developmental mechanisms control climacteric and non-climacteric ripening.

assessment of whether such genes represent regulatory mechanisms common to both climacteric and non-climacteric fruit species.

Cell Wall Metabolism and Softening

Within the context of fruit ripening, tomato PG has been the most widely studied cell wall hydrolase. This is due in large part to initial observations of a high-level extractable endo-PG activity that increased in parallel with the ripening process. These observations led to the pursuit of the tomato endo-PG gene and the hypothesis regarding the role of PG in ripening-related textural modification (reviewed in 50). Gene isolation, and the subsequent functional characterization of tomato fruit PG in transgenic plants, indicated that PG activity alone is not sufficient to significantly impact texture (49, 129, 131); thus, it is likely to function in concert with additional factors. Kramer et al suggested that fruit PG may also play a role in mediating the fruit ripening–associated increase in susceptibility to opportunistic pathogens (73).

Enzymes in addition to PG that are involved in cell wall metabolism have been identified in ripening fruit and, in some cases, have been tested for function. Pectin-methyl-esterase (PME) shows activity throughout fruit development and may increase accessibility of PG to its pectin substrate. Antisense repression of a tomato fruit PME resulted in decreased pectin degradation, but consistent with PG repression, it did not alter additional ripening characteristics, including softening (145). Two tomato β-glucanases (hemicellulases) that show differential expression in ripening fruit and are designated CEL1 and CEL2 were repressed via antisense without observable impact on fruit ripening and softening (20, 79). It is interesting to note that CEL1 repression inhibited pedicel abscission (79), whereas CEL2 repression inhibited fruit abscission (20). Expression of these genes during fruit ripening is suggestive of a function in fruit cell wall metabolism; however, the lack of observable ripening phenotypes in the available transgenic lines indicates that the roles they play are functionally redundant and/or components of a more complicated metabolic process. Repression of additional ripening-related cell wall metabolism enzymes, such as members of the β-galactosidase gene family (132), in addition to pyramiding of multiple cell wall metabolism antisense genes through crosses of available transgenic lines, may shed additional light on the genetic regulation of this complicated metabolic process.

Some of the most definitive results concerning ripening-related texture modification have emerged from analysis of tomato expansins. Expansins are cell wall proteins associated with numerous tissues and developmental stages undergoing (often rapid) changes in size and shape (for review, see 29). Tomato and strawberry expansin genes upregulated during fruit ripening have been isolated (26, 124), and repression of a fruit ripening-specific expansin (Exp1) in tomato resulted in reduced softening. Overexpression of Exp1 resulted in enhanced softening, including softening of mature green fruit owing to ectopic expression via the CaMV35s promoter (21). These results suggest that, although the activity of fruit cell wall hydrolases may well be important for in vivo textural modifications associated with ripening, fruit expansins contribute significantly and definitively to softening effects. It is important to keep in mind that methods for measuring softening do not reflect all of the nuances associated with this process and are approximate at best. Nevertheless, the transgenic lines described in this section, when combined with sexual hybridization and assessed via more comprehensive genomics approaches, represent a powerful reservoir of genetic tools that will shed considerable insight into ripening associated textural changes.

Light Signal Transduction and Fruit Carotenoid Accumulation

To date, molecular regulation of the role of light in fruit ripening has been studied most thoroughly in tomato, and available evidence suggests that light has its greatest impact on pigmentation, with apparently little effect on additional ripening phenomena (4).

The green to red color transition typical of ripening tomato fruit is largely due to the developmental transition of chloroplasts to chromoplasts; as photosynthetic membranes are degraded, chlorophyll is metabolized, and carotenoids, including β-carotene and lycopene, accumulate (54). The regulation of carotenoid biosynthesis during ripening is due, at least in part, to ripening-related and ethylene-inducible gene expression in both tomato (45, 52, 86, 88, 123) and melon (63). Although numerous tomato mutants that are altered in pigment accumulation have been reported (117, 118), few that result in net carotenoid accumulation have been identified. Nevertheless, a combination of elegant biochemical and genetic approaches has resulted in the isolation of a key gene, *lycopene-ε-cyclase*, responsible for the relative levels of β-carotene and lycopene in tomato fruit (122). Discovery of this gene also led to the elucidation of the molecular basis of the tomato β (*Beta*) and *cr* (*crimson*, often referred to as *og*) mutants, which result in fruit that has shifted toward accumulation of either β-carotene or lycopene, depending on enhanced or reduced expression of the cyclase gene, respectively. Genetic analysis of pepper suggests that numerous loci responsible for tomato fruit pigmentation may be conserved in pepper (144) and thus might be conserved among a wide range of species.

A particularly interesting mutation from the standpoint of fruit carotenoid accumulation is the recessive *high pigment-1* (*hp-1*) mutation. In contrast to most tomato carotenoid mutations, *hp-1* results in increased accumulation of both lycopene and β-carotene during fruit development. It is also responsible for heightened levels of chlorophyll in leaves and green fruit at all stages of development in lines homozygous for the mutant allele (152). A mutation similar in phenotype to *hp-1*, named *hp-2*, was described by Soressi (133) and is non-allelic with *hp-1* (151).

Key to understanding the basis of the *hp-1* mutation is the fact that tomato seedlings homozygous for the *hp-1* allele demonstrate an exaggerated photomorphogenic de-etiolation response (112). In short, *hp-1/hp-1* seedlings are characterized by inhibition of hypocotyl elongation and intense anthocyanin pigmentation, relative to seedlings of normal NILs, with maximal phenotypic expression in response to red light (111). Tomato seedling de-etiolation is a phytochrome (red light) response, which can be enhanced by blue light, suggesting that hp-1 may influence phytochrome and blue light receptor action and/or signaling. Overexpression of oat phytochrome A in tomato resulted in phenotypes similar to those observed in the hp-1 mutant, including increased carotenoid accumulation in ripe fruit (18). Furthermore, Peters et al (111) showed that the hp-1 phenotype was repressed when associated with the phytochrome deficient *aurea* mutant, confirming the role of hp-1 in phytochrome responses. Quantification of phytochrome levels in normal and hp-$1/hp$-1 seedlings indicates that the amplified phytochrome responses observed in the hp-1 mutant occur within the context of normal phytochrome concentration and stability, suggesting that the normal HP-1 gene product acts as a negative regulator of phytochrome signal transduction in tomato (1, 111).

Arabidopsis is the most widely studied plant system for analysis of the genetic basis of light signal transduction, and a number of mutations have been identified and hypothesized to represent genes that function as negative regulators of light signaling (24, 25, 115). Such genes may be similar in function to the normal Hp-1 allele. Indeed, researchers recently found that the tomato hp-2 mutation represents a tomato homologue of *Arabidopsis DE-ETIOLATED1* (100, 110). This result confirms the role of general light signaling in fruit pigment accumulation and suggests that a greater understanding of these processes may lead to successful efforts in fruit quality and nutrient modification. Efforts toward the isolation of the hp-1 locus via a positional cloning strategy are ongoing (160).

Regulation of Gene Expression

The isolation of fruit ripening–related genes has resulted not only in tools for studying the direct effects of specific gene products on ripening but also in opportunities to isolate and study gene regulatory elements that may illuminate regulatory mechanisms. Ripening-related genes have been isolated from a number of species in addition to tomato (53, 89, 103, 137); however, most attempts to study ripening gene regulatory sequences have focused on tomato genes. Genes responding to ethylene and non-ethylene signals have been identified (33, 130). Sequences directing fruit, and in some cases ripening-specific, expression have been localized via promoter-reporter constructs for the PG (99, 104), E8 (31), 2A11 (150), and ACO1 (16) genes, whereas the ripening-induced (but not fruit-specific) E4 (98) gene revealed the presence of regulatory sequences likely associated with more general ethylene regulatory mechanisms that are shared with additional fruit-specific and ripening-related genes (15, 150). The fact that both ethylene and additional developmental factors regulate several of these genes enhanced the possibility that the relationship between both signaling systems could be examined at the molecular level. Indeed, *cis*-elements that impact fruit specificity, in addition to those that mediate ripening-associated developmental and ethylene-mediated regulation, could be separated. Furthermore, *trans*-factors that bind to corresponding sequences were identified (31, 99, 150). Genes corresponding to the factors that result in the observed promoter binding activities remain unknown, thus limiting knowledge that is relative to specific genetic regulatory mechanisms that controll expression of fruit-specific and ripening-related genes. However, as many of the ripening-related genes that have undergone promoter analysis are impacted by the *rin* and *nor* mutations, the recent cloning of these putative transcription factors will provide opportunities to test for specific interactions of the RIN and NOR proteins with functionally characterized regulatory sequences.

Tomato has also been utilized as a heterologous system to test the function of putative promoter sequences that are isolated from fruit species, such as apple (10) and pepper (76), which are not as easily transformed and (in the case of apple) require a much longer time to reach maturity. Apple ACO and PG promoter-reporter constructs demonstrated upregulation during ripening, confirming that a complement of sufficient regulatory sequences to control expression during ripening had been recovered (10). Perhaps more significant is the fact that these results demonstrated that common regulatory mechanisms are conserved at the molecular level among widely different species that exhibit climacteric ripening of fleshy fruit. Equally significant, if not more intriguing, was the observation by Kuntz et al (76) that promoters from two ripening-induced genes (capsanthin/capsorubin synthase and fibrillin) from non-climacteric pepper were induced in transgenic tomato fruit in parallel with ripening. Expression of both genes was enhanced by application of ethylene, suggesting that climacteric and non-climacteric ripening may share common molecular underpinnings.

OPPORTUNITIES IN FRUIT DEVELOPMENT RESEARCH

The molecular investigations into fruit development and ripening reviewed here, in addition to the advent of recent technologies facilitating functional and comparative genomics (2, 75, 78), have put the field in a position to make significant advances in coming years. The last decade has seen the unraveling of many of the mysteries regarding ethylene biosynthesis and perception, in addition to significant inroads into the control of cell wall metabolism and textural changes associated with fruit ripening. Major genes regulating fruit carotenoid biosynthesis have been discovered, and tantalizing observations regarding the role of light in fruit ripening may lead to opportunities for modification of fruit quality and nutrient content. A number of pioneering attempts in this regard have been undertaken (47, 68, 121), though greater impact is likely to result following a more complete understanding of the regulatory processes influencing such factors (47, 68). Regulation and synergy of the multiple processes contributing to the ripe phenomena remain unknown and may be addressed in coming years with genomic and proteomic approaches. Finally, insights into early regulation of fruit development, and common regulatory mechanisms among climacteric and non-climacteric ripening, represent avenues through which future research activities will follow for the dissection of common regulatory control systems, in addition to identification of discrete molecular mechanisms specific to unique fruit development traits that differentiate fruiting species.

ACKNOWLEDGMENTS

Special thanks to Ruth White who helped in many of the technical aspects associated with preparation of this manuscript. Thanks to Drs. Harry Klee, David Clark, and Steve Tanksley for providing figures and Drs. Cornelius Barry and Julia Vrebalov for useful discussion and suggestions. We are grateful to the following that have supported work on fruit development, ripening, and ethylene response in the Giovannoni Laboratory: USDA-NRI (92-37300-7653, 95-37300-1575, 00-35300-9356), NSF (IBN-9604115, DBI-9872617), Zeneca Agrochemicals, Lipton Foods, Seminis Seeds, Texas Agricultural Experiment Station, and USDA-ARS. This review is dedicated to the memory of the late Dr. Kevin Alpert whose energy and enthusiasm are continuing inspirations.

Visit the Annual Reviews home page at www.AnnualReviews.org

LITERATURE CITED

1. Adamse P, Peters JL, Jaspers PAPM, van Tuinen A, Koornneef M, Kendrick RE. 1989. Photocontrol of anthocyanin synthesis in tomato seedlings: a genetic approach. *Photochem. Photobiol.* 50:107–11
2. Aharoni A, Keizer LCP, Bouwmeester HJ, Sun Z, Alvarez HM, et al. 2000. Identification of the SAAT gene involved in strawberry flavor biogenesis by use of DNA microarrays. *Plant Cell* 12:647–61
3. Akhtar MS, Goldschmidt EE, John I, Rodoni S, Matile P, Grierson D. 1999. Altered patterns of senescence and ripening in gf, a stay-green mutant of tomato (*Lycopersicon esculentum* Mill.). *J. Exp. Bot.* 50:1115–22
4. Alba R, Cordonnier-Pratt MM, Pratt LH. 2000. Fruit-localized phytochromes regulate lycopene accumulation independently of ethylene production in tomato. *Plant Physiol.* 123:363–70
5. Alonso JM, Chamaro J, Granell A. 1995. Evidence for the involvement of ethylene in the expression of specific RNAs during maturation of the orange, a non-climacteric fruit. *Plant Mol. Biol.* 29:385–90
6. Alpert KB, Grandillo S, Tanksley SD. 1995.

Fw2.2: A major QTL controlling fruit weight is common to both red- and green-fruited tomato species. *Theor. Appl. Genet.* 91:994–1000
7. Alpert KB, Tanksley SD. 1996. High-resolution mapping and isolation of a yeast artificial chromosome contig containing fw2.2: a major fruit weight quantitative trait locus in tomato. *Proc. Natl. Acad. Sci. USA* 93:15503–7
8. Alvarez-Buylla ER, Pelaz S, Liljegren SJ, Gold SE, Burgeff C, et al. 2000. An ancestral MADS-box gene duplication occurred before the divergence of plants and animals. *Proc. Natl. Acad. Sci. USA* 97:5328–33
9. Arumuganathan K, Earle E. 1991. Nuclear DNA content of some important plant species. *Plant Mol. Biol. Rep.* 9:208–18
10. Atkinson RG, Bolitho KM, Wright MA, Iturriagagoitia BT, Reid SJ, Ross GS. 1998. Apple ACC-oxidase and polygalacturonase: ripening-specific gene expression and promoter analysis in transgenic tomato. *Plant Mol. Biol.* 38:449–60
11. Azpiroz LR, Feldman KA. 1997. T-DNA

insertion mutagenesis in Arabidopsis: going back and forth. *Trends Genet.* 13:152–56

12. Barry CS, Llop-Tous I, Grierson D. 2000. The regulation of 1-aminocyclopropane-1-carboxylic acid synthase gene expression during the transition from system-1 to system-2 ethylene synthesis in tomato. *Plant Physiol.* 123:979–86

13. Bassett CL, Artlip TS. 1999. Isolation of an ETR1 ethylene receptor homologue from peach (*Prunus persica* (L.) Batsch). *HortScience* 34:542

14. Bishop GJ, Harrison K, Jones JDG. 1996. The tomato Dwarf gene isolated by heterologous transposon tagging encodes the first member of a new cytochrome P450 family. *Plant Cell* 8:959–69

15. Blume B, Barry CS, Hamilton AJ, Bouzayen M, Grierson D. 1997. Identification of transposon-like elements in non-coding regions of tomato ACC oxidase genes. *Mol. Gen. Genet.* 254:297–303

16. Blume B, Grierson D. 1997. Expression of ACC oxidase promoter-GUS fusions in tomato and *Nicotiana plumbaginifolia* regulated by developmental and environmental stimuli. *Plant J.* 12:731–46

17. Bonnema G, Hontelez J, Verkerk R, Zhang YQ, Van Daelen R, et al. 1996. An improved method of partially digesting plant megabase DNA suitable for YAC cloning: application to the construction of a 5.5 genome equivalent YAC library of tomato. *Plant J.* 9:125–33

18. Boylan MT, Quail PH. 1989. Oat phytochrome is biologically active in transgenic tomatoes. *Plant Cell* 1:765–73

19. Browleader MD, Jackson P, Mobasheri A, Pantelides AT, Sumar S, et al. 1999. Molecular aspects of cell wall modifications during fruit ripening. *Crit. Rev. Food Sci. Nutr.* 39:149–64

20. Brummell DA, Hall BD, Bennett AB. 2000. Antisense suppression of tomato endo-1,4-beta-glucanase Cel2 mRNA accumulation increases the force required to break fruit abscission zones but does not affect fruit softening. *Plant Mol. Biol.* 40:615–22

21. Brummell DA, Harpster MH, Civello PM, Palys JM, Bennett AB, Dunsmuir P. 1999. Modification of expansin protein abundance in tomato fruit alters softening and cell wall polymer metabolism during ripening. *Plant Cell* 11:2203–16

22. Bucheli P, Voirol E, DeLaTorre R, Lopez J, Rytz A, et al. 1999. Definition of volatile markers for flavor of tomato (*Lycopersicon esculentum* Mill.) as tools in selection and breeding. *J. Agric. Food Chem.* 47:659–64

23. Budiman MA, Mao L, Wood TC, Wing RA. 2000. A deep-coverage tomato BAC library and prospects toward development of an STC framework for genome sequencing. *Genome Res.* 10:129–36

24. Chamovitz DA, Deng XW. 1996. Light signaling in plants. *Crit. Rev. Plant Sci.* 15:455–78

25. Chory J. 1993. Out of darkness: mutants reveal pathways controlling light-regulated development in plants. *Trends Genet.* 9:167–72

26. Civello PM, Powell ALT, Sabehat A, Bennett AB. 1999. An expansin gene expressed in ripening strawberry fruit. *Plant Physiol.* 121:1273–79

27. Clough SJ, Bent AF. 1998. Floral dip: a simplified method for Agrobacterium-mediated transformation of *Arabidopsis thaliana*. *Plant J.* 16:735–43

28. Cohen JD. 1996. In vitro tomato fruit cultures demonstrate a role for indole-3-acetic acid in regulating fruit ripening. *J. Am. Soc. Hortic. Sci.* 121:520–24

29. Cosgrove DJ. 2000. New genes and new biological roles for expansins. *Curr. Opin. Plant Biol.* 3:73–78

30. Davies C, Robinson SP. 1996. Sugar accumulation in grape berries: cloning of two putative vacuolar invertase cDNAs and their expression in grapevine tissues. *Plant Physiol.* 111:275–83

31. Deikman J, Kline R, Fischer RL. 1992.

Organization of ripening and ethylene regulatory regions in a fruit-specific promoter from tomato (*Lycopersicon esculentum*). *Plant Physiol.* 100:2013–17

32. Deikman J, Xu R, Kneissl ML, Ciardi JA, Kim KN, Pelah D. 1998. Separation of *cis* elements responsive to ethylene, fruit development, and ripening in the 5′-flanking region of the ripening-related E8 gene. *Plant Mol. Biol.* 37:1001–11

33. DellaPenna D, Lincoln JE, Fischer RL, Bennett AB. 1989. Transcriptional analysis of polygalacturonase and other ripening associated genes in Rutgers, *rin, nor*, and *Nr* tomato fruit. *Plant Physiol.* 90:1372–77

34. Doganlar S, Tanksley SD, Mutschler MA. 2000. Identification and molecular mapping of loci controlling fruit ripening time in tomato. *Theor. Appl. Genet.* 100:249–55

35. Ecker JR. 1995. The ethylene signal transduction pathway in plants. *Science* 268:667–75

36. Eshed Y, Zamir D. 1994. A genomic library of *Lycopersicon pennellii* in *L. esculentum*: a tool for fine mapping of genes. *Euphytica* 79:175–79

37. Ferrandiz C, Liljegren SJ, Yanofsky MF. 2000. Negative regulation of the SHATTERPROOF genes by FRUITFULL during Arabidopsis fruit development. *Science* 289:436–38

38. Ferrandiz C, Pelaz S, Yanofsky MF. 1999. Control of carpel and fruit development in Arabidopsis. *Annu. Rev. Biochem.* 99:321–54

39. Ficcadenti N, Sestili S, Pandolfini T, Cirillo C, Rotino GL, Spena A. 1999. Genetic engineering of parthenocarpic fruit development in tomato. *Mol. Breed.* 5:463–70

40. Filipecki MK, Sommer H, Malepszy S. 1997. The MADS-box gene CUS1 is expressed during cucumber somatic embryogenesis. *Plant Sci.* 125:63–74

41. Fillatti J, Kiser J, Rose B, Comai L. 1987. Efficient transformation of tomato and the introduction and expression of a gene for herbicide tolerance. In *Tomato Biotechnology*, ed. D Nevins, R Jones, pp. 199–210. New York: Liss

42. Fluhr R, Mattoo AK. 1996. Ethylene: biosynthesis and perception. *Crit. Rev. Plant Sci.* 15:479–523

43. Folkertsma RT, Spassova MI, Prins M, Stevens MR, Hille J, Goldbach RW. 1999. Construction of a bacterial artificial chromosome (BAC) library of *Lycopersicon esculentum* cv. Stevens and its application to physically map the Sw-5 locus. *Mol. Breed.* 5:197–207

44. Frary A, Nesbitt TC, Frary A, Grandillo S, van der Knaap E, et al. 2000. fw2.2: a quantitative trait locus key to the evolution of tomato fruit size. *Science* 289:85–88

45. Fray RG, Grierson D. 1993. Identification and genetic analysis of normal and mutant phytoene synthase genes of tomato by sequencing, complementation, and cosuppression. *Plant Mol. Biol.* 22:589–602

46. Fray RG, Grierson D. 1993. Molecular genetics of tomato fruit ripening. *Trends Genet.* 9:438–43

47. Fray RG, Wallace A, Fraser PD, Valero D, Hedden P, et al. 1995. Constitutive expression of a fruit phytoene synthase gene in transgenic tomatoes causes dwarfism by redirecting metabolites from the gibberellin pathway. *Plant J.* 8:693–701

48. Giovannoni JJ. 1993. Molecular biology of fruit development and ripening. *Methods Plant Mol. Biol.* 10:253–87

49. Giovannoni JJ, DellaPenna D, Bennett AB, Fischer RL. 1989. Expression of a chimeric polygalacturonase gene in transgenic rin (ripening inhibitor) tomato fruit results in polyuronide degradation but not fruit softening. *Plant Cell* 1:53–63

50. Giovannoni JJ, DellaPenna D, Bennett A, Fischer R. 1991. Polygalacturonase and tomato fruit ripening. *Hortic. Rev.* 13:67–103

51. Grandillo S, Ku HM, Tanksley SD. 1999. Identifying the loci responsible for natural variation in fruit size and shape in tomato. *Theor. Appl. Genet.* 99:978–87

52. Gray JE, Picton S, Giovannoni JJ, Grierson D. 1994. The use of transgenic and naturally occurring mutants to understand and manipulate tomato fruit ripening. *Plant Cell Environ.* 17:557–71

53. Gray JE, Picton S, Shabbeer J, Schuch W, Grierson D. 1992. Molecular biology of fruit ripening and its manipulation with antisense genes. *Plant Mol. Biol.* 19:69–87

54. Grierson D, Purton M, Knapp J, Bathgate B. 1987. Tomato ripening mutants. *Developmental Mutants in Higher Plants*, ed. H Thomas, D Grierson, pp. 73–94. London: Cambridge Univ. Press

55. Gu Q, Ferrandiz C, Yanofsky MF, Martienssen R. 1998. The fruitfull mads-box gene mediates cell differentiation during Arabidopsis fruit development. *Development* 125:1509–17

56. Hall AE, Chen QG, Findell JL, Schaller GE, Bleecker AB. 1999. The relationship between ethylene binding and dominant insensitivity conferred by mutant forms of the ETR1 ethylene receptor. *Plant Physiol.* 121:291–99

57. Hamilton A, Lycett G, Grierson D. 1990. Antisense gene that inhibits synthesis of the hormone ethylene in transgenic plants. *Nature* 346:284–87

58. Hamilton CM, Frary A, Xu Y, Tanksley SD, Zhang HB. 1999. Construction of tomato genomic DNA libraries in a binary-BAC (BIBAC) vector. *Plant J.* 18:223–29

59. Hua J, Meyerowitz EM. 1998. Ethylene responses are negatively regulated by a receptor gene family in *Arabidopsis thaliana*. *Cell* 94:261–71

60. Ishida BK, Jenkins SM, Say B. 1998. Induction of AGAMOUS gene expression plays a key role in ripening of tomato sepals in vitro. *Plant Mol. Biol.* 36:733–39

61. Jenkins J, Mackinney G. 1955. Carotenoids of the apricot tomato and its hybrids with yellow and tangerine. *Genetics* 40:715–20

62. Johnson PR, Ecker JR. 1998. The ethylene gas signal transduction pathway: a molecular perspective. *Annu. Rev. Genet.* 32:227–54

63. Karvouni Z, John I, Taylor JE, Watson CF, Turner AJ, Grierson D. 1995. Isolation and characterisation of a melon cDNA clone encoding phytoene synthase. *Plant Mol. Biol.* 27:1153–62

64. Kerr E. 1981. Linkage studies of *green ripe* and *never ripe*. *Rep. Tomato Genet. Co-op.* 31:7

65. Kerr E. 1982. *Never ripe-2* (*Nr-2*) a slow ripening mutant resembling *Nr* and *Gr*. *Rep. Tomato Genet. Co-op.* 32:33

66. Kieber JJ. 1997. The ethylene response pathway in Arabidopsis. *Annu. Rev. Plant Physiol. Plant Mol. Biol.* 48:277–96

67. Kita M, Hisada S, Endo IT, Omura M, Moriguchi T. 2000. Changes in the levels of mRNAs for putative cell growth-related genes in the albedo and flavedo during citrus fruit development. *Plant Cell Rep.* 19:582–87

68. Klann EM, Hall B, Bennett AB. 1996. Antisense acid invertase (TIV1) gene alters soluble sugar composition and size in transgenic tomato fruit. *Plant Physiol.* 112:1321–30

69. Klee HJ, Hayford MB, Kretzmer KA, Barry GF, Kishore GM. 1991. Control of ethylene synthesis by expression of a bacterial enzyme in transgenic tomato plants. *Plant Cell* 3:1187–93

70. Knapp S, Larondelle Y, Rossberg M, Furtek D, Klaus T. 1994. Transgenic tomato lines containing Ds elements at defined genomic positions as tools for targeted transposon tagging. *Mol. Gen. Genet.* 243:666–73

71. Koornneef M, Alonso BC, Peeters AJM. 1997. Genetic approaches in plant physiology. *New Phytol.* 137:1–8

72. Kopeliovitch E, Rabinowitch HD, Mizrahi Y, Kedar N. 1981. Mode of inheritance of alcobaca, a tomato fruit ripening mutant. *Euphytica* 30:223–25

73. Kramer M, Sanders R, Sheehy R, Melis M,

Kuehn M, Hiatt W. 1990. Field evaluation of tomatoes with reduced polygalacturonase by antisense RNA. In *Horticultural Biotechnology*, ed. A Bennett, S O'Neill, pp. 347–55. New York: Liss

74. Ku HM, Doganlar S, Chen KY, Tanksley SD. 1999. The genetic basis of pear-shaped tomato fruit. *Theor. Appl. Genet.* 99:844–50

75. Ku HM, Vision T, Liu J, Tanksley SD. 2000. Comparing sequenced segments of the tomato and Arabidopsis genomes: large-scale duplication followed by selective gene loss creates a network of synteny. *Proc. Natl. Acad. Sci. USA* 97:9121–26

76. Kuntz M, Chen HC, Simkin AJ, Romer S, Shipton CA, et al. 1998. Upregulation of two ripening-related genes from a non-climacteric plant (pepper) in a transgenic climacteric plant (tomato). *Plant J.* 13:351–61

77. Lanahan MB, Yen HC, Giovannoni JJ, Klee HJ. 1994. The *Never Ripe* mutation blocks ethylene perception in tomato. *Plant Cell* 6:521–30

78. Lander ES, Weinberg RA. 2000. Genomics: journey to the center of biology. *Science* 287:1777–82

79. Lashbrook CC, Giovannoni JJ, Hall BD, Fischer RL, Bennett AB. 1998. Transgenic analysis of tomato endo-beta-1,4-glucanase gene function. Role of cel1 in floral abscission. *Plant J.* 13:303–10

80. Lashbrook CC, Tieman DM, Klee HJ. 1998. Differential regulation of the tomato ETR gene family throughout plant development. *Plant J.* 15:243–52

81. Lelievre JM, Latche A, Jones B, Bouzayen M, Pech JC. 1997. Ethylene and fruit ripening. *Physiol. Plant.* 101:727–39

82. Liljegren SJ, Ditta GS, Eshed Y, Savidge B, Bowman JL, Yanofsky MF. 2000. SHATTERPROOF MADS-box genes control seed dispersal in Arabidopsis. *Nature* 404:766–70

83. Liljegren S, Ferrandiz C, Alvarez-Buylla E, Pelaz S, Yanofsky M. 1998. Arabidopsis MADS-box genes involved in fruit dehiscence. *Flower. Newsl.* 25:9–19

84. Lincoln JE, Campbell AD, Oetiker J, Rottmann WH, Oeller PW, et al. 1993. LE-ACS4, a fruit ripening and wound-induced 1-aminocyclopropane-1-carboxylate synthase gene of tomato (*Lycopersicon esculentum*): expression in *Escherichia coli* structural characterization, expression characteristics, and phylogenetic analysis. *J. Biol. Chem.* 268:19422–30

85. Lincoln JE, Cordes S, Read E, Fischer RL. 1987. Regulation of gene expression by ethylene during *Lycopersicon esculentum* (tomato) fruit development. *Proc. Natl. Acad. Sci. USA* 84:2793–97

86. Lois LM, Rodriguez CM, Gallego F, Campos N, Boronat A. 2000. Carotenoid biosynthesis during tomato fruit development: regulatory role of 1-deoxy-D-xylulose 5-phosphate synthase. *Plant J.* 22:503–13

87. Lukowitz W, Gillmor CS, Scheible WR. 2000. Positional cloning in Arabidopsis. Why it feels good to have a Genome Initiative working for you. *Plant Physiol.* 123:795–805

88. Mann V, Pecker I, Hirschberg J. 1994. Cloning and characterization of the gene for phytoene desaturase (Pds) from tomato (*Lycopersicon esculentum*). *Plant Mol. Biol.* 24:429–34

89. Manning K. 1998. Isolation of a set of ripening-related genes from strawberry: their identification and possible relationship to fruit quality traits. *Planta* 205:622–31

90. Martienssen RA. 1998. Functional genomics: probing plant gene function and expression with transposons. *Proc. Natl. Acad. Sci. USA* 95:2021–26

91. Martin GB, Ganal MW, Tanksley SD. 1992. Construction of a yeast artificial chromosome library of tomato and identification of cloned segments linked to two disease resistance loci. *Mol. Gen. Genet.* 233:25–32

92. Martineau B, Houck CM, Sheehy RE, Hiatt WR. 1994. Fruit-specific expression of the *A. tumefaciens* isopentenyl transferase gene in tomato: effects on fruit ripening and defense-related gene expression in leaves. *Plant J.* 5:11–19

93. Mathews H, Wagoner W, Kellogg J, Bestwick R. 1995. Genetic transformation of strawberry: stable integration of a gene to control biosynthesis of ethylene. *In Vitro Cell. Dev. Biol. Plant* 31:36–43

94. Maunder M, Holdsworth M, Slater A, Knapp J, Bird C, et al. 1987. Ethylene stimulates the accumulation of ripening-related mRNAs in tomatoes. *Plant Cell Environ.* 10:177–84

95. Mazzucato A, Taddei AR, Soressi GP. 1998. The parthenocarpic fruit (pat) mutant of tomato (*Lycopersicon esculentum* Mill.) sets seedless fruits and has aberrant anther and ovule development. *Development* 125:107–14

96. Meissner R, Chague V, Zhu Q, Emmanuel E, Elkind Y, Levy AA. 2000. A high throughput system for transposon tagging and promoter trapping in tomato. *Plant J.* 22:265–74

97. Meyerowitz EM. 1998. Genetic and molecular mechanisms of pattern formation in Arabidopsis flower development. *J. Plant Res.* 111:233–42

98. Montgomery J, Goldman S, Deikman J, Margossian L, Fischer RL. 1993. Identification of an ethylene-responsive region in the promoter of a fruit ripening gene. *Proc. Natl. Acad. Sci. USA* 90:5939–43

99. Montgomery J, Pollard V, Deikman J, Fischer RL. 1993. Positive and negative regulatory regions control the spatial distribution of polygalacturonase transcription in tomato fruit pericarp. *Plant Cell* 5:1049–62

100. Mustilli AC, Fenzi F, Ciliento R, Alfano F, Bowler C. 1999. Phenotype of the tomato high pigment-2 mutant is caused by a mutation in the tomato homolog of DEETIOLATED1. *Plant Cell* 11:145–57

101. Nakata K, Tanaka H, Ito T, Sasagawa N, Chung IK, et al. 1993. Construction and some characterization of a yeast artificial chromosome library from DNA of a tomato line having four disease resistance traits. *Biosci. Biotechnol. Biochem.* 57:1790–92

102. Nakatsuka A, Murachi S, Okunishi H, Shiomi S, Nakano R, et al. 1998. Differential expression and internal feedback regulation of 1-aminocyclopropane-1-caboxylate synthase, of 1-aminocyclopropane-1-caboxylate oxidase, and ethylene receptor genes in tomato during development and ripening. *Plant Physiol.* 118:1295–305

103. Nam YW, Tichit L, Leperlier M, Cuerq B, Marty I, Lelievre JM. 1999. Isolation and characterization of mRNAs differentially expressed during ripening of wild strawberry (*Fragaria vesca* L.) fruits. *Plant Mol. Biol.* 39:629–36

104. Nicholass FJ, Smith Christopher JS, Schuch W, Bird CR, Grierson D. 1995. High levels of ripening-specific reported gene expression directed by tomato fruit polygalacturonase gene-flanking regions. *Plant Mol. Biol.* 28:423–35

105. Oeller PW, Wong LM, Taylor LP, Pike DA, Theologis A. 1991. Reversible inhibition of tomato fruit senescence by antisense 1-aminocyclopropane-1-carboxylate. synthase. *Science* 254:427–39

106. O'Neill SD. 1997. Pollination regulation of flower development. *Annu. Rev. Plant Physiol. Plant Mol. Biol.* 48:547–74

107. Osborne B, Corr C, Prince J, Hehl R, Tanksley S, et al. 1991. *Ac* transposition from a T-DNA can generate linked and unlinked clusters of insertions in the tomato genome. *Genetics* 129:833–44

108. Parinov S, Sundaresan V. 2000. Functional genomics in Arabidopsis: Large-scale insertional mutagenesis complements the genome sequencing project. *Curr. Opin. Biotechnol.* 11:157–61

109. Payton S, Fray RG, Brown S, Grierson D. 1996. Ethylene receptor expression is regulated during fruit ripening, flower senescence and abscission. *Plant Mol. Biol.* 31:1227–31

110. Pepper A, Delaney T, Washburn T, Poole D, Chory J. 1994. DET1, a negative regulator of light-mediated development and gene expression in Arabidopsis, encodes a novel nuclear-localized protein. *Cell* 78:109–16

111. Peters JL, Schreuder MEL, Verduin SJW, Kendrick RE. 1992. Physiological characterization of a high-pigment mutant of tomato. *Photochem. Photobiol.* 56:75–82

112. Peters JL, van Tuinen A, Adamse P, Kendrick RE, Koornneef M. 1989. High pigment mutants of tomato exhibit high sensitivity for phytochrome action. *J. Plant Physiol.* 134:661–66

113. Picton S, Barton SL, Bouzayen M, Hamilton AJ, Grierson D. 1993. Altered fruit ripening and leaf senescence in tomatoes expressing an antisense ethylene-forming enzyme transgene. *Plant J.* 3:469–81

114. Pnueli L, Hareven D, Rounsley SD, Yanofsky MF, Lifschitz E. 1994. Isolation of the tomato AGAMOUS gene TAG1 and analysis of its homeotic role in transgenic plants. *Plant Cell* 6:163–73

115. Quail PH, Boylan MT, Short TW, Xu Y, Wagner D. 1995. Phytochrome: photosensory perception and signal transduction. *Science* 268:675–80

116. Rhodes MJC. 1980. The maturation and ripening of fruits. In *Senescence in Plants*, ed. KV Thimann, pp. 157–205. Boca Raton, FL: CRC Press

117. Rick CM. 1956. New mutants. *Rep. Tomato Genet. Coop.* 6:22–23

118. Rick CM. 1980. Tomato linkage survey. *Rep. Tomato Genet. Coop.* 30:2–17

119. Rick CM, Butler L. 1956. Cytogenetics of the tomato. *Adv. Genet.* 8:267–382

120. Riechmann JL, Krizek BA, Meyerowitz EM. 1996. Dimerization specificity of Arabidopsis MADS domain homeotic proteins APETALA1, APETALA3, PISTILLATA, and AGAMOUS. *Proc. Natl. Acad. Sci. USA* 93:4793–98

121. Romer S, Fraser PD, Kiano JW, Shipton CA, Misawa N, et al. 2000. Elevation of the provitamin A content of transgenic tomato plants. *Nat. Biotechnol.* 18:666–69

122. Ronen G, Carmel GL, Zamir D, Hirschberg J. 2000. An alternative pathway to beta-carotene formation in plant chromoplasts discovered by map-based cloning of Beta and old-gold color mutations in tomato. *Proc. Natl. Acad. Sci. USA* 97:11102–7

123. Ronen G, Cohen M, Zamir D, Hirschberg J. 1999. Regulation of carotenoid biosynthesis during tomato fruit development: Expression of the gene for lycopene epsilon-cyclase is down-regulated during ripening and is elevated in the mutant Delta. *Plant J.* 17:341–51

124. Rose JKC, Lee HH, Bennett AB. 1997. Expression of a divergent expansin gene is fruit-specific and ripening-regulated. *Proc. Natl. Acad. Sci. USA* 94:5955–60

125. Rosin FM, Hannapel D. 1999. RNA localization of a strawberry MADS-box gene (SAG1) involved in fruit development. *HortScience* 34:457

126. Sato NK, Yuhashi KI, Higashi K, Hosoya K, Kubota M, Ezura H. 1999. Stage- and tissue-specific expression of ethylene receptor homolog genes during fruit development in muskmelon. *Plant Physiol.* 120:321–29

127. Schaller GE, Bleecker AB. 1995. Ethylene-binding sites generated in yeast expressing the Arabidopsis ETR1 gene. *Science* 270:1809–11

128. Seymour GB, Taylor JE, Tucker GA, eds. 1993. *Biochemistry of Fruit Ripening*. London: Chapman & Hall. 442 pp.

129. Sheehy R, Kramer M, Hiatt W. 1988. Reduction of polygalacturonase activity in tomato fruit by antisense RNA. *Proc. Natl. Acad. Sci. USA* 85:8805–9

130. Sitrit Y, Bennett AB. 1998. Regulation of tomato fruit polygalacturonase mRNA accumulation by ethylene: a reexamination. *Plant Physiol.* 116:1145–50

131. Smith C, Watson C, Ray J, Bird C, Morris P, et al. 1988. Antisense RNA inhibition of polygalacturonase gene expression in transgenic tomatoes. *Nature* 334:724–26

132. Smith DL, Gross KC. 2000. A family of at least seven beta-galactosidase genes is expressed during tomato fruit development. *Plant Physiol.* 123:1173–83

133. Soressi GP. 1975. New spontaneous or chemically-induced fruit ripening tomato mutants. *Tomato Genet. Coop. Rep.* 25:21–22

134. Stepanova AN, Ecker JR. 2000. Ethylene signaling: from mutants to molecules. *Curr. Opin. Plant Biol.* 3:353–60

135. Sung SK, An G. 1997. Molecular cloning and characterization of a MADS-Box cDNA clone of the Fuji apple. *Plant Cell Physiol.* 38:484–89

136. Sung SK, Yu GH, Nam J, Jeong DH, An G. 2000. Developmentally regulated expression of two MADS-box genes, MdMADS3 and MdMADS4, in the morphogenesis of flower buds and fruits in apple. *Planta* 210:519–28

137. Suyama T, Yamada K, Mori H, Takeno K, Yamaki S. 1999. Cloning cDNAs for genes preferentially expressed during fruit growth in cucumber. *J. Am. Soc. Hortic. Sci.* 124:136–39

138. Tanksley SD, Ganal MW, Prince JP, de Vicente MC, Bonierbale MW, et al. 1992. High density molecular linkage maps of the tomato and potato genomes. *Genetics* 132:1141–60

139. Tattersall DB, Van Heeswijck R, Hoj PB. 1997. Identification and characterization of a fruit-specific, thaumatin-like protein that accumulates at very high levels in conjunction with the onset of sugar accumulation and berry softening in grapes. *Plant Physiol.* 114:759–69

140. Tesniere C, Verries C. 2000. Molecular cloning and expression of cDNAs encoding alcohol dehydrogenases from *Vitis vinifera* L. during berry development. *Plant Sci.* 157:77–88

141. Theissen G, Saedler H. 1999. The Golden Decade of molecular floral development (1990–1999): a cheerful obituary. *Dev. Genet.* 25:181–93

142. Theologis A, Oeller PW, Wong LM, Rottmann WH, Gantz DM. 1993. Use of a tomato mutant constructed with reverse genetics to study fruit ripening, a complex developmental process. *Dev. Genet.* 14:282–95

143. Thompson AJ, Tor M, Barry CS, Vrebalov J, Orfila C, et al. 1999. Molecular and genetic characterization of a novel pleiotropic tomato-ripening mutant. *Plant Physiol.* 120:383–89

144. Thorup TA, Tanyolac B, Livingstone KD, Popovsky S, Paran I, Jahn M. 2000. Candidate gene analysis of organ pigmentation loci in the Solanaceae. *Proc. Natl. Acad. Sci. USA* 97:11192–97

145. Tieman DM, Harriman RW, Ramamohan G, Handa AK. 1992. An antisense pectin methylesterase gene alters pectin chemistry and soluble solids in tomato fruit. *Plant Cell* 4:667–79

146. Tieman DM, Taylor MG, Ciardi JA, Klee HJ. 2000. The tomato ethylene receptors NR and LeETR4 are negative regulators of ethylene response and exhibit functional compensation within a multigene family. *Proc. Natl. Acad. Sci. USA* 97:5663–68

147. Tigchelaar E, McGlasson W, Buescher R. 1978. Genetic regulation of tomato fruit ripening. *Hortic. Sci.* 13:508–13

148. Tucker GA, Brady CJ. 1987. Silver ions interrupt tomato fruit ripening. *J. Plant Physiol.* 127:165–69

149. Tucker GA, Schindler CB, Roberts JA. 1984. Flower abscission in mutant tomato Lycopersicon plants. *Planta* 160:164–67

150. Van Haaren MJJ, Houck CM. 1993. A

functional map of the fruit-specific promoter of the tomato 2A11 gene. *Plant Mol. Biol.* 21:625–40

151. van Tuinen A, Cordonnier-Pratt MM, Pratt LH, Verkerk R, Zabel P, Koornneef M. 1997. The mapping of phytochrome genes and photomorphogenic mutants of tomato. *Theor. Appl. Genet.* 94:115–22

152. Wann EV, Jourdain EL, Pressey R, Lyon BG. 1985. Effect of mutant genotypes *hp og^c* and *dg og^c* on tomato fruit quality. *J. Am. Soc. Hortic. Sci.* 110:212–15

153. Wilkinson JQ, Lanahan MB, Clark DG, Bleecker AB, Chang C, et al. 1997. A dominant mutant receptor from Arabidopsis confers ethylene insensitivity in heterologous plants. *Nat. Biotechnol.* 15:444–47

154. Wilkinson JQ, Lanahan MB, Conner TW, Klee HJ. 1995. Identification of mRNAs with enhanced expression in ripening strawberry fruit using polymerase chain reaction differential display. *Plant Mol. Biol.* 27:1097–108

155. Wilkinson J, Lanahan M, Yen H, Giovannoni JJ, Klee HJ. 1995. An ethylene-inducible component of signal transduction encoded by *Never-ripe*. *Science* 270:1807–9

156. Yamasaki S, Fujii N, Takahashi H. 2000. The ethylene-regulated expression of CS-ETR2 and CS-ERS genes in cucumber plants and their possible involvement with

sex expression in flowers. *Plant Cell Physiol.* 41:608–16

157. Yang SF. 1985. Biosynthesis and action of ethylene. *HortScience* 20:41–45

158. Yao JL, Kvarnheden A, Morris B. 1999. Seven MADS-box genes in apple are expressed in different parts of the fruit. *J. Am. Soc. Hortic. Sci.* 124:8–13

159. Yen H, Lee S, Tanksley S, Lanahan M, Klee HJ, Giovannoni JJ. 1995. The tomato *Never-ripe* locus regulates ethylene-inducible gene expression and is linked to a homologue of the *Arabidopsis ETR1* gene. *Plant Physiol.* 107:1343–53

160. Yen H, Shelton A, Howard L, Vrebalov J, Giovannoni JJ. 1997. The tomato *high pigment* (*hp*) locus maps to chromosome 2 and influences plastome copy number and fruit quality. *Theor. Appl. Genet.* 95:1069–79

161. Yueming J, Jiarui F. 2000. Ethylene regulation of fruit ripening: molecular aspects. *Plant Growth Regul.* 30:193–200

162. Zegzouti H, Jones B, Frasse P, Marty C, Maitre B, et al. 1999. Ethylene-regulated gene expression in tomato fruit: characterization of novel ethylene-responsive and ripening-related genes isolated by differential display. *Plant J.* 18:589–600

163. Zhou D, Kalaitzis P, Mattoo AK, Tucker ML. 1996. The mRNA for an ETR1 homologue in tomato is constitutively expressed in vegetative and reproductive tissues. *Plant Mol. Biol.* 30:1331–38

Annu. Rev. Plant Physiol. Plant Mol. Biol. 2001. 52:751–84

CYTOKINESIS AND BUILDING OF THE CELL PLATE IN PLANTS

Desh Pal S Verma

Department of Molecular Genetics and Plant Biotechnology Center, Ohio State University, Columbus, Ohio 43210-1002; e-mail: verma.1@osu.edu

Key Words   cell division, phragmoplast, vesicle fusion, callose synthase, plant cytoskeleton, cell wall, phragmoplastin, exocytosis

■ **Abstract**   Cytokinesis in plant cells is more complex than in animals, as it involves building a cell plate as the final step in generating two cells. The cell plate is built in the center of phragmoplast by fusion of Golgi-derived vesicles. This step imposes an architectural problem where ballooning of the fused structures has to be avoided to create a plate instead. This is apparently achieved by squeezing the vesicles into dumbbell-shaped vesicle-tubule-vesicle (VTV) structures with the help of phragmoplastin, a homolog of dynamin. These structures are fused at their ends in a star-shaped body creating a tubulovesicular "honeycomb-like" structure sandwiched between the positive ends of the phragmoplast microtubules. This review summarizes our current understanding of various mechanisms involved in budding-off of Golgi vesicles, delivery and fusion of vesicles to initiate cell plate, and the synthesis of polysaccharides at the forming cell plate. Little is known about the molecular mechanisms involved in determining the site, direction, and the point of attachment of the growing cell plate with the parental cell wall. These gaps may be filled soon, as many genes that have been identified by mutations are analyzed and functions of their products are deciphered.

CONTENTS

INTRODUCTION

Because of the presence of a cell wall and the absence of cell migration in plants, the division of one cell into two is a more complex process than in animals. The timing and positioning of cell division, including the orientation of the cell wall, is important for proper plant growth and development. The plane of cell division is particularly vital for the embryo development where the initial direction of the cell plate determines the polarity of the embryo and the tissue type that each daughter cell gives rise to. The geometrical relationship of the cell wall that is established during cytokinesis is usually retained despite cell enlargement and has a direct impact on the direction of cell elongation and the morphology of the resulting tissue. Thus, a successful cytokinesis is essential not only for correct morphogenesis of all plant organs but also for the proper architecture of the plant body.

Cytokinesis in plant cells involves building an "extracellular compartment" within the cell; therefore, additional steps are required to complete cytokinesis in plants as compared to that in animal cells. Many plant mutations have been identified in genes affecting cytokinesis and cell plate formation, suggesting that this final step in cell division involves many genes and possible checkpoints, as occur at early phases of cell division. The process of cytokinesis and cell plate formation has been extensively studied from the morphological and cytological perspectives using electron microscopy (EM) and immunological approaches, and it is summarized in a number of recent reviews (48, 63, 115, 143, 150, 154). These studies have described a basic framework that is followed in building the cell plate in both vegetative and endosperm cells as well as in meiotic cell divisions in both male and female gametophytes (20, 114, 130).

The cell plate is a disk-like, membrane-bound structure, laid down in the center of the phragmoplast at cytokinesis (48, 58, 150). The phragmoplast is a loose cytoskeletal structure held together by two arrays of microtubule bundles and also contains actin. It acquires sufficient subcellular integrity to be fractionated as an organelle (4a, 79). The phragmoplast is formed at anaphase by the reassembly of mitotic microtubules (Figure 1A, see color insert) (58, 168). Golgi-derived vesicles carry the components of the forming cell plate (78, 130, 149, 150) and accumulate at the center of the phragmoplast between the two stacks of microtubules. This event is marked by the appearance of phragmoplastin, a dynamin-like protein, which is associated with the cell plate vesicles (56). The cell plate is first built within the phragmoplast proper, and it then extends in a centrifugal manner to the parental cell wall (57, 130) as shown in Figure 1*B* and *C* (see color insert).

The plane of the cell division is predetermined before the onset of mitosis. The first indication of the future cell division plane is the appearance of the preprophase band (PPB), an array of annular cortical microtubules laid down just beneath the plasma membrane during the G2 phase of the cell cycle (58, 99; for review see 98). Although the PPB disappears during mitosis, the division plane is imprinted by an unknown mechanism. The future cell plate precisely fuses with the parental membrane at this site.

Many questions remain about the mechanisms involved in cell plate formation. Among these, two are most important: First, how do vesicles fuse to give rise to a plate instead of a large ballooned vesicular body in the center of the phragmoplast as expected from a simple fusion event (without a target) of small vesicles? Second, how is polysaccharide biosynthesis (callose and cellulose) initiated de novo? A molecular dissection of the machinery involved in vesicle fusion that prevents ballooning of the membrane structure at the forming cell plate, and the initiation of callose synthesis followed by a switch to cellulose synthesis, is of fundamental importance. Also, understanding the mechanism involved in the orientation and growth of the cell plate is important for possibly altering plant architecture.

CYTOKINESIS

The division of one cell into two not only must ensure a full complement of chromosomes (karyokinesis) but also must appropriately partition the cytoplasm, including organelles (cytokinesis). The mitotic spindle plays a key role in cytokinesis in animal cells. Picket-Heaps and colleagues (121) have proposed a basic principle of "cellular tensegrity," which suggests that the mitotic spindle might originally have evolved as the mechanism by which a single "tensegral unit" (cytoplast) is divided into two cytoplasts. The use of the spindle for segregating chromosomes may represent an adaptation of this basic function. The forces involved in this process and the participation of various cytoskeletal proteins in generating such forces, however, are not fully understood.

In animal cells, cytokinesis can be divided into five steps: (*a*) The mitotic spindle defines the site at which cleavage furrow is formed. (*b*) A contactile ring containing actin and myosin is formed at this site. (*c*) Contraction of this ring creates a furrow that pulls the overlying plasma membrane and (*d*) forms a transient structure, the midbody. (*e*) The common membrane that surrounds the cell increases in surface area and divides the two daughter cells. There is a set of conserved families of proteins that is involved in yeast (49) and animal cell cytokinesis (54). This set is made up of tubulins, septins, myosin, formin, IQGAP, Cdc15, kinesin, and polo kinases (46). Homologs of some of these have also been identified from plants, which suggests a basic conservation of at least some of the mechanisms involved in this process. Various GTPases and their binding partners are also necessary for cytokinesis.

Recently, a gene (*spg1*) encoding a GTPase was identified in *Schizosaccharomyces pombe* that appears to have an important regulatory function in cell division (136). Mutation in this gene fails to form the septum, even though the actin ring formation is not affected. Overexpression of this gene forms multiple septa that can occur at any stage of the cell cycle. This gene, therefore, uncouples karyokinesis from cytokinesis. Spg1p forms a complex with Cdc7 kinase and is probably regulated by a GTPase-activating protein and a guanine nucleotide exchange factor (54). Identification of a homolog of this gene from plants may provide a clue about the missing link between the PPB and the alignment of the cell plate to the position marked by the PPB.

In contrast to animal cells that divide by forming a constriction, plant cells build a cell wall at the position marked by PPB. The manner in which the new cell wall is laid down varies considerably from algae to higher plants and differs with cell types, as well as with the type of division, i.e. mitotic vs meiotic. Cytokinesis in algae ranges from formation of a cleavage furrow, as in *Chlamydomonas* and septum formation in *Cylindrocapsa* to proper cell plate formation, e.g. in *Fucus*. Septum formation in *Cylindrocapsa* takes place in a narrow layer of cytoplasm that separates postmitotic nuclei (140). In this organism, the daughter nuclei develop a cytoplasmic invagination containing numerous strands of rough endoplasmic reticulum (ER). Smooth membranes are generated by rough ER that subsequently coalesce to form the membranous transverse septum. Thus, formation of this structure does not follow any of the known basic cytokinetic patterns in green plants, and instead it represents a novel type of membrane flow, which does not appear to involve the Golgi apparatus. This type of cell wall formation may represent an evolutionary intermediate between the primitive method of plasma membrane furrowing and the more advanced cell-plate system observed in higher plants (140). Most vegetative cells of higher plants, including gymnosperms, make cell plates that arise in the center of the phragmoplast and grow centrifugally as shown in Figure 1 (see color insert).

Irrespective of the type of cell plate, the cytokinesis process in plants requires generation of new cell surface. This process involves exocytosis and must be coordinated with the cell cycle. For example, cytokinesis must not occur prior to chromosome segregation and must be controlled by various checkpoints that are the hallmark of cell cycle progression in eukaryotic cells.

The Preprophase Band and the Orientation of Cell Division

The PPB is laid down prior to the commencement of cell division, thereby marking the future site of the cell plate. It not only determines the division site but also influences the cell polarity and formation of the mitotic spindle. The PPB is constituted by an array of unique cortical microtubules and actin that form a band around the nucleus, and it disappears at the prophase transition stage but leaves behind an imprint that is follwed by the cell plate at the division site. The dynamics of the PPB is well summarized in a recent review by Mineyuki

(98), which suggests that this key event in cell division is very complex and may involve cyclin-dependent kinases (see below) that are organ/cell type-specific. The PPB is absent in microsporogenesis (69), megasporogenesis (172, 176), and the first asymmetrical mitosis of the embryo (157). The endosperm cells do not have any cortical microtubules, and the division site is established in this tissue by nuclear microtubules (20, 114). The *ameiotic* gene of maize when mutated replaces the first meiotic division with synchronized mitotic divisions (151), indicating that this gene may encode a product that inhibits PPB formation (98) because the PPB is required for the mitotic divisions but not for the meiotic divisions.

Although much of the data suggest that the PPB determines the future division site, the asymmetric cell division patterns (see below), and the change in the division plane due to physical injury show that cortical actin filaments may play an early role in fixing the axis of cell division. This step is followed by rearrangement of cortical microtubules into a broad band around the nucleus. This process becomes irreversible by the narrowing of the PPB that finally determines the future site of the cell plate (98). Cortical actin filaments appear to play a critical role in positioning and fixing the site of the PPB as shown by EM studies (38). The F-actin network is also associated with phragmoplast in both algae and higher plants and is present throughout mitosis and cytokinesis (80, 161). However, in a plant mutant lacking the PPB, a proper cell plate is still formed (160). The actin band disappears during breakdown of PPB microtubules in some cases, although it persists in others (for review, see 98). An actin-depleted zone is formed at the center of the phragmoplast as shown by microinjection of rhodamin-phloidin (33), and the cell plate is built precisely in this area. However, actin is abundantly present in the cell plate region of *Fucus* (18). The cyclin-dependent kinases (CDKs) may be involved in the disassembly of PPB microtubules as shown by microinjection experiments (74), using active mitosis-promoting factor, which contains Cdc2 kinase and cyclin. Centrin-like protein has also been localized at the PPB (37, 60). Finally, experimental obliteration of the PPB causes incorrect insertion of cell plate (105), confirming the role of PPB in laying an imprint that directs the cell plate to the correct position.

Cytoskeletal Elements and the Formation of Phragmoplast

As the cell enters cytokinesis, microtubules from the remnants of the mitotic spindle align perpendicular to the plane of the future cell plate with their plus ends pointing toward the equatorial region (44). As the cell plate expands, the microtubules depolymerize in the center and repolymerize along the edge of the growing cell plate (56, 58). Thus, microtubules in the expanding phragmoplast form two rings surrounding the growing edge of the cell plate (55, 56, 99, 150). The microtubule cytoskeleton plays a major role in all stages of cell cycle, particularly in cytokinesis, as it provides guidance and a support for the vesicles to travel to the forming cell plate (see below). The dynamics of microtubules in living cells have been studied following microinjection of labeled tubulin (187) and expression of green fluorescence protein (GFP) fused with the microtubule-binding domain of MAP4 (55). It is apparent that the microtubule arrangement is clearly different in cells undergoing meiosis than in mitosis (69, 137, 157). The *pilz* group of genes affects microtubule organization in both embryo and endosperm (95). Recently, γ-tubulin was identified in plant cells (119), but it is not clear whether it is a part of the normal tubulin network or if it forms its own network (76).

Actin microfilaments (AMFs) are also present in the phragmoplast structure (161), but the role of actin is unclear. AMF depolymerization with profilin causes a delay in cell plate formation and sometimes disintegrates the plate that is already initiated (163). AMFs are aligned perpendicular to the plane of the cell plate (33). In addition, strands of F-actin bridge the leading margin of the growing phragmoplast to the opposing cortex (161). Radial AMFs may well provide a memory mechanism for the predetermined division site that is marked by the PPB. Recent studies suggest an acto-myosin-based mechanism involved in cell plate guidance. This is based on the effects that 2,3-butanedione 2-monoxime, a myosin ATPase inhibitor, has on cell plate formation in *Tradescantia* stamen hair cells (101). As a result of this treatment, the cell plate fails to expand centrifugally and the phragmoplast is misaligned. This observation suggests that the driving force that aligns the cell plate to the previously defined division site may be generated with the help of actin and myosin. Actin is present in the forming cleavage furrow during telophase and cytokinesis in *Chlamydomonas*, and at the forming cell plate in *Fucus* (10, 18) and *Sphacelaria* (80). In *Fucus* embryos, actin mRNA has been localized at the cell plate (18), indicating possible synthesis and delivery of actin at this location. No other mRNA localization event has been described in plants, although this phenomenon is common in yeast and many animal systems (175). We have recently identified a phragmoplastin-interacting protein (PhIP1) that has features of a putative RNA-binding protein (Z Hong & DPS Verma, unpublished data). Further characterization of this protein and the type of RNA it may bind might shed light on the possible role of this protein in RNA localization in plants and how it may affect the process of cytokinesis and cell plate formation.

Several kinesin-like microtubule plus and minus end–binding proteins have been identified in plants (4a, 19, 85, 88, 145). A kinesin-related protein, DSK1, is involved in anaphase spindle elongation in *Cylindrotheca fusiformis* and appears to concentrate in the gap that forms as the two half-spindles separate, suggesting that DSK1 may be part of a nonmicrotubule spindle matrix (173). Asada et al (4) identified a novel kinesin, TKRP125, from tobacco cells and showed that it is colocalized with microtubules at all stages of the cell cycle (Figure 2, see color insert). The pattern of antibody localization against this protein superimposes the microtubules (except the cortical microtubules) at all stages of the cell cycle, suggesting its role in arranging the microtubules in an orderly array, first in the mitotic spindle and then in the phragmoplast. The TKRP125 is distributed along microtubules in the PPB. During the M phase, TKRP125 is distributed along spindle microtubules and accumulates at the equatorial plane of the spindle as the spindle elongates. During cytokinesis, TKRP125 is colocalized with phragmoplast microtubules. The expression of TKRP125 is cell cycle–dependent and was not detected in cells at the G1 phase. It begins to appear at the S phase and accumulates during the G2 phase (Figure 2). This protein appears to facilitate reorganization of microtubules, particularly during mitosis and the assembly of phragmoplast.

Another kinesin-related protein, AtPAKRP1, becomes associated with the positive ends of phragmoplast microtubules at the late anaphase when the kinetochore microtubules become very short, and it was localized to the central region of the interzonal microtubules (85). The localization of AtPAKRP1 did not overlap with the already formed cell plate, as revealed by calcofluor staining. Microtubule depolymerization induced by colchicine completely abolished the AtPAKRP1 localization pattern. However, this protein, when fused with GST, did not sediment with microtubules (85). This may be due to some posttranslational modifications of the native peptide that are missing in the GST-tagged recombinent peptide expressed in *Escherichia coli*. AtPAKRP1 is a 145-KD protein with a classical motor domain at its amino end, but its function is not yet established (85).

The kinesin-related proteins might be activators of MAPK3 in the phragmoplast (93). In a recent study (170), the role of another kinesin-like calmodulin-binding protein (KCBP) was shown by microinjection in *Tradescantia* stamen hair cells. The KCBP is a minus end–directed microtubule motor protein (145). This protein interacts with microtubules in vitro and has been localized with PPB microtubules, mitotic spindle, and phragmoplast microtubules but not with the cortical microtubules (142). Antibodies raised against the calmodulin-binding domain of this protein inhibit calmodulin binding. When such antibodies were microinjected into mitotic cells, chromosomes condensed as if the cells were arrested at the metaphase. Injection of cells at late metaphase or early anaphase caused telophase arrest without formation of the cell plate. KCBP is involved in microtubule assembly at metaphase as shown by labeling of microtubules. Calmodulin inhibits the interaction of microtubules with KCBP in the presence of Ca^{2+}. This suggests that Ca^{2+} may be involved in reorganization of the microtubule cytoskeleton at different stages of the cell cycle (see below). Kinesin along with dynamin is also involved in vesicle transport from the Golgi (82). It would be of great interest to see if any of the plant kinesins identified to date can interact with phragmoplastin and thus take part in vesicle transport.

Phragmoplastin, a Marker for the Phragmoplast and Initiation of the Cell Plate

Although the phragmoplast structure has long been known, no specific molecular marker for this organelle was available. Early observations on cell plate formation were based primarily on staining with dyes that show callose deposited on the forming cell plate. This event, however, occurs much later than the initiation of cell plate by fusion of the Golgi-derived vesicles. We identified a dynamin-like protein from soybean (56), which has homology to the *Arabidopsis* dynamin-like (ADL) protein (39). Immunofluorescence microscopy localized this protein to the cell plate in dividing soybean root tip cells (56). Based on the temporal and spatial organization of this protein in the phragmoplast, it was termed phragmoplastin. Double-labeling using antibodies against soybean phragmoplastin and tubulin (56) as well as GFP fusion experiments (57) demonstrated that phragmoplastin is located across the newly formed cell plate, with a higher concentration at the ends where vesicle fusion is most active (Figure 1*C*, see color insert). Once the cell plate is completed, phragmoplastin disappears, leaving some punctate structures scattered in the cell. The latter may be associated with Golgi apparati that become redistributed after cell plate is completed (107). Phragmoplastin has been localized on both mitotic and meiotic cell plates and is also associated with endosperm phragmoplasts (84). The function of phragmoplastin might be to create VTV structures at the forming cell plate (see below); but a large family of these proteins (19 in *Arabidopsis*) exists, and they clearly have other functions in plant cells similar to dynamins in animal cells.

Potential Kinases Involved in Cytokinesis

Various cell cycle–dependent kinases (CDKs) play a role in yeast, animal, and plant cytokinesis. Several protein kinases have been implicated in the metaphase/anaphase transition in plants (179), and some of them appear to be involved in cytokinesis and cell plate formation (16). The intitiation of cytokinesis requires inactivation of CDK1, which affects microtubule dynamics and phosphorylation of myosin (see 46). The colocalization of Cdc2 kinase with three microtubular structures, the PPB, the spindle, and the cell plate (35, 152), suggests that there are several possible targets of the Cdc2 kinases. This protein is differentially regulated in the cytoplasm and nucleus (16). A possible target is the kinesin-related protein TKRP125 that has been localized to the PPB and phragmoplast (4a). Another important kinase in yeast and animal cytokinesis is polo kinase, which promotes CDK1 inactivation. The polo kinase in *S. pombe* interacts directly with Mid1p, a contractile ring component (6). No plant polo kinase homolog has yet been characterized and shown to be involved in cytokinesis, although several partly homologous sequences exist in the *Arabidopsis* genome.

Two mitosis-specific mitogen-activated protein kinases (MAP kinases) have recently been identified from plants (16, 100, 111), and kinesin-related proteins have been proposed to activate the MMK3 cascade, whose targets have not yet been identified. A *Nicotiana* protein kinase 1 (NPK1), which is related to MAPK3, is activated by NPK1-activating kinesin-like protein (NACK1) (111). NACK1 is also able to activate NPK1 when coexpressed in yeast cells (93, 111). Immunohistochemical studies have localized NPK1 and NACK1 to the equatorial region of the phragmoplast (106). Furthermore, expression of a kinase-minus construct of the

NPK1 in tobacco BY-2 cells affects cell plate formation and produces multinucleate cells. The tobacco MAP kinase, p43^{Ntf6}, showed activity only in dividing cells and appears to localize at the cell plate (25). MAP kinases also phosphorylate microtubule-associated proteins (72), but none has been characterized from plants. These data suggest that kinase cascade pathways play important roles in regulating cytokinesis in plants. The identification of the targets of various kinases induced during cytokinesis (179) may help in understanding the signal cascade involved in cytokinesis and cell plate formation.

BUILDING THE CELL PLATE

Based on EM studies, investigators have divided cell plate formation in plants into five major steps: (*a*) the transport and arrival of Golgi-derived vesicles to the equatorial region of the cell, (*b*) the formation of the tubulovesicular network (TVN), (*c*) consolidation of TVN into a smooth tubular network and fenestrated plate-like structure filled with callose, (*d*) fusion of the margin of the cell plate with the parental cell membrane, and (*e*) synthesis of cellulose and the maturation of the cell plate into the cell wall (130). Each step has specific morphological characteristics, and the completion of each step most likely requires different protein machineries and checkpoints. Mechanistically, cell plate formation involves four processes: first, organization of microtubules by a plus end–directed motor; second, generation and transport of vesicles along the microtubules (by an unidentified motor); third, formation of VTV structures with the help of phragmoplastin; and fourth, homotypic fusion of vesicles by KNOLLE syntaxin (84) (Figure 3, see color insert). Callose begins to appear as the TVN is formed (130). Generally, cell plate completion takes less than 60 min, but the process is sensitive to environmental conditions such as temperature and osmotic stress. The dynamics of cell plate growth can now be more precisely measured in living cells using GFP-tagged cell plate–specific proteins, as we have done with phragmoplastin (57).

Origin of Vesicles for Building the Cell Plate

The process of cell plate building is an exocytotic event (9, 158) that creates an extracellular compartment de novo at the designated site inside the cell. Because this process has to be completed in a short and defined time, the entire exocytotic machinery becomes engaged in this event for which a large number of vesicles need to be generated by the Golgi apparatus. Thus, very little or no exocytosis at the plasma membrane may occur during cytokinesis, although this has not been well established experimentally. During cytokinesis, stacks of Golgi are positioned at the ends of the phragmoplast, and some are redistributed around the phragmoplast, particularly near the junction where the cell plate will fuse with the parental cell wall (107). A continuous supply of vesicles is essential for cell plate completion, and disassembly of the Golgi apparatus by treatment with brefeldin A (BFA) blocks the completion of cytokinesis, apparently by shutting off the supply of cell-plate vesicles (135, 149, 182, 184). This, however, does not occur immediately, as a sufficient number of vesicles are in transit and the cell plate continues to be built for some time after the disruption of the Golgi. The inhibition of cell plate growth might also be due to the depolymerization of phragmoplast microtubules by BFA (182). The BFA treatment is reversible, and the supply of vesicles may resume as the Golgi is reassembled after the removal of BFA (149).

We have determined, using a GTPase domain–mutated phragmoplastin (Z Hong & DPS Verma, unpublished data), that budding of vesicles from the Golgi may involve phragmoplastin, a phenomenon similar to that of dynamin observed in animal cells (75). Recently, a homolog of VPS45 was isolated from *Arabidopsis*; this protein is involved in vesicle formation at the *trans* Golgi (8). In addition, profilin I is required for formation of vesicles at the *trans* Golgi in animal cells (41). A critical balance between actin and profilin may be essential as microinjection of profilin in *Tradescantia* cells affects cell plate formation (163).

Recent progress in understanding vesicle formation in yeast and animal systems (174) and the isolation of homologous proteins from plants (9, 129, 133) are providing some details about the mechanism of plant vesicle generation and targeting. The assembly of vesicles at the *trans* Golgi may follow the basic mechanism common to all eucaryotes that involves the coat protein (COP) system (174), and some of the COP homologs have been identified from plants (103, 121a). Vesicles are generally initiated by attachment of small GTPases at the membrane, followed by binding of heterooligomeric proteins that induce deformation of the membrane. Donor membrane proteins play an important role in both sorting cargo for delivery and recruiting other soluble proteins necessary for the vesicle to bud off from the membrane. In the case of cell plate vesicles, the cargo must contain pectin and hemicellulose, and the vesicle membrane contains cell wall synthesizing enzymes (see below). The exact membrane composition and the contents of the cell plate vesicles, however, have not yet been fully characterized, as it is difficult to prepare these vesicles free of contamination from other endo membranes. Isolated phragmoplasts may serve as a source of cell plate vesicles (78, 168), and following solubilization of microtubules, these vesicles may be isolated. This can be facilitated using antibodies against cell-plate-specific proteins (see below). Eventually, the proteomics of purified cell plate vesicles may provide a complete picture of the players involved in building the cell plate at cytokinesis in plants.

Delivery of Cell Plate Vesicles

Originating from the Golgi apparatus, the vesicles are delivered to a predetermined site that is marked by the PPB. Vesicles are transported to the center of the phragmoplast via microtubules. The bundles of microtubules that assemble with their positive ends facing each other leave a space in between that seems to be devoid of any cellular structures. Physical association of microtubules and the vesicles has been observed in both intact tissues and in isolated phragmoplasts (79, 130). No vesicle-associated motor protein has yet been identified, nor has it been possible

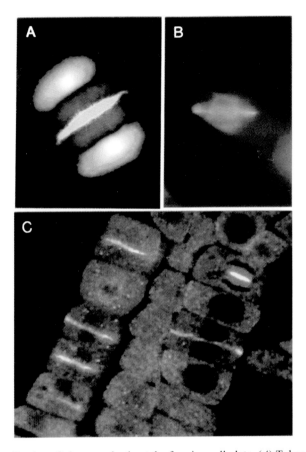

Figure 1 Localization of phragmoplastin at the forming cell plate. (*A*) Tobacco BY-2 cell was reacted with DAPI (Blue), antibody to tubulin (Red), and antibody to phragmoplastin (Green). Images were recorded separately and superimposed. (*B*) Dividing Tobacco BY-2 cell expressing GFP-phragmoplastin on the forming cell plate (reproduced from Gu & Verma, 1997; 57). (*C*) Double labeling of soybean root tip cells with tubulin antibodies (Red) and phragmoplastin antibodies (Green). Images were taken using a confocal microscope (reproduced from Gu and Verma, 1996; 56). Note the localization of phragmoplastin at different stages of cell plate formation.

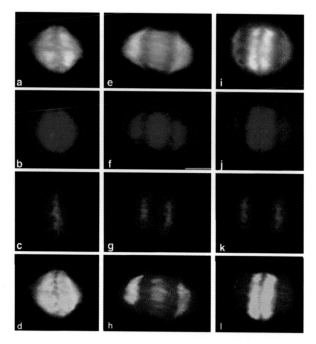

Figure 2 Distribution of TKRP125 kinesin in tobacco BY-2 cells. Tobacco BY-2 cells with a metaphase spindle (*a–d*), an anaphase spindle (*e–h*), and a phragmoplast (*i–l*) were stained with antibodies to tubulin (yellow: *a, e, i*), with PAb125m (purple: *b, f, j*), and with DAPI (red: *c, g, k*), colored artificially. Figures *d, h,* and *l* were generated by superimposing the corresponding images. Bar, 5 μm (modified from Asada et al, 1997; 4a)

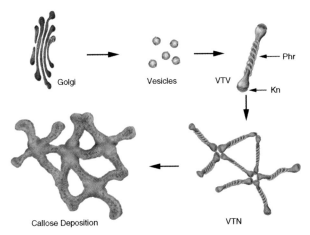

Figure 3 A proposed model for cell plate formation in plants. The Golgi-derived vesicles traverse along the microtubules and carry callose synthase, phragmoplastin, and other associated proteins. Once they reach the PPB area, they are squeezed by phragmoplastin into tubules forming dumbbell-shaped VTV structures. These structures fuse end-to-end creating a tubular fence and thus avoiding ballooning of the fused structures. The fusion brought about by KNOLLE syntaxin is followed by activation of callose synthase; the callose synthesized dilates these tubules and closes the gaps, forming a flat sheet at the forming cell plate. Phragmoplastin is then removed once the callose synthase is activated.

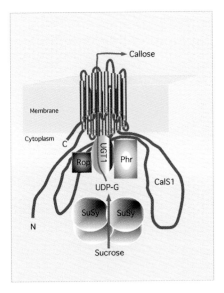

Figure 5 A model of callose synthase complex at the forming cell plate. Interaction of cell plate-specific callose synthase (CalS1) with phragmoplastin and a novel UDP-glucose transferase as well as possibly with sucrose synthase (for details, see 70, 71).

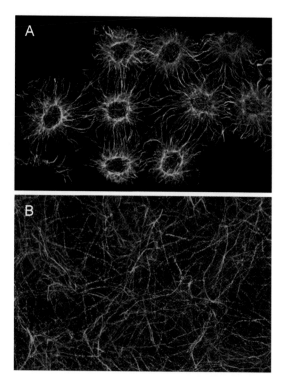

Figure 6 Confocal micrographs of microtubules and F-actin in the endosperm of *Cornopus didymous* (provided by R Brown, unpublished results). (*A*) Microtubules were labeled with antibodies to tubulin (Green), and the nuclei were labeled with propidium iodide (Red). (*B*) Localization of actin in early syncitial endosperm by staining with anti-actin antibody and secondry antibody conjugated to DTAF (pseudo-colored in blue for contrast).

to isolate cell plate vesicles. Because kinesin, along with dynamin, can act as a motor for Golgi vesicles (82), the 125-KD plus end–directed kinesin (4a) or any other kinesin along with phragmoplastin or its homolog may play a role in the transport of cell plate vesicles. Other proteins likely to be involved in the transport of vesicles belong to the Rab family of low-molecular-weight GTPases, and many of them have been isolated from plants (17, 30, 167, 169). A brief molecular characterization of plant transport vesicles has been attempted (126), but the generation of different types of vesicles and their transport to specific sites is much more complex, as evident from analysis of vesicles in yeast and animal systems (42, 59, 123).

Application of taxol (a microtubule stabilizing agent) to cells, once the cell plate is initiated, immediately freezes the outward growth of the cell plate (57), suggesting that the dynamics of microtubules is very important in guiding vesicles to the forming cell plate. Disruption of microfilaments causes oblique cell plates, but it does not prevent the formation of the cell plate (137). In taxol-treated cells, the cell plate is much thicker and more microtubule-associated vesicles are present in isolated phragmoplasts (183). These data suggest that the depolymerization of microtubules is not essential for the translocation of vesicles per se but that the depolymerization of microtubules in the center is necessary for repolymerization at the ends of growing cell plate in order to deliver vesicles to the growing ends of the plate (56, 130). If added early, taxol inhibits initiation of the cell plate, which requires depolymerization of mitotic spindle microtubules and repolymerization into phragmoplast microtubules (187). Researchers need to develop a suitable method to isolate vesicles in order to determine their membrane composition and contents, and eventually develop an in vitro vesicle translocation system. Such preparations are also needed for an in vitro membrane fusion system to study the machinery involved in this process, as has been accomplished for the synaptic membrane fusion complex (62).

Possible Role of Phragmoplastin in Generating VTV Structures

Phragmoplastin and dynamin share significant sequence homology, especially in the GTP-binding domain and the so-called self-assembly motif that is identified in dynamins and phragmoplastin (56, 68, 190). Phragmoplastin lacks the proline-rich domain (characteristic of the dynamin family of proteins) and interacts with a different set of proteins than dynamin. Therefore, phragmoplastin might perform a function at the cell plate different from that of dynamin at the plasma membrane. The functions of the dynamin family of proteins are very diverse. Dynamins are primarily involved in endocytic processes both at the plasma membrane as well as on the *trans* Golgi, generating vesicles for exocytosis. Mutations in dynamin completely block the generation and transport of secretory vesicles (26). Both dynamin and phragmoplastin are located at the membrane, but as neither has any transmembrane domain, they must become associated with membranes by interacting with other proteins, lipids, or by posttranslational modifications. Synaptobrevin, a dynamin-associated protein, becomes palmitoylated in order to attach to the membrane (166), and Rop1 (86) is isoprenylated so that it can attach to the membrane (87). The latter interacts with the callose synthase complex with which phragmoplastin also interacts (see below).

Dynamin forms helical structures in the presence of GTP-γ-S (155, 156). In the *Drosophila* mutant, *shibire*, specific amino acid substitutions in dynamin prevent endocytosis and cause the formation of elongated tubules on the plasma membrane (28). This is due to the ability of dynamin to polymerize and wrap around the biological membranes (68, 155), and we have shown that phragmoplastin has similar properties in being able to form helical structures (190). We postulated that polymerization of phragmoplastin on the surface of the cell plate vesicles may result in squeezing the vesicles into dumbbell-shaped tubular structures, thereby creating VTV. The presence of dense spiral structures observed at VTVs in cells expressing a GTPase domain–mutated phragmoplastin confirms this hypothesis. Mutation in the GTPase domain also results in the retention of most of the phragmoplastin in the Golgi apparatus (J Geisler-Lee & DPS Verma, unpublished data). These results are similar to those obtained by using purified dynamin in the presence of GTP-γ-S (155, 156). Thus, the function of phragmoplastin may be to create dumbbell-shaped VTV structures at the cell plate. This step may help to avoid direct vesicle-vesicle fusion and prevent ballooning of the fused structures at the forming cell plate.

We have also identified an *Arabidopsis* dynamin homolog (AtDH) that is localized at the cell plate (C Wang & DPS Verma, unpublished findings). This molecule resembles dynamin II, which is involved in endocytosis at the plasma membrane but not in the generation of secretory vesicles at the Golgi (81). AtDH might be involved in membrane recycling via clatherin-coated vesicles that are present on the cell plate (130). That AtDH and phragmoplastin may have different roles in cell plate formation is supported by recent observations that phragmoplastin interacts with several cell-plate proteins, e.g. PhIP1, CalS, and UDP-GT (71), whereas AtDH interacts with 14-3-3 (C Wang & DPS Verma, unpublished data), a protein involved in signal transduction (180, 189). Our data also suggest that phragmoplastin becomes associated with the exocytic vesicles as they leave the Golgi and that pinching of vesicles from the Golgi involves phragmoplastin in a manner similar to that of dynamin in animal and yeast systems (75).

Vesicle Fusion and the Role of KNOLLE

Because vesicles forming the cell plate do not have a target membrane with which to fuse, the entire process is initiated de novo. The vesicle fusion machinery is not well studied in plants, although some players have been identified. This process is well worked out in yeast and animal cells. Most researchers accept a general model of vesicle transport and fusion (14, 123, 126, 133, 167) in all eukaryotic organisms. Protein transport between membranes involves interactions of v- and t-SNARE proteins for fusion of vesicles with appropriate target membrane compartments (133, 167). Mammalian SNARE proteins have been observed to interact with NSF and SNAP proteins. This suggests that SNARE proteins are structurally similar among eukaryotes and can be classified into two groups depending on whether they interact via conserved glutamine (Q-SNARE) or arginine (R-SNARE). Furthermore, the same subset of proteins that is required for budding-off of Golgi vesicles is involved in homotypic fusion to generate vacuoles (123). For homotypic fusion, both v- and t-SNARE may occur in the same vesicle (14), and there may not be specific t-SNARE-only–containing vesicles among the cell plate vesicles. The product of the *KNOLLE* gene (92) is a homolog of syntaxin 1 (t-SNARE), and it appears to be involved in homotypic fusion at the cell plate vesicles (84). There are several syntaxins in plants and they may provide specificity for different types of vesicle fusion (191). A syntaxin 5 homolog encoding a presumptive tSNARE has been isolated from *Arabidopsis* (133, 191). Syntaxins interact with synaptotagmins (138) and the latter interact with dynamins, which are homologs of phragmoplastins, but no synaptotagmin-like protein has been identified in plants.

A more important question is how a direct vesicle-to-vesicle fusion is prevented at the cell plate, which would otherwise result in the formation of a larger ballooned structure in the center of the phragmoplast. As indicated above, phragmoplastin may play a role in this event by creating VTV structures. Once the VTVs are formed, the only way they can fuse with each other is by end-to-end homotypic fusion. This is achieved with the help of a novel syntaxin that is encoded by the *KNOLLE* gene (84, 92). The resulting branched or stellate bodies that are likely to be formed by such fusions have been observed at the forming cell plate with arms radiating in the plane of the cell plate (64). The result of this orchestrated process is the creation of the TVN as described by Samuels et al (130). In this model, the involvement of phragmoplastin precedes that of KNOLLE. This is confirmed by the studies on *knolle* mutants in which phragmoplastin (referred to as ADL) was still localized at the cell plate (84). The model presented in Figure 3 (see color insert) outlines the major events thought to be associated with membrane fusion at the forming cell plate, thereby leading to TVN formation. This structure when filled by callose (see below) becomes a fenestrated sheat of membrane; thus, the ballooning of this structure is prevented.

The TVN of the forming cell plate expands outward and a centrifugal growth of the cell plate occurs, as observed in real time using GFP:phragmoplastin (57) or by staining of the cell plate by aniline blue. The latter stains 1,3-β-glucan (callose), which is the first cell wall polymer synthesized (79, 112, 130). Callose applies a spreading force and helps the cell plate expand by closing the holes in the fenestrated tubular structure (Figure 3). As the cell plate reaches the parental cell wall, callose is replaced by 1,4-β-glucan (cellulose) (130).

PLAYERS IN SEARCH OF ROLES

Centrin, a Ca^{2+}-binding protein (12), is involved in nucleation of centromeres. This protein has been detected at the forming cell plate (37, 60, 153). Centrin may carry positional information for the cell plate based on its role in microtubule organizing centers in animal cells. Antibodies against centrin produce a punctate structure in root cell plates and is localized with plasmodesmata (13). Centrin is suggested to be a component of the Ca^{2+}-sensitive contractile nanofilaments located in the neck region of plasmodesmata as shown by EM immunolocalization. In addition, antibodies against the microtubule organizing center (MTOC) and phosphoprotein MPM-2 are associated with the phragmoplast (141). MTOCs are morphologically diverse cellular structures involved in nucleation of microtubules and are analogous to animal centrosomes (164). Several proteins associated with centrosomes have been localized with MTOCs.

A LIM domain protein (WLIM1), which is characterized by the presence of one or several double zinc finger motifs, has been isolated from sunflower (104). This protein may play a role in actin cytoskeleton-membrane interaction during cytokinesis. The WLIM1 is related to the muscle proteins CRPs, which are involved in anchoring the actin cytoskeleton to sites of membrane adhesion in animal cells. In late anaphase and early telophase, WLIM1 accumulates in the phragmoplast. Using antibodies, researchers have localized a vinculin-like protein at the cell plate, but they have not identified its plant homolog (43). A homolog of CDC48 has been isolated from *Arabidopsis* that can complement the *cdc*48 mutation in yeast, but its exact function is not known (45). Several genes that have been identified by mutations have yet to be cloned and characterized to decipher their functions in cytokinesis and cell plate formation. In addition, the function of several proteins encoded by mutants known to affect cytokinesis and cell plate formation (see below) is undetermined.

Role of Ca^{2+} in Cell Plate Formation

Ca^{2+} appears to play several critical roles during cytokinesis and in cell plate formation. The levels of Ca^{2+} rise abruptly during anaphase (14, 66, 122). Using chlorotetracyclin, which fluoresces in the presence of Ca^{2+}, investigators detected a high concentration of membrane-bound Ca^{2+} in the forming cell plate (7, 178). Also, the level of free Ca^{2+} increases during anaphase (67). Researchers suggest that arrays of ER, which are present in the cell plate region, may regulate the level of Ca^{2+} (65). A role for Ca^{2+} in the acto-myosin system, assembly and disassembly of microtubules, and exocytosis of vesicles has been proposed (65). Further, the early phases of cell plate formation, which include vesicle fusion, are most sensitive to the level of Ca^{2+} (77). Ca^{2+} may also control the GTPase activity of phragmoplastin, which is necessary for its function in creating VTV structures; it may be involved in phosphorylation of phragmoplastin by a Ca^{2+}-activated kinase; it may facilitate homotypic fusion of vesicles; and finally, it may help activate callose synthase. The polymerization of phragmoplastin is facilitated by Ca^{2+} although its GTPase activity may be reduced by high levels of Ca^{2+} as is the case for dynamin (36); thus, Ca^{2+} may control VTV formation by modulating phragmoplastin GTPase activity. Inhibition of dynamin GTPase by using a GTP analog or mutation facilitates the creation of tubular structures from vesicles (155, 156). Ca^{2+} also enhances callose synthase activity at the cell plate (79). In fact, Ca^{2+} is required by most callose synthases for their optimal activities.

One Ca^{2+} effector might be calmodulin, and a high level of calmodulin has been reported in the phragmoplast (58). A cell plate–specific Ca^{2+}/calmodulin-dependent protein kinases cascade may exist and regulate cytokinesis and cell plate formation. Treatment with caffeine dissociates the forming cell plate (66, 130, 132) by preventing the thin fusion tube network from converting into the stable TVN. When applied to the partly formed cell plate, it reverts to vesicles that are then reabsorbed (57, 132). Caffeine may reduce the Ca^{2+} levels, which in turn affect Ca^{2+}/calmodulin-dependent protein kinase(s) that plays a role(s) in cell plate formation. KNOLLE shares homology with human syntaxin A1, which interacts with a Ca^{2+} channel; thus, KNOLLE-induced vesicle fusion may control Ca^{2+} levels. Finally, a high level of Ca^{2+} is required for callose synthesis, although the Ca^{2+} level must be reduced for cellulose synthesis to commence during cell plate maturation. The prolonged presence of high levels of Ca^{2+} at the nascent cell plate may continue callose synthesis and delay cell plate maturation as observed in *cyt1* mutant (109).

SYNTHESIS OF POLYSACCHARIDES AT THE FORMING CELL PLATE

Except for callose, which has long been identified in young cell plates by aniline blue staining and immunocytochemical studies (112), the contents of the developing cell plate are largely unknown. Though noncellulosic matrix polysaccharides are synthesized in the Golgi apparatus and transported to the cell plate (135, 188), callose is synthesized de novo once the vesicles have fused to form new plasma membrane at the TVN. Accordingly, isolated phragmoplasts are able to synthesize callose in vitro, although the transport vesicles and the Golgi apparatus do not (79). In addition to callose, other cell wall matrix polysaccharides, such as xyloglucan (102), pectin (135), and arabinogalactan, have been identified at the cell plate using specific antibodies (112). Pectin makes up a significant part (20%–40%) of the plant cell walls; is a complex mixture of homogalacturonan and rhamnogalaturonan, with complex side chains that include arabinose and galactose; and is synthesized primarily in the Golgi apparatus (147). Thus, Golgi-derived vesicles carry pectin to the forming cell plate where it is deposited via exocytosis by fusion of the vesicles.

We have cloned a full-length cDNA encoding catalytic subunit of callose synthase that shares a sequence homology with yeast and fungal 1,3-β-glucan synthases. We have also shown that there is a cell plate–specific enzyme (CalS1) that is a part of a family of callose synthases that exists in a plant (70). The *CalS1* locus on the *Arabidopsis* chromosome 1 is located immediately upstream of a novel UDP-glucose transferase (UDP-GT) that interacts with phragmoplastin (71). UDP-GT also interacts with Rop1, a Rho-like protein, and this interaction occurs in the GTP-bound configuration. Rho is a regulatory subunit of 1,3-β-glucan synthase in yeast (125). UDP-GT appears to be a part of the CalS complex that may also include sucrose synthase (SuSy) in a manner proposed for cellulose synthase (2).

Location of UDP-GT in the callose synthase complex is consistent with an earlier observation (50) that a ~57-KD peptide that binds to radioactive UDP-glucose is associated with CalS activity. This peptide might be a homolog of our UDP-GT that has a molecular mass of about 60 kD. Using a product-entrapment procedure, we purified this complex and showed that UDP-GT and CalS1 copurify as a part of this complex (71). That CalS1 is indeed a cell plate–specific enzyme was shown by its fusion with GFP and its direct localization at the forming cell plate (70). Furthermore, CalS1:GFP copurify with the CalS complex. Overexpression of CalS1 cDNA enhances callose deposition at the cell plate and increases callose synthase activity, confirming that it is a cell plate–specific callose synthase involved in callose deposition at the forming cell plate. Formation of a functional complex between CalS, UDP-GT, and possibly SuSy, which has been localized at the cell plate (2), may create a substrate channel for UDP-glucose, which would ensure rapid deposition of callose at the forming cell plate. Because the cell plate has to be built in a very short time, a delay in its formation may alter the composition of the structure being formed and produce daughter cells with altered cell walls.

Callose deposition at the cell plate occurs in response to temporal and spatial signals. It begins to accumulate as TVN is established (130). Callose is also detected at the T junction of the parental cell wall (Figure 4A). Cell walls at the division site often become differentially thickened (51), which may prepare the parental cell wall to receive the daughter cell plate and establish a firm connection at this position. This thickening may result from the direct fusion of vesicles that accumulate in this region during the PPB formation (see 98) and prepare the parental cell wall for fusion with the new wall that attaches at this place. The synthesis of callose at the forming cell plate apparently occurs independently of any primer, although the search for a primer for both callose and cellulose synthesis continues. Little is known about how callose synthesis is turned on during cell plate formation and how it is turned off during cell wall maturation, although changes in the levels of Ca^{2+} is one likely factor. In a *cyt1* mutant (109), the absence of cellulose biosynthesis causes incomplete cell walls and excessive callose accumulation without forming cellulose (see 109). The cell wall is not completed and the fenestrated callose sheet acts only as a temporary, incomplete cell wall, which later dissolves. Overexpression of phragmoplastin also causes accumulation of callose, which appears to delay cell wall maturation (J Geiser-Lee & DPS Verma, unpublished observation). Because phragmoplastin and callose synthase interact directly, and phragmoplastin also interacts with UDP-GT, its overexpression is expected to affect callose synthase activity (70).

Cellulose is detected as the plate begins to mature and fuse with the parental plasma membrane (Figure 4B). This suggests that cellulose synthase is delivered to the cell plate via the vesicles transported from the Golgi apparatus. If cellulose synthase arrives simultaneously with the callose synthase, it may be activated later, as the Ca^{2+} level drops within the forming cell plate. Clearly, CalS and CelS are two different enzymes, and callose and cellulose are not synthesized by the

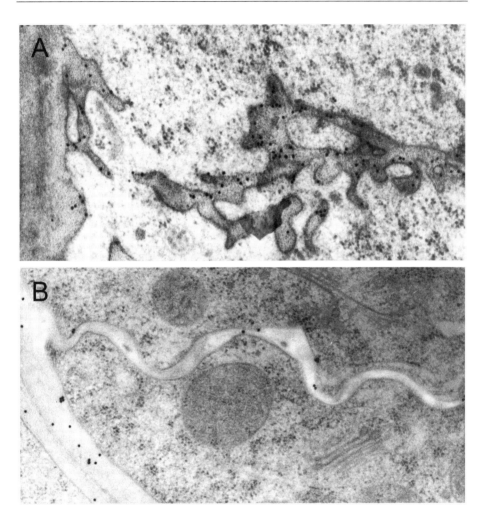

Figure 4 Synthesis of callose and cellulose during cell plate formation. (*A*) Callose, labeled with a monoclonal antibody to callose, is synthesized in the forming cell plate and in parts of the parental cell wall at the T-junction. (*B*) Cellulose, labeled with cellobiohydrolase I-gold, begins to be synthesized when the cell plate fuses with the parental cell wall [reproduced from Samuels et al 1995 (130)].

same enzyme as had been suggested (2). Callose is a constituent of the cell plate only until the growing plate matures, when it gradually disappears. Persistance of callose affects cell plate maturation (109) and may prevent cellulose synthesis. The herbicide dichlobenil that prevents cellulose synthesis affects flattening of the cell plate and dichlobenil-treated cells contain up to 20 times more callose at their cell plates (165).

Not all proteins involved in the synthesis of callose and cellulose at the cell plate are known because each is a large, multisubunit complex. Nor do researchers know whether there are two separate complexes or a single complex that shares UDP-GT and SuSy to provide UDP glucose for the growing polymer chains. Based on our current data (23, 70, 71), we propose a model of callose synthase complex at the forming cell plate, as shown in Figure 5 (see color insert). A more precise interaction of various proteins, particularly that of SuSy, which has been suggested to be a part of the cellulose/callose synthase complex, remains to be determined. For a Ca^{2+}-mediated switch between callose and cellulose synthesis, proteins homologous to animal calcineurinor or synaptobrevin may participate in this mechanism. These proteins are part of the synaptosomal complex and are involved in a dynamin-mediated exocytotic event (83). Annexin has also been implicated as a component of the callose synthase complex (3), and several annexins have been identified from plants (3, 124).

Several questions remain on the de novo biosynthesis of polysaccharides at the forming cell plate. What are the primers for callose synthase and cellulose synthases? Do these enzymes form a separate complex or share the machinery of the same complex? May a change in Ca^{2+} level switch callose synthesis to cellulose synthesis, or is a specific protein involved in this switching mechanism?

MATURATION OF THE CELL PLATE

The final stage in the completion of the cell plate is the maturation stage, a process that transforms the fluid and wrinkled cell plate to a stiff and flat cell wall. This process is accompanied by the replacement of callose by cellulose. Very little is known about the maturation process that integrates, along with cellulose, many cell wall proteins. How and when cell wall proteins begin to integrate with the polysaccharide matrix to form the mature cell wall is not clear. Furthermore, how plasmodesmata are formed is not understood. Fusion of the cell plate with the parental plasma membrane at the exact division site marked by the PPB is necessary for the maturation process to be completed. If the cell plate is forced to anchor elsewhere on the parental plasma membrane by physical displacement, the cell plate does not flatten. Following displacement of the cell plate, its recovery process becomes sensitive to cytochalasin B and phalloidin, both of which affect F-actin (117), suggesting the involvement of F-actin in guiding phragmoplast and the growing cell plate to the parental cell wall. Furthermore, myosin VIII has been localized with the postcytokinesis cell wall (127). The division site is thought to contain recognition and cell-wall maturation factors essential for the completion of cell-plate maturation (99). Caffeine inhibits the maturation process by inhibiting callose deposition (132), and inhibitors of cellulose synthesis such as dichlobenil also inhibit cell plate maturation (169).

The *KORRIGAN* gene of *Arabidopsis* encodes an endo-1,4-β-glucanase (192), a plasma membrane–associated enzyme required for normal cell wall biosynthesis

(110). This enzyme has been localized on both Golgi and plasma membranes (22). This is a unique glucanase with its enzymatic domain next to a transmembrane domain, which may limit its activity in the membrane near the cellulose synthase. Whether this enzyme forms a part of the cellulose synthase complex has not been determined. Polarized targeting of this enzyme to the cell plate plays a critical role in the maturation of the plate, and it may be involved in cellulose biosynthesis. That the presence of a glucanase affects cell wall synthesis indicates that this enzyme may act as a part of the synthase complex and is probably involved in a proofreading mechanism of the polymer being synthesized (27). Thus, not only the synthesis but also the degradation of polysaccharides are essential for an orderly maturation of the cell plate; however, nothing is known about the enzyme that degrades callose during cell plate maturation.

Although the establishment of the division/fusion site is poorly understood at the molecular level, increasing evidence suggests that proteins of the extracellular matrix (ECM)-cytoskeletal continuum might be involved. Preferential adhesion of the cell wall to the cell cortex at the future division site has been observed after mild plasmolysis, indicating the close association of the ECM with the plasma membrane at this site. Evidence suggests that bridges involving a vitronectin-like protein connect the cell wall to the cytoskeletal network inside the cell (171). In addition, a vinculin-like antigen is present at this site (43). Identification of proteins of the ECM-cytoskeleton continuum, which remains localized at the division site throughout mitosis and cytokinesis, may help elucidate the mechanism involved in the orientation of the plane of the cell plate. This orientation is of particular importance in cells undergoing unequal division or arched cell plate, as in supporting cells of stomata (143).

Overexpression of phragmoplastin affects cell plate formation in transgenic cells and regenerated plants. This change in the orientation of the cell plate seems to have no effect on the direction of cell elongation (57). The persistence of callose that is caused by overexpression and dominant negative mutants (which are created by the expression of GTPase domain–mutated phragmoplastin) apparently affects cell plate maturation. This results in the arrest of both root and shoot growth, suggesting that phragmoplastin plays an essential role in cell plate formation in both root and shoot meristem cells (J Geisler-Lee & DPS Verma, unpublished observations).

UNCOUPLING OF CELL PLATE FORMATION FROM NUCLEAR DIVISION

In plant endosperm and megagametophyte development, cell plate formation is uncoupled from nuclear division (11). Moreover, endosperm cells do not form a PPB, which is a charateristic of somatic cells. Rather, a new type of cell plate is formed. In the syncytial endosperm cells that are formed by repeated nuclear divisions without cytokinesis (11, 20), anticlinal cell walls are thought to be formed by tip growth (113). However, a recent study using cryofixation of *Arabidopsis*

(115) indicated that no mitotic phragmoplasts are present in these cells, but rather mini-phragmoplasts are formed. Because mitotic spindle microtubules disappear in these cells, new arrays of microtubules radiating from the nuclei are assembled like sprockets of a wheel (Figure 6a, see color insert). The position where the positive ends of these microtubules face each other constitutes a site (Figure 6a) where the cell plate is formed by assembling mini-phragmoplast structures (114). The actin cytoskeleton is more pronounced in endosperm cells and follows a cage-like structure surrounding each nuclei as shown in *Cornopus* endosperm cells (Figure 6b). Although interzonal phragmoplasts appear initially at this site, they do not make the cell plates and are replaced by a radial microtubule system. All mini-phragmoplasts appear in a synchronized manner (114). The Golgi-derived vesicles travel to the mini-phragmoplasts and fuse in a manner similar to that in somatic cells, but instead of forming dumbbell-shaped structures like those found on normal cell plates, hourglass-shaped structures are observed (114). Phragmoplastin was not localized in this study, but it was localized in a study by Lauber et al (84). The presence of phragmoplastin at the cell plate in endosperm suggests that this molecule may also be involved in creating hourglass structures, as it creates dumbbell-shaped VTV structures. A ring is detectable around the neck of the hour-glass structures (114), possibly formed by phragmoplastin (115). This finding points to a similarity between the processes in vegetative and endosperm cell plate formation. Several mini-phragmoplasts appear to participate in making a single plate by independently initiating vesicle fusion events at several locations simultaneously. Mechanistically, therefore, the process in vegetative cells and the endosperm is very similar, but the composition of the cell wall seems to be different.

All endosperm cell plates contain $1\text{-}3\text{-}\beta$-glucan but not $1\text{-}3,1\text{-}4\text{-}\beta$-glucans. The callosic endosperm walls remain thin, and callose seems to persist much longer in these cell plates; perhaps due to the function of this tissue, little structural support is needed, and the main function of these cells is to provide nutrition to the growing embryo. The endosperm cell plate appears to lack fucosyl residue on the xyloglucans. An *A. thaliana* mutant (*mur1*) has little or no L-fucose in the primary cell walls (186), indicating that the *mur1* gene may control fucosylation of xyloglucans and that this gene is downregulated in endosperm, resulting in a lack of fucose at the endosperm cell plate. Furthermore, the fact that the *mur1* mutant survives questions the hypothesis that fucose is an essential component of the biologically active cell wall xyloglucans. L-fucose is replaced by L-galactose in this mutant, which does not apparently alter the biological activity of the xyloglucan.

ASYMMETRIC CELL DIVISIONS

Asymmetric cell divisions give rise to daughter cells with different fates. In plants, asymmetric cell divisions mark the beginning of embryogenesis and the development of cell complexes, such as cells involved in the differentiation of stomata. The resulting cells are different not only developmentally but also physically in shape and size. Asymmetric cell divisions are common throughout plant development. Formation of these structures depends on the proper positioning of cell walls, which is determined during cytokinesis. Several plant mutants have been identified in both *Arabidopsis* and *Zea maize* that affect stomata development. Sack and colleagues have isolated several mutants that affect stomatal morphology, but the genes involved have not yet been cloned (181). These mutants result from altered cell division patterns. A stomatal meristemoid cell is formed by an asymmetric cell division of a protodermal cell. The smaller cell becomes the meristemoid that undergoes several asymmetric cell divisions to finally convert into a guard cell mother cell (GMC). A symmetric cell division of GMC produces two guard cells (181). In the *four lips* mutant, the gene product is needed to restrict the divisions of the GMC to one; whereas in *flp* mutants, GMCs keep dividing a variable number of times (F Sack, personal communication). The cell plate dividing the guard cells is unique, as it creates a hole in the center, presumably by dissolving pectin, but how this process is carried out awaits determination.

The cytokinesis event that gives rise to guard cells of stomata and forms supporting cells in monocot plants is affected by additional genes that control the unequal partitioning of the cytoplasm and formation of a curved cell plate, such as those demonstrated in *discordia* mutants (52). These mutants disrupt the spatial regulation of cytokinesis during asymmetric cell division without affecting the symmetric cell divisions. In *discordia* mutants, the phragmoplast appears to be normal but fails to move to the predetermined PPB position and does not curve along the actin patch. These mutations specifically affect asymmetric cell division plates and not normal cell plates. Because these mutations can be phenocopied by cytochalasin D (31), they affect some actin-dependent processes unique to asymmetric cell divisions (52). This suggests that actin plays a major role in asymmetric cell divisions. In the leaves of the *tangled-1* mutant of maize where the orientation of the cell plate is altered, cells in all tissues divide transversely at normal frequencies, but longitudinal divisions are largely substituted by a variety of differently oriented cell divisions (144). This gene product is involved in controlling the cytoskeletal array (34). However, the overall shape of the mutant leaves appears almost normal at all stages of growth. In the *warty-1* mutant, cells in the leaf blade become abnormally enlarged (128), often doubling in length and width, and create abnormal swelling on the leaf surface. These cells show misoriented cell plates and incomplete cell walls, suggesting a correlation between cell size and cytokinesis regulation, which becomes altered when a particular size limit is reached. This finding may also explain why cells after reaching a certain size no longer divide and become terminal. This phenomenon is very common in cell culture.

In *Volvox*, an asymmetric division sets apart cells of the germ and somatic lineages during embryogenesis. Using transposon tagging, investigators have cloned a *glsA* gene and shown that this gene is expressed maximally in asymmetrically dividing embryos (97). The *glsA* gene encodes a 748 amino acid protein that is associated with the mitotic spindle, but the actual function of this gene product is not known.

CELL PLATE FORMATION DURING MEIOTIC DIVISIONS

Cell plate formation differs between the mitotic and meiotic divisions in plants and also in meiotic divisions between the male and female gametophyte. Cytokinesis during microsporogenesis involves the formation of cleavage furrows from the parental cell wall (116), and KNOLLE protein appears to not be involved in this type of cell division (84). The PPB has not been observed during female gameto-phyte cellularization in *Arabidopsis*, but nuclear-MT arrays similar to those shown in Figure 6 (see color insert) have been found, suggesting that the cell plates in the female gametophyte are assembled in a manner similar to that in endosperm. This process is affected in the *female gametophyte4* mutant of *Arabidopsis*, which exhibits an altered cellularization pattern in the embryo sac (32). This mutation likely affects cytoskeleton organization and nuclear microtubules. Furthermore, researchers have identified a *dyad* gene in *Arabidopsis* that affects progression of female meiosis (139).

Cell plates during pollen grain development arise via normal phragmoplasts, fol-lowing an asymmetric cell division (162). Two genes, *STUD* and *TETRASPORE*, specifically affect cell plate at meiosis in male gametophytes (73, 148). In the *Arabidopsis* mutant *sidecar pollen*, microspores undergo a symmetric division. One of the two resulting cells again undergoes asymmetric division and gives rise to a generative and a vegetative cell, whereas the other develops into a vegeta-tive cell (29). The *gemini pollen1* mutation also shows a phenotype consistent with spatial uncoupling of karyokinesis and cytokinesis (185). The second mi-totic division during pollen development takes place in the generative cell, giving rise to two sperm cells. This division can occur either inside the pollen grain or the pollen tube and involves phragmoplast formation. In contrast, this division is achieved in *Tradescantia* via a cleavage furrow (118). These observations sug-gest that the same result can be achieved by different routes in different systems (115).

OTHER MUTATIONS AFFECTING CELL PLATE FORMATION

Other plant mutations have been identified that directly or indirectly affect cytoki-nesis and cell plate formation. Some of these mutations only affect a particular cell type, such as stomata in vegetative or reproductive organs (52, 181), whereas others affect all organs. The *cyt1* mutation is embryo-lethal and results in excessive callose synthesis and incomplete cell wall formation (109). The pea *cyd* mutant forms multinucleate cells with partial cell plates (89). In the *keule* mutant of *Ara-bidopsis*, multinucleate cells with incomplete cell plates are formed (5). The *keule* gene product apparently functions downstream of KNOLLE, and keule protein may interact with KNOLLE. The pluripotent cells of the apical meristem in the 16-cell embryo are maintained by the *WUSCHEL* gene, which when mutated, mis-specifies the stem meristem (96). The *first* gene alters the cell division plane and radial pattern of embryo differentiation (40), whereas EMB 506 controls normal development of the embryo (1).

Several *Arabidopsis* genes affecting postembryonic development have been identified and cloned, but their functions are undetermined. A mutation, *hobbit*, was identified as affecting only hypophyseal cells of the developing embryo, resulting in seedlings with very short roots. This gene controls cell morphology postembryonically (177). The *hobbit* mutant roots lack a recognizable quiescent center and mitotically active root meristem, resulting in the lack of supply of new cells that arrest root growth. The *GNOM* gene affects the position of cell plate and pattern formation (24, 94). The *titan* mutant affects cell division only during seed development (90).

The *tso1* mutant improperly organizes floral meristem and produces abnormal sepals and callus-like cells in the center of the flower, but cell plate formation appears to be normal (91). *TSO1* encodes a protein with two cystein-rich regions bearing similarity to the *zeste* enhancer of *Dropsophila* (146). The TSO1 protein may act as a transcriptional regulator that modulates expression of genes encoding cytoskeleton elements specifically in floral organs (61). Cytokinesis regulation may therefore vary in vegetative and reproductive organs.

The *titan* mutant affects cytokinesis only during seed development (90). A mutation in the *GURKE* gene abolishes cotyledon development, but the root meristem appears normal. This mutation is traced back to the heart-shaped embryos where the cells giving rise to cotyledons are affected (159). The *fass* and *ton* mutants are defective in PPB formation but develop normal cell plates (159, 160). The mitotic spindle and phragmoplast are normal in these mutants, but the phragmoplast does not rotate to special orientation. These mutations apparently affect cytoskeletal elements. A group of mutations has been identified in *Arabidopsis* in which the cell wall does not adhere tightly, and the daughter cells fall apart (120). The *TFA1* locus leads to ectopic cell separation in young seedlings. This group of genes may encode proteins involved in pectin biosynthesis because pectin acts as a glue to hold cells together.

Perspectives

Building of the cell plate creats an extracellular compartment inside the cell where the components of the cell wall begin to assemble. This process involves extensive exocytotic and endocytotic activities to deliver the cargo from the Golgi and to recycle the extra membrane after fusion of the vesicles. The site of cell plate assembly is determined by the PPB, followed by the fusion of vesicles in a unique manner to avoid ballooning of the fused structures. The latter step is facilitated by phragmoplastin, a member of the dynamin family of proteins with ability to form membrane tubules. The endocytotic event mediated by the clatherin-coated vesicles may be facilitated by the homolog of dynamin (AtDH) also located on the cell plate. Researchers still need to identify other proteins necessary for this machinery to function and to develop an in vitro membrane fusion system. Similarly, they need to identify proteins involved in the functioning of callose synthase and cellulose synthase complexes, and they need to study the regulation of these two steps in detail to understand the de novo synthesis of callose and cellulose on the forming cell plate. Several other proteins have been localized at the cell plate, including centrin, cdc48, annexin, calmodulin, SuSy, a vincullin-like protein, cytokinesis-specific MAP kinase (MMK3), and a novel phragmoplastin-interacting protein (PhIP1); but their functions are not known. Finally, identification and understanding of the role of proteins in imprinting the division site marked by PPB during the G2 phase of cell cycle is of paramount importance to altering the plane of cell division that affects embryogenesis and the architecture of plant organs, and thus of the entire plant.

Building the cell plate is a complex process controlled by many genes; and the process is not only cell type–specific, but it also varies in mitotic and meiotic cells. Further genetic studies on plant mutations affecting cell plate formation, position, orientation and size of cells, and the use of double mutations in combination with molecular studies may allow us to decipher the function of various genes in cytokinesis and cell plate formation in plants.

ACKNOWLEDGMENTS

This study was supported by NSF grant IBN 9724014. The author thanks Drs. Ashton Delauney, Eric Gotewold, and Fred Sack for their comments and Dr. Zongli Hong and Jane Geisler-Lee for their help in the preparation of illustrations for this manuscript. I wish to thank Drs. Roy Brown, Andrew Staehelin, and H Shibaoka for providing their figures for reproduction.

Visit the Annual Reviews home page at www.AnnualReviews.org

LITERATURE CITED

1. Albert S, Despres B, Guilleminot J, Bechtold N, Pelletier G, et al. 1999. The EMB 506 gene encodes a novel ankyrin repeat containing protein that is essential for the normal development of Arabidopsis embryos. *Plant J.* 17:169–79

2. Amor Y, Haigler CH, Johnson S, Wainscott M, Delmer DP. 1995. A membrane-associated form of sucrose synthase and its potential role in synthesis of cellulose and callose in plants. *Proc. Natl. Acad. Sci. USA* 92:9353–57

3. Andrawis A, Solomon M, Delmer DP. 1993. Cotton fiber annexins: a potential role in the regulation of callose synthase. *Plant J.* 3:763–72

4. Asada T, Kuriyama R, Shibaoka H. 1997. TKRP125, a kinesin-related protein involved in the centrosome-independent organization of the cytokinetic apparatus in tobacco BY-2 cells. *J. Cell Sci.* 110:179–89

4a. Asada T, Shibaoka H. 1994. Isolation of polypeptides with microtubule-translocating activity from phragmoplasts of tobacco BY-2 cells. *J. Cell Sci.* 107:2249–57

5. Assaad FF, Mayer U, Wanner G, Jürgens G. 1996. The *KEULE* gene is involved in cytokinesis in *Arabidopsis*. *Mol. Gen. Genet.* 253:267–77

6. Bahler J, Steever AB, Wheatley S, Wang Y-L, Pringle JR, et al. 1998. Role of polo kinase and Mid1p in determining the site

of cell division in fission yeast. *J. Cell Biol.* 143:1603–16

7. Baskin TI, Cande WZ. 1990. The structure and function of the mitotic spindle in flowering plants. *Annu. Rev. Plant Physiol. Plant Mol. Biol.* 41:277–315

8. Bassham DC, Sanderfoot AA, Kovaleva V, Zheng H, Raikhel NV. 2000. AtVPS45 complex formation at the *trans* Golgi network. *Mol. Biol. Cell* 11:2251–65

9. Battey NH, James NC, Greenland AJ, Brownlee C. 1999. Exocytosis and endocytosis. *Plant Cell* 11:643–59

10. Belanger KD, Quatrano RS. 2000. Membrane recycling occurs during asymmetric tip growth and cell plate formation in *Fucus disticus* zygotes. *Protoplasma* 212:28–32

11. Berger F. 1999. Endosperm development. *Curr. Opin. Plant Biol.* 2:28–32

12. Bhattacharya D, Steinkotter J, Melkonian M. 1993. Molecular cloning and evolutionary analysis of the Ca^{2+}-modulated contractile protein, centrin, in green algae and land plants. *Plant Mol. Biol.* 23:1243–54

13. Blackman LM, Harper JD, Overall RL. 1999. Localization of a centrin-like protein to higher plant plasmodesmata. *Eur. J. Cell Biol.* 78:297–304

14. Blatt MR, Leyman B, Geelen D. 1999. Molecular events of vesicle trafficking and control by SNARE proteins in plants. *New Phytol.* 144:389–418

15. Deleted in proof

16. Bogre L, Calderini O, Binarova P, Mattauch M, Till S, et al. 1999. A MAP kinase is activated late in plant mitosis and becomes localized to the plane of cell division. *Plant Cell* 11:101–13

17. Borg S, Brandstrup B, Jensen TJ, Poulsen C. 1997. Identification of new protein species among 33 different small GTP-binding proteins encoded by cDNAs from *Lotus japonicus*, and expression of corresponding mRNAs in developing root nodules. *Plant J.* 11:237–50

18. Bouget F-Y, Gerttula S, Shaw SL, Quatrano RS. 1996. Localization of actin mRNA during the establishment of cell polarity and early cell division in *Fucus* embryos. *Plant Cell* 8:189–201

19. Bowser J, Reddy ASN. 1997. Localization of a kinesin-like calmodulin-binding protein in dividing cells of *Arabidopsis* and tobacco. *Plant J.* 12:1429–37

20. Brown RC, Lemmon BE, Nguyen H, Olson O-A. 1999. Development of endosperm in *Arabidopsis thaliana. Sex. Plant Reprod.* 12:32–42

21. Deleted in proof

22. Brummell DA, Catella C, Lashbrook CC, Bennett AB. 1997. A membrane anchored E-type endo 1,4-β glucanase is localized on Golgi and plasma membranes of higher plants. *Proc. Natl. Acad. Sci. USA* 94:4794–99

23. Buckeridge MS, Vergara CE, Carpita NC. 1999. The mechanism of synthesis of a mixed-linkage 1,3, 1,4 β-D-glucan in maize. Evidence for multiple sites of glucosyl transfer in the synthase complex. *Plant Physiol.* 120:1105–16

24. Busch M, Mayer U, Jurgens G. 1996. Molecular analysis of the *Arabidopsis* pattern formation gene *GNOM*: gene structure and intragenic complementation. *Mol. Gen. Genet.* 250:681–91

25. Calderini O, Bögre L, Vicente O, Binarova P, Heberle-Bors E, Wilson C. 1998. A cell cycle regulated MAP kinase with a possible role in cytokinesis in tobacco cells. *J. Cell Sci.* 111:3091–100

26. Cao H, Thompson HM, Krueger EW, McNiven MA. 2000. Disruption of Golgi structure and function in mammalian cells expressing a mutant dynamin. *J. Cell Sci.* 113:1993–2002

27. Chapple C, Carpita N. 1998. Plant cell walls as targets for biotechnology. *Curr. Opin. Plant Biol.* 1:179–85

28. Chen MS, Obar RA, Schroeder CC, Austin TW, Poodry CA, et al. 1991. Multiple forms of dynamin are encoded by *shibire*, a *Drosophila* gene involved in endocytosis. *Nature* 35:583–86

29. Chen Y-CS, McCormick S. 1996. *sidecar pollen*, an *Arabidopsis thaliana* male gametophytic mutant with aberrant cell divisions during pollen development. *Development* 122:3243–53

30. Cheon C-I, Lee N-G, Siddique ABM, Bal AK, Verma DPS. 1993. Roles of plant homologs of Rab1p and Rab7p in biogenesis of peribacteroid membrane, a subcellular compartment formed *de novo* during root nodule symbiosis. *EMBO J.* 12:4125–35

31. Cho S-O, Wick SM. 1990. Distribution and function of actin in the developing stomatal complex of winter rye (*Secale cereale* cv Puma). *Protoplasma* 157:154–64

32. Christensen CA, Subramanian S, Drews GN. 1998. Identification of gametophytic mutations affecting female gametophyte development in *Arabidopsis*. *Dev. Biol.* 202:136–51

33. Cleary AL, Gunning BS, Wasteneys GO, Hepler PK. 1992. Microtubules and F-actin dynamics at the division site in living *Tradescantia* stamen hair cells. *J. Cell Sci.* 103:977–88

34. Cleary AL, Smith LG. 1998. The *tangled 1* gene is required for spatial control of cytoskeletal arrays associated with cell division during maize leaf development. *Plant Cell* 10:1875–88

35. Colasanti J, Cho S-O, Wick S, Sundaresan V. 1993. Localization of the functional p34-cdc2 homolog of maize in root tip and stomatal complex cells: association with predicted division sites. *Plant Cell* 5:1101–11

36. Cousin MA, Robinson PJ. 2000. Ca^{2+} inhibits dynamin and arrests syneptic vesicles endocytosis at the active zone. *J. Neurosci.* 20:949–57

37. Del Vecchio AJ, Harper JDI, Vaughn KC, Baron AT, Salisbury JL, Overall RL. 1997. Centrin homologues in higher plants are prominently associated with the developing cell plate. *Protoplasma* 196:224–34

38. Ding B, Turgeon R, Parthasarathy MV. 1991. Microfilaments of the preprophase

band of freeze substituted preprophase band. *Protoplasma* 165:209–11

39. Dombrowski JE, Raikhel NV. 1995. Isolation of cDNA encoding a novel GTP-binding protein of *Arabidopsis thaliana*. *Plant Mol. Biol.* 28:1121–26

40. Don SM, Drews GN, Fischer RL, Harada JJ, Goldberg RB, Koltunow AM. 1997. *first*: an *Arabidopsis* mutant with altered cell division planes and radial pattern disruption during embryogenesis. *Sex. Plant Reprod.* 10:358–67

41. Dong J, Radau B, Otto A, Muller E, Lindschau C, Westermann P. 2000. Profilin I attached to the Golgi is required for the formation of constitutive transport vesicles at the trans-Golgi network. *Biochim. Biophys. Acta* 1497:253–60

42. Emr SD, Gary JD, Odorizzi GC, Babst M, Wurmser AE. 1999. Phosphoinositide kinase signaling in vesicle transport. *Mol. Biol. Cell* 10:233a

43. Endlé M-C, Stoppin V, Lambert A-M, Schmit A-C. 1998. The growing cell plate of higher plants is a site of both actin assembly and vinculin-like antigen recruitment. *Eur. J. Cell Biol.* 77:10–18

44. Euteneuer U, Jackson WT, McIntosh JR. 1982. Polarity of spindle microtubules in *Haemanthus* endosperm. *J. Cell Biol.* 94:644–53

45. Feiler HS, Desprez T, Santoni V, Kronenberger J, Caboche M, Traas J. 1995. The higher plant *Arabidopsis thaliana* encodes a functional CDC48 homologue which is highly expressed in dividing and expanding cells. *EMBO J.* 14:5626–37

46. Field C, Li R, Oegema K. 1999. Cytokinesis in eucaryotes: a mechanistic comparision. *Curr. Opin. Cell Biol.* 11:68–80

47. Deleted in proof

48. Fishkind DJ, Wang Y-L. 1995. New horizons for cytokinesis. *Curr. Biol.* 7:23–31

49. Flescher EG, Madden K, Snyder M. 1993. Components required for cytokinesis are important for bud site selection in yeast. *J. Cell Biol.* 122:373–86

50. Frost DJ, Read SM, Drake RR, Haley BE, Wasserman BP. 1990. Identification of the UDP-glucose binding polypeptide of callose synthase from *Beta vulgaris* L. by photoaffinity labeling with 5-azido-UDP-glucose. *J. Biol. Chem.* 265:2162–67

51. Galatis B, Apostolakos P, Katsaros C, Lokari H. 1982. Preprophase microtubule band and local wall thickening in guard cell mother cells of some Leguminosae. *Ann. Bot.* 50:779–91

52. Gallagher K, Smith LG. 1999. *discordia* mutations specifically misorient asymmetric cell divisions during development of maize leaf epidermis. *Development* 126:4623–33

53. Deleted in proof

54. Glotzer M. 1997. The mechanism of control of cytokinesis. *Curr. Opin. Cell Biol.* 9:815–23

55. Granger CL, Cyr RJ. 2000. Microtubule reorganization in tobacco BY-2 cells stably expressing GFP-MBD. *Planta* 210:502–9

56. Gu X, Verma DPS. 1996. Phragmoplastin, a dynamin-like protein associated with cell plate formation in plants. *EMBO J.* 15:695–704

57. Gu X, Verma DPS. 1997. Dynamics of phragmoplastin in living cells during cell plate formation and uncoupling of cell elongation from the plane of cell division. *Plant Cell* 9:157–69

58. Gunning BES, Wick SM. 1985. Preprophase bands, phragmoplasts, and spatial control of cytokinesis. *J. Cell Sci.* 2(Suppl.):157–79

59. Hannah MJ, Schmidt AA, Huttner WB. 1999. Synaptic vesicle biogenesis. *Annu. Rev. Cell Dev. Biol.* 15:733–98

60. Harper JDI, Fowke LC, Gilmer S, Overall RL, Marc J. 2000. A centrin homologue is localised across the developing cell plate in gymnosperms and angiosperms. *Protoplasma* 211:207–16

61. Hauser BA, He JQ, Park SO, Gasser CS. 2000. TSO1 is a novel protein that modulates cytokinesis and cell expansion in *Arabidopsis. Development* 127:2219–26

62. Hayashi T, Yamasaki S, Nauenburg S, Binz T, Niemann H. 1995. Disassembly of the reconstituted synaptic vesicle membrane fusion complex in vitro. *EMBO J.* 14:2317–25

63. Heese M, Mayer U, Jürgens G. 1998. Cytokinesis in flowering plants: cellular processes and developmental integration. *Curr. Opin. Plant Biol.* 1:486–91

64. Hepler PK. 1982. Endoplasmic reticulum in the formation of the cell plate and plasmodesmata. *Protoplasma* 111:121–33

65. Hepler PK. 1994. The role of calcium in cell division. *Cell Calcium* 16:322–30

66. Hepler PK, Bonsignore CL. 1990. Caffeine inhibits cytokinesis: ultrastructure of cell plate formation/degradation. *Protoplasma* 157:182–92

67. Hepler PK, Callaham DA. 1987. Free calcium increases during anaphase in stamen hair cells of *Tradescantia. J. Cell Biol.* 105:2137–43

68. Hinshaw JE, Schmid SL. 1995. Dynamin self-assembles into rings suggesting a mechanism for coated vesicle budding. *Nature* 374:190–92

69. Hogan CJ. 1987. Microtubule patterns during meiosis in two higher plant species. *Protoplasma* 138:126–36

70. Hong Z, Delauney AJ, Verma DPS. 2001. A cell plate-specific callose synthase and its interaction with phragmoplastin. *Plant Cell.* In press

71. Hong Z, Zhang Z, Olson JM, Verma DPS. 2001. A novel UDP-glucose transferase forms a complex with callose synthase and interacts with phragmoplastin at the forming cell plate. *Plant Cell.* In press

72. Hoshi M, Ohta Y, Mori A, Murofushi H, Sakai H, Nishida E. 1992. Mitogen-activated-protein-kinase-catalysed phosphorylation of microtubule-associated proteins, microtubule-associated protein 2 and microtubule-associated protein 4, induces an alteration in their function. *Eur. J. Biochem.* 203:43–52

73. Hulskamp M, Parekh NS, Grini P, Schneitz K, Zimmerman I, et al. 1997. The *STUD* gene is required male-specific cytokinesis after telophase II of meiosis in *Arabidopsis thaliana* mutant. *Plant J.* 11:659–69

74. Hush J, Wu L, John PC, Hepler LH, Hepler PK. 1996. Plant mitosis promoting factor disassembles the microtubule preprophase band and accelerates prophase progression in *Tradescantia*. *Cell Biol. Int.* 20:275–87

75. Jones SM, Howell KE, Henley JR, Cao H, McNiven MA. 1998. Role of dynamin in the formation of transport vesicles from the trans-Golgi network. *Science* 279:573–77

76. Joshi HC, Palevitz BA. 1996. γ-Tubulin and microtubule organization in plants. *Trends Cell Biol.* 6:41–44

77. Jurgens M, Hepler LH, Rivers BA, Hepler PK. 1994. BAPTA-calcium buffers modulate cell plate formation in stamen hairs of *Tradescantia*: evidence for calcium gradients. *Protoplasma* 183:86–99

78. Kakimoto T, Shibaoka H. 1988. Cytoskeletal ultrastructure of phragmoplast-nuclei complexes isolated from cultured tobacco cells. *Protoplasma* 2(Suppl.):95–103

79. Kakimoto T, Shibaoka H. 1992. Sythesis of polysaccharides in phragmoplasts isolated from tobacco BY-2 cells. *Plant Cell Physiol.* 33:353–61

80. Karyophyllis D, Katsaros C, Dimitriadis I, Galatis B. 2000. F-actin organization during the cell cycle of *Sphacelaria rigidula* (Phaeophyceae). *Euro. J. Phycol.* 35:25–33

81. Kasai K, Shin HW, Shinotsuka C, Murakami K, Nakayama K. 1999. Dynamin II is involved in endocytosis but not in the formation of transport vesicles from the *trans*-Golgi network. *J. Biochem.* 125:780–89

82. Kreitzer G, Marmorstein A, Okamoto P, Vallee R, Rodriguez-Boulan E. 2000. Kinesin and dynamin are required for post-Golgi transport of a plasma-membrane protein. *Nat. Cell Biol.* 2:125–27

83. Lai MM, Hong JJ, Ruggiero AM, Burnett PE, Slepnev VI, et al. 1999. The calcineurin-dynamin 1 complex as a calcium sensor for synaptic vesicle endocytosis. *J. Biol. Chem.* 274:25963–66

84. Lauber MH, Waizenegger I, Steinmann T, Schwarz H, Mayer U, et al. 1997. The *Arabidopsis* KNOLLE protein is a cytokinesis specific syntaxin. *J. Cell Biol.* 139:1485–93

85. Lee Y-RJ, Liu B. 2000. Identification of a phragmoplast-associated kinesin-related protein in higher plants. *Curr. Biol.* 10:797–800

86. Li H, Wu G, Ware D, Davis KR, Yang Z. 1998. *Arabidopsis* Rho-related GTPase: differential gene expression in pollen and polar localization in fission yeast. *Plant Physiol.* 118:407–17

87. Lin Y, Wang Y, Zhu J-K, Yang Z. 1996. Localization of a Rho GTPase implies a role in tip growth and movement of the generative cell in pollen tubes. *Plant Cell* 8:293–303

88. Liu B, Palevitz BA. 1996. Localization of a kinesin-like protein in generative cells of tobacco. *Protoplasma* 195:78–89

89. Liu CM, Johnson S, Wang TL. 1995. *cyd*, a mutant of pea that alters embryo morphology is defective in cytokinesis. *Dev. Genet.* 16:321–31

90. Liu CM, Meinke DW. 1998. The *titan* mutants of *Arabidopsis* are disrupted in mitosis and cell cycle control during seed development. *Plant J.* 16:21–31

91. Liu Z, Running MP, Meyerowitz EM. 1997. *TSO1* functions in cell division during *Arabidopsis* flower development. *Development* 124:665–72

92. Lukowitz W, Mayer U, Jurgens G. 1996. Cytokinesis in the *Arabidopsis* embryo involves the syntaxin-related *KNOLLE* gene product. *Cell* 84:61–71

93. Machida Y, Nakashima M, Morikiyo K, Banno H, Ishikawa M, et al. 1998. MAPKKK-related protein kinase NPK1: regulation of the M phase of plant cell cycle. *J. Plant Res.* 111:243–46

94. Mayer U, Buttner G, Jurgens G. 1993.

Apical-basal pattern formation in the *Arabidopsis* embryo. Studies on the role of *GNOM* gene. *Development* 117:149–62

95. Mayer U, Herzog U, Berger F, Inzé D, Jurgens G. 1999. Mutations in the *pilz* group genes disrupt the microtubule cytoskeleton and uncouple cell cycle progression from cell division in *Arabidopsis* embryo and endosperm. *Eur. J. Cell Biol.* 78:100–8

96. Mews M, Sek FJ, Moore R, Volkmann D, Gunning BES, John PCL. 1997. Mitotic cyclin distribution during maize division: implications for the sequence diversity and function of cyclins in plants. *Protoplasma* 200:128–45

97. Miller SM, Kirk DL. 1999. *glsA*, a *Volvox* gene required for asymmetric division and germ cell specification encodes a chaperone-like protein. *Development* 126:649–58

98. Mineyuki Y. 1999. The preprophase band of microtubules: its function as cytokinetic apparatus in higher plants. *Int. Rev. Cytol.* 187:1–49

99. Mineyuki Y, Gunning BES. 1990. A role for preprophase bands of microtubules in maturation of new cell walls and a general proposal on the function of preprophase band sites in cell division in higher plants. *J. Cell Sci.* 97:527–37

100. Mizoguchi T, Gotoh Y, Nishida E, Yamaguchi-Shinozaki K, Hayashida N, et al. 1994. Characterization of two cDNAs that encode MAP kinase homologues in *Arabidopsis thaliana* and analysis of the possible role of auxin in activating such kinase activities in cultured cells. *Plant J.* 5:111–22

101. Molchan TM, Valster AH, Hepler PK. 1999. Actomyosin promotes cell plate alignment and lateral expansion in plant cells. *Mol. Biol. Cell* 10:15a

102. Moore P, Staehelin LA. 1988. Immunogold localization of the cell-wall-matrix polysaccharides rhamnogalacturonan I

and xyloglucan during cell expansion and cytokinesis in *Trifolium pratense* L.: implications for secretory pathways. *Planta* 174:433–45

103. Movafeghi A, Happel N, Pimpl P, Tai G-H, Robinson DG. 1999. *Arabidopsis* Sec21p and Sec23p homologs. Probable coat proteins of plant COP-coated vesicles. *Plant Physiol.* 119:1437–45

104. Mundel C, Baltz R, Eliasson Å, Bronner R, Grass N, et al. 2000. A LIM-domain protein from sunflower is localized to the cytoplasm and/or nucleus in a wide variety of tissues and is associated with the phragmoplast in dividing cells. *Plant Mol. Biol.* 42:291–302

105. Murata T, Wada M. 1991. Effects of centrifugation on preprophase band formation in *Adiantum protonemata*. *Plant Cell Physiol.* 32:1145–51

106. Nakashima M, Hirano K, Nakashima S, Banno H, Nishihama R, Machida Y. 1998. Expression pattern of the gene for NPK1 protein kinase related to mitogen-activated protein kinase kinase kinase (MPKKK) in a tobacco plant: correlation with cell proliferation. *Plant Cell Physiol.* 39:690–700

107. Nebenfuhr A, Frohlick JA, Staehelin LA. 2000. Redistribution of Golgi stacks and other organelles during mitosis and cytokinesis in plant cells. *Plant Physiol.* 124:135–51

108. Deleted in proof

109. Nickle TC, Meinke DW. 1998. A cytokinesis-defective mutant of *Arabidopsis: cyt1* characterized by embryonic lethality, incomplete cell walls, and excessive callose accumulation. *Plant J.* 15:321–32

110. Nicol F, His I, Jauneau A, Vernhettes S, Canut H, Hofte H. 1998. A plasma membrane-bound putative endo-1,4-β-D-glucanase is required for normal wall assembly and cell elongation in Arabidopsis. *EMBO J.* 17:5563–76

111. Nishihama R, Machid Y. 2000. The MAP

kinase cascade that includes MAPKKK-related protein kinase NPK1 controls a mitotic process in plant cells. In *MAP Kinases in Plant Signal Transduction, Results and Problems in Cell Differentiation,* ed. H Hirt, 27:119–30. Berlin: Springer-Verlag

112. Northcote DH, Davet R, Lay J. 1989. Use of antisera to localize callose, xylan and arabinogalactan in the cell plate, primary and secondary walls of plant cells. *Planta* 178:353–66

113. Olson O-A, Brown RC, Lemmon BE. 1995. Pattern and process of wall formation in developing endosperm. *BioEssays* 17:803–12

114. Otegui M, Staehelin LA. 2000. Syncytial-type cell plate: a novel kind of cell plate invoved in endosperm cellularization of Arabidopsis. *Plant Cell* 12:933–47

115. Otegui M, Staehelin LA. 2001. Cytokinesis in flowering plants: more than one way to divide a cell. *Curr. Opin. Plant Biol.* 3:493–502

116. Owen HA, Makaroff CA. 1995. Ultrastructure of microsporogenesis and microgametogenesis in *Arabidopsis thaliana* (L.) Heynh. ecotype Wassilewskija (Brassicaceae). *Protoplasma* 185:7–21

117. Palevitz BA. 1980. Comparative effects of phalloidin and cytochalasin B on motility and morphogenesis in *Allium. Can. J. Bot.* 58:773–85

118. Palevitz BA, Tiezzi A. 1992. Organization, composition and function of the generative cell and sperm cytoskeleton. *Int. Rev. Cytol.* 40:338–48

119. Panteris E, Apostolakos P, Galatis B. 2000. Gamma-tubulin colocalizes with microtubule arrays and tubulin paracrystals in dividing vegetative cells of higher plants. *Protoplasma* 210:179–87

120. Patterson SE, Quinn AT, Sussman MR, Bleecker AB. 1997. Things fall apart: Mutations at the TFA1 locus lead to ectopic cell separation. *Arabidopsis Conf.,* 1997. Abstr. 8–19

121. Pickett-Heaps JD, Gunning BES, Brown RC, Lemmon BE, Cleary AL. 1999. The cytoplast concept in dividing plant cells: cytoplasmic domains and the evolution of spatially organized cell division. *Am. J. Bot.* 86:153–72

121a. Pimpl P, Movafegli A, Coughlan S, Denecke J, Hillmer S, Robinson DG. 2000. In situ localization and in vitro induction of COPI-coated vesicles. *Plant Cell* 22:19–36

122. Poenie M, Alderton J, Steinhardt R, Tsien R. 1986. Calcium rises abruptly and briefly throughout the cell on the onset of anaphase. *Science* 233:886–89

123. Price A, Wickner W, Ungermann C. 2000. Proteins needed for vesicle budding from the Golgi complex are also required for the docking step of homotypic vacuole fusion. *J. Cell Biol.* 148:1223–29

124. Proust J, Houlné G, Schantz M-L, Shen W-H, Schantz R. 1999. Regulation of biosynthesis and cellular localization of Sp32 annexins in tobacco BY2 cells. *Plant Mol. Biol.* 39:361–72

125. Qadota H, Python CP, Inoue SB, Arisawa M, Anraku Y, et al. 1996. Identification of yeast Rho1p GTPase as a regulatory subunit of 1,3-beta glucan synthase. *Science* 272:279–81

126. Ragnini-Wilson A. 1999. How to get to the right place at the right time: Rab/Ypt small GTPases and vesicle transport. *Protoplasma* 209:19–27

127. Reichelt S, Knight AE, Hodge TP, Baluska F, Samaj J, et al. 1999. Characterization of the unconventional myosin VIII in plant cells and its localization at the post-cytokinetic cell wall. *Plant J.* 19:555–67

128. Reynolds JO, Eisses JF, Sylvester AW. 1998. Balancing division and expansion during maize leaf morphogenesis: analysis of the mutant *warty-1. Development* 125:259–68

129. Robinson DG, Hinz G, Holstein SHE. 1998. The molecular characterization of transport vesicles. *Plant Mol. Biol.* 38:49–76

130. Samuels AL, Giddings TH, Staehelin LA. 1995. Cytokinesis in tobacco BY-2 and root tip cells: a new model of cell plate formation in higher plants. *J. Cell Biol.* 130:1345–57

131. Deleted in proof

132. Samuels AL, Staehelin LA. 1996. Caffeine inhibits cell plate formation by disrupting membrane reorganization just after the vesicle fusion step. *Protoplasma* 195:144–55

133. Sanderfoot AA, Raikhel NV. 1999. The specificity of vesicle trafficking: coat proteins and SNAREs. *Plant Cell* 11:629–41

134. Deleted in proof

135. Satiat-Jeunemaitre B, Cole L, Bourett R, Howard R, Hawes C. 1996. Brefeldin A effects in plant and fungal cells: something new about vesicle trafficking? *J. Microsc.* 181:162–77

136. Schmidt S, Sohmann M, Hofmann K, Woodlard A, Simanie V. 1997. Spg1p GTPase is an essential dosage-dependent inducer of septum formation in *Schizosaccharomyces pombe*. *Genes Dev.* 11:1519–34

137. Schopfer CR, Hepler PK. 1991. Distribution of membranes and the cytoskeleton during cell plate formation in pollen mother cells of *Tradescantia*. *J. Cell Sci.* 100:717–28

138. Shao XG, Fernandez I, Zhang XY, Sudhof TC, Rizo J. 1997. Synaptotagmin-syntaxin interaction: the C2 domain as a Ca^{2+}-dependent electrostatic switch. *Neuron* 18:133–42

139. Siddiqi I, Ganesh G, Grossniklaus U, Subbiah V. 2000. The *dyad* gene is required for progression through female meiosis in *Arabidopsis*. *Development* 127:197–207

140. Sluiman HJ. 1984. A pathway of plasma membrane biogenesis bypassing the Golgi apparatus during cell division in the green alga *Cylindrocapsa geminella*. *J. Cell Sci.* 72:89–100

141. Smirnova EA, Cox DL, Bajer AS. 1995. Antibodies against phosphorylated proteins MPM-2 recognizes mitotic microtubules in endosperm cells of higher plant *Haemanthus*. *Cell Motil. Cytoskelet.* 31:34–44

142. Smirnova EA, Reddy ASN, Bowser J, Bajer AS. 1998. Minus end-directed kinesin-like protein, KCBP, localizes to anaphase spindle poles in *Haemanthus* endosperm. *Cell Motil. Cytoskelet.* 41:271–80

143. Smith LG. 1999. Divide and conquer: cytokinesis in plant cells. *Curr. Opin. Plant Biol.* 2:447–53

144. Smith LG, Hake S, Sylvester AW. 1996. The *tangled-1* mutation alters cell division orientation throughout maize leaf development without altering leaf shape. *Development* 122:481–89

145. Song H, Golovkin M, Reddy ASN, Endow SA. 1997. *In vitro* motility of AtKCBP, a calmodulin-binding kinesin protein of *Arabidopsis*. *Proc. Natl. Acad. Sci. USA* 94:322–27

146. Song J-Y, Leung T, Ehler LK, Wang C, Liu Z. 2000. Regulation of meristem organization and cell division by *TSO1*, an *Arabidopsis* gene with cystein-rich repeats. *Development* 127:2207–17

147. Sorensen SO, Pauly M, Bush M, Skjot M, McCan MC, et al. 2000. Pectin engineering: modification of potato pectin by in vivo expression of an endo-1,4-β-D-galactanse. *Proc. Natl. Acad. Sci. USA* 97:7639–44

148. Spielman M, Preuss D, Li F-L, Browne WE, Scott RJ. 1997. *TETRASPORE* is required for male meiotic cytokinesis in *Arabidopsis thaliana*. *Development* 124:2645–57

149. Staehelin LA, Driouich A. 1997. BrefeldinA effects in plants. *Plant Physiol.* 114:401–3

150. Staehelin LA, Hepler PK. 1996. Cytokinesis in higher plants. *Cell* 84:821–24

151. Staiger CJ, Cande WZ. 1992. *ameiotic*, a gene that controls meiotic chromosome and cytoskeletal behavior in maize. *Dev. Biol.* 154:226–30

152. Stals H, Bauwens S, Traas J, van Montagu M, Engler G, Inzé D. 1997. Plant CDC2 is not only targeted to the preprophase band, but also colocalized with the spindle, phragmoplast and chromosomes. *FEBS Lett.* 418:229–34

153. Stoppin-Mellet V, Canaday J, Lambert AM. 1999. Characterization of microsome associated tobacco BY-2 centrins. *Eur. J. Cell Biol.* 78:842–48

154. Sylvester AW. 2000. Division decisions and the spatial regulation of cytokinesis. *Curr. Opin. Plant Biol.* 3:58–66

155. Takei K, McPherson PS, Schmid SL, de Camilli P. 1995. Tubular membrane invaginations coated by dynamin rings are induced by GTP-γ-S in nerve terminals. *Nature* 374:186–90

156. Takei K, Mundigl O, Daniell L, de Camilli P. 1996. The synaptic vesicle cycle: a single vesicle budding step involving clathrin and dynamin. *J. Cell Biol.* 133:1237–50

157. Terasaka O, Niitsu T. 1990. Unequal cell division and chromatin differentiation in pollen grain cells II. Microtubule dynamics associated with the unequal cell division. *Bot. Mag.* 103:133–42

158. Thiel G, Battey N. 1998. Exocytosis in plants. *Plant Mol. Biol.* 38:111–25

159. Torres-Ruiz RA, Lohner A, Jurgens G. 1996. The *GURKE* gene is required for normal organization of the apical region in the *Arabidopsis* embryo. *Plant J.* 10:1005–16

160. Traas JA, Bellini C, Nacry P, Kronenberger J, Bouchez D, Caboche M. 1995. Normal differentiation pattern in plants lacking microtubular preprophase band. *Nature* 375:676–77

161. Traas JA, Doonan JH, Rawlins DJ, Shaw PJ, Watts J, Lloyd CW. 1987. An actin network is present in the cytoplasm throughout the cell cycle of carrot cells and associates with the dividing nucleus. *J. Cell Biol.* 105:387–95

162. Twell D, Park SK, Lalanne E. 1998. Asymmetric division and cell-fate determination in developing pollen. *Trends Plant Sci.* 3:305–10

163. Valster AH, Pierson ES, Valenta R, Hepler PK, Emons AMC. 1997. Probing the plant actin cytoskeleton during cytokinesis and interphase by profilin microinjection. *Plant Cell* 9:1815–24

164. Vaughn KC, Harper JD. 1998. Microtubule-organizing centers and nucleating sites in land plants. *Int. Rev. Cytol.* 181:75–149

165. Vaughn KC, Hoffman JC, Hahn MG, Staehelin LA. 1995. The herbicide dichlobenil disrupts cell plate formation: immunogold characterization. *Protoplasma* 194:117–32

166. Veit M, Becher A, Ahnert-Hilger G. 2000. Synaptobrevin 2 is palmitoylated in synaptic vesicles prepared from adult, but not from embryonic brain. *Mol. Cell Neurosci.* 15:408–16

167. Verma DPS, Cheon C-I, Hong Z. 1994. Small GTP-binding proteins and membrane biogenesis in plants. *Plant Physiol.* 106:1–6

168. Verma DPS, Gu X. 1996. Vesicle dynamics during cell plate formation in plants. *Trends Plant Sci.* 1:145–49

169. Verma DPS, Hong Z. 1996. Biogenesis of the peribacteroid membrane in root nodules. *Trends Microbiol.* 4:364–68

170. Vos JW, Safadi F, Reddy ASN, Hepler PK. 2000. The kinesin-like calmodulin binding protein is differentially involved in cell division. *Plant Cell* 12:979–90

171. Wagner VT, Leigh B, Quatrano RS. 1992. Role of a vitronectin-like molecule in embryo adhesion of the brown alga

Fucus. Proc. Natl. Acad. Sci. USA 89:3644–48

172. Webb MC, Gunning BES. 1990. Embryo sac development in *Arabidopsis thaliana*. 1. Megasporogenesis, including the microtubular cytoskeleton. *Sex. Plant Reprod.* 3:244–56

173. Wein H, Bass HW, Cande WZ. 1998. DSK1, a kinesin-related protein involved in anaphase spindle elongation, is a component of a mitotic spindle matrix. *Cell Motil. Cytoskelet.* 41:214–24

174. Wieland F, Harter C. 1999. Mechanisms of vesicle formation: insight from the COP system. *Curr. Opin. Cell Biol.* 11:440–46

175. Wilheim JE, Valle RD. 1993. RNA on the move: the mRNA localization pathway. *J. Cell Biol.* 123:269–74

176. Willemse MTM, Van Lammeren AA. 1988. Structure and function of the microtubular cytoskeletan during megasporogenesis and embryo sac development in *Gasteria verrucosa* (Mill) H. Duval. *Sex. Plant Reprod.* 1:74–82

177. Willemsen V, Wolkenfelt H, Vrieze G, Weisbeek P, Scheres B. 1998. The *HOBBIT* gene is required for formation of the root meristem in the *Arabidopsis* embryo. *Development* 125:521–31

178. Wolniak SM, Hepler PK, Jackson WT. 1980. Detection of membrane-calcium distribution during mitosis in *Halmanthus* endosperm with chlorotetracyclin. *J. Cell Biol.* 87:23–32

179. Wolniak SM, Larsen PM. 1995. The timing of protein kinase activation events in the cascade that regulates mitotic progression in *Tradescantia* stamen hair cells. *Plant Cell* 7:431–45

180. Wu K, Rooney M, Ferl RJ. 1997. The Arabidopsis 14-3-3 multigene family. *Plant Physiol.* 114:1421–31

181. Yang M, Sack FD. 1995. The *too many mouths* and *four lips* mutations affect stomatal production in *Arabidopsis*. *Plant Cell* 7:2227–39

182. Yasuhara H, Shibaoka H. 2000. Inhibition of cell-plate formation by brefeldin A inhibited the depolymerization of microtubules in the central region of the phragmoplast. *Plant Cell Physiol.* 41:300–10

183. Yasuhara H, Sonobe S, Shibaoka H. 1993. Effects of taxol on the development of cell plate and of the phragmoplast in tobacco BY-2 cells. *Plant Cell Physiol.* 34:21–29

184. Yasuhara H, Sonobe S, Shibaoka H. 1995. Effects of brefeldin A on the formation of the cell plate in tobacco BY-2 cells. *Eur. J. Cell Biol.* 66:274–81

185. Yu HS, Russell SD. 1993. 3-dimensional ultrastructure of generative cell mitosis in the pollen tube of *Nicotiana tabacum*. *Eur. J. Cell Biol.* 61:338–48

186. Zablackis E, York WS, Pauly M, Hantus S, Reiter W-D, et al. 1996. Substitution of L-fucose by L-galactose in cell walls of *Arabidopsis mur1*. *Science* 27:1808–10

187. Zhang D, Wadsworth P, Hepler P. 1990. Microtubule dynamics in living dividing plant cells. Confocal imaging of microinjected fluorescent brain tubulin. *Proc. Natl. Acad. Sci. USA* 87:8820–24

188. Zhang GF, Staehelin LA. 1992. Functional compartmentalization of the Golgi apparatus of plant cells. An immunocytochemical analysis of high-pressure-frozen and freeze-substituted sycamore maple suspension culture cells. *Plant Physiol.* 99:1070–83

189. Zhang H, Wang J, Hwang I, Goodman HM. 1995. Isolation and expression of an *Arabidopsis* 14-3-3-like protein gene. *Biochem. Biophys. Acta* 1266:113–16

190. Zhang Z, Hong Z, Verma DPS. 2000. Phragmoplastin polymerizes into spiral coiled structures via intermolecular interaction of two self-assembly domains. *J. Biol. Chem.* 275:8779–84

191. Zheng H, Bassham DC, da Silva Conceicao A, Raikhel NV. 1999. The syntaxin

family of proteins in *Arabidopsis*: a new syntaxin homologue shows polymorphism between two ecotypes. *J. Exp. Bot.* 50:915–24

192. Zuo J, Niu Q-W, Nishizawa N, Wu Y, Kost B, Chua N-H. 2000. KORRIGAN, an *Arabidopsis* endo-1,4-β glucanase, localized to the cell plate by polarized targeting is essential for cytokinesis. *Plant Cell* 12:1137–52

Annu. Rev. Plant Physiol. Plant Mol. Biol. 2001. 52:785–816

RIBOSOME-INACTIVATING PROTEINS:
A Plant Perspective

Kirsten Nielsen and Rebecca S Boston
Department of Botany, North Carolina State University, Raleigh, North Carolina 27695-7612; e-mail: knielse@unity.ncsu.edu; boston@unity.ncsu.edu

Key Words RIP, protein synthesis inhibitor, plant toxins, cytotoxicity, 28S ribosomal RNA

■ **Abstract** Ribosome-inactivating proteins (RIPs) are toxic N-glycosidases that depurinate the universally conserved α-sarcin loop of large rRNAs. This depurination inactivates the ribosome, thereby blocking its further participation in protein synthesis. RIPs are widely distributed among different plant genera and within a variety of different tissues. Recent work has shown that enzymatic activity of at least some RIPs is not limited to site-specific action on the large rRNAs of ribosomes but extends to depurination and even nucleic acid scission of other targets. Characterization of the physiological effects of RIPs on mammalian cells has implicated apoptotic pathways. For plants, RIPs have been linked to defense by antiviral, antifungal, and insecticidal properties demonstrated in vitro and in transgenic plants. How these effects are brought about, however, remains unresolved. At the least, these results, together with others summarized here, point to a complex biological role. With genetic, genomic, molecular, and structural tools now available for integrating different experimental approaches, we should further our understanding of these multifunctional proteins and their physiological functions in plants.

CONTENTS

1040-2519/01/0601-0785$14.00

INTRODUCTION

Proteins with selective toxicity have been investigated for use in ways as varied as murder weapons by mystery writers (38) and espionage agents (39, 92), to transgenic plant protection by biologists (110, 112, 117), "silver bullet" therapies by cancer researchers (53, 96, 139, 145, 171, 183), and biological weaponry by military groups (39, 200). One class of such proteins, ribosome-inactivating proteins (RIPs), are found in genera throughout the plant kingdom as well as in certain fungi and bacteria. These proteins act as N-glycosidases to modify large rRNAs and render them incapable of sustaining further translation. The K_{cat} for nonplant ribosomes is greater than 10^3 min^{-1} for the RIPs abrin (from *Abrus precatorius*) and ricin (from *Ricinus communis*; 139). Thus, a single molecule has the potential to kill a cell.

Because of their selective toxicity, RIPs have been primary candidates for the toxic moiety of immunotherapeutics (139). As a result, much of the RIP literature reflects attempts to isolate and characterize RIPs from new plant sources and to exploit these RIPs as anticancer agents (8, 56, 173). Numerous other studies have focused on enzymology, uptake of lectin-associated RIPs into target cells, and subsequent transport to ribosomal targets in the cytosol (116, 140, 162). These investigations have provided a broad knowledge base for understanding biochemical and medicinal properties of RIPs. Less prevalent, however, are investigations into the biological function of RIPs in plants. In recent years, such investigation of RIP activities has increased, especially as tools for gene isolation and transgenic expression became available. These studies have led to an improved understanding of RIP gene expression and activity against pathogens but have also uncovered new enzymatic activities that are suggestive of RIP biology being quite complex. This review summarizes work related to RIP activities and considers unresolved issues in how these activities may affect plant metabolism and protection.

BACKGROUND

Historically, RIPs have been linked to plant defense, with reports appearing as early as 1925 describing inhibition of viral infection by extracts of pokeweed [*Phytolacca americana*; summarized in (83)]. Pioneering work was performed by L Barbieri, F Stirpe, and coworkers who assayed extracts from over 50 plants and found that most had translational inhibitory activity in vitro (8, 56, 173). Subsequent purification of the inhibitory proteins led to their identification as RIPs. As searches for additional RIPs were carried out, they were found not only in a few exotic plants but also in crop plants such as wheat, maize, and barley [(40)

see comprehensive reviews by Barbieri (8) and Stirpe et al (173) for detailed lists of RIPs, their source plants, and abundance in various organs]. For many years after the first RIPs were characterized, the mechanism by which they inactivated translation was not known. In a major breakthrough, Endo and coworkers showed that the enzymatic activity of RIPs was an N-glycosidation to remove a specific adenine corresponding to residue A4324 in rat 28S rRNA (49, 50). This adenine lies within a 14-nucleotide region that is known as the α-sarcin loop and is conserved in large rRNAs from bacteria to humans (122). A GAGA sequence in which the first A is the RIP substrate forms the core of a putative tetraloop surrounded by a short base-paired stem (41, 65, 143). Irreversible modification of the target A residue blocks elongation factor (EF)-1- and EF-2-dependent GTPase activities and renders the ribosome unable to bind EF-2, thereby blocking translation (133).

Because this translational inhibitory activity is toxic, RIPs were seen as having great potential for use as selective cell-killing agents and interest in them shifted toward medical exploitation [for review see (139, 145, 171, 173)]. With the development of monoclonal antibodies as tools for identifying and targeting cell surface markers, researchers gained the ability to couple antibodies to RIPs and thus deliver the toxic protein directly to specific cells. The potential for using RIPs as cell destructive agents in the immunotoxins stimulated intense efforts to isolate and characterize such proteins from many different plant sources [reviewed in (53, 145)]. Unfortunately, RIP-derived immunotoxins are not perfect clinical tools. For example, they are generally highly antigenic and promote immune responses in animals receiving prolonged treatment with the immunotoxins [reviewed in (8)]. A second problem is with vascular leak syndrome, a deleterious side effect that limits clinical efficacy as a cancer therapy (96). Nevertheless, refined approaches to inhibit toxicity are showing promise (7, 76) and a number of clinical trials are ongoing (53, 96).

CLASSIFICATION OF RIPs

RIPs are classified into three groups based on their physical properties (Figure 1) (127). Type 1 RIPs, such as pokeweed antiviral protein (PAP), saporin (from soapwort, *Saponaria officinalis* L.), and barley (*Hordeum vulgare*) translation inhibitor, are monomeric enzymes, each with an approximate Mr of 30,000 (3, 8, 82). They are basic proteins that share a number of highly conserved active cleft residues and secondary structure within the active site region (8, 81, 124, 126) but are distinctly different in overall sequence homology and posttranslational modifications (71). To date, most RIPs that have been characterized fall into the type 1 class (8).

Type 2 RIPs, like ricin and abrin, are highly toxic heterodimeric proteins with enzymatic and lectin properties in separate polypeptide subunits, each of approximate M_r of 30,000 (138, 139, 175). One polypeptide with RIP activity (A-chain) is linked to a galactose binding lectin (B-chain) through a disulfide bond (138, 139, 175). The lectin chain can bind to galactosyl moieties of glycoproteins and/or glycolipids

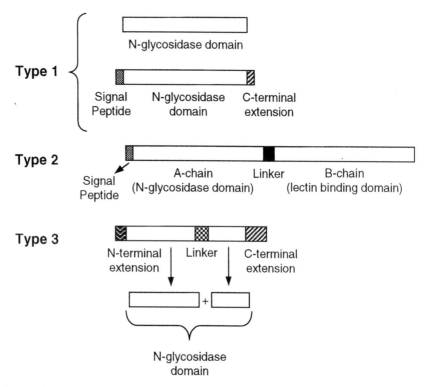

Figure 1 Alignment of RIPs showing a comparison of primary structures. Filled, stippled, and hatched boxes denote regions absent in the active enzymes (shown as blank boxes). The N-terminal signal peptides on type 1 and type 2 RIPs target the proteins to the endomembrane system. Once there, they move to various subcellular compartments such as vacuoles, protein bodies or the periplasmic space. The N-terminal extensions of type 3 RIPs do not appear to have targeting functions because the proteins remain in the cytosol.

found on the surface of eukaryotic cells (105, 140, 158, 172, 180) and mediate retrograde transport of the A-chain to the cytosol (16, 139, 160, 191). Once it reaches the cytosol, the RIP has access to the translational machinery and readily disrupts protein synthesis. The type 2 RIPs have been very useful for studies of endocytosis and intracellular transport in mammalian cells (reviewed in 74, 114, 116, 161, 162).

Type 3 RIPs are synthesized as inactive precursors (proRIPs) that require proteolytic processing events to occur between amino acids involved in formation of the active site (127). These RIPs are much less prevalent than type 1 or type 2 RIPs. To date, type 3 RIPs have been characterized only from maize and barley (14, 34, 151, 196), although several close relatives of maize, including sorghum, appear to accumulate type 3 RIPs in seeds as judged by size and immunological cross-reactivity with antibodies to maize proRIP (75, 165). In maize, proRIPs are acidic proteins that are cleaved in vivo to release amino acids from an internal region as well as short segments at both NH_2- and COOH-termini. These processing events result in proteins with tightly associated polypeptide subunits of M_r 16,500 and 8,500 (196). The two RIPs that have been characterized in maize are both type 3 proteins (13, 14, 196). Barley, in contrast, has one type 1 RIP and one type 3 RIP. The latter, called JIP60, is induced by jasmonic acid and activated after proteolytic cleavage to remove internal and COOH-terminal domains (34). The internal insertions of JIP60 occur at approximately the same position within the primary amino acid sequence as in the maize RIPs. However, the JIP60 has a much larger C-terminal region (>20 kDa) and shares homology with eukaryotic initiation factor 4γ subunits (34).

The function of the extra domains in the type 3 RIPs is not known. Once they are removed, the processed active protein is similar in charge and enzymatic activity to type 1 RIPs (75, 95, 196). For maize, the extra domains are unlikely to be protective features to prevent self-inactivation of maize ribosomes because ribosomes from seed and other plant parts are resistant to maize proRIP and active RIP (14, 75, 95). For barley, however, induction of JIP60 was reported to coincide with a decrease in protein synthesis followed by a decrease in polysome size (151). Thus, the possibility of JIP60 accumulating as a proenzyme to protect barley ribosomes cannot be ruled out.

RIBOSOME SUSCEPTIBILITY TO RIP INACTIVATION

The enzymology of RIPs has been well characterized, more so than their biological function. As a result, the role of RIPs in planta remains open to speculation. One factor contributing to the difficulty in ascertaining biological function occurs because many RIPs seem to share few properties aside from the capacity to depurinate ribosomes at the α-sarcin loop. In fact, even this activity varies among different substrates. RIPs such as PAP are very active against both animal and plant ribosomes, but RIPs from cereals generally have low activity against plant ribosomes [117a; reviewed in (70, 71)]. An exception to this rule is the RIP of wheat leaves, which can modify plant ribosomes at concentrations where the seed RIP does not (119).

Large differences in efficiency are observed between depurination of RNA and ribosomes. For example, 10^4-fold more ricin is needed to depurinate oligonucleotides and 10^3-fold more to depurinate wheat ribosomes than to kill mammalian cells (30, 48, 114). A few RIPs have activity against prokaryotic ribosomes, but usually very large amounts of RIP are necessary for these targets (31).

One difference among RIPs contributing to their translational inhibitory activity is the requirement for cofactors. Gelonin from *Gelonium multiflorum*, barley RIP, PAP, and tritin-S from wheat require ATP for maximal activity (27, 156, 170), but other RIPs such as bryodin-R from *Bryonia dioica*, mormordin from *Momordica chorantia*, and saporin do not (27). Brigotti and coworkers have demonstrated that tRNAs affect translational inhibitory activity, with the specificity of the stimulation depending on both the RIP and the particular tRNA. Tritin-S was fairly nonspecific in being stimulated equally by different tRNAs, whereas gelonin was stimulated only by tRNA^{Trp} from mammalian and avian cells and not by other tRNAs or tRNA^{Trp} from yeast (20–23). Given the variety of assays and assay conditions used for RIP analysis, some differences observed in previous studies may be explained by cofactor requirements. It is not known, however, whether the need for cofactors simply represents a mechanism for increasing enzyme efficiency or if it is linked to additional biological activities.

An important long-standing question is: "What factors contribute to the resistance or susceptibility of a ribosome to RIP inactivation?" To date, the accumulated results are at least as confounding as clarifying. Endo's discovery that RIPs depurinate the A^{4324} residue from the strictly conserved α-sarcin loop eliminated the possibility of target site differences between susceptible and resistant ribosomes and left little doubt that factors other than nucleic acid sequences must be the key determinants (49). Chaddock et al (32) approached the question by swapping domains of ricin (which has little effect on plant or bacterial ribosomes) and PAP (which is highly effective at modifying plant and bacterial ribosomes). Surprisingly, rather than gaining the capacity to attack prokaryotic ribosomes, the chimeric molecules lost the promiscuous RIP activity associated with PAP. Vater et al (192) used chemical cross-linking to identify interactions between ricin A-chain and rat liver ribosomal proteins L9 and P0 (previously known as L10e). This finding was intriguing because L9 and P0 are located in the region of the ribosome called the acidic stalk, which is involved in interactions with elongation factors (153, 188). Furthermore, Vater et al suggest that sequence divergence among these proteins is sufficient to account for a lack of prokaryotic recognition by ricin (192). An additional component of the acidic stalk, P3, appears to be unique to higher plants and may contribute to structural differences that affect RIP interactions with plant ribosomes (4, 5).

Hudak et al (79) recently discovered a different interaction, this one occurring between the yeast ribosomal protein L3 and PAP. A mutant with two amino acid substitutions in yeast L3 is resistant to PAP and the mutant L3 protein loses the capacity to be cross-linked to PAP. Because the altered amino acid residues are highly conserved among fungal, mammalian, and plant cells, the RIP-L3 interaction is not likely to be a determinant of species-specific sensitivity or resistance to RIPs. Nevertheless, the RIP-L3 interaction appears to be necessary for the enzymatic modification of ribosomes by RIPs.

An intriguing concept that ribosome susceptibility to RIPs may be a dynamic process rather than an innate property arose from studies with the type 3 barley RIP, JIP60. Incubation of polysomes with JIP60 resulted in a shift to monosomes only if the polysomes had been prepared from stressed leaf tissue that had undergone 36 h of desiccation or 24 h of methyl jasmonate treatment. In contrast, water-treated controls had no change in polysome size (150, 151). These data should be interpreted with caution, however, as ribosomes were not assayed for depurination at the α-sarcin loop. Further questions about whether the N-glycosidase activity is responsible for polysome cleavage arise because of a report that JIP60 is not competent for translational inhibition unless proteolytic processing with at least two cleavage events has occurred (34).

WHAT PURPOSE(S) DO RIPs SERVE IN PLANTS?

The diversity among RIPs and their activities toward different targets calls into question how far one can extrapolate results in attempting to characterize RIP activity in planta. A presumed role in plant defense could be argued from circumstantial evidence gained both in vitro and in vivo. Data with fungal and insect systems are covered here and antiviral activities are discussed later in the review.

In bioassays, two type 1 RIPs from *Mirabilis expansa* roots were active at microgram levels against several soilborne bacterial species, the first such demonstration of antibacterial activity from a plant RIP in bioassays. In addition, these RIPs were active against a wide variety of both pathogenic and nonpathogenic fungi including *Fusarium* and *Trichoderma* species (195). Surprisingly, in some cases fungal species from the same genus showed differential sensitivity. For example, *Pythium irregulare* was sensitive, whereas *P. ultimum* was resistant. Treatment of fungal spores with proteolytically activated maize RIP, but not its proRIP form, produced morphological alterations in hyphae of *Aspergillus flavus* but induced autolysis of *A. nidulans* (132). Addition of the type 1 barley RIP was inhibitory to fungal growth on solid media when tested against *Trichoderma reesei* (155). Inhibition of growth in liquid media, however, was minimal with barley RIP alone but increased dramatically when chitinase was also included (100).

This apparent defense role against pathogens also extends to certain insect pests as assayed in feeding studies. Insect bioassays with ricin and saporin showed extreme toxicity to larvae of two *Coleopteran* species but had no detrimental effect on *Lepidoptera* (57). Cinnamomin, a type 2 RIP from seeds of the camphor tree *Cinnamomum camphora*, was toxic to larvae of mosquito (*Culex pipines pallens*) and cotton bollworm [*Helicoverpa armigra* (207)]. In both studies, the capacity of insect gut homogenates to hydrolyze the RIP was associated with a decrease in effectiveness of the RIP against insects. Thus, the apparent resistance seen in these studies may simply indicate that the RIP was degraded before it could be internalized into target cells. Another demonstration of insect susceptibility came from two type 2 RIPs of *Eranthis hyemalis* that were highly toxic (90%–100% mortality at 1.0 mg/ml) to the southern corn rootworm *Diabrotica undecimpunctata howardii* in feeding trials (97). Toxicity to insects has also been shown for maize proRIP and active RIP, which deterred feeding of adult beetles of *Carpophilus freemani*, *C. lugubris*, *Stelidota germinata*, and *Sitophilus zeamais* in assays in which the insects were given a choice of diets. In contrast, only active RIP was toxic to caterpillars in no-choice assays (46). Cabbage loopers (*Trichoplusia ni*), which do not feed on maize, were most severely affected, whereas Indian meal moths

(*Ploidia interpunctella*), which commonly feed on stored maize grain, showed no significant difference from controls. Fall armyworms (*Spodoptera frugiperda*, preferential leaf feeders), corn earworms (*Helicoverpa zea*), and corn borers (*Ostrinia nubilalis*; preferential immature seed feeders) had intermediate levels of susceptibility. Thus, differences in susceptibility of caterpillar species to active RIP varied in apparent accordance to host adaptation (or lack thereof), but factors contributing to the differential susceptibility or resistance of these insects have not been identified.

The fungal and insect bioassays offer the advantage of testing a single protein for its effect. Furthermore, tests can be done with concentrations of the protein equivalent to those found in particular plant organs (46). However, the use of a purified protein creates an artificial situation because the amount of RIP that would actually be released from cells during an endogenous insect-plant or fungal-plant interaction can only be approximated. Ectopic expression of RIPs in transgenic plants can solve this problem by allowing exposure of the pest or pathogen to the RIP only during interactions with the plant. Several such studies with different RIP genes confirm that these proteins can provide protection against plant pathogens [reviewed in (70)]. The type 1 barley RIP expressed by a 35S-CaMV promoter or a wound-inducible promoter in tobacco conferred some reduction to disease symptoms caused by the fungus *Rhizoctonia solani* (112). Addition of a signal sequence to target the RIP to the endomembrane system improved resistance in transgenic plants producing detectable levels of the RIP (84). Transgenic wheat plants, however, exhibited variable (0–40%) resistance against infection by the fungal pathogen *Erysiphe graminis* (19b). The significance of this resistance is questionable because the highest resistance did not correlate with the highest expression of the transgene. Expression of PAP, as well as an enzymatically inactive mutant, conferred fungal resistance and also led to overproduction of pathogenesis-related (PR) proteins in transgenic tobacco (209). This coordinate expression of RIP and PR proteins appears to be specific for the PAP-producing transgenic tobacco, as PR protein induction has not been seen in organs of nontransformed plant species even when RIPs accumulate to 10–20% of the soluble protein. Maize proRIP, when expressed in tobacco, was implicated as a defense protein against the fungus *R. solani* (117). Whether this resistance required proteolytic processing of the maize proRIP to an active *N*-glycosidase was not determined. However, tobacco containing a deletion construct of the kernel proRIP equivalent to the processed, active form of the enzyme was more resistant than control plants to insect feeding (P Dowd & R Boston, unpublished observations). Knowledge gained from ectopic expression studies with transgenic plants is valuable from the standpoint of agricultural biotechnology applications. But finding that RIPs can decrease susceptibility to damage by pathogens does not preclude additional and even more important roles for those proteins. Discovery of such roles would likely involve comparative analysis of plants in which RIP function has been removed (such as by mutation, insertional inactivation, or cosuppression). To date, gene knockout studies have not been reported for RIPs, but data are available from maize in which expression of the abundant seed proRIP is regulated by the transcriptional activator Opaque-2 (44, 69, 88, 123, 169). Levels of proRIP and storage proteins are both decreased (more than 100-fold for proRIP) in *o2* mutants (12, 169; AD Mehta & RS Boston, unpublished results) and kernels from mutant plants have increased susceptibility to fungal attack (111) and insect feeding (64). The increased susceptibility in the absence of the proRIP is consistent with its having a defense function, but the experimental results cannot be attributed to the maize proRIP a priori because Opaque-2 regulates transcription of many genes that may contribute to a complex mutant phenotype. Thus, definitive loss-of-function analyses are needed.

Taken together, data from mutants, transgenic plants, bioassays, and feeding studies suggest that defense is at least one component of RIP biology. Given that amino acids important for active site cleft formation, but few others, are conserved in all RIPs for which sequence information is available, it could be argued that retention of enzymatic activity is the most important selective pressure for RIP genes and that accumulation of RIPs in storage organs offers an advantage in plant defense. Developing seeds accumulate large quantities of endosperm- or cotyledon-specific proteins for use as nutrient sources during germination. These resources must be protected during grain fill and early stages of seedling growth when the seed is especially vulnerable to both mechanical damage and competition for storage reserves between the embryo and pests and pathogens. Thus, an abundant RIP could provide seeds with both nutritional benefits and protection against pathogen invasion. As discussed above, the maize proRIP accumulates under control of the same transcriptional activator, Opaque-2, that is responsible for directing gene expression for the major storage proteins in the seed. Saporin activity (8) is also highest in mature seeds, as is ricin and the type 1 barley RIP (100, 114). Accumulation of RIPs is not limited to seeds but also occurs in other storage organs. Vivanco et al have characterized RIPs from Andean root crops and reported levels up to 20% of the soluble root proteins of *Mirabilis expansa* (195). Likewise, trichosanthin accumulates to levels estimated at more than 20% of the soluble protein in storage roots of *Trichosanthes kirilowii* (163) and a RIP is the most abundant protein in Iris bulbs (190a). Thus, coordinate accumulation of RIPs and storage proteins would appear to put in place a preformed deterrent to damage by invading pests and pathogens.

But RIPs also accumulate in other organs, and recent reports link expression of some RIP genes to various stresses and even circadian control. A clone for JIP60, the type 3 RIP from barley, was originally identified from a cDNA library of jasmonic acid–induced genes (17). Expression of this gene is not linked strictly to jasmonic acid but is also induced by osmotic stress and desiccation (151). Similarly, RNA encoding the *Phytolacca insularis* antiviral protein, PIP2, accumulated in leaves exposed to jasmonic acid. RNA for this RIP also increased after treatment of plants with abscisic acid or mechanical wounding (169a). RIP activity from leaves of pokeweed and *Hura crepitans* increased during osmotic stress and also as a function of leaf age when green leaves were compared to senescent leaves (174).

Interestingly, in pokeweed, RIP activity increased in response to cold treatment and heat shock, whereas in *H. crepitans*, RIP activity increased in response to heat shock but not cold shock (174).

A RIP from the ice plant *Mesembryanthemum crystallinum* is expressed at low levels in unstressed plants but is induced by salt stress (154). RIP RNA levels from both stressed and unstressed ice plants fluctuated diurnally, with the highest levels appearing during the middle of the light cycle at midday (154). A diurnal effect was also observed with the kernel-specific maize proRIP gene. In this experiment, however, the proRIP RNA accumulated to highest levels during the dark phase of a 24-h clock with 14-h light periods (A Viotti, P Ciceri & R Schmidt, personal communication). Interestingly, a second maize proRIP gene that had been previously found to be expressed at low levels throughout the plant (13) also appears to be regulated by stress. In this case, the proRIP gene was induced 30–40-fold from nearly undetectable levels by both shading and drought stress in postpollinated ear and kernel samples (T Helentjaris, personal communication).

Stress induction of RIP genes is not limited to abiotic stresses but also occurs in some plants in response to biotic signals. For example, trichosanthin, a type 1 RIP from root tubers of *Trichosanthes kirilowii*, accumulated up to 19-fold more in roots of plants cocultivated with microorganisms than in sterile soil or culture medium (202). Beetin 27 and 29, type 1 RIPs from sugar beet leaves, were induced by several different viruses (58). The beetin 27 and 29 RIPs were also induced by H_2O_2 and salicylic acid, two signaling components of systemic acquired resistance in plants. Taken together, these observations suggest that RIPs may play a more dynamic role in the plant than was previously thought. However, insufficient information is currently available to determine whether or not stress-induction is a widespread phenomenon among RIPs. As more data become available from genomic investigations of gene expression, we may well uncover additional information about RIP gene expression and identify pathways common to its regulation in different plants.

OTHER RIP ENZYMATIC ACTIVITIES

The site-specific *N*-glycosidase activity has long been the defining characteristic of RIPs. However, additional activities have also been reported. The most widespread of these is a polynucleotide:adenosine glycosidase that depurinates DNA as well as RNA from sites other than the A^{4324} of rRNA (10, 11, 11a, 102, 130). This activity was found for all of 52 RIPs surveyed by Barbieri and coworkers (10). Nuclease activity of several RIPs against supercoiled DNA and both single- and double-stranded DNAs was detectable but relatively inefficient compared to the reaction on ribosomes (45, 106, 107, 129, 130, 157, 197). However, Nicolas et al suggest that the K_{cat} against oligoribonucleotides is comparable to that of multisubunit DNA glycosylases that normally act on damaged DNA bases (130a). Prior to having access to RIP DNA and amino acid sequences, researchers were hampered in investigating RIP activities by the possibility that they were working with impure protein preparations. As a result, there was confusion and concern about the reliability of claims of alternative activities and controversy as to whether they existed at all (42). Part of the difficulty in analyzing other activities comes from some but not all apparently sharing active site residues with the N-glycosidase such that mutations affect not just one but multiple activities. Additionally, assay conditions can vary and the alternative functions have yet to be tied to functions that occur in planta.

Some discrepancies in activities reported by different research groups may even be due to variations in the actual proteins assayed. For example, PAP cleaved double-stranded supercoiled DNA, but a point mutant of PAP (PAPx) that cannot depurinate ribosomes failed to nick the same supercoiled plasmid templates (197). In contrast, recombinant PAP produced in *Escherichia coli* retained N-glycosidase activity but showed no capacity to nick supercoiled DNA (42). These studies, while apparently in conflict, may also reflect differences of the proteins synthesized in the three systems. For example, Tumer's group assayed PAP produced in pokeweed and the mutant PAPx produced in transgenic tobacco, whereas Day and coworkers assayed PAP produced in *E. coli* from a clone in which sequences corresponding to the carboxy terminal 29 amino acids of the natural protein had been deleted.

Most likely, some additional activities observed experimentally do reflect the presence of proteins other than RIPs. Valbonesi et al (190) and Fong et al (50a) separated a previously reported RNase activity from momordin II (125), but residual RNase activity was still detected (50a). Likewise, Day et al (42) used gel filtration chromatography to separate DNase activity from N-glycosidase activity of ricin. In addition, these authors found differences in DNase and N-glycosidase activities of PAP with heat and DEPC treatments that they attributed to the presence of at least two different proteins.

These examples point out the need for stringent control of RIP purity, but they do not rule out at least some RIPs having enzymatic activities in addition to depurination at the α-sarcin loop. Recently, Wang et al (198) used NMR to obtain a high-resolution solution structure of MAP30, a RIP from bitter melon. MAP30 preparations cleave supercoiled DNA and also exhibit DNA glycosylase/apurinic/apyrimidinic (AP) lyase activity (103, 198). These authors assigned DNA and RNA N-glycosidase activities to one site and AP lyase activity to a different but contiguous subsite of the protein. In this model, DNA would be depurinated by MAP30 after which it would be cleaved by the AP lyase activity. Wang et al also showed that divalent cations interact with negatively charged regions of MAP30 and are likely to facilitate interactions with DNA. Thus, the cations would have a role in enhancing MAP30 activity instead of being associated with contaminating nucleases (42, 198). A sequential lyase activity was also suggested by Ogasawara et al (137). These authors, however, showed cleavage of the α-sarcin loop by a separate RNA apurinic site-specific lyase following depurination of the RNA by gypsophilin, a RIP from *Gypsophilia elegans*.

Antiviral Activity

Antiviral activities of RIPs have been known for ~75 years [reviewed in (8, 70, 185)]. They were presumed to provide a plant defense function by acting on ribosomes of infected plant cells [reviewed in (8)]. This conclusion was supported by links between susceptibility of host ribosomes to N-glycosidase activity and antiviral activity (182) as well as the absence in viral RNAs of any sequence similarity to the N-glycosidase target site of the α-sarcin loop. In addition, viruses that were incubated with PAP lost infectivity but recovered it once the PAP was removed (184). Antiviral activity is not confined to plant cells but is also seen for both RNA and DNA viruses of animal cells and even retroviruses of yeast (2, 102, 104, 148, 187, 189, 205).

The antiviral effect has been noted for a number of type 1 and type 2 RIPs, but the mechanism of antiviral activity has not been resolved [reviewed in (8, 197a)]. Several lines of evidence, however, suggest that antiviral activity can be separated from depurination at the α-sarcin loop (2, 78, 104, 121, 205). The most definitive demonstration was made by Tumer et al who assayed a deletion mutant of a PAP gene in transgenic tobacco. Even though the mutant protein was unable to depurinate the α-sarcin loop, it still conferred viral resistance against *Potato virus X* (186).

Hudak et al (80) recently extended this work with the report of a novel activity of PAP to depurinate selectively RNAs that had a 5′ terminal m7GpppG cap. In this study, capped and uncapped mRNAs were transiently exposed to PAP or PAP mutants and assayed for translational competence in vitro. Significant reductions were seen in translation of capped mRNAs that had been exposed to PAP. In contrast, PAP had no significant effect on uncapped mRNAs. Analysis of the capped mRNAs after incubation showed that they had been degraded at high concentrations of PAP and depurinated presumably at multiple sites at low PAP concentrations. From these observations, the authors concluded that the capped mRNAs could serve as targets for depurination. When the assays were carried out with PAP mutants lacking the capacity to depurinate ribosomes at the α-sarcin loop, selective translational inhibition of capped RNAs still occurred for mutants that had been altered in N- or C-terminal regions. However, the capped RNAs remained translationally competent after treatment with protein resulting from a point mutation in the putative active site of the enzyme. Thus, although the N-glycosidase activity was important for inactivation of capped RNAs, ribosome depurination was not.

Direct depurination of capped viral RNA could explain the antiviral activity of PAP against the Sindbis-like viruses, *Tobacco mosaic virus* (TMV), *Brome mosaic virus* (BMV), and *Cucumber mosaic virus* (CMV), all of which have 5′ terminal caps (60, 178). It falls short of providing a comprehensive explanation of the PAP antiviral activity, however, because many viruses inhibited equally well lack 5′ cap structures. For example, Chen et al assayed *Potato virus Y* (PVY), which has a 5′ terminal protein in place of a m7GpppG cap, on *Chenopodium amaranticolor*

(35). Application of PAP to *C. amaranticolor* leaves inhibited formation of local lesions by PVY and the extent of inhibition was even greater than for the capped viruses TMV and CMV (35). PAP also inhibited infection by the uncapped animal viruses influenza virus, poliovirus, and herpes simplex virus [a DNA virus (2, 189)]. Molecules other than capped viral RNAs have also been shown to be targets for antiviral activity. Lee-Huang and colleagues demonstrated activity of MAP30 and GAP31 (from *Gelonium multiflorum*) against HIV integrase at doses tenfold lower than those needed for translational inhibition (78, 103). Furthermore, they showed that limited proteolysis of the RIPs removed translational inhibitory activity but did not affect the capacity of the RIPs to inhibit HIV integration, proliferation of tumor cells, or HIV protein production in infected lymphocyte cells (78, 103). Strong inhibition of HIV-1 integrase in vitro was also seen for gelonin, luffin, α-momorcharin, β-momorcharin, saporin, and trichosanthin but not agrostin (3a). In addition to the data from enzymatic analyses and bioassays, structural studies support a conclusion of RIPs interfering with viral integration as well. Wang et al used NMR to examine interactions between MAP30 and the HIV long-terminal repeat (LTR) DNA and concluded that the MAP30 binds to the LTR perhaps in competition with the viral integrase in vivo (198).

Taken together, these studies are suggestive that the antiviral properties of RIPs are quite complex. Furthermore, the mechanism of viral inhibition may vary among different viruses and different RIPs. It is clear, however, that development of sensitive assays for detecting depurination and other modifications of nucleic acids has expanded the enzymatic activities that can be assigned to RIPs. Structural studies as well as studies of mutants have demonstrated the usefulness of these approaches in defining the various protein domains and determining their importance for the different activities. With the availability of cloned DNAs for many RIPs, questions of endogenous or contaminating activities can be answered. Finally, as enzymatic activities are identified in vitro, analysis can move to plants for investigation of whether these activities are relevant under physiological conditions.

ENTRY OF RIPs INTO CELLS

Assuming that ribosome depurination is at least one biologically important activity of RIPs, then the RIPs must gain access to the ribosome-containing cytosol of target cells. Many RIPs likely evolved to have individualized methods for protecting their host cell ribosomes from inactivation while at the same time providing a means by which the protein could come into contact with target cells. This requirement would have to be met regardless of whether RIPs are acting as defense proteins against heterologous ribosomes and/or viral RNAs or regulating cell metabolism by modifying orthologous ribosomes. Here, we first address ways by which synthesis and sequestration of RIPs may protect the host cell and then consider the situation where RIPs must breach at least two barriers—the host cell membrane and the cell membrane of the heterologous target cell.

Secreted and Compartmentalized RIPs

RIPs are localized extracellularly as well as in compartments that vary among different host cells. Most RIPs appear to have N-terminal signal sequences that target them for cotranslational entry into the endomembrane system (Figure 1) (71). The endomembranes then provide a barrier between the RIP and the orthologous ribosomes. RIPs, however, can be transported bidirectionally—both forward and in reverse through the endomembrane system. As a result, additional protective steps are necessary to prevent subsequent retrograde transport of a newly synthesized RIP back to the ribosome-containing cytosol (retrograde transport of RIPs is discussed later). One strategy is synthesis as inactive pro-proteins. PIP2, saporin, sechiumin (from *Sechium edule*), trichoanguin (from *Trichosanthes anguina*), and trichosanthin are all type 1 RIPs with short carboxy terminal extensions that are encoded by the corresponding genes but not found on proteins isolated from plants (18, 28, 36, 37, 169a, 204) (Figure 1). The C-terminal extensions are similar in sequence to those found on vacuolar proteins and may act as vacuolar targeting signals (128, 194). Recombinant trichosanthin and sechiumin that contain the C-terminal amino acid peptides are ~fivefold less active in translational inhibition assays than the corresponding native proteins (204, 208). Thus, in addition to targeting, the extensions may prevent these RIPs from becoming active prior to reaching the storage organelles.

The importance of sequential processing and localization of RIPs away from ribosomes was recently demonstrated by studies to express various ricin constructs in transgenic tobacco protoplasts and determine their cellular fates (55). Ricin, a type 2 RIP, undergoes a complex maturation process. It is produced in castor bean as a precursor polypeptide (preproricin) that contains a signal peptide as well as the A (enzymatic) and B (lectin) chains joined by a short linker peptide (26, 98) (Figure 1). Proricin is generated by cleavage of the N-terminal signal peptide from preproricin and transported from its site of synthesis at the ER to vacuoles via the Golgi complex (113). Only after proricin has reached the vacuole is the linker peptide cleaved to produce the mature active protein. When the ricin A-chain was expressed alone in transgenic tobacco protoplasts, it could be detected in ER, but its continued expression was toxic (55). This toxicity indicates that the active A-chain can most likely be transported from ER into the cytosol where it would interact with ribosomes. When the native preproricin construct was assayed, processing, glycosylation, and targeting to the vacuole occurred normally and no toxicity was seen (166). Thus, it appears that to prevent toxicity to the host cell, ricin, and most likely a number of other type 2 RIPs, must be produced as proproteins and targeted to the vacuole prior to activation by cleavage of the peptide linker between the A- and B-chains.

Besides those RIPs localized in vacuoles, there are others such as PAP and some forms of saporin that are secreted to a final destination in the cell wall matrix (28, 149; also see 71). Like RIPs localized in vacuoles, these proteins would be physically separated from orthologous ribosomes. Furthermore, the host cell would not be a barrier for activity against target cells.

Cytosolic RIPs

Exceptions to the RIPs that are sequestered from host ribosomes are those from cereals. These RIPs lack obvious signal sequences and appear to reside in the cytosol where they would constantly come in contact with host ribosomes (66, 100, 196). In general, cereal RIPs have little if any activity against plant ribosomes at concentrations found in vivo. The apparent lack of ribosome sensitivity to RIPs from the same plant extends to type 3 RIPs even after they have been proteolytically activated (14, 34, 95, 182), The cytosolic RIPs are also distinct in that they apparently lack antiviral activity (182), but they retain antifungal activity (100, 117, 132, 155). At present, the significance of the specialized localizations and ribosome specificity is unclear.

For vacuolar or cytosolically localized RIPs the question arises as to how they exit the host cell. One plausible explanation is that lysis of the plasma or vacuolar membranes upon cell attack by a pest or pathogen would release the RIP. For those type 3 RIPs requiring proteolytic activation, lysis of cellular membranes would likely release both the inactive proRIPs and the proteases required to activate them. Alternatively, activation could occur as a result of proteolysis by enzymes produced by an invading pest or pathogen.

RIP Interactions with Membranes and Receptors

Once a RIP had been released from the host cell, the next barrier would be encountered at the target cell where uptake would require binding of the RIP to the cell surface, transport into the cell, and finally entry into the cytosol. The presence of the lectin B-chain of type 2 RIPs allows binding to galactosyl moieties found on the surface of most eukaryotic cells. Studies of this binding and subsequent uptake of the disulfide bonded A-chain have been reviewed recently and thus are not covered in detail here (74, 114, 161, 162). Instead, we focus on uptake of type 1 and type 3 RIPs for which the uptake process remains mostly unknown.

Type 1 and 3 RIPs lack the lectin chain that facilitates entry and accounts for the extreme toxicity of type 2 RIPs to intact cells (176). Some type 1 RIPs such as gelonin (176), dianthin (177), and *Momordica charantia* inhibitor (9) are glycosylated and presumably bind to carbohydrate receptors on the cell membrane (reviewed in 8, 87), Similar binding has been shown for the ricin A-chain that carries mannose oligosaccharides capable of binding to mannose receptors even in the absence of the B-chain (51, 54, 91, 152, 167).

Carbohydrate binding is not the only means for recognition and entry, however, nor perhaps the most efficient. Comparison of toxicity of unglycosylated saporin and the glycosylated RIPs, dianthin and gelonin, to a variety of animal cells failed to show a correlation between toxicity and the presence of carbohydrates (8, 15). A better correlation was seen between toxicity and binding to members of the low-density lipoprotein (LDL) receptor family, which interact with a wide spectrum of ligands that are internalized via clathrin-coated pits (59). Saporin and trichosanthin (also unglycosylated) bind specifically to α-macroglobulin and me-galin receptors (29, 33). Saporin was more toxic to macrophages and liver cells that had LDL receptors than to T lymphocytes that did not. Additional cell surface receptor–RIP interactions will likely be discovered as better tools become available for tracking these proteins. In fact, trichosanthin was recently shown to bind to different chemokine receptors and stimulate chemotaxis and G-protein activation of cultured animal cells (206). Equivalent activation, however, was also seen when a mutant trichosanthin with 4000-fold lower ribosome-inactivating activity was used (131, 206). Whether these data reflect a very low threshold for RIP action or an activity unrelated to N-glycosidation is unresolved.

Although interactions between RIPs and receptors at the cell surface would seem to indicate a protein-mediated uptake, receptor-independent mechanisms of mem-brane binding are also supported by experimental evidence. Studies with reconsti-tuted liposomes have implicated negatively charged phospholipids in conferring selective binding and uptake of the fungal RIP α-sarcin (141, 142). Alpha-sarcin (89, 203) is similar to many type 1 RIPs in that it is a single-chain nonglycosylated protein with no strikingly hydrophobic zones to allow for crossing of the membrane bilayer. Furthermore, binding to protein receptors has not been documented, yet α-sarcin was found to associate with phospholipid vesicles (141). This association has been attributed to aggregation of α-sarcin into oligomeric forms in the presence of negatively charged phospholipids (142). The type 1 RIP, saporin, was shown to promote fusion of membranes containing negatively charged phospholipids, but uptake into liposomes was not assayed (68, 108).

The diversity of proteins and phospholipids able to interact with type 1 RIPs makes it hard to offer a single model for introduction into cells. For type 3 RIPs, even less is known, including whether these proteins interact with cells as the proRIP zymogens, the activated (processed) RIPs, or in both forms. Based on studies with type 2 RIPs and with the ricin A-chain, uptake might be expected to be quite complex. For the ricin holoenzyme, the primary means of uptake is endocytosis via clathrin-coated pits with transport through the Golgi apparatus to the ER (161, 162, 168). When clathrin-mediated uptake was inhibited, an alterna-tive method of uptake was revealed (61, 161, 162). This alternative internalization is clathrin independent and highly regulated through complex signaling pathways involving protein kinases, G-proteins, cAMP, and cell polarity (47, 77, 85, 109).

Retrograde Transport of RIPs

For RIPs that enter the cell by way of vesicles, further transport is necessary to gain access to cytosolic ribosomes. Type 2 RIPs follow a retrograde transport pathway through endosomes or Golgi to the ER and then the cytosol (115, 116, 162, 168, 199). This retrograde movement has been studied extensively for type 2 RIPs as well as for the ricin A-chain alone, which has often been taken to be a model for the single-chain type 1 RIPs (116, 161, 162, 179). Recent advances in eluci-dating the terminal steps of retrograde transport are described briefly here even though their importance for type 1 and 3 RIPs can only be hypothesized at present.

The last step in retrograde transport, exit from the ER, is mediated by a protein conducting translocon in the ER. This translocon serves a dual function in export of unfolded or misfolded proteins from the ER to the cytosol for degradation and in import of nascent polypeptides from the RER into the secretory pathway (24, 120). Polypeptides that are to be exported from the ER are identified as being modified or partially unfolded by quality control proteins such as the ER molecular chaperones that bind to nonnative domains and target the proteins for degradation by the proteasome (24). RIPs have been proposed to subvert this pathway such that as they exit the ER through the translocon, they escape to the cytosol rather than interact with the proteasome (74, 114). Work by Simpson et al (168) provides experimental support for translocon-mediated entry. These authors found that a large proportion (80%) of recombinant ricin A-chain polypeptides produced in wild-type yeast were rapidly degraded, whereas almost no degradation was seen in yeast strains defective in the ER-associated degradation (ERAD) pathway. The ricin A-chain molecules found in the cytosol of wild-type yeast were presumed to have entered by passing through the translocon and escaping degradation by the proteasome.

Use of the translocon by ricin A-chain suggests that it was recognized in the ER as having unfolded or misfolded domains. Consistent with this notion is recent evidence that the conformational stability of ricin A-chain favors an unfolded state in the ER and that refolding in the cytosol could be mediated by ribosomes (1). Because of structural similarities between the ricin A-chain and the type 1 and 3 RIPs, a hypothesis of retrograde transport based on the ricin A-chain seems to be a good basis for investigating entry of type 1 and type 3 RIPs into the cytosol from the ER.

PHYSIOLOGICAL MANIFESTATIONS OF RIP ACTIVITY

Although the enzymatic mechanism of RIP activity is well defined, the physiological steps by which ribosome inactivation leads to cell death are not well understood. In cultured mammalian cells, both type 1 and type 2 RIPs have been linked to a programmed cell death, or apoptosis (19a, 63, 99, 146, 147, 201). RIP-treated cells exhibited the morphological features characteristic of apoptosis including condensation and fragmentation of cell nuclei, cytoplasmic densification, breakdown of nuclear DNA into discrete fragments, and mitochondrial membrane alterations (19a, 25, 63, 72, 90, 99, 118, 135, 159, 193, 201). In addition, use of inhibitors and pharmacological agents that perturb signal transduction pathways leading to programmed cell death add further support to the idea that apoptosis is initiated by RIPs. For example, production of reactive oxygen species (ROS) was detected in single cells treated with trichosanthin (205a). Cell viability increased, however, upon preincubation with α-tocopherol, a protective agent against ROS-induced cell death. Similarly, when the apoptotic protease activities of caspases and serine proteases were inhibited, treatment of cells with ricin failed to bring about programmed cell death (93, 136). Treatment with the thiol antioxidant N-acetylecysteine (NAC) blocked cytotoxicity of ricin and led to the conclusion that redox regulation of proteins via their thiol groups also plays a role in ricin-induced programmed cell death (134). The redox regulation, however, appears to act through a signaling pathway distinct from the protease-mediated pathway because NAC treatment did not affect the generation of caspase activity. Signaling through a third molecule, tumor-necrosis factor-α (TNF-α), has also been implicated in ricin-induced apoptosis as judged by the lack of a ricin effect in cells in which TNF receptors had been blocked (73).

Promotion of RIP-induced cell death through multiple pathways may have important therapeutic implications for RIP-based immunotoxins. For example, many cancer cells are resistant to apoptosis and thus would not likely be killed by action through caspases and serine proteases but might well be susceptible through the thiol or TNF pathway. For plant, fungal, and insect cells, however, the presence of a dual response pathway has not been explored.

Because apoptosis is an indirect effect that occurs downstream of the known RIP enzymatic activities, several investigations were focused on the importance of the ribosome-inactivating activity of RIPs in the apoptotic response. Initial reports had suggested that the B-chain lectin of type 2 RIPs can induce programmed cell death in mammalian cells (67). More recent reports, however, have shown that highly purified B-chain subunits alone cannot induce programmed cell death (193). The role of the B-chain in this process is most likely only as a carrier to allow the A-chain to have access to the cell (135). Site-directed mutagenesis of the type 2 RIP mistletoe lectin 1 showed a strict positive correlation between the enzymatic ribosome-inactivating activity of the A-chain and programmed cell death (99).

Not all type 1 RIPs induce apoptosis, however. Presumably, these differences in response are due to differential uptake of the RIP into cells because conjugation of a nontoxic type 1 RIP, bryodin-1 from *Bryonia dioica* roots, to an antibody that recognized the cell surface protein CD40, resulted in prompt cytotoxicity in TS1 cells (52).

The necessity of having ribosome-inactivating activity for subsequent apoptosis is consistent with the hypothesis that reduction in protein synthesis is a trigger for programmed cell death in mammalian cells. Indirect evidence for such a hypothesis comes from work with an interferon-induced, dsRNA-dependent protein kinase [PKR; reviewed in (86)]. PKR inactivates the translational initiation factor, eIF2α, by phosphorylating it such that initiation of translation and subsequent protein synthesis are severely inhibited (101, 144). Overexpression of PKR in cultured cells increases their sensitivity to inducers of apoptosis, whereas overexpression of a dominant negative PKR confers resistance to inducers of programmed cell death (6, 43).

In a separate study, Sandvig and coworkers found that either ricin or cyclo-hexamide blocked protein synthesis in mammalian cell cultures, but only ricin treatment led to programmed cell death. However, if cyclohexamide was added to the ricin-treated cells at the cessation of protein synthesis, programmed cell death did not occur (159). These observations at first seem to run counter to the idea that a reduction in protein synthesis leads to programmed cell death. They can be explained, however, by the finding that cyclohexamide inhibits autophagy, a key degradative step in apoptosis (94, 159). By inhibiting autophagy, cyclohexamide likely blocked the ricin induction of apoptosis following translational inhibition. Thus, the idea that RIPs induce apoptosis by blocking protein synthesis remains viable.

The finding that RIPs can induce apoptosis in mammalian cell cultures is important for defining mechanisms of activity and designing targeted applications for these proteins. Extrapolating these results to effects on whole organisms, however, may be more complex. For example, a side effect of the antibody-targeted use of RIPs as anticancer agents is vascular leak syndrome (VLS) characterized by an increase in vascular permeability that leads to organ failure. Recent results by Baluna et al (6a, 7) suggest that VLS may not be induced by the ribosome-inactivating activity of RIPs but instead by a three–amino acid structural motif that interacts with and damages vascular endothelial cells. Whether RIPs with this motif would also have a detrimental effect on insect, fungal, or plant cells is an interesting but unanswered question. Although fungal bioassays and insect feeding studies point to RIPs from all three structural classes as being toxic, how those RIPs actually affect cells from organisms other than mammals is less clearly defined.

Ectopic expression of PAP and the type 3 barley RIP, JIP60, produced abnormal phenotypes in transgenic tobacco (62, 110). For PAP, only those plants making large amounts of enzymatically active proteins produced morphologically aberrant plants (110, 186). Bioassays to determine the effect of RIPs on insects have primarily depended on gross changes in the growth or survival of the insect and not effects on individual cells (46, 57, 97).

The most common bioassays to determine RIP antifungal activity are based on inhibition of fungal colony growth (100, 155, 164, 195). Recently, however, microscopic examination of fungi has offered some insight into what effect RIP treatment might be having on individual fungal cells. Hyphae of *Trichoderma reesei* treated with two type 1 RIPs from *Mirabilis expansa* were found to be narrower than control hyphae, and to have extensive septum formation and enlarged tips (195). Treatment of *Aspergillus nidulans* spores with an active form of maize RIP led to apparently normal germination but autolysis of hyphae prior to septum formation. The autolysis depended on both ribosome-inactivating activity of the protein and G-protein signaling in the cells (132; K Nielsen, GA Payne & RS Boston, unpublished results). Confocal imaging of maize RIP labeled with the fluorophore Texas Red and nuclei stained with the DNA binding dye DAPI showed localization of RIP within the cell and a decrease in nuclear staining prior to the autolytic event (K Nielsen, GA Payne & RS Boston, unpublished results). These observations suggest that fungi, like mammalian cells, have a programmed cell death pathway whereby the nuclear degradation observed prior to autolysis in *A. nidulans* cells is analogous to the programmed cell death observed with RIP treatment of mammalian cells. Taken together, the above observations suggest that the effect of RIPs on individual cells from various organisms may be manifested by similar pathways.

FUTURE PERSPECTIVES

After years of being investigated as tools to be exploited for their toxicity, RIPs are stimulating interest for their biological functions in plants. Transgenic plant technologies have introduced new avenues for targeting RIPs to additional sites within plants, expressing RIPs in plants that lack endogenous RIP activity, and inactivating endogenous RIP genes to determine the breadth of their influence on plant phenotype. Understanding the process of RIP uptake and transport in cells is benefiting from new concepts in retrotranslocation and development of tools for nondestructive imaging (181). These approaches should also be valuable for comparative analysis. In particular, investigation of how type 1 and type 3 RIPs enter cells of potential pests and pathogens lags far behind studies of type 2 RIPs and their effects on animal cells. Recent invention of a photochemical internalization method for introducing membrane-impermeable molecules into cells has removed a major obstacle, namely, the lack of an efficient internalization of the proteins (19, 166a). Much is left to be learned from comparing RIPs from the different structural classes and with different substrate affinities. New insights into antiviral mechanisms have begun to increase our understanding of properties important for interfering with viral infection. Moreover, they have opened investigation into the likelihood that RIP activity may not be limited to ribosomal substrates but may also damage DNA or RNA of pathogen and/or host cells (147a). Discovery of multiple enzymatic activities and dynamic fluctuation of some RIPs in response to biotic and abiotic signals has prompted exploration into the possibility of RIPs participating in maintaining organismal homeostasis, perhaps by facilitating macromolecular turnover (34, 154, 157, 174). The next few years are likely to be an exciting phase for fundamental RIP research as we obtain insights into the functional significance for medicinal and agronomic applications of emerging discoveries.

ACKNOWLEDGMENTS

We thank colleagues for sharing results prior to publication and acknowledge past or current research support by the National Science Foundation, the US Department of Agriculture, the North Carolina Agricultural Research Service, the NC Biotechnology Center and training grant support from the McKnight Foundation, and a NSF-DOE-USDA program for Interdisciplinary Research Training.

Visit the Annual Reviews home page at www.AnnualReviews.org

LITERATURE CITED

1. Argent RH, Parrott AM, Day PJ, Roberts LM, Stockley PG, et al. 2000. Ribosome-mediated folding of partially unfolded ricin A-chain. *J. Biol. Chem.* 275:9263–69

2. Aron G, Irvin JD. 1980. Inhibition of herpes simplex virus multiplication by the pokeweed antiviral protein. *Antimicrob. Agents Chemother.* 17:1032–33

3. Asano K, Svensson B, Poulsen FM. 1984. Isolation and characterization of inhibitors of animal cell-free protein synthesis from barley seeds. *Carlsberg Res. Commun.* 49:619–26

3a. Au TK, Collins RA, Lam TL, Ng TB, Fong WP, Wan DCC. 2000. The plant ribosome inactivating proteins luffin and saporin are potent inhibitors of HIV-1 integrase. *FEBS Lett.* 471:169–72

4. Bailey-Serres J. 1998. Cytoplasmic ribosomes of higher plants. See Ref. 4a, pp. 125–44

4a. Bailey-Serres J, Gallie DR, eds. 1998. *A Look Beyond Transcription: Mechanisms Determining mRNA Stability and Translation in Plants.* Rockville, MD: Am. Soc. Plant Physiol.

5. Bailey-Serres J, Vangala S, Szick K, Lee CH. 1997. Acidic phosphoprotein complex of the 60S ribosomal subunit of maize seedling roots. Components and changes in response to flooding. *Plant Physiol.* 114:1293–305

6. Balachandran S, Kim CN, Yeh WC, Mak TW, Bhalla K, Barber GN. 1998. Activation of the dsRNA-dependent protein kinase, PKR, induces apoptosis through FADD-mediated death signaling. *EMBO J.* 17:6888–902

6a. Baluna R, Coleman E, Jones C, Ghetie V, Vitetta ES. 2000. The effect of a monoclonal antibody coupled to ricin A chain-derived peptides on endothelial cells in vitro: insights into toxin-mediated vascular damage. *Exp. Cell Res.* 258:417–24

7. Baluna R, Rizo J, Gordon BE, Ghetie V, Vitetta ES. 1999. Evidence for a structural motif in toxins and interleukin-2 that may be responsible for binding to endothelial cells and initiating vascular leak syndrome. *Proc. Natl. Acad. Sci. USA* 96:3957–62

8. Barbieri L, Battelli MG, Stirpe F. 1993. Ribosome-inactivating proteins from plants. *Biochim. Biophys. Acta* 1154:237–82

9. Barbieri L, Lorenzoni E, Stirpe F. 1979. Inhibition of protein synthesis in vitro by a lectin from *Momordica charantia* and by other haemagglutinins. *Biochem. J.* 182:633–35

10. Barbieri L, Valbonesi P, Bonora E, Gorini P, Bolognesi A, Stirpe F. 1997. Polynucleotide: adenosine glycosidase activity of ribosome-inactivating proteins: effect on DNA, RNA and poly(A). *Nucleic Acids Res.* 25:518–22

11. Barbieri L, Valbonesi P, Gorini P, Pession A, Stirpe F. 1996. Polynucleotide: adenosine glycosidase activity of saporin-L1: effect on DNA, RNA and poly(A). *Biochem. J.* 319:507–13

11a. Barbieri L, Valbonesi P, Govoni M, Pession A, Stirpe F. 2000. Polynucleotide: adenosine glycosidase activity of saporin-L1: effect on various forms of mammalian DNA. *Biochim. Biophys. Acta* 1480:258–66

12. Bass HW, Goode JH, Greene TW, Boston RS. 1994. Control of ribosome-inactivating protein (RIP) RNA levels during maize seed development. *Plant Sci.* 101:17–30

13. Bass HW, OBrian GR, Boston RS. 1995. Cloning and sequencing of a second ribosome-inactivating protein gene from

maize (*Zea mays* L.). *Plant Physiol.* 107:661–62

14. Bass HW, Webster C, OBrian GR, Roberts JKM, Boston RS. 1992. A maize ribosome-inactivating protein is controlled by the transcriptional activator Opaque-2. *Plant Cell* 4:225–34

15. Battelli MG, Montacuti V, Stirpe F. 1992. High sensitivity of cultured human trophoblasts to ribosome-inactivating proteins. *Exp. Cell Res.* 201:109–12

16. Beaumelle B, Alami M, Hopkins CR. 1993. ATP-dependent translocation of ricin across the membrane of purified endosomes. *J. Biol. Chem.* 268:23661–69

17. Becker W, Apel K. 1992. Isolation and characterization of a cDNA clone encoding a novel jasmonate-induced protein of barley (*Hordeum vulgare* L.). *Plant Mol. Biol.* 19(6):1065–67

18. Benatti L, Nitti G, Solinas M, Valsasina B, Vitale A, et al. 1991. A Saporin-6 cDNA containing a precursor sequence coding for a carboxyl-terminal extension. *FEBS Lett.* 291:285–88

19. Berg K, Selbo PK, Prasmickaite L, Tjelle TE, Sandvig K, et al. 1999. Photochemical internalization: a novel technique for delivery of macromolecules into cytosol. *Cancer Res.* 59:1180–83

19a. Bergamaschi G, Perfetti V, Tonon L, Novella A, Lucotti C, et al. 1996. Saporin, a ribosome-inactivating protein used to prepare immunotoxins, induces cell death via apoptosis. *Br. J. Haematol.* 93:789–94

19b. Bieri S, Potrykus I, Fütterer J. 2000. Expression of active barley seed ribosome-inactivating protein in transgenic wheat. *Theor. Appl. Genet.* 100:755–63

20. Brigotti M, Carnicelli D, Alvergna P, Pallanca A, Lorenzetti R, et al. 1995. 3′-immature tRNA(Trp) is required for ribosome inactivation by gelonin, a plant RNA N-glycosidase. *Biochem. J.* 310:249–53

21. Brigotti M, Carnicelli D, Alvergna P, Pallanca A, Sperti S, Montanaro L. 1996. tRNA(Trp) as cofactor of gelonin, a ribosome-inactivating protein with RNA-N-glycosidase activity. Features required for the cofactor activity. *Biochem. Mol. Biol. Int.* 40:181–88

22. Brigotti M, Carnicelli D, Pallanca A, Rizzi S, Accorsi P, et al. 1999. Identity elements in bovine tRNA(Trp) required for the specific stimulation of gelonin, a plant ribosome-inactivating protein. *RNA* 5:1357–63

23. Brigotti M, Keith G, Pallanca A, Carnicelli D, Alvergna P, et al. 1998. Identification of the tRNAs which up-regulate agrostin, barley RIP and PAP-S, three ribosome-inactivating proteins of plant origin. *FEBS Lett.* 431:259–62

24. Brodsky JL, McCracken AA. 1999. ER protein quality control and proteasome-mediated protein degradation. *Semin. Cell Dev. Biol.* 10:507–13

25. Bussing A, Wagner M, Wagner B, Stein GM, Schietzel M, et al. 1999. Induction of mitochondrial Apo2.7 molecules and generation of reactive oxygen-intermediates in cultured lymphocytes by the toxic proteins from *Viscum album* L. *Cancer Lett.* 139:79–88

26. Butterworth AG, Lord JM. 1983. Ricin and *Ricinus communis* agglutinin subunits are all derived from a single-size polypeptide precursor. *Eur. J. Biochem.* 137:57–65

27. Carnicelli D, Brigotti M, Montanaro L, Sperti S. 1992. Differential requirement of ATP and extra-ribosomal proteins for ribosome inactivation by eight RNA N-glycosidases. *Biochem. Biophys. Res. Commun.* 182:579–82

28. Carzaniga R, Sinclair L, Fordham-Skelton AP, Harris N, Croy RDR. 1994. Cellular and subcellular distribution of saporins, type-1 ribosome-inactivating proteins, in soapwort (*Saponaria officinalis* L.). *Planta* 194:461–70

29. Cavallaro U, Nykjaer A, Nielsen M, Soria MR. 1995. Alpha 2-macroglobulin receptor mediates binding and cytotoxicity of

plant ribosome-inactivating proteins. *Eur. J. Biochem.* 232:165–71

30. Cawley DB, Hedblom ML, Hoffma EJ, Houston LL. 1977. Differential sensitivity of rat liver and wheat germ ribosomes to polyuridylic acid translation. *Arch. Biochem Biophys.* 182:690–95

31. Chaddock JA, Lord JM, Hartley MR, Roberts LM. 1994. Pokeweed antiviral protein (PAP) mutations which permit *E. coli* growth do not eliminate catalytic activity towards prokaryotic ribosomes. *Nucleic Acids Res.* 22:1536–40

32. Chaddock JA, Monzingo AF, Robertus JD, Lord JM, Roberts LM. 1996. Major structural differences between pokeweed antiviral protein and ricin A-chain do not account for their differing ribosome specificity. *Eur. J. Biochem.* 235:159–66

33. Chan WL, Shaw PC, Tam SC, Jacobsen C, Gliemann J, Nielsen MS. 2000. Trichosanthin interacts with and enters cells via LDL receptor family members. *Biochem. Biophys. Res. Commun.* 270:453–57

34. Chaudhry B, Mueller UF, Cameron Mills V, Gough S, Simpson D, et al. 1994. The barley 60 kDa jasmonate-induced protein (JIP60) is a novel ribosome-inactivating protein. *Plant J.* 6:815–24

35. Chen Z, White RF, Antoniw JF, Lin Q. 1991. Effect of pokeweed antiviral protein (PAP) on the infection of plant viruses. *Plant Pathol.* 40:612–20

36. Chow LP, Chou MH, Ho CY, Chuang CC, Pan FM, et al. 1999. Purification, characterization and molecular cloning of trichoanguin, a novel type I ribosome-inactivating protein from the seeds of *Trichosanthes anguina. Biochem. J.* 338:211–19

37. Chow TP, Feldman RA, Lovett M, Piatak M. 1990. Isolation and DNA sequence of a gene encoding alpha-trichosanthin, a type I ribosome-inactivating protein. *J. Biol. Chem.* 265:8670–74

38. Christie A. 1929. House of lurking death. In *Partners in Crime.* New York: Dodd, Mead

39. Christopher GW, Cieslak TJ, Pavlin JA, Eitzen EM Jr. 1997. Biological warfare. A historical perspective. *JAMA* 278:412–17

40. Coleman WH, Roberts WK. 1982. Inhibitors of animal cell-free protein synthesis from grains. *Biochim. Biophys. Acta* 696:239–44

41. Correll CC, Munishkin A, Chan YL, Ren Z, Wool IG, Steitz TA. 1998. Crystal structure of the ribosomal RNA domain essential for binding elongation factors. *Proc. Natl. Acad. Sci. USA* 95:13436–41

42. Day PJ, Lord JM, Roberts LM. 1998. The deoxyribonuclease activity attributed to ribosome-inactivating proteins is due to contamination. *Eur. J. Biochem.* 258:540–45

43. Der SD, Yang YL, Weissmann C, Williams BR. 1997. A double-stranded RNA-activated protein kinase-dependent pathway mediating stress-induced apoptosis. *Proc. Natl. Acad. Sci. USA* 94:3279–83

44. Di-Fonzo N, Manzocchi L, Salamini F, Soave C. 1986. Purification and properties of an endospermic protein of maize associated with the *opaque-2* and *opaque-6* genes. *Planta* 167:587–94

45. Di Maro A, Valbonesi P, Bolognesi A, Stirpe F, De Luca P, et al. 1999. Isolation and characterization of four type-1 ribosome-inactivating proteins, with polynucleotide:adenosine glycosidase activity, from leaves of *Phytolacca dioica* L. *Planta* 208:125–31

46. Dowd PF, Mehta AD, Boston RS. 1998. Relative toxicity of the maize endosperm ribosome-inactivating protein to insects. *J. Agric. Food Chem.* 46:3775–79

47. Eker P, Holm PK, van Deurs B, Sandvig K. 1994. Selective regulation of apical endocytosis in polarized Madin-Darby canine kidney cells by mastoparan and cAMP. *J. Biol. Chem.* 269:18607–15

48. Endo Y, Gluck A, Wool IG. 1991. Ribosomal RNA identity elements for ricin A-chain recognition and catalysis. *J. Mol. Biol.* 221:193–207

49. Endo Y, Mitsui K, Motizuki M, Tsurugi K. 1987. The mechanism of action of ricin and related toxic lectins on eukaryotic ribosomes: the site and the characteristics of the modification in 28S ribosomal RNA caused by the toxins. *J. Biol. Chem.* 262:5908–12

50. Endo Y, Tsurugi K. 1987. RNA N-glycosidase activity of ricin A-chain: mechanism of action of the toxic lectin ricin on eukaryotic ribosomes. *J. Biol. Chem.* 262:8128–30

50a. Fong WP, Mock WY, Ng TB. 2000. Intrinsic ribonuclease activities in ribonuclease and ribosome-inactivating proteins from the seeds of bitter gourd. *Int. J. Biochem. Cell Biol.* 32:571–77

51. Foxwell BM, Donovan TA, Thorpe PE, Wilson G. 1985. The removal of carbohydrates from ricin with endoglycosidases H, F and D and alpha-mannosidase. *Biochim. Biophys. Acta* 840:193–203

52. Francisco JA, Gawlak SL, Miller M, Bathe J, Russell D, et al. 1997. Expression and characterization of bryodin 1 and a bryodin 1-based single-chain immunotoxin from tobacco cell culture. *Bioconjug. Chem.* 8:708–13

53. Frankel AE, FitzGerald D, Siegall C, Press OW. 1996. Advances in immunotoxin biology and therapy: a summary of the Fourth International Symposium on Immunotoxins. *Cancer Res.* 56:926–32

54. Frankel AE, Fu T, Burbage C, Tagge E, Harris B, et al. 1997. Lectin-deficient ricin toxin intoxicates cells bearing the D-mannose receptor. *Carbohydr. Res.* 300:251–58

55. Frigerio L, Vitale A, Lord JM, Ceriotti A, Roberts LM. 1998. Free ricin A chain, proricin, and native toxin have different cellular fates when expressed in tobacco protoplasts. *J. Biol. Chem.* 273:14194–99

56. Gasperi-Campani A, Barbieri L, Battelli MG, Stirpe F. 1985. On the distribution of ribosome-inactivating proteins amongst plants. *J. Nat. Prod.* 48:446–54

57. Gatehouse A, Barbieri L, Stirpe F, Croy RRD. 1990. Effects of ribosome inactivating proteins on insect development—differences between Lepidoptera and Coleoptera. *Entomol. Exp. Appl.* 54:43–51

58. Girbes T dTC, Iglesias R, Ferreras JM, Mendez E. 1996. RIP for viruses. *Nature* 379:777–78

59. Gliemann J. 1998. Receptors of the low density lipoprotein (LDL) receptor family in man. Multiple functions of the large family members via interaction with complex ligands. *Biol. Chem.* 379:951–64

60. Goldbach R. 1986. Molecular evolution of plant RNA viruses. *Annu. Rev. Phytopathol.* 24:289–310

61. Gonatas NK, Gonatas JO, Stieber A. 1998. The involvement of the Golgi apparatus in the pathogenesis of amyotrophic lateral sclerosis, Alzheimer's disease, and ricin intoxication. *Histochem. Cell Biol.* 109:591–600

62. Gorschen E, Dunaeva M, Hause B, Reeh I, Wasternack C, Parthier B. 1997. Expression of the ribosome-inactivating protein JIP60 from barely in transgenic tobacco leads to an abnormal phenotype and alterations on the level of translation. *Planta* 202:470–78

63. Griffiths GD, Leek MD, Gee DJ. 1987. The toxic plant proteins ricin and abrin induce apoptotic changes in mammalian lymphoid tissues and intestine. *J. Pathol.* 151:221–29

64. Gupta SC, Asnani VL, Khare BP. 1970. Effect of the opaque-2 gene in maize (*Zea mays* L.) on the extent of infestation by *Sitophilus oryzae* L. *Stored Prod. Res.* 6:191–94

65. Gutell RR, Gray MW, Schnare MN. 1993. A compilation of large subunit (23S and 23S-like) ribosomal RNA structures: 1993. *Nucleic Acids Res.* 21:3055–74

66. Habuka N, Kataoka J, Miyano M, Tsuge H, Ago H, Noma M. 1993. Nucleotide sequence of a genomic gene encoding tritin, a ribosome-inactivating protein from

Triticum aestivum. Plant Mol. Biol.
22:171–76

67. Hajto T, Hostanska K, Frei K, Rordorf C, Gabius HJ. 1990. Increased secretion of tumor necrosis factors alpha, interleukin 1, and interleukin 6 by human mononuclear cells exposed to beta-galactoside-specific lectin from clinically applied mistletoe extract. *Cancer Res.* 50:3322–26

68. Hao Q, Yan L, Yang H, Zhang Y, Gao G, et al. 1996. Aggregation of phospholipid vesicles induced by the ribosome inactivating protein saporin. *Biochem. Mol. Biol. Int.* 38:701–9

69. Hartings H, Lazzaroni N, Spada A, Thompson R, Salamini F, et al. 1989. The b-32 protein from endosperm: characterization of genomic sequences. *Maize Genet. Coop. Newsl.* 63:29–30

70. Hartley MR, Chaddock JA, Bonness MS. 1996. The structure and function of ribosome-inactivating proteins. *Trends Plant Sci.* 1:254–60

71. Hartley MR, Lord JM. 1993. Structure, function and applications of ricin and related cytotoxic proteins. In *Biosynthesis and Manipulation of Plant Products*, ed. D Griesson, pp. 210–39. New York: Chapman & Hall

72. Hassoun EA, Wang X. 1999. Time- and concentration-dependent production of superoxide anion, nitric oxide, DNA damage and cellular death by ricin in the J774A.1 macrophage cells. *J. Biochem. Mol. Toxicol.* 13:179–85

73. Hassoun E, Wang X. 2000. Ricin-induced toxicity in the macrophage J744A.1 cells: the role of TNF-alpha and the modulation effects of TNF-alpha polyclonal antibody. *J. Biochem. Mol. Toxicol.* 14:95–101

74. Hazes B, Read RJ. 1997. Accumulating evidence suggests that several AB-toxins subvert the endoplasmic reticulum-associated protein degradation pathway to enter target cells. *Biochemistry* 36:11051–54

75. Hey TD, Hartley M, Walsh TA. 1995. Maize ribosome-inactivating protein (b-

32). Homologs in related species, effects on maize ribosomes, and modulation of activity by pro-peptide deletions. *Plant Physiol.* 107:1323–32

76. Hirao I, Madin K, Endo Y, Yokoyama S, Ellington AD. 2000. RNA aptamers that bind to and inhibit the ribosome-inactivating protein, pepocin. *J. Biol. Chem.* 275:4943–48

77. Holm PK, Eker P, Sandvig K, van Deurs B. 1995. Phorbol myristate acetate selectively stimulates apical endocytosis via protein kinase C in polarized MDCK cells. *Exp. Cell Res.* 217:157–68

78. Huang PL, Sun Y, Chen HC, Kung HF, Lee-Huang S. 1999. Proteolytic fragments of anti-HIV and anti-tumor proteins MAP30 and GAP31 are biologically active. *Biochem. Biophys. Res. Commun.* 262:615–23

79. Hudak KA, Dinman JD, Tumer NE. 1999. Pokeweed antiviral protein accesses ribosomes by binding to L3. *J. Biol. Chem.* 274:3859–64

80. Hudak KA, Wang P, Tumer NE. 2000. A novel mechanism for inhibition of translation by pokeweed antiviral protein: depurination of the capped RNA template. *RNA* 6:369–80

81. Husain J, Tickle IJ, Wood SP. 1994. Crystal structure of momordin, a type I ribosome inactivating protein from the seeds of *Momordica charantia. FEBS Lett.* 342:154–58

82. Irvin JD. 1975. Purification and partial characterization of the antiviral protein from *Phytolacca americana* which inhibits eukaryotic protein synthesis. *Arch. Biochem. Biophys.* 169:522–28

83. Irvin JD. 1983. Pokeweed antiviral protein. *Pharmacol. Ther.* 21:371–87

84. Jach G, Görnhardt B, Mundy J, Logemann J, Pinsdorf E, et al. 1995. Enhanced quantitative resistance against fungal disease by combinatorial expression of different barley antifungal proteins in transgenic tobacco. *Plant J.* 8:97–109

85. Jackman MR, Ellis JA, Gray SR, Shurety

W, Luzio JP. 1999. Cell polarization is required for ricin sensitivity in a Caco-2 cell line selected for ricin resistance. *Biochem. J.* 341:323–27

86. Jagus R, Joshi B, Barber GN. 1999. PKR, apoptosis and cancer. *Int. J. Biochem. Cell Biol* 31:123–38

87. Jimenez A, Vazquez D. 1985. Plant and fungal protein and glycoprotein toxins inhibiting eukaryote protein synthesis. *Annu. Rev. Microbiol.* 39:649–72

88. Jones RA, Larkins BA, Tsai CY. 1977. Storage protein synthesis in maize. II. Reduced synthesis of a major zein component by the opaque-2 mutant of maize. *Plant Physiol.* 59:525–29

89. Kao R, Davies J. 1995. Fungal ribotoxins: a family of naturally engineered targeted toxins? *Biochem. Cell Biol.* 73:1151–59

90. Keppler-Hafkemeyer A, Brinkmann U, Pastan I. 1998. Role of caspases in immunotoxin-induced apoptosis of cancer cells. *Biochemistry* 37:16934–42

91. Kimura Y, Hase S, Kobayashi Y, Kyogoku Y, Ikenaka T, Funatsu G. 1988. Structures of sugar chains of ricin D. *J. Biochem.* 103:944–49

92. Knight B. 1979. Ricin—a potent homicidal poison. *Br. Med. J.* 1:350–51

93. Komatsu N, Oda T, Muramatsu T. 1998. Involvement of both caspase-like proteases and serine proteases in apoptotic cell death induced by ricin, modeccin, diphtheria toxin, and pseudomonas toxin. *J. Biochem.* 124:1038–44

94. Kominami E, Hashida S, Khairallah EA, Katunuma N. 1983. Sequestration of cytoplasmic enzymes in an autophagic vacuole-lysosomal system induced by injection of leupeptin. *J. Biol. Chem.* 258:6093–100

95. Krawetz JE, Boston RS. 2000. Substrate specificity of a maize ribosome-inactivating protein differs across diverse taxa. *Eur. J. Biochem.* 267:1966–74

96. Kreitman RJ. 1999. Immunotoxins in cancer therapy. *Curr. Opin. Immunol.* 11:570–78

97. Kumar MA, Timm DE, Neet KE, Owen WG, Peumans WJ, Rao AG. 1993. Characterization of the lectin from the bulbs of *Eranthis hyemalis* (winter aconite) as an inhibitor of protein synthesis. *J. Biol. Chem.* 268:25176–83

98. Lamb FI, Roberts LM, Lord JM. 1985. Nucleotide sequence of cloned cDNA coding for preproricin. *Eur. J. Biochem.* 148:265–70

99. Langer M, Mockel B, Eck J, Zinke H, Lentzen H. 1999. Site-specific mutagenesis of mistletoe lectin: the role of RIP activity in apoptosis. *Biochem. Biophys. Res. Commun.* 264:944–48

100. Leah R, Tommerup H, Svendsen I, Mundy J. 1991. Biochemical and molecular characterization of three barley seed proteins with antifungal properties. *J. Biol. Chem.* 266:1564–73

101. Lee SB, Melkova Z, Yan W, Williams BR, Hovanessian AG, Esteban M. 1993. The interferon-induced double-stranded RNA-activated human p68 protein kinase potently inhibits protein synthesis in cultured cells. *Virology* 192:380–85

102. Lee-Huang S, Huang PL, Bourinbaiar AS, Chen HC, Kung HF. 1995. Inhibition of the integrase of human immunodeficiency virus (HIV) type 1 by anti-HIV plant proteins MAP30 and GAP31. *Proc. Natl. Acad. Sci. USA* 92:8818–22

103. Lee-Huang S, Huang PL, Chen HC, Bourinbaiar A, Huang HI, Kung HF. 1995. Anti-HIV and anti-tumor activities of recombinant MAP30 from bitter melon. *Gene* 161:151–56

104. Lee-Huang S, Kung HF, Huang PL, Bourinbaiar AS, Morell JL, et al. 1994. Human immunodeficiency virus type 1 (HIV-1) inhibition, DNA-binding, RNA-binding, and ribosome inactivation activities in the N-terminal segments of the plant anti-HIV protein GAP31. *Proc. Natl. Acad. Sci. USA* 91:12208–12

105. Lehar SM, Pedersen JT, Kamath RS, Swimmer C, Goldmacher VS, et al. 1994.

Mutational and structural analysis of the lectin activity in binding domain 2 of ricin B chain. *Protein Eng.* 7:1261–66

106. Li M, Yeung HW, Pan LP, Chan SI. 1991. Trichosanthin, a potent HIV-1 inhibitor, can cleave supercoiled DNA *in vitro*. *Nucleic Acids Res.* 19:6309–12

107. Ling J, Liu WY, Wang TP. 1994. Cleavage of supercoiled double-stranded DNA by several ribosome-inactivating proteins in vitro. *FEBS Lett.* 345:143–46

108. Liu G, Hao Q, Zhang Y, Gao G, Yan G, et al. 1997. Fusion of phospholipid vesicles induced by the ribosome inactivating protein saporin. *Biochem. Mol. Biol. Int.* 42:873–80

109. Llorente A, van Deurs B, Garred O, Eker P, Sandvig K. 2000. Apical endocytosis of ricin in MDCK cells is regulated by the cyclooxygenase pathway. *J. Cell Sci.* 113:1213–21

110. Lodge JK, Kaniewski WK, Tumer NE. 1993. Broad-spectrum virus resistance in transgenic plants expressing pokeweed antiviral protein. *Proc. Natl. Acad. Sci. USA* 90:7089–93

111. Loesch PJ Jr, Foley DC, Cox DF. 1976. Comparative resistance of *opaque-2* and normal inbred lines of maize to ear-rotting pathogens. *Crop Sci.* 16:841–42

112. Logemann J, Jach G, Tommerup H, Mundy J, Schell J. 1992. Expression of a barley ribosome-inactivating protein leads to increased fungal protection in transgenic tobacco plants. *BioTechnology* 10:305–8

113. Lord JM. 1985. Precursors of ricin and *Ricinus communis* agglutinin. Glycosylation and processing during synthesis and intracellular transport. *Eur. J. Biochem.* 146:411–16

114. Lord JM, Roberts LM. 1996. The intracellular transport of ricin: why mammalian cells are killed and how Ricinus cells survive. *Plant Physiol. Biochem.* 34:253–61

115. Lord JM, Roberts LM. 1998. Retrograde transport: going against the flow. *Curr. Biol.* 8:R56–58

116. Lord JM, Roberts LM. 1998. Toxin entry: retrograde transport through the secretory pathway. *J. Cell Biol.* 140:733–36

117. Maddaloni M, Forlani F, Balmas V, Donini G, Stasse L, et al. 1997. Tolerance to the fungal pathogen *Rhizoctonia solani* AG4 of transgenic tobacco expressing the maize ribosome-inactivating protein b-32. *Transgenic Res.* 6:393–402

117a. Madin K, Sawasaki T, Ogasawara T, Endo Y. 2000. A highly efficient and robust cell-free protein synthesis system prepared from wheat embryos: plants apparently contain a suicide system directed at ribosomes. *Proc. Natl. Acad. Sci. USA* 97:559–64

118. Martin SJ, Lennon SV, Bonham AM, Cotter TG. 1990. Induction of apoptosis (programmed cell death) in human leukemic HL-60 cells by inhibition of RNA or protein synthesis. *J. Immunol.* 145:1859–67

119. Massiah AJ, Hartley MR. 1995. Wheat ribosome-inactivating proteins: seed and leaf forms with different specificities and cofactor requirements. *Planta* 197:633–40

120. Matlack KE, Mothes W, Rapoport TA. 1998. Protein translocation: tunnel vision. *Cell* 92:381–90

121. McGrath MS, Hwang KM, Caldwell SE, Gaston I, Luk KC, et al. 1989. GLQ223: an inhibitor of human immunodeficiency virus replication in acutely and chronically infected cells of lymphocyte and mononuclear phagocyte lineage. *Proc. Natl. Acad. Sci. USA* 86:2844–48

122. Mehta AD, Boston RS. 1998. Ribosome-inactivating proteins. See Ref. 4a, pp. 145–52

123. Mertz ET, Bates LS, Nelson OE. 1964. Mutant gene that changes protein composition and increases lysine content of maize endosperm. *Science* 145:279–80

124. Mlsna D, Monzingo AF, Katzin BJ, Ernst S, Robertus JD. 1993. Structure of recombinant ricin A chain at 2.3 Å. *Protein Sci.* 2:429–35

125. Mock JW, Ng TB, Wong RN, Yao QZ, Yeung HW, Fong WP. 1996. Demonstration of ribonuclease activity in the plant ribosome-inactivating proteins alpha- and beta-momorcharins. *Life Sci.* 59:1853–59

126. Monzingo AF, Robertus JD. 1992. X-ray analysis of substrate analogs in the ricin A-chain active site. *J. Mol. Biol.* 227:1136–45

127. Mundy J, Leah R, Boston R, Endo Y, Stirpe F. 1994. Genes encoding ribosome-inactivating proteins. *Plant Mol. Biol. Rep.* 12:S60–62

128. Neuhaus JM, Rogers JC. 1998. Sorting of proteins to vacuoles in plant cells. *Plant Mol. Biol.* 38:127–44

129. Nicolas E, Beggs JM, Haltiwanger BM, Taraschi TF. 1997. Direct evidence for the deoxyribonuclease activity of the plant ribosome inactivating protein gelonin. *FEBS Lett.* 406:162–64

130. Nicolas E, Beggs JM, Haltiwanger BM, Taraschi TF. 1998. A new class of DNA glycosylase/apurinic/apyrimidinic lyases that act on specific adenines in single-stranded DNA. *J. Biol. Chem.* 273:17216–20

130a. Nicolas E, Beggs JM, Taraschi TF. 2000. Gelonin is an unusual DNA glycosylase that removes adenine from single-stranded DNA, normal base pairs and mismatches. *J. Biol. Chem.* 275:31399–406

131. Nie H, Cai X, He X, Xu L, Ke X, et al. 1998. Position 120-123, a potential active site of trichosanthin. *Life Sci.* 62:491–500

132. Nielsen K, Payne GA, Boston RS. 2001. Maize ribosome-inactivating protein 1 has antifungal activity against *Aspergillus flavus* and *Aspergillus nidu-*

lans. *Mol. Plant-Microbe Interact.* 14:164–72

133. Nilsson L, Asano K, Svensson B, Poulsen FM, Nygard O. 1986. Reduced turnover of the elongation factor EF-1 X ribosome complex after treatment with the protein synthesis inhibitor II from barley seeds. *Biochim. Biophys. Acta* 868:62–70

134. Oda T, Iwaoka J, Komatsu N, Muramatsu T. 1999. Involvement of N-acetyl-cysteine-sensitive pathways in ricin-induced apoptotic cell death in U937 cells. *Biosci. Biotechnol. Biochem.* 63:341–48

135. Oda T, Komatsu N, Muramatsu T. 1997. Cell lysis induced by ricin D and ricin E in various cell lines. *Biosci. Biotechnol. Biochem.* 61:291–97

136. Oda T, Komatsu N, Muramatsu T. 1998. Diisopropylfluorophosphate (DFP) inhibits ricin-induced apoptosis of MDCK cells. *Biosci. Biotechnol. Biochem.* 62:325–33

137. Ogasawara T, Sawasaki T, Morishita R, Ozawa A, Madin K, Endo Y. 1999. A new class of enzyme acting on damaged ribosomes: ribosomal RNA apurinic site-specific lyase found in wheat germ. *EMBO J.* 18:6522–31

138. Olsnes S, Pihl A. 1973. Isolation and properties of abrin: a toxic protein inhibiting protein synthesis. Evidence for different biological functions of its two constituent-peptide chains. *Eur. J. Biochem.* 35:179–85

139. Olsnes S, Pihl A. 1982. Chimeric toxins. *Pharmacol. Ther.* 15:355–81

140. Olsnes S, Sandvig K. 1988. How protein toxins enter and kill cells. *Cancer Treat. Res.* 37:39–73

141. Onaderra M, Mancheno JM, Gasset M, Lacadena J, Schiavo G, et al. 1993. Translocation of alpha-sarcin across the lipid bilayer of asolectin vesicles. *Biochem. J.* 295:221–25

142. Onaderra M, Mancheno JM, Lacadena J, de los Rios V, Martinez del Pozo A,

Gavilanes JG. 1998. Oligomerization of the cytotoxin alpha-sarcin associated with phospholipid membranes. *Mol. Membr. Biol.* 15:141–44

143. Orita M, Nishikawa F, Shimayama T, Taira K, Endo Y, Nishikawa S. 1993. High-resolution NMR study of a synthetic oligoribonucleotide with a tetranucleotide GAGA loop that is a substrate for the cytotoxic protein, ricin. *Nucleic Acids Res.* 21:5670–78

144. Pain VM. 1996. Initiation of protein synthesis in eukaryotic cells. *Eur. J. Biochem.* 236:747–71

145. Pastan I, Fitzgerald D. 1991. Recombinant toxins for cancer treatment. *Science* 254:1173–76

146. Poma A, Marcozzi G, Cesare P, Carmignani M, Spano L. 1999. Antiproliferative effect and apoptotic response in vitro of human melanoma cells to liposomes containing the ribosome-inactivating protein luffin. *Biochim. Biophys. Acta* 1472:197–205

147. Poma A, Zarivi O, Bianchini S, Spanò L. 1999. The plant ribosome inactivating protein saporin induces micronucleus formation in peripheral human lymphocytes in vitro. *Toxicol. Lett.* 105:67–73

147a. Putnam CD, Tainer JA. 2000. The food of sweet and bitter fancy. *Nat. Struct. Biol.* 7:17–18

148. Rajamohan F, Venkatachalam TK, Irvin JD, Uckun FM. 1999. Pokeweed antiviral protein isoforms PAP-I, PAP-II, and PAP-III depurinate RNA of human immunodeficiency virus (HIV)-1. *Biochem. Biophys. Res. Commun.* 260:453–58

149. Ready MP, Brown DT, Robertus JD. 1986. Extracellular localization of pokeweed antiviral protein. *Proc. Natl. Acad. Sci. USA* 83:5053–56

150. Reinbothe S, Mollenhauer B, Reinbothe C. 1994. JIPs and RIPs: the regulation of plant gene expression by jasmonates in response to environmental cues and pathogens. *Plant Cell* 6:1197–209

151. Reinbothe S, Reinbothe C, Lehmann J, Becker W, Apel K, Parthier B. 1994. JIP60, a methyl jasmonate-induced ribosome-inactivating protein involved in plant stress reactions. *Proc. Natl. Acad. Sci. USA* 91:7012–16

152. Riccobono F, Fiani ML. 1996. Mannose receptor dependent uptake of ricin A1 and A2 chains by macrophages. *Carbohydr. Res.* 282:285–92

153. Rich BE, Steitz JA. 1987. Human acidic ribosomal phosphoproteins P0, P1, and P2: analysis of cDNA clones, in vitro synthesis, and assembly. *Mol. Cell. Biol.* 7:4065–74

154. Rippmann JF, Michalowski CB, Nelson DE, Bohnert HJ. 1997. Induction of a ribosome-inactivating protein upon environmental stress. *Plant Mol. Biol.* 35:701–9

155. Roberts W, Stewart TS. 1979. Purification and properties of a translational inhibitor from wheat germ. *Biochemistry* 18:2615–21

156. Roberts WK, Selitrennikoff CP. 1986. Isolation and partial characterization of two antifungal proteins from barley. *Biochim. Biophys. Acta* 880:161–70

157. Roncuzzi L, Gasperi-Campani A. 1996. DNA-nuclease activity of the single-chain ribosome-inactivating proteins dianthin 30, saporin 6 and gelonin. *FEBS Lett.* 392:16–20

158. Sandvig K, Olsnes S, Pihl A. 1976. Kinetics of binding of the toxic lectins abrin and ricin to surface receptors of human cells. *J. Biol. Chem.* 251:3977–84

159. Sandvig K, van Deurs B. 1992. Toxin-induced cell lysis: protection by 3-methyladenine and cycloheximide. *Exp. Cell Res.* 200:253–62

160. Sandvig K, van Deurs B. 1994. Endocytosis and intracellular sorting of ricin and Shiga toxin. *FEBS Lett.* 346:99–102

161. Sandvig K, van Deurs B. 1996. Endocytosis, intracellular transport, and cytotoxic action of Shiga toxin and ricin. *Physiol. Rev.* 76:949–66

162. Sandvig K, van Deurs B. 1999. Endocytosis and intracellular transport of ricin: recent discoveries. *FEBS Lett.* 452:67–70

163. Savary BJ, Flores HE. 1994. Biosynthesis of defense-related proteins in transformed root cultures of *Trichosanthes kirilowii* Maxim. var *japonicum* (Kitam.). *Plant Physiol.* 106:1195–204

164. Schlumbaum A, Mauch F, Vogeli U, Boller T. 1986. Plant chitinases are potent inhibitors of fungal growth. *Nature* 324:365–67

165. Seetharaman K, Waniska RD, Rooney LW. 1996. Physiological changes in sorghum antifungal proteins. *J. Agric. Food Chem.* 44:2435–41

166. Sehnke PC, Ferl RJ. 1999. Processing of preproricin in transgenic tobacco. *Protein Expr. Purif.* 15:188–95

166a. Selbo PK, Sandvig K, Kirveliene V, Berg K. 2000. Release of gelonin from endosomes and lysosomes to cytosol by photochemical internalization. *Biochim. Biophys. Acta* 1475:307–13

167. Simmons BM, Stahl PD, Russell JH. 1986. Mannose receptor-mediated uptake of ricin toxin and ricin A chain by macrophages. Multiple intracellular pathways for a chain translocation. *J. Biol. Chem.* 261:7912–20

168. Simpson JC, Roberts LM, Romisch K, Davey J, Wolf DH, Lord JM. 1999. Ricin A chain utilises the endoplasmic reticulum-associated protein degradation pathway to enter the cytosol of yeast. *FEBS Lett.* 459:80–84

169. Soave C, Tardani L, Di-Fonzo N, Salamini F. 1981. Zein level in maize endosperm depends on a protein under control of the *opaque-2* and *opaque-6* loci. *Cell* 27:403–10

169a. Song SK, Choi Y, Moon YH, Kim SG,

Choi YD, Lee JS. 2000. Systemic induction of a *Phytolacca insularis* antiviral protein gene by mechanical wounding, jasmonic acid, and abscisic acid. *Plant Mol. Biol.* 43:439–50

170. Sperti S, Brigotti M, Zamboni M, Carnicelli D, Montanaro L. 1991. Requirements for the inactivation of ribosomes by gelonin. *Biochem. J.* 277:281–84

171. Spooner RA, Lord JM. 1990. Immunotoxins: status and prospects. *Trends Biotechnol.* 8:189–93

172. Steeves RM, Denton ME, Barnard FC, Henry A, Lambert JM. 1999. Identification of three oligosaccharide binding sites in ricin. *Biochemistry* 38:11677–85

173. Stirpe F, Barbieri L, Battelli MG, Soria M, Lappi DA. 1992. Ribosome-inactivating proteins from plants: present status and future prospects. *Biotechnology* 10:405–12

174. Stirpe F, Barbieri L, Gorini P, Valbonesi P, Bolognesi A, Polito L. 1996. Activities associated with the presence of ribosome-inactivating proteins increase in senescent and stressed leaves. *FEBS Lett.* 382:309–12

175. Stirpe F, Gasperi-Campani A, Barbieri L, Lorenzoni E, Montanaro L, et al. 1978. Inhibition of protein synthesis by modeccin, the toxin of *Modecca digitata*. *FEBS Lett.* 85:65–67

176. Stirpe F, Olsnes S, Pihl A. 1980. Gelonin, a new inhibitor of protein synthesis, nontoxic to intact cells. Isolation, characterization, and preparation of cytotoxic complexes with concanavalin A. *J. Biol. Chem.* 255:6947–53

177. Stirpe F, Williams DG, Onyon LJ, Legg RF, Stevens WA. 1981. Dianthins, ribosome-damaging proteins with antiviral properties from *Dianthus caryophyllus* L. (carnation). *Biochem. J.* 195:399–405

178. Strauss JH, Strauss EG. 1988. Evolution of RNA viruses. *Annu. Rev. Microbiol.* 42:657–83

179. Svinth M, Steighardt J, Hernandez R, Suh JK, Kelly C, et al. 1998. Differences in cytotoxicity of native and engineered RIPs can be used to assess their ability to reach the cytoplasm. *Biochem. Biophys. Res. Commun.* 249:637–42

180. Swimmer C, Lehar SM, McCafferty J, Chiswell DJ, Blattler WA, Guild BC. 1992. Phage display of ricin B chain and its single binding domains: system for screening galactose-binding mutants. *Proc. Natl. Acad. Sci. USA* 89:3756–60

181. Tagge E, Harris B, Burbage C, Hall P, Vesely J, et al. 1997. Synthesis of green fluorescent protein-ricin and monitoring of its intracellular trafficking. *Bioconjug. Chem.* 8:743–50

182. Taylor S, Massiah A, Lomonossoff G, Roberts LM, Lord JM, Hartley M. 1994. Correlation between the activities of five ribosome-inactivating proteins in depurination of tobacco ribosomes and inhibition of tobacco mosaic virus infection. *Plant J.* 5:827–35

183. Thorpe PE, Edwards DC, Davies AJS, Ross WCJ. 1982. Monoclonal antibody-toxin conjugates: aiming the magnetic bullet. In *Monoclonal Antibodies in Clinical Medicine*, ed. J Fabre, A McMichael, pp. 167–201. London: Academic

184. Tomlinson JA, Walker VM, Flewett TH, Barclay GR. 1974. The inhibition of infection by cucumber mosaic virus and influenza virus by extracts from *Phytolacca americana*. *J. Gen. Virol.* 22:225–32

185. Tumer NE, Hudak K, Di R, Coetzer C, Wang P, Zoubenko O. 1999. Pokeweed antiviral protein and its applications. *Curr. Top. Microbiol. Immunol.* 240:139–58

186. Tumer NE, Hwang DJ, Bonness M. 1997. C-terminal deletion mutant of pokeweed antiviral protein inhibits viral infection but does not depurinate host ribosomes. *Proc. Natl. Acad. Sci. USA* 94:3866–71

187. Tumer NE, Parikh BA, Li P, Dinman JD. 1998. The pokeweed antiviral protein specifically inhibits Ty1-directed +1 ribosomal frameshifting and retrotransposition in *Saccharomyces cerevisiae*. *J. Virol.* 72:1036–42

188. Uchiumi T, Wahba AJ, Traut RR. 1987. Topography and stoichiometry of acidic proteins in large ribosomal subunits from *Artemia salina* as determined by crosslinking. *Proc. Natl. Acad. Sci. USA* 84:5580–64

189. Ussery MA, Irvin JD, Hardesty B. 1977. Inhibition of poliovirus replication by a plant antiviral peptide. *Ann. NY Acad. Sci.* 284:431–40

190. Valbonesi P, Barbieri L, Bolognesi A, Bonora E, Polito L, Stirpe F. 1999. Preparation of highly purified momordin II without ribonuclease activity. *Life Sci.* 65:1485–91

190a. Van Damme EJ, Barre A, Barbieri L, Valbonesi P, Rouge P, et al. 1997. Type 1 ribosome-inactivating proteins are the most abundant proteins in iris (*Iris hollandica* var. Professor Blaauw) bulbs: characterization and molecular cloning. *Biochem. J.* 324:963–70

191. van Deurs B, Tonnessen TI, Petersen OW, Sandvig K, Olsnes S. 1986. Routing of internalized ricin and ricin conjugates to the Golgi complex. *J. Cell Biol.* 102:37–47

192. Vater CA, Bartle LM, Leszyk JD, Lambert JM, Goldmacher VS. 1995. Ricin A chain can be chemically cross-linked to the mammalian ribosomal proteins L9 and L10e. *J. Biol. Chem.* 270:12933–40

193. Vervecken W, Kleff S, Pfuller U, Bussing A. 2000. Induction of apoptosis by mistletoe lectin I and its subunits. No evidence for cytotoxic effects caused by isolated A- and B-chains. *Int. J. Biochem. Cell Biol.* 32:317–26

194. Vitale A, Raikhel NV. 1999. What do proteins need to reach different vacuoles? *Trends Plant Sci.* 4:149–55

195. Vivanco JM, Savary BJ, Flores HE. 1999. Characterization of two novel

type I ribosome-inactivating proteins from the storage roots of the Andean crop *Mirabilis expansa. Plant Physiol.* 119:1447–56

196. Walsh TA, Morgan AE, Hey TD. 1991. Characterization and molecular cloning of a proenzyme form of a ribosome-inactivating protein from maize: novel mechanism of proenzyme activation by proteolytic removal of a 2.8-kilodalton internal peptide segment. *J. Biol. Chem.* 266:23422–27

197. Wang P, Tumer NE. 1999. Pokeweed antiviral protein cleaves double-stranded supercoiled DNA using the same active site required to depurinate rRNA. *Nucleic Acids Res.* 27:1900–5

197a. Wang P, Tumer NE. 2000. Virus resistance mediated by ribosome inactivating proteins. *Adv. Virus Res.* 55:325–55

198. Wang YX, Neamati N, Jacob J, Palmer I, Stahl SJ, et al. 1999. Solution structure of anti-HIV-1 and anti-tumor protein MAP30: structural insights into its multiple functions. *Cell* 99:433–42

199. Wesche J, Rapak A, Olsnes S. 1999. Dependence of ricin toxicity on translocation of the toxin A-chain from the endoplasmic reticulum to the cytosol. *J. Biol. Chem.* 274:34443–49

200. Wiener SL. 1996. Strategies for the prevention of a successful biological warfare aerosol attack. *Mil. Med.* 161:251–56

201. Williams JM, Lea N, Lord JM, Roberts LM, Milford DV, Taylor CM. 1997. Comparison of ribosome-inactivating proteins in the induction of apoptosis. *Toxicol. Lett.* 91:121–27

202. Wong RNS, Mak NK, Choi WT, Law PTW. 1995. Increased accumulation of trichosanthin in *Trichosanthes kirilowii* induced by microorganisms. *J. Exp. Bot.* 46:355–58

203. Wool IG, Gluck A, Endo Y. 1992. Ribotoxin recognition of ribosomal RNA and a proposal for the mechanism of translocation. *Trends Biochem. Sci.* 17:266–69

204. Wu TH, Chow LP, Lin JY. 1998. Sechiumin, a ribosome-inactivating protein from the edible gourd, *Sechium edule* Swartz—purification, characterization, molecular cloning and expression. *Eur. J. Biochem.* 255:400–8

205. Zarling JM, Moran PA, Haffar O, Sias J, Richman DD, et al. 1990. Inhibition of HIV replication by pokeweed antiviral protein targeted to CD4+ cells by monoclonal antibodies. *Nature* 347:92–95

205a. Zhang CY, Gong YX, Ma H, An CC, Chen DY. 2000. Trichosanthin induced calcium-dependent generation of reactive oxygen species in human choriocarcinoma cells. *Analyst* 125:1539–42

206. Zhao J, Ben LH, Wu YL, Hu W, Ling K, et al. 1999. Anti-HIV agent trichosanthin enhances the capabilities of chemokines to stimulate chemotaxis and G protein activation, and this is mediated through interaction of trichosanthin and chemokine receptors. *J. Exp. Med.* 1:101–11

207. Zhou X, Li XD, Yuan JZ, Tang ZH, Liu WY. 2000. Toxicity of cinnamomin—a new type II ribosome-inactivating protein to bollworm and mosquito. *Insect Biochem. Mol. Biol.* 30:259–64

208. Zhu RH, Ng TB, Yeung HW, Shaw PC. 1992. High level synthesis of biologically active recombinant trichosanthin in Escherichia coli. *Int. J. Pept. Protein Res.* 39:77–81

209. Zoubenko O, Uckun F, Hur Y, Chet I, Tumer N. 1997. Plant resistance to fungal infection induced by nontoxic pokeweed antiviral protein mutants. *Nat. Biotechnol.* 15:992–96

Annu. Rev. Plant Physiol. Plant Mol. Biol. 2001. 52:817–45

PLANT PLASMA MEMBRANE H+-ATPases: Powerhouses for Nutrient Uptake

Michael G Palmgren

Department of Plant Biology, The Royal Veterinary and Agricultural University,
Thorvaldsensvej 40, DK-1871 Frederiksberg C, Denmark; e-mail: palmgren@biobase.dk

Key Words Arabidopsis, proton pump, genome sequencing, T-DNA knockouts, gene family, 14-3-3, structure

■ **Abstract** Most transport proteins in plant cells are energized by electrochemical gradients of protons across the plasma membrane. The formation of these gradients is due to the action of plasma membrane H^+ pumps fuelled by ATP. The plasma membrane H^+-ATPases share a membrane topography and general mechanism of action with other P-type ATPases, but differ in regulatory properties. Recent advances in the field include the identification of the complete H^+-ATPase gene family in Arabidopsis, analysis of H^+-ATPase function by the methods of reverse genetics, an improved understanding of the posttranslational regulation of pump activity by 14-3-3 proteins, novel insights into the H^+ transport mechanism, and progress in structural biology. Furthermore, the elucidation of the three-dimensional structure of a related Ca^{2+} pump has implications for understanding of structure-function relationships for the plant plasma membrane H^+-ATPase.

CONTENTS

1040-2519/01/0601-0817$14.00

817

INTRODUCTION

Plasma membrane H$^+$-ATPases constitute a family of proton pumps driven by hydrolysis of ATP and are found exclusively in the plasma membrane of plants and fungi. Here their primary role is to provide an energy source for transport of nutrients into the cell. The plasma membrane H$^+$-ATPase is an electrogenic enzyme since it extrudes positive charges (H$^+$) and thus forms a membrane potential (negative on the inside). In plant cells this membrane potential may exceed -200 mV (52). As protons accumulate on the outside of the cell, the pH of the apoplast decreases typically to reach values of pH 5–6, substantially more acidic than the cytoplasm. The combined electrochemical gradient of charge and matter constitutes a driving force for solutes to enter the cell. Cations are attracted by the cell because of the membrane potential, negative inside, and may enter the cell simply through channel proteins. Cations, anions, and neutral solutes are all able to enter the cell through various carrier proteins through which transport is energized by the concomitant uptake of protons. Thus, most of the hundreds of membrane-bound transport proteins that have been identified in plants are energized indirectly through the action of plasma membrane H$^+$-ATPases (Figure 1; see color insert).

In this review, I focus on recent advances that have increased our knowledge of plant plasma membrane H$^+$-ATPases. These include new insights into the evolution of H$^+$-ATPases, progress in understanding the physiological roles of H$^+$-ATPases and their regulation, and advances in structural biology that have helped us to understand structure-function relationships. Other aspects of plasma membrane H$^+$-ATPases are discussed in a number of recent reviews (79, 82 95, 96, 109, 123, 131, 133).

EVOLUTION

Plasma membrane H$^+$-ATPase differ markedly from V-type and F-type H$^+$-ATPases in the vacuolar and mitochondrial inner membranes, respectively, with respect to their biochemistry, subunit organization, mechanism of action and evolutionary origin. Plant plasma membrane H$^+$-ATPase is a single polypeptide of around 100 kDa that forms a covalent enzyme-phosphate transition state during the reaction cycle (20, 136). Hence, this enzyme is classified as a P-type ATPase (to reflect the presence of the E-P form). P-type ATPases constitute a large family of cation pumps that (*a*) form an aspartyl phosphate reaction cycle intermediate, (*b*) are inhibited by vanadate, and (*c*) share a common domain organization (12, 73, 80, 106). Other ATPases belonging to this family include the fungal plasma membrane H$^+$-ATPases; the animal Na$^+$/K$^+$-ATPase; the gastric H$^+$/K$^+$-ATPase; the Ca^{2+}-ATPases in the sarcoplasmic reticulum and in the plasma membrane, vacuolar membrane, and ER of plants, fungi, and animals; heavy metal ATPases in bacteria and eukaryotes; and bacterial K$^+$-ATPases. In all these ATPases, the amino acid sequence surrounding the phosphorylated aspartate residue is conserved: DKTGT[L/I/V/M][T/I] (the D is phosphorylated). This motif (ProSite PS00154; ATPASE_E1_E2) can be used as a signature pattern to identify P-type ATPases.

P-type ATPases are structurally related to a large superfamily of hydrolases that are typified by the L-2 haloacid dehalogenase (HAD) (8). Sequence and structure comparisons suggest that the catalytic phosphorylation site and other regions are related in P-type ATPases and haloacid dehalogenases (130, 134). However, in P-type ATPases, a nucleotide binding domain has been inserted into the haloacid dehalogenase fold (130, 134). It was therefore hypothesized that P-type ATPases first evolved from the fusion of a HAD-like phophatase with a nucleotide-binding protein (Figure 2; see color insert). A soluble P-type ATPase was recently identified in the archaebacterium *Methanococcus jannaschii* (91) and might represent an ancestral P-type ATPase.

Later, soluble P-type ATPases might have fused with a membrane-bound carrier protein (Figure 2). The soluble P-type ATPase of *M. jannaschii* has sequence homology with the membrane-bound KdpB-ATPase (91). This primitive bacterial P-type ATPase has only six putative transmembrane segments, whereas present-day plasma membrane H$^+$-ATPases are believed to have ten transmembrane segments. Acquisition of the four additional membrane-spanning segments might have been the result of subsequent protein fusions.

The KdpB ATPase of eubacteria is unlike other P-type ATPases because it is organized in a complex with three other polypeptides, KdpA, KdpC, and KdpF (2, 42). The Kdp-ATPase complex is involved in K$^+$ transport but, intriguingly, KdpA, and not KdpB, constitutes the K$^+$ pathway in the complex (23, 32). It has been suggested (12) that KdpB might be involved in the outward transport of another cation (which could be H$^+$), thus generating a membrane potential that could drive uptake of K$^+$ through the KdpA subunit, which resembles a K$^+$ channel (32); however, experimental evidence for this hypothesis is lacking.

It is not yet clear whether transport of protons by P-type ATPases is to be considered a primitive character. Sequences belonging to the subfamily of P-type H$^+$-ATPases have been identified in plants, fungi, protozoa, and in *M. jannaschii* (12). However, related genes have not been identified in other archaebacteria (five complete genomes are available so far) and not at all in eubacteria. All bacterial P-type ATPases investigated to date transport divalent cations (heavy metals, Ca^{2+}, and Mg^{2+}) except for the Kdp-ATPase complex.

THE PLASMA MEMBRANE H⁺-ATPase GENE FAMILY

The first plant plasma membrane H^+-ATPase genes to be cloned—and the first genes encoding plasma membrane proteins—were Arabidopsis *AHA1* and *AHA3* (49, 101). It soon became apparent that in this organism there is a multigene family encoding H^+-ATPases (47, 48, 54) and, as the Arabidopsis genome sequencing project (17) has reached its completion (133a), we now know that there are 12 Arabidopsis H^+-ATPase genes (Table 1). One of the genes (*AHA12*) carries two large deletions and thus might represent a pseudogene. In the *Nicotiana plumbaginifolia* genome, nine H^+-ATPase genes have been identified (18a, 94), which supports the notion that a large family of plasma membrane H^+-ATPases is present in every plant. References to H^+-ATPase genes in other plants are given in (82) and at the P-type ATPase database web-site (http://biobase.dk/~axe/Patbase.html).

A phylogenetic tree based on the available amino acid sequences reveals the presence of a number of H^+-ATPase subfamilies (Figure 3, see color insert).

TABLE 1   Overview of the plasma membrane H^+-ATPase gene family in *Arabidopsis thaliana*

Accession no.	Gene name	Chromosomal location (Centimorgans)[a]	Mol.Wt.[b]	pI	Length (amino acids)
P20649[c]/AC003673[d]	AHA1/At2g18960	2; 35	104313	6.3	949
P19456/AL161576	AHA2/At4g30190	4; 81	104401	6.5	948
P20431/AB019233	AHA3/At5g57350	5; 114	104449	6.7	949
Q9SU58/AL049658	AHA4/At3g47950	3; 65	105679	6.1	960
Q9SJB3/AC006954	AHA5/At2g24520	2; 39	104739	6.8	949
Q9SH76/AC007662	AHA6/At2g07560	2; 19	105012	5.8	949
Q9LY32/AL163852	AHA7/At3g60330	3; 78	105520	6.4	961
Q9M2A0/AL138640	AHA8/At3g42640	3; 53	104131	5.5	948
Q42556/AC011713	AHA9/At1g80660	1; 124	105208	6.0	954
Q43128/S74033[e]	AHA10/At1g17260	1; 23	104815	6.0	947
Q9LV11/AB020751	AHA11/At5g62670	5; 119	105123	6.1	956
Q9T0E0/AL049500[f]	AHA12/At4g11730	4; 40	90439	6.4	813

[a]The position in centimorgans is the position of the nearest known genetic marker according to the Arabidopsis Information Resource (http://www.arabidopsis.org).

[b]Mol. wt., calculated molecular weight.

[c]SWISS-PROT database accession no.

[d]EMBL/GenBank/DDBJ databases accession no.

[e]The original protein sequence is partly derived from genomic DNA data. A proposed exon border has been changed by one amino acid removing a one amino acid gap only found in this sequence.

[f]This sequence is atypical as it is missing 100 amino acid residues from a conserved area and the C-terminal also seems to be missing. In its current form it cannot be an active ATPase, but could be a pseudo-gene or have another function in the cell.

Arabidopsis AHA1, AHA2, AHA3, and AHA5 group together with *N. plumbagini-folia* PMA4. Arabidopsis AHA6, AHA8, and AHA9 belong to a cluster with *N. plumbaginifolia* PMA6. The remaining H$^+$-ATPases form three small branches, each with representatives from both Arabidopsis and *N. plumbaginifolia*.

When the structures of the Arabidopsis and *N. plumbaginifolia* H$^+$-ATPase genes are compared and grouped according to their exon split boundaries, the H$^+$-ATPase genes form three clusters with very similar exon structures (Figure 4; see color insert). The H$^+$-ATPases cluster as in the phylogenetic tree, except that one cluster (III) comprises three of the small branches in the phylogenetic tree.

We might conclude that at least two H$^+$-ATPase gene duplications have occurred early in plant evolution, well before the split between Arabidopsis and *N. plumbaginifolia*. These have been followed by several more recent gene duplications and have given rise to additional subfamilies of H$^+$-ATPases, each with one or more members depending on the organism.

Is there functional analogy between the H$^+$-ATPases in each subfamily? For example, Arabidopsis AHA3 and *N. plumbaginifolia* PMA4 are members of the same subfamily (I) and are both localized to the phloem (see below) where they may have the same function. Whether this reflects the general picture, however, is still too early to say.

Another important question is: Do the various members of the H$^+$-ATPase family in a given species have different catalytic properties? This problem has been tackled by producing individual plant H$^+$-ATPase isoforms in a heterologous system such as yeast. Subsequent analysis has revealed a number of quantitative differences in catalytic and regulatory properties between isoforms (27a, 72, 97). In yeast, plant H$^+$-ATPase isoforms are phosphorylated to various degrees by an endogenous protein kinase at residues important for regulation (27a, 39, 76). Are some of the observed differences in catalytic properties between isoforms partly or fully the result of this posttranslational modification in the heterologous host? Identification and disruption of the protein kinase(s) having plant H$^+$-ATPase as its substrate might help resolve this question.

PHYSIOLOGICAL ROLES

Plasma membrane H$^+$-ATPases are found throughout the plant in every cell type investigated. However, certain cell types have much higher concentrations of H$^+$-ATPase than others. For a comprehensive description of the expression pattern of seven isoforms of the *N. plumbaginifolia* plasma membrane H$^+$-ATPase, the reader is referred to (94). An overview of the localization of plant plasma membrane H$^+$-ATPases is given in Table 2. In general, cell types with abundant H$^+$-ATPase are specialized for intensely active transport and accumulate solutes from their surroundings. Although this indicates a role of H$^+$-ATPases in energizing transport, direct demonstration of the role of H$^+$-ATPases in the various parts of the plant has to come from genetic studies.

TABLE 2   Localization of specific plasma membrane H^+-ATPase isoforms in the plant body

Tissue	H^+-ATPase protein	Plant	References
Seedlings			
Cotyledon	PMA1, PMA2, PMA4	*N. plumbaginifolia*	79a, 81
Primary root	PMA1, PMA4	*N. plumbaginifolia*	79a, 81
Root:			
Cortex parenchyma	PMA2, PMA3, PMA4	*N. plumbaginifolia*	1
Extension zone	PMA4	*N. plumbaginifolia*	81
Lateral root initials	PMA2, PMA4	*N. plumbaginifolia*	81
Lateral roots	PMA4, PMA9	*N. plumbaginifolia*	81, 94
Root hair and	PMA1, PMA3, PMA4	*N. plumbaginifolia*	79a, 81
epidermis	MHA2	*Zea mays*	36a
Root cap	PMA2, PMA4	*N. plumbaginifolia*	81
Stele (central cylinder)	PMA2, PMA3, PMA4	*N. plumbaginifolia*	81
Uninfected host cells in root nodules	BHA1	*Phaseolus vulgaris*	24a
Stem:			
Axillary buds	PMA2, PMA4, PMA9	*N. plumbaginifolia*	81, 94
Cortex parenchyma	PMA1, PMA2, PMA4	*N. plumbaginifolia*	79a, 81
Pith	PMA4	*N. plumbaginifolia*	81
Vascular tissue	PMA2, PMA3, PMA4, PMA9	*N. plumbaginifolia*	81, 94
	MHA2	*Zea mays*	36a
	AHA3	*A. thaliana*	30, 31
Leaf:			
Guard cells	PMA2, PMA4	*N. plumbaginifolia*	79a, 81
	VHA1, VHA2	*Vicia faba*	51
	MHA2	*Zea mays*	36a
Mesophyll	PMA2, PMA4	*N. plumbaginifolia*	81
	VHA1, VHA2	*Vicia faba*	51
Trichomes (long)	PMA4	*N. plumbaginifolia*	81
Trichomes (short)	PMA6	*N. plumbaginifolia*	94
Vascular tissue	PMA2, PMA3, PMA4	*N. plumbaginifolia*	81
	MHA2	*Zea mays*	36a
	AHA3	*A. thaliana*	30, 31

(Continued)

TABLE 2   (*Continued*)

Tissue	H$^+$-ATPase protein	Plant	References
Flower			
Carpel	PMA2	*N. plumbaginifolia*	81
Ovules	PMA1, PMA2, PMA3, PMA4, PMA6, PMA9	*N. plumbaginifolia*	79a, 81, 94
	AH3	*A. thaliana*	30
	AHA10	*A. thaliana*	48
Nectaries	PMA2	*N. plumbaginifolia*	81
Stamen (filament, anther); pollen (grains, tubes)	PMA1, PMA2, PMA3, PMA4, PMA6, PMA9	*N. plumbaginifolia*	79a, 81, 94
	AHA3	*A. thaliana*	30
	AHA9	*A. thaliana*	54
Style	PMA1, PMA3, PMA4	*N. plumbaginifolia*	79a, 81
Vascular tissue	PMA1, PMA2, PMA3, PMA4, PMA6	*N. plumbaginifolia*	79a, 81, 94
	AHA3	*A. thaliana*	30

Massive screening of Arabidopsis lines carrying T-DNA insertions has so far resulted in the identification of individual mutant lines carrying knockouts in all H$^+$-ATPase genes except for AHA6 and AHA12 (66, 67, 149a). Several mutant alleles have been identified for a number of isoforms (149a). The analysis of knockout lines is likely to concentrate first on the identification of essential genes. In those cases where there is redundancy of gene function, single gene mutations might not result in a visible phenotype. However, knockouts in more than a single H$^+$-ATPase gene can in principle be generated by crossing mutant lines.

In this review, focus is on the role of H$^+$-ATPase in phloem loading, the movements of stomatal guard cells, energization of nutrient uptake into the roots, and for the growth of root hairs and pollen tubes. The participation of plasma membrane H$^+$-ATPases in other important physiological processes such as salt and osmotolerance, leaf movements, intracellular pH regulation, and acid growth is discussed elsewhere (79, 82, 94, 96, 123, 131).

Role in Phloem Loading

The plasma membrane H$^+$-ATPase is highly concentrated in the phloem, a specialized tissue for long-distance transport of mostly organic compounds. This was first shown by immunodecoration of this tissue with anti-H$^+$-ATPase antibodies (103, 139). The expression patterns of the *GUS* reporter gene fused to the promoter region of Arabidopsis *AHA3* (29), and *N. plumbaginifolia PMA4* (81) indicate that these H$^+$-ATPase isoforms are phloem localized.

Transgenic *N. plumbaginifolia* plants that cosuppress *PMA4* are stunted in growth and accumulate sugars in the leaves (152). The retarded growth might result from the inability of established leaves to export sugars to sink organs such as the root and developing leaves. This would suggest that the plasma membrane H^+-ATPase is crucial for the loading of sucrose and probably other photosynthetic assimilates into the phloem (152).

The exact localization of H^+-ATPase in the phloem has been studied in some detail. Arabidopsis AHA3 H^+-ATPase was equipped with a viral epitope and expressed in transgenic plants (31). Immunological detection localized the tagged protein to phloem companion cells. These cells are rich in mitochondria and hence are able to synthesize the large amounts of ATP required by the H^+-ATPase. In Arabidopsis (129, 135) and *Plantago major* (128), sucrose/H^+ cotransporters are found in the plasma membrane of phloem companion cells. Sucrose taken up by these cells is subsequently transported into the sieve elements by passive diffusion through plasmodesmata.

Surprisingly, sucrose/H^+ cotransporters in tobacco, potato, and tomato are localized exclusively in the plasma membrane of enucleate sieve elements (68). These cells contains few mitochondria, and the H^+-ATPase has not been localized to this cell type. How the H^+-ATPase in the companion cells is able to energize sucrose transport by sucrose/H^+ cotransporters in the sieve elements is not understood. Whether H^+-ATPase has escaped detection in enucleate sieve elements needs to be investigated.

Role in Regulation of the Size of the Stomatal Aperture

When guard cells take up solutes and water, the cells swell and the stomatal aperture widens, allowing CO_2 to enter the leaves through the stomatal pore and to be utilized for photosynthesis. Immunological methods have shown that the plasma membrane H^+-ATPase is enriched in guard cells (16, 139). Two H^+-ATPase genes of *Vicia faba* (*VHA1* and *VHA2*), two H^+-ATPases of *N. plumbaginifolia* (*PMA2* and *PMA4*), and maize *MHA2* are expressed in guard cells. In addition, *V. faba*, *N. plumbaginifolia*, and maize express these genes in many other cell types (Table 2).

Transgenic *N. plumbaginifolia* plants that cosuppress expression of *PMA4* have closed stomatal apertures (152). This is true even in the presence of the fungal phytotoxin fusicoccin, which normally induces strong irreversible activation of H^+-ATPases. The H^+-ATPase is thus likely to be required for the opening process.

Opening and closure of the stomatal aperture are controlled by many factors (9, 150). For example, a short pulse of blue light is sufficient to initiate the opening process. Blue light is presumably registered by a light receptor in the guard cells and the signal transmitted to the guard cell plasma membrane H^+-ATPase. In *V. faba*, this activation occurs less than a minute after the light signal is received, thus activating electrogenic H^+ pumping (5, 10, 63, 116, 122). The complete signal transduction pathway from the blue light receptor to the H^+-ATPase has not been identified, but involves a protein kinase that by phosphorylation of the H$^+$-ATPase creates a binding site for regulatory 14-3-3 protein (see below) (63).

Role in Solute Uptake in the Roots

Epidermal cells of plant roots have a very high affinity for anti-H$^+$-ATPase antibody (55, 119). Several candidate H$^+$-ATPases have emerged that might be involved in energization of the uptake of nutrients from the soil into the roots. Since they are localized to root epidermal cells and root hairs (Table 2). In Arabidopsis, the mRNA of *AHA2* accumulates in the roots (47), and evidence based on the analysis of the expression patterns of promoter-*GUS* fusions in Arabidopsis have suggested that AHA2 is localized in the root epidermis as well as in other parts of the plant (JF Harper, personal communication; K Drumm & MG Palmgren, unpublished results).

In roots, apart from the epidermal cells, high amounts of immunodetectable H$^+$-ATPase are apparent in the endodermis (55, 103). The localization of H$^+$-ATPase in root endodermal tissues suggests a role for the pump in the active loading of solutes into the xylem (103). In Arabidopsis, AHA4 is expressed most strongly in the root endodermis, but also in flowers, as suggested by promoter/*GUS* reporter assays (JF Harper, personal communication).

Role in Tip Growing Systems

Tip-growing systems are single-cell systems that expand in one direction only. Prominent examples of plant tip-growing systems are pollen tubes and root hairs (Figure 5, see color insert).

High amounts of plasma membrane H$^+$-ATPase have been localized immunologically to pollen grains, but only low amounts to pollen tubes (87). Large numbers of H$^+$-ATPase isoforms have been localized by *GUS*-promoter fusion analysis to pollen grains (Table 2).

Using a self-referencing (vibrating) electrode, electric fields can be detected around germinating lily pollen (147). Measurements by proton-selective vibrating microelectrodes have revealed that these currents are generated by fluxes of protons (35). Two closed loops of proton fluxes are present in a long ($\sim$800 μM) pollen tube: The first circuit is around the grain, with protons leaving the pollen grain and entering the pollen tube at its basal end, immediately after the pore; the second proton circuit is localized to the growing tip, with protons leaving the tube below the tip and entering the tube at the extreme apex. The first proton circuit, at the base of the pollen tube, is compatible with the high level of plasma membrane H$^+$-ATPase at the corresponding position (87). However, the second proton circuit, at the tip of the pollen tube, is not compatible with the apparent lack of H$^+$-ATPase at this location (87). Further studies are therefore required to clarify the localization of H$^+$-ATPase in pollen tubes.

The pattern of cytoplasmic pH in the growing pollen tube correlates well with the localization of proton fluxes. Cytosolic pH has been measured in the growing pollen tube using a wide-field imaging system that allows visualization at low concentrations (less than 1 μM) of the pH-sensitive fluorescent probe 2',7'-bis-(2-carboxyethyl)-5-(and-6)-carboxyfluorescein (BCECF) (35). Higher concentrations of the indicator dye are often used (37, 77, 104), but apparently dissipate local pH gradients (35). The tip of the growing pollen tube possesses a distinct pH gradient (Figure 5). Thus, the cytoplasm of the extreme apex is slightly acidic (pH $\sim$ 6.8), with an alkaline region (pH up to 7.8) observed immediately below (35). The cytoplasmic pH at the position of the alkaline band oscillates with time, and a clear correlation exists between alkalinization and increased rates of pollen tube growth (35).

Root hairs of barley contain high amounts of immunodetectable plasma membrane H^+-ATPase (119), and several isoforms localize to this structure in other species (see above). Proton-selective vibrating electrodes have also revealed a proton circuit in root hairs (58, 146): Protons enter the root hair at the extreme tip and leave the hair just below the tip (58) (Figure 5). This pattern of proton influx and efflux closely resembles that detected in the pollen tube. However, it is still not known whether proton fluxes in the root hair correlate with changes in cytoplasmic pH and spatial localization of the plasma membrane H^+-ATPase.

Confocal ratio imaging of root hairs has been used to reveal the pH of the cell wall and in the cytoplasm. Root hair initiation in Arabidopsis is associated with a slight alkalinization of the cytoplasm (from approximately pH 7.3 pH up to pH 7.7) and a local wall acidification (from pH 6 down to pH 4.5) at the site of initiation (18). The initiation process is reversibly stopped by adding buffers to raise extracellular pH. These localized changes in pH at the initiation site could be due to changes in plasma membrane H^+-ATPase activity; this proposition should be tested, possibly by a genetic approach.

REGULATION

The C-terminal end of the plasma membrane H^+-ATPase (the C-terminal regulatory domain, hence the R-domain) serves a role as an autoinhibitory regulatory domain. This was demonstrated initially from studies showing that a C-terminal fragment of the H^+-ATPase could be removed by proteases resulting in increased H^+-ATPase activity (98, 99). It was hypothesized that a posttranslational modification in vivo might displace the R-domain, which would lead to pump activation and an enzyme with high affinity for its ligands (95). According to this model, physiological factors that increase H^+-ATPase activity are likely to have this domain as their ultimate target.

Several lines of evidence have suggested a molecular mechanism involving the R-domain that leads to activation of the plasma membrane H^+-ATPase (Figure 6, see color insert). This model involves 14-3-3 protein, which are regulatory proteins that bind to a large number of target proteins in eukaryotic systems (25, 36, 38).

Typically, 14-3-3 proteins will only bind if a Ser (85, 149) or a Thr (39, 76, 132) is phosphorylated in the 14-3-3 binding site of the target. A family of twelve 14-3-3 proteins is found in Arabidopsis and the isoforms have somewhat different affinities for a given target within the cell (116a).

Several lines of evidence led to the identification of 14-3-3 proteins as candidate regulatory proteins of H$^+$-ATPases: (a) 14-3-3 proteins copurified with the binding activity of fusicoccin, a fungal toxin that activates the H$^+$-ATPase (64, 75, 88); (b) proteolytic studies showed that fusicoccin activates plasma membrane H$^+$-ATPase by a mechanism involving the R-domain (57, 69, 92, 111); and (c) there was a strict correlation between the amount of fusicoccin bound to the plasma membrane and the activation of the plasma membrane H$^+$-ATPase, as would be expected if the fusicoccin receptor interacts directly with the H$^+$-ATPase (28).

Later it was shown that 14-3-3 protein interacts directly with the R-domain (40, 56, 90). Phosphorylation of the penultimate Thr in the R-domain (Thr948, Thr947, and Thr955 in spinach H$^+$-ATPase, Arabidopsis AHA2, and *N. plumbaginifolia* PMA2, respectively) results in the formation of the binding site for 14-3-3 protein (39, 76, 132). Binding of 14-3-3 protein to the R-domain is stabilized by the addition of fusicoccin. Interestingly, the fusicoccin binding site is generated only following interaction of the 14-3-3 protein with the R-domain (14, 89, 108). Fusicoccin causes the dissociation rate to diminish, resulting in the formation of an almost irreversible complex (39). Fusicoccin can induce binding of 14-3-3 protein to the R-domain even in the absence of a phosphothreonine at the penultimate position, but the binding is less tight.

Plant plasma membrane H$^+$-ATPase is phosphorylated at several positions in vivo. A phosphotreonine residue has been identified in purified spinach H$^+$-ATPase at the penultimate position of the R-domain and is protected from dephosphorylation by 14-3-3 protein (93). Blue light activation of the mung bean H$^+$-ATPase involves protein kinase–mediated phosphorylation of the pump (63). This phosphorylation involves Ser and Thr residues at the R-domain and is concomitant with binding of 14-3-3 protein. Oat root plasma membrane H$^+$-ATPase is likewise phosphorylated at both Ser and Thr residues (120) but whether this results in the formation of 14-3-3 binding site(s) is not known.

Binding of 14-3-3 protein to the R-domain results in activation of H$^+$-ATPase activity (14, 76, 132). To reverse the activation, which is induced by the protein kinase-mediated generation of the 14-3-3 binding site, the R-domain would need to be dephosphorylated by a protein phosphatase (Figure 6). A protein phosphatase 2A activity that could serve such a role has been purified from maize membranes (24).

Intriguingly, it has been reported that plasma membrane H$^+$-ATPases in some systems is inhibited by phosphorylation and activated by dephosphorylation (29, 71, 138, 148), which is in contrast to the results reported above. In beet root, inhibitory phosphorylation of H$^+$-ATPase is Ca^{2+} dependent (71). The residue(s) in the H$^+$-ATPase involved in this negative regulation have not been identified but might be apart from the R-domain (29).

Other factors contribute to posttranslational regulation of H^+-ATPase activity. Lysophospholipids and free fatty acids activate H^+-ATPase activity (100, 105) by a mechanism involving the R-domain (57, 99, 112). Lysophospholipids and free fatty acids are generated when phospholipids are hydrolyzed by a reaction catalyzed by phospholipase A_2. This enzyme, which has been proposed to serve an important role in regulation of the H^+-ATPase in vivo (95, 100, 121) was first identified in oat roots (100) and has been purified from leaves of *Vicia faba* (61, 62).

Other aspects of regulation of the activity of H^+-ATPase are discussed in recent reviews (82, 95, 96, 109). Regulation of the amount of H^+-ATPase in the plant occurs at several levels. Transcriptional and translational levels of regulation have been described elsewhere (82). In addition, controlling the amount of H^+-ATPase by exocytosis and protein turnover has been suggested as a regulatory mechanism (46).

ENZYMOLOGY

P-type ATPases are believed to alternate between at least two major conformations, E_1 and E_2. The E_1 form has high affinity for ATP as well as the ion to be transported out of the cytoplasm. The E_2 form has low affinity for both ligands, but has high affinity for the inhibitor vanadate. Transport of a bound cation from one side of the membrane to the other is associated with the conformational change between E_1 and E_2 (Figure 7, see color insert). According to the Post-Albers scheme (1, 110), the cation enters from the cytoplasmic side and is bound to the enzyme in the E_1 conformation. Phosphorylation of the invariant aspartyl residue results in the E_1P form of the enzyme, which is then converted to E_2P. The cation, now bound with lower affinity to the same site as before, is then released on the other side of the membrane. Phosphate is released by hydrolysis of the aspartyl phosphate bond, and the E_2 form of the enzyme reverts to E_1. According to this model, the pump operates much like the lock of a waterway, which also has an enclosed section with alternating accessibility to either side.

Protons are ligands of the H^+-ATPase, and therefore pH is expected to strongly influence pump activity. Indeed, kinetic data suggest that protonation on an ionizable group in the AHA2 H^+-ATPase with a pK of ~ 6.7 stabilizes the high-affinity conformation (E_1) of the enzyme (112).

Similarly, in the Na^+/K^+-ATPase and muscle sarcoplasmic reticulum Ca^{2+}-ATPase, the cations to be bound from the cytoplasmic side (Na^+ and Ca^{2+}, respectively) stabilize the enzyme in the E_1 conformation (59).

When plant plasma membrane H^+-ATPase is activated by mechanisms involving the R-domain, the ATP affinity increases and pH optimum of the pump is displaced towards neutral values, which might reflect an increased H^+ affinity (98, 99, 112). In line with the discussion above, this would suggest that in the activated state the conformational equilibrium of the enzyme has been shifted toward the E_1 form.

STRUCTURE-FUNCTION RELATIONSHIPS

Quaternary Structure

The quaternary structure of the red beet plasma membrane H$^+$-ATPase has been studied by radiation inactivation experiments. This analysis revealed a H$^+$-ATPase target size of about 225 kDa in plasma membrane vesicles and 218 kDa in reconstituted liposomes, corresponding to a dimeric form of the enzyme (21). The H$^+$-ATPase solubilized with the detergent Zwittergent 3-14 enzyme has a target size of 129 kDa, corresponding to the expected mass of a monomer (21). Because the solubilized enzyme is still active, the minimal functional unit of the H$^+$-ATPase is likely to be a monomer (21). In line with these results, it has been demonstrated that reconstituted monomers of N. crassa H$^+$-ATPase are active proton pumps (43).

Tertiary Structure

Information on the three-dimensional structure of a membrane protein can be obtained from analysis of well-ordered crystals of the purified protein in either two or three dimensions. Only very recently has it been possible to crystallize purified recombinant plant plasma membrane H$^+$-ATPase for this purpose (T Jahn, J Dietrich, B Andersen, C Otter, C Briving, MG Palmgren, submitted). These crystals of AHA2 diffract to 8 Å resolution, but so far the crystals have been studied only in one plane. The crystal unit cell suggests that the H$^+$-ATPase is organized in the membrane as a dimer. Furthermore, the cytoplasmic portion of the molecule appears to be divided into three distinct densities, which could correspond to distinct domains of the enzyme.

The plasma membrane H$^+$-ATPase of the fungus Neurospora crassa has been crystallized in two dimensions (11). From analysis of the crystals by cryoelectron microscopy, a structure resolved to 8 Å resolution was obtained. The H$^+$-ATPase forms hexamers, and ten transmembrane helices are apparent in the crystal structure of each H$^+$-ATPase molecule. The pump is exposed to both sides of the membrane; however, most of the H$^+$-ATPase (around 70%) is exposed to one side of the membrane, presumably the cytoplasmic side, and is separated into four more-or-less separated domains.

The recent solution of the crystal structure of the sarcoplasmic reticulum Ca^{2+}-ATPase to 2.6 Å resolution (134) is a landmark in our understanding of structure/function relationships in cation pumps. Since this is the only structure of a P-type ATPase solved at atomic resolution, it serves as a model for the structure of related pumps such as the plasma membrane H$^+$-ATPase.

In the structure of the Ca^{2+}-ATPase (134), a large cytoplasmic protrusion is associated with a bundle of ten membrane spanning alpha-helices, as in the Neurospora H$^+$-ATPase (11). Although the borders of the membrane are not clearly defined in the structure, some of the transmembrane helices are very long and protrude into the cytoplasmic region of the pump. Very little of the protein mass is exposed to the extracytoplasmic side. The cytoplasmic region is divided into three well-separated domains: A, P, and N (Figure 8; see color insert). The actuator domain (A) includes the N-terminal region and the portion of the molecule formed by the small cytosolic loop between M2 and M3. The phosphorylation (P) domain is bounded by M4 and M5 and includes the aspartyl residue to be phosphorylated during catalysis. The nucleotide (N) binding domain is fused to the P-domain and contains the ATP binding site. Thus, the domain structure of the Ca^{2+}-ATPase corresponds very well to the domain organization suggested above in the discussion on the evolution of P-type ATPases.

The primary structure of the Arabidopsis plasma membrane H^+-ATPase AHA2 is indicated in Figure 9; (see color insert). The various domains of the enzyme, as revealed from sequence comparison with the Ca^{2+}-pump, are indicated in colors. The sequence analysis method of von Heijne (143) predicts all ten transmembrane segments in SERCA1 correctly, and similarly predicts ten transmembrane helices in the AHA2 H^+-ATPase (96).

H^+-Binding Site(s)

A 1:1 stoichiometric relationship between ATP being hydrolysed and protons being transported is supported by measurements under a number of experimental conditions (19, 22, 125). However, this does not preclude the possibility that other ratios are possible under other conditions (15, 84) or that one or more protons could be counter-transported by the H^+-ATPase. Thus, hydrolysis of ATP might e.g. result in two protons pumped out and one pumped in (Figure 10; see color insert). Other P-type ATPases are involved in counter-transport of cations, and in the case of the Ca^{2+}-ATPase, the counterions are indeed protons. Binding of counterions in a number of P-type ATPases appears to be required for hydrolysis of the E_2P phosphoenzyme (80).

By comparison with other ion pumps, at least two models for ion binding can be envisioned. According to the first model, protons will follow a pathway of different polar groups during transport through the membrane (19a). Such a proton-wire mechanism appears to be true for well-characterized H^+ pumps such as bacteriorhodopsin (50, 67a) and cytochrome c oxidase (78, 127). According to the second model, the ion to be transported binds to a specific pocket surrounded by coordinating groups (19a). This model appears to be valid for related P-type ATPases, such as the Ca^{2+}- and Na^+/K^+-ATPase. Assuming a similar transport mechanism in the H^+-ATPase, this raises the question as to whether H^+ is transported as H_3O^+ (18b, 19a), which has about the same ionic radius and Na^+ and Ca^{2+} (Table 3). The observation that heavy water (D_2O) inhibits plasma membrane H^+-ATPase activity in isolated plasma membrane vesicles (118) supports a model that involves translocation of water.

Site-directed mutagenesis and preferably structural studies are required to test which residues are involved in binding of protons by the H^+-ATPase. It has been proposed (134) that binding of Ca^{2+} to the Ca^{2+}-ATPase requires step-wise dehydration of Ca^{2+}, whereas dissociation is associated with rehydration of the bound

TABLE 3 Ionic radii of
selected dehydrated cations

Ion	Crystal radii (Å)
H$_3$O$^+$	1.15
Na$^+$	1.12
K$^+$	1.44
Ca^{2+}	1.06

Ca^{2+}. A similar mechanism might be valid for H$^+$-ATPases as a hydrated H$_3$O$^+$ ion binds three to four water molecules (Figure 11; see color insert). Likewise, specific binding of a transported H$_3$O$^+$ is not likely to involve more than three to four liganding groups per bound H$_3$O$^+$ as hydrogen bonding partners. It has been suggested that negatively charged or polar residues in the transmembrane region of H$^+$-ATPases could be involved in H$^+$ binding (145). When H$^+$-ATPase sequences are compared in their presumed transmembrane regions, just one acidic residue is strictly conserved, namely Asp684 (AHA2 numbering) in M6, and among the polar residues only two are conserved (Gln760 and Ser762; both in the middle of M8) (Figure 12; see color insert).

In the Arabidopsis H$^+$-ATPase AHA2, Asp684 has been replaced by Asn (22a). This conservative substitution has no effect on folding of the enzyme but completely abolishes proton pumping by the ATPase. The mutagenized enzyme is able to proceed to E_1 P but from here it appears to be blocked in its catalytic cycle. Thus, these data are compatible with Asp684 being involved in coordination of H$^+$. In the yeast H$^+$-ATPase PMA1, many residues in transmembrane regions have been individually mutated (4, 33, 45, 124), including Asp730 (45; in M6), which corresponds to AHA2 Asp684. However, in the yeast enzyme, Asp730 cannot be substituted alone since this residue is apparently involved in forming a salt bridge with Arg695 in M5, and in its absence, PMA1 does not fold properly (45).

In the calcium pump structure, two calcium ions are bound side by side in the same plane as the membrane (134). Site I is located between M5 and M6, whereas site II is between M4 and M6) (Figure 13; see color insert). In site II, three carbonyl groups of hydrophobic amino acid residues contribute to coordination of the bound Ca^{2+} (Figure 14; see color insert). Carbonyl groups are normally hidden in the core of alpha-helices, but two prolines separated by three residues partially unfold the alpha-helical structure of M4 and allow the coordinating carbonyl groups to get into close proximity to Ca^{2+}. In M6, Asp800 (corresponding to AHA2 Asp684) plays a key role as it is coordinating both of the two Ca^{2+} ions bound and is in close proximity to the unwound part of M4 (Figure 15; see color insert).

A three-dimensional model of the first six transmembrane segments of AHA2 has been built from the coordinates of the Ca^{2+}-pump structure by homology modeling (J Bukrinsky, MJ Buch-Pedersen, S Larsen, MG Palmgren, submitted) (Figure 13). The details of this model are only suggestions, but it might serve as a useful tool to predict the roles of various residues and domains of the plant H^+-ATPase. In the model of the AHA2 H^+-ATPase, there appears to be no analogy to site I in the SERCA1 Ca^{2+}-ATPase, since the binding pocket apparently is occupied by the side chain of a basic residue, Arg655 (Figure 14). On the other hand, the two proline residues in M4 are strictly conserved between Ca^{2+}- and H^+-ATPases. Accordingly, in the model of the AHA2 H^+-ATPase, M4 is also unfolded (Figure 15) and the position of carbonyl groups in this region would easily allow for coordination of a bound H_3O^+ (Figure 14). Thus, four residues in the transmembrane region of plant plasma membrane H^+-ATPase emerge as candidate coordinating residues in a H_3O^+ binding site: Asp684 in M6 could contribute with its side chain whereas three residues in M4 (Ile282, Gly283, and Ile285) each might contribute with carbonyls (Figure 14). At this location, the H^+ might be shared between the bound water molecule and the carboxyl group of Asp684. In yeast PMA1, the corresponding residues in M4 (Ile331, Ile332, and Val334) have been substituted individually with Ala. These mutants have reduced (around 30%) H^+-ATPase activity but are still able to pump protons (4).

ATP Binding Site

Fluorescein isothiocyanate inhibits activity of the *N. crassa* PMA1 H^+-ATPase by reacting with Lys474 (which in AHA2 corresponds to Lys423) in the well-conserved sequence motif KGAP. Since ATP protects Lys474 from fluorescein isothiocyanate, it was suggested that this residue is located at the nucleotide-binding domain (102). Indeed, in the Ca^{2+}-ATPase structure, the corresponding residue is positioned at the bottom of the predicted ATP binding site formed by the N-domain (134). As noted by Toyoshima and coworkers (134), the ATP binding site in the crystal structure is far (about 25 Å distance) from the aspartyl residue that is phosphorylated by the gamma-phosphoryl group of the bound ATP. This could imply that a substantial conformational change takes place between binding of ATP and formation of the phosphoenzyme.

Mg^{2+} Binding Site

Mg^{2+} is absolutely required by the plasma membrane H^+-ATPase for ATP hydrolysis (136). Modeling the active site of P-type ATPases on the dehalogenase fold (114) has suggested that the Mg^{2+} ion is coordinated by two aspartate residues that in AHA2 H^+-ATPase would correspond to Asp588 and Asp592 (Figure 16; see color insert) that are part of the segment [587]GDGVNDAPALKKA, which is highly conserved among P-type ATPases (12). The bound Mg^{2+} is proposed to be in close proximity to residues that correspond to AHA2 Asp329, the aspartyl residue in the P-domain that gets phosphorylated during catalysis. Mutagenesis studies with the Na^+/K^+-ATPase support the notion that at least Asp710 in Na^+/K^+-ATPase (corresponding to AHA2 Asp588) contribute to Mg^{2+} binding during transfer of the gamma-phosphate of ATP to the aspartyl residue (106a). The role of the bound

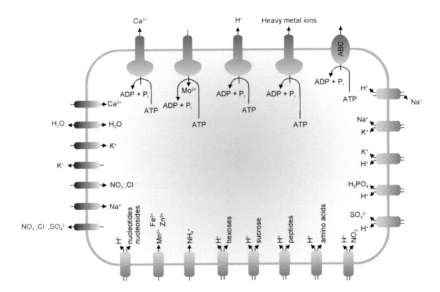

Figure 1 Overview of transport proteins in the plasma membrane of plant cells and their proposed transport specifities. Transport through most channel proteins (red) and carrier proteins (orange) is energized by the membrane potential (negative on the inside) and proton gradient generated by the plasma membrane H$^+$-ATPase (blue, middle).

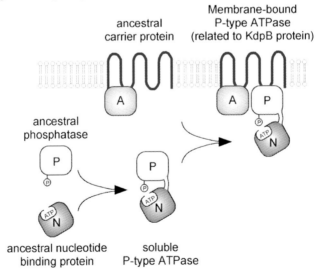

Figure 2 Proposed evolution of plasma membrane H$^+$-ATPases. Two soluble proteins, a protein phosphatase (P) and a nucleotide-binding protein (N), fused to form a soluble P-type ATPase. This later fused with a membrane-bound carrier protein with six trans-membrane spanning segments to form an ATP-fueled cation pump. As a result of additional fusion events, present day H$^+$-ATPases have ten trans-membrane segments.

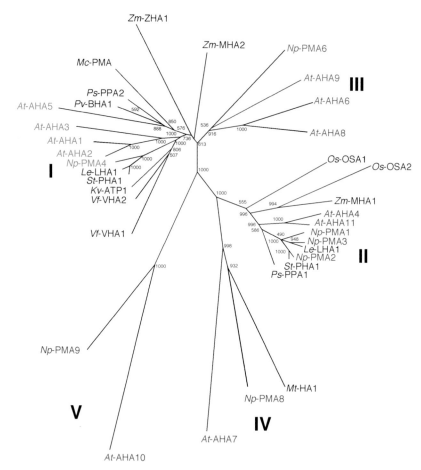

Figure 3 Phylogenetic tree showing the predicted relationship among plant plasma membrane H⁺-ATPases. The PHYLIP program (J Felsenstein, University of Washington) was used to construct the phylogenetic tree from the amino acid sequences deduced from genomic and cDNA clones. Colors indicate H⁺-ATPases that have a very similar exon structure (see Figure 4). Sequences are from *Arabidopsis thaliana* (AHA1: P20649; AHA2: P19456; AHA3: P20431; AHA4: Q9SU58; AHA5: Q9SJB3; AHA6: Q9SH76; AHA7: Q9LY32; AHA8: Q9M2A0; AHA9: Q42556; AHA10: Q43128; AHA11: Q9LV11), *Nicotiana plumbaginifolia* (PMA1: Q08435; PMA2: Q42932; PMA3: Q08436; PMA4: Q03194; PMA6: Q9SWH2; PMA8: Q9SWH1; PMA9: Q9SWH0), *Kosteletzkya virginica* (KvATP1: O22613), *Lycopersicon esculentum* (LHA1: P22180; LHA2: Q9SPD5; LHA4: Q96578), *Medicago truncatula* (ha1: Q9M4N4), *Mesembryanthemum crystallinum* (PMA: P93265), *Oryza sativa* (OSA1: Q43001; OSA2: Q43002), *Phaseolus vulgaris* (BHA1: Q43106), *Prunus persica* (PPA1: Q9M460; PPA2: Q9M461), *Solanum tuberosum* (PHA1: Q43182; PHA2: Q41378), *Vicia faba* (VHA1: Q43131; VHA2: Q9SAW3), *Zea mays* (MHA1: Q43243; MHA2: Q43271), *Zostera marina* (ZHA1: Q43275).

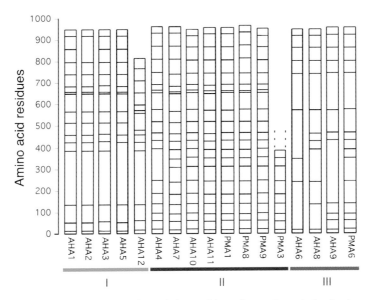

Figure 4 Schematic representation of the position of exon boundaries in the genomic sequences of Arabidopsis and *Nicotiana plumbaginifolia* H⁺-ATPases. The positions of introns are shown by a horizontal line within a box representing the coding sequence.

```
AHA2....274 idnlLvllIgGiPiamPtVlsvT 296
            ----L---I-G-P---P-V---T         M4
SERCA1..296 FkiaVaLAVAAIPEGLPAViTtc 318
            F---V-LAVAAIPEGLPAV-T--


AHA2....644 nYtiYavsitirivfgfmlialI 666
            -Y--Y-------------L---I         M5
SERCA1..759 qFIRYliSsNvGEvvcIfltaal 781
            -FIRY--S-N-GE---I------


AHA2....671 fsafmvliIAIlnDgtimtIskD 693
            --------IAI--D-----I--D         M6
SERCA1..787 LiPvQlLWvNLVTDGlPAtALGf 809
            L-P-Q-LW-NLVTDG-PA-ALG-
```

Figure 12 Alignment of selected trans-membrane segments of the AHA2 plasma membrane H⁺-ATPase and the sarcoplasmic reticulum Ca²⁺-ATPase SERCA1. Conserved residues in both pumps are boxed. Residues conserved in 30 out of 39 H⁺-ATPase sequences and 46 out of 58 Ca²⁺-ATPase sequences in the databases are indicated by capital letters. Residues involved in Ca²⁺ binding are colored red. Residues proposed to be involved in H⁺ binding are colored blue.

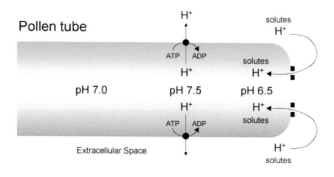

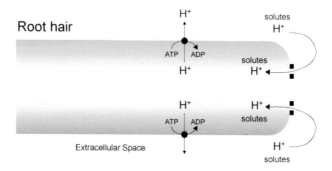

Figure 5 A model for proton gradients in pollen tubes and root hairs. Data related to pollen tubes are from Feijo et al (35).

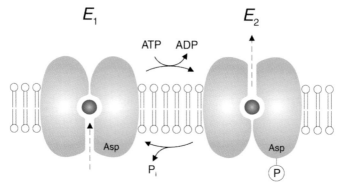

Figure 7 A model for the transport mechanism of plasma membrane H^+-ATPase. H^+ (or H_3O^+) binds to a specific ion binding pocket, the accessibility of which is alternating between the two sites of the membrane during the catalytic cycle. In the E_1 conformation, the ion binding pocket is accessible to the cytoplasmic side of the membrane only. In the E_2 conformation, the ion binding pocket is accessible to the extracellular side of the membrane. Differences in affinity of the ion binding site in the two conformations dictate whether the ion is bound or released.

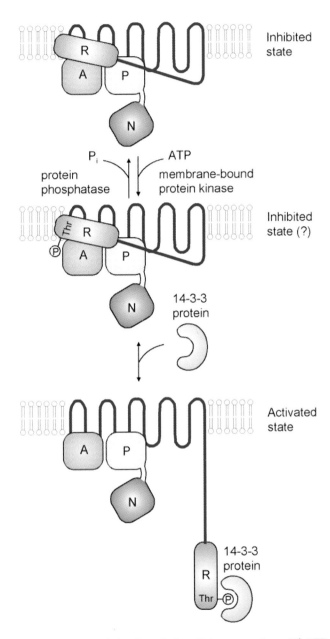

Figure 6 A model for posttranslational regulation of plasma membrane H^+-ATPase involving a protein kinase and protein phosphatase pair that has the R-domain as its target. Regulatory 14-3-3 protein recognizes a binding site generated by phosphorylation of the R-domain.

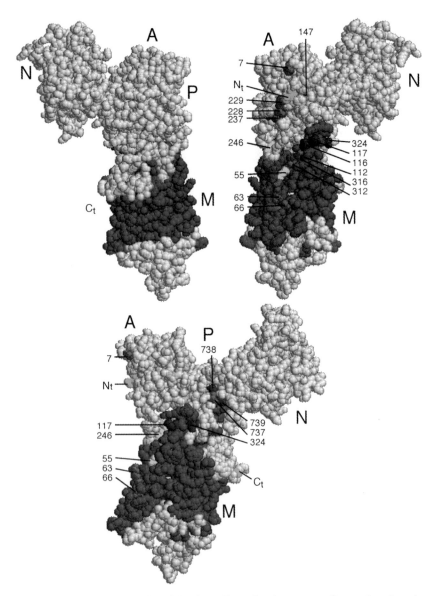

Figure 8 Space-filling model of the three-dimensional structure of sarcoplasmic reticulum Ca^{2+}-ATPase (PDB entry 1eul; 134). The corresponding residues that in a number of other P-type ATPases give rise to activation of pump activity when mutated are colored pink (*N. plumbaginifolia* PMA2 H^+-ATPase), red (*Saccharomyces cerevisiae* PMA1 H^+-ATPase), and yellow (*A. thaliana* ACA4 Ca^{2+}-ATPase). A complete list of these residues is presented in Table 4. Dark gray indicates membrane-spanning alpha-helices. The protein model was generated with the RasMol software program (22).

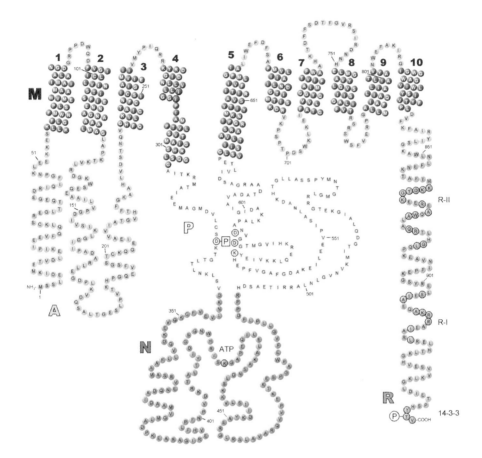

Figure 9 Schematic presentation of the AHA2 plasma membrane H⁺-ATPase. The various domains (A, P, N, and R) of the enzyme are indicated by colored residues. Encircled residues are discussed further in the text. The positions of transmembrane segments M1-M7 are in accordance with the corresponding residues in the sarcoplasmic reticulum Ca^{2+}-ATPase (134). The predicted topologies of M8-M10 were analyzed by the method of von Heijne (143). R-I: Region I; R-II: Region-II; 14-3-3: 14-3-3 protein binding site.

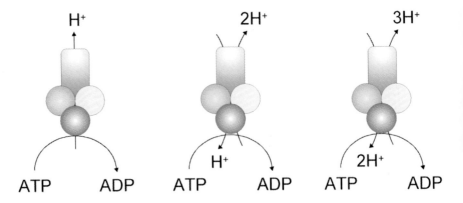

Figure 10 Models for proton pumping by plasma membrane H^+-ATPase that result in a 1:1 stoichiometry between ATP hydrolyzed and net proton transport.

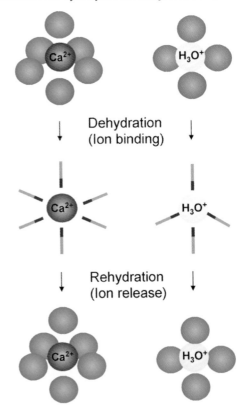

Figure 11 Proposed model for dehydration and rehydration of Ca^{2+} and H^+ accompanying binding and release from the cation binding pockets in the Ca^{2+} and H^+-ATPases, respectively.

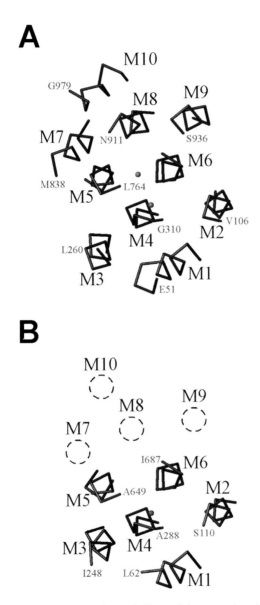

Figure 13 Top view of the transmembrane helices of the sarcoplasmic reticulum Ca^{2+}-ATPase SERCA1 (*A*) and in the model of AHA2 plasma membrane H^+-ATPase (*B*). The pictures were constructed (*A*) from the Protein Database (PDB) entry 1eul (134) or (*B*) from a homology model of AHA2 (J Bukrinsky, MJ Buch-Pedersen, S Larsen, MG Palmgren, submitted). Ten residues are shown from each of the helices shown. Dashed circles indicate transmembrane helices that could not be modeled. Green spheres, Ca^{2+}; red sphere, H_3O^+. The figure was generated using the program TURBO-FRODO (117).

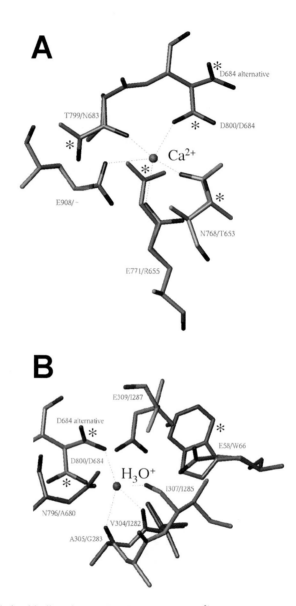

Figure 14 Cation binding sites I (*A*) and II (*B*) in the Ca^{2+}-ATPase SERCA1 (*upper label*) superimposed on the corresponding residues from the model of AHA2 (*lower label*, marked by asterisks). The model of AHA2 (J Bukrinsky, MJ Buch-Pedersen, S Larsen, MG Palmgren, submitted) is based on the structure of the sarcoplasmic reticulum Ca^{2+}-ATPase SERCA1 (PDB entry 1eul; 134). Green sphere, Ca^{2+}; red sphere: H_3O^+. The figure was generated using the program TURBO-FRODO (117).

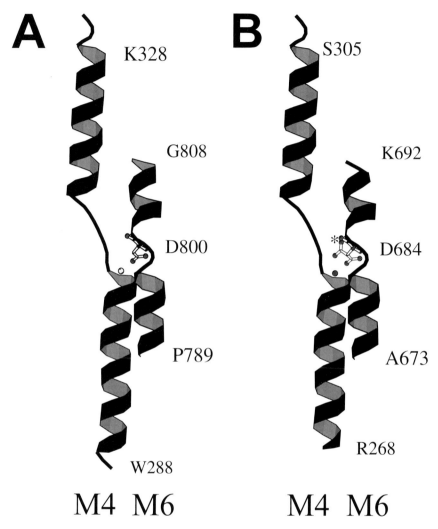

Figure 15 Transmembrane helices M4 and M6 in ribbon from the sarcoplasmic reticulum Ca^{2+}-ATPase SERCA1 (*A*) and a homology model of the AHA2 plasma membrane H$^+$-ATPase (*B*). (*A*) D800 in SERCA1 (PDB) entry 1eul (134), which is bridging the two Ca^{2+} ions bound, is shown in ball-and-stick. (*B*) The corresponding arrangement in the model of AHA2 (J Bukrinsky, MJ Buch-Pedersen, S Larsen, MG Palmgren, submitted), with D684 shown in two possible conformations (one of which is marked by an asterisk). Yellow sphere, Ca^{2+}; red sphere, H$_3$O$^+$. This figure was produced with the program MOLSCRIPT (65).

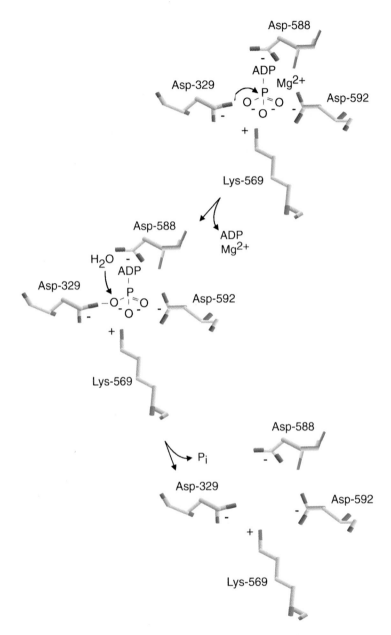

Figure 16 Proposed reaction scheme for the phosphorylation during catalysis of plasma membrane H^+-ATPases. For details see the text.

Mg^{2+} might be to neutralize the negatively charged phosphate group and, in addition, it could be involved in activation of the attacking neutrophile, polarization of the P–O bond, and stabilization of the leaving group (114).

Catalytic Mechanism

Koonin and coworkers (8) have suggested a reaction scheme for P-type ATPases based on the structural homology between these pumps and haloacid dehalogenases. The reaction scheme of haloacid dehalogenases is known in considerable detail (53, 70, 115). Modified for the plant plasma membrane H$^+$-ATPase, the following reaction scheme can be proposed (Figure 16): First, Asp329 forms a transition state complex with the gamma-phosphoryl group of ATP. In this complex, one of the excessive negative charges is stabilized by the positive charge of a nearby basic residue, Lys569, and the other charge is balanced by Mg^{2+} (see above). This leads to formation of the aspartyl phosphate pump intermediate. Mg^{2+} would leave again together with ADP. A water molecule is then consumed for hydrolysis of the acylphosphate bond and phosphate is released. It has been proposed that the A domain is involved in catalyzing this phosphatase reaction (123).

Position of the R-domain and Its Intramolecular Receptor

The R-domain of the plant plasma membrane H$^+$-ATPase comprises approximately 110 residues (Figure 8). Substitutions at several residues in the R-domain of the *N. plumbanifolia* PMA2 result in activated H$^+$-ATPases in which the R-domain is more vulnerable to proteolytic attack compared to that of the wild-type enzyme (83, 84). Since the substitutions mimic the effect of proteolytic removal of the R-domain, it is plausible that they result in displacement of this domain from the rest of the molecule (83, 84). A mutational study of AHA2 through 87 consecutive residues in the C-terminal domain has revealed that single amino acid substitutions at 23 positions lead to increased pump activity (13). The amino acid substitutions resulting in this phenotype cluster in two groups, regions I and II (Figure 8), that together are likely to form the autoinhibitory region of the R-domain.

The R-domain is likely to interact with a portion of the pump molecule and in this way to exert its negative effect on enzyme activity. Genetic strategies have been employed to identify this intramolecular receptor for the R-domain. Yeast strains containing no endogenous H$^+$-ATPase activity have been allowed to express plant H$^+$-ATPase and spontaneous mutations in the plant gene that result in an upregulated H$^+$-ATPase could be isolated because they increase the growth rate of the transformed yeast cells. Many of the mutations obtained in this way cluster in regions I and II of the R-domain (15, 83, 84) but, in addition, large numbers of mutations have been observed in other regions of the pump molecule. Thus, in the *N. plumbaginifolia* PMA2 H$^+$-ATPase polypeptide such mutations are found in the presumed A- and P-domains and in M1 and M4 (83, 84) (Table 4). A similar strategy has been employed to identify regulatory residues in the yeast PMA1 H$^+$-ATPase (34) and substitutions have been found in essentially the same domains

TABLE 4 Single point mutations in various P-type ATPases that result in activation of pump activity. Mutations identified in R-domains are not indicated

| | | Corresponding residue in other pumps | | |
| | | AHA2 | SERCA1 | |
ATPase	Mutation	#	#	Domain
Np-PMA2 (83,84)	E14D,Q,G	E10	K7	A
	P72A	P68	R63	M1 (middle)
	W75C	W71	L66	M1 (middle)
	P154R	P150	P147	A
	V220G	V216	V228	A
	H221N,D	H217	S229	A
	H229D	H225	D237	A-"leg" junction
	P294Q	P290	P312	M4 (top)
	S298L	S294	T316	M4 (top)
	N510K	N506	R620	P
	E626G	E622	D737	P-M5 junction
Sc-PMA1 (34)	A165V	A117	A112	M2 (top)
	V169I/D170N	A121/A122	I116/E117	M2 (top)
	A350T	S301	T323	M4 (top)
	A351T	H302	R324	M4 (top)
	P536L	P489	P603	P-N junction
	A565T	G518	A632	P
	G587N	H541	G655	P
	G648S	G602	G717	P
	P669L	P623	D738	P-M5 junction
	G670S	G624	N739	P-M5 junction
At-ACA2 (27)	E167K	K60	E55	M1 (top)
	D219N	E113	Q108	M2 (top)
	E341K	V233	K246	M3 (top)

but also in M2 (Table 4). Likewise, in the plant Ca^{2+}-ATPase ACA2 (27), which is regulated by an N-terminal regulatory domain, regulatory residues are found in the predicted M1, M2, and M3 (Table 4). The various P-type ATPases regulated by terminal autoinhibitory domains were aligned with the SERCA1 Ca^{2+}-ATPase and the corresponding residues in this pump are indicated in Table 4.

A note of caution is necessary before interpreting these results since "regulatory" mutants might involve the basic machinery involved in conformational transitions rather than specific regulatory properties. Thus, a large number of mutants in both the yeast H^+-ATPase (3) and in the SERCA1 Ca^{2+}-ATPase (7, 26, 41, 113, 140–142, 151) have been identified that are impeded in their ability to undergo the E_1P-E_2P conformational change. In these mutants, the conformational equilibrium is shifted toward the E_1 form, which is characterized by high affinity for ATP. The mutated residues group in several domains of the ATPases, such as the A- and P-domains, as well as M1, M2, and M4, much like the "regulatory" mutants described above. Ca^{2+}-ATPase E_1P-E_2P conformational change mutants that appear to have the same phenotype behave very differently when the fast kinetics are analyzed in detail by rapid quench experiments (126). Thus, they group into several classes that could involve conformational change mutants, regulatory mutants, etc.

Nevertheless, when residues in the Ca^{2+}-ATPase corresponding to the regulatory substitutions in the various P-type ATPases regulated by terminal autoinhibitory domains are marked in the structure of the Ca^{2+}-pump an interesting picture emerges (Figure 9). The residues affected form an almost continuous line of surface-exposed groups extending from the P-domain to the middle of M1. This raises the question as to whether the R-domain is placed horizontally relative to the rest of the pump molecule in the plane of the membrane, possibly extending into the membrane.

A few lines of evidence support the notion that the R-domain might indeed be close to or partially embedded in the membrane. Thus, (*a*) lysophosphatidylcholine, a lipid molecule, and free fatty acids, that incorporates into membranes, activate plant H$^+$-ATPase by a mechanism involving the R-domain (see above); (*b*) fusicoccin, which interacts with the R-domain, is a strongly hydrophobic compound and is likely to partition into the membrane; (*c*) a protein kinase identified in spinach that phosphorylates the R-domain of the plasma membrane H$^+$-ATPase is membrane-associated (132).

CONCLUDING REMARKS

Recent advances in the plasma membrane H$^+$-ATPase field have allowed links to be made from the level of protein structure and enzyme regulation to cellular function and plant physiology. Important questions that remain to be answered are: What are the cellular and organismal function of all the different H$^+$-ATPase isoforms? What are the natures of the signal transduction pathways that regulate pump activity? Where are the active sites in H$^+$-ATPases? What are the structural changes mediating proton translocation? Will it be possible to improve nutrient uptake from the soil by the genetic manipulation of H$^+$-ATPase crop plants? These and other important questions are already subjected to intense research in several laboratories and exciting new discoveries are expected in the near future.

ACKNOWLEDGMENTS

The author is indebted to Jens Bukrinsky for his work on modeling the AHA2 pump structure, to Kristian B. Axelsen for database searches and construction of phylogenetic trees, to Nina Rasmussen for excellent art work, and to Tom Roberts for editing the manuscript. The work in the author's laboratory was supported by the European Union's Biotechnology Programme and the Human Frontier Science Program Organization.

Visit the Annual Reviews home page at www.annualreviews.org

LITERATURE CITED

1. Albers RW. 1967. Biochemical aspects of active transport. *Annu. Rev. Biochem.* 36: 727–56
2. Altendorf K, Siebers A, Epstein W. 1992. The KDP ATPase of *Escherichia coli. Ann. NY Acad. Sci.* 671:228–43
3. Ambesi A, Miranda M, Petrov VV, Slayman CW. 2000. Biogenesis and function of the yeast plasma-membrane H^+-ATPase. *J. Exp. Biol.* 203:155–60
4. Ambesi A, Pan RL, Slayman CW. 1996. Alanine-scanning mutagenesis along membrane segment 4 of the yeast plasma membrane H^+-ATPase. Effects on structure and function. *J. Biol. Chem.* 271: 22999–3005
5. Amodeo G, Srivastava A, Zeiger E. 1992. Vanadate inhibits blue light-stimulated swelling of *Vicia* guard–cell protoplasts. *Plant Physiol.* 100:1567–70
6. Andersen JP, Vilsen B. 1998. Structure-function relationships of the calcium binding sites of the sarcoplasmic reticulum Ca^{2+}-ATPase. *Acta Physiol. Scand. Suppl.* 643:45–54
7. Andersen JP, Vilsen B, Leberer E, MacLennan DH. 1989. Functional consequences of mutations in the beta-strand sector of the Ca^{2+}-ATPase of sarcoplasmic reticulum. *J. Biol. Chem.* 264:21018–23
8. Aravind L, Galperin MY, Koonin EV. 1998. The catalytic domain of the P-type ATPase has the haloacid dehalogenase fold. *Trends Biochem. Sci.* 23:127–29
9. Assmann SM, Shimazaki K. 1999. The multisensory guard cell. Stomatal responses to blue light and abscisic acid. *Plant Physiol.* 119:809–16
10. Assmann SM, Simoncini L, Schroeder JI. 1985. Blue light activates electrogenic ion

pumping in guard cell protoplasts of *Vicia faba* L. *Nature* 318:285–87
11. Auer M, Scarborough GA, Kuhlbrandt W. 1988. Three-dimensional map of the plasma membrane H^+-ATPase in the open conformation. *Nature* 392:840–43
12. Axelsen KB, Palmgren MG. 1998. Evolution of substrate specificities in the P-type ATPase superfamily. *J. Mol. Evol.* 46:84–101
13. Axelsen KB, Venema K, Jahn T, Baunsgaard L, Palmgren MG. 1999. Molecular dissection of the C-terminal regulatory domain of the plant plasma membrane H^+-ATPase AHA2: mapping of residues that when altered give rise to an activated enzyme. *Biochemistry* 38:7227–34
14. Baunsgaard L, Fuglsang AT, Jahn T, Korthout HA, de Boer AH, Palmgren MG. 1998. The 14-3-3 proteins associate with the plant plasma membrane H^+-ATPase to generate a fusicoccin binding complex and a fusicoccin responsive system. *Plant J.* 13:661–71
15. Baunsgaard L, Venema K, Axelsen KB, Villalba JM, Welling A, et al. 1996. Modified plant plasma membrane H^+-ATPase with improved transport coupling efficiency identified by mutant selection in yeast. *Plant J.* 10:451–58
16. Becker D, Zeilinger C, Lohse G, Depta H, Hedrich R. 1993. Identification and biochemical characterization of the plasma membrane H^+-ATPase in guard cells of *Vicia faba* L. *Planta* 190:44–50
17. Bevan M, Bancroft I, Mewes HW, Martienssen R, McCombie R. 1999. Clearing a path through the jungle: progress in Arabidopsis genomics. *BioEssays* 21:110–20
18. Bibikova TN, Jacob T, Dahse I, Gilroy S.

1998. Localized changes in apoplastic and cytoplasmic pH are associated with root hair development in *Arabidopsis thaliana. Development* 125:2925–34

18a. Boutry M, Michelet B, Goffeau A. 1989. Molecular cloning of a family of plant genes encoding a protein homologous to plasma membrane H$^+$-translocating AT-Pases. *Biochem. Biophys. Res. Commun.* 162:567–74

18b. Boyer PD. 1988. Bioenergetic coupling to protonmotive force: Should we be considering hydronium ion coordination and not group protonation? *Trends Biochem. Sci.* 13:5–7

19. Briskin DP, Basu S, Assmann SM. 1995. Characterization of the red beet plasma membrane H$^+$-ATPase reconstituted in a planar bilayer system. *Plant Physiol.* 108:393–98

19a. Briskin DP, Hanson JB. 1992. How does the plant plasma membrane H$^+$-ATPase pump protons? *J. Exp. Bot.* 43:269–89

20. Briskin DP, Poole RJ. 1983. Plasma membrane ATPase of red beet forms a phosphorylated intermediate. *Plant Physiol.* 71:507–12

21. Briskin DP, Reynolds-Niesman I. 1989. Change in target molecular size of the red beet plasma membrane ATPase during solubilization and reconstitution. *Plant Physiol.* 90:394–97

22. Briskin DP, Reynolds-Niesman I. 1991. Determination of H$^+$/ATP stoichiometry for the plasma membrane H$^+$-ATPase from red beet (*Beta vulgaris* L.) storage tissue. *Plant Physiol.* 95:242–50

22a. Buch-Pedersen MJ, Venema K, Serrano R, Palmgren MG. 2000. Abolishment of proton pumping and accumulation in the E_1P conformational state of a plant plasma membrane H$^+$-ATPase by substitution of a conserved aspartyl residue in transmembrane segment 6. *J. Biol. Chem.* 275:39167–73

23. Buurman ET, Kim KT, Epstein W. 1995. Genetic evidence for two sequentially occupied K$^+$ binding sites in the Kdp transport ATPase. *J. Biol. Chem.* 270: 6678–85

24. Camoni L, Iori V, Marra M, Aducci P. 2000. Phosphorylation-dependent interaction between plant plasma membrane H$^+$-ATPase and 14-3-3 proteins. *J. Biol. Chem.* 275:9919–23

24a. Campos F, Perez-Castineira JR, Villalba JM, Culianez-Marcia FA, Sanchez F, Serrano R. 1996. Localization of plasma membrane H$^+$-ATPase in nodules of *Phaseolus vulgaris* L. *Plant Mol. Biol.* 32:1043–53

25. Chung HJ, Sehnke PC, Ferl RJ. 1999. The 14-3-3 proteins: cellular regulators of plant metabolism. *Trends Plant Sci.* 4:367–71

26. Clarke DM, Loo TW, MacLennan DH. 1990. Functional consequences of alterations to polar amino acids located in the transmembrane domain of the Ca^{2+}-ATPase of sarcoplasmic reticulum. *J. Biol. Chem.* 265:6262–67

27. Curran AC, Hwang I, Corbin J, Martinez S, Rayle D, et al. 2000. Autoinhibition of a calmodulin dependent calcium pump involves a structure in the stalk that connects the transmembrane domain to the ATPase catalytic domain. *J. Biol. Chem.* 275:30301–8

27a. Dambly S, Boutry M. 2000. The two major plant plasma membrane H$^+$-ATPases display different regulatory properties. *J. Biol. Chem.* In press

28. De Michelis MI, Rasi-Caldogno F, Pugliarello MC, Olivari C. 1996. Fusicoccin binding to its plasma membrane receptor and the activation of the plasma membrane H$^+$-ATPase. 3. Is there a direct interaction between the fusicoccin receptor and the plasma membrane H$^+$-ATPase? *Plant Physiol.* 110:957–64

29. Desbrosses G, Stelling J, Renaudin JP. 1998. Dephosphorylation activates the purified plant plasma membrane

H$^+$-ATPase—possible function of phosphothreonine residues in a mechanism not involving the regulatory C-terminal domain of the enzyme. *Eur. J. Biochem.* 251:496–503

30. DeWitt ND, Harper JF, Sussman MR. 1991. Evidence for a plasma membrane proton pump in phloem cells of higher plants. *Plant J.* 1:121–28

31. DeWitt ND, Sussman MR. 1995. Immunocytological localization of an epitope-tagged plasma membrane proton pump (H$^+$-ATPase) in phloem companion cells. *Plant Cell* 2053–67

32. Durell SR, Bakker EP, Guy HR. 2000. Does the KdpA subunit from the high affinity K$^+$-translocating P-type KDP-ATPase have a structure similar to that of K$^+$ channels? *Biophys. J.* 78:188–99

33. Dutra MB, Ambesi A, Slayman CW. 1998. Structure-function relationships in membrane segment 5 of the yeast Pma1 H$^+$-ATPase. *J. Biol. Chem.* 273:17411–17

34. Eraso P, Portillo F. 1994. Molecular mechanism of regulation of yeast plasma membrane H$^+$-ATPase by glucose. Interaction between domains and identification of new regulatory sites. *J. Biol. Chem.* 269:10393–99

35. Feijo JA, Sainhas J, Hackett GR, Kunkel JG, Hepler PK. 1999. Growing pollen tubes possess a constitutive alkaline band in the clear zone and a growth-dependent acidic tip. *J. Cell Biol.* 144:483–96

36. Finnie C, Borch J, Collinge DB. 1999. 14-3-3 proteins: eukaryotic regulatory proteins with many functions. *Plant Mol. Biol.* 40:545–54

36a. Frias I, Caldeira MT, Perez-Castineira JR, Navarro-Avino JP, Culianez-Macia FA, et al. 1996. A major isoform of the maize plasma membrane H$^+$-ATPase: characterization and induction by auxin in coleoptiles. *Plant Cell* 8:1533–44

37. Fricker MD, White NS, Obermeyer G. 1997. pH gradients are not associated with tip growth in pollen tubes of *Lilium longiflorum*. *J. Cell Sci.* 110:1729–40

38. Fu H, Subramanian RR, Masters SC. 2000. 14-3-3 proteins: structure, function, and regulation. *Annu. Rev. Pharmacol. Toxicol.* 40:617–47

39. Fuglsang AT, Visconti S, Drumm K, Jahn T, Stensballe A, et al. 1999. Binding of 14-3-3 protein to the plasma membrane H$^+$-ATPase AHA2 involves the three C-terminal residues Tyr^{946}-Thr-Val and requires phosphorylation of Thr^{947}. *J. Biol. Chem.* 274:36774–80

40. Fullone MR, Visconti S, Marra M, Fogliano V, Aducci P. 1998. Fusicoccin effect on the in vitro interaction between plant 14-3-3 proteins and plasma membrane H$^+$-ATPase. *J. Biol. Chem.* 273:7698–702

41. Garnett C, Sumbilla C, Belda FF, Chen L, Inesi G. 1996. Energy transduction and kinetic regulation by the peptide segment connecting phosphorylation and cation binding domains in transport ATPases. *Biochemistry* 35:11019–25

42. Gassel M, Mollenkamp T, Puppe W, Altendorf K. 1999. The KdpF subunit is part of the K$^+$-translocating Kdp complex of *Escherichia coli* and is responsible for stabilization of the complex in vitro. *J. Biol. Chem.* 274:37901–7

43. Goormaghtigh E, Chadwick C, Scarborough GA. 1986. Monomers of the *Neurospora* plasma membrane H$^+$-ATPase catalyze efficient proton translocation. *J. Biol. Chem.* 261:7466–71

44. Guex N, Peitsch MC. 1997. SWISS-MODEL and the Swiss-PdbViewer: an environment for comparative protein modelling. *Electrophoresis* 18:2714–23

45. Gupta SS, DeWitt ND, Allen KE, Slayman CW. 1998. Evidence for a salt bridge between transmembrane segments 5 and 6 of the yeast plasma-membrane H$^+$-ATPase. *J. Biol. Chem.* 273:34328–34

46. Hager A, Debus G, Edel HG, Stransky H, Serrano R. 1991. Auxin-induced

exocytosis and the rapid synthesis of a high-turnover pool of plasma–membrane H$^+$-ATPase. *Planta* 185:527–37

47. Harper JF, Manney L, DeWitt ND, Yoo MH, Sussman MR. 1990. The *Arabidopsis thaliana* plasma membrane H$^+$-ATPase multigene family. Genomic sequence and expression of a third isoform. *J. Biol. Chem.* 265:13601–8

48. Harper JF, Manney L, Sussman MR. 1994. The plasma membrane H$^+$-ATPase gene family in Arabidopsis: genomic sequence of AHA10 which is expressed primarily in developing seeds. *Mol. Gen. Genet.* 244:572–87

49. Harper JF, Surowy TK, Sussman MR. 1989. Molecular cloning and sequence of cDNA encoding the plasma membrane proton pump (H$^+$-ATPase) of *Arabidopsis thaliana*. *Proc. Natl. Acad. Sci. USA* 86:1234–38

50. Heberle J. 2000. Proton transfer reactions across bacteriorhodopsin and along the membrane. *Biochim. Biophys. Acta* 1458:135–47

51. Hentzen AE, Smart LB, Wimmers LE, Fang HH, Schroeder JI, Bennett AB. 1996. Two plasma membrane H$^+$-ATPase genes expressed in guard cells of *Vicia faba* are also expressed throughout the plant. *Plant Cell Physiol.* 37:650–59

52. Hirsch RE, Lewis BD, Spalding EP, Sussman MR. 1998. A role for the AKT1 potassium channel in plant nutrition. *Science* 280:918–21

53. Hisano T, Hata Y, Fujii T, Liu JQ, Kurihara T, et al. 1996. Crystal structure of L-2-haloacid dehalogenase from *Pseudomonas* sp. YL. An alpha/beta hydrolase structure that is different from the alpha/beta hydrolase fold. *J. Biol. Chem.* 271:20322–30

54. Houlne G, Boutry M. 1994. Identification of an *Arabidopsis thaliana* gene encoding a plasma membrane H$^+$-ATPase whose expression is restricted to anther tissue. *Plant J.* 5:311–17

55. Jahn T, Baluska F, Michalke W, Harper JF, Volkmann D. 1998. Plasma membrane H$^+$-ATPase in the root apex: evidence for strong expression in xylem parenchyma and asymmetric localization within cortical and epidermal cells. *Physiol. Plant.* 104:311–16

56. Jahn T, Fuglsang AT, Olsson A, Bruntrup IM, Collinge DB, et al. 1997. The 14-3-3 protein interacts directly with the C-terminal region of the plant plasma membrane H$^+$-ATPase. *Plant Cell* 9:1805–14

57. Johansson F, Sommarin M, Larsson C. 1993. Fusicoccin activates the plasma membrane H$^+$-ATPase by a mechanism involving the C-terminal inhibitory domain. *Plant Cell* 5:321–27

58. Jones DL, Shaff JE, Kochian LV. 1995. Role of calcium and other ions in directing root hair tip growth in *Limnobium stoloniferum* L. 1. Inhibition of tip growth by aluminium. *Planta* 197:672–80

59. Jorgensen PL, Andersen JP. 1988. Structural basis for E1-E2 conformational transitions in Na,K-pump and Ca-pump proteins. *J. Membr. Biol.* 103:95–120

60. Jorgensen PL, Nielsen JM, Rasmussen JH, Pedersen PA. 1998. Structure-function relationships of E1-E2 transitions and cation binding in Na,K-pump protein. *Biochim. Biophys. Acta* 1365:65–70

61. Jung KM, Kim DK. 2000. Purification and characterization of a membrane-associated 48-kilodalton phospholipase A$_2$ in leaves of broad bean. *Plant Physiol.* 123:1057–67

62. Kim DK, Lee HJ, Lee Y. 1994. Detection of two phospholipase A$_2$(PLA2) activities in leaves of higher plant *Vicia faba* and comparison with mammalian PLA2's. *FEBS Lett.* 343:213–18

63. Kinoshita T, Shimazaki K. 1999. Blue light activates the plasma membrane H$^+$-ATPase by phosphorylation of the C terminus in stomatal guard cells. *EMBO J.* 18:5548–58

64. Korthout HAAJ, de Boer AH. 1994. A fusicoccin-binding protein belongs to the family of 14-3-3 brain protein homologs. *Plant Cell* 6:1681–92

65. Kraulis PJ. 1991. MOLSCRIPT—a program to produce both detailed and schematic plots of protein structures. *J. Appl. Crystallogr.* 24:946–50

66. Krysan PJ, Young JC, Sussman MR. 1999. T-DNA as an insertional mutagen in Arabidopsis. *Plant Cell* 11:2283–90

67. Krysan PJ, Young JC, Tax F, Sussman MR. 1996. Identification of transferred DNA insertions within Arabidopsis genes involved in signal transduction and ion transport. *Proc. Natl. Acad. Sci. USA* 93:8145–50

67a. Kühlbrandt W. 2000. Bacteriorhodopsin—the movie. *Nature* 406:569–70

68. Kühn C, Franceschi VR, Schulz A, Lemoine R, Frommer WB. 1997. Macromolecular trafficking indicated by localization and turnover of sucrose transporters in enucleate sieve elements. *Science* 275:1298–300

69. Lanfermeijer FC, Prins HBA. 1994. Modulation of H⁺-ATPase activity by fusicoccin in plasma–membrane vesicles from oat (*Avena sativa* L.) roots—a comparison of modulation by fusicocin, trypsin, and lysophosphatiylcholine. *Plant Physiol.* 104:1277–85

70. Li YF, Hata Y, Fujii T, Hisano T, Nishihara M, et al. 1998. Crystal structures of reaction intermediates of L-2-haloacid dehalogenase and implications for the reaction mechanism. *J. Biol. Chem.* 273:15035–44

71. Lino B, Baizabal-Aguirre VM, Gonzalez de la Vara LE. 1998. The plasma-membrane H⁺-ATPase from beet root is inhibited by a calcium-dependent phosphorylation. *Planta* 204:352–59

72. Luo H, Morsomme P, Boutry M. 1999. The two major types of plant plasma membrane H⁺-ATPases show different enzymatic properties and confer differen-

tial pH sensitivity of yeast growth. *Plant Physiol.* 119:627–34

73. Lutsenko S, Kaplan JH. 1995. Organization of P-type ATPases: significance of structural diversity. *Biochemistry* 34:15607–13

74. MacLennan DH, Rice WJ, Green NM. 1997. The mechanism of Ca²⁺ transport by sarco(endo)plasmic reticulum Ca²⁺-ATPases. *J. Biol. Chem.* 272:28815–18

75. Marra M, Fullone MR, Fogliano V, Masi S, Mattei M, et al. 1994. The 30 kilodalton protein present in purified fusicoccin receptor preparations is a 14-3-3-like protein. *Plant Physiol.* 106:1497–501

76. Maudoux O, Batoko H, Oecking C, Gevaert K, Vandekerckhove J, et al. 2000. A plant plasma membrane H⁺-ATPase expressed in yeast is activated by phosphorylation at its penultimate residue and binding of 14-3-3 regulatory proteins in the absence of fusicoccin. *J. Biol. Chem.* 275:17762–70

77. Messerli M, Robinson KR. 1997. Tip localized Ca²⁺ pulses are coincident with peak pulsatile growth rates in pollen tubes of *Lilium longiflorum*. *J. Cell Sci.* 110:1269–78

78. Michel H. 1998. The mechanism of proton pumping by cytochrome c oxidase. *Proc. Natl. Acad. Sci. USA* 95:12819–24

79. Michelet B, Boutry M. 1995. The plasma membrane H⁺-ATPase—a highly regulated enzyme with multiple physiological functions. *Plant Physiol.* 108:1–6

79a. Michelet B, Lukaszewicz M, Dupriez V, Boutry M. 1994. A plant plasma membrane proton-ATPase gene is regulated by development and environment and shows signs of a translational regulation. *Plant Cell* 6:1375–89

80. Moller JV, Juul B, le Maire M. 1996. Structural organization, ion transport, and energy transduction of P-type ATPases. *Biochim. Biophys. Acta* 1286:1–51

81. Moriau L, Michelet B, Bogaerts P, Lambert L, Michel A, et al. 1999. Expression analysis of two gene subfamilies encoding the plasma membrane H^+-ATPase in *Nicotiana plumbaginifolia* reveals the major transport functions of this enzyme. *Plant J.* 19:31–41

82. Morsomme P, Boutry M. 2000. The plant plasma membrane H^+-ATPase: structure, function and regulation. *Biochim. Biophys. Acta* 1465:1–16

83. Morsomme P, Dambly S, Maudoux O, Boutry M. 1998. Single point mutations distributed in 10 soluble and membrane regions of the *Nicotiana plumbaginifolia* plasma membrane PMA2 H^+-ATPase activate the enzyme and modify the structure of the C-terminal region. *J. Biol. Chem.* 273:34837–42

84. Morsomme P, de Kerchove d'Exaerde A, De Meester S, Thines D, Goffeau A, Boutry M. 1996. Single point mutations in various domains of a plant plasma membrane H^+-ATPase expressed in *Saccharomyces cerevisiae* increase H^+-pumping and permit yeast growth at low pH. *EMBO J.* 15:5513–26

85. Muslin AJ, Tanner JW, Allen PM, Shaw AS. 1996. Interaction of 14-3-3 with signaling proteins is mediated by the recognition of phosphoserine. *Cell* 84:889–97

86. Nakajima N, Saji H, Aono M, Kondo N. 1995. Isolation of cDNA for a plasma membrane H^+-ATPase from guard cells of *Vicia faba*. *Plant Cell Physiol.* 36:919–24

87. Obermeyer G, Lutzelschwab M, Heumann HG, Weisenseel MN. 1992. Immunolocalization of H^+-ATPases in the plasma-membrane of pollen grains and pollen tubes of *Lilium longiflorum*. *Protoplasma* 171:55–63

88. Oecking C, Eckerskorn C, Weiler EW. 1994. The fusicoccin receptor of plants is a member of the 14-3-3 superfamily of eukaryotic regulatory proteins. *FEBS Lett.* 352:163–66

89. Oecking C, Hagemann K. 1999. Association of 14-3-3 proteins with the C-terminal antoinhibitory domain of the plant plasma-membrane H^+-ATPase generates a fusicoccin-binding complex. *Planta* 207:480–82

90. Oecking C, Piotrowski M, Hagemeier J, Hagemann K. 1997. Topology and target interaction of the fusicoccin-binding 14-3-3 homologs of *Commelina communis*. *Plant J.* 12:441–53

91. Ogawa H, Haga T, Toyoshima C. 2000. Soluble P-type ATPase from an archaeon, *Methanococcus jannaschii*. *FEBS Lett.* 471:99–102

92. Olivari C, Pugliarello MC, Rasi-Caldogno F, De Michelis MI. 1993. Characteristics and regulatory properties of the H^+-ATPase in a plasma-membrane fraction purified from *Arabidopsis thaliana*. *Bot. Acta* 106:13–19

93. Olsson A, Svennelid F, Ek B, Sommarin M, Larsson C. 1998. A phosphothreonine residue at the C-terminal end of the plasma membrane H^+-ATPase is protected by fusicoccin-induced 14-3-3 binding. *Plant Physiol.* 118:551–55

94. Oufattole M, Arango M, Boutry M. 2000. Identification and expression of three new *Nicotiana plumbaginifolia* genes which encode isoforms of a plasma-membrane H^+-ATPase, and one of which is induced by mechanical stress. *Planta* 10:715–22

95. Palmgren MG. 1991. Regulation of plasma membrane H^+-ATPase activity. *Physiol. Plant.* 83:314–23

96. Palmgren MG. 1998. Proton gradients and plant growth: Role of the plasma membrane H^+-ATPase. *Adv. Bot. Res.* 28:1–70

97. Palmgren MG, Christensen G. 1994. Functional comparisons between plant plasma membrane H^+-ATPase isoforms expressed in yeast. *J. Biol. Chem.* 269:3027–33

98. Palmgren MG, Larsson C, Sommarin M. 1990. Proteolytic activation of the plant plasma membrane H^+-ATPase by removal of a terminal segment. *J. Biol. Chem.* 265:13423–26

99. Palmgren MG, Sommarin M, Serrano R, Larsson C. 1991. Identification of an autoinhibitory domain in the C-terminal region of the plant plasma membrane H^+-ATPase. *J. Biol. Chem.* 267:20470–75

100. Palmgren MG, Sommarin M, Ulvskov P, Jørgensen PL. 1988. Modulation of plasma membrane H^+-ATPase by lysophosphatidylcholine, free fatty acids and phospholipase A_2. *Physiol. Plant.* 74:11–19

101. Pardo JM, Serrano R. 1989. Structure of a plasma membrane H^+-ATPase gene from the plant *Arabidopsis thaliana. J. Biol. Chem.* 264:8557–62

102. Pardo JP, Slayman CW. 1988. The fluorescein isothiocyanate-binding site of the plasma-membrane H^+-ATPase of *Neurospora crassa. J. Biol. Chem.* 263:18664–68

103. Parets-Soler A, Pardo JM, Serrano R. 1990. Immunocytolocalization of plasma membrane H^+-ATPase. *Plant Physiol.* 93:1654–58

104. Parton RM, Fischer S, Malho R, Papasouliotis O, Jelitto TC, et al. 1997. Pronounced cytoplasmic pH gradients are not required for tip growth in plant and fungal cells. *J. Cell Sci.* 110:1187–98

105. Pedchenko VK, Nasirova GF, Palladina TA. 1990. Lysophosphatidylcholine specifically stimulates plasma membrane H^+-ATPase from corn roots. *FEBS Lett.* 275:205–8

106. Pedersen PL, Carafoli E. 1987. Ion motive ATPases. I. Ubiquity, properties and significance to cell function. *Trends Biochem. Sci.* 12:146–50

106a. Pedersen PA, Jorgensen JR, Jorgensen PL. 2000. Importance of conserved α-subunit segment ^{709}GDGVND for Mg^{2+} binding, phosphorylation, and energy transduction in Na,K-ATPase. *J. Biol. Chem.* 275:37588–95

107. Peitsch MC. 1996. ProMod and Swiss-Model: internet-based tools for automated comparative protein modelling. *Biochem. Soc. Trans.* 24:274–79

108. Piotrowski M, Morsomme P, Boutry M. 1998. Complementation of the *Saccharomyces cerevisiae* plasma membrane H^+-ATPase by a plant H^+-ATPase generates a highly abundant fusicoccin binding site. *J. Biol. Chem.* 273:30018–23

109. Portillo F. 2000. Regulation of plasma membrane H^+-ATPase in fungi and plants. *Biochim. Biophys. Acta* 1469:31–42

110. Post RL, Hegyvary C, Kume S. 1972. Activation by adenosine triphosphate in the phosphorylation kinetics of sodium and potassium ion transport adenosine triphosphatase. *J. Biol. Chem.* 247:6530–40

111. Rasi-Caldogno F, Pugliarello MC, Olivari C, De Michelis MI. 1993. Controlled proteolysis mimics the effect of fusicoccin on the plasma membrane H^+-ATPase. *Plant Physiol.* 103:391–98

112. Regenberg B, Villalba JM, Lanfermeijer FC, Palmgren MG. 1995. C-terminal deletion analysis of plant plasma membrane H^+-ATPase: yeast as a model system for solute transport across the plant plasma membrane. *Plant Cell* 7:1655–66

113. Rice WJ, MacLennan DH. 1996. Scanning mutagenesis reveals a similar pattern of mutation sensitivity in transmembrane sequences M4, M5, and M6, but not in M8, of the Ca^{2+}-ATPase of sarcoplasmic reticulum (SERCA1a). *J. Biol. Chem.* 271:31412–19

114. Ridder IS, Dijkstra BW. 1999. Identification of the Mg^{2+}-binding site in the P-type ATPase and phosphatase members of the HAD (haloacid dehalogenase) superfamily by structural similarity to the response regulator protein CheY. *Biochem. J.* 339:223–26

115. Ridder IS, Rozeboom HJ, Kalk KH, Dijkstra BW. 1999. Crystal structures of intermediates in the dehalogenation of

haloalkanoates by L-2-haloacid dehalogenase. *J. Biol. Chem.* 274:30672–78

116. Roelfsema MRG, Staal M, Prins HBA. 1998. Blue light-induced apoplastic acidification of *Arabidopsis thaliana* guard cells: Inhibition by ABA is mediated through protein phosphatases. *Physiol. Plant.* 103:466–74

116a. Rosenquist M, Sehnke P, Ferl RJ, Sommarin M, Larsson C. 2000. Evolution of the 14-3-3 protein family: Does the large number of isoforms in multicellular organisms reflect functional specificity? *J. Mol. Evol.* 51:446–58

117. Roussel A, Cambillau C. 1992. TURBO-FRODO, Biographics and AFMB (architecture et fonction des macromolécules biologiques), Marseilles, France

118. Sacchi GA, Cocucci M. 1992. Effects of deuterium oxide on growth, proton extrusion, potassium influx and *in vitro* plasma membrane activities in maize root segments. *Plant Physiol.* 100:1962–67

119. Samuels AL, Fernando M, Glass ADM. 1992. Immunofluorescent localization of plasma membrane H$^+$-ATPase in barley roots and effects of K nutrition. *Plant Physiol.* 99:1509–14

119a. Sayle R. 1996. RasMol Version 2.6 Molecular Visualization Program, Glaxo Wellcome Research Development, Stevenage, United Kingdom

120. Schaller GE, Sussman MR. 1988. Phosphorylation of the plasma-membrane H$^+$-ATPase of oat roots by a calcium-stimulated protein kinase. *Planta* 173:509–18

121. Scherer GF. 1994. Phospholipid signalling by phospholipase A$_2$ in plants. The role of mastoparan and lysophospholipids as weak 'auxin-like' agonists. *Symp. Soc. Exp. Biol.* 48:229–42

122. Schroeder JI. 1988. K$^+$ transport properties of K$^+$ channels in the plasma membrane of *Vicia faba* guard cells. *J. Gen. Physiol.* 92:667–83

123. Serrano R. 1989. Structure and function of plasma membrane ATPase. *Annu. Rev. Plant Physiol. Plant Mol. Biol.* 40:61–94

124. Seto-Young D, Hall MJ, Na S, Haber JE, Perlin DS. 1996. Genetic probing of the first and second transmembrane helices of the plasma membrane H$^+$-ATPase from *Saccharomyces cerevisiae. J. Biol. Chem.* 271:581–87

125. Slayman CL, Sanders D. 1985. Steady-state kinetic analysis of an electroenzyme. *Biochem. Soc. Symp.* 50:11–29

126. Sorensen TL, Dupont Y, Vilsen B, Andersen JP. 2000. Fast kinetic analysis of conformational changes in mutants of the Ca^{2+}-ATPase of sarcoplasmic reticulum. *J. Biol. Chem.* 275:5400–8

127. Soulimane T, Buse G, Bourenkov GP, Bartunik HD, Huber R, Than ME. 2000. Structure and mechanism of the aberrant ba_3-cytochrome c oxidase from *Thermus thermophilus. EMBO J.* 19:1766–76

128. Stadler R, Brandner J, Schulz A, 1995. Phloem loading by the *PmSUC2* sucrose carrier from *Plantago major* occurs into companion cells. *Plant Cell* 7:1545–54

129. Stadler R, Sauer N. 1996. The *Arabidopsis thaliana AtSUC2* gene is specifically expressed in companion cells. *Bot. Acta* 109:299–306

130. Stokes DL, Green NM. 2000. Modeling a dehalogenase fold into the 8-A density map for Ca^{2+}-ATPase defines a new domain structure. *Biophys. J.* 78:1765–76

131. Sussman MR. 1994. Molecular analysis of proteins in the plant plasma membrane. *Annu. Rev. Plant Physiol. Plant Mol. Biol.* 45:211–34

132. Svennelid F, Olsson A, Piotrowski M, Rosenquist M, Ottman C, et al. 1999. Phosphorylation of Thr-948 at the C terminus of the plasma membrane H$^+$-ATPase creates a binding site for the regulatory 14-3-3 protein. *Plant Cell* 11:2379–92

133. Sze H, Li X, Palmgren MG. 1999. Energization of plant cell membranes by H^+-pumping ATPases. Regulation and biosynthesis. *Plant Cell* 11:677–90

133a. The Arabidopsis Genome Initiative. 2000. Analysis of the genome sequence of the flowering plant *Arabidopsis thaliana*. *Nature* 408:796–815

134. Toyoshima C, Nakasako M, Nomura H, Ogawa H. 2000. Crystal structure of the calcium pump of sarcoplasmic reticulum at 2.6 Å resolution. *Nature* 405:647–55

135. Truernite E, Sauer N. 1995. The promoter of the *Arabidopsis thaliana SUC2* sucrose-H^+ symporter gene directs expression of beta-glucoronidase to the phloem—evidence for phloem loading and unloading by SUC2. *Planta* 196:564–70

136. Vara F, Serrano R. 1982. Partial purification and properties of the proton-translocating ATPase of plant plasma membranes. *J. Biol. Chem.* 257:12826–30

137. Vara F, Serrano R. 1983. Phosphorylated intermediate of the ATPase of plant plasma membranes. *J. Biol. Chem.* 258:5334–36

138. Vera-Estrella R, Barkla BJ, Higgins VJ, Blumwald E. 1994. Plant defence response to fungal pathogens—activation of host-plasma membrane H^+-ATPase by elicitor-induced enzyme dephosphorylation. *Plant Physiol.* 104:209–15

139. Villalba JM, Lützelschwab M, Serrano R. 1991. Immunocytolocalization of plasma-membrane H^+-ATPase in maize coleoptiles and enclosed leaves. *Planta* 185:458–61

140. Vilsen B, Andersen JP, Clarke DM, MacLennan DH. 1989. Functional consequences of proline mutations in the cytoplasmic and transmembrane sectors of the Ca^{2+}-ATPase of sarcoplasmic reticulum. *J. Biol. Chem.* 264:21024–30

141. Vilsen B, Andersen JP, MacLennan DH. 1991. Functional consequences of alterations to amino acids located in the hinge domain of the Ca^{2+}-ATPase of sarcoplasmic reticulum. *J. Biol. Chem.* 266:16157–64

142. Vilsen B, Andersen JP, MacLennan DH. 1991. Functional consequences of alterations to hydrophobic amino acids located at the M4S4 boundary of the Ca^{2+}-ATPase of sarcoplasmic reticulum. *J. Biol. Chem.* 266:18839–45

143. von Heijne G. 1992. Membrane protein structure prediction. Hydrophobicity analysis and the positive-inside rule. *J. Mol. Biol.* 225:487–94

144. Vonck J. 2000. Structure of the bacteriorhodopsin mutant F219L N intermediate revealed by electron crystallography. *EMBO J.* 19:2152–60

145. Wach A, Schlesser A, Goffeau A. 1992. An alignment of 17 deduced protein sequences from plant, fungi, and ciliate H^+-ATPase genes. *J. Bioenerg. Biomembr.* 24:309–17

146. Weisenseel MH, Dorn A, Jaffe LF. 1979. Natural H^+ currents traverse growing roots and root hairs of barley (*Hordeum vulgare* L.) *Plant Physiol.* 64:512–18

147. Weisenseel MH, Nuccitelli R, Jaffe LF. 1975. Large electrical currents traverse growing pollen tubes. *J. Cell Biol.* 66:556–67

148. Xing T, Higgins VJ, Blumwald E. 1996. Regulation of plant defense response to fungal pathogens: two types of protein kinases in the reversible phosphorylation of the host plasma membrane H^+-ATPase. *Plant Cell* 8:555–64

149. Yaffe MB, Rittinger K, Volinia S, Caron PR, Aitken A, et al. 1997. The structural basis for 14-3-3:phosphopeptide binding specificity. *Cell* 91:961–71

149a. Young JC, Krysan PJ, Sussman MR. 2001. Efficient screening of Arabidopsis T-DNA insertion lines using degenerate primers. *Plant Physiol.* 125:513–18

150. Zeiger E. 1983. The biology of stomatal guard cells. *Annu. Rev. Plant Physiol.* 34:441–75

151. Zhang Z, Sumbilla C, Lewis D, Summers S, Klein MG, Inesi G. 1995. Mutational analysis of the peptide segment linking phosphorylation and Ca^{2+}-binding domains in the sarcoplasmic reticulum Ca^{2+}-ATPase. *J. Biol. Chem.* 270:16283–90

152. Zhao R, Dielen V, Kinet JM, Boutry M. 2000. Cosuppression of a plasma membrane H$^+$-ATPase isoform impairs sucrose translocation, stomatal opening, plant growth, and male fertility. *Plant Cell* 12:535–46

Annu. Rev. Plant Physiol. Plant Mol. Biol. 2001. 52:847–75

THE COHESION-TENSION MECHANISM AND THE ACQUISITION OF WATER BY PLANT ROOTS

Ernst Steudle

Lehrstuhl Pflanzenökologie, Universität Bayreuth, D-95440 Bayreuth, Germany;
e-mail: ernst.steudle@uni-bayreuth.de

Key Words   cavitation, cohesion-tension theory, composite-transport model, pressure probe, root hydraulics

■ **Abstract**   The physical basis and evidence in support of the cohesion-tension theory of the ascent of sap in plants are reviewed. The focus is on the recent discussion of challenges to the cohesion-tension mechanism based on measurements with the pressure probe. Limitations of pressure probes to measure tensions (negative pressures) in intact transpiring plants are critically assessed. The possible role of the cohesion-tension mechanism during the acquisition of water and solutes by plant roots is discussed.

CONTENTS

1040-2519/01/0601-0847$14.00
847

INTRODUCTION

In recent years, the validity of the cohesion-tension (CT) theory of the ascent of sap in plants has been questioned by Professor Ulrich Zimmermann and his colleagues at the University of Würzburg, Germany (4, 59, 143–145). Since the theory established over 100 years ago by Böhm (7) plays a key role in our understanding of the functioning of plants, the challenge has provoked a lively ongoing debate (e.g. 19a, 61, 67, 91, 97, 98, 113, 117, 128). New experimental approaches have been used to test the validity of the theory (19, 41, 73, 127, 129). Alternative or additional mechanisms have been proposed to explain the movement of water up to the top of the tallest trees (13, 14, 144). The topic has been reviewed recently by Tyree (117), who concluded that the evidence in favor of the cohesion-tension mechanism is strong, and by Tomos & Leigh (113), who discussed some aspects of pressure probe techniques involving the measurement of negative pressure. Unlike Tyree, Tomos & Leigh, perhaps still mindful of the intensity induced by the challenge to the cohesion-tension mechanism, avoid a clear judgment, namely a critical assessment of the use of pressure probes to measure tensions (negative pressures).

This review provides the physical background of the CT-mechanism, which necessitates a brief historical perspective, then discusses problems with the mechanism and recent evidence for and against it. The second part of the review considers the role of the cohesion-tension mechanism in the context of water acquisition by plant roots: how plants use both variable tension in the xylem and variable hydraulic properties of roots to regulate water uptake. Evidence that the uptake of certain solutes and their transport across the root may be affected by the CT-mechanism is reviewed.

ESSENTIAL FEATURES OF THE COHESION-TENSION MECHANISM

The CT-theory relies on basic physical properties of water and on some assumptions that may be summarized as follows:

- Water has high cohesive forces. It can be subjected to from some ten to several hundred MPa before columns break. When subjected to tensions, water is in a metastable state, i.e. pressure in xylem vessels is much smaller than the equilibrium water vapor pressure at the given temperature.
- Walls of vessels represent the weak part of the system. They may contain air or seeds of water vapor. When a critical tension is reached in the lumen

of xylem vessels, pits in vessel walls allow the passage of air through them, resulting in cavitation (embolism).

- Water in vessels of higher plants forms a continuous system from evaporating surfaces in the leaves to absorbing surfaces of the roots and into the soil (soil-plant-air-continuum; SPAC). With few exceptions, water flow within the SPAC is hydraulic in nature, and the system can be described as a network of resistors arranged in series and in parallel (123a).

- Evaporation from leaves lowers their water potential and causes water to move from the xylem to evaporating cells across leaf tissue. This reduces the pressure in the xylem, often to values well below zero (vacuum).

- Gradients in pressure (water potential) are established along transpiring plants; this causes an inflow of water from the soil into the roots and to the transpiring surfaces in the leaves.

According to these features, the cohesion-tension theory provides both a mechanism for the flow across the plant and the force driving it. The difference in water potential between the atmosphere and soil would usually be sufficient to provide enough force for even the tallest trees. However, the mechanism requires high tensions in the xylem to operate, and it is hard to envisage how these tensions could be maintained long enough. For example, it is difficult to construct a mechanical pump that would suck water from the top of a water column longer than 10 m (equivalent to 1 bar of pressure) without causing failure by cavitation. It is much easier to use positive pressures applied at the bottom. The critical question therefore is whether the tensile strength of water is sufficient to sustain states of high tension and, if so, what are the conditions required to maintain it.

TENSILE STRENGTH OF WATER, CAVITATION AVOIDANCE, AND GAS-SEEDING THEORY

Unlike the gas phase, the forces acting between molecules are high in condensed phases. Hence, liquids and solids can be subjected to high tensional forces until they fail. This may be understandable with solids such as a bar of steel, but is less intuitive for liquids. Failure by cavitation (gas embolism) is much more likely in liquids, allowing seeding caused by bubbles of water vapor or air to dominate. Liquids free of such seeds should be able to withstand very high tensions. Their tensile strength measured as the tension to be applied to cause failure is high. For a polar liquid such as water, measured values range between 5 and 140 MPa (6, 11, 80, 123, 136); the range is much smaller for nonpolar liquids such as liquid helium (1 MPa; 55). The theory of tensile properties of liquids is well developed (29, 55, 90, 112, 114). Experimental values are smaller by one to two orders of magnitude than the theoretical, because heterogenous rather than the homogenous nucleation usually dominates. During heterogenous nucleation, cavitation is initiated by gas seeds of a critical size at surfaces of vessels or by solid impurities in the liquid, i.e. by residues of air lodged on these surfaces. Homogenous nucleation is initiated by bubbles of water vapor produced spontaneously within the liquid. This process of spontaneous formation of gas bubbles is much less probable than embolism caused by preexisting seeds. From a thermodynamic point of view, a liquid under tension is in a metastable state, i.e., it tends to proceed to a state equilibrium and to form bubbles in which the vapor assumes the equilibrium value at the given temperature, which is larger than zero (vacuum) for all liquids. For water, the equilibrium vapor pressure would be 2.3 kPa at 20°C.

THEORETICAL APPROACHES

In a simple theoretical approach, the tensile strength may be calculated from the energy stored in hydrogen bonds. Taking a value of 25 kJ/mole stored in these bonds (44), an internal (cohesion) pressure of 1400 MPa (14,000 bar) is calculated by dividing the figure given by the molar volume of water ($18 \cdot 10^{-6}$ m^3/mole). This is a high value that may be reduced by the fact that, because of thermal motion, not all of the bonds will be intact at room temperature. However, even if only 80% were intact, the resulting figure of 1,100 MPa is still high, far in excess of what a plant would need to pull water from the soil into the transpiring leaf of the tallest trees.

In a more rigorous approach, the attractive forces acting in a liquid between molecules can be expressed as a change in internal energy (U) divided by the change in volume (V) of the liquid, i.e. by $(\partial U/\partial V)_T$. This term has the dimension of a pressure at constant temperature (T), and is called internal pressure. The action of the internal pressure caused by the attraction between molecules will be counteracted by the thermal pressure, which derives from the thermal motion of molecules tending to increase volume, i.e. $T(\partial P/\partial T)_V$. $(\partial P/\partial T)_V$ is called the thermal coefficient of pressure. In contrast to the energetic term, $(\partial P/\partial T)_V$ represents an entropic term ($= (\partial S/\partial V)_T$) as is easily understood. Together with the external (measurable) pressure or tension (P) acting in a liquid (such as the positive turgor pressure of cells or the negative pressure exerted on water in a vessel of a transpiring plant), the internal pressure just balances the thermal pressure, i.e.:

$$(\partial U/\partial V)_T + P = T(\partial P/\partial T)_V. \qquad 1.$$

Interestingly, physical chemists sometimes call $(\partial U/\partial V)_T$ 'cohesion pressure' of a liquid or solid, which relates to the background of the cohesion-tension theory of botanists and is based on a high $(\partial U/\partial V)_T$ of xylem solution. For water, there are tabulated values of either $(\partial P/\partial T)_V$, or of the more common coefficients of thermal expansivity, $\alpha = 1/V \cdot (\partial V/\partial T)_P$, and isothermal compressibility, $\beta = -1/V \cdot (\partial V/\partial P)_T$, which are related to the coefficient of thermal tension by $(\partial P/\partial T)_V = \alpha/\beta$ (see textbooks of physical chemistry). For liquids, $\alpha \approx 10^{-3}$ K^{-1} and $\beta \approx 10^{-3}$ MPa^{-1}. Hence, we obtain an estimate of 300 MPa

(3000 bars) for the cohesion pressure of water ($T = 300$ K). For solids, both the thermal coefficient and the compressibility are lower than for liquids which results in similar values for the coefficient of thermal tension. From a thermodynamic point of view, the cohesion-tension mechanism has a sound basis. In the presence of gas, the tensile strength of the xylem liquid would be lost. By definition, $(\partial U/\partial V)_T$ is zero for an ideal gas.

Other attempts to calculate the tensile strength of liquid water have employed the van der Waals equation, or critical tensions have been derived from the latent heat of evaporation (e.g. 112). In summary, the different theoretical approaches resulted in values for the tensile strength of water ranging between 50 and 1400 MPa. For condensed phases, it is difficult to estimate maximum tensions because there is no unique equation of state.

EXPERIMENTAL VALUES OF TENSILE STRENGTH

The Belgian chemist Donny (25) and the French physical chemist Berthelot (6) were problably the first to demonstrate experimentally tensions in liquids. Donny used a U-shaped glass tube in which one arm was sealed and the other left open or connected to a vacuum pump. When the sealed arm of the U-tube was filled with concentrated sulphuric acid, the height of the liquid column was larger than that equivalent to atmospheric pressure. Berthelot encased water in quartz tubes at elevated temperature. When the tubes were subsequently cooled, they were able to withstand tensions of up to 5 MPa (50 bar) before failing, with an audible click and with the appearance of a bubble of water vapor. Tensions within the liquid were caused by the water in the tubes contracting more than the quartz. Reynolds (77) performed experiments similar to Donny's, using mercury to fill the tubes. Later, Reynolds (78) also used U-shaped tubes that he rotated to produce centrifugal forces on the liquid, which resulted in tensions. This technique has later received greater attention in experiments by Briggs (11), and more recently by Holbrook et al (41) and Pockman et al (73). Ursprung (123) was the first to estimate the tensile strength of liquid water using a botanical object. The annulus cells of fern sporangia open at a sufficient tension within the cell sap that is usually caused by withdrawal of liquid water by evaporation. Imitating evaporation, Ursprung used highly concentrated sucrose solutions to produce a surroundings of low water potential next to the fern sporangia. He measured a maximum tensile strength of water of as large as 30 MPa (300 bar). Briggs (11) found a similar value in his famous spinning experiments with Z-shaped glass capillaries (see above).

More recently, Roedder (80) found evidence for high tensions in microscopic inclusions of water or electrolyte solution in certain naturally occurring minerals. The water in the inclusions melted at temperatures substantially higher than $0°C$, even at $+6.5°C$ in one case. Extrapolation from the melting point line indicated that this corresponded to a tension as large as 95 MPa. Zheng et al (136) used an inclusion technique to artificially prepare microfissures of water in quartz and other minerals, which were healed at high temperature and pressure to provide a high density of the water within the inclusions. When recovered at room temperature, some of the inclusions developed tensions of up to 140 MPa at densities of the liquid water substantially smaller than 1 g/cm^3 (0.5–0.7 g/cm^3). Hence, the water was substantially stretched and tensions came close to the limit at which the compressibility should become infinite (i.e. $(\partial P/\partial V)T = 0$) and the velocity of sound zero. The theory predicts a 'spinodal line' at which this is the case (90). This line originates at the critical point and extends into the range of negative pressure. Since the spinodal line is not expected to be reached, the figure of 140 MPa of Zheng et al (136) may indicate a value of the tensile strength of water close to the ultimate limit. Maris & Balibar (55) recently performed experiments similar to those with water using liquid helium close to the absolute zero. According to the nonpolar nature of this solute, maximum tensions were only a few bar, with a maximum at 9.5 bar. Although liquid helium may be an exotic substance in plant physiology, the figure is instructive nevertheless because it indicates a lower limit of the tensile strength of liquids. The large differences between measured values of tensile strength for water are due to problems in eliminating heterogenous nucleation during the measurement.

VAPOR-SEEDING MECHANISMS (HOMOGENOUS NUCLEATION)

At a first sight, nucleation (vapor-seeding) in the bulk xylem sap may seem important, but actually it is not. On the contrary, spontaneous seeding in bulk solution (liquids) is an extremely rare event. When gas bubbles appear in a bulk solution under tension, they would need to reach a certain critical size in order to cause cavitation. Most of the very small seeds will rapidly disappear. As small bubbles grow, much more energy must be invested to overcome surface tension (surface energy) than is gained by volume expansion owing to the pressure gradient between bubble and the liquid under tension (volume work). The capillary pressure, P_{cap}, would be relevant, i.e. $P_{cap} = 2T/r$ (T = surface tension; $2r$ = diameter of void). When we look at the overall work (A) performed by a vapor bubble, we have:

$$A = 4\pi r^2 \cdot T + 4\pi/3r^3(P - P_w).$$ 1.

Here, the terms $4\pi r^2 \cdot T$ and $4\pi/3r^3(P - P_w)$ represent the surface energy and volume work, respectively, and P and P_w represent the pressure in the solution and the water vapor pressure in the bubble. Since $P < 0$ and $|P| \gg P_w \approx 0$, the first term on the right side of Equation 1 has a positive and the other one a negative sign. With increasing bubble size, the volume work term grows faster than the surface tension term. Hence, there should be a maximum of A, where it holds that $dA/dr = 0$. At the maximum, we get from Equation 1:

$$P_{cap} = 2T/r.$$ 2.

This is the equation for capillary pressure, mentioned above. Physically, it means that at maximum A, the capillary pressure just balances the forces externally exerted. When the bubble size is increased further, there is a dramatic increase in size, i.e. a cavitation. We may use the value of P_{cap} to calculate the work done by the system in the maximum, A_{max}:

$$A_{max} = \frac{16\pi \cdot T^3}{3 \cdot P^2}.$$
3.

The rate for the formation of 'successful' gas seeds (J) can be now given using the Boltzmann distribution function, i.e. by describing the rate of gas seeding in a way analagous to the Arrhenius equation used to express rates of chemical reactions as a function of temperature (29):

$$J = J_o \cdot \exp -\{(A_{max} + \Delta h_V)/kT\}.$$
4.

The heat of evaporation of water Δh_V has to be added to the overall activation energy because the growth of seeds requires evaporation of liquid water to maintain P_w at the saturation value. However, this second term is usually negligible compared with A_{max}. In the context of seeding processes as they occur in the xylem of transpiring plants, A_{max} decreases with second power of tension (P), i.e. at high tensions the probability of homogenous gas seeding should be much more pronounced than at low tensions. However, since the exponential factor is usually very small at tensions that are of interest in the xylem, homogenous nucleation rarely causes cavitation. It should be noted that the constant factor J_o in Equation 4 is proportional to the amount of liquid (water) under consideration. This reminds of the traditional view that events of cavitation should occur more often in vessel members having a bigger volume than tracheids (141). According to the very small absolute value of the exponential term this is, however, meaningless. Air-seeding through pit membranes should dominate, i.e. heterogenous nucleation.

HETEROGENOUS NUCLEATION AND EFFECTS OF GASES DISSOLVED IN XYLEM SAP

Heterogenous nucleation may occur at vessel walls due to existing gas (air) residues or in some kind of a catalytic process at these surfaces (for a classification of processes, see 117). Alternatively, air-seeding occurs across pit membrane pores. The critical pressure difference at which this occurs is again given by the capillary pressure equation, with 2r being the diameter of the pores. Since homogenous nucleation is such a rare event, most of the seeding should occur at or through surfaces such as the glass or metal surfaces of a container without pores or the xylem vessels containing pit pores. According to the size of the fissures and the gas residues contained by a glass surface, cavitation will occur when a critical size of tension is reached in the solution. From the equation for capillary pressure (Equation 2), one can calculate that a bubble diameter of 3 μm refers to a critical tension (pressure difference) of 0.1 MPa (1 bar). Accordingly, 1 MPa (10 bar) tension refers to 0.3 μm or 300 nm, i.e. to a bubble size that is smaller than the wavelength of visible light. The highest tensions of about 10 MPa that have been indirectly measured in the xylem of transpiring plants could only tolerate gas impurities as small as 30 nm without cavitation. This is an extremely small figure. Hence, the existence of such high tensions in the xylem has been questioned.

Xylem vessel walls are different in construction from those of a glass or metal container, which will have surface microfissures even when carefully polished. Hence, cavitation is unavoidable in these containers when critical tensions are attained. Xylem walls consist of a porous net of wettable polymers (cellulose, lignin, hemicelluloses, etc). Pores (interfibrillar spaces) are of an order of 10 nm, which corresponds to 30 MPa of capillary pressure. Hence the porous hydrophilic matrix will be imbibed with water like a sponge. According to the high capillary forces (negative matric potentials), no space will be left for air-seeds of sufficient size to cause embolism. The special capacity of xylem vessels to allow for a high tensile strength is based primarily on the porous structure of its completely wettable walls rather than on the tensile strength of the bulk xylem solution, which is not the limiting factor. Since interfibrillar spaces in vessel walls are smaller than the diameters of pores in pit membranes, the latter should usually limit the tension at which air-seeding occurs. This is in accordance with experiments in which air-seeding across pit membranes has been directly demonstrated in the double-ended pressure chamber and other techniques (see below).

The fact that xylem solution usually contains dissolved gases (N_2, O_2, CO_2) should not affect its ability to withstand tensions. As for the formation of bubbles of water vapor in bulk solution, the formation of bubbles even in saturated or supersaturated solutions is a rare event. Kenrick et al (50) saturated liquids with gas at 100 atm and reduced pressure to 1 atm without effervescence. Kenrick et al (49) superheated water to 270°C under atmospheric pressure before it exploded. A superheated or supersaturated liquid should behave similarly to a liquid under tension. In the experiments, where water was superheated to 270°C, substantial internal tensions could be estimated. The supersaturation experiments indicate that air dissolved in the xylem sap should not affect its tensile strength. Therefore gases such as oxygen and nitrogen dissolved in the water taken up by plant roots or CO_2 developed by respiratory processes should pose no problem as long as they stay dissolved. An increase in temperature of xylem sap on its passage up the shoot may cause a problem when the solubility limit is reached. Freezing of xylem sap also reduces solubility, which would then cause cavitation. This phenomenon has long been known (141).

OLDER EVIDENCE IN FAVOR OF THE CT-THEORY

The Austrian botanist Böhm (7), the formulator of the CT-theory, was the first to conceive that states of tensions are involved in the ascent of sap in plants. He devised model experiments similar to those of Reynolds, but included transpiring shoots to raise the column of mercury above atmospheric. Cavitation problems, however, seriously impeded the experiments. Nevertheless, Böhm demonstrated convincingly that cohesion-tension is the basic mechanism for the ascent of sap, even in tall trees. Böhm's experiments were continued by Dixon & Joly (24) and Askenasy (1), but broad acceptance of the idea of a cohesion-tension mechanism was slow in taking hold. Other mechanisms were favored such as tricky mechanisms of the ascent of sap in vessels in the presence of air bubbles ['Jaminsche Ketten', see (71); imbibition mechanism, see (82)]. The imbibition mechanism theory proposed that water moved up the plant by matric forces in the walls, as in a wick. Early on botanists had deduced that axial (long-distance) transport in the xylem is driven by passive mechanisms. Killing the cells around conducting vessels had no effect on the functioning of xylem (109). Thus the contribution of metabolism (vitalistic mechanisms) to the movement of water across the xylem received increasingly less attention. Recently, there have been attempts to revive these mechanisms. It has been claimed that tissue pressure (which originates from metabolic processes) supports the ascent of sap in the xylem and plays an important role during the refilling of cavitated vessels. However, these speculations have no real thermodynamic basis (13, 14; see below).

In 1911, Renner (76) provided the first quantitative data on the tensions present in shoots of transpiring plants. To measure transpiration, he used a capillary filled with water (potometer) that he attached to an excised transpiring twig. Using a clamp, he was able to partially interrupt the transport along the xylem, thus increasing the axial hydraulic resistance and tension. However, the high forces exerted in the vessels by transpiration made it difficult to completely interupt the flow. More important, Renner compared the suction force created by the twig with that of a vacuum pump and found that the tensions created by the twig were larger by a factor of up to 10 to 20 than that provided by the pump. He concluded that the pressures created by transpiration within the xylem must have been substantially smaller than vacuum. These experiments provided incontrovertible evidence that the tensions in the xylem were sufficient to move water, even through tall trees, and helped to resolve the controversies surrounding the mechanisms for the ascent of sap in plants (23). It was agreed that the ascent of water was a passive process ultimately driven by the evaporation of water from leaves, i.e. by the water potential difference between soil and the dry air, and that, in the absence of transpiration as the force driving water flow across the soil-plant-air-continuum, root pressure would serve as the auxiliary engine. Root exudation, however, is dependent on metabolic energy to create an osmotic gradient between soil solution and xylem.

THE SCHOLANDER-HAMMEL PRESSURE BOMB

Current support for the CT-mechanism comes mainly from indirect measurement of xylem pressure (water potential) using the pressure chamber re-invented by Scholander et al in 1965 (84, 119, 120). The pressure chamber or Scholander-Hammel bomb is a compensation technique used widely to measure the water potential of shoots or parts thereof. When a transpiring shoot is excised from a plant, the tension (negative pessure) in the xylem is released to atmospheric causing an uptake of water into the leaf and stem cells. The original status of completely filled functioning vessels is then restored by applying air pressure to the sample in the chamber. When the vessels are refilled with xylem solution, the compensating or balancing pressure (P_b) is equal to the pressure in the xylem, as it was before excision, i.e. $P_x = -P_b$. Since the osmotic pressure of the xylem sap (π_x) is usually small in transpiring plants, $-P_b$ would also be a good measure of the water potential of the shoot, twig, or leaf under investigation. Note that the Scholander-Hammel bomb is based on osmotic (thermodynamic) equilibrium. Gradients within the sample prior to excision are leveled out. These gradients could be due either to a drop in water potential across the transpiring leaf (between stomata and xylem vessels) or to gradients within a shoot, a potentially important problem in rapidly transpiring leaves. By definition, the technique averages these gradients (5, 115). Consequently, there may be differences between the P_x measured directly in an intact plant and the average P_x measured with the pressure chamber (117, 127, 129), a factor sometimes overlooked when questioning the validity of the Scholander-Hammel bomb in measuring xylem pressure (4, 59). Nevertheless, averaged xylem pressures (water potentials) as measured with the Scholander-Hammel bomb have their physiological and ecological significance in that they represent a quantitative measure of the water status of plant samples and a measure of the force driving water between different parts of plant, e.g. between the root and the shoot.

Recently, Holbrook et al (41) combined the spinning technique of Reynolds (78) with the pressure chamber technique. They used excised stem segments with a single leaf attached at the midpoint of the segment, which they then rotated by a motor-driven shaft. Rotation caused a centrifugal tension at the midpoint that was sensed by the attached leaf. The P_x at the midpoint was calculated from the segment length and angular velocity of rotation and this value was then compared with the P_b measured in the leaf with a pressure chamber after centrifugation to check the validity of the measurements with the bomb. A 1:1 relationship was found between the two values for P_x values down to -1.8 MPa.

Using the Scholander-Hammel bomb, P_x values of as low as -10 MPa have been measured in water-stressed shoots (e.g. 52). According to theory this requires xylem solution that is quite free of air or water vapor seeds. Since capillary pressure also governs the seeding of air across vessel walls, pit pore diameters should also have been low. The porosity of pit-membranes rather than the volume of vessel members is critical in preventing dysfunction of vessels and, hence, withstanding drought stress (92). The genetics of pit morphology and porosity are hypothesized to have been under high selective pressure for plants that are adapted to arid habitats (117).

The mechanism of air-seeding across pit pores has been tested in double-ended pressure chambers (19). In this elegant technique, a shoot or branch sectioned at both ends is bent around in a large pressure chamber so that the cut ends protrude into the atmosphere. With a capillary attached to one end, water could be passed continually through the segment under positive pressure from a water column and the flow rate measured by weighing at the other side. When gas (air) pressure is applied to the section in the bomb, the flow will decrease substantially to the point where the pressure difference between xylem (which is at atmospheric pressure) and bomb pressure exceeds the minimal value to cause air-seeding across pit pores. Vulnerability curves obtained in this technique indicate that air-seeding across pit pores is the mechansim driving most of the cavitation events (91). In a modification of this experiment (41), Pockman et al (73) also used centrifugation to cause cavitation in cut segments of shoots that were subjected to different tensional stresses in the xylem. Cavitation was then followed by measuring the axial hydraulic resistance of stem segments. As in the double-ended pressure chamber, air-seeding across pit pores was induced at pressure differences of a few MPa between atmosphere and xylem lumen.

RECENT EVIDENCE AGAINST THE CT-THEORY

For over 100 years, the validity of the cohesion-tension theory has occasionally been called into question [see Sachs (82); Pfeffer (71)]. More recently, Greenidge (34), Plumb & Bridgman (72), and Canny (13, 14) have questioned whether the tissue surrounding vessels contributes to the axial flow or if osmotic mechanisms play a significant role in transpiring plants. Given the large volume of water passing through transpiring plants, mechanisms based entirely on osmotic pressure provided by roots would cause enormous problems in getting rid of the osmotic solutes (e.g. nutrient salts) in the shoot as the water evaporates. Such elimination would only be possible by recycling via the phloem, resulting in a rapid turnaround of solutes at high metabolic costs.

Over the past decade, Zimmermann and his co-workers have been collecting evidence against the cohesion-tension mechanism. The Würzburg group used the cell pressure probe, earlier used to measure turgor of individual cells, to assess xylem pressure in intact transpiring plants (45, 95, 108, 113). The equipment, then called a 'xylem pressure probe' (4), was filled with water instead of low-viscosity silicone oil. The tip of the probe was carefully introduced into the xylem and its actual location was identified by the change in pressure, which tended to become negative (smaller than vacuum) as the xylem was punctured. These were the first direct measurements of xylem pressure in intact transpiring plants. They showed that xylem pressure was less negative (the tension smaller) than expected from measurements taken in the pressure chamber. The Scholander-Hammel bomb had not, therefore, been correctly measuring xylem pressure, P_x (water potential). In absolute terms, tensions of only a few tenths of a MPa (only a few bars) were found. In many cases, only subatmospheric pressures were recorded. However, as precision was gained, P_x values became more negative, with a minimum close to -1 MPa.

Even more remarkable was the finding that xylem pressure was not or was hardly affected by transpiration (4, 142). The finding of low tensions and the lack of dependence on transpiration led to the conclusion that the CT-mechanism of the ascent of sap in plants was not correct, or at the very least, it was not the dominating mechanism hitherto proposed. Other mechanisms such as the osmotic uptake of water into the xylem (i.e. root and stem pressures) or capillarity were more likely alternatives (144). Since problems with cavitations make direct measurement of tensions difficult experimentally, the finding that tensions measured with a probe tended to become bigger (pressure was more negative) may indicate greater skill in measuring tensions, which, in turn, made the authors more willing to accept the CT-theory, at least as an additive mechanism. Throughout, Zimmermann and co-workers barely discuss the actual position of the pressure probe in the tissue and the criteria whereby they ensured its location. Largely, it was the reaction in pressure that convinced them that the probe was in the lumen of functioning vessels. Under these conditions, they obtained less negative xylem pressures with the probe than with the Scholander-Hammel bomb. However, in a recent paper, a 1:1 relationship was demonstrated between xylem pressures measured with the pressure probe and the pressure chamber for corn and sugar cane under conditions of low transpiration (see above; 59). This relationship is in line with other observations and may indicate a change forthcoming in the debate (145). The conclusions from the pressure probe experiments by Zimmermann's group remain: (*a*) Cohesion-tension is not the dominating mechanism driving water across the SPAC, and (*b*) the Scholander-Hammel bomb incorrectly measures xylem tension.

This challenge to a key theory in plant water relations has had repercussions for other researchers in the field. The apparent difficulty of the CT-theory in explaining how water under high tension is sustained for long periods of time caused widespread reevaluation of the validity of the CT-mechanism. The problems with direct measurements underscore the fact that the xylem is a vulnerable pipe. The controversy over direct measurements of xylem pressure and the mechanism of refilling cavitated vessels remains very much alive (13, 14, 121, 146).

RECENT EVIDENCE FROM PRESSURE PROBE EXPERIMENTS IN FAVOR OF THE CT-MECHANISM

Direct measurements of xylem P_x with pressure probes may appear to be straightforward, with no further tests or critical assessments needed to check their validity, but this is not so. Earlier measurements in my lab in Bayreuth have shown that the pressure probe or similar devices may be used to measure tensions in small compartments such as in the root xylem or artificial osmotic cells (39, 97, 102, 137). While making these measurements, it became clear that the equipment was limited in its application to ranges of tensions smaller than $\sim$0.8 MPa. These ranges, however, are smaller than those of interest within the context of the CT-theory.

In 1997/98, the problem was reanalyzed in collaboration with Dr. Tyree and his student Chungfang Wei from the University of Vermont, using intact maize plants (127, 129). When properly secured, functioning vessels in the midribs of the leaves were accessible to puncturing with the probe. To improve the rate of puncturing, the pots with the roots of the plants were encased in big pressure chambers to apply pneumatic pressure to the root, thereby increasing P_x (lowering tension). By applying pulses of pressure to the roots, it was possible to follow rates of propagation of pressure (change in water potential) within the xylem from roots to shoots. According to the CT-theory and to the fact that root hydraulic conductance was high, pressure changes should rapidly propagate along the xylem when the pressure probe was in a functioning xylem vessel. If this condition did not obtain, measurements were disregarded. Hence, the proper position of the tip of the pressure probe could be tested rigorously.

When the tip of the probe was not located in a functioning vessel, there was a delay in the response, although the pressure was negative. When the tip was positioned outside the vessels, this may have resulted in a drop in pressure and in a response smaller than 1:1 between pressure applied to the root and pressure measured with the pressure probe. When pneumatic pressures were applied to the root, it was possible to verify whether the system was functioning properly. The tests ensured that during measurement, the tips of pressure probes remained open to allow for good hydraulic contact between the xylem vessel and the pressure transducer of the probe. With these precautions, P_x was measured in a range down to -1 MPa (-10 bars). However, the tendency of the system to cavitate increased with mounting tension (129). This result accords with earlier findings with artificial osmotic cells (102). In agreement with the CT-mechanism, xylem pressure immediately decreased when light intensity was increased, which caused a simultaneous increase in the measured rate of transpiration. In the early experiments from the Zimmermann lab, this response was missing or was hardly detectable (4, 142). The papers from the Zimmermann lab gave no indication how the functioning of the system was tested other than the occurrence of a negative pressure. In our experiments, it was shown that step changes in the applied pneumatic pressure caused a 1:1 response in P_x (see above). However, as P_x exceeded atmospheric pressure, the response in P_x became much smaller than 1:1. Under these conditions, guttation occurred at the leaf margins, which indicated that the drop in response was attributable to leakage out of the xylem. This explanation is reasonable in terms of shoot hydraulics and is in line with the CT-mechanism.

In separate experiments, xylem pressure, P_x, was first measured at a given rate of transpiration. The leaf tip in which the measurements had been performed was then harvested and P_x determined with the aid of a pressure chamber. Both results were in good agreement, i.e. there was a 1:1 agreement between $|P_x|$ and P_b. P_x of leaves of transpiring plants was slighty smaller, on average, than that of nontranspiring plants. However, as transpiration rates were small during the experiments, gradients within leaves should have been also small. The results obtained with the Scholander-Hammel bomb and with the cell pressure probe were therefore similar, at least in a range of xylem pressures of down to −1 MPa.

Most important was the fact that tensions were measurable only up to 1 MPa (10 bars) despite care to avoid cavitations caused by vibration, shaking of fixed leaves, etc. The pressure probe itself or the set-up with the probe in a vessel could well have been the reason for the limitation. We therefore tested the tensile strength of the probes in a series of experiments where tips of pressure probes completely filled with silicone oil were closed with glue. In a Berthelot-type experiment, tensions were set up by cooling the capillaries of probes with dry ice. The maximum tensile strength was about 1.6 to 1.8 MPa, which was much smaller than that of liquids in the absence of air-seeds at the walls (see above), but larger than the critical value of 1 MPa found during the experiments when the tip was in xylem vessels. The tensile strength of the probe may be regarded as low. However, a tensile strength of 1.6 to 1.8 MPa would be equivalent to seed diameters of $2r = 190$ to 170 nm, which is a fairly small value (wavelength of visible light: 400–800 nm). Because internal surfaces in the probes are of differing materials (perspex, glass, silicone rubber, silicon), heterogenous seeding may occur at lower tensions than in the classical experiments that used only quartz tubes (6, 112). Tensile strength of 1.6 to 1.8 MPa is currently the limit for pressure probes. With the tip in a vessel, this limit was reduced further, perhaps because puncturing created porous by-passes in the wall next to the glass tip. Detailed tests of the tensile strength of pressure probes filled either with oil or with water indicated no substantial differences in their ability to sustain tensions (129). Indeed, oil-filled probes (used in Bayreuth) had a somewhat higher tensile strength than water-filled probes (used in Würzburg).

REFILLING MECHANISMS

Usually, it is assumed that refilling of cavitated vessels occurs when transpiration is switched off. Under these conditions, root and stem pressures play a predominant role. However, there are observations that refilling can occur even during the day, i.e. when xylem sap is still under tension (13, 14). Refilling has been followed by cryo-scanning electron microscopy just counting the number of cavitated vessels and measuring the water potential of the shoot during the day. It has been proposed that the tissue pressure generated by xylem parenchyma may cause refilling (and may also support the ascent of sap; 13). It is thought that the production of osmotic solutes (such as sugars derived from the degradation of starch) creates a high turgor in xylem parenchyma cells, which then causes some squeezing out of water from the tissue protoplasts into vessel lumina (14). Others have speculated that water would be driven into cavitated vessels by capillary forces (41a, 146). This, in turn, would increase the volume of droplets sitting at the vessel walls at atmospheric pressure or nearly so. A positive pressure would be created in the liquid phase that would compress the air and eventually remove it from the vessel.

For this latter model to work, it has been claimed that vessel walls and pits would be lined up with hydrophobic material to reduce its permeability to water to close to zero. Hence, vessels would be hydraulically isolated from surrounding tissue and would be just filled via the pits. Both types of models are highly speculative and, in fact, violate basic physical (thermodynamic) principles. They ignore the fact that vessel walls are quite permeable to water (e.g. 70a). The models postulate (in the absence of an active water transport) an uphill movement of water from regions of a low (tissue) to those of a high water potential (xylem lumen), which is not possible. Recently, it has been demonstrated in a model experiment that the observation of cavitated vessels by cryo-scanning electron microscopy may be prone to artifacts (18a, 19a). It was shown that cavitations may occur artifactually during the freezing of samples, even when attempts are made to perform this very rapidly. Furthermore, the frequency at which cavitations occur, may increase when vessels are under tension (see also 54a). When this turns out to be true, the discussion about the filling of cavitated vessels under conditions where other vessels are under high tension and the water potential of surrounding tissue is low, would have to be reconsidered. Test experiments are missing to show that artifacts can be excluded. However, it remains true that mechanisms that are evidently impossible (because they violate basic principles) can *a priori* be excluded (121).

ROLE OF COHESION-TENSION DURING WATER ACQUISITION AND TRANSPORT BY ROOTS

It has been proposed that the cohesion-tension mechanism causes variability and even adjustment in the hydraulic resistance of the xylem [resistance to long-distance transport of water (92, 117, 118, 122)]. Transpiration under conditions of water shortage should result in high tensions in the xylem that, in turn, may cause vessel dysfunction. When critical tensions are reached, air-seeding will occur across pit membrane pores. Failure of vessels and increased axial resistance would result in an increased tension in remaining intact vessels, which should then also cavitate in a vicious cycle (runaway cavitation). Eventually, reduction of water supply to the shoot would cause negative shoot-water potentials and a closure of stomata. To operate as a feedback system this would require an effective mechanism(s) of refilling of vessels when tensions are switched off during the night (see above). According to the diameter of pit pores, different species may regulate the axial hydraulic resistance at different set points (117).

Regulation of water flow across the SPAC by reversible xylem dysfunction would be a means by which plants could operate under conditions of low water potential and severe drought stress. To function properly it requires that (*a*) stomata closure is induced at even lower water potentials and that (*b*) the water supply by the root is not sufficient to balance the water status of the shoot. In the past, there has been a strong emphasis on the former process, i.e. on the output function [regulation of stomatal conductance (21, 47, 87)]. Little attention has been paid to the input function, i.e. to the regulation of water acquisition by roots and how this would be affected by xylem tension. The input function is as important for the water balance as are water losses. The reason for the lack in our knowledge of the input function is that, unlike the shoot, the hydraulic architecture of roots in the soil is much more difficult to assess. Comprehensive understanding of root hydraulics involves the measurement of water relations at the cell and tissue/organ level in addition to the xylem in a developing structure. Root morphology and anatomy must be taken into account, which vary in reponse to growing conditions. Furthermore, there are interactions between solute (nutrient) relations and the water, i.e. there are osmotic processes besides the purely hydraulic movement of water as is usually discussed within the framework of the CT-mechanism. Roots are not just 'hydraulic machines'. Osmotic and even active solute transport processes complicate the analysis of root water. They are most obvious in the phenomenon of root pressure, which relates to active uptake of solutes and plays a role during the water supply of shoots under conditions of low transpiration. In the following, hydraulic properties of plant roots will be reviewed in order to work out possible mechanisms of an adjustment or even a regulation of water uptake according to the needs of the shoot. There will be a focus on the role of cohesion mechanisms during these processes. Most of the results will refer to excised roots (individual roots and root systems), where most of the data have been collected.

VARIABLE ROOT HYDRAULIC RESISTANCE

Root hydraulic resistance (inverse of the root hydraulic conductance) is often adjusted by the size of the root system, i.e. a certain root:shoot ratio is maintained by root growth to supply the shoot with water and nutrients and to allow for mechanical stability of the shoot. Furthermore, water flow is adjusted or is even regulated by a variable hydraulic conductivity of roots at a given size and root system structure (anatomy). Depending on the species and conditions, changes can be up to three orders of magnitude. Since water uptake of a given root is proportional to its surface area, root hydraulic conductivity (root Lp_r) should be referred to unit surface area in m^2 (if known) and to unit pressure (osmotic or hydrostatic) driving the flow from the soil solution to the root xylem. Hence, root Lp_r would have the dimensions of $m^3 \cdot m^{-2} \cdot s^{-1} \cdot MPa^{-1}$ or $m \cdot s^{-1} \cdot MPa^{-1}$. That roots increase their hydraulic conductivity according to demands from the shoot, i.e. in response to tensions developing in root xylem, has long been known (8–10,12,20,27,54,66,81,94,98,103,107,126).

The radial rather than the axial component of water transport limits water uptake by roots (30,31,43,63,107). Near the root tip, where xylem vessels are not yet fully developed and offer considerable resistance, both radial and axial components have to be taken into account (31,60). Variable root hydraulic resistance has been explained in terms of different models. Brewig (10) assumed an adjustment of the permeability of root cell membranes. The development of the root's endodermis clearly also plays an important role. In the endodermis, the development of apoplastic barriers (Casparian bands, suberin lamellae, and secondary wall thickening) are thought to interrupt the apoplastic path that forces water to cross membranes. In mature roots, the endodermis is thought to be the major limiting barrier for water uptake at least in mature roots. The exodermis (hypodermis) also plays a role (64, 65, 68, 69, 79, 107, 110, 140); the exodermis undergoes a development similar to that of the endodermis, albeit with a time lag. Under stress conditions, the existence of an exodermis may cause a substantial reduction in the hydraulic conductivity of roots (22, 79, 93, 140). Another component could be plasmodesmata, which may act in a valve-like fashion to allow water uptake under favorable conditions (66, 134).

PATHWAYS FOR WATER AND SOLUTES

The hydraulic and osmotic properties of roots are related to their structure and anatomy, critical data when interpreting root transport. Depending on the species, growth conditions, and developmental state, there are large differences in roots. Roots do not behave like ideal osmometers (62, 96, 98, 105–107), as shown by measuring root reflection coefficients (σ_{sr}) that were smaller than unity, although in some cases values of close to unity have been reported (28, 33). Deviation in the behavior of roots from that of ideal osmometers (in analogy to cells) is caused by some or partial by-pass of water and solutes (nutrients, test solutes) in the apoplast even in the presence of Casparian bands and suberin lamellae in the endo- and exodermis, although these structures impede solute movement depending on the polarity and charge of the latter. Owing to the existence of apoplastic barriers, roots are not leaky, but tend to have permeability coefficients of solutes (nutrient salts) similar to those of cells (96, 140). In addition to the apoplast, there are two more parallel pathways in the root cylinder: the transcellular and the symplastic path. The transcellular path is across cell membranes and is dominated by water channels (aquaporins), whereas the symplastic path is mediated by plasmodesmata. To date, the transcellular and the symplastic pathways have not been separated experimentally, so they are summarized as a cell-to-cell path. However, evidence suggests that the transcellular component is dominating cell-to-cell Lp.

COMPOSITE TRANSPORT MODEL OF ROOT

According to root structure, there will be both hydraulic and osmotic water flow across roots. The relative contribution of the two components varies depending on conditions. The simple view describing water movement across roots in terms of osmotic processes in which root membranes play the dominant role [osmometer model of root (53)] does not hold as does the view that roots can be treated as simple and constant hydraulic resistors within the SPAC. Both views do not account for adjustments of root Lp_r and low root σ_{sr}. Because there are no membranes along the apoplast, hydraulic flow dominates along this path. Flow across the apoplast is through a porous medium exhibiting no selective properties, i.e. the reflection coefficient of the apoplast will be zero or close to it. Consequently, gradients in osmotic pressure will cause little or no water flow, unlike the cell-to-cell path. Here, osmotic gradients have to be considered besides the hydrostatic ones. Unlike walls, membranes have selective properties; their reflection coefficient is close to unity. Because there are parallel pathways of different selectivity in roots (as in other plant tissue), the intensity by which disparate components of water potential act on the two pathways is different. Responses of roots differ depending on whether there is a difference in either hydrostatic pressure (such as tensions in root xylem during transpiration) or osmotic pressure between xylem sap and soil solution, which causes root pressure in the absence of transpiration. Differences should disappear in the presence of apoplastic barriers that completely interrupt the apoplastic water flow or in the presence of a very high permeability of cell membranes for water. Both extremes, a dominating apoplastic transport in the presence of hydrostatic gradients and a dominating cell-to-cell transport, are found in plant roots (96, 98, 100, 107).

Work with root and cell pressure probes and with other techniques has provided a composite transport model of the root. The composite root structure is comparable to that of membranes, which exhibit arrays of differential permeability and selectivity and form the basis of a composite transport model (48, 101) that has been adapted to roots. The composite transport model of the root explains (*a*) differences between osmotic and hydraulic water flow and the variabilty of root Lp_r, (*b*) low reflection coefficients, and (*c*) differences in root hydraulics among species.

Differences between hydraulic and osmotic water flow can be considerable: by an order of magnitude in herbaceous species and up to three orders of magnitude in woody species (96, 104, 107). Differences are expected from the composite transport model. In the absence of hydrostatic pressure gradients such as the tension in the root xylem, the apoplastic path should be inefficient because of its low reflection coefficient. Therefore, only the cell-to-cell component is left for water movement, which has a much higher resistance. Hence, when switching from hydrostatic to nonhydrostatic water flow, there should be a change in the resistance as is observed when measuring nonlinear pressure-flow curves of roots (20, 27, 66, 81, 104). The finding explains the unresolved problem of variable hydraulic resistance in terms of a switch between transport models (apoplastic versus cell-to-cell), which is related to the intensity of transpiration and the consequent existence of tensions in the root xylem.

Low reflection coefficients of roots are a consequence of apoplastic by-passes in arrays where Casparian bands are not yet developed, or even of some by-pass flow across the Casparian band itself. The latter conclusion derives from a comparison of root Lp_r and cell Lp, in experiments in which the endodermis was punctured and from chemical analyses of Casparian bands (42a, 70, 85, 86, 99, 100, 105–107,

133, 139). In the presence of two parallel pathways with different reflection coefficients or passive selectivity, reflection coefficients of individual pathways contribute to the overall reflection coefficient according to their hydraulic conductance. In the root, the reflection coefficient of the cell-to-cell pathway will be close to unity and that of the apoplast close to zero. Hence, the overall value should be somewhere in between (as was indeed found). It should depend on the efficiency by which apoplastic barriers interrupt water flow. The model predicts that at low overall hydraulic conductivity, effects of by-passes should be relatively high and root reflection coefficients low, as found for woody species. On the other hand, when artificial by-passes are created, root σ_{sr} decreases, also as expected. Both the absolute values of root σ_{sr} and the differences found between species support the model.

PHYSIOLOGICAL CONSEQUENCES OF COMPOSITE TRANSPORT AND ROLE OF COHESION TENSION

The most obvious consequence of the model is that it provides a means of increasing root Lp_r as transpiration develops and demands for water from the shoot increase. In terms of the model, this is mediated by an increase in the hydraulic component in the presence of increased tensions in the root xylem. Tensions cause a switch from osmotic cell-to-cell transport to hydraulic apoplastic transport. On the other hand, root Lp_r will be low at low rates of transpiration, i.e. during the night and during periods of water stress. Under these conditions, roots will be protected from excessive water loss to the soil by their low root Lp_r. Thus, the composite transport model provides an optimization of the water balance under different conditions, simply by a physical adjustment. This has been termed a coarse regulation of the water balance (96, 98, 100, 107), whereas a fine regulation is obtained by the activity of water channels (see below). As a result of composite transport, roots exhibit a high and adjustable water permeability in the presence of a low solute permeability. These unique transport properties are optimal for roots. They could be hardly achieved by a semipermeable endodermis in which the apoplastic path is completely blocked off (classical model of endodermis). In the context of the cohesion mechanism, tensions in the root xylem caused by a demand for water from the shoot increase root Lp_r, which is useful.

   The traditional osmometer model fails to explain the variable Lp_r and low reflection coefficients. The Fiscus model (27) explains the variability in terms of a dilution of xylem sap, i.e. a decrease in the osmotic driving force in the xylem. However, detailed quantitative studies have shown that this cannot fully explain the measured effects (140). Since there are, for technical reasons, no direct measurements of the contribution of plasmodesmata (symplastic transport component), the quantitative contribution of plasmodesmata is not known although it has been suggested to play a role (66, 134). However, since water channels contribute to most of the root cell Lp, the role of plasmodesmata may be much smaller than thought originally (116, 135).

As the composite transport model proposes substantial apoplastic transport of water even in the endo- and exodermis, a considerable drag of solutes such as nutrient salts might also be suggested. However, this is not the case. When apoplastic dyes such as PTS (trisodium 3-hydroxy-5,8,10-pyrenetrisulfonate) are added to the root medium, they are found only in small quantities in the root xylem. Less than 1% of the concentration offered in the root medium has been found in the root xylem of different species, suggesting that PTS is filtered off at the exodermis and endodermis (35, 89, 140). These results compared with the quantitative data available for the overall and cell-to-cell passage of water might also suggest substantial differences between water and ionic and polar dyes used to trace water movement. However, for rice roots it has been proposed that sodium passes apoplastically in much higher quantities than is usually the case for dyes (131, 132).

From experiments on roots of *Arabidopsis thaliana*, it has recently been proposed that most of the calcium would arrive at the shoot after passing across the root apoplastically (130). There was no competition between Ca^{2+}, Ba^{2+}, and Sr^{2+} added to the mechanism. The conclusions are problematic in view of the fact that Ca^{2+} should move slowly across the apoplast even when there are no apoplastic barriers. Calcium is usually thought to travel with the transpiration stream in the root cortical apoplast up to the endodermis where the Casparian band prevents further movement. An uptake into the endodermal symplast is required (17, 56), using either Ca^{2+}-ATPases or Ca^{2+}-channels in the presence of a favorable electrochemical potential gradient (26). The thesis of a substantial apoplastic transport of Ca^{2+} was derived from results showing that transpiration linearly increased calcium uptake by the shoot even in the presence of Ba^{2+} and Sr^{2+} (130). Whether Ca^{2+} transport by membrane proteins in the plasmamembrane of endodermal cells is sufficient to allow for the high calcium requirements of the shoot is undetermined. High rates of transcellular calcium flux may also present a problem because of the risk of compromising intracellular Ca^{2+} levels required during $[Ca^{2+}]_{cyt}$ signals. The finding of an apoplastic transport of Ca^{2+} across the entire root cylinder is intriguing, but is at variance to other results which showed that there was no close coupling between Ca^{2+}-uptake and water uptake or transpiration (1a, 25a). It differs from results obtained with the root pressure probe during the past two decades (42a, 98, 100, 106). These results indicate that roots behave like osmometers although not as perfect ones. Most of the salts are effectively filtered off at the endo- and exodermis. However, in rice, the contribution of apoplastic transport to the overall uptake of NaCl was much larger than that given for the apoplastic tracer PTS (131, 132). The physicochemical basis of the differences in the selective properties of apoplastic barriers in the root (which may vary during root development) are not yet understood nor is the fine structure of apoplastic barriers known in sufficient detail (42a).

For the stress hormone abscisic acid (ABA), an apoplastic transport across the root cylinder affected by transpiration (cohesion tension) has been proposed in numerous studies with seedlings of maize, sunflower, and aspen (31, 32, 42, 42a, 124, 125). The results indicate a considerable by-pass flow of ABA when added in nM up to 100 μM concentrations to the root medium. About 10% of the externally applied concentration of ABA was found in the root xylem. The apoplastic flow of ABA compensated, or even overcompensated, for the dilution by water flow in the xylem. Hence, the ABA signal (xylem concentration) was strongly affected by apoplastic ABA flow. In corn roots, the existence of an exodermis reduced both the flow of water and ABA, but did not change the xylem concentration much. In corn, ABA also specifically affected water channel activity (42). The results show that overall water flow (transpiration), which is usually thought to be regulated with the aid of the stress hormone ABA at the level of stomata, may interact with the ABA signal from the root in some kind of feedback loop. On the other hand, ABA may increase water uptake via water channel activity in the root under nontranspiring conditions, thus inducing water uptake along the cell-to-cell path (42).

ROLE OF COHESION TENSION ON WATER CHANNELS IN ROOTS

Water channels are transmembrane proteins with a molecular weight of about 30 kDa and six transmembrane helices spanning the membrane, thus forming a pore of an internal diameter just sufficient to allow the passage of water in a single file (16, 51, 57, 83, 116). Four of these functional units are arranged in the membrane to form a stable tetramer. Water channels can be reversibly affected by mercurials that bind to SH groups of cysteine (58, 88, 101, 111). The activity of water channels is also affected by high salinity, solute concentration, temperature, heavy metals, oxidative stress, and by the deprivation of nutrients to the roots (15, 36, 36a, 38, 74, 75, 101). In some species, there is a diurnal rhythm in the hydraulic properties (root Lp_r) that correlates with a rhythm in the level of m-RNA encoding for putative aquaporins (18, 37). Whether tension in the xylem or pressure gradients across a root membrane such as at the endodermis could affect the open/closed state of aquaporins is more difficult to answer than whether xylem tensions affect apoplastic water flow. Water potential in the root apoplast is suggested to affect water channel activity (46). In roots, high salinity causes changes in both root Lp_r and root cell Lp, but more extensively in the latter parameter (2, 3). This may be interpreted as an effect of ion concentration or of dehydration of cell membranes and shrinkage of membrane pores caused by tensions within water channels, as once proposed for ion channels (138).

CONCLUSIONS

Older and more recent evidence provides strong support for the cohesion-tension theory of the ascent of sap in plants. The CT-mechanism has a solid physical basis. Direct measurements of xylem pressure in transpiring plants have shown that responses of P_x to changes in transpiration or to pressure applied to the root are as predicted by the cohesion-tension theory. The disagreement found in earlier measurements with the probe performed by Zimmermann and co-workers is most likely due to experimental limitations and artifacts that have not been checked for properly. At present, the limit for the use of pressure probes in the xylem of transpiring plants is at a P_x of about -1 MPa (-10 bar), which is less than the highest tensions of up to 10 MPa (100 bars) claimed to exist in the xylem. Within these limits, measurements of xylem pressure conducted with the probe agreed with those conducted with the Scholander-Hammel bomb. To extend the range of the pressure probe, the technique needs to be further refined.

The cohesion-tension mechanism plays a role during the acquisition of water by plant roots. Tensions provide a strong gradient in hydrostatic pressure that favors the apoplastic component of water uptake in relation to the cell-to-cell component. This results in nonlinear pressure-flow relations (increase of root hydraulic conductivity with increasing xylem tension) and in a coarse regulation of water uptake by plants in accord with the composite transport model of the root. According to the model, tensions in the xylem set up by transpiration cause a switch from cell-to-cell to apoplastic water transport, which increases root hydraulic conductivity and the ability to take up water even at low soil water potential. On the other hand, when transpiration is switched off at night or during water stress, hydraulic resistance would be high, thus minimizing the loss of water to the dry soil. Water channels would provide a fine regulation of water uptake in the presence of effective apoplastic barriers (roots grown under unfavorable conditions). Water channel (aquaporin) activity in plasma membranes of roots is under metabolic control and is affected by many external parameters. It is not yet clear whether water channel activity is also affected by pressure gradients set up across the root cylinder in response to high tensions in the xylem.

ACKNOWLEDGMENTS

I thank Drs. David T. Clarkson, Department of Plant Sciences, IACR-Long Ashton Research Station, University of Bristol, UK, and Hervé Cochard, INRA Clermont-Ferrand, France, for reading and discussing the manuscript. Financial support from the Deutsche Forschungsgemeinschaft, Schwerpunktprogramm "Apoplast" is acknowledged.

Visit the Annual Reviews home page at www.AnnualReviews.org

LITERATURE CITED

1. Askenasy E. 1895. Über das Saftsteigen. Bot. Zentralbl. 62:237–38
1a. Atkinson CJ, Ruiz LP, Mansfield TA. 1992. Calcium in xylem sap and the regulation of its delivery to the shoot. J. Exp. Bot. 43:1315–1324
2. Azaizeh H, Gunse B, Steudle E. 1992. Effects of NaCl and CaCl$_2$ on water transport

across root cells of maize (*Zea mays* L.) seedlings. *Plant Physiol.* 99:886–94

3. Azaizeh H, Steudle E. 1991. Effects of salinity on water transport of excised maize (*Zea mays* L.) roots. *Plant Physiol.* 97:1136–45

4. Balling A, Zimmermann U. 1990. Comparative measurements of the xylem pressure of *Nicotiana* plants by means of the pressure bomb and pressure probe. *Planta* 182:325–38

5. Begg JE, Turner NC. 1970. Water potential gradients in field tobacco. *Plant Physiol.* 46:343–46

6. Berthelot M. 1850. Sur quelques phénomènes de dilatation forcée des liquides. *Ann. Chim. Phys.* 30:2321–42

7. Böhm J. 1893. Capillarität und Saftsteigen. *Ber. Dtsch. Bot. Ges.* 11:203–12

8. Boyer JS. 1974. Water transport in plants: mechanism of apparent changes in resistance during absorption. *Planta* 117:187–207

9. Boyer JS. 1985. Water transport. *Annu. Rev. Plant Physiol.* 36:473–516

10. Brewig A. 1937. Permeabilitätsänderungen der Wurzelgewebe, die vom Spross beeinflusst werden. *Z. Bot.* 31:481–540

11. Briggs LJ. 1950. Limiting negative pressure of water. *J. Appl. Phys.* 21:721–22

12. Brouwer R. 1954. The regulating influence of transpiration and suction tension on the water and salt uptake by roots of intact *Vicia faba* plants. *Acta Bot. Neerl.* 3:264–312

13. Canny MJ. 1995. A new theory for the ascent of sap: cohesion supported by tissue pressure. *Ann. Bot.* 75:343–57

14. Canny MJ. 1998. Transporting water in plants. *Am. Sci.* 86:152–59

15. Carvajal M, Cooke DT, Clarkson DT. 1996. Responses of wheat plants to nutrition deprivation may involve the regulation of water-channel function. *Planta* 199:372–81

16. Chrispeels MJ, Maurel C. 1994. Aquaporins: the molecular basis of facilitated water

movement through living plant cells. *Plant Physiol.* 105:9–15

17. Clarkson DT. 1993. Roots and the delivery of solutes to the xylem. *Philos. Trans. R. Soc. London Ser. B* 341:5–17

18. Clarkson DT, Carvajal M, Henzler T, Waterhouse RN, Smyth AJ, et al. 2000. Root hydraulic conductance: diurnal aquaporin expression and the effects of nutrient stress. *J. Exp. Bot.* 51:61–70

18a. Cochard H, Bodet C, Ameglio T, Cruiziat P. 2000. Cryo-scanning electron microscopy observations of vessel content during transpiration in walnut petioles. Facts or artifacts? *Plant Physiol.* 124:1191–202

19. Cochard H, Cruiziat P, Tyree MT. 1992. Use of positive pressures to establish vulnerability curves: further support for the air-seeding hypothesis and possible problems for pressure-volume analysis. *Plant Physiol.* 100:205–9

19a. Cochard H, Ameglio T, Cruiziat P. 2001. The recurrent debate about vessel content in plants. *Trends Plant Sci.* In press

20. Colombo SJ, Asselstine MF. 1989. Root hydraulic conductivity and root growth capacity of black spruce (*Picea mariana*) seedlings. *Tree Physiol.* 5:73–81

21. Cowan IR. 1977. Stomatal behaviour and environment. *Adv. Bot. Res.* 4:117–228

22. Cruz RT, Jordan WR, Drew MC. 1992. Structural changes and associated reduction of hydraulic conductance in roots of *Sorghum bicolor* L. following exposure to water deficit. *Plant Physiol.* 99:203–12

23. Dixon HH. 1924. *The Transpiration Stream*. London: Univ. London Press. 80 pp.

24. Dixon HH, Joly J. 1894. On the ascent of sap. *Philos. Trans. R. Soc London Ser. B* 186:563–76

25. Donny HMF. 1846. Sùr la cohésion des leqùides, et sùr leùr adhérence aùx corps soliders. *Ann. Chim. Phys.* 16:167–90

25a. Engels C. 1999. Regulation of xylem transport of calcium from roots to shoots of maize by growth-related demand. *J. Plant Nutr. Soil Sci.* 162:287–94

26. Felle HH, Tretyn A, Wagner G. 1992. The role of the plasma membrane Ca^{2+}-ATPase in Ca^{2+} homeostasis in *Sinapis alba* root hairs. *Planta* 188:305–13

27. Fiscus EL. 1975. The interaction between osmotic- and pressure-induced water flow in plant roots. *Plant Physiol.* 55:917–22

28. Fiscus EL. 1986. Diurnal changes in volume and solute transport coefficients of *Phaseolus* roots. *Plant Physiol.* 80:752–59

29. Fisher JC. 1948. The fracture of liquids. *J. Appl. Phys.* 19:1062–67

30. Frensch J. 1998. Primary responses of root and leaf elongation to water deficits in the atmosphere and soil solution. *J. Exp. Bot.* 48:985–99

31. Frensch J, Steudle E. 1989. Axial and radial hydraulic resistance to roots of maize (*Zea mays* L.). *Plant Physiol.* 91:719–26

32. Freundl E, Steudle E, Hartung W. 1998. Water uptake by roots of maize and sunflower affects the radial transport of abscisic acid and the ABA concentration in the xylem. *Planta* 207:8–19

33. Freundl E, Steudle E, Hartung W. 2000. Apoplastic transport of abscisic acid through roots of maize: effect of the exodermis. *Planta* 210:222–31

34. Greenidge KNH. 1957. Ascent of sap. *Annu. Rev. Plant Physiol.* 8:237–56

35. Hanson PJ, Sucoff EI, Markhart AH. 1985. Quantifying apoplastic flux through red pine root systems using trisodium 3-hydroxy-5,8,10-pyrenetrisulfonate. *Plant Physiol.* 77:21–24

36. Henzler T, Steudle E. 1995. Reversible closing of water channels in *Chara* internodes provides evidence for a composite transport model of the plasma membrane. *J. Exp. Bot.* 46:199–209

36a. Henzler T, Steudle E. 2000. Transport and metabolic degradation of hydrogen peroxide in *Chara corallina:* model calculations and measurements with the pressure

probe suggest transport of H_2O_2 across water channels. *J. Exp. Bot.* 51:2053–66

37. Henzler T, Waterhouse RN, Smyth AJ, Carvajal M, Cooke DT, et al. 1999. Diurnal variations in hydraulic conductivity and root pressure can be correlated with the expression of putative aquaporins in the root of *Lotus japonicus. Planta* 210:50–60

38. Hertel A, Steudle E. 1997. The function of water channels in *Chara*: the temperature dependence of water and solute flows provides evidence for composite membrane transport and for a slippage of small organic solutes across water channels. *Planta* 202:324–35

39. Heydt H, Steudle E. 1991. Measurement of negative pressure in the xylem of excised roots. *Planta* 184:389–96

40. Deleted in proof

41. Holbrook NM, Burns MJ, Field CB. 1995. Negative xylem pressures in plants: a test of the balancing pressure technique. *Science* 270:1193–94

41a. Holbrook NM, Zwienicki MA. 1999. Field CB. 1999. Embolism repair and xylem tension: do we need a miracle? *Plant Physiol.* 120:7–10

42. Hose E, Steudle E, Hartung W. 2000. Abscisic acid and the hydraulic conductivity of roots: a cell- and root-pressure probe study. *Planta.* 211:874–82

42a. Hose E, Clarkson DT, Steudle E, Schreiber L, Hartung W. 2001. The exodermis—a variable apoplastic barrier. *J. Exp. Bot.* In press

43. Hsiao TC, Xu LK. 2000. Growth of roots vs. leaves and other implications of water transport. *J. Exp. Bot.* 51:1595–616

44. Huheey JE, Keiter EA, Keiter RL. 1993. *Inorganic Chemistry. Principles of Structure and Reactivity.* New York: Harper Collins

45. Hüsken D, Steudle E, Zimmermann U. 1978. Pressure probe technique for measuring water relations of cells in higher plants. *Plant Physiol.* 61:158–63

46. Johansson I, Larsson C, Ek B, Kjellbom P. 1996. The major integral proteins of spinach leaf plasma membranes are putative aquaporins and are phoshorylated in response to Ca^{2+} and apoplastic water potential. *Plant Cell* 8:1181–91

47. Jones HG. 1998. Stomatal control of photosynthesis and transpiration. *J. Exp. Bot.* 49:387–98

48. Kedem O, Katchalsky A. 1963. Permeability of composite membranes. Part 2. Parallel elements. *Trans. Faraday Soc.* 59:1931–40

49. Kenrick FB, Gilbert CB, Wismer KL. 1924. The superheating of liquids. *J. Phys. Chem.* 28:1297–307

50. Kenrik FB, Wismer KL, Wyatt KS. 1924. Supersaturation of gases in liquids. *J. Phys. Chem.* 28:1308–15

51. Kjellbom P, Jarsson C, Johansson I, Karlsson M, Johanson U. 1999. Aquaporins and water homeostasis in plants. *Trends Plant Sci.* 4:308–14

52. Kolb KJ, Davis SD. 1994. Drought-induced xylem embolism in co-occurring species of coastal sage and chaparral of California. *Ecology* 75:648–59

53. Kramer PJ, Boyer JS. 1995. *Water Relations of Plants and Soils.* Orlando: Academic

53a. Lange OL, Nobel PS, Osmond CB, Ziegler H, eds. 1982. *Encyclopedia of Plant Physiology.* Berlin: Springer-Verlag. Vol. 12B

54. Lopushinsky W. 1964. Effect of water movement on ion movement into the xylem of tomato roots. *Plant Physiol.* 39:494–501

54a. Lybeck BR. 1959. Winter freezing in relation to the rise of sap in tall trees. *Plant Physiol.* 34:482–86

55. Maris H, Balibar S. 2000. Negative pressure and cavitation in liquid helium. *Phys. Today* 53:29–34

56. Marschner H. 1995. *Mineral Nutrition of Higher Plants.* London: Academic

56a. Martre P, North GB, Nobel PS. 2001.

Hydraulic conductivity and mercury-sensitive water transport for roots of *Opuntia acanthocarpa* in relation to soil drying and rewetting. *Plant Physiol.* In press

57. Maurel C. 1997. Aquaporins and water permeability of plant membranes. *Annu. Rev. Plant Physiol. Plant Mol. Biol.* 48:399–429

58. Maurel C, Reizer J, Schroeder JI, Chrispeels MJ. 1993. The vacuolar membrane protein gamma-TIP creates water specific channels in *Xenopus* oocytes. *EMBO J.* 12:2241–47

59. Melcher PJ, Meinzer FC, Yount DE, Goldstein G, Zimmermann U. 1998. Comparative measurements of xylem pressure in transpiring and nontranspiring leaves by means of the pressure chamber and the xylem pressure probe. *J. Exp. Bot.* 49:1757–60

60. Melchior W, Steudle E. 1993. Water transport in onion (*Allium cepa* L.) roots. Changes of axial and radial hydraulic conductivities during root development. *Plant Physiol.* 101:1305–15

61. Milburn JA. 1996. Sap ascent in vascular plants: challenges to the cohesion theory ignore the significance of immature xylem and the recycling of Münch water flow. *Ann. Bot.* 78:399–407

62. Miller DM. 1985. Studies of root function in *Zea mays.* III. Xylem sap composition at maximum root pressure provides evidence of active transport into the xylem and a measurement of the reflection coefficient of the root. *Plant Physiol.* 77:162–67

63. North GB, Nobel PS. 1991. Changes in hydraulic conductivity and anatomy caused by drying and rewetting roots of *Agave desertii* (Agavaceae). *Am. J. Bot.* 78:906–15

64. North GB, Nobel PS. 1995. Hydraulic conductivity of concentric root tissues of *Agave deserti* Engelm. under wet and drying conditions. *New Phytol.* 130:47–57

65. North GB, Nobel PS. 1996. Radial

hydraulic conductivity of individual root tissues of *Opuntia ficus-indica* (L.) Miller as soil moisture varies. *Ann. Bot.* 77:133–42

66. Passioura JB. 1988. Water transport in and to roots. *Annu. Rev. Plant Physiol. Plant Mol. Biol.* 39:245–65

67. Passioura JB. 1991. An impasse in plant water relations? *Bot. Acta* 104:405–11

68. Peterson CA. 1988. Exodermal Casparian bands: their significance for ion uptake in roots. *Physiol. Plant.* 72:204–8

69. Peterson CA, Emanuel ME, Humphreys GB. 1981. Pathways of movement of apoplastic fluorescent dye tracers through the endodermis at the site of secondary root formation in corn (*Zea mays*) and broad bean (*Vicia faba*). *Can. J. Bot.* 59:618–25

70. Peterson CA, Murrmann M, Steudle E. 1993. Location of major barriers to water and ion movement in young roots of *Zea mays* L. *Planta* 190:127–36

70a. Peterson CA, Steudle E. 1993. Lateral hydraulic conductivity of early metaxalem vessels in *Zea mays* L. roots. *Planta* 189:288–297

71. Pfeffer W. 1897. *Pflanzenphysiologie. Ein Handbuch der Lehre vom Stoffwechsel und Kraftwechsel der Pflanze. Erster Band: Stoffwechsel.* Leipzig: Verlag Engelmann

72. Plumb RC, Bridgman WB. 1972. Ascent of sap in trees. *Science* 176:1129–31

73. Pockman WT, Sperry JS, O'Leary JW. 1995. Sustained and significant negative water pressure in xylem. *Nature* 378:715–16

74. Radin J, Eidenbock MP. 1984. Hydraulic conductance as a factor limiting leaf expansion of phosphorus-deficient cotton plants. *Plant Physiol.* 75:372–77

75. Radin JW, Matthews MA. 1989. Water transport properties of cells in the root cortex of nitrogen- and phosphorous-deficient cotton seedlings. *Plant Physiol.* 89:264–68

76. Renner O. 1911. Experimentelle Beiträge zur Kenntnis der Wasserbewegung. *Flora (Leipzig)* 103:171–247

77. Reynolds O. 1882. On the internal cohesion of liquids and the suspension of a column of mercury to a height of more than double that of the barometer. *Mem. Manch. Lit. Philos. Soc.* 7:1–19

78. Reynolds O. 1901. *Papers on Mechanical and Physical Subjects,* 2:578–87. Cambridge: Cambridge Univ. Press

79. Rieger M, Litvin P. 1999. Root system hydraulic conductivity in species with contrasting root anatomy. *J. Exp. Bot.* 50:201–09

80. Roedder E. 1967. Metastable superheated ice in liquid-water inclusions under high negative pressure. *Science* 155:1413–16

81. Rüdinger M, Hallgren SW, Steudle E, Schulze ED. 1994. Hydraulic and osmotic properties of spruce roots. *J. Exp. Bot.* 45:1413–25

82. Sachs J. 1865. *Handbuch der Experimentalphysiologie der Pflanzen.* Leipzig: Verlag Engelmann

83. Schäffner AR. 1998. Aquaporin function, structure, and expression: There are still surprises to come up in water relations. *Planta* 204:131–39

84. Scholander PF Hammel HT, Bradstreet ED, Hemmingsen EA. 1965. Sap pressure in vascular plants. *Science* 148:339–46

85. Schreiber L, Breiner HW, Riederer M, Düggelin M, Guggenheim R. 1994. The Casparian strip of *Clivia miniata* Reg. roots: isolation, fine structure and chemical nature. *Bot. Acta* 107:353–61

86. Schreiber L, Hartmann K, Skrabs M, Zeier J. 1999. Apoplastic barriers in roots: chemical composition of endodermal and hypodermal cell walls. *J. Exp. Bot.* 50:1267–80

87. Schulze ED. 1986. Carbon dioxide and water vapor exchange in response to drought in the atmosphere and soil. *Annu. Rev. Plant Physiol.* 37:247–74

88. Schütz K, Tyerman SD. 1997. Water channels in *Chara corallina. J. Exp. Bot.* 48:1511–18

89. Skinner RH, Radin JW. 1994. The effect of phosphorus nutrition on water flow through the apoplastic bypass of cotton roots. *J. Exp. Bot.* 45:423–28

89a. In Smith JAC, Griffith H, eds. 1993. *Water Deficits: Plant Responses from Cell to Community.* Oxford: BIOS Sci.

90. Speedy RJ. 1982. Stability-limit conjecture. An interpretation of the properties of water. *J. Phys. Chem.* 86:982–91

91. Sperry JS, Saliendra NZ, Pockman WT, Cochard H, Cruiziat P, et al. 1996. New evidence for large negative xylem pressures and their measurement by the pressure chamber method. *Plant Cell Environ.* 19:427–36

92. Sperry JS, Tyree MT. 1988. Mechanism of water-stress-induced xylem embolism. *Plant Physiol.* 88:581–87

93. Stasovsky E, Peterson CA. 1993. Effects of drought and subsequent rehydration on the structure, vitality and permeability of *Allium cepa* adventitious roots. *Can. J. Bot.* 71:700–7

94. Steudle E. 1989. Water flows in plants and its coupling with other processes: an overview. *Methods Enzymol.* 174:183–225

95. Steudle E. 1993. Pressure probe techniques: basic principles and application to studies of water and solute relations at the cell, tissue, and organ level. See Ref. 89a, pp. 5–36

96. Steudle E. 1994. Water transport across roots. *Plant Soil* 167:79–90

97. Steudle E. 1995. Trees under tension. *Nature* 378:663–64

98. Steudle E. 2000. Water uptake by roots: effects of water deficit. *J. Exp. Bot.* 51:1531–42

99. Steudle E, Frensch J. 1989. Osmotic responses of maize roots: water and solute relations. *Planta* 177:281–95

100. Steudle E, Frensch J. 1996. Water transport in plants: role of the apoplast. *Plant Soil* 187:67–79

101. Steudle E, Henzler T. 1995. Water channels in plants: Do basic concepts of water transport change? *J. Exp. Bot.* 46:1067–76

102. Steudle E, Heydt H. 1988. An artificial osmotic cell: a model system for simulating osmotic processes and for studying phenomena of negative pressure in plants, *Plant Cell Environ.* 11:629–37

103. Steudle E, Heydt H. 1997. Water transport across tree roots. In *Trees—Contributions to Modern Tree Physiology,* ed. H Rennenberg, W Eschrich, H Ziegler, pp. 239–55. Leiden, The Netherlands: Backhuys

104. Steudle E, Meshcheryakov AB. 1996. Hydraulic and osmotic properties of oak roots. *J. Exp. Bot.* 47:387–401

105. Steudle E, Murrmann M, Peterson CA. 1993. Transport of water and solutes across maize roots modified by puncturing the endodermis. Further evidence for the composite transport model of the root. *Plant Physiol.* 103:335–49

106. Steudle E, Oren R, Schulze ED. 1987. Water transport in maize roots. *Plant Physiol.* 84:1220–32

107. Steudle E, Peterson CA. 1998. How does water get through roots? *J. Exp. Bot.* 49:775–88

108. Steudle E, Zimmermann U. 1971. Hydraulische Leitfähigkeit von *Valonia utricularis. Z. Naturforsch. Teil B* 26:1276–82

109. Strasburger E. 1891. *Über den Bau und die Verrichtungen der Leitungsbahnen in Pflanzen.* Jena: Fischer

110. Taleisnik E, Peyrano G, Cordoba A, Arias C. 1999. Water retention capacity in root segments differing in the degree of exodermis development. *Ann. Bot.* 83:19–27

111. Tazawa M, Asai K, Iwasaki N. 1996. Characteristics of Hg- and Zn-sensitive water channels in the plasma membrane of *Chara* cells. *Bot. Acta* 109:388–96

112. Temperley HNV. 1947. The behaviour of water under hydrostatic tension III. *Proc. Phys. Soc. London* 59:199–208

113. Tomos AD, Leigh RA. 1999. The pressure probe: a versatile tool in plant cell physiology. *Annu. Rev. Plant Physiol. Plant Mol. Biol.* 50:447–72

114. Trevena DH. 1987. *Cavitation and Tension in Liquids*. Bristol, UK: Adam Hilger

115. Turner NC. 1981. Correction of flow resistances of plants measured from covered and exposed leaves. *Plant Physiol.* 68:1090–92

116. Tyerman SD, Bohnert HJ, Maurel C, Steudle E, Smith JAC. 1999. Plant aquaporins: their molecular biology, biophysics and significance for plant water relations. *J. Exp. Bot.* 50:1055–71

117. Tyree MT. 1997. The cohesion-tension theory of sap ascent. current controversies. *J. Exp. Bot.* 48:1753–65

118. Tyree MT, Davis SD, Cochard H. 1994. Biophysical perspectives of xylem evolution: Is there a tradeoff of hydraulic efficiency for vulnerability dysfunction? *IAWA J.* 15:335–60

119. Tyree MT, Hammel HT. 1972. The measurement of the turgor pressure and the water relations of plants by the pressure-bomb technique. *J. Exp. Bot.* 23:267–82

120. Tyree MT, Jarvis PG. 1982. Water in tissues and cells. See Ref. 53a, pp. 35–77

121. Tyree MT, Salleo S, Nardini A, Assunta Lo Gullo M, Mosca R. 1999. Refilling of embolized vessels in young stems of laurel. Do we need a new paradigm? *Plant Physiol.* 120:11–22

122. Tyree MT, Sperry JS. 1989. The vulnerability of xylem to cavitation and embolism. *Annu. Rev. Plant Physiol. Plant Mol. Biol.* 40:19–38

123. Ursprung A. 1915. Über die Kohäsion des Wassers im Farnannulus. *Ber. Dtsch. Bot. Ges.* 33:153–62

123a. van den Honert TH. 1948. Water transport in plants as a catenary process. *Discuss. Faraday Soc.* 3:146–53

124. Wan X, Zwiazek JJ. 1999. Mercuric chloride effects on root water transport in aspen seedlings. *Plant Physiol.* 121:939–46

125. Wan X, Zwiazek JJ. 2001. Root water flow and leaf stomatal conductance in aspen (*Populus tremuloides*) transport in aspen seedlings. *Planta.* In press

126. Weatherley PE. 1982. Water uptake and flow into roots. See Ref. 53a, pp. 79–109

127. Wei C, Steudle E, Tyree MT. 1999. Water ascent in plants: Do ongoing controversies have a sound basis? *Trends Plant Sci.* 4:372–5

128. Wei C, Steudle E, Tyree MT. 2000. Reply: Water ascent in plants. *Trends Plant Sci.* 5:146–47

129. Wei C, Tyree MT, Steudle E. 1999. Direct measurement of xylem pressure in leaves of intact maize plants: a test of cohesion-tension theory taking into account hydraulic architecture. *Plant Physiol.* 121:1191–205

130. White PJ. 2001. The pathways of calcium movement to the xylem. *J. Exp. Bot.* In press

131. Yadav R, Flowers TJ, Yeo AR. 1996. The involvement of the transpirational bypass flow in sodium uptake by high- and low-sodium-transporting lines of rice developed through intravarietal selection. *Plant Cell Environ.* 19:329–36

132. Yeo AR, Yeo ME, Flowers TJ. 1987. The contribution of an apoplastic pathway to sodium uptake by rice roots in saline conditions. *J. Exp. Bot.* 192:1141–53

133. Zeier J, Schreiber L. 1998. Comparative investigation of primary and tertiary endodermal cell walls isolated from the roots of five monocotyledoneous species: chemical composition in relation to root fine structure. *Planta* 206:349–61

134. Zhang WH, Tyerman SD. 1991. Effect of low O_2 concentration and azide on hydraulic conductivity and osmotic volume

of the cortical cells of wheat roots. *Aust. J. Plant Physiol.* 18:603–13

135. Zhang WH, Tyerman SD. 1999. Inhibition of water channel activity by $HgCl_2$ in intact wheat root cells. *Plant Physiol.* 120:849–58

136. Zheng Q, Durben DJ, Wolf GH, Angell CA. 1991. Liquids at large negative pressures: water at the homogenous nucleation limit. *Science* 254:829–32

137. Zhu JJ, Steudle E, Beck E. 1989. Negative pressure produced in an artificial osmotic cell by extracellular freezing. *Plant Physiol.* 91:1454–59

138. Zimmerberg J, Parsegian VA. 1986. Polymer inaccessible volume changes during opening and closing of a voltage-dependent ionic channel. *Nature* 323:36–39

139. Zimmermann HM, Hartmann K, Schreiber L, Steudle E. 2000. Chemical composition of apoplastic transport barriers in relation to radial hydraulic conductivity of corn roots (*Zea mays* L.). *Planta* 210:302–11

140. Zimmermann HM, Steudle E. 1998. Apoplastic transport across young maize roots: effects of the exodermis. *Planta* 206:7–19

141. Zimmermann MH. 1983. *Xylem structure and the Ascent of Sap*. Berlin: Springer-Verlag, 143 pp.

142. Zimmermann U, Benkert R, Schneider J, Rygol J, Zhu JJ, Zimmermann G. 1993. Xylem pressure and transport in higher plants and tall trees. See Ref. 89a, pp. 87–108

143. Zimmermann U, Haase A, Langbein D, Meinzer FC. 1993. Mechanism of long-distance water transport in plants: a reexamination of some paradigms in the light of new evidence. *Philos. Trans. R. Soc. London Ser. B* 341:19–31

144. Zimmermann U, Meinzer FC, Benkert R, Zhu JJ, Schneider H, et al. 1994. Xylem water transport: Is the available evidence consistent with the cohesion-tension theory? *Plant Cell Environ.* 17:1169–81

145. Zimmermann U, Wagner HJ, Schneider H, Rokitta M, Haase A, Bentrup FW. 2000. Water ascent in plants: the ongoing debate. *Trends Plant Sci.* 5:145–46

146. Zwienicki MA, Holbrook NM. 2000. Bordered pit structure vessel wall surface properties. Implications from embolism and repair. *Plant Physiol.* 123:1015–20

Subject Index

and, 446
Pseudomonas aeruginosa
ascorbic acid biosynthesis
and, 443, 445
organic anion exudation
from roots and, 547
Pseudotsuga menzesii
defensive resin
biosynthesis in conifers
and, 697
psr1 mutant
macronutrient utilization
and, 189–90
Purines
alkaloid biosynthesis and,
43
ribosome-inactivating
proteins and, 784–804
transporters for
nitrogenous solutes and,
659, 677–78
Putrescine
alkaloid biosynthesis and,
41–42, 46, 48, 52–53
Pyrobaculum aerophilum
tonoplast transporters and,
476
Pythium spp.
ribosome-inactivating
proteins and, 791
PZE40 gene
endosperm development
and, 251

Q

Quantitative trait loci
fruit maturation and
ripening, 732–33
Quaternary structure
plasma membrane
H⁺-ATPases and, 829
Quercus spp.
isoprene emission and,
424
Quinine
alkaloid biosynthesis and,
31

R

Radial microtubular systems
endosperm development
and, 233, 241–46
Ranunculus scleratus
endosperm development
and, 242–43
Rauwolfia serpentina
alkaloid biosynthesis and,
32, 34
rbcS gene
macronutrient utilization
and, 177
molecular engineering of
C₄ photosynthesis and,
303
R-domain
plasma membrane
H⁺-ATPases and, 833–34
REACH-OUT program
history of research, 26
Reactive oxygen species
macronutrient utilization
and, 163
mitochondria and oxidative
stress, 561–82
Receptors
cytokinin metabolism and
action, 89, 103
plasma membrane
H⁺-ATPases and, 833–34
ribosome-inactivating
proteins and, 799–800
Recombinant DNA
technology
molecular engineering of
C₄ photosynthesis and,
297–310
Redox
isoprene emission and, 407
Mo-based nitrogenase and,
269–88
photosystem I and, 593,
609–11
Refilling mechanisms
cohesion-tension and water
uptake, 860–61

Resin biosynthesis
in conifers
defensive, 689–718
(S)-Reticuline
alkaloid biosynthesis and,
40, 44
Retrograde transport
ribosome-inactivating
proteins and, 800
Reverse genetics
guard cell signal
transduction and, 645–46
Rhizoctonia solani
ribosome-inactivating
proteins and, 792
Rhizophagus spp.
defensive resin
biosynthesis in conifers
and, 696
Rhizosphere
organic anion exudation
from roots and, 527–50
Rhodococcus fascians
cytokinin metabolism and
action, 98
Rhodospirillum rubrum
Mo-based nitrogenase and,
270
tonoplast transporters and,
476
Rht mutant
gibberellin signaling and,
71–72
Ribes nigrum
seed-storage lipid
biosynthesis and, 346
28S Ribosomal RNA
ribosome-inactivating
proteins and, 785–804
Ribosome-inactivating
proteins (RIPs)
antiviral activity, 796–97
background, 786–87
classification, 787–89
compartmentalized RIPs,
798
cytosolic RIPs, 799

CUMULATIVE INDEXES

CONTRIBUTING AUTHORS, VOLUMES 42–52

CHAPTER TITLES, VOLUMES 42–52

Prefatory Chapters

Biochemistry and Biosynthesis

Genetics and Molecular Biology

Cell Differentiation

Tissue, Organ, and Whole Plant Events

Methods